ANNUAL REVIEW OF PHYSIOLOGY

ANNUAL REVIEW OF PHYSIOLOGY

VOLUME 51, 1989

JOSEPH F. HOFFMAN, *Editor*

Yale University School of Medicine

PAUL De WEER, *Associate Editor*

Washington University School of Medicine

ANNUAL REVIEW INC.   4139 EL CAMINO WAY,   P.O. BOX 10139   PALO ALTO, CALIFORNIA 94303-0897

ANNUAL REVIEWS INC.
Palo Alto, California, USA

International Standard Serial Number: 0066–4278
International Standard Book Number: 0–8243–0351-2
Library of Congress Catalog Card Number: 39–15404

∞   The paper used in this publication meets the minimum requirements of American National Standard for Information Sciences—Permanence of Paper for Printed
Library Materials, ANSI Z39.48-1984.

Typesetting by Kachina Typesetting Inc., Tempe, Arizona; John Olson, President
Typesetting coordinator, Janis Hoffman

PRINTED AND BOUND IN THE UNITED STATES OF AMERICA

Annual Review of Physiology
Volume 51, 1989

CONTENTS

(*continued*) v

OTHER REVIEWS OF INTEREST TO PHYSIOLOGISTS

From the *Annual Review of Biochemistry*, Volume 58 (1989):

ATP Synthase (H⁺-ATPase): Results by Combined Biochemical and Molecular Biological Approaches, M. Futai, T. Noumi, and M. Maeda
Growth Factors, T. Maciag and W. H. Burgess
The Biochemistry of P-Glycoprotein-Mediated Multidrug Resistance, J. A. Endicott and V. Ling
Molecular Basis of Fertilization, D. L. Garbers
DNA Conformation and Protein Binding, A. A. Travers
Biochemistry of Oxygen Toxicity, E. Cadenas
The Structure and Regulation of Protein Phosphatases, P. Cohen
Topography of Membrane Proteins, M. L. Jennings
The Bacterial Photosynthetic Reaction Center as a Model for Membrane Proteins, D. C. Rees, H. Komiya, T. O. Yeates, J. P. Allen, and G. Feher
The Multi-subunit Interleukin-2 Receptor, T. A. Waldman

From the *Annual Review of Medicine*, Volume 40 (1989):

Acid-Base Disorders in Critical Care Medicine, V. Fencl and T. H. Rossing
Preeclampsia: Pathophysiology, Diagnosis, and Management, M. D. Lindheimer and A. I. Katz
Corticotropin-Releasing Hormone: Clinical Application, L. K. Nieman and D. L. Loriaux
Neuropeptides and Inflammation: The Role of Substance P, D. G. Payan
Diabetes and Thyroid-Hormone-Induced Changes in Cardiac Function and Their Molecular Basis, W. H. Dillmann
Pulmonary Surfactant, L. G. Dobbs
Phosphoinositide Metabolism and Hormone Action, K. J. Catt and T. Balla

From the *Annual Review of Neuroscience* Volume 12 (1989):

The Journey of a Neuroembryologist, V. Hamburger
Short-Term Synaptic Plasticity, R. S. Zucker
Structure of the Adrenergic and Related Receptors, B. F. O'Dowd, R. J. Lefkowitz, and M. G. Caron
Axonal Growth-Associated Proteins, J. H. Pate Skene
The Function of Synaptic Transmitters in the Retina, N. W. Daw, W. J. Brunken, and D. Parkinson
Fluorescent Probes of Cell Signaling, R. Y. Tsien

Cyclic GMP-Activated Conductance of Retinal Photoreceptor Cells, K.-W. Yau and D. A. Baylor

The Cell Biology of Vertebrate Taste Receptors, S. D. Roper

Spider Toxins: Recent Applications in Neurobiology, H. Jackson and T. N. Parks

Acute Regulation of Tyrosin Hydroxylase by Nerve Activity and by Neurotransmitters via Phosphorylation, R. E. Zigmond, M. A. Schwarzschild, and A. R. Rittenhouse

From the *Annual Review of Pharmacology and Toxicology*, Volume 29 (1989):

The Biochemical Pharmacology of Atrial Peptides, P. Needleman, E. H. Blaine, J. E. Greenwald, M. L. Michener, C. B. Saper, P. T. Stockman, and E. H. Tolunay

Thromboxane, Prostoglandin, and Leukotriene Receptors, P. V. Halushka, D. E. Mais, P. R. Mayeux, and T. Morinelli

The Excitatory Amino Acid Receptors, D. T. Monaghan, R. J. Bridges, and C. W. Cotman

Modulation of Glutamate Receptors: Molecular Mechanisms and Functional Implications, J. T. Wroblewski and W. Danysz

Neurotransmitter Receptors and Phosphoinositide Turnover, D.-M. Chuang

ANNUAL REVIEWS INC. is a nonprofit scientific publisher established to promote the advancement of the sciences. Beginning in 1932 with the *Annual Review of Biochemistry*, the Company has pursued as its principal function the publication of high quality, reasonably priced *Annual Review* volumes. The volumes are organized by Editors and Editorial Committees who invite qualified authors to contribute critical articles reviewing significant developments within each major discipline. The Editor-in-Chief invites those interested in serving as future Editorial Committee members to communicate directly with him. Annual Reviews Inc. is administered by a Board of Directors, whose members serve without compensation.

ANNUAL REVIEWS OF

Anthropology	Medicine	SPECIAL PUBLICATIONS
Astronomy and Astrophysics	Microbiology	
Biochemistry	Neuroscience	Excitement and Fascination
Biophysics and Biophysical Chemistry	Nuclear and Particle Science	of Science, Vols. 1, 2, 3,
Cell Biology	Nutrition	and 4
Computer Science	Pharmacology and Toxicology	
Earth and Planetary Sciences	Physical Chemistry	Intelligence and Affectivity,
Ecology and Systematics	Physiology	by Jean Piaget
Energy	Phytopathology	
Entomology	Plant Physiology &	
Fluid Mechanics	Plant Molecular Biology	
Genetics	Psychology	
Immunology	Public Health	
Materials Science	Sociology	

For the convenience of readers, a detachable order form/envelope is bound into the back of this volume.

Robert L. Post

Annu. Rev. Physiol. 1989. 51:1–15

SEEDS OF SODIUM, POTASSIUM ATPase

Robert L. Post

Department of Molecular Physiology and Biophysics, Vanderbilt University Medical School, Nashville, Tennessee 37232

> For who "can look into the seeds of time,
>
> And say which grain will grow and which will not"?
>
> Adapted from Shakespeare: *Macbeth* I,iii
>
> "There are more things in heaven and earth, Horatio,
>
> Than are dreamt of in your philosophy."
>
> Shakespeare: *Hamlet* I,v

HISTORY

Comroe (7) examined the history of medical discovery to find out how it is done and how to do it better. I describe part of the natural history of one discovery as a correlation and adjustment of interlocking ideas until new priorities and more effective combinations are found.

My Background

My father was Professor of Greek at a small Quaker college in Haverford outside Philadelphia. He believed that Western Civilization began with the ancient Greeks. The fundamental problems and solutions started there; a perspective of more than 2,000 years was his frame of reference for current events.

1

0066-4278/89/0315-0001$02.00

He sent me to the best schools he could afford. At Harvard College, even though I had studied Latin for six years and Greek for three years, I was more attracted to science. Isaac Newton was my boyhood hero; Newton's Laws of Motion expressed more understanding in fewer words than anything I had encountered. I did an experimental thesis in Biochemical Sciences under J. T. Edsall and Jeffries Wyman. After college I wanted contact with "real" life and chose Harvard Medical School. In my second year, George Acheson (later Chairman of Pharmacology at University of Cincinnati) asked if I would like to investigate the mechanism of digitalis: I could isolate an endogenous factor from the plasma that would mimic its effects. Fortunately I declined; that problem is still unsolved! After medical school, a rotating internship nearly finished me. The necessity to stay awake required constant attention; we had only every other night off duty. I knew I did not understand what I was doing, so I devised a shorthand and kept a record of every patient I saw. If I had enough of these and organized them, I thought I could make sense out of the system. At its lowest level, the practice of medicine requires only that one do what any other physician would do next.

Life is short

And the art long

The occasion instant

Experiment perilous

Decision difficult.

An inscription at Harvard Medical School

The problems come to you, regardless of your understanding. A major advantage of a career in research is that one can choose one's problem.

After my internship, an opening in the Department of Physiology at the University of Pennsylvania under H. C. Bazett led me to research on the circulation of the blood. A later opening at Vanderbilt under H. J. Curtis introduced me to electrophysiology. When Howard Curtis left, my new chairman, Rollo Park introduced me to membrane transport.

Rationalization of Concentration Differences Between Cytoplasm and Extracellular Fluid in the 1950s

MEMBRANE TRANSPORT   At this time there was a well-developed understanding of the plasma membrane as a lipid barrier through which specialized transport, including active transport, could take place. Active transport was considered net movement away from thermodynamic equilibrium. It was also defined as dependent on metabolism. The difference between the two definitions was often neglected. Kepner has collected key papers on these ideas (24).

SORPTION However, some investigators thought that the plasma membrane did not do anything, even if it did exist. (The electron microscope had only recently been invented.) Troshin took coacervates of gelatin and gum arabic, for instance, as a model of protoplasm; both systems took up solutes from their surrounding medium in a nonlinear fashion. He made a scholarly and complete survey of the literature arguing for "sorption" (49). Ling, who invented the intracellular microelectrode, found that the membrane potential of muscle cells persists in the presence of metabolic poisons and developed an elaborate a priori physicochemical model, his "association-induction hypothesis" (27), to explain an assumed selective binding of potassium to cytoplasm and the basis of action potentials.

OUTCOME The membrane and sorption models are not contradictory except in the minds of their advocates. Both models postulate binding sites that are variably selective for sodium or potassium. The sorption model envisions a great many of them attached to macromolecules of the cytoplasm; membrane transport envisions a few embedded in the membrane and varying their selectivity as they move sodium or potassium from one side of the membrane to the other. Sorption keeps cell components from separating by forces between the components; membrane transport confines the components by means of a double Donnan equilibrium across the membrane. Robinson compared this controversy to that over the nature of combustion in the eighteenth century (40). He likened the membrane theory to oxygen and the association-induction theory to phlogiston. But proteins do bind water and can bind some ions (8), but not to the extent imagined in the sorption theory.

Counter-Transport of Glucose

In those days, "active transport" usually meant, as now, transport against an electrochemical gradient, away from equilibrium, "uphill" (8a) although some writers did not distinguish this from carrier-mediated transport. Carrier-mediated transport showed saturation kinetics, chemical specificity for the transported substrate, and competitive inhibition by structurally related molecules. The imagined carrier was a small lipid-soluble molecule in the membrane that formed a molecular complex with the transported substrate and allowed it to move through the hydrophobic barrier of the membrane. Today an ionophore, valinomycin, embodies this model for transport of potassium ion.

Rollo Park aimed to show that insulin regulated a glucose carrier in the plasma membrane of rat diaphragm. First he studied rabbit erythrocytes, and I was his consultant. After a while we realized that we could distinguish a mobile carrier from a selective channel if we could drive glucose uphill by transporting a competitive substrate downhill in the opposite direction, as predicted by Widdas (24). The experiments worked (34). Rosenberg & Wilbrandt (41) showed the same phenomenon in the more difficult human erythrocyte system and named it counterflow. They also reasoned that active transport implied a "mobile carrier" model rather than a fixed binding site in the membrane.

Active Transport of Sodium and Potassium

In 1954 active transport of sodium, with or without potassium, had been demonstrated in erythrocytes, skeletal muscle, giant axons, and across frog skin. Sodium transport across frog skin occurred between aqueous solutions at equilibrium and carried an electric current (51). This active transport was proportional to an increment in oxygen consumption.

CARDIOACTIVE STEROIDS   In 1953 Schatzmann published a most significant paper (42). He showed that the active transport of sodium and potassium in erythrocytes was inhibited by cardioactive steroids. This project was based on work done elsewhere in the 1930s showing that digitalis provoked a loss of potassium from muscle. Schatzmann's mentor, Wilbrandt, thought that adrenal mineralocorticoids might be the putative lipid-soluble sodium carrier and that the lactone ring of the cardioactive steroids might displace the carrier.

DEPENDENCE OF ACTIVE TRANSPORT SPECIFICALLY ON ATP   In 1954 in Hungary, Gárdos, using F. B. Straub's new technique of reversible hemolysis of erythrocytes, incorporated extracellular ATP into these cells and showed that this ATP supported potassium uptake (13). In 1960 in Cambridge, England, Caldwell et al (5) stimulated radioactive sodium efflux and potassium influx in the squid axon by injecting arginine phosphate into the cytoplasm. Injection of ATP stimulated only sodium efflux.

LINKAGE OF ACTIVE SODIUM AND POTASSIUM TRANSPORT   In 1956 Glynn (13a) gave an elegant and scholarly analysis of kinetics of radioactive tracer fluxes in erythrocytes. He related his findings to a cyclical carrier hypothesis for active transport as follows.

> It is supposed that K^+ and Na^+ can only cross the membrane in combination with the carriers X and Y, X being K^+ specific and Y being Na^+ specific. . . . X and Y are, by hypothesis, interconvertible and are in equilibrium at the outer surface of the membrane; at the inside surface, X is converted into Y with the expenditure of metabolic energy.

STOICHIOMETRY OF ACTIVE SODIUM AND POTASSIUM ION TRANSPORT IN ERYTHROCYTES   In 1954 I chose to work with human erythrocytes because they are simple, structurally and metabolically, and easy to get (from myself, at times!), and they permit aliquots. A new instrument, the flame photometer, made the analyses convenient. Incubation for a week or two in the cold room moved ion concentrations toward equilibrium, increasing cell sodium and reducing cell potassium. Subsequent warming with added metabolic substrates restored the normal composition in a few hours, moving both ions away from equilibrium and demonstrating active transport. In order to estimate cell content rather than concentration, I measured the ratio of the cations to hemoglobin. I avoided radioactive tracers because I thought that net transport was more fundamental. In 1957 Post & Jolly reported a stoichiometry of 3 Na^+ outward per 2 K^+ inward for the component of transport inhibited by a cardioactive steroid; "The discrepancy in the pumping rates for sodium and potassium would have a considerable effect on the membrane potential due to the net movement of positive charge if it were not for the fact that the erythrocyte membrane is freely permeable to small anions . . . " (36).

AN ELECTROGENIC SODIUM PUMP   In 1957 Ritchie & Straub carefully characterized posttetanic hyperpolarization in small nerve fibers, showing that it was produced by the sodium pump. They hesitated to conclude that the pump itself was electrogenic (39). Unfortunately, I was not aware of this work at that time.

Na,K-ATPase

In 1954 Na,K-ATPase, was unknown. In 1945 Racker & Krimsky (38) reported that sodium ions inhibited glycolysis in a mouse brain homogenate. In further work on inhibition by sodium, Utter (52) wrote in 1950, " . . . the dephosphorylation of ATP and ADP was stimulated. The stimulation of Apyrase was shown . . . at low levels of Na^+ and to be dependent upon . . . Mg^{++}." " . . . one or more of the enzymes affected by Na^+ is removed by centrifugation."

In 1957 Skou (46) noted in the introduction to his landmark paper that metabolic poisons inhibited active transport of sodium ions out of giant axons (21) and reduced their content of energy-rich phosphate esters (4). "A further study on the ATPase in nerves and its possible role in the active outward transport of sodium ions seems warranted" (46). He based his experiments on those of Abood & Gerard (1), who found ATPase activity in the light microsomal fraction of a homogenate of rat peripheral nerve. From this fraction of crab nerve, Skou obtained and characterized an ATPase activity highly specific for sodium ions. He summarized,

Leg nerves from the shore crab *(Carcinus maenas)* contain an adenosine triphosphatase which is located in the submicroscopic particles. . . . Sodium ions increase the activity when magnesium ions are present. Potassium ions increase the activity when the system contains both magnesium and sodium ions. . . . This observation, as well as some other characteristics of the system, suggest that the adenosine triphosphatase studied here may be involved in the active transport of sodium from the nerve fibre (46).

In 1957 it was hardly credible that active sodium transport could be generated by anything so simple as a specific sodium and potassium ion-transport ATPase embedded in the plasma membrane of almost every animal cell. When Skou's paper appeared, it aroused little immediate attention. Nevertheless, before his paper the rain of evidence trickled in diverse streams or sat in puddles. After his paper, it flowed in a progressively larger and broader river. Input came from both membrane transport and enzymology. My colleagues and I were fortunate to contribute seven drops of convergent evidence that the Na^+-K^+ pump and the Na,K-ATPase were a single entity (37).

Calcium Ion-Transport ATPase from Sarcoplasmic Reticulum

Na,K-ATPase was soon joined by the calcium ion-transport ATPase of sarcoplasmic reticulum of skeletal muscle. A particulate ATPase of W. W. Keilley and O. Meyerhof in 1948–50 and B. B. Marsh's "relaxing factor" of muscular contraction in 1952 converged in the work of S. Ebashi in 1958 and became a calcium pump in the work of W. Hasselbach and M. Makinose in 1960 and of S. Ebashi & F. Lipmann in 1962 (18). It was a complicated system. Much effort was expended before it was realized that free calcium ion in the cytoplasm catalyzed contraction and that resealed vesicles of sarcoplasmic reticulum pumped calcium into their interior to produce relaxation.

THE CURRENT SCENE

I apologize to all those authors who might reasonably expect to find their work cited here and who do not find it, especially those who sent me reprints. I apologize to readers who might reasonably expect to find a better coverage. By the time I warmed up to my task, there was no more time.

Reviews

Glynn has written a comprehensive review (14). Nørby contributed further informaton and perspective (32). Jørgensen reviewed the function and regulation of the enzyme in the kidney (22). Fambrough et al reviewed regulation of the pump from the perspective of a molecular biologist (11). Skou has written a very nice overview (47).

Subunit Interactions

The formation of two-dimensional crystals in the lipid bilayer shows that subunit interactions by lateral association of $\alpha\beta$-protomers can occur (30). Retention of many functions by solubilized protomers shows that protomer interactions are not necessary (53). Although many partial answers have been offered, the question whether protomer interactions modify function in the native membrane-bound enzyme remains open. There is at least one report of retention of some function by an isolated α-subunit (29). Askari has written a mini-review (2). See also a contribution from Schoner's laboratory (43).

Endodigin

Endodigin is Arnold Schwartz's name for endogenous digoxin, a putative regulatory substance of the pump in animals, reflected in the high specificity of cardioactive steroids for inhibition of this enzyme. It may be involved in hypertension.

A major stumbling block to finding this substance is the necessity of a major commitment to a tissue source, a means of extraction, and an assay system before knowing if the right ones were chosen.

If endodigin is a regulatory substance in multicellular organisms, then Na,K-ATPase in unicellular organisms such as protozoa should not be sensitive to cardioactive steroids.

For recent articles, see the book edited by Mulrow & Schreier (31) and two reviews (15, 17). Inagami's laboratory reported a substance with properties very close to those of a cardioactive steroid (48).

Na,K-ATPase AS AN OSCILLATOR

Qualifications

For an enzyme to qualify as an oscillator, its reaction sequence should consist in a single cycle that includes at least two reactive states. Two of these reactive states should exhibit maximum and minimum values of some parameter, such as the volume, the dipole moment, or the fluorescence intensity of a probe attached to or part of the enzyme. I refer to these reactive states as principal reactive states. The turnover number of the enzyme, thus, corresponds to the frequency of the oscillator. The frequency depends not only on the enzyme but also on the reaction mixture in which it functions, particularly on the concentrations of substrates and products.

Experimental Limitations

A major limitation to detecting a signal from such an enzyme is the necessity to synchronize the molecules and to keep them synchronized. Even if the enzyme molecules all oscillate at the same frequency, no signal can be detected if the molecules have a random phase relationship to each other. In principle, they can be synchronized by varying a force, such as pressure or an electric field, if the principal conformations of the enzyme differ in a corresponding displacement such as volume or dipole moment respectively. For instance, if the volume of the enzyme is different in the principal conformations, as each molecule turns over, it will emit a tiny sound wave at a frequency corresponding to its turnover number. Now, if a sound wave is applied to the reaction mixture from an external source at the frequency of the turnover number, those enzyme molecules that are out of phase with the applied wave will be brought into phase with it. The ones that are ahead of the applied wave, leading the phase, will be slowed slightly and the ones that are behind, lagging the phase, will be speeded up slightly until all the molecules are in phase with the applied sound wave. Most of the energy is supplied by the splitting of the substrate of the enzyme; the sound energy is needed only for synchronization. [Emission of sound produced by flashes of light was used to estimate enthalpy changes in the reaction sequence of bacteriorhodopsin (26a)].

An Acoustic Oscillator

EXPERIMENTS   John Wikswo and Pablo Vasallo helped me with this project. We used Na,K-ATPase from the outer medulla of dog kidney prepared by Jørgensen's zonal method (23). For the output signal we chose the fluorescence intensity of a fluorescein isothiocyanate molecule attached to lysine residue number 501 of the α-subunit (sheep kidney sequence). Its intensity is 20% greater in the presence of Na^+ than in the presence of K^+. An SLM-Aminco DW-2c spectrophotometer was available with a fluorescence attachment. This instrument can respond to frequencies as high as 250 cycles per second. For the input parameter we chose pressure since it was simple to apply sound vibrations to the enzyme by coupling a loudspeaker driver to a cuvette in the spectrofluorometer. For a substrate we chose acetylphosphate since the enzyme derivatized in this way shows no response to ATP. In using acetylphosphate we had to separate the Na^+,K^+-dependent activity with this substrate from the K^+-dependent activity. We did this by choosing Na^+ and K^+ concentrations that permitted the Na^+,K^+-dependent acetylphosphatase activity and prevented K^+-dependent p-nitrophenylphosphatase activity. We obtained a turnover number of 17 per second for the acetylphosphatase activity at 20°C. [This was an upper limit since the Na^+,K^+-activity can stimulate a little K^+-dependent activity; when K^+ gets on the enzyme, it tends to come off slowly (35).]

In order to improve the ratio of signal to noise we used a lock-in amplifier. This device filters a noisy input signal. It also accepts a signal from a reference oscillator and reports the amplitude and phase of the component of the noisy signal that is at the frequency of the reference signal. We fed it the output from the spectrophotometer and a reference signal from the oscillator that was driving the loudspeaker. If the enzyme was synchronized to the sound waves, we thought we would detect a modulation of the fluorescent intensity at the same frequency and at a constant phase relationship to the driving signal.

When we got the derivatized enzyme, the reaction mixture, and the apparatus all together, we varied the frequency of the applied sound wave from 5 to 100 cycles per second and looked for a response from the lock-in amplifier. There were several sharply tuned responses. But the inhibitor ouabain, which stops the acetylphosphatase activity, had no effect. All the responses were artifacts produced by vibrations of the mirrors of the spectrophotometer caused by the vibrations of the loudspeaker driver.

SIGNIFICANCE   If we had obtained a usable signal, we could have determined whether the sodium form, E_1 conformation, or the potassium form, E_2 conformation, of the enzyme had the smaller volume. For instance, if the potassium form had the smaller volume, then the minimum of the fluorescence intensity should have coincided with the compression of the sound wave and not with the rarefaction. In the calcium ATPase of sarcoplasmic reticulum, Blasie et al found that the protein of that enzyme moved from a position outside of the membrane slightly into the membrane when that enzyme went from an E_1 to an E_2 conformation (3). This motion does not necessarily imply a change in volume, of course.

EPILOGUE   We learned later by a personal communication from George Fortes that a pressure of about 1,000 atm is needed to inhibit Na,K-ATPase. Since out apparatus produced a peak-to-peak change of pressure of a little more than one atm, we were applying too little pressure to have an effect.

An Electric Oscillator

This was not the end of our experiments, however. The enzyme might be an electric oscillator, if not an acoustic oscillator. Na,K-ATPase is an electrogenic pump, characteristically transporting 3 Na^+ outward per 2 K^+ inward per cycle and thus generating a net movement of one positive charge per cycle, a small electric current. Furthermore, it is the outward sodium stroke of the cycle that moves the charge (9).

Even apart from sodium transport, the enzyme may respond to and therefore generate oscillating electrical fields. There are occluded conformations for both the sodium phosphoenzyme and the potassium dephosphoenzyme. In an occluded conformation, the enzyme holds a transported substrate (ion) without allowing it access to either the solution of origin or the solution of destination. Such an enzyme must have two gates, one on either side of the active center or cavity of occlusion. In the occluded state both gates are shut. Furthermore, in the course of the transport step only one gate may be open at one time. If both gates open simultaneously, the pump becomes a channel and the transported ion rushes across the membrane toward equilibrium, impairing the function of the pump.

In the voltage-gated sodium channels of electrically excitable membranes, the gates flicker transiently open and shut. The fraction of time in which they are open is regulated by the electrical potential across the membrane. This regulation implies a "sensor," a dipole in the protein that moves in response to the electric field across the membrane. The motion of the sensor generates in turn a transient electric current, a gating current, that has been demonstrated experimentally (20). Such flickering gates have been reported in preparations of Na,K-ATPase incorporated into artificial lipid bilayers (25, 26, 29). Forbush has proposed a flickering gate model to explain transient kinetics of rubidium release from the enzyme (12). In the secondary structure of proteins there are alpha helices. An alpha helix of more than two turns has a dipole moment equivalent to one-half charge at either end, even in the absence of charged residues. The amino-terminal end is positive (28). Thus, even the secondary structure of a protein can have a dipole moment. Gresalfi & Wallace reported that the secondary structure of Na,K-ATPase differs greatly between the sodium and the potassium forms (16) although this conclusion has been denied elsewhere (6, 19).

Finally, consider the experiments of Dux & Martonosi (10) on the related calcium ATPase of sarcoplasmic reticulum. They crystallized this enzyme in its native vesicles by adding vanadate or decavanadate and observed the rate of crystallization. The enzyme crystallizes preferentially in the presence of E_2 ligands, namely inorganic phosphate or vanadate, magnesium ion, and ethyleneglycol-bis-(β-aminoethyl ether)N,N,N',N'-tetraacetic acid (i.e. in the absence of calcium ion). Dux & Martonosi studied the effect of membrane potential on the rate of crystallization. They varied the membrane potential by applying suitable salt concentration gradients across the membrane. The rate of crystallization was faster when the cytoplasmic side of the membrane was negative. When it was positive, crystals that had already formed broke up. Thus the E_2 conformation was stabilized by a negative membrane potential, and the E_1 conformation was stabilized by a positive membrane potential. This stabilization implies a difference in the orientation of a dipole in the enzyme.

All these indirect considerations suggested that it might be possible to make the enzyme vibrate between sodium (E_1) and potassium (E_2) conformations by applying an oscillating electric field across the membrane. The alternating electrical field would move a dipole, which would alter the conformation of the enzyme. The change in conformation would change the intensity of fluorescence of the probe.

The membranes containing Na,K-ATPase in the Jørgensen preparation are discs about 0.2–0.4 μm in diameter. To apply an electric field uniformly, all the discs must first be oriented in the same direction at right angles to the electric field. Fortunately, Ormos et al oriented purple membranes of bacteriorhodopsin by applying a steady electrical potential (33). We applied 30 V along 3 cm of a cuvette. To this potential we added an alternating sine wave potential of 50 V peak-to-peak and varied its frequency. The derivatized enzyme was suspended in 4 mM imidazole/3-(N-morpholino) propanesulfonic acid buffer at pH 7.1 at 23°C. At 5 cycles per second, the lowest frequency available, we obtained a signal about 0.5% as large as the maximum change in fluorescence intensity produced by changing sodium and potassium ion concentrations. This signal was three to five fold larger than the noise level. As we increased the frequency, the phase of the response lagged and the amplitude decreased, disappearing at about 10 cycles per second. The response required about 10 seconds to reach its maximal level. Both the steady and the sine wave components of the stimulus were required. Addition of the inhibitor, ouabain, did not affect the response. Ouabain locks the enzyme in an inhibited conformation. Thus the response was probably not due to a conformational change. The membrane fragments containing the enzyme visibly migrated toward the anode in this system. We speculated that they were tumbling at the frequency of the alternating potential. As they tumbled, they could variably shadow the fluorescent probe.

In a different reaction system, Serpersu & Tsong stimulated the pump electrically. They stimulated ouabain-inhibited net rubidium uptake into human red blood cells with an alternating electric field (44, 45). Their optimum stimulation was a sinusoidal potential of 12 mV across the membrane at 1,000 cycles per second. The temperature coefficient of the stimulated uptake was less than that of the unstimulated, metabolically driven uptake so that the stimulated uptake was about fourfold greater than the unstimulated uptake at 6°C and about one half as great at 26°C. The stimulated uptake was an increment above the unstimulated uptake. Efflux of rubidium or potassium and influx or efflux of sodium were not stimulated correspondingly. The kinetics with respect to extracellular rubidium concentration were similar for the unstimulated and the stimulated uptakes at 26°C. Intracellular sodium was required with about the same affinity for both uptakes ($K_m \simeq 8$ mM). The stimulated uptake was less dependent on the ATP concentration and was less inhibited by vanadate than was the unstimulated uptake. From a mathematical model they concluded that a net or cyclic charge translocation across the membrane and an asymmetric stability of the enzyme states could account for the results (50). Since the unstimulated potassium transport step is electrically neutral (9), an outward movement of an empty carrier, presumably carrying two negative charges, is required for the stimulated uptake. Since there was no stimulation of Na^+ efflux, their stimulation must have displaced the cytoplasmic Na^+, which was required for the Rb^+ influx, to permit the empty charged transport site to gain access to the extracellular face of the membrane. They estimated a turnover number of their enzyme at 10 cycles per second at a stoichiometry of 2 Rb^+ per cycle (45). Thus, their stimulation frequency of 1,000 cycles per second was far above the turnover number. They were probably not vibrating the whole enzyme but only a part of it, possibly the "lobe" that extends from the massive "body" of the enzyme in the parts farthest from the membrane (30). Presumably, they were not only driving cytoplasmic Na^+ out of the transport site but were also making one or both of the gates of the empty occluded transport site flicker.

ACKNOWLEDGMENT

This work was supported by a grant, R01 HL01974, from the National Heart, Lung, and Blood Institute of the National Institutes of Health.

MAXIMS FOR A YOUNG INVESTIGATOR

If we could first know where we are and whither we are tending, then we could better judge what to do and how to do it.

Abraham Lincoln

Whenever a new discovery is reported to the scientific world, they say first, "It is probably not true." Thereafter, when the truth of the new proposition has been demonstrated beyond question, they say, "Yes, it may be true, but it is not important." Finally, when sufficient time has elapsed to fully evidence its importance, they say, "Yes, surely it is important, but it is no longer new."

Montaigne

One of the principal objects of theoretical research in any department of knowledge is to find the point of view from which the subject appears in its greatest simplicity.

J. Willard Gibbs

THINK BIG!

Sidney Colowick

Do it right the first time.

C. R. Park

Most things don't work. Confirm anything that does.

Murphy

Put yourself in a position to be lucky. Be lucky. Know that you have been lucky. Persuade others that you were lucky.

R. L. Post

Literature Cited

1. Abood, L. G., Gerard, R. W. 1954. Enzyme distribution in isolated particulates of rat peripheral nerve. *J. Cell. Comp. Physiol.* 43:379–92
2. Askari, A. 1987. ($Na^+ + K^+$)-ATPase: on the number of the ATP sites of the functional unit. *J. Bioenerg. Biomembr.* 19:359–74
3. Blasie, J. K., Herbette, L. G., Pascolini, D., Skita, V., Pierce, D. H., Scarpa, A. 1985. Time-resolved x-ray diffraction studies of the sarcoplasmic reticulum membrane during active transport. *Biophys. J.* 48:9–18
4. Caldwell, P. C. 1956. The effects of certain metabolic inhibitors on the phosphate esters of the squid giant axon. *J. Physiol.* 132:35P
5. Caldwell, P. C., Hodgkin, A. L., Keynes, R. D., Shaw, T. I. 1960. The effects of injecting 'energy-rich' phosphate compounds on the active transport of ions in the giant axons of *Loligo*. *J. Physiol.* 152:561–90
6. Chetverin, A. B., Brazhnikov, E. V. 1985. Do sodium and potassium forms of Na,K-ATPase differ in their secondary structure? *J. Biol. Chem.* 260:7817–19
7. Comroe, J. H. 1977. *Retrospectroscope. Insights into Medical Discovery*, p. 186. Menlo Park, Calif.: Von Gehr
8. Creighton, T. E. 1984. *Proteins. Structures and Molecular Principles*, pp. 153, 243, 251–52, 377, 387. New York: Freeman
8a. Davson, H. 1951. *A Textbook of General Physiology*, pp. 274–77. Phila. Blakiston
9. De Weer, P., Gadsby, D. C., Rakowski, R. F. 1988. Voltage dependence of the Na-K pump. *Ann. Rev. Physiol.* 50:225–41
10. Dux, L., Martonosi, A. 1983. The regulation of ATPase-ATPase interactions in sarcoplasmic reticulum membrane. II. The influence of membrane potential. *J. Biol. Chem.* 258:11903–7
11. Fambrough, D. M., Wolitzky, B. A., Tamkun, M. M., Takeyasu, K. 1987. Regulation of the sodium pump in excitable cells. *Kidney Int.* 32(Suppl. 23):S97–S112
12. Forbush, B. 1987. Rapid release of ^{42}K or ^{86}Rb from two distinct sites on the Na,K-pump in the presence of P_i or vanadate. *J. Biol. Chem.* 262:11116–27
13. Gárdos, G. 1954. Akkumulation der Kaliumionen durch menschliche Blutkorperchen. *Acta Physiol. Hung.* 6:191–99
13a. Glynn, I. M. 1956. Sodium and potassium movements in human red cells. *J. Physiol.* 134:278–310
14. Glynn, I. M. 1985. The Na^+,K^+-Transporting Adenosine Triphosphatase. In *The Enzymes of Biological Membranes*, ed. A. N. Martonosi, pp. 35–114. New York: Plenum. 2nd ed.
15. Graves, S. W., Williams, G. H. 1987. Endogenous digitalis-like natriuretic factors. *Ann. Rev. Med.* 38:433–44
16. Gresalfi, T. J., Wallace, B. A. 1984. Secondary structural composition of the Na/K-ATPase E1 and E2 conformers. *J. Biol. Chem.* 259:2622–28
17. Haber, E., Haupert, G. T. 1987. The search for a hypothalamic Na^+,K^+-ATPase inihbitor. *Hypertension* 9:315–24
18. Hasselbach, W. 1964. Relaxing factor and the relaxation of muscle. *Prog. Biophys.* 14:167–222
19. Hastings, D. F., Reynolds, J. A., Tanford, C. 1986. Circular dichroism of the two major conformational states of mammalian ($Na^+ + K^+$)-ATPase. *Biochim. Biophys. Acta* 860:566–69
20. Hille, B. 1984. *Ionic Channels of Excitable Membranes*, pp. 345–47. Sunderland, Mass.: Sinauer
21. Hodgkin, A. L., Keynes, R. D. 1955. Active transport of cations in giant axons from *Sepia* and *Loligo*. *J. Physiol.* 128:28–60
22. Jørgensen, P. L. 1986. Structure, func-

tion and regulation of Na,K-ATPase in the kidney. *Kidney Int.* 29:10–20

23. Jørgensen, P. L. 1988. Purification of Na$^+$,K$^+$-ATPase: enzyme sources, preparative problems, and preparation from mammalian kidney. *Methods Enzymol.* 156:29–43

24. Kepner, G. R. 1979. *Cell Membrane Permeability and Transport. Benchmark Papers in Human Physiology.* Stroudsburg, Penn.: Dowden, Hutchinson Ross

25. Kumazawa, N., Tsujimoto, T., Fukushima, Y. 1986. Influence of voltage and ATP on ion-channel of (Na,K)ATPase incorporated into solvent-free phospholipid planar bilayers. *Biochem. Biophys. Res. Commun.* 136:767–72

26. Last, T. A., Gantzer, M. L., Tyler, C. D. 1983. Ion-gated channel induced in planar bilayers by incorporation of (NA$^+$,K$^+$)-ATPase. *J. Biol. Chem.* 258:2399–2404

26a. LeGrange, J., Cahen, D., Caplan, S. R. 1982. Photoacoustic calorimetry of purple membranes. *Biophys. J.* 37:4–6

27. Ling, G. N. 1962. *A Physical Theory of the Living State: The Association-Induction Hypothesis; With Considerations of the Mechanisms Involved in Ion Specificity.* New York: Blaisdell

28. Matthew, J. B. 1985. Electrostatic effects in proteins. *Ann. Rev. Biophys. Chem.* 14:387–417

29. Mironova, G. D., Bocharnikova, N. I., Mirsalikova, N. M., Mironov, G. P. 1986. Ion-transporting properties and ATPase activity of (Na$^+$ + K$^+$)-ATPase large subunit incorporated into bilayer lipid membranes. *Biochim. Biophys. Acta* 861:224–36

30. Mohraz, M., Simpson, M. V., Smith, P. R. 1987. The three-dimensional structure of the Na,K-ATPase from electron microscopy. *J. Cell Biol.* 105:1–8

31. Mulrow, P. J., Schreier, R. 1987. *Atrial Hormones and Other Natriuretic Factors*, pp. 127–71. Bethesda, Md.: Am. Physiol. Soc.

32. Nørby, J. G. 1987. Na,K-ATPase: Structure and kinetics. Comparison with other ion transport systems. Nobel Symposium 66 Membrane Proteins: Structure, Function, Assembly. *Chem. Scr.* 27B:119–30

33. Ormos, P., Dancsházy, Z. S., Keszthelyi, L. 1980. Electric response of a back photoreaction in the bacteriorhodopsin photocycle. *Biophys. J.* 31:207–13

34. Park, C. R., Post, R. L., Kalman, C. F., Wright, J. H., Johnson, L. H., Morgan, H. E. 1956. The transport of glucose and

other sugars across cell membranes and the effect of insulin. *Ciba Found. Colloq. Endocrinol.* 9:240–60

35. Post, R. L., Hegyvary, C., Kume, S. 1972. Activation by adenosine triphosphate in the phosphorylation kinetics of sodium and potassium ion transport adenosine triphosphatase. *J. Biol. Chem.* 247:6530–40

36. Post, R. L., Jolly, P. C. 1957. The linkage of sodium, potassium, and ammonium active transport across the human erythrocyte membrane. *Biochim. Biophys. Acta* 25:118–28

37. Post, R. L., Merritt, C. R., Kinsolving, C. R., Albright, C. D. 1960. Membrane adenosine triphosphatase as a participant in the active transport of sodium and potassium in the human erythrocyte. *J. Biol. Chem.* 235:1796–1802

38. Racker, E., Krimsky, I. 1945. Effect of nicotinic acid amide and sodium on glycolysis and oxygen uptake in brain homogenates. *J. Biol. Chem.* 161:453–61

39. Ritchie, J. M., Straub, R. W. 1957. The hyperpolarization which follows activity in mammalian non-medullated fibres. *J. Physiol.* 136:80–97

40. Robinson, J. D. 1982. The sodium pump and its rivals: an example of conflict resolution in science. *Perspect. Biol. Med.* 25:486–95

41. Rosenberg, T., Wilbrandt, W. 1957. Uphill transport induced by counterflow. *J. Gen. Physiol.* 41:289–96

42. Schatzmann, H.-J. 1953. Herzglycoside als Hemmstoffe für den aktiven Kalium- und Natriumtransport durch die Erythrocytenmembran. *Helv. Physiol. Acta* 11:346–54

43. Scheiner-Bobis, G., Fahlbusch, K., Schoner, W. 1987. Demonstration of cooperating α subunits in working (Na$^+$ + K$^+$)-ATPase by the use of the MgATP complex analog cobalt tetrammine ATP. *Eur. J. Biochem.* 168:123–31

44. Serpersu, E. H., Tsong, T. Y. 1983. Stimulation of ouabain-sensitive Rb$^+$ uptake in human erythrocytes with an external electric field. *J. Membr. Biol.* 74:191–201

45. Serpersu, E. H., Tsong, T. Y. 1984. Activation of electrogenic Rb$^+$ transport of (Na,K)-ATPase by an electric field. *J. Biol. Chem.* 259:7155–62

46. Skou, J. C. 1957. The influence of some cations on an adenosine triphosphatase from peripheral nerves. *Biochim. Biophys. Acta* 23:394–401

47. Skou, J. C. 1988. Overview: the Na,K-pump. *Methods Enzymol.* 156:1–25

48. Tamura, M., Lam, T.-T., Inagami, T. 1988. Isolation and characterization of a specific endogenous Na$^+$,K$^+$-ATPase inhibitor from bovine adrenal. *Biochemistry* 27:4244–53

49. Troshin, A. S. 1966. *Problems of Cell Permeability*. London: Pergamon

50. Tsong, T. Y., Astumian, R. D. 1988. Electroconformational coupling: how membrane-bound ATPase transduces energy from dynamic electrical fields. *Ann. Rev. Physiol.* 50:273–90

51. Ussing, H. H., Zerahn, K. 1951. Active transport of sodium as the source of electric current in the short-circuited isolated frog skin. *Acta Physiol. Scand.* 23:110–27

52. Utter, M. F. 1950. Mechanism of inhibition of anaerobic glycolysis of brain by sodium ions. *J. Biol. Chem.* 185:499–517

53. Vilsen, B., Andersen, J. P., Petersen, J., Jørgensen, P. L. 1987. Occlusion of ^{22}Na$^+$ and ^{86}Rb$^+$ in membrane-bound and soluble protomeric $\alpha\beta$-subunits of Na,K-ATPase. *J. Biol. Chem.* 262:10511–17

RENAL AND ELECTROLYTE PHYSIOLOGY

BIOLOGY OF RENAL GROWTH

Introduction, Carl W. Gottschalk, M.D., *Section Editor*

The Renal and Electrolyte Physiology Section presents a minisymposium on the Biology of Renal Growth. The morphological aspects of growth in the size of the kidney, usually termed renal hypertrophy, have long interested renal pathologists. Oliver and others clearly defined the two separate processes that may cause an increase in renal mass, (*a*) enlargement of cells (hypertrophy) and (*b*) increase in cell number (hyperplasia), and identified circumstances in which one or both occurred and speculated on their cause. This symposium presents a contemporary view of the cellular and molecular aspects of these processes.

Drs. Fine and Norman consider the cellular events leading to renal hypertrophy in various circumstances. They discuss the initiating events, changes in physiological processes, cellular metabolism of DNA, RNA, and proteins, and gene expression.

Drs. Mendley and Toback discuss the autocrine and paracrine regulation of kidney epithelial cell growth by polypeptide growth factors, which can be either inhibitory or stimulatory. The review focuses on new knowledge of

17

growth factors produced by renal epithelial and mesangial cells in culture and those isolated from kidney tissue.

Androgenic hormones are known to stimulate cellular growth. Depending upon the tissue, they may cause an increase in cell size, cell number or both. As Dr. Berger points out, the tissue-specific effects probably reflect the particular genes that respond rather than differences in mechanism of hormone action. He discusses androgenic effects on the kidney.

Epidermal growth factor belongs to an extensive class of molecules that mediates cell growth and differentiation. Drs. Fischer, Salido, and Barajas discuss the ontogenesis, characteristics, origin, localization, and role of epidermal growth factor in the kidney.

Annu. Rev. Physiol. 1989. 51:19–32

CELLULAR EVENTS IN RENAL HYPERTROPHY

Leon G. Fine and Jill Norman

Division of Nephrology, Department of Medicine, UCLA School of Medicine, Los Angeles, California 90024

DEFINITIONS AND CAUSES

Growth in the size of the kidney is loosely referred to as renal hypertrophy. At a cellular level the term hypertrophy is entirely appropriate since kidney mass increases predominantly by a process of cell enlargement rather than by cell proliferation (32, 33). This is reflected by an increase in protein per cell, protein per DNA, and cell size. Since the bulk of the kidney mass consists of the proximal tubule, this part of the nephron contributes most to hypertrophy. However, all parts of the nephron increase in size in response to renal ablation, including glomeruli (2, 50) and proximal (4, 18, 44, 57) and distal tubular elements (4, 36). Given the unique structure of the renal tubule, in which a single layer of epithelium encloses a narrow lumen, growth by hypertrophy is a feasible way to increase tubular mass; a proliferative response, i.e. hyperplasia (such as occurs following partial ablation of the liver), would lead to piling up of cells and tubular obstruction, and would only be economical if it followed loss of cells with denudation of the basement membrane.

The causes of renal hypertrophy are numerous (see Table 1). The pattern of cell growth described above is not uniform for all forms of renal hypertrophy. Even the ablation model yields different growth patterns depending upon the specific experimental conditions. Thus, in the neonatal animal, compensatory renal growth following uninephrectomy occurs predominantly by hyperplasia whereas in the adult, total DNA content increases only marginally (11). In the adult, the extent of renal ablation appears to influence the cellular growth response: the more extensive the ablation, the greater the increase in DNA content per nephron (37). While it is usually assumed that this increase in DNA content reflects hyperplasia in a tubule that is increasing in length, the

19

phenomenon has not been well studied at a cellular level. For instance, it is not known whether nuclear polyploidy occurs or whether an increase in mitochondrial DNA contributes to the increased DNA per nephron (discussed below).

Renal growth in response to certain dietary manipulations also departs from the pattern seen in compensatory hypertrophy following partial renal ablation. Chronic potassium depletion leads not only to overall hypertrophy, but also to a unique proliferative response in the collecting tubules in which papillary projections of epithelial cells are seen (54, 55). This phenomenon may be related to the observation that reduction in medium potassium concentration stimulates mitogenesis in BSC-1 (African Green Monkey epithelial) cells (62) in vitro. The effects of a high protein diet are also intriguing; such a diet is additive with renal ablation in causing proximal tubular hypertrophy (23, 34, 44). On the other hand, a high protein diet appears to cause a disproportionate increase in the size of the thick ascending limbs in the inner stripe of the outer medulla relative to other parts of the nephron (9). A similar pattern of hypertrophy has been described in Brattleboro rats receiving vasopressin (8). Bouby et al suggested that hypertrophy of these nephron segments may be directly related to increased activity of the urinary concentrating mechanism (8, 9).

INITIATING EVENTS IN RENAL HYPERTROPHY

Glomerular Filtration Rate

We have previously pointed out that a common denominator in many seemingly disparate causes of renal hypertrophy is an elevation of glomerular

Table 1 Causes of renal hypertrophy[a]

Category	Cause
With elevation of GFR	Ablation of renal mass or nephron destruction
	High protein diet/total parenteral nutrition
	Pregnancy
	Hormone administration (thyroid, ACTH, growth hormone, testosterone, vasopressin)
	Chronic volume expansion with mineralocorticoid and sodium chloride
	Insulin-dependent diabetes mellitus
	Alcoholic liver disease
Without elevation of GFR	Potassium depletion
	Ammonium chloride loading (metabolic acidosis)
With associated hyperplasia	Renal ablation in neonatal period
	Extensive renal ablation in adults
	Potassium depletion

[a]GFR = glomerular filtration rate.

filtration rate (GFR) (14a). While there are isolated exceptions, the over-whelming evidence suggests that an early rise in GFR initiates renal growth following ablation. Maneuvers that alter the growth response, such as protein intake, hypothyroidism, hyperthyroidism, and pregnancy, are associated with primary changes in GFR (14a). Furthermore, in chronic experimental glomerulonephritis, where nephron injury is heterogeneous, in those nephrons with hyperfiltering, large glomeruli, the attached tubules are large, whereas those with partially destroyed glomerular tufts are attached to small tubules (1, 29, 43, 44). This strongly suggests that local factors may be more relevant to initiation of tubular hypertrophy than a putative kidney-specific growth factor released at a distant site, which would presumably cause growth of all nephrons in an indiscriminate fashion.

The link between GFR and enlargement of renal tubular cells is not understood. Direct effects of an increased flow rate over a 2 h period in rabbit proximal tubules perfused in vitro does not lead to a consistent increase in fluid absorption (L. G. fine, unpublished observations). An increase in tubular reabsorptive function takes place in vivo within 24 h of uni-nephrectomy, and this precedes a measurable increase in tubular cell size (52).

Na^+-H^+ Exchange

There is extensive literature on the role of intracellular pH and, more specifi-cally, on the role of the Na^+-H^+ exchange in the initiation of mitogenesis following exposure to growth factors (see 38 for a review). The studies cited focus almost exclusively on cell proliferation. Given that the brush border membrane Na^+-H^+ exchange system is the principal mechanism whereby Na^+ is transported from the tubular lumen to the interior of the proximal tubular cell, the activity of this system in relation to renal hypertrophy is of interest. In isolated brush border membrane vesicles of remnant kidneys from dog (13), rat (23), and rabbit (39), Na^+-H^+ exchange activity is increased. This is a V_{max} (39) effect and is not due to a change in the internal or external pH dependence of the system (61). The only study that has attempted to determine whether this increase in V_{max} is due to an increase in the turnover number of a fixed population of antiporters versus an increased number of transporters was performed on a solubilized brush border membrane prepara-tion using [3H]ethylpropylamiloride, a high-affinity ligand for the Na^+-H^+ antiporter. This study concluded that an increased turnover number of a fixed population of transporters occurs in the remnant kidney. However, since solubilization could have incorporated transporters associated with, but not inserted into, the membrane, this conclusion requires confirmation with intact cells or isolated membranes.

Interestingly, the increase in Na^+-H^+ exchange in the brush border is not paralleled by an increase in the V_{max} of Na^+-dependent cotransport processes (e.g. Na-glucose and Na-alanine) (13, 23, 39). Since transtubular transport of organic substrates is increased in the remnant kidney, this suggests that these systems probably operate below V_{max} in vivo and can increase adaptively in a substrate-dependent manner, whereas systems that normally operate close to V_{max}, such as Na^+-H^+ exchange in the presence of 140 mM NaCl in the tubular lumen, increase their transport capacities by an increase in V_{max}.

Is an increase in Na^+-H^+ exchange necessary for the initiation of the hypertrophic response? If it is, it should occur early and should be universally present in vivo and in vitro; its absence or inhibition, should prevent hypertrophy. In two models of renal cell hypertrophy in vitro (see below) we have shown that Na^+-H^+ exchange activity increases early (within 30 min of the initiation of cell enlargement) (15, 16). No definitive studies have been performed on cells lacking the antiporter or on cells in which the antiporter is selectively inhibited. Thus a causal relationship remains to be established. The recent demonstration that thyroid hormone stimuates the antiporter without causing hypetrophy at least indicates that activation of Na^+-H^+ exchange activity does not, per se, initiate the growth response (65).

Na,K-ATPase and Other Transport Systems

The activity of the basolaterally-located sodium-potassium pump (Na,K-ATPase) is magnified in the proximal tubule of the remnant kidney (49). The number of pump sites increases in proportion to the amount of protein per cell. Interestingly, the surface area of the basolateral membrane increases out of proportion to the luminal membrane surface area, but, despite this, the functional activity of the Na^+-K^+ pump appears to increase in proportion to the overall cell protein per cell (49).

In vitro, proximal tubular hypertrophy is also associated with enhanced activity of the basolateral Na^+-K^+ pump; the increase Na^+-K^+ pump activity is inhibited by 10^{-4}-M amiloride, which directly inhibits the brush border Na^+-H^+ exchanger (15). This finding is consistent with the general view that the basolateral pump, which normally operates below its V_{max} with respect to intracellular Na^+, is able to maintain intracellular Na^+ concentration at a relatively constant level. Following an acute influx of Na^+, a parallel efflux of Na^+ is achieved by acutely increasing the rate of transport of existing pumps. When the stimulus to Na^+ influx is sustained, the cell adapts by inserting additional transporters into the membrane, each of which presumably operates close to the original rate of transport (22, 47, 64).

Other transport systems have received little attention in relation to renal hypertrophy. Na^+-dependent phosphate transport in brush border membrane vesicles of dog remnant kidney is decreased in the presence of elevated circulating parathyroid hormone (PTH) levels (26). It is not clear if PTH, per se, regulates the process of hypertrophy, but circumstantial evidence indicates that it may play a role. Maintenance of animals on a low calcium diet (which stimulates PTH production) or administration of exogenous PTH leads to renal hypertrophy (31). Since PTH has been shown to stimulate inositol triphosphate and diacylglycerol production, and a rise in cytosolic calcium concentration in renal tubular cells (27), PTH could be a signal for initiating growth. PTH is mitogenic for canine proximal tubular cells in primary culture (K. Hruska, personal communication). The observation that bradykinin (which causes a rise in intracellular calcium concentration in proximal tubular cells similar to that observed with PTH) is not mitogenic (40) indicates that common signalling events do not imply the same ultimate effects on cell function.

Ammoniagenesis

An increased rate of ammoniagenesis per nephron characterizes the hypertrophy of renal ablation, protein loading, potassium depletion, and ammonium chloride loading (17). Kurtz's group recently demonstrated that addition of ammonium chloride to the medium of JTC cells (a proximal tubular cell line) induces hypertrophy over a period of 3–4 days at concentrations as low as 2 mM (21). Since internal and external pH was perturbed only minimally, increased cellular ammonia availability, per se, may act as a stimulus to hypertrophy and may also increase the activity of the Na^+-H^+ exchanger by acting as a substrate for the transporter on its cytoplasmic side. Alternately, the generation of HCO_3^- in the ammoniagenic process may activate a Na^+-HCO_3^- cotransport process at the basolateral surface, which would lower intracellular Na^+ concentration, thereby generating an increased Na^+ gradient across the luminal membrane. This would also increase the activity of the antiporter. Particularly intriguing is the potassium depletion model (56), in which increased ammonia production is associated with renal hypertrophy without an increase in GFR, but with an increase in Na^+-H^+ exchange (51).

DNA, RNA, AND PROTEIN METABOLISM IN RENAL HYPERTROPHY

While it generally requires 24 h for demonstrable increases of kidney dry weight, protein, and RNA content to occur following uninephrectomy, studies of synthetic rates measured by incorporation of radiolabeled precursors have provided information about the early events in DNA and RNA metabolism.

DNA Metabolism

Normally, less than 0.3% of renal tubular cells incorporate precursors into DNA in vivo (63), and following unilateral nephrectomy in the adult rat and the mouse there is a minimal increase in kidney DNA content, which reaches

10% above control values at 9 days (36). The percentage of cells in mitosis in the cortex increases from 0.03–0.23% by 48 h (48). It is possible that manipulation of the kidney, per se, could cause stimulation of mitotic activity in the contralateral kidney, and that this is not necessarily part of the hypertrophic process. Thus, in the mouse, damage to one kidney, without its removal, leads to an increase in mitotic activity in the contralateral kidney after 2 days (3). As a rule, however, the contribution of cell proliferation to overall growth is small. Cell cycle analysis of proximal tubular cells of uninephrectomized rabbit shows no evidence of a shift into the S_1, G_2, or M phases of the cell cycle (41).

The contribution of mitochondrial DNA to the small observed increase in DNA content following partial renal ablation needs further investigation. We have shown that mitochondrial density (mitochondrial volume per unit cell volume) is unchanged in the remnant kidney, which indicates that mitochondria grow in parallel with the overall increase in cell size (49). Ch'ih & Devlin demonstrated a 30% increase in the DNA/protein ratio in isolated mitochondria 24 h after uninephrectomy; this ratio returns to control values by 36 h as mitochondrial protein content increases (12). Since there was no increase in [^{3}H]thymidine incorporation into DNA, which would have explained the increased DNA/protein ratio, it was assumed that transient stabilization of this DNA pool occurs.

The foregoing information indicates that mitogenesis plays a quantitatively small role in compensatory growth of the adult kidney, and that growth in cell size is the predominant adaptation.

RNA Metabolism

In contrast to the relatively stable DNA content of the hypertrophied adult kidney, RNA content rises progressively following partial ablation of renal mass (36). Measurable changes in the RNA/DNA ratio (an increase of approximately 25%) occur around 24 h (30, 36).

Different approaches have been used to determine the cause of the increased RNA levels. Injection of radiolabeled precursors (orotic acid or uridine) have yielded conflicting results, probably because the size of the unlabeled precursor pool may change following uninephrectomy. Thus Hill et al, by measuring the specific activity of the uridine triphosphate (UTP) pool, were unable to demonstrate an increase in [5-^{3}H]uridine incorporation into RNA 48 h after nephrectomy (25). Cortes et al, on the other hand, showed a paradoxical decrease in incorporation of radiolabeled orotic acid and uridine in vitro (14). These investigators found that the UTP pool had increased by 21% 24 h after nephrectomy, which suggests that the isotopic incorporation rate is invalid as a measure of RNA synthesis in this model. When they infused [5-^{3}H]orotic acid in vivo for 2 h and measured the true specific activity of the isotope, they found an increase in RNA synthesis by 12 h and a plateau in the synthetic rate after 24 h. Since the majority of cellular RNA is ribosomal RNA (rRNA), changes in total RNA pools mostly reflect rRNA and may obscure small but important changes in mRNA levels. Since the period of labeling (2 h) was only a fraction of the estimated half-life of renal rRNA [4–6 days (45)], it is unlikely that changes in degradation could explain their findings. Indeed, Hill measured the degradation rate of RNA labeled prior to uninephrectomy and found no evidence of increased degradation up to 5 days after the operation (24); he also found that synthesis of RNA precursors was the same in uninephrectomy as in controls. Assuming that precursor pools were identical, he concluded that rRNA accretion must involve decreased degradation of newly synthesized rather than preexisting rRNA.

The controversy over increased transcription versus decreased degradation of rRNA has apparently been laid to rest by the definitive study of Ouellette and colleagues, who demonstrated, by direct measurement of transcription, using in vitro nuclear run-off methods, that nuclei from kidneys obtained 6–48 h after uninephrectomy show an increase of up to 150% in the rate of transcription of ribosomal precursor RNA (46). Increased rates of transcription were evident as early as 6 h after uninephrectomy. In contrast to the increasing ribosomal RNA levels, steady state levels of mRNAs for the ribosomal proteins S16 and L10 were unchanged. If coordinate increases in the levels of rRNA and ribosomal proteins are required for ribosome synthesis, increasingly efficient translation of existing ribosomal protein mRNAs or posttranscriptional stabilization must occur. The mechanism that increases rRNA transcription is unknown; Oulette et al suggest that this is due to recruitment of normally inactive genes (46). It is of interest that a decrease in renal mass, induced by a protein-depleted diet, is associated with a decrease in rRNA mass (28), which suggests that changes in rRNA levels closely parallel increases and decreases of kidney mass.

Vandewalle et al have shown that the most active sites of RNA synthesis in the nephron, as measured by [^{3}H]uridine incorporation, are the thick ascending limb and the distal convoluted tubule (60). Administration of DOCA, a mineralocorticoid that acts predominantly on the collecting tubule, increases RNA synthesis predominantly in this segment (59). However, despite the fact that the proximal tubule is not a target site for DOCA, an increase in uridine incorporation was also observed. This is presumably linked to the increase in GFR and tubular hypertrophy (35) that accompanies volume expansion with salt plus mineralocorticoid.

Information on mRNA metabolism is scanty, and since mRNA constitutes only a small fraction of total RNA, no inferences can be drawn from studies of total rRNA. Ouellette demonstrated the stability of mouse kidney poly A$^+$

mRNA by pulse-chase analysis using [^{3}H]orotate (45). A biphasic decay was noted: one component decayed with a half-life of 24 h and the other with a half-life of 6 h. These decay rates were not influenced by uninephrectomy. He was also able to label an mRNA pool with a half-life of only 1–2 h, but studies of its turnover in hypertrophy are not available.

Additional information on mRNA is discussed below in the context of specific gene expression.

Protein Metabolism

Surprisingly, very little work has been done in this area in the last decade. Although an increase in the protein/cell ratio is the hallmark of hypertrophy, it is still not clear whether this is achieved predominantly by a process of increased synthesis or decreased degradation. Using [^{3H}]leucine incorporation, Coe & Korty showed that protein synthesis following uninephrectomy is unchanged within the first 24 h, increases to 20% above control values within 48 h, and then remains constant up to 96 h despite the fact that renal protein content rises continuously from 0–96 h (12a). These data, which must be interpreted with caution since leucine transport rates and intracellular pools of leucine were not measured, support the notion that decreased protein degradation plays an important role in protein accumulation, but that an increase in synthetic rate accounts for the earliest increase in protein content.

In the renal hypertrophy of streptozotocin-induced diabetes mellitus, the activities of the intralysosomal proteolytic enzymes cathepsin B and cathepsin L are decreased in the proximal tubule and this may contribute to decreased protein degradation (58). Hypertrophy can be induced in cultured proximal tubular cells by adding insulin to the medium (15). Serum deprivation stimulates proteolysis in these cells, an effect that is completely inhibited by insulin (58). Thus, there is accumulating evidence that decreased degradation contributes to protein accretion in various models of hypertrophy. The role of coordinate changes in synthetic and degradative rates requires further study.

GENE EXPRESSION IN RENAL HYPERTROPHY

While a large body of literature exists on patterns of gene expression in cycling cells, i.e. in hyperplasia, the predominant growth pattern in the adult kidney is not cell proliferation but hypertrophy. hence, extrapolations from these studies and from studies on regeneration, such as occurs in the liver (20), are not applicable to renal hypertrophy One fundamental difference between liver regeneration and compensatory renal growth is the expression of gene products required for ribosomal synthesis. Whereas genes for pre-rRNA constituents are induced in renal hypertrophy (45), they are not in liver regeneration (20). Another important difference lies in steady state mRNA levels for various proto-oncogenes (c-*myc,* c-*ras*^{Ha}, c-*ras*^{K} and c-*fos*). These are all increased with different and specific time-courses following partial hepatectomy whereas significant change in mRNA levels occur within the first 72 h after uninephrectomy (5).

One approach to understanding gene expression in renal growth is to examine models in which the molecular mechanisms of gene expression can be modified by a single factor; androgen-induced renal growth is one such model (6, 7, 10). This review does not address this topic. One important observation, however, requires attention. Whereas the concentrations of several mRNA's in mouse kidney increase in response to testosterone, this is achieved not by an increased rate of transcription but by mRNA stabilization (7). It is obviously important to determine whether such posttranscriptional mechanisms apply to other forms of renal hypertrophy.

THE NATURE OF CELL GROWTH IN RENAL HYPERTROPHY

In the terminology of the traditional cell cycle, enlargement of the cell and an increase in protein content starts during the G_1, or pre-DNA synthetic, phase. Since renal cells are basically nondividing cells with low mitotic rates, they can be thought of as being in a quiescent state, otherwise referred to as G_o. There are two basic mechanisms whereby the cell may increase in size and protein content without entering DNA synthesis or undergoing division. In the first case the cell may exit from G_o, enter and progress through G_1, and be inhibited at some point in G_1 prior to the S phase of DNA synthesis. Alternately, the growth in size and protein content may occur by a process that is fundamentally different from that which occurs early in the cell cycle.

In support of the first mechanism we have shown that it is possible to produce hypertrophy of proximal tubular cells in vitro by adding an inhibitor of DNA synthesis to a combination of mitogens. A combination of insulin plus hydrocortisone is mitogenic for these cells. When the growth inhibitor derived from BSC-1 monkey kidney epithelial cells (shown to be virtually identical to transforming growth factor β) was added together with the above mitogens, the increase in [^{3}H]thymidine incorporation was inhibited, but enlargement of the cells and an increase in protein content occurred (16). These studies show that it is possible to induce hypertrophy by inhibiting DNA synthesis, but the relationship to in vivo hypertrophy is not clear.

One approach to differentiating between the two patterns of growth described above is to examine gene expression in the early period following the stimulus to hypertrophy or proliferate. For instance, specific inhibition of the S phase of the cell cycle with cytochalasin does not alter the pattern of gene expression prior to the point of inhibition of DNA synthesis (53). Thus, by comparing cells undergoing hyperplasia versus hypertrophy in vivo, the pattern of early gene expression in cycling cells can be compared with that observed in hypertrophying cells. If inhibition in G_1 is the basic mechanism of hypertrophy, the patterns of early gene expression should be the same in hypertrophy and hyperplasia, whereas if alternate mechanisms of hypertrophy exist, mRNA levels would not be expected to follow the pattern observed early in the hyperplastic response.

We have recently compared steady state mRNA levels for a variety of proto-oncogenes, transport proteins, and structural proteins in kidneys induced to undergo regenerative hyperplasia following acute folic acid–induced injury or compensatory hypertrophy following uninephrectomy. All of these genes are expressed in a cell-cycle-dependent fashion. These studies showed that the patterns of expression of mRNAs for c-*fos*, c-*myc*, c-*ras*[Ha], B-actin, vimentin, Na,K-ATPase (α and β subunits) ADP-ATP translocase, and calcyclin were fundamentally different in the two models (42). Whereas in regenerative hyperplasia there are rapid transient increases in mRNA levels, with a peak at 4–6 h, in the hypertrophy following uninephrectomy, most mRNA levels show a slow, progressive increase and remain elevated for up to 2 weeks. By studying mRNA levels over an extended period in the latter model we were able to show that the earlier observation that mRNA levels increase only minimally within 72 h of uninephrectomy (5) represents only the earliest phase of a process that takes longer to evolve. As long as the cell continues to increase in size, it appears as if most mRNA levels increase in parallel. Since cells obtained from uninephrectomized animals do not incorporate [^{3}H]thymidine into DNA and do not enter the S, G_2, or M phases of the cell cycle (42), it is possible to conclude that cell enlargement in renal hypertrophy is due not to an interruption of the normal cycle but to a unique growth process that requires further definition. This process can be regarded as one of "sustained message amplification."

CONCLUSION

Figure 1 summarizes our present understanding of the process of renal hypertrophy. Studies of gene expression and initiating events in renal hypertrophy are in their infancy. It is important to know if there are unique signalling events that initiate the unique process of cell enlargement, which is the hallmark of hypertrophy. If a single gene product is responsible for

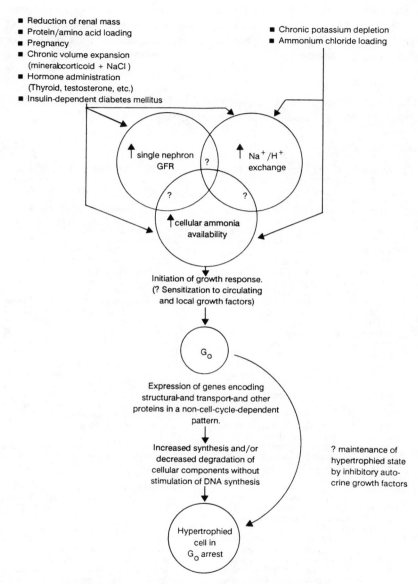

Figure 1   Putative sequence of events leading to renal tubular hypertrophy.

initiating a cascade of events that ultimately leads to symmetrical hypertrophy of all of the cell's constituents, it may become possible to induce or inhibit renal hypertrophy by the appropriate in vivo manipulation of transcriptional or posttranscriptional events.

ACKNOWLEDGMENTS

This work was supported by grants ROI DK25301, ROI DK36955, and ROI DK34049 from the National Institutes of Health.

Literature Cited

1. Allison, M. E. M., Wilson, C. B., Gottschalk, C. W. 1974. Pathophysiology of experimental glomerulitis in rats. *J. Clin. Invest.* 53:1402–23
2. Arataki, M. 1926. Experimental researches on the compensatory enlargement of the surviving kidney after unilateral nephrectomy (albino rat). *Am. J. Anat.* 36:437–50
3. Argyrus, T. S., Trimble, M. E. 1964. The growth promoting effects of damage in the damaged and contralateral kidneys in the mouse. *Anat. Rec.* 150:1–10
4. Arrizurieta de Muchnik, E. E., Lipham, E. M., Gottschalk, C. W. 1969. Form and function in normal and hypertrophied nephrons. In *Compensatory Renal Hypertrophy*, ed. W. W. Nowinski, R. J. Goss, pp. 29–42. New York: Academic
5. Beer, D. G., Zweifel, K. A., Simpson, D. P., Pitot, H. C. 1987. Specific gene expression during compensatory renal hypertrophy in the rat. *J. Cell. Physiol.* 131:29–35
6. Berger, F. G., Gross, K. W., Watson, G. 1981. Isolation and characterization of a DNA sequence complementary to an androgen-inducible messenger RNA from mouse kidney. *J. Biol. Chem.* 256:7006–13
7. Berger, F. G., Loose, D., Meisner, H., Watson, G. 1986. Androgen induction of messenger RNA in mouse kidney is posttranscriptional. *Biochemistry* 25:1170–75
8. Bouby, N., Bankir, L., Trinh-Trang-Tan, M. M., Minuth, W. W., Kriz, W. 1985. Selective ADH-induced hypertrophy of the medullary thick ascending limb in Brattleboro rats. *Kidney Int.* 28:456–66
9. Bouby, N., Trinh-Trang-Tan, M. M., Laouari, D., Kleinkuecht, C., Grünfeld, J. P., et al. 1988. *Kidney Int.* In press
10. Catterall, J. F., Kontula, K. K., Watson, C. S., Seppanen, P. J., Funkenstein, B., et al. 1986. Regulation of gene expression by androgens in murine kidney. *Recent Progr. Horm. Res.* 42:71–109
11. Celsi, G., Jakobssen, B., Aperia, A. 1986. Influence of age on compensatory renal growth in rats. *Pediatr. Res.* 20:347–50
12. Ch'ih, J. J., Devlin, T. M. 1973. Biogenesis of mammalian mitochondria in the reniprival kidney. II. Aspects of mitochondrial DNA synthesis. *Arch. Biochem. Biophys.* 156:26–33
12a. Coe, F. L., Korty, P. R. 1967. Protein synthesis during compensatory renal renal hypertrophy. *Am. J. Physiol.* 213:1585–89
13. Cohn, D. E., Hruska, K. A., Klahr, S., Hammerman, M. R. 1982. Increased Na^+-H^+ exchange in brushborder vesicles from dogs with renal failure. *Am. J. Physiol.* 243:F293–F299
14. Cortes, P., Levin, N. W., Martin, P. R. 1976. Ribonucleic acid synthesis in the renal cortex at the initiation of compensatory growth. *Biochem. J.* 158:457–70
14a. Fine, L. G. 1986. The biology of renal hypertrophy. *Kidney Int.* 29:619–34
15. Fine, L. G., Badie-Dezfooly, B., Lowe, A. G., Hamzeh, A., Wells, J., et al. 1985. Stimulation of Na^+/H^+ antiport is an early event in hypertrophy of renal proximal tubular cells. *Proc. Natl. Acad. Sci. USA* 32:1736–40
16. Fine, L. G., Holley, R. W., Nasri, H., Badie-Dezfooly, B. 1985. BSC-1 growth inhibitor transforms a mitogenic stimulus into a hypertrophic stimulus for renal proximal tubular cells: Relationship to Na^+/H^+ antiport activity. *Proc. Natl. Acad. Sci. USA* 82:6163–66
17. Fine, L. G., Nord, E. P., Danovitch, G. M., Kurtz, I., Bacallao, R. 1988. Pathophysiology and nephron adaptation in chronic renal failure. In *Diseases of the Kidney*, ed. R. W. Shrier, C. W.

Gottschalk, pp. 2985–3018. Boston: Little Brown

18. Fine, L. G., Trizna, W., Bourgoignie, J. J., Bricker, N. S. 1978. Functional profile of the isolated uremic nephron. Role of compensatory hypertrophy in the control of fluid reabsorption by the proximal straight tubule. *J. Clin. Invest.* 61:1508–18

19. Deleted in proof

20. Friedman, J. M., Chung, E. Y., Darnell, J. E. Jr. 1984. Gene expression during liver regeneration. *J. Mol. Biol.* 179:37–53

21. Golchini, K., Norman, J., Kurtz, I. 1988. NH_4Cl in the absence of extracellular acidemia induces hypertrophy and increased Na^+/H^+ antiport activity in monkey proximal tubule cells (JTC cells). *Kidney Int.* 33:157 (Abstr.)

22. Haber, R. S., Pressley, T. A., Loeb, J. N., Edelman, I. S., Ismail-Beigi, F. 1987. Ionic dependence of active Na-K transport: "clamping" of cellular Na with monensin. *Am. J. Physiol.* 253:F26–F33

23. Harris, R. C., Seifter, J. L., Brenner, B. M. 1984. Adaptation of Na^+-H^+ exchange in renal nicrovillus membrane vesicles. Role of dietary protein and nephrectomy. *J. Clin. Invest.* 74:1979–87

24. Hill, J. M. 1975. Ribosomal RNA metabolism during renal hypertrophy. Evidence of decreased degradation of newly synthesized ribosomal RNA. *J. Cell Biol.* 64:260–65

25. Hill, J. M., Geert, A. B., Malt, R. A. 1974. Ribonucleic acid labelling and nucleotide pools during compensatory hypertrophy. *Biochem. J.* 144:447–53

26. Hruska, K. A., Klahr, S., Hammerman, M. R. 1982. Decreased luminal membrane transport of phosphate in chronic renal failure. *Am. J. Physiol.* 242:F17–F22

27. Hruska, K. A., Urowskowitz, D., Esbrit, P., Civitelli, R., Westbrook, S., et al. 1987. Stimulation of inositol triphosphate and diacylglycerol production in renal tubular cells by parathyroid hormone. *J. Clin. Invest.* 79:230–39

28. Iapalucci-Espinoza, S., Bur, J. A., Pucciarelli, M. G., Corde, R. D. 1986. Decreased formation and keeping of ribosomes during dietary recovery of mouse kidney. *Am. J. Physiol.* 251:E266–E272

29. Ichikawa, I., Hoyer, J. R., Seiler, M. W., Brenner, B. M., 1982. Mechanism of glomerulotubular balance in the setting of heterogenous glomerular injury. *J. Clin. Invest.* 69:185–98

30. Jelinek, J., Vesela, H., Valvova, S.

1964. The effect of nortestosterone phenylpronate on compensatory hypertrophy of the remaining kidney after unilateral nephrectomy. *Acta Endocrinol.* 46:352–59

31. Jobin, J., Taylor, C. M., Caverzasio, J., Bonjouir, J. P. 1984. Calcium restriction and parathyroid hormone enhance renal compensatory growth. *Am. J. Physiol.* 246:F685–F690

32. Johnson, H. A. 1969. Cytoplasmic response to overwork. See Ref. 4, pp. 9–25

33. Johnson, H. A., Vera Roman, J. M. 1966. Compensatory renal enlargement: hypertrophy vs. hyperplasia. *Am. J. Pathol.* 49:1–13

34. Johnston, J. R., Brenner, B. M., Hebert, S. C. 1987. Uniphrectomy and dietary protein affect fluid absorption in rabbit proximal straight tubule. *Am. J. Physiol.* 253:F222–F233

35. Knepper, M. A., Burg, M. B. 1981. Increased fluid absorption and cell volume in isolated rabbit proximal straight tubules after in vivo DOCA administration. *Am. J. Physiol.* 241:F502–F508

36. Malt, R. A. 1969. Compensatory growth of the kidney. *N. Engl. J. Med.* 280:1446–54

37. Miskell, C. A., Simpson, D. P. 1988. The effects of dietary protein on DNA and protein synthsis after sham, unilateral and 5/6 nephrectomy. *Kidney Int.* 33:380 (Abstr.)

38. Moolenaar, W. H. 1986. Effects of growth factors on intracellular pH regulation. *Ann. Rev. Physiol.* 48:363–76

39. Nord, E. P., Hafezi, A., Kaunitz, J., Trizna, W., Fine, L. G. 1985. pH gradient-dependent increased Na^+-H^+ antiport capacity of the rabbit remnant kidney. *Am. J. Physiol.* 249:F90–F98

40. Nord, E. P., Schlosser, J., Norman, J. 1988. Bradykinin and EGF stimulate c-myc mRNA expression in rabbit proximal tubule cells but result in disparate effects on cell proliferation. *Kidney Int.* 33:168 (Abstr.)

41. Norman, J. T., Bowen, J., McDonough, A., Fine, L. G. 1988. Early gene expression differs in renal cortical cells undergoing hypertrophy or hyperplasia. *Kidney Int.* 33:168 (Abstr.)

42. Norman, J. T., Bohman, R., Fischmann, G., Bowen, J. W., McDonough, A., et al. 1988. Patterns of mRNA expression during early cell growth differ in kidney epithelial cells destined to undergo compensatory hypertrophy versus regenerative hyperplasia. *Proc. Natl. Acad. Sci. USA* 85:6768–72

43. Oliver, J. 1939. In *Architecture of the Kidney in Chronic Bright's Disease.* New York: Hoeber
44. Oliver, J. 1944. New directions in renal morphology: A method, its results and its future. *Harvey Lect.* 40:102–55
45. Ouellette, A. J. 1978. Messenger RNA in compensatory renal hypertrophy. *Yale J. Biol. Med.* 51:413–18
46. Ouellette, A. J., Moonka, R., Zelenitz, A. D., Malt, R. A. 1987. Regulation of ribosome synthesis during compensatory renal hypertrophy in mice. *Am. J. Physiol.* 253:C506–C513
47. Pressley, T. A., Haber, R. S., Loeb, J. N., Edelman, I. S., Ismail-Beigi, F. 1986. Stimulation of Na, K-activated adenosine triphosphatase and active transport by low external K^+ in a rat liver cell line. *J. Gen. Physiol.* 87:591–606
48. Reiter, R. J. 1965. Cellular preparation of deoxyribonucleic acid synthesis in compensating kidneys of mice and the effect of food and water restriction. *Lab. Invest.* 14:1636–43
49. Salehmoghaddam, S., Bradley, T., Mikhail, N., Badie-Dezfooly, B., Nord, E. P., et al. 1985. Hypertrophy of basolateral Na-K-pump activity in the proximal tubule of the remnant kidney. *Lab. Invest.* 53:443–52
50. Saphir, O. 1927. The state of the glomerulus in experimental hypertrophy of the kidneys of rabbits. *Am. J. Pathol.* 3:329–42
51. Seifter, J. L., Harris, R. C. 1984. Chronic K^+ depletion increases Na^+-H^+ exchange in rat renal cortical brush border membrane vesicles. *Kidney Int.* 24:302 (Abstr.)
52. Tabei, K., Levinson, D. J., Brenner, B. M. 1983. Early enhancement of fluid transport in rabbit proximal straight tubules after loss of contralateral renal excretory function. *J. Clin. Invest.* 72:871–81
53. Takasuka, T., Ishibashi, S., Ide, T. 1987. Expression of cell cycle dependent genes in serum stimulated cells whose entry into S phase is blocked by cytochalasin D. *Biochim. Biophys. Acta* 909:161–64
54. Toback, F. G. 1984. Phosphatidylcholine metabolism during renal growth and regeneration. *Am. J. Physiol.* 246:F249–F259
55. Toback, F. G., Havener, L. J., Spargo, B. H. 1977. Stimulation of renal phospholipid formation during potassium depletion. *Am. J. Physiol.* 233:E212–E218
56. Tolins, J. P., Hostetter, M. K., Hostetter, T. H. 1987. Hypokalemic nephropathy in the rat. Role of ammonia in chronic tubular injury. *J. Clin. Invest.* 79:1447–58
57. Trizna, W., Yanagawa, N., Bar-Khayim, Y., Houston, B., Fine, L. G. 1978. Functional profile of the isolated uremic nephron. Evidence of proximal tubular "memory" in experimental renal disease. *J. Clin. Invest.* 68:760–67
58. Tsao, T., Mortimore, G. E., Crapoe, E., Rabkin, R. 1988. Insuling inhibits accelerated proteolysis in serum-deprived cultured kidney cells. *Kidney Int.* 33:396 (Abstr.)
59. Vandewalle, A. 1984. Heterogeneity of uridine incorporation along the rabbit nephron. II. Effect of DOCA. *Am. J. Physiol.* 246:F427–F436
60. Vandewalle, A., Farman, N., Cluzeaud, F., Bonvalet, J. P. 1984. Heterogeneity of uridine incorporation along the rabbit nephron. I. Autoradiographic study. *Am. J. Physiol.* 246:F417–F426
61. Vigne, P., Jean, T., Baoboy, P., Frelin, C., Fine, L. G., et al. 1985. [^{3}H] ethylpropylamiloride, a ligand to analyze the properties of the Na^+/H^+ exchange system in the membranes of normal and hypertrophied kidneys. *J. Biol. Chem.* 260:12120–25
62. Walsh-Reitz, M. M., Toback, F. G. 1983. Kidney epithelial cell growth is stimulated by lowering extracellular potassium concentration. *Am. J. Physiol.* 244:C249–C432
63. Wilson, G. D., Soranson, J. A., Heurs, A. A. 1987. Cell kinetics of mouse kidney using bromodeoxyuridine incorporation and flow cytometry: Preparation and staining. *Cell Tissue Kinet.* 20:125–33
64. Wolitsky, B. A., Fambrough, D. M. 1986. Regulation of the $(Na^+ + K^+)$-ATPase in cultured chick skeletal muscles. Modulation of expression by the demand for ion transport. *J. Biol. Chem.* 261:9990–99
65. Yokemura, K., Cheng, L., Sacktor, B. 1988. Effect of L-triiodo-thyronine in Na^+-H^+ exchange activity in cultured opposum kidney cells. *Kidney Int.* 33:177 (Abstr.)

Annu. Rev. Physiol. 1988. 51:33–50

AUTOCRINE AND PARACRINE REGULATION OF KIDNEY EPITHELIAL CELL GROWTH

Susan R. Mendley and F. Gary Toback

Department of Medicine, The University of Chicago, Chicago, Illinois 60637

INTRODUCTION

Cell growth is a restrained and highly regulated phenomenon in most tissues, including the adult kidney (76). The growth response to loss of renal mass is largely hypertrophic, which leads to an increase in tubule length and cell size (44); only 25% of the compensatory enlargement of the remaining kidney after uninephrectomy is believed to be due to hyperplasia (57, 95). Proliferation of renal epithelial cells is normal following tubular necrosis, but it is self-limited and orderly. Unregulated proliferation is pathological; in the kidney it manifests itself as carcinoma and cystic disease. This review examines the mechanisms that regulate renal cell growth.

From the standpoint of proliferation, a population of cells can be divided into three groups (8). Cells in the first group divide continuously, going from mitosis through the G_1 (resting) phase of the cell cycle, the S (DNA synthesis) phase, the G_2 phase, and then to another mitosis. The rapidly proliferating cells of the bone marrow, which probably have no counterpart in adult kidney, are a good example of this group. The second group includes cells that leave the cell cycle after a few divisions and differentiate, never to divide again. Mature granulocytes are such terminally differentiated cells. Lastly, some cells temporarily leave the cycle and remain reproductively dormant (in G_o phase) although they still perform their differentiated functions. This seems to describe the state of most cells of the kidney (8). These cells can be induced to reenter the cell cycle by an appropriate environmental signal.

What types of environmental signals trigger division of quiescent renal cells? It appears that extracellular polypeptide messengers, termed growth

33

0066-4278/89/0315-0033$02.00

factors, can stimulate dormant cells to reenter S phase from G_o. These proteins affect target cells by binding to specific cell surface receptors. This ligand-receptor interaction results in the activation of an intracellular effector component, which is often the tyrosine kinase domain of the receptor (54). Studies are underway in many laboratories to define the cascade of postreceptor events that initiate DNA synthesis following the interaction of a growth factor with its receptor. An increased understanding of the physiological roles of many growth factors has resulted from their purification and subsequent determination of their amino acid sequence. In addition, isolation of complementary DNAs (cDNAs) encoding the growth factors indicates that most growth factors are derived from larger molecules by proteolytic processing (54) (Table 1). Moreover, the isolation of cDNA probes has facilitated studies of the regulation of the genes encoding these proteins. Additional studies, stimulated by the availability of purified growth factors, indicate that many of these proteins have physiological effects unrelated to their mitogenic properties.

Epidermal growth factor (EGF) and the insulin-like growth factors (IGFs) act on renal cells to enhance exit from the G_o/G_1 phase of the cell cycle (48, 53, 110). By contrast, transforming growth factor-type beta (TGF-β) acts as a growth inhibitor of kidney epithelial cells in culture and impedes their exit from G_o (47, 49, 118). Thus, it appears that renal cells may be subject to both tonic inhibition and stimulation of growth. These observations and the low mitotic index (0.1%) in renal tissue in vivo (76) suggest that growth inhibitory controls normally predominate. This balance can be shifted when growth is required.

Table 1 Structural characteristics of polypeptide growth factors.

Growth factor[a]	Protein size[b]		mRNA Size[c]	Signal Peptide	References
	Precursor	Mature			
hTGF-β1	390	112	2.5	Yes	28, 29
mTGF-β2	414	112	2.4	Yes	42
hEGF	1207	53	5.0	Yes	11
hTGF-α	160	50	4.8	Yes	30
hIGF-I	156	70	9.0, 5.3, 7.7	Yes	12, 55, 90
hIGF-II	180	67	4.9, 6.0[d]	Yes	12, 13, 89
hPDGF-A	211	125	1.9, 2.3, 2.8	Yes	15
hPDGF-B	240	160	4.2	Yes	15
haFGF	155	140	4.8	No	56
hbFGF	155	146	2.2, 4.6	No	2, 3

[a]Source of growth factor: h, human; m, monkey. TGF, transforming growth factor; EGF, epidermal growth factor; IGF, insulin-like growth factor; PDGF, platelet-derived growth factor; aFGF, acidic fibroblast growth factor; bFGF, basic fibroblast growth factor.
[b]Values are number of amino acids.
[c]Values are number of kilobases.
[d]Values are for adult kidney tissue; sizes differ in fetal kidney and other tissues.

Figure 1 illustrates various mechanisms whereby cell-cell communication can be mediated by peptide messengers. Endocrine signaling occurs when hormones are secreted into blood or lymph for transport to distant cell target sites. A paracrine signaling cell secretes proteins that affect only adjacent target cells that have functional growth factor receptors on their surface. In autocrine signaling, cells respond to protein factors that they have released themselves. Thus, cells participating in an autocrine mechanism both secrete the growth factor and express receptors for it on the plasma membrane (105). Autocrine and paracrine mechanisms seem to represent more primitive regulatory mechanisms; endocrine systems are probably a later evolutionary development. Recently, a mechanism that is entirely intracellular was described for autocrine stimulation in v-*sis* transformed cells: the growth factor and its receptor interact in the cell and binding takes place within intracellular compartments (63). At present, it appears that this mechanism is limited to v-*sis* transformed cells.

Autocrine secretion of growth factors may occur as a transient, normal physiological process during repair of tissue injury or during embryological development, when particularly rapid growth of cells is necessary. The autocrine hypothesis of Sporn & Todaro states that one way a cancer cell can become independent of external growth inhibitory control is by synthesizing growth factors for which it possesses receptors (105). In fact, excess secretion may not be the only means of autocrine stimulation. Unrestrained growth of malignant cells could be mediated by increased receptor number or affinity, enhanced intracellular response to ligand-receptor binding, or abnormal regulation of receptor biosynthesis, e.g. failure of the ligand to reduce the number

ENDOCRINE   PARACRINE   AUTOCRINE

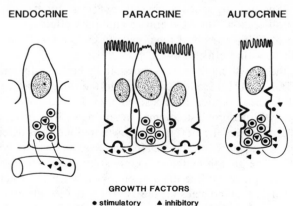

GROWTH FACTORS
● stimulatory   ▲ inhibitory

Figure 1   Schema for growth regulation by autocrine, paracrine, and endocrine mechanisms. The cells shown are capable of synthesis and release of growth-inhibitory and growth-stimulatory polypeptide messengers such as growth factors, which are depicted as zymogens in the cytoplasm. The thickened curved and angular regions of the plasma membrane indicate receptor sites for growth-promoting and growth-inhibitory molecules, respectively.

of cell surface receptors (down-regulation) (103). Other possible mechanisms involve diminished tonic release of a growth inhibitor or a reduction in the number or responsiveness of its cellular receptors (122).

New knowledge about growth factors has begun to make an impact on the study of renal cell physiology. This review focuses on growth factors produced by renal epithelial and mesangial cells in culture and those isolated from kidney tissue.

TRANSFORMING GROWTH FACTOR β

The low mitotic index of many tissues in the adult organism, including kidney, suggested to many investigators that a negative-feedback system exists to limit cell growth. In 1962, Bullough (19) used the term "chalone" to describe a substance extracted from skin that inhibited mitosis in epidermal cells, and in 1978, Holley and coworkers provided evidence (47) for a growth inhibitor protein produced by renal epithelial cells in culture. The presence of growth-inhibitory activity was inferred from observations made on crowded cultures of nontransformed monkey kidney epithelial cells of the BSC-1 line. It was found that stimulation of [³H]thymidine incorporation into DNA occurred when conditioned medium containing 0.1% serum was replaced by fresh, serum-free medium. Additional studies indicated that initiation of DNA synthesis was due to the removal of a growth inhibitor(s) in the conditioned medium (47). The purified inhibitor protein arrested sparse cultures of growing cells in G_1, but proliferation resumed when the inhibitor was removed. This reversible effect on cell growth and the low concentration required for inhibition (1 ng/ml) suggested a physiological role for the inhibitor in the control of proliferation. Since the growth inhibitory effect could be overcome by addition of EGF, growth of renal cells in culture could be regulated by factors with opposing effects (49).

In 1984, the growth inhibitor was shown to be biologically and chemically similar to TGF-β (118). Both factors bind to the same cell receptor, inhibit [³H]thymidine incorporation in mouse-embryo derived AKR-2B cells, and stimulate growth of fibroblast colonies in soft agar. Recently, the complete amino acid sequence of the BSC-1 cell growth inhibitor was determined from the nucleotide sequence of the cDNA and was shown to correspond to TGF-$\beta2$ (42). The growth inhibitor is derived by proteolytic processing of a 414–amino acid precursor; the mature, biologically active protein comprises the C-terminal 112 amino acids (Table 1). There is 71% identity between the sequences of monkey TGF-$\beta2$ and human TGF-$\beta1$ (28), two closely related proteins with similar properties.

The TGFs are a group of polypeptides first found in the medium of virally-transformed 3T3 fibroblasts and were characterized by their ability to induce reversibly the transformed phenotype (anchorage-independent growth in soft agar) in nontransformed fibroblasts (25). TGF-β requires the concommitant binding of EFG or TGF-α to induce transformation (104). Human TGF-β1 has an apparent M_r of 25,000 and is composed of two chains linked by disulfide bonds. TGF-β1 (a homodimer of two linked β1 chains) has been isolated from a number of different mammalian tissues including bovine kidney and human platelets (4,92); it is identical to cartilage-inducing factor A. TGF-β2 (a homodimer of two β2 chains), which is apparently identical to cartilage-inducing factor B, is found in porcine, but not human, platelets (104). Recently, a heterodimer form has been described, TGF-β1.2 (23). There is a family of TGF-β receptors that bind the various forms of the ligand; moreover, each receptor has a different affinity for each form of TGF-β (23). The physiological role of this variation in affinities is not known but may permit modulation of the effects of TGF-β through control of receptor expression.

TGF-β is probably made by all cells but its effects depend on cell type (104). It is mitogenic for cells of mesenchymal origin, but anti-mitogenic for epithelial cells, endothelial cells, and T and B lymphocytes in culture. TGF-β is released in an inactive precursor form and is unable to bind to receptors until activated by proteolytic cleavage or exposure to an acidic pH (67, 68). Since the cellular receptor seems to be universally expressed, activation of latent TGF-β may be an important step regulating the physiological function of the molecule.

Several effects of TGF-β2 have been described in both epithelial and fibroblast lines. Within 5 hours of adding TGF-β2 to BSC-1 cells, a protein of apparent M_r 48,000 was secreted (81). This inhibitor-inducible protein was termed IIP48. The addition of actinomycin D or cycloheximide blocked production of IIP48, which indicates that mRNA and protein synthesis are necessary for its appearance. Subsequent work has shown a dissociation between the TGF-β2-induced inhibition of DNA synthesis and production of IIP48, which suggests that IIP48 does not mediate the arrest of cells in G_1 (112). IIP48 is immunoprecipitated by an antibody to bovine endothelial plasminogen activator inhibitor. As a protease-inhibitor, the physiological role of IIP48 may be to limit the proteolytic cleavage of TGF-β2 and to prevent formation of the active peptide. Thus, one of its effects may be feedback inhibition of further activation of TGF-β2.

In studies of primary cultures of rabbit proximal tubular cells, TGF-β2 has been shown to transform a mitogenic stimulus into a hypertrophic one (33). In this system, insulin and hydrocortisone increase [^{3}H]thymidine incorporation, cell volume, and the amount of protein per cell. Addition of purified TGF-β2 inhibited stimulation of [^{3}H]thymidine incorporation in a dose-dependent fashion, but did not inhibit increases in cell volume or protein per cell. Thus, hypertrophy of cells occurred in the absence of mitogenesis. These observations may be relevant to compensatory renal growth after uninephrectomy. Perhaps release of a growth inhibitor by kidney cells in vivo converts what might otherwise have been a hyperplastic response into cellular hypertrophy.

In renal epithelial cells (BSC-1 line), TGF-β2 inhibited the increase in cell sodium content (125) that characterizes the onset of growth (24, 64, 101). Studies in fibroblast lines have demonstrated an effect of TGF-β1 on glucose and amino acid uptake (16, 52). In 3T3 and BALB/MK-1 cells, TGF-β1 stimulated uptake of 2-deoxyglucose in an EGF-dependent fashion (52). In NRK-49F fibroblasts, TGF-β1 has been shown to stimulate glycolysis by a methionine-sensitive mechanism (16). The uptake of amino acids via system A was studied with methylaminoisobutyrate and was found to be stimulated by TGF-β1 and EGF.

A major effect of TGF-β1 is its contribution to the production and maintenance of the extracellular matrix. TGF-β1-induced synthesis of fibronectin and its incorporation into the matrix have been demonstrated in a lung epithelial line and several different fibroblast lines (51, 93). Actinomycin D can block the increase in fibronectin, which indicates that transcription of mRNA is required for the increase in fibronectin production. In cells that do not make fibronectin, proteins of apparent molecular masses of 140, 170, and 190 kilodaltons (kDa), probably procollagens, are synthesized and incorporated into the matrix in response to TGF-β1 (51). These effects of TGF-β1 on production of matrix proteins appear to enhance wound healing (51, 80, 93). It is not known if TGF-β participates in renal regeneration after tubular injury.

EPIDERMAL GROWTH FACTOR

EGF is the most extensively studied and best characterized stimulatory polypeptide growth factor discussed in this review. Originally isolated from extracts of mouse submandibular gland, EGF causes precocious eyelid opening and incisor eruption when injected into newborn mice (21). EGF has since been found in urine, milk, saliva, plasma, and many tissues of humans and other species. It is a potent mitogen for cells in culture, including those of renal epithelial origin (48). Human EGF is identical to urogastrone, a gastric antisecretory hormone isolated from human urine (21). Mouse and human EGF are single chain polypeptides of 53 amino acids with an apparent M_r of 6045, containing three intramolecular disulfide bonds that are required for biological activity.

Specific saturable receptors for EGF have been demonstrated using [^{125}I]EGF in a wide variety of tissues and cultured cells (20). The EGF receptor protein (M_r 170,000) has a tyrosine kinase domain coupled to its receptor moiety. It is a single chain, integral membrane protein of 1186 amino acids with extracellular, transmembrane, and cytoplasmic domains. The tyrosine kinase activity of the cytoplasmic domain is considered the primary effector of the transmembrane signaling response. Similar tyrosine kinase activity has been demonstrated in other receptors, including those for insulin, IGF-I, platelet-derived growth factor (PDGF), and colony stimulating factor-1. The tyrosine kinase activity of the EGF receptor appears to be able to function catalytically without the rest of the receptor structure (9). Amino acid sequencing has shown that the cytoplasmic and transmembrane domains of the EGF receptor have an extremely high level of sequence homology to the erb-B oncogene of the avian erythroblastosis virus (65, 106, 126). It is likely that the EGF receptor is the proto-oncogene from which the viral erb-B gene was derived.

Several proteins are known to be phosphorylated at tyrosine residues in an EGF-dependent manner. Of particular interest are the lipocortins, also known as pp34–39 or the calpactins (50). The lipocortins have been reported to inhibit the activity of phospholipase A_2, and phosphorylation of these proteins is reported to remove their inhibitory effect (46, 121). This suggests that treatment of cells with EGF should result in the mobilization of free arachidonate and the formation of eicosanoid products. Indeed, Madin-Darby canine kidney (MDCK) epithelial cells exposed to low concentrations of EGF are stimulated to produce prostaglandin $F_{2\alpha}$ ($PGF_{2\alpha}$) and prostaglandin E_2 (PGE_2), and to accumulate free arachidonate (70).

EGF induces mitogenesis and differentiation in many cell lines. Cells of the BSC-1 line respond to EGF much as they do to serum stimulation, with an increase in DNA synthesis and final cell density (48). The binding of EGF to BSC-1 cells is dependent upon cell density. The number of EGF receptors is approximately tenfold higher at low cell density than at high density without an apparent change in receptor affinity. The mechanism for this is not entirely clear, but it seems likely that EGF receptors are internalized at higher cell densities. It is also possible that crowding of cells leads to steric hindrance or immobilization of EFG receptors. One or both of these mechanisms may contribute to density-dependent growth (48). Thus, EGF receptors may be unmasked in the event of epithelial cell injury. Once normal or maximal cell density is restored, limitations could again be imposed on EGF binding as a means of terminating the regenerative response.

EGF affects many aspects of cell metabolism in vitro although the role of this growth factor on physiological processes in vivo is uncertain. EGF mediates constriction of rat aorta (14) and may also play a role in modulating renal blood flow (RBF) and glomerular filtration rate (GFR) by inducing contraction of mesangial cells (5). Intrarenal infusions of EGF in the rat cause a decline in RBF and GFR due to afferent and efferent arteriolar constriction

(5). There is also a decrease in K_f, the glomerular capillary ultrafiltration coefficient, which suggests the participation of mesangial cell contraction. Mesangial cells appear to have specific receptors for EGF, and the growth factor stimulates prostaglandin production by these cells in culture (43, 73). It is not clear if the local concentration of EGF in the glomerulus is high enough to produce this effect since circulating levels in serum are very low (130–250 pg/ml) (85) and production of EGF by glomerular cells has not been demonstrated.

It is not yet known if EGF regulates transport function in the kidney although preliminary reports show that EGF inhibits sodium and water transport in isolated perfused rabbit cortical collecting tubules (18, 119).

The discovery of significant amounts of EGF in human and animal urine caused much speculation as to its source and possible function. Several studies suggested that clearance of EGF from plasma does not adequately explain the relative high concentration of EGF in urine (75, 83, 84); however, it has not been conclusively shown that EGF is produced in renal tissue. (See Fisher et al, this volume, for additional information.)

Prepro-EGF

An abundance of the mRNA that encodes the EGF precursor is clearly demonstrated in mouse and human kidney (86); it appears to be localized to cells lining the distal tubule. In the submandibular gland, the precursor is processed to EGF, but in the kidney there is no evidence of cleavage to smaller peptides. The large amounts of unprocessed EGF precursor are unlikely to be incidental and suggest an alternate function in the distal tubule, perhaps as a membrane-bound transporter. Such a role would be supported by the homology of the EGF precursor with the low-density lipoprotein receptor (11). Levels of renal prepro-EGF mRNA have been studied in ischemic and toxic models of acute renal failure. In both cases, there is a reduction in the amount of this mRNA, which appears to correlate with renal cell injury (96). Although prepro-EGF mRNA is abundant in adult human and mouse kidney, it could not be detected in human fetal kidney tissue, Wilms' tumor (renal embryonal origin), or various kidney epithelial cell lines (11).

The human EGF precursor is a 1207–amino acid protein (apparent M_r 134,000) that includes the sequence of EGF near its carboxyterminus and encodes an additional 8 putative proteins with sequences similar, but not identical, to EGF (11,100). The human prepro-EGF molecule includes a strongly hydrophobic region 3' to EGF, which may function as a transmembrane domain. The likelihood that prepro-EGF functions as a membrane receptor is supported by studies of COS cells (SV40 transformed monkey kidney cells) into which the cDNA for prepro-EGF has been introduced (11). In these cells, prepro-EGF is transiently expressed on the cell surface as a membrane protein with its amino terminus in an extracellular location.

The function of the EGF precursor remains unclear. Perhaps this membrane-bound protein, whose extracellular EGF domain projects into the lumen of the nephron, is cleaved by urinary proteases to liberate EGF into the urine. This could account for the ~50 μg of the growth factor excreted daily by humans (11).

TRANSFORMING GROWTH FACTOR α

TGF-α is produced by virally transformed cells and can confer the transformed phenotype on nontransformed cells (25). Amino acid sequencing has demonstrated that human TGF-α is a 50–amino acid protein (apparent M_r 6000), initially translated as an internal part of a 160–amino acid precursor from which it is cleaved by proteolysis (30). TGF-α is structurally related to EGF and exerts its effects by binding to the EGF receptor (22, 74, 117). It can cause anchorage-independent growth in soft agar without the concommitant stimulation of other growth factors, but this effect is stronger if serum or TGF-β1 are added. TGF-α is produced by renal carcinomas and other human tumors (27), and this growth factor can sometimes be recovered from the urine (109). It is not produced by kidney epithelial cells of the BSC-1 line (F. G. Toback, unpublished observations), but the mRNA for this growth factor is detected in normal adult human kidney (G. I. Bell, unpublished observations).

LOW-POTASSIUM GROWTH FACTOR

The observation that a potassium-deficient diet induces renal growth was made over fifty years ago (97). In fact, sustained mild hypokalemia in rats is associated with a doubling of renal mass (102) that is due to both hyperplasia and hypertrophy of kidney cells. Cell proliferation occurs in the collecting tubules, interstitium, and thick ascending limb of Henle's loop (116). In the medullary collecting duct, the growing cells form adenomatous masses that protrude into the tubular lumen and appear to obstruct it (82). This cell multiplication is associated with an increase in glycolysis, a decrease in mitochondrial energy production, and an inhibition of the Pasteur effect: a pattern that simulates the bioenergetics of tumor cells (115).

In cell culture, nontransformed monkey kidney epithelial cells (BSC-1) proliferate when the extracellular potassium concentration is reduced from 5.4 to 3.2 mM (124). Thus, these cells perceive a reduction in the potassium concentration of the medium as a mitogenic signal. After an exposure of one hour, the cells release a growth-stimulatory activity into the conditioned medium (CM) (78). Activity in the CM persists even when the potassium concentration is corrected to the control value. This growth-promoting activity can be antagonized by the addition of purified TGF-β2.

Preliminary attempts to isolate and characterize the growth-promoting activity indicate that it is a molecule(s) with an apparent M_r of 12,000–30,000 (78). Its activity is destroyed by heating to 56°C for 30 min, but it is stable at 4°C for at least 3 days. This activity differs from other previously described growth factors. Further work will be required to purify the factor and determine its amino acid sequence and molecular mechanism of action. Its role in renal physiology and in the pathogenesis of potassium depletion nephropathy is not yet known.

LOW-SODIUM GROWTH FACTORS

Augmented influx of sodium ions occurs during the onset of proliferation in many cell types (24, 64, 101), and addition of NaCl to the culture medium can induce accelerated growth of confluent BSC-1 cells (114). Surprisingly, a reduced extracellular sodium concentration also stimulates proliferation of BSC-1 cells (123). After exposure of confluent cultures for only five minutes to a low-sodium medium (130 mM; control concentration is 155 mM), the cells release two growth-stimulatory factors (apparent M_r 6200 and 9000). Release of growth-stimulatory activity is not dependent upon new protein synthesis since it occurs in the presence of cycloheximide. The activity in CM is stable at 56°C for 30 min and is retained after freezing for several weeks. Treatment with trypsin abolishes the growth-promoting effect, whereas dithiothreitol does not, which suggests that the low-sodium growth factor has no accessible disulfide bonds required for activity. The growth response to a reduction in extracellular sodium concentration appears to be cell-type specific, since a low-sodium medium does not stimulate proliferation of fibroblasts. Release of growth factor activity is also cell-type specific since CM from fibroblasts exposed to a reduced extracellular sodium concentration is not stimulatory for epithelial cells. The low-sodium growth factors appear chemically and functionally different from other known growth factors.

The release of active factors by renal epithelial cells in culture in response to alterations in the ionic milieu suggests that kidney cells may respond similarly in vivo. Although the factors released in reponse to low-sodium and low-potassium media induce proliferation in cell culture, their physiological role may be different in the intact kidney. These factors may act as messengers between glomerular and tubular cells in different parts of the nephron in response to changes in peritubular or luminal ion concentrations.

INSULIN-LIKE GROWTH FACTORS

The IGFs, also termed somatomedins, are peptide growth factors that were first isolated from human plasma fractions. All IGFs share the following biological activities: stimulation of sulfate incorporation into cartilage, insulin-like activity on glucose metabolism, and a mitogenic effect on different cell types (10). The differences between the human IGFs became much clearer after their sequencing and immunological characterization. IGF-I, also known as somatomedin C, is a basic, single chain polypeptide of 70 amino acids with an apparent M_r of 7649 (90). IGF-II is a slightly acidic peptide of 67 amino acids with an apparent M_r of 7471; there is 62% identity between IGF-I and IGF-II, and both have a high degree of homology with human proinsulin (89). Both IGF-I and IGF-II are derived by proteolytic processing of larger precursors (13,55) (Table 1)

The site of production of IGF-I was originally considered to be the liver, from which it is released in response to growth hormone (GH) (10). However, recent evidence indicates that IGF-I is produced by most, if not all tissues, and thus likely acts as an autocrine or paracrine effector (26). Moreover, alterations in its serum level have less significance than changes within a tissue (26). IGF-I synthesis and secretion are regulated by GH, and the growth factor mediates some or all of the peripheral effects of this pituitary hormone. IGF-I production (and its growth hormone dependence) has been demonstrated in rat kidney, as well as other rat tissues (79). IGF-I mRNA is also present in adult human kidney although its distribution within the organ has not been determined (12).

IGF-II is less directly under GH control and is believed to be an important fetal growth factor (88, 99). IGF-II mRNA is present in both fetal and adult human kidney; however, it is 10–100-fold more abundant in the fetal organ.

Two types of IGF receptors have been described (87). Type I receptors bind IGF-I with an equal or greater affinity than IGF-II and bind insulin with low affinity, whereas type II receptors bind IGF-II with greater affinity than IGF-I and do not interact with insulin. The type I receptor is structurally homologous to the insulin receptor with two disulfide-linked α subunits, which bind the peptide, and two β subunits, which have intrinsic tyrosine kinase activity. The type II receptor is a single polypeptide without tyrosine kinase activity, which is identical to the mannose 6-phosphate receptor, a membrane protein that targets proteins to lysosomes (71). The type I receptor likely mediates the mitogenic response to both IGF-I and II in most systems. The physiological role for the type II receptor in mediating the tissue response to IGF-II is unknown (87).

Both types of IGF receptors have been identified in various tissues, including kidney (111). Type I and II IGF receptors are present on MDCK cells, which lack insulin receptors (66), and IGF-I has been shown to stimulate DNA synthesis in these cells (53,110). The distribution of IGF receptors has been studied on proximal tubular cells isolated from canine kidney (39–41). IGF-I binds to both basolateral and brush border membranes with approximately equal affinities, but the specific binding capacity is severalfold higher on the basolateral membrane. IGF-I-stimulated phosphorylation of the β subunit of the IGF-I receptor has been demonstrated only in preparations of basolateral membranes and not in those from brush border. IGF-II receptors appear to be equally distributed on basolateral and brush border membranes.

The function of IGFs in adult kidney has not been determined. During compensatory growth after uninephrectomy in the rat, IGF-I levels were elevated in the compensating kidney after five days, but not at 24 h or 30 days (107). This could be a consequence of either increased binding of circulating IGF-I or increased synthesis and secretion by the kidney; the available data do not distinguish between these possibilities. An increase in the amount of IGF-I mRNA (4- to 6-fold) has also been reported during compensatory renal growth (32). The precise contribution of IGFs to the control of renal growth remains to be clarified by further studies.

PLATELET-DERIVED GROWTH FACTOR

PDGF is produced by cells of mesodermal origin, such as fibroblasts and smooth muscle cells (31). The factor is found in abundance in the α granules of platelets so that whole serum and out-dated platelets are frequently used as sources from which to purify the protein. PDGF is also a potent mitogen for cells of mesenchymal origin. It is a dimeric protein comprised of A and/or B chains linked by disulfide bonds (31, 45). It is most commonly found as a heterodimer (A-B) although biologically active homodimers (A-A and B-B) have been described. The human PDGF A chain is synthesized as a precursor of 211 amino acids and is processed to a mature protein of 125 amino acids; the B chain precursor comprises 240 amino acids and is processed to a protein of 160 residues (15). The amino acid sequence of the B chain is nearly identical to the putative transforming protein of the simian sarcoma virus, which is encoded by the v-*sis* oncogene; the cellular homologue is termed c-*sis* (58, 59). Some transformed cells can release PDGF-like proteins and express PDGF receptors (69, 72). This suggests that an autocrine mechanism contributes to their proliferation.

Studies of rat mesangial cells in culture demonstrate that, like other cells of mesenchymal origin, they produce a PDGF-like protein that is secreted into the medium (1). Purified PDGF is mitogenic for mesangial cells (17) and causes mesangial cell contraction at a concentration of 10^{-10} M (77). It also causes transient elevation of free intracellular calcium and increased membrane phosphoinositide turnover (17, 77). Glomerular endothelial cells also proliferate in response to PDGF (108), which implies both a paracrine and an autocrine mechanism of action for PDGF produced by mesangial cells. These observations suggest that PDGF released by these cells could play a central role in glomerular cell proliferation.

High density, quiescent cultures of BSC-1 cells release PDGF activity into their medium (60). The gene for the B chain of PDGF (c-*sis*) is apparently constitutively expressed in these cells. No PDGF A chain mRNA could be detected in these cells, which appear to synthesize and secrete only the B-B homodimer. TGF-β2, the BSC-1 growth inhibitor, and adenosine diphosphate (ADP), the most potent mitogen yet described for BSC-1 cells (61, 62), both stimulated the expression of mRNA for the PDGF B chain gene. However, TGF-β2 inhibited DNA synthesis while release of PDGF activity was minimal, despite accumulation of PDGF B chain mRNA. In contrast, ADP stimulated DNA synthesis in quiescent cultures and increased three-fold both the amount of PDGF B chain mRNA and the release of PDGF activity. Interestingly, neither growing nor quiescent BSC-1 cells respond to the mitogenic potential of PDGF nor do they express the PDGF receptor. These results suggest that if the PDGF-like protein is released by renal epithelial cells in vivo, it could operate by a paracrine mechanism on neighboring connective or vascular tissue.

Cultures from Wilms' tumor cells have been shown to produce PDGF (34). Tumor-derived cell lines with either fibroblastic or epithelial features secrete 2–3 ng growth factor /10^6 cells/48 h into the medium. This high level is comparable to that produced by some bladder and liver carcinoma cell lines. However, human fetal kidney cells also produce high levels of PDGF. Thus, production of the growth factor by Wilms' tumor cells may be a marker for their embryonic origin rather than their malignant phenotype. Like the BSC-1 line, cells from Wilms' tumor and fetal kidney bind little PDGF, which suggests a paracrine function for the growth factor in vivo.

FIBROBLAST GROWTH FACTORS

The earliest evidence for the existence of FGFs is found in descriptions of mitogenic activity in brain tissue made nearly fifty years ago (113). The activity was recently purified and characterized as two closely related polypeptides with different isoelectric points, designated acidic FGF (aFGF) and basic FGF (bFGF). cDNA clones encoding both of these proteins have been isolated, and the predicted amino acid sequences indicate 55% structural homology between these two growth factors (2). FGFs are mitogenic for most, if not all, nonterminally differentiated cells of mesodermal or neuroectodermal origin: fibroblasts, endothelial cells, myoblasts, chondrocytes, osteoblasts, glial cells, and neuroblasts. FGFs are also potent inducers of blood vessel growth. They are chemotactic for vascular endothelial cells and induce these cells to express plasminogen activators and collagenases, proteolytic enzymes that presumably mediate tissue remodeling.

An important feature noted early in work with the FGFs is their avid binding to heparin, which has been exploited in purification procedures (36, 37, 98). Heparin stabilizes FGFs and augments the mitogenic activity of aFGF on cells in culture. FGFs also bind to heparan sulfates, the principle molecules of the extracellular matrix (ECM), and are found in large quantity in the matrix of cells in culture (7, 120). Their presence in the ECM suggests that they mediate proliferation of cells adjacent to the basement membrane. In addition, medium conditioned by endothelial cells has no growth-promoting activity, whereas seeding the cells on their own denuded ECM induces rapid proliferation and appearance of the expected phenotype (38). This suggests that FGF is not secreted into the medium, but likely exerts its effects through its integration into the ECM. In this manner it could act as a local growth regulator and could induce regeneration after denudation of the overlying cell layer. This may explain some of its capacity to promote wound healing. It has been difficult to define the mechanism by which FGF is deposited into the ECM, as both aFGF and bFGF lack a classic leader sequence required for cellular secretion (2, 56). In fact, when bFGF is experimentally fused to a signal peptide (which mediates cotranslational insertion into the endoplasmic reticulum), it acquires the ability to transform cells (94). These cells become morphologically aberrant and highly tumorigenic. Clearly this is not the usual mode of cellular release of FGF; if it were, the transformed phenotype would be routine in cells that produce this growth factor. It is not known whether FGF is released only from damaged or dying cells, is delivered to sites of injury or inflammation by stimulated macrophages, or is secreted by an as yet uncharacterized mechanism (56).

Until recently, aFGF was thought to exist only in neural tissue, but both acidic and basic FGF have now been isolated from bovine kidney (6, 35). Little work has been done to assess the effects of FGF on kidney cells, although aFGF has been found to stimulate proliferation of BSC-1 cells (F. G. Toback & K. Thomas, unpublished observations). Whether FGF is present in glomerular or tubular basement membranes or participates in renal cell regeneration after injury is thus far unknown.

Studies in embryonic kidney suggest a role for FGF in renal angiogenesis (91). During embryonic development, kidney differentiation is driven by the interaction of cells of different types. Contact with the epithelial ureteric bud induces the nephrogenic mesenchyme to differentiate, which then leads to a stimulation of blood vessel ingrowth. Induced nephrogenic mesenchyme stimulates angiogenesis in rabbit cornea and in chorioallantoic membrane, and a heparin-binding endothelial cell growth factor that retains this angiogenic activity has been isolated from embryonic mouse kidneys (91). It has not yet been sequenced, but its pattern of purification suggests it is an aFGF-like protein.

SUMMARY AND UNRESOLVED QUESTIONS

Understanding of the physiological roles of renal growth factors is in its infancy. Additional factors are likely to be discovered. Moreover, most of the mechanisms by which the known polypeptides affect kidney function remain to be elucidated. The presence of growth-inhibitory TGFs in renal tissue and their production by kidney epithelial cells in culture suggests that cells of the nephron may be subject to tonic inhibitory as well as stimulatory growth factors. Production of biologically active EGF in renal tissue has not been convincingly demonstrated although its unprocessed precursor has been localized in cells of the distal nephron. The low-potassium and low-sodium growth factors demonstrate the ability of renal epithelial cells to transduce changes in their ionic milieu into the release of specific proteins and could provide a means of intercellular communication and adaptation. Both IGF-I and IGF-II are probably synthesized in the kidney, however, their physiological functions in the organ are unknown. PDGF could function as an autocrine or paracrine factor in the glomerulus. Since mesangial cells both synthesize and respond to PDGF, it could play a role in autoregulation of blood flow or cell proliferation during glomerular inflammation. FGFs appear to play a role in angiogenesis during renal embryonic development.

Repair of kidney tissue following cell injury or necrosis could be regulated by one or more epithelial mitogens. In this hypothesis, intact cells adjacent to the site of injury could participate in the regeneration of their neighbors by releasing growth factors. In addition, if FGF were deposited in the basement membrane, it could be called upon to stimulate mitogenesis. Limitations may be placed on growth by the local release of TGF-β, thereby completing the regenerative response and preventing unopposed tubular cell growth. In addition, the compensatory hypertrophy and hyperplasia that follow unilateral nephrectomy could be mediated in part by growth factors with opposing actions, such as IGF-I and TGF-β. The aberrant tubular cell proliferation that characterizes cyst formation may be due to inappropriate production of autocrine or paracrine growth factors, or excessive responsiveness to them.

Do growth factors that act on the kidney contribute to homeostatic control of the internal milieu? Do these peptide messengers participate in the regulation of sodium and water reclamation, potassium balance, or acid excretion and bicarbonate regeneration by affecting ion exchangers and channels?

Studies addressing these questions could uncover a heretofore unrecognized system for regulation of renal function.

ACKNOWLEDGMENTS

We wish to thank Graeme I. Bell for valuable advice and a critical reading of the manuscript. Susan R. Mendley is a Research Fellow of the National Kidney Foundation. Support for studies cited in the text was provided by National Institutes of Health Grants DK39689, DK18413, and DK37227.

Literature Cited

1. Abboud, H. E., Poptic, E., DiCorleto, P. 1987. *J. Clin. Invest.* 80:675–83
2. Abraham, J. A., Mergia, A., Whang, J. L., Tumolo, A., Friedman, J., et al. 1986. *Science* 233:545–48
3. Abraham, J. A., Whang, J. L., Tumolo, A., Mergia, A., Friedman, J., et al. 1986. *EMBO J.* 5:2523–28
4. Assoian, R. K., Komoriya A., Meyers, C. A., Miller, D. M., Sporn, M. B. 1983. *J. Biol. Chem.* 258:7155–60
5. Badr, K. F., Harris, R. C. 1987. *Clin. Res.* 35:542 (Abstr.)
6. Baird, A., Esch, F., Böhlen, P., Ling, N., Gospodarowicz, D. 1985. *Reg. Peptides* 12:201–13
7. Baird, A., Ling, N. 1987. *Biochem. Biophys. Res. Commun.* 142:428–35
8. Baserga, R. 1981. *N. Engl. J. Med.* 304:453–59
9. Basu, M., Biswas, R., Das, M. 1984. *Nature* 311:477–80
10. Baxter, R. C. 1986. *Adv. Clin. Chem.* 25:49–115
11. Bell, G. I., Fong, N. M., Stempien, M. M., Wormsted, M. A., Caput, D., et al. 1986. *Nucleic Acids Res.* 14:8427–46
12. Bell, G. I., Gerhard, D. S., Fong, N. M., Sanchez-Pescador, R., Rall, L. B. 1985. *Proc. Natl. Acad. Sci. USA* 82:6450–54
13. Bell, G. I., Merryweather, J. P., Sanchez-Pescador, R., Stempien, M. M., Priestley, L. M., et al. 1984. *Nature* 310:775–77
14. Berk, B. C., Brock, T. A., Webb, R. C., Taubman, M. B., Atkinson, W. J., et al. 1985. *J. Clin. Invest.* 75:1083–86
15. Betsholtz, D., Johnsson, A., Heldin, C.-H., Westermark, B., Lind, P., et al. 1986. *Nature* 320:695–99
16. Boerner, P., Resnick, R. J., Racker, E. 1985. *Proc. Natl. Acad. Sci. USA* 82:1350–53
17. Bonventre, J. V., Weber, P. C., Gronich, J. H. 1988. *Am. J. Physiol.* 254:F87–94
18. Breyer, M. D., Jacobson, H. R., Breyer, J. 1988. *Kidney Int.* 33:255 (Abstr.)
19. Bullough, W. S. 1962. *Biol. Rev.* 37: 307–42
20. Carpenter, G. 1987. *Ann. Rev. Biochem.* 56:881–914
21. Carpenter, G., Cohen, S. 1979. *Ann. Rev. Biochem.* 48:193–216
22. Carpenter, G., Stoscheck, C. M., Preston, Y. A., DeLarco, J. E. 1983. *Proc. Natl. Acad. Sci. USA* 801:5627–30
23. Cheifetz, S., Weatherbee, J. A., Tsang, M. L.-S., Anderson, J. K., Mole, J. E., et al. 1987. *Cell* 48:409–15
24. Cone, C. D. Jr., Tongier, M. Jr. 1973. *J. Cell. Physiol.* 82:373–86
25. DeLarco, J. E., Todaro, G. J. 1978. *Proc. Natl. Acad. Sci. USA* 75:4001–5
26. D'Ercole, A. J., Stiles, A. D., Underwood, L. E. 1984. *Proc. Natl. Acad. Sci. USA* 81:935–39
27. Derynck, R., Goeddel, D. V., Ullrich, A., Gutterman, J. U., Williams, R. D., et al. 1987. *Cancer Res.* 47:707–12
28. Derynck, R., Jarrett, J. A., Chen, E. Y., Eaton, D. H., Bell, J. R., et al. 1985. *Nature* 316:701–5
29. Derynck, R., Rhee, L., Chen, E. Y., Van Tilburg, A. 1987. *Nucleic Acids Res.* 15:3188–89
30. Derynck, R., Roberts, A. B., Winkler, M. E., Chen, E. Y., Goeddel, D. V. 1984. *Cell* 38:287–97
31. Deuel, T. F., Pierce, G. F., Yeh, H. J., Shawver, L. K., Milner, P. G., Kimura, A. 1987. *J. Cell. Physiol. Suppl.* 5:95–99
32. Fagin, J. A., Melmed, S. 1987. *Endocrinology* 120:718–24
33. Fine, L. G., Holley, R. W., Nasri, H., Badie, B. 1985. *Proc. Natl. Acad. Sci. USA* 82:6163–66
34. Fraizer, G. E., Bowen-Pope, D. F., Vogel, A. M. 1987. *J. Cell. Physiol.* 133:169–74
35. Gautschi-Sova, P., Jiang, Z.-P., Fräter-

Schröder, M., Böhlen, P. 1987. *Biochemistry* 26:5844–47
36. Gimenez-Gallego, G., Conn, G., Hatcher, V. B., Thomas, K. A. 1986. *Biochem. Biophys. Res. Commun.* 135: 541–48
37. Gospodarowicz, D., Cheng, J. 1986. *J. Cell. Physiol.* 128:475–84
38. Gospodarowicz, D., Ferrara, N., Schweigerer, L., Neufeld, G. 1987. *Endocr. Rev.* 8:95–114
39. Hammerman, M. R., Gavin, J. R. 1984. *J. Biol. Chem.* 259:13511–17
40. Hammerman, M. R., Gavin, J. R. 1986. *Am. J. Physiol.* 251:E32–41
41. Hammerman, M. R., Rogers, S. 1987. *Am. J. Physiol.* 253:F841–47
42. Hanks, S. K., Armour, R., Baldwin, J. H., Maldonado, F., Spiess, J., Holley, R. W. 1988. *Proc. Natl. Acad. Sci. USA* 85:79–82
43. Harris, R. C., Hoover, R. L., Jacobson, H. R., Badr, K. F. 1988. *Kidney Int.* 33:266 (Abstr.)
44. Hayslett, J. P., Kashgarian, M., Epstein, F. H. 1968. *J. Clin. Invest.* 47:774–82
45. Heldin, C.-H., Westermark, B. 1987. *J. Cell. Physiol. Suppl.* 5:31–34
46. Hirata, F., Matsuda, K., Notsu, Y., Hattori, T., del Carmine, R. 1984. *Proc. Natl. Acad. Sci. USA* 81:4717–21
47. Holley, R. W., Armour, R., Baldwin, J. H. 1978. *Proc. Natl. Acad. Sci. USA* 75:1864–66
48. Holley, R. W., Armour, R., Baldwin, J. H., Brown, K. D., Yeh, Y.-C. 1977. *Proc. Natl. Acad. Sci. USA* 74:5046–50
49. Holley, R. W., Böhlen, P., Fava, R., Baldwin, J. H., Kleeman, G., Armour, R. 1980. *Proc. Natl. Acad. Sci. USA* 77:5989–92
50. Huang, K.-S., Wallner, B. P., Mattaliano, R. J., Tizard, R., Burne, C., et al. 1986. *Cell* 46:191–99
51. Ignotz, R., Massagué, J. 1986. *J. Biol. Chem.* 261:4337–45
52. Inman, W. H., Colowick, S. P. 1985. *Proc. Natl. Acad. Sci. USA* 82:1346–49
53. Izumi, T., White, M. F., Kadowaki, T., Takaku, F., Akanuma, Y., Kasuga, M. 1987. *J. Biol. Chem.* 262:1282–87
54. James, R., Bradshaw, R. A. 1984. *Ann. Rev. Biochem.* 53:259–92
55. Jansen, M., van Schaik, F. M. A., Ricker, A. T., Bullock, B., Woods, D. E., et al. 1983. *Nature* 306:609–11
56. Jaye, M., Howk, R., Burgess, W., Ricca, G. A., Chiu, I.-M., et al. 1986. *Science* 233:541–45
57. Johnson, H. A., Vera Roman, J. M. 1966. *Am. J. Pathol.* 49:1–13
58. Johnsson, A., Heldin, C.-H., Wasteson,

Å., Westermark, B., Deuel, T. F., et al. 1984. *EMBO J.* 3:921–28
59. Josephs, S. F., Grio, C., Ratner, L., Wong-Staal, F. 1984. *Science* 223:487–90
60. Kartha, S., Bradham, D. M., Grotendorst, G. R., Toback, F. G. 1988. *Am. J. Physiol.* In press
61. Kartha, S., Sukhatme, V. P., Toback, F. G. 1987. *Am. J. Physiol.* 252:F1175–79
62. Kartha, S., Toback, F. G. 1985. *Am. J. Physiol.* 249:F967–72
63. Keating, M. T., Williams, L. T. 1988. *Science* 239:914–16
64. Koch, K. S., Leffert, H. L. 1979. *Cell* 18:153–63
65. Kondo, I., Shimizu, N. 1983. *Cytogen. Cell Genet.* 35:9–14
66. Krett, N. L., Heaton, J. H., Geleherter, T. D. 1986. *Biochem. Biophys. Res. Commun.* 134:120–27
67. Lawrence, D. A., Pircher, R., Jullien, P. 1985. *Biochem. Biophys. Res. Commun.* 133:1026–34
68. Lawrence, D. A., Pircher, R., Kryceve-Martinerie, C., Jullien, P. 1984. *J. Cell. Physiol.* 121:184–88
69. Leof, E. B., Proper, J. A., Goustin, A. S., Shipley, G. D., DiCorleto, P. E., Moses, H. L. 1986. *Proc. Natl. Acad. Sci. USA* 83:2453–57
70. Levine, L., Hassid, A. 1977. *Biochem. Biophys. Res. Commun.* 76:1181–87
71. MacDonald, R. G., Pfeffer, S. R., Coussens, L., Tepper, M. A., Brocklebank, C. M., et al. *Science* 239:1134–37
72. Mäkelä, T. P., Alitalo, R., Paulsson, Y., Westermark, B., Heldin, C.-H., Alitalo, K. 1987. *Mol. Cell. Biol.* 7:3653–62
73. Margolis, B. L., Bonventre, J. V., Kremer, S. G., Kudlow, J. E., Skorecki, K. L. 1988. *Biochem. J.* 249: 587–92
74. Massagué, J. 1983. *J. Biol. Chem.* 258:13614–20
75. Mattila, A-L., Pasternack, A., Viinikka, L., Perheentupa, J. 1986. *J. Clin. Endocrinol. Metab.* 62:1180–83
76. McCreight, C. E., Sulkin, N. M. 1959. *J. Gerontol.* 14:440–43
77. Menè, P., Abboud, H. E., Dubyak, G. R., Scarpa, A., Dunn, M. J. 1987. *Am. J. Physiol.* 253:F458–63
78. Mordan, L. J., Toback, F. G. 1984. *Am. J. Physiol.* 246:C351–54
79. Murphy, L. J., Bell, G. I., Duckworth, M. L., Friesen, H. G. 1987. *Endocrinology* 121:684–91
80. Mustoe, T. A., Pierce, G. F., Thomason, A., Gramates, P., Sporn, M. B., Deuel, T. F. 1987. *Science* 237:1333–36

81. Nilsen-Hamilton, M., Holley, R. W. 1983. *Proc. Natl. Acad. Sci. USA* 80:5636–40
82. Oliver, J., MacDowell, M., Welt, L. G., Holliday, M. A., Hollander, W. Jr., et al. 1957. *J. Exp. Med.* 106:563–74
83. Olsen, P. S., Nexø, E., Poulsen, S. S., Hansen, H. F., Kirkegaard, P. 1984. *Regul. Peptides* 10:37–45
84. Perheentupa, J., Lakshmanan, J., Fisher, D. A. 1985. *Acta Endocrinol.* 108:428–32
85. Perheentupa, J., Lakshmanan, J., Hoath, S. B., Beri, U., Kim, H., et al. 1985. *Am. J. Physiol.* 248:E391–96
86. Rall, L. B., Scott, J., Bell, G. I., Crawford, R. J., Penschow, J. D., et al. 1985. *Nature* 313:228–31
87. Rechler, M. M., Nissley, S. P. 1986. *Hormone Res.* 24:152–59
88. Reeve, A. E., Eccles, M. R., Wilkins, R. J., Bell, G. I., Millow, L. J. 1985. *Nature* 317:258–60
89. Rinderknecht, E., Humbel, R. E. 1978. *FEBS Lett.* 89:283–86
90. Rinderknecht, E., Humbel, R. E. 1978. *J. Biol. Chem.* 253:2769–76
91. Risau, W., Ekblom, P. 1986. *J. Cell Biol.* 103:1101–7
92. Roberts, A. B., Anzano, M. A., Meyers, C. A., Wideman, J., Blacher, R., et al. 1983. *Biochemistry* 22:5692–98
93. Roberts, A. B., Sporn, M. B., Assoian, R. K., Smith, J. M. Roche, N. S., et al. 1986. *Proc. Natl. Acad. Sci. USA* 83:4167–71
94. Rogelj, S., Weinberg, R. A., Fanning, P., Klagsbrun, M. 1988. *Nature* 331:173–75
95. Rollason, H. D. 1949. *Anat. Rec.* 104:263–85
96. Safirstein, R., Rucker, S., Price, P. 1988. *Clin. Res.* 36:597A(Abstr.)
97. Schrader, G. A., Prickett, C. O., Salmon, W. D. 1937. *J. Nutr.* 14:85–110
98. Schreiber, A. B., Kenney, J., Kowalski, W. J., Friesel, R., Mehlman, T., Maciag, T. 1985. *Proc. Natl. Acad. Sci. USA* 82:6138–42
99. Scott, J., Cowell, J., Robertson, M. E., Priestley, L. M., Wadey, R., et al. 1985. *Nature* 317:260–62
100. Scott, J., Urdea, M., Quiroga, M., Sanchez-Pescador, R., Fong, N., et al. 1983. *Science* 221:236–40
101. Smith, J. B., Rozengurt, E. 1978. *Proc. Natl. Acad. Sci. USA* 75:5560–64
102. Spargo, B. H. 1954. *J. Lab. Clin. Med.* 43:802–14
103. Sporn, M. B., Roberts, A. B. 1985. *Cancer Surv.* 4:627–32
104. Sporn, M. B., Roberts, A. B., Wake-field, L. M., de Crombrugghe, B. 1987. *J. Cell. Biol.* 105:1039–45
105. Sporn, M. B., Todaro, G. J. 1980. *N. Engl. J. Med.* 303:878–80
106. Spurr, N. K., Solomon, E., Jansson, M., Sheer, D., Goodfellow, P. N., et al. 1984. *EMBO J.* 3:159–63
107. Stiles, A. D., Sosenko, I. R. S., D'Ercole, A. J., Smith, B. T. 1985. *Endocrinology* 117:2397–2401
108. Striker, G. E., Sodeland, C., Bowen-Pope, D. F., Gown, A. M., Schmer, G., et al. 1984. *J. Exp. Med.* 160:323–28
109. Stromberg, K., Hudgins, W. R., Orth, D. N. 1987. *Biochem. Biophys. Res. Commun.* 144:1059–68
110. Sukegawa, I., Hizuka, N., Takano, K., Asakawa, K., Shizume, K. 1987. *Endocrinol. Jpn.* 34:339–46
111. Taylor, J. E., Scott, C. D., Baxter, R. C. 1987. *J. Endocrinol.* 115:35–41
112. Thalacker, F. W., Nilsen-Hamilton, M. 1987. *J. Biol. Chem.* 262:2283–90
113. Thomas, K. A. 1987. *FASEB J.* 1:434–40
114. Toback, F. G. 1980. *Proc. Natl. Acad. Sci. USA* 77:6654–56
115. Toback, F. G., Aithal, H. N., Ordóñez, N. G., Spargo, B. H. 1979. *Lab. Invest.* 41:265–67
116. Toback, F. G., Ordóñez, N. G., Bortz, S. L., Spargo, B. H. 1976. *Lab. Invest.* 34:115–24
117. Todaro, G. J., Fryling, C., DeLarco, J. E. 1980. *Proc. Natl. Acad. Sci. USA* 77:5258–62
118. Tucker, R. F., Shipley, G. D., Moses, H. L., Holley, R. W. 1984. *Science* 226:705–7
119. Vehaskari, V. M., Hering-Smith, K., Moskowitz, D., Hamm, L. 1988. *FASEB J.* 2:708A (Abstr.)
120. Vlodavsky, I., Folkman, J., Sullivan, R., Fridman, R., Ishai-Michaeli, R., et al. 1987. *Proc. Natl. Acad. Sci. USA* 84:2292–96
121. Wallner, B. P., Mattaliano, R. J., Hession, C., Cate, R. L., Tizard, R., et al. 1986. *Nature* 320:77–81
122. Walsh-Reitz, M. M., Feldman, R. I., Toback, F. G. 1988. *Am. J. Physiol.* 254:F747–53
123. Walsh-Reitz, M. M., Gluck, S. L., Waack, S., Toback, F. G. 1986. *Proc. Natl. Acad. Sci. USA* 83:4764–48
124. Walsh-Reitz, M. M., Toback, F. G. 1983. *Am. J. Physiol.* 244:C429–32
125. Walsh-Reitz, M. M., Toback, F. G., Holley, R. W. 1984. *Proc. Natl. Acad. Sci. USA* 81:793–96
126. Yamamoto, T., Hishida, T., Miyajima, N., Kawai, S., Ooi, T., Toyoshima, K. 1983. *Cell* 35:71–78

Annu. Rev. Physiol. 1989. 51:51–65

ANDROGEN-REGULATED GENE EXPRESSION

Franklin G. Berger

Department of Biology, University of South Carolina, Columbia, South Carolina 29208

Gordon Watson

Department of Genetics, University of California at Berkeley, Berkeley, California 94720

INTRODUCTION

Androgenic hormones exert a variety of effects upon mammalian tissues, including modification of gene expression and control of cellular growth and differentiation. Historically, the effects of androgens have been classified as either androgenic or anabolic (4). Androgenic effects are those associated with differentiation of the male phenotype and occur primarily in reproductive tract tissues. Anabolic effects occur within nonreproductive tissues such as liver, kidney, and muscle. This classification may not be very meaningful since it is likely that the primary mechanisms of androgen action do not differ significantly from tissue to tissue.

An important consequence of androgen action is the stimulation of cellular growth, which includes increases in cell size (hypertrophy), in cell number (hyperplasia), or both, depending upon the tissue. For example, in the submaxillary gland, testosterone induces DNA synthesis, which results in cellular proliferation within the tissue (36). In contrast, in the mouse kidney, the primary growth effect of androgens is hypertrophy, with little or no DNA synthesis (65). Such tissue-specific growth effects of androgens probably reflect the particular genes that respond to hormone, rather than fundamental differences in the mechanisms of hormone action. An important goal

51

0066–4278/89/0315–0051$02.00

of current research is to understand the detailed biochemical and molecular events that are initiated by androgens and that result in cellular growth.

Several gene products, produced in different androgen-responsive tissues, have become major models for studies of the biochemical and molecular mechanisms of androgen action. Most of the products are abundantly produced and rather limited in their tissue distributions. The major exception to this is the kidney, where a variety of "housekeeping" genes, expressed at low levels, respond to testosterone.

MECHANISMS OF STEROID HORMONE ACTION

The last several years have seen an explosion of information on the molecular mechanisms of steroid hormone action (87, 110). It is now accepted that steroids function primarily through the modulation of gene transcription. This occurs by the direct binding of a steroid–steroid receptor complex to a *cis*-acting DNA sequence, termed the hormone response element (HRE), that is within or flanking the gene under its control. Receptor binding to the HRE, possibly in cooperation with the binding of other factors, stimulates transcription initiation (51, 100, 110). In most cases, the HRE behaves as a classical enhancer element; it functions independently of orientation and position and can confer hormone regulation upon a heterologous promoter (110). Sequence analysis of a variety of HREs has enabled identification of a short, palindromic consensus sequence that defines the binding site for the steroid–steroid receptor complex (48). Small 15–base pair oligonucleotides containing these HRE sequences can confer steroid regulation upon nearby promoters (52, 94). The close sequence relationships among HREs for various steroids may underlie the multiple control of single genes by several steroid hormones (12, 79, 100).

Analysis of cloned sequences corresponding to various steroid receptors (33, 56, 57) has shown that each is comprised of a DNA binding domain, located near the center of the polypeptide, and a hormone binding domain, located in the C-terminal region. The DNA binding domains are characterized by a conserved cysteine-rich sequence that may form "finger" structures, which are metal ion-stabilized polypeptide configurations commonly found in DNA binding proteins (26, 107). The hormone binding domain determines the specificity for steroid. Studies with mutated receptor molecules indicate that in the absence of hormone, this domain inhibits receptor binding to DNA, an effect that is attenuated in the presence of hormone (34).

Steroids affect gene expression at levels other than transcription. Alterations in mRNA stability (11, 69), protein processing (86), and protein turnover (43, 91) have been documented. However, it remains to be determined whether these are primary effects of the hormone or secondary effects resulting from steroid action at other sites. In fact, the distinction between primary and secondary effects must also be made for transcriptional regulation by steroids, for in certain cases, hormonal induction of transcription has been shown to be indirect (20, 108).

MOLECULAR MECHANISMS OF GENE REGULATION BY ANDROGENS

Like other steroids, androgens exert their effects at several levels. Nuclear run-on assays have shown that hormonal inductions of the major urinary proteins in mouse liver (24) and of ovalbumin and ovomucoid in chick oviduct (21) occur through increases in transcription of the corresponding genes. In contrast, androgen-mediated induction of the rat prostatic steroid binding proteins (70), as well as several mRNAs of the mouse kidney (6, 86a), may involve posttranscriptional mechanisms. The induction of ornithine decarboxylase levels in mouse kidney involves stabilization of the protein (43, 91).

Much of the work on the molecular mechanisms of androgen regulation has been driven by the notion that a *cis*-acting DNA element, the HRE, binds the androgen–androgen receptor complex to stimulate transcription. Although some data consistent with this model has been obtained, direct proof is lacking. Sequence analysis of the upstream regions of seven androgen-regulated genes revealed only a few modest homologies of 7–10 base pairs each (109); no sequence motifs were strong enough to be considered important in hormonal modulation. Kandala et al (47) identified a 30 nucleotide sequence that is conserved within the upstream regions of the genes encoding the androgen-regulated prostatic steroid binding proteins and the seminal vesicle secretory proteins of the rat. This sequence bears no resemblance to HREs for other steroid hormones, and no functional studies have been done to determine whether or not it is involved in hormonal regulation.

Several systems offer promise as models for dissection of the molecular elements involved in testosterone-regulated gene expression. These include the steroid binding protein gene family in rat prostate (70, 71, 77–79), the sex-limited protein gene in mouse liver (89, 93), and the mouse mammary tumor virus (12, 23, 79). Transfection experiments with cloned sequences indicate that the androgen regulation of these genes is conferred by nearby DNA elements. In the case of the mammary tumor virus, it has been shown that the glucocorticoid-responsive HRE within the long-terminal repeat of the viral genome (18, 42, 110) is also responsible for androgen and progestin regulation of expression (12, 79). A role for the androgen receptor in gene expression has been inferred primarily from studies in animals bearing the testicular feminization *(Tfm)* mutation, which defines an X-linked gene and causes a marked reduction in measurable androgen receptors in various tissues (29, 32). Putative interactions between the receptor and HRE-like sequences are largely undefined although one study has reported the binding of androgen receptors to specific DNA regions within the prostatic steroid binding protein gene (88).

In summary, research to date is consistent with the theory that the primary effect of androgens is generated at the level of gene transcription and occurs through the interaction of a steroid receptor and a *cis*-acting DNA sequence in the vicinity of the responding gene. However, direct evidence in support of this model is lacking. In particular, it has not yet been demonstrated that *cis*-acting DNA elements, which mediate androgen regulation and exist within or around genes under their control, bind the androgen receptor.

ANDROGEN REGULATED GENES OF THE MOUSE KIDNEY

General Features

The kidney has been recognized for quite some time as an androgen target organ, particularly in mice. The hormone stimulates hypertrophy of proximal tubule and Bowman's capsule cells (4). This process, which involves little or no stimulation of DNA synthesis (65), is accompanied by marked structural and morphological changes in cellular organelles (54). Significant effects upon protein and RNA synthesis have been measured (44, 53), as have inductions of a number of specific gene products. The importance of specific mRNA concentrations in the androgen induction of these gene products was initially recognized by Paigen and coworkers, who determined that β-glucuronidase induction involves mRNA (73). In later work, two androgen-inducible gene products, the KAP (kidney androgen-regulated protein) and *RP2* mRNAs, were identified through analyses at the RNA level (5, 97). It has become clear from these studies, as well as from numerous others that have been performed since, that a predominant effect of androgens in the mouse kidney is the modulation of mRNA concentrations.

Experiments have been conducted to directly assess the role of gene transcription in the androgen induction of mRNA levels in the kidney. Nuclear run-on assays, which measure transcription in isolated nuclei in vitro, indicated that inductions of several mRNAs are predominantly posttranscriptional, occurring at the level of transcript processing and/or stability (6). This finding was supported by kinetic analysis of mRNA induction and deinduction following hormone administration and withdrawal, respectively (6). However, more recent nuclear run-on experiments, which include use of small, single-stranded probes from various regions of the genes in question, indicate that the inductions do involve substantial increases in the relative rates of gene transcription (86a). The lack of measurable transcription induction in earlier analyses (6) may reflect the high degree of "aberrant" transcription that occurs in both the sense and anti-sense directions in isolated nuclei, obscuring detection of relevant transcripts (86b). The biological significance, if any, of this phenomenon is not known.

An in vivo protocol for measuring mRNA synthesis in whole animals has recently been developed (105). This method, which does not distinguish between nuclear precursor RNAs and mature cytoplasmic transcripts, measures both gene transcription and RNA maturation, and has been used to show that the relative synthetic rates for several androgen-regulated mRNAs increase in response to testosterone. However, posttranscriptional effects of androgens on mRNA turnover are also likely since in several instances the increases in RNA synthesis do not completely account for inductions of mRNA concentration (105).

The Mouse as a Genetic Model

A genetic approach, which involves the study of variation among closely related strains or species of organisms, can provide insights into the evolutionary origins of particular gene expression phenotypes and can generate opportunities to analyze the genetic elements that govern them. In addition, such a strategy may shed light on the function of certain regulatory phenotypes, based upon the extent of evolutionary conservation.

The mouse (genus *Mus*) has been of great value as a model of mammalian genetics, primarily due to the availability of a large number of genetically diverse inbred strains and wild-derived species. The phylogeny of the *Mus* genus, derived from a number of paleotological, morphological, biochemical, and molecular studies (9), is relatively well understood. The commonly used inbred strains have been classified as *Mus domesticus,* which derives from a lineage that separated relatively recently (9). Other species represent lineages that separated earlier, up to 10 million years ago. The availability of species comprising a genus that is relatively well understood in terms of its biology and systematics makes the mouse a powerful system for evolutionary studies.

β-Glucuronidase (GUS)

The biochemistry and genetics of murine GUS have been reviewed previously (13, 72, 96). The enzyme, which is a housekeeping protein whose concentration varies from tissue to tissue, exists as a tetramer of four identical subunits encoded by a single gene on chromosome 5 (13, 72). Tissue specificity of GUS expression is determined at the level of protein synthesis and/or processing rather than at the level of mRNA concentration (10). The enzyme is selectively and dramatically induced in the proximal tubule kidney cells of mice treated with androgens (28, 74, 96). This induction occurs at the level of mRNA. Among inbred strains of mice, the concentration of GUS mRNA is induced some 30–120 fold (76, 101, 103). Androgen response is drastically reduced in hypophysectomized mice, but can be restored by daily injections of growth hormone (95, 96), whose effects are observed only when the hormone is delivered in a "pulsatile" fashion (66). None of the other androgen-regulated mRNAs in kidney has a requirement for pituitary hormones (5, 8, 27).

Genetic loci affecting GUS expression include *Tfm* (14) and *pearl* (67), both of which operate at the mRNA level. In addition, several loci that are tightly linked to *Gus-s* and that affect various aspects of GUS expression have been identified. *Gus-u* modulates the levels of GUS in all tissues and appears to be *cis*-acting (59, 72, 83). *Gus-t* is a *trans*-acting locus that determines the developmental expression of GUS (38, 59, 63, 72). Finally, *Gus-r* determines the rate and extent of GUS induction by androgens in the kidney (72, 84, 85, 102). Both *Gus-u* and *Gus-t* control the rate of enzyme synthesis, but have no effect on mRNA levels (10, 83, 103). In contrast, *Gus-r* affects mRNA concentrations (72, 76, 101–104).

Several putative *Gus-r* alleles have been described in inbred and wild-derived mice (19, 72, 99). The wild-derived species *M. hortulanus* shows a noninducible phenotype that is specific to GUS, is due to a *cis*-acting genetic locus, and is generated at the mRNA level (58). Most wild-derived *Mus* species behave similarly to *M. hortulanus;* only *M. spretus* and *M. saxicola* display an inducible phenotype (99). Several other *Gus-r* alleles, most of which operate at the mRNA level, have been distinguished on the basis of variations in the kinetics of GUS induction (58, 102, 104).

Pulse-labeling experiments in whole animals indicate that GUS mRNA synthesis increases in response to testosterone, which accounts for a major part of the induction of mRNA levels (105); however, effects on transcript stability cannot be ruled out in the absence of direct measurements of mRNA turnover. Since the in vivo rates of synthesis measurements do not distinguish between transcription and nuclear processing, it is theoretically possible that androgens determine the fraction of primary transcripts that are correctly processed to mRNA (105).

Several mechanisms may explain the slow, progressive activation of the GUS gene in response to testosterone. The hormone–receptor complex may interact directly with multiple binding sites within or near the [GUS] gene complex; the degree of gene activation might, in such a case, be a function of the number of binding sites occupied. Almagor & Paigen (2) presented a mathematical model that is based upon this mechanism and that fits well with the experimental data.

The complete sequence of GUS mRNA from the mouse has been determined and used to derive the amino acid sequence of the protein (30, 31).

The genomic organization and complete sequence of the gene have been determined for the *Gus-s*[a] allele (22, 30).

Ornithine Decarboxylase (ODC)

Polyamines play an important, though not well understood, role in cell growth. Inhibition of polyamine biosynthesis causes cessation of cellular proliferation, which can be reinitiated by the addition of exogenous polyamines (80, 81). ODC, which is the first enzyme of the polyamine biosynthetic pathway, has been of interest both for its high turnover rate as well as for its rapid response to a variety of stimuli, particularly those affecting cell growth (80).

ODC activity levels are highly responsive to androgens in the mouse kidney. Testosterone treatment induces a 300–500-fold increase in the enzyme in female mice (37, 75). This reflects induction of the ODC protein concentration (90), which in turn is a consequence of both an increase in the relative rate of ODC synthesis (82) as well as a decrease in turnover of the ODC polypeptide (43, 91). ODC cDNA clones have been used to show that kidney ODC mRNA levels undergo a 10–20-fold induction in response to testosterone (8, 39, 45, 55, 61). This mRNA increase is generated predominantly at the transcriptional level (86c), a finding that contrasts with earlier conclusions (6). Since the increase in mRNA may not fully account for induction of ODC synthesis, which has been estimated to be at least 25-fold (82), it is possible that androgen regulation of ODC mRNA translation may occur. In some circumstances, translational regulation of ODC is an important control mechanism (41, 46, 60); therefore, it is worth considering the role of such a mechanism in the androgen induction of ODC synthesis in the kidney.

Androgen regulation of ODC expression has been examined in a variety of inbred and wild-derived mice (62, 99). Variations in ODC response to androgens among inbred strains do not correlate with inter-strain differences in androgen receptor levels, circulating androgen concentrations, or expression of other androgen-regulated gene products (62). Among the more divergent wild-derived *Mus* species, androgen induction of ODC is, in general, greater than in inbred mice. Most species respond to hormone with a 30–100-fold increase in mRNA levels accompanied by a 1,000–5,000-fold induction of the enzyme (86c, 99). Thus, similar to inbred mice, enzyme induction is not fully accounted for by increases in mRNA and must involve changes in mRNA translation and/or enzyme stability.

Two closely-related species, *M. cervicolor* and *M. cookii,* show reduced responses to androgens. In *M. cervicolor,* ODC mRNA concentrations increase by only 3–5-fold, while in *M. cookii,* they increase by 2-fold at most (99). Enzyme induction in the latter species is 60-fold and must be generated at the translational and/or posttranslational level. The near absence of mRNA induction in *M. cookii* is associated with the lack of an androgen effect upon ODC gene transcription, as measured by nuclear run-on assays (86c).

It has been suggested that ODC is of primary importance in androgen regulated gene expression in the mouse kidney (35). The observation that androgen-mediated cellular hypertrophy and induction of enzymes are attenuated in the kidneys of mice treated with difluoromethylornithine, an inhibitor of ODC, has led to the proposal that androgen effects are indirect and are due to expansion of the polyamine pool that occurs subsequent to ODC induction (35). However, in a different study, no evidence for the mediation of androgen induction by polyamines was obtained (7), and the issue remains open.

The RP2 Gene

The androgen-inducible mRNAs encoded by the *RP2* gene were originally identified by a plasmid, pMK908, which was isolated from a kidney cDNA library (5). The *RP2* mRNAs, which have also been denoted the MAK mRNAs (92), encode a 43,000 dalton polypeptide of unknown function (5). Their sequence has been determined and used to deduce the sequence of the 357–amino acid polypeptide (50). Variation in *RP2* mRNA length among inbred strains correlates with a restriction fragment length polymorphism in genomic DNA and has been used to map the *RP2* gene to chromosome 7, very near the *Gpi-1* locus (25). This variation was shown to derive from the insertion of a DNA element, representing the *B1* repetitive family, into the 3'-untranslated region of the mRNA (49).

The *RP2* mRNAs are expressed in all tissues, but are induced by testosterone only in the kidney (5, 98). An androgen-mediated increase in *RP2* gene transcription has recently been measured, but does not account for full induction of the mRNA (86a). This is consistent with the participation of a posttranscriptional control (6).

RP2 mRNA regulation by testosterone has been examined in several *Mus* species (98). The correlation of variations in inter-species response with phylogeny suggests that *RP2* inducibility arose during *Mus* evolution and occurred in two steps: acquisition of a modest, 2–4-fold response followed by its maximization to about 10–15-fold (98). Nuclear run-on measurements indicate that the acquisition step may have occurred at the posttranscriptional level, while the maximization step occurred at the transcriptional level (86a). Thus, multiple mechanisms of hormonal regulation may have evolved independently and may contribute differentially to gene expression phenotypes in various species.

Kidney Androgen-Regulated Protein (KAP)

KAP is an abundant polypeptide whose mRNA is induced 3–10-fold by testosterone in the mouse kidney (13, 97, 105). In situ hybridization experiments have shown that KAP is expressed in the epithelial cells of the proximal convoluted tubules (64). Specific antibodies have been used to demonstrate that KAP is induced in kidney to the same extent as its mRNA (13). Low levels of KAP can be detected in liver, submaxillary gland, and urine. The presence of KAP in the urine suggests that the protein is excreted, much like other androgen-inducible proteins in kidney (13).

The role of the androgen receptor in KAP induction is not clear. Two laboratories have reported that KAP mRNA does not respond to testosterone in mice carrying the *Tfm* mutation (97, 105); however, Watson et al (106) observed induction in such animals. *Tfm* mutants have been shown to have residual androgen binding activity (29), which may be sufficient to partially induce the apparently hypersensitive KAP gene (15, 106). However, the possible participation of a second receptor protein in the induction cannot be excluded.

In vivo pulse-labeling experiments indicate that induction of KAP mRNA synthesis in response to testosterone accounts for the increase in mRNA concentrations (105). The relative rates of KAP mRNA synthesis both before and after testosterone treatment are disproportionately low compared to KAP mRNA concentrations. Thus, the mRNA may be unusually stable, a suggestion supported by preliminary pulse-chase experiments (G. Watson, unpublished observations).

Alcohol Dehydrogenase (ADH)

The *Adh-1* gene on mouse chromosome 3 (17) encodes the major ADH isoenzyme expressed in liver and kidney (40). The products of the *Adh-2* and *Adh-3* genes have different catalytic properties and are expressed in other tissues (1, 40). Control of ADH activity in liver and kidney appears to be independent. Thus, while the enzyme is induced in the kidney in response to androgens (68), it is unaffected in the liver. In addition, a genetic locus has been described that regulates activity in liver, yet has no effect in kidney (3).

In response to androgens, ADH undergoes a 10–12-fold induction over a period of several days (16, 27). Comparable inductions occur in the rate of ADH synthesis and in the concentration of ADH mRNA (16, 27). Thus, in contrast to ODC, ADH turnover does not change after the administration of androgen. Also, the translational efficiency of ADH mRNA appears to remain constant. Rates of mRNA synthesis, as determined by in vivo pulse labeling of RNA, indicate that testosterone induces ADH mRNA synthesis 6-fold. An identical level of induction has been found using nuclear run-on assays, which suggests that ADH mRNA is regulated at the transcriptional level (27). However, a 2-fold stabilization of the mRNA by androgen is still possible. Induction of ADH is progressive and occurs with kinetics that fit the multiple binding site model of Almagor & Paigen (2).

SUMMARY AND CONCLUSIONS

While a great deal of knowledge on the mechanisms of steroid hormone regulated gene expression now exists, specific information relating to androgens is lacking. A number of experimental systems have been developed and show promise as models for molecular studies of androgen regulation. Further development of these models must address the issue of whether or not the androgen receptor behaves similarly to other steroid receptors. This will require progress in the purification of the receptor itself or the cloning of its gene.

Several features of androgen-regulated gene expression in the mouse kidney are applicable to a number of important biological problems. First, the presence of a variety of inducible mRNAs, whose responses to androgen are controlled at several genetic and molecular levels, should be valuable in obtaining basic information on mechanisms of gene regulation by hormones. Second, a genetic approach, for which the mouse is a convenient organism, will enable identification of novel regulatory elements that are responsible for variations in the hormonal activation of genes and that drive the evolution of species-specific gene expression phenotypes. Finally, the trophic effects of androgens in the mouse kidney afford opportunities to study a gene expression phenotype that is involved in cell growth; it will be of interest to determine how androgen induction of gene expression in kidney proximal tubule cells relates to the hormone-mediated growth of these cells.

Acknowledgments

We thank Carol Rheaume, Karen Barbour, Kristen French, and Susan Elliger for help in preparation of this manuscript. Work in the authors' laboratories is supported by National Institutes of Health grants DK37265 and GM31656.

Literature Cited

1. Algar, E. M., Seeley, T.-L., Holmes, R. S. 1983. Purification and molecular properties of mouse alcohol dehydrogenase isozymes. *Eur. J. Biochem.* 137:139–47
2. Almagor, H., Paigen, K. 1988. Chemical kinetics of induced gene expression: Activation of transcription by non-cooperative binding of multiple regulatory molecules. *Biochemistry* 27:2094–2102
3. Balak, K. J., Keith, R. H., Felder, M. R. 1982. Genetic and developmental regulation of mouse liver alcohol dehydrogenase. *J. Biol. Chem.* 257:15000–7
4. Bardin, C. W., Catterall, J. F. 1981.

Testosterone: A major determinant of extragenital sexual development. *Science* 24:1285–94
5. Berger, F. G., Gross, K. W., Watson, G. 1981. Isolation and characterization of a DNA sequence complementary to an androgen-inducible messenger RNA from mouse kidney. *J. Biol. Chem.* 256:7006–13
6. Berger, F. G., Loose, D. S., Meisner, H., Watson, G. 1986. Androgen induction of messenger RNA concentrations in mouse kidney is post-transcriptional. *Biochemistry* 25:1170–75
7. Berger, F. G., Porter, C. W. 1986. Putrescine does not mediate the androgen-response in mouse kidney. *Biochem.*

Biophys. Res. Commun. 138:771–77

8. Berger, F. G., Szymanski, P., Read, E., Watson, G. 1984. Ornithine decarboxylase mRNAs of mouse kidney. *J. Biol. Chem.* 259:7941–46

9. Bonhomme, F. 1986. Evolutionary relationships in the genus *Mus. Curr. Top. Microbiol. Immunol.* 127:19–34

10. Bracey, L. T., Paigen, K. 1987. Changes in translational yield regulate tissue specific expression of β-glucuronidase. *Proc. Natl. Acad. Sci. USA* 84:9020–24

11. Brock, M. L., Shapiro, D. J. 1983. Estrogen stabilizes vitellogenin mRNA against cytoplasmic turnover. *Cell* 34:207–14

12. Cato, A. C. B., Henderson, D., Ponta, H. 1987. The hormone response element of the mouse mammary tumor virus DNA mediates the progestin and androgen induction of transcription in the proviral long terminal repeat region. *EMBO J.* 6:363–68

13. Catterall, J. F., Kontula, K. K., Watson, C. S., Seppanen, P. J., Funkenstein, B., et al. 1986. Regulation of gene expression by androgens in murine kidney. *Recent Prog. Horm. Res.* 42:71–108

14. Catterall, J. F., Leary, S. L. 1983. Detection of early changes in androgen-induced mouse renal β-glucuronidase messenger ribonucleic acid using cloned complementary deoxyribonucleic acid. *Biochemistry* 22:6049–53

15. Catterall, J. F., Watson, C. S., Kontula, K. K., Janne, O. A., Bardin, C. W. 1985. Differential sensitivity of specific genes in mouse kidney to androgens and antiandrogens. In *Molecular Mechanism of Steroid Hormone Action,* ed. V. K. Moudgil. New York: de Gruyter 587 pp.

16. Ceci, J. D., Lawther, R., Duester, G., Hatfield, G. W., Smith, M., et al. 1986. Androgen induction of alcohol dehydrogenase in mouse kidney, studied using a cDNA probe confirmed by nucleotide sequence analysis. *Gene* 41:217–24

17. Ceci, J. D., Zheng, Y.-W., Felder, M. R. 1987. Molecular analysis of mouse alcohol dehydrogenase: Nucleotide sequence of the *Adh-1* gene and genetic mapping of a related nucleotide sequence to chromosome 3. *Gene* 59:171–82

18. Chandler, V. L., Maler, B. A., Yamamoto, K. R. 1983. DNA sequences bound specifically by glucocorticoid receptor in vitro render a heterologous promoter hormone responsive in vivo. *Cell* 33:489–99

19. Chapman, V. M., Miller, D. R., Novak, E., Elliott, R. W. 1986. Alleles of β-glucuronidase found in wild mice. *Curr. Topics Microbiol. Immunol.* 127:114–23

20. Chen, C. L. C., Feigelson, P. 1979. Hormonal control of alpha$_{2u}$-globulin synthesis and its mRNA in isolated hepatocytes. *Ann. NY Acad. Sci.* 349:28–45

21. Compere, S. J., McKnight, G. S., Palmiter, R. D. 1981. Androgens regulate ovomucoid and ovalbumin gene expression independently of estrogen. *J. Biol. Chem.* 256:6341–47

22. D'Amore, M. A., Gallagher, P. M., Korfhagen, T. R., Ganschow, R. E. 1988. The complete sequence and organization of the murine β-glucuronidase gene. *Biochemistry.* Submitted for publication

23. Darbre, P., Page, M., King, R. J. B. 1986. Androgen regulation by the long terminal repeat of mouse mammary tumor virus. *Mol. Cell. Biol.* 6:2847–54

24. Derman, E. 1981. Isolation of a cDNA clone for mouse major urinary proteins: Age- and sex-related expression of mouse urinary protein genes is transcriptionally controlled. *Proc. Natl. Acad. Sci. USA* 78:5425–29

25. Elliott, R. W., Berger, F. G. 1983. DNA sequence polymorphism in an androgen-regulated gene is associated with alteration in the encoded mRNAs. *Proc. Natl. Acad. Sci. USA* 80:501–4

26. Evans, R. M., Hollenberg, S. M. 1988. Zinc fingers: Gilt by association. *Cell* 52:1–3

27. Felder, M. R., Watson, G., Huff, M., O'Malley, M., Ceci, J. D. 1988. Androgen-induced stimulation of transcription of the *Adh-1* gene. *J. Biol. Chem.* In press

28. Fishman, W. H., Abraham, R., DeLellis, D. 1966. β-glucuronidase response to androgens as a histochemical model for a hormone-enzyme relation. *Ann. Histochem.* 11:391–402

29. Fox, T. O., Blank, D., Politch, J. A. 1983. Residual androgen binding in testicular feminization (Tfm). *J. Steroid Biochem.* 19:577–81

30. Funkenstein, B., Leary, S. L., Stein, J. C., Catterall, J. F. 1988. Genomic organization and sequence of the *Gus-s*^{a} allele of the murine β-glucuronidase gene. *Mol. Cell. Biol.* 8:1160–68

31. Gallagher, P. M., D'Amore, M. A., Lund, S. D., Ganschow, R. E. 1988. The complete nucleotide sequence of murine β-glucuronidase mRNA and its

deduced polypeptide. *Genomics*. Submitted for publication.

32. Gehring, U., Tompkins, G. M. 1974. Characterization of a hormone receptor defect in the androgen-insensitivity mutant. *Cell* 3:59–64

33. Giguere, V., Hollenberg, S. M., Rosenfeld, M. G., Evans, R. M. 1986. Functional domains of the human glucocorticoid receptor. *Cell* 46:645–52

34. Godowski, P. J., Rusconi, S., Miesfield, R., Yamamoto, K. 1987. Glucocorticoid receptor mutants that are constitutive activators of transcriptional enhancement. *Nature* 325:365–68

35. Goldstone, A., Koenig, H., Lu, C. 1982. Testosterone-dependent sexual dimorphism of the mouse kidney is mediated by polyamines. *Biochem. Biophys. Res. Commun.* 104:165–72

36. Gresik, E. W. 1980. Postnatal developmental changes in submandibular glands of rats and mice. *J. Histochem. Cytochem.* 28:860–70

37. Henningsson, S., Persson, L., Rosengren, E. 1978. Polyamines and nucleic acids in the mouse kidney induced to growth by testosterone proprionate. *Acta Physiol. Scand.* 102:385–93

38. Herrup, K., Mullen, R. J. 1977. Biochemical and genetic factors in the heat inactivation of murine β-glucuronidase. *Biochem. Genet.* 15:641–53

39. Hikok, N. J., Seppanen, P. J., Kontula, K. K., Janne, P. A., Bardin, C. W., Janne, O. A. 1985. Two ornithine decarboxylase mRNA species in mouse kidney arise from size heterogeniety at their 3'-termini. *Proc. Natl. Acad. Sci. USA* 83:594–98

40. Holmes, R. S., Albanese, R., Whitehead, F. D., Duley, J. A. 1981. Mouse alcohol dehydrogenase isozymes: Products of closely localized duplicated genes exhibiting divergent kinetic properties. *J. Exp. Zool.* 215:151–57

41. Holtta, E., Pohjanpelto, P. 1986. Control of ornithine decarboxylase in Chinese hamster ovary cells. Translational inhibition of synthesis and acceleration of degradation of the enzyme by putrescine, spermidine, and spermine. *J. Biol. Chem.* 261:9502–8

42. Hynes, N., van Ooyen, A. J. J., Kennedy, N., Herrlich, P., Ponta, H., Groner, B. 1983. Subfragments of the large terminal repeat cause glucocorticoid-responsive expression of mouse mammary tumor virus and of an adjacent gene. *Proc. Natl. Acad. Sci. USA* 80:3637–41

43. Isomaa, V. V., Pajunen, A. E. I.,

44. Janne, O., Bullock, L. P., Bardin, C. W., Jacob, S. T. 1976. Early androgen action in kidney of normal and androgen-insensitive (tfm/y) mice. Changes in RNA polymerase and chromatin template activities. *Biochem. Biophys. Acta* 418:330–43

45. Kahana, C., Nathans, D. 1984. Isolation of cloned cDNA encoding mammalian ornithine decarboxylase. *Proc. Natl. Acad. Sci. USA* 81:3645–49

46. Kahana, C., Nathans, D. 1985. Translational regulation of mammalian ornithine decarboxylase by polyamines. *J. Biol. Chem.* 260:15390–93

47. Kandala, J. C., Kistler, M. K., Kistler, W. S. 1985. Androgen regulated genes from prostrate and seminal vesicle share upstream sequence homologies. *Biochem. Biophys. Res. Commum.* 126:948–52

48. Karin, M., Haslinger, A., Holtgreve, H., Richards, R. I., Krauter, P., Westphal, H. M., Beato, M. 1984. Characterization of DNA sequences through which cadmium and glucocorticoid hormones induce human metallothionein-IIA gene. *Nature* 308:513–19

49. King, D., Snider, L. D., Lingrel, J. B. 1986. Polymorphism in an androgen-regulated mouse gene is the result of the insertion of a B1 repetitive element into the transcription unit. *Mol. Cell. Biol.* 6:209–17

50. King, D., Sun, Y. H., Lingrel, J. B. 1986. Amino acid sequence of the testosterone-regulated mouse kidney *RP2* protein determined from its complementary DNA sequence. *Nucleic Acids Res.* 14:5159–70

51. Klein-Hitpass, L., Schorpp, M., Wagner, U., Ryffel, G. U. 1986. An estrogen-responsive element derived from the 5'-flanking region of the *Xenopus* vitellogenin A2 gene functions in transfected human cells. *Cell* 46:1053–61

52. Klock, G., Strahle, U., Schutz, G. 1987. Oestrogen and glucocorticoid responsive elements are closely related but distinct. *Nature* 329:734–36

53. Kochakian, C. D., Hill, J., Aonuma, S. 1963. Regulation of protein biosynthesis in mouse kidney by androgens. *Endocrinology* 72:354–63

54. Koenig, H., Goldstone, A., Blume, G., Lu, C. Y. 1980. Testosterone-mediated

Bardin, C. W., Janne, O. A. 1983. Ornithine decarboxylase in mouse kidney. Purification, characterization, and radioimmunological determination of the enzyme protein. *J. Biol. Chem.* 258:6735–40 sexual demorphism of mitochondria and lysosomes in mouse kidney tubule cells. *Science* 209:1023–26

55. Kontula, K. K., Torkkeli, T. K., Bardin, C. W., Janne, O. A. 1984. Androgen induction of ornithine decarboxylase mRNA in mouse kidney as studied by complementary DNA. *Proc. Natl. Acad. Sci. USA* 81:731–35

56. Kumar, V., Green, S., Stack, G., Berry, M., Jin, J.-R., Chambon, P. 1987. Functional domains of the human estrogen receptor. *Cell* 51:941–51

57. Loosefelt, H., Atger, M., Misrahi, M., Guiochon-Mantel, A., Meriel, C., et al. 1986. Cloning and sequence analysis of rabbit progesterone-receptor complementary DNA. *Proc. Natl. Acad. Sci. USA* 83:9045–49

58. Lund, S. D., Miller, D., Chapman, V., Ganschow, R. E. 1988. Androgen regulation of murine β-glucuronidase expression: Identification and characterization of a non-response variant. *Genetics* 119:151–56

59. Lusis, A. J., Chapman, V. M., Wangenstein, R. W., Paigen, K. 1983. A trans-acting temporal locus within the β-glucuronidase gene complex. *Proc. Natl. Acad. Sci. USA* 80:4398–4402

60. McConlogue, L., Dana, S. L., Coffino, P. 1986. Multiple mechanisms are responsible for altered expression of ornithine decarboxylase in overproducing variant cells. *Mol. Cell. Biol.* 6:2865–71

61. McConlogue, L., Gupta, M., Wu, L., Coffino, P. 1984. Molecular cloning and expression of the mouse ornithine decarboxylase gene. *Proc. Natl. Acad. Sci. USA* 81:540–44

62. Melanitou, E., Cohn, D. A., Bardin, C. W., Janne, O. A. 1987. Genetic variation in androgen regulation of ornithine decarboxylase gene expression in inbred strains of mice. *Mol. Endocrinol.* 1:266–73

63. Meredith, S. A., Ganschow, R. E. 1978. Apparent *trans* control of murine β-glucuronidase synthesis by a temporal genetic element. *Genetics* 90:725–34

64. Mesegner, A., Catterall, J. F. 1987. Mouse kidney androgen-regulated mRNA is expressed in the proximal convoluted tubules. *Mol. Endocrinol.* 1:535–41

65. Mills, N. C., Mills, T. M., Yurkiewicz, W. J., Bardin, C. W. 1979. Actions of androgens on the kidney of female mice: Strain differences in the DNA and β-glucuronidase responses. *Int. J. Androl.* 2:371–84

66. Norstedt, G., Palmiter, R. 1984. Secretory rhythm of growth hormone regulates sexual differentiation of mouse liver. *Cell* 36:805–12

67. Novak, E. K., Swank, R. T. 1979. Lysosomal dysfunctions associated with mutations at mouse pigment genes. *Genetics* 92:189–204

68. Ohno, S., Stenius, C., Christian, L., Harris, C., Ivey, C. 1970. More about the testosterone induction of kidney alcohol dehydrogenase activity in the mouse. *Biochem. Genet.* 4:565–77

69. Paek, I., Axel, R. 1987. Glucocorticoids enhance stability of human growth hormone mRNA. *Mol. Cell. Biol.* 7:1496–1507

70. Page, M. J., Parker, M. G. 1982. Effect of androgen on the transcription of rat prostatic binding protein genes. *Mol. Cell. Endocrinol.* 27:343–55

71. Page, M. J., Parker, M. G. 1983. Androgen-regulated expression of a cloned rat prostatic C3 gene transfected into mouse mammary tumor cells. *Cell* 32:495–502

72. Paigen, K. 1979. Acid hydrolases as models of genetic control. *Ann. Rev. Genet.* 13:417–66

73. Paigen, K., Labarca, C., Watson, G. 1979. A regulatory locus for mouse β-glucuronidase induction, *Gur*, controls messenger RNA activity. *Science* 203:554–56

74. Paigen, K., Swank, R. T., Tomino, S., Ganschow, R. E. 1975. The molecular genetics of mammalian glucuronidase. *J. Cell. Physiol.* 85:379–92

75. Pajunen, A. E. I., Isomaa, V. V., Janne, O. A., Bardin, C. W. 1982. Androgenic regulation of ornithine decarboxylase activity in mouse kidney and its relationship to changes in cytosol and nuclear androgen receptor concentrations. *J. Biol. Chem.* 257:8190–98

76. Palmer, R., Gallagher, P. M., Boyko, W. L., Ganschow, R. E. 1983. Genetic control of levels of murine kidney glucuronidase mRNA in response to androgen. *Proc. Natl. Acad. Sci. USA* 80:7596–7600

77. Parker, M., Hurst, H., Page, M. 1984. Organization and expression of the prostatic steroid binding protein genes. *J. Steroid Biochem.* 20:67–71

78. Parker, M. G., Scrace, G. T., Mainwaring, W. I. P. 1978. Testosterone regulates the synthesis of major proteins in rat ventral prostate. *Biochem. J.* 170:115–21

79. Parker, M. G., Webb, P., Needham, M., White, R., Hain, J. 1987. Identi-

fication of androgen response elements in mouse mammary tumour virus and the rat prostate C3 gene. *J. Cell. Biochem.* 35:285–92

80. Pegg, A. E. 1986. Recent advances in the biochemistry of polyamines in eucaryotes. *Biochem. J.* 234:249–62

81. Pegg, A. E., McCann, P. P. 1982. Polyamine metabolism and function. *Am. J. Physiol.* 243:C212-C221

82. Persson, L., Seely, J. E., Pegg, A. E. 1984. Investigation of structure and rate of synthesis of ornithine decarboxylase protein in mouse kidney. *Biochemistry* 23:3777–83

83. Pfister, K., Chapman, V., Watson, G., Paigen, K. 1985. Genetic variation for enzyme structure and systemic regulation in two new haplotypes of the β-glucuronidase gene of Mus musculus castaneus. *J. Biol. Chem.* 260:11588–94

84. Pfister, K., Paigen, K., Watson, G., Chapman, V. 1982. Expression of β-glucuronidase haplotypes in prototype and congenic mouse strains. *Biochem. Genet.* 20:519–36

85. Pfister, K., Watson, G., Chapman, V., Paigen, K. 1984. Kinetics of β-glucuronidase induction by androgen: Genetic variation in the first order rate constant. *J. Biol. Chem.* 259:5816–20

86. Rabindran, S. K., Danielson, M., Firestone, G. L., Stallcup, M. R. 1987. Glucocorticoid-dependent maturation of viral proteins in mouse lymphoma cells: isolation of defective and hormone-independent cell variants. *Somat. Cell Mol. Genet.* 13:131–43

86a. Rheaume, C., Barbour, K., Tseng-Crank, J., Berger, F. G. 1988. Molecular genetics of androgen-inducible RP2 gene transcription in the mouse kidney. *Mol. Cell. Biol.* Submitted for publication

86b. Rheaume, C., Latimer, J. J., Baumann, H., Berger, F. G. 1988. Tissue- and species-specific regulation of murine α$_1$-antitrypsin gene transcription. *J. Biol. Chem.* In press

86c. Rheaume, C., Schonfeld, C., Porter, C., Berger, F. G. 1988. Evolution of androgen-regulated ornithine decarboxylase expression in mouse kidney. *Mol. Endocrinol.* Submitted for publication

87. Ringold, G. 1985. Steroid hormone regulation of gene expression. *Ann. Rev. Pharmacol. Toxicol.* 25:529–66

88. Rushmere, N. K., Parker, M. G., Davies, C. 1987. Androgen receptor-binding regions of an androgen responsive gene. *Mol. Cell. Endocrinol.* 51:259–65

89. Schreffler, D. C. 1976. The S region of the mouse major histocompatability complex (H-2): Genetic variation and functional role in complement system. *Transplant. Rev.* 32:140–67

90. Seely, J. E., Pegg, A. E. 1983. Changes in mouse kidney ornithine decarboxylase activity are brought about by changes in the amount of enzyme protein as measured by radioimmunoassay. *J. Biol. Chem.* 258:2496–2500

91. Seely, J. E., Poso, H., Pegg, A. E. 1982. Effect of androgens on turnover of ornithine decarboxylase in mouse kidney. Studies using labeling of the enzyme by reaction with [^{14}C]-difluoromethylornithine. *J. Biol. Chem.* 257:7549–53

92. Snider, L. D., King, D., Lingrel, J. B. 1985. Androgen regulation of MAK mRNAs in mouse kidney. *J. Biol. Chem.* 260:9884–93

93. Stavenhagen, J., Loreni, F., Hemenway, C., Kalff, M., Robins, D. M. 1987. Molecular genetics of androgen-dependent and -independent expression of mouse sex-limited protein. *Mol. Cell. Biol.* 7:1716–24

94. Strahle, U., Klock, G., Schutz, G. 1987. A DNA sequence of 15 base pairs is sufficient to mediate glucocorticoid and progesterone induction of gene expression. *Proc. Natl. Acad. Sci. USA* 84:7871–75

95. Swank, R. T., Davey, R., Joyce, L., Reid, P., Macey, M. R. 1977. Differential effect of hypophysectomy on the synthesis of β-glucuronidase and other androgen-inducible enzymes in mouse kidney. *Endocrinology* 100:473–80

96. Swank, R. T., Paigen, K., Davey, R., Chapman, V., Labarca, C., et al. 1978. Genetic regulation of mammalian β-glucuronidase. *Rec. Prog. Horm. Res.* 34:401–36

97. Toole, J. J., Hastie, N. D., Held, W. A. 1979. An abundant androgen-regulated mRNA in the mouse kidney. *Cell* 17:441–48

98. Tseng-Crank, J., Berger, F. G. 1987. Evolution of steroid-inducible RP2 mRNA expression in the mouse kidney. *Genetics* 116:593–99

99. Tseng-Crank, J., Schonfeld, C., Berger, F. G. 1988. Evolution of androgen-regulated mRNA expression in mouse kidney. *Mol. Biol. Evol.* 5:442–54

100. von der Ahe, D., Janich, S., Scheidereit, C., Renkawitz, R., Schutz, G., Beato, M. 1985. Glucocorticoid and progesterone receptors bind to the same

sites in two hormonally regulated promoters. *Nature* 313:706–9

101. Watson, C. S., Catterall, J. F. 1986. Genetic regulation of androgen-induced accumulation of mouse renal β-glucuronidase messenger ribonucleic acid. *Endocrinology* 118:1081–86

102. Watson, G., Davey, R. A., Labarca, C., Paigen, K. 1981. Genetic determination of kinetic parameters in β-glucuronidase induction by androgen. *J. Biol. Chem* 256:3005–11

103. Watson, G., Felder, M., Rabinow, L., Moore, K., Labarca, C., et al. 1985. Properties of rat and mouse β-glucuronidase mRNA and cDNA, including evidence for sequence polymorphism and genetic regulation of mRNA levels. *Gene* 36:15–25

104. Watson, G., Paigen, K. 1987. Genetic variations in the kinetic constants that describe β-glucuronidase mRNA induction in androgen treated mice. *Mol. Cell. Biol.* 7:1085–90

105. Watson, G., Paigen, K. 1988. mRNA synthesis rates in vivo for androgen-inducible sequences in mouse kidney. *Mol. Cell. Biol.* 8:2117–24

106. Watson, C. S., Salomon, D., Catterall, J. F. 1984. Structure and expression of androgen-regulated genes in mouse kidney. *Ann. NY Acad. Sci.* 438:101–14

107. Weinberger, C., Hollenberg, S. M., Rosenfeld, M. G., Evans, R. M. 1985. Domain structure of human glucocorticoid receptor and its relationship to the *v-erbA* oncogene product. *Nature* 318:670–72

108. Widman, L. E., Chasin, L. A. 1982. Multihormonal induction of alpha$_{2u}$-globulin in an established rat hepatoma cell line. *J. Cell. Physiol.* 112:316–26

109. Williams, L., McDonald, C., Higgins, S., 1985. Sequence organization of rat seminal vesicle F gene: Location of transcriptional start point and sequence comparison with six other androgen-regulated genes. *Nucleic Acids Res.* 13:659–72

110. Yamamoto, K. R. 1985. Steroid receptor regulated transcription of specific genes and gene networks. *Ann. Rev. Genet.* 19:209–52

Annu. Rev. Physiol. 1989. 51:67–80

EPIDERMAL GROWTH FACTOR AND THE KIDNEY

Delbert A. Fisher, Eduardo C. Salido, and Luciano Barajas

Departments of Pediatrics, Medicine, and Pathology, University of California, Los Angeles School of Medicine, Harbor-UCLA Medical Center, Los Angeles, California 90509

INTRODUCTION

Epidermal growth factor (EGF) belongs to an extensive class of molecules, referred to as growth factors, that mediates cell growth and differentiation (7, 8, 12). These factors also may stimulate acute cell responses. Their effects are mediated via autocrine, paracrine, or endocrine mechanisms. EGF was isolated and characterized by Cohen & Taylor (7), Deuel (8), and Gospodarowicz (12) from the adult mouse salivary gland. The human analogue was purified from urine by Cohen & Carpenter (6), Starkey et al (55), and (as urogastrone) Gregory (14). EGF is a 53–amino acid, 6045–molecular weight peptide that acts via specific plasma membrane receptors to evoke a remarkable variety of biological responses (6–8, 12). Human and mouse EGF share a 70% homology in amino acid structure and have similar locations for the three disulfide bonds (6, 14). Mouse EGF is derived from a 1217–amino acid precursor molecule that contains at least seven EGF-like sequences (13, 54). The human EGF precursor molecule is a 1207–amino acid molecule with 66% homology to the mouse protein (2a). The EGF sequence is blanked by segments of 970 and 184 residues at the aminoterminal and carboxyterminal, respectively. EGF binds to a well characterized 170–185-kilodalton (kDa) glycoprotein receptor that undergoes tyrosine phosphorylation. EGF receptors are widely distributed, and EGF is mitogenic for a variety of epidermal and mesodermal cell types. It has important maturative effects, accelerating tooth eruption and eyelid opening in rodents, accelerating lung maturation in fetal sheep, and stimulating thyroid and liver growth and gastrointestinal development in rodents (3, 6–8, 12, 42, 45, 64).

67

0066-4278/89/0315-0067$02.00

ONTOGENESIS OF KIDNEY EGF

In adult humans EGF is detectable by immunoassay or immunoctyochemistry in salivary glands, gut, pancreas, bone marrow, prostate gland, and several endocrine glands (pituitary, adrenal, and thyroid) (18, 24). Tissue levels are comparable and highest (about 4 ng/gram net weight) in kidney, pancreas, and thyroid (18). EGF mRNA has been identified in mammalian kidney tissue, and EGF is present in relatively high concentration in urine (4, 6, 11, 14, 18, 19, 32, 55). Studies of the ontogenesis of EGF in urine and kidney of the mouse have shown low levels in urine before 6 days of age (1–3 ng/mg urea N) with a rapid increase by 18 days (to about 90 ng/mg urea N) and a more gradual increase thereafter to adult concentrations (about 200 ng/mg urea N) by 3–4 months (37). Kidney tissue concentrations increase similarly, reaching adult levels approximating 1.0 ng/mg protein (37).

Plasma and serum EGF levels are similar in the mouse; adult serum concentrations are achieved by 30–60 days in females and by 3–4 months in males (39). Adult serum EGF levels approximate 400 pg/mg (39). Adult mouse kidney contains relatively large concentrations of prepro EGF mRNA (44); the EGF mRNA level in kidney is half that in submandibular gland, and 100- to 1000-fold greater than in most other tissues (Table 1). Prepro EGF mRNA appears in mouse kidney by 10–14 days of postnatal age (15, 43)

There is a sexual dimorphism of EGF concentrations in both mouse kidney and urine, with higher EGF levels in the female. This dimorphism appears between 1 and 3 months (37). A similar sexual dimorphism has been observed for kidney prepro EGF mRNA levels, with higher concentrations in adult females than males (15). The mRNA dimorphism appears by 2 to 3 weeks of postnatal age (15, 43). The sexual dimorphism of kidney EGF and prepro EGF mRNA levels in the rodent (female levels greater than male) differs from that in submandibular gland or serum, where values for males exceed those for females (4, 7, 12, 15, 39). Thyroxine and growth hormone have been

Table 1 Prepro EGF mRNA and EFF protein in mouse tissues[a]

Tissue	Relative prepro EGF mRNA abundance	Relative EGF protein abundance
Kidney	1	1
Submaxillary gland (male)	2	2000
Pancreas	0.008	0.43
Duodenrum	0.004	0.33
Brain	0.002	<0.02
Lung	0.002	<0.02
Spleen	<0.002	0.33

[a]Abundances normalized to kidney values. Table modified from Rall et al (44), including data from Bynny et al (4).

Table 2 Hormones modulating EGF concentrations in salivary gland and urine of the mouse[a]

Hormones	EGF concentrations	
	Salivary gland	Urine
Testosterone	Increase	No effect
Estrogen	No effect	Increase ?
Glucocorticoid	Increase	?
Thyroxine	Increase	Increase
Growth Hormone	?	Increase

[a]From references 15, 36, 37, 40.

shown to stimulate urine EGF concentrations, and these effects become manifest during the first week of postnatal life (36, 40) (Table 2).

Studies of the maturation of human urinary immunoreactive EGF indicate a progressive increase in concentration during infancy to a peak between 1 and 2 years of age (about 70 ng/ml or 235 ng/mg creatinine), with a plateau thereafter at 70–80 ng/ml through 20 years of age (28, 30). Levels between 30 and 55 years range from 30 to 50 ng/ml and fall to <20 ng/ml at 70 years (28). Urinary EGF falls between 2 and 16 years to a level of 30–60 ng/mg creatinine, plateaus through 55 years, and falls again to a value of 10–20 ng/mg at 70 years (28, 30). As in the rodent, human urine EGF concentrations are higher in females than in males but are not affected by the menstrual cycle, oral contraceptives, or postmenopausal estrogen therapy (28). However, urine EGF concentrations increase about two fold during pregnancy, reaching peak levels of 100–200 ng/g creatinine at 20 weeks (20).

The role of EGF during fetal life is not clear. As discussed above, EGF and EGF mRNA levels become detectable in rodents only during the neonatal period. However, EGF receptors have been reported in fetal tissues, including kidney, and in placenta (1, 11a, 31a, 35a). The ligand for these receptors may be alpha transforming growth factor (α-TGF), a 6000–molecular weight, 50–amino acid, EGF-like protein that is identified by its ability to transform nonneoplastic cells (27c). α-TGF has a 35% homology with mouse EGF and a 44% homology with human EGF (urogastrone) (27b,c). It is produced by a variety of virus transformed cells and has been identified in a number of solid tumors, as well as in normal tissues (27b,c) Lee et al reported that α-TGF mRNA is detectable in the 8–10 day whole rat embryo, but was not detectable by day 18 (26a). Whether EGF, α-TGF or both are present in fetal blood remains to be clarified.

The receptor for α-TGF appears to be very similar or identical to the EGF receptor. Massague et al conducted affinity labeling cross-linking studies, which indicated that both [^{125}I]EGF and [^{125}I]α-TGF bound to a 140–160-kDa receptor in normal rat kidney (NRK) and A431 cells (27e). Receptor binding could be inhibited by addition of either cold EGF or cold α-TGF; similar kinetics suggest that both factors interact with the same receptor. [^{125}I]α-TGF cross-linked specifically to a 60-kDa receptor postulated to mediate the anchorage independent growth. Additional studies using human placental membranes or A431 carcinoma cells demonstrated equivalent membrane binding affinity and capacity for both EGF and α-TGF (27d). Moreover, response to lectins and receptor down-regulation in the presence of 30 nm EGF and α-TGF also were found to be similar (27d). Others have shown that both EGF and α-TGF interact with receptors possessing tyrosine kinase activity. Also, the degree of receptor phosphorylation is similar for the two peptides, which further supports the single receptor hypothesis (41a).

CHARACTERISTICS OF URINE EGF

Immunoreactive EGF in adult human urine consists of the intact 53–amino acid, 6045–molecular weight peptide plus several fragments (EGF 1–52, 1–51, and 1–50) that represent carboxyterminal cleavage of 1 to 3 aminoacids, presumably by urinary exopeptidases (31). All have similar immunoreactive and placental membrane-binding activities (31). Mouse immunoreactive urinary EGF also has (Sephadex) chromatographic properties similar to purified intact mouse salivary gland EGF (36). Immunoreactive rat urine EGF is more heterogenous, showing two to four peaks by chromatofocusing or high performance liquid chromatography (HPLC)(35). A high molecular weight form of human urine EGF has been purified to a molecular weight of approximately 30,000 (59). Tryspin digestion yields 6-kDa fragments. The N-terminal sequence of the 30,000–molecular weight molecule is identical with residues 829–848 of the predicted prepro EGF sequence and appears to represent a protein transcript distal to the transmembrane domain (54, 59).

Kidney tissue EGF in the mouse is reported to have a relative molecular mass of 130,000 kDa, similar to that predicted for prepro EGF (44). A 6-kDa species also has been identified by isoelectric focusing and HPLC (23).

RENAL ORIGIN OF URINE EGF

The mouse salivary gland is a major storage site for EGF that is available for secretion into saliva or blood (7, 15, 38). In contrast, there is little or no storage of EGF in kidney (Table 1). EGF mRNA abundance is high in the kidney, however, and the EGF production rate in urine is high. This is reflected by the fact that 1 ml of adult mouse urine (with 20–25 ng urea/ml) contains the same amount of EGF as 100 pairs of adult kidneys (37). During development, urine EGF increases about 100-fold relative to urea concentration and 1000-fold relative to urine volume (37). Studies of human EGF have consistently shown a high correlation between EGF and creatinine concentrations, which suggests that urine EGF is filtered from plasma (5, 28, 29, 56). Recent observations, however, indicate that EGF is not detectable or is present in very low concentrations (<20 pg/ml) in human plasma (5). EGF circulating in humans, in contrast to the mouse, is largely confined to blood platelets and is released during the process of blood coagulation (5, 34). Human serum contains 20–40 ng EGF/mg creatinine or 1–2 ng EGF/ml (5, 34).

In a recent study, levels of human plasma and urine creatinine and creatinine clearance were measured hourly for a 3 hour period in 12 adult male and 8 adult female subjects. EGF was not detectable in plasma by radioimmunoassay (<20 pg/mg), whereas relatively high levels were measured in serum (5). Urine EGF excretion averaged (± SE) 1641 ± 233 ng/hr in males and 1507 ± 191 ng/hr in females, and a significant correlation was observed between urine creatinine and EGF concentrations in both male and female subjects. Urine EGF excretion approximated 1.5 μg/hr or 25 μg/mg creatinine (5). The level of plasma EGF necessary to account for the urine EGF by glomerular filtration would have had to exceed 200 pg/ml. The authors concluded that more than 90% or urine EGF must be derived from the kidney (5). This is in agreement with results in the rat and mouse. In the mouse, EGF clearance exceeds urea clearance by 150-fold (38); in the rat, urine EGF clearance exceeds creatinine clearance 5-fold (35).

Salivary gland excision in rodents has no effect on urine EGF excretion (35, 38). In addition, thyroxine administration increases salivary gland EGF and urine EGF concentration, but does not increase serum EGF levels in the mouse (36, 38); testosterone increases salivary gland and plasma EGF, but has no effect on urine EGF concentration or apparent EGF clearance (38). Finally, salivary gland excision increases urine EGF clearance, and administration of salivary gland extract has no effect on kidney or urine EGF levels (38). This information further supports the view that the bulk of urine EGF (>90%) is derived from the kidney; very little is filtered via the glomerulus. Nevertheless, there is a high correlation between urine EGF and urine creatinine concentrations. Studies in adults with renal disease and decreased urine EGF levels indicate that the correlation between urine EGF and creatinine clearance persists in these subjects (29). Thus, there is a functional relationship between glomerular filtration and the process of renal EGF excretion. The mechanism remains unclear. Further characterization of the control of renal EGF synthesis and excretion is necessary to delineate the factors conditioning this glomerular filtration–tubular EGF balance.

LOCALIZATION OF EGF IN THE KIDNEY

EGF has been immunolocalized to the apical portion of the cells lining the thick ascending limb of Henle (TALH) and the distal convoluted tubule (DCT) (49). The macula densa (MD), in contrast, lacks EGF immunoreactivity (Figure 1). The presence of EGF immunoreactivity in the mouse kidney is likely to be the result of EGF synthesis at this level rather than sequestration of serum EGF. The demonstration of prepro EGF mRNA in the mouse kidney not only by dot blot and northern blot analyses of mRNA extracts but also by in situ hybridization using ^{32}P prepro EGF cDNA supports this view. In situ hybridization with the probe labeled with ^{32}P showed that the prepro EGF mRNA is limited to the distal nephron (44). More recent studies in our laboratory of the distribution of prepro EGF mRNA in the mouse kidney using a tritiated prepro EGF cDNA probe permitted better morphological resolution and showed a distribution of prepro EGF that parallels the distribution of EGF as shown by immunocytochemistry: Labeling was localized to the TALH and the DCT, but was absent from the MD (1a). As judged by immunoelectron microscopy, EGF immunoreactivity is present on the luminal plasma membrane and apical vesicles of the cells of the TALH (Figure 2) and the DCT; the MD showed no immunoreactivity. (50).

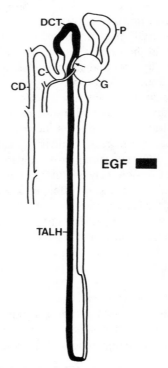

Figure 1 Diagrammatic illustration of the distribution of EGF-immunoreactivity in the tubular nephron. EGF-immunoreactivity is present in the thick ascending limb of Henle (TALH) and distal convoluted tubule (DCT). The macula densa (arrow), proximal tubule (P), connecting tubule (C), and collecting duct (CD) lacked EGF-immunoreactivity. G, glomerulus.

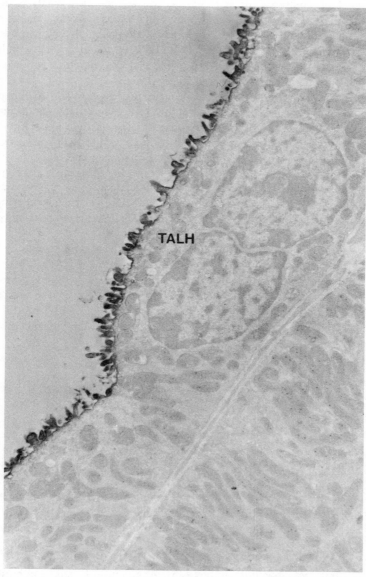

Figure 2   EGF immunoreactivity present on the luminal plasma membrane of cells of the thick ascending limb of Henle (TALH). Electron micrograph, x7,000 (reprinted with permission from 50).

These findings are consistent with the concept that EGF is synthesized as a transmembrane prepro EGF molecule, as was suggested by analysis of the EGF cDNA (13, 54). It has been proposed that prepro EGF is a membrane-attached protein with a membrane-spanning hydrophobic domain adjacent to the EGF moiety (9). Prepro EGF mRNA has been found in relatively large amounts in the mouse kidney (44), whereas EGF protein levels are exceedingly low in kidney tissue (about 5 ng/gm wet weight) (4, 44). It has been suggested that either the EGF precursor is not processed to the small peptide in the kidney (44) or it is not easily solubilized from the cell membrane during the extraction process (23). The immunolocalization of EGF in the kidney is compatible with either hypotheses since the antiserum to EGF can recognize the EGF moiety as a part of the larger EGF precursor molecule. It is also possible that both prepro EGF and processed peptides are represented in the apical immunoreactive material. Aminopeptidase and other proteolytic enzymes are localized to the apical cell surface of kidney epithelial cells and do appear in urine. Their role in prepro EGF processing remains to be determined (27).

It is interesting that EGF is localized in the same renal tubular areas (TALH and DCT) as human uromodulin (Tamm-Horsfall protein) (17). There is a 32% structural homology between the prepro EGF molecule (amino acids 399 to 491) and the amino-terminal regions (amino acids 37 to 135) of uromodulin, but the intron structure of the genes differs; the significance of this structural homology is unclear (17). There is no obvious functional homology between the two molecules.

ROLE OF EGF IN THE KIDNEY

The role of EGF in the kidney is unclear. A mitogenic role for tubular cells has been proposed. Thorburn and colleagues infused EGF (300–400 μg/day for 3–5 days) into chronically catheterized, third trimester fetal sheep (a period comparable developmentally to the neonatal period in rodents), and the sheep demonstrated a significant increase in kidney weight (from 9.4 ± 3.5 to 12.9 ± 4.9 g/kg body weight, $P<0.002$) (58). EGF has been shown to be a mitogen for rabbit kidney cortical collecting tubule (CCT), cortical thick ascending limb of Henle (TALH), and proximal tubule (PT) cells (33, 61). In the CCT and TALH cells, dexamethasone, insulin, and prolactin seemed to augment the effect of EGF on thymidine incorporation (33). In PT cells, EGF increased DNA synthesis 18-fold above the level in quiescent cells, and angiotensin II potentiated this effect (33). Angiotensin II is a local hormone known to activate phosphatidylinositol turnover in renal tubular cells (62). EGF binding to receptors in renal tubular cells activated phosphatidylinositol turnover to cause a rise in cytosolic free calcium levels, which suggests that the augmentation of EGF mitogenesis by angiotensin may be mediated via increases in cell free calcium (33, 62). EGF also has been shown to increase guanylate cyclase activity in kidney tissue of mice within 4 hours after an exogenous dose of 1 μg EGF per gram body weight (52). Breyer & Harris showed that EGF binds to specific EGF receptors on rabbit medullary interstitial cells in culture and stimulates thymidine incorporation in these cells (3a). NRK cells also have been utilized to study the effects of EGF. These "immortal" fibroblast cells are known to possess EGF receptors, and EGF is strongly mitogenic for this cell line (60). Also, NRK cells can be transformed by exposure to specific combinations of polypeptide growth factors, including EGF.

During the process of compensatory renal hypertrophy in rodents, there is a dramatic hypertrophy of the proximal tubules, and to a lesser degree of the distal tubules, without a change in the number of nephrons (10, 16, 26). There are associated increases in cell protein, RNA, and poly A+ RNA, and increased activities of a variety of enzymes without significant change in DNA content (2, 10, 25). Proto-oncogene expression shows little or no change (including c-*myc,* c-H-*ras,* c-K-*ras,* and *fos*), whereas mRNA levels for tubular cell enzymes (including ornithine aminotransferase and gamma glutamyl transpeptidase) are increased within 6 to 24 hours (2). Insulinlike growth factor I (IGF-I) levels also are increased in contralateral kidney tissue of rats 5 days, but not 24 hours, after unilateral nephrectomy, and the increase is restricted to cells of the collecting ducts and TALH (22, 57).

The possible involvement of EGF in compensatory renal hypertrophy has been investigated recently by immunoassay and in situ hybridization (21, 51). Significant increases in immunoreactive EGF in contralateral kidney tissue are observed by 7 days, but not 2 days, after unilateral nephrectomy in the mouse (51); increased levels of expression of prepro EGF mRNA are observed in the TALH and distal tubule within 7 days (21, 51). It is interesting that most of the increase in contralateral kidney weight occurs rapidly (before 7 days) after unilateral nephrectomy, as do the increases in enzyme mRNA levels. Thus, the increases in EGF and perhaps IGF-I synthesis and concentration seem to be relatively late events in the process of compensatory hypertrophy; the role of EGF in this process is not clear.

Recent studies have shown a functional role for EGF in CCTs. Breyer et al reported that EGF inhibits vasopressin-stimulated hydraulic conductivity of isolated microperfused rabbit CCT (3b). Pretreatment with peritubular EGF showed a dose response relationship over the range of 10^{-8} to 10^{-12} M EGF. Pretreatment with 10^{-8} M EGF had no effect when microperfused via the luminal surface. Peritubular EGF also inhibited cAMP-stimulated hydraulic conductivity, which indicates a postreceptor site of EGF action. The inhibitory effect of EGF was not blocked by indomethacin, which suggests that prostaglandins do not mediate the EGF effect (3b). Recent studies of Madin-Darby canine kidney (MDCK) epithelial cells in culture showed localization of EGF receptors to the basal surface and unidirectional transport of EGF in the apical direction (27a). These studies support a role for circulating EGF acting via EGF receptors on the basal (peritubular) surface of renal tubular cells.

Rall et al suggested that EGF may serve as a receptor on the cells of the distal tubules regulating membrane transport events (44). The sequence homology between the EGF precursor and the low density lipoprotein (LDL) receptor (48, 63), as well as the structural similarity between the EGF precursor and the receptors for EGF and insulin (41), suggests that the EGF precursor could function as receptor. If so, the ligand mediator and the effect remain to be defined. In support of this possibility, changes in urine flow and ionic composition have been reported after infusion of EGF into sheep renal artery (53), and EGF has been shown to increase transmembrane ion flux in cultured fibroblasts (46, 47).

It also has been suggested that EGF may be important in maintaining the integrity of the epithelial surfaces of the urinary tract (44). The high correlation between EGF and urinary creatinine indicates a fairly constant EGF excretory/secretory process. If the prepro EGF is localized to or anchored in the apical cell membrane of the TALH and DCT, the molecule could be cleaved to release the 30,000–molecular weight fragment, which in turn is rapidly cleaved to EGF 1–53 by enzymes present in urine. Carboxyterminal processing to EGF 1–52, 1–51, and 1–50 analogues follows (31). Tubular cell synthesis and membrane anchorage of prepro EGF could provide an alternative system to intracellular sequestration in storage granules (which are not seen in the kidney) and would provide for relatively constant availability of EGF to the luminal glomerular filtrate. Recent studies cited above demonstrated that EGF receptors are located on the basal (peritubular) surface of renal tubular cells and that EGF does not affect hydraulic conductivity of CCT cells when microperfused via the luminal surface (3b, 27a). To date there is no evidence that there are EGF receptors on the luminal surface of renal epithelial cells and no evidence for a luminal effect of EGF.

SUMMARY

Current information indicates that the mammalian kidney is a significant site of EGF synthesis, second only to the salivary gland in the rodent and probably exceeding most other tissues in the human species. The prepro EGF mRNA is localized to the cells of the TALH and the DCT. The EGF mRNA transcript in kidney is similar to that in salivary gland; the molecular mass of the prepro

EGF protein in kidney approximates 130,000 kDa. Several EGF peptides are excreted in urine, including 6000-molecular weight peptides (composed of EGF 1–53, 1–52, 1–51, and 1–50) and a 30,000-molecular weight species with an aminoterminus portion corresponding to amino acids 829–848 of the prepro molecule. It has been suggested that prepro EGF could be a membrane protein since it contains an internal hydrophobic domain (amino acids 1039–1058) adjacent to the EGF sequence (amino acids 976–1029). The 30,000-molecular weight urinary product appears to represent a protein derived from amino acids 829 to approximately 1029 of prepro EGF, adjacent (distal) to the hydrophobic domain. Moreover, immunoelectron microscopy localizes the EGF immunoreactivity to the apical plasma membrane of the TALH and DCT cells.

The molecular form of this apically localized, EGF immunoreactivity is not yet clear. Proximal, distal, and TALH cells of the renal tubules and renal medullary interstitial cells appear to have EGF receptors and respond to EGF with increased DNA synthesis and mitogenesis. Also, there is a relatively late increase in prepro EGF mRNA levels in TALH and DCT cells during the process of renal hypertrophy. Limited evidence suggests a role of EGF on tubular function mediated via basal EGF receptors. EGF peptides processed intracellularly or by membrane localized peptidases appear to be continuously excreted and secreted into urine from the apical membrane surface of the TALH and DCT cells. This urinary EGF is constantly bathing urinary tract epithelial surfaces and could play a role in maintaining surface integrity. A similar role for salivary gland EGF in saliva has been proposed for the gastrointestinal tract. It also is possible that prepro EGF is anchored in the apical membrane, where it could function as a receptor, and a role for renal tubular EGF in regulation of membrane transport events has been proposed.

Literature Cited

1. Adamson, E. D., Meek, J. 1984. Epidermal growth factor receptors during mouse development. *J. Dev. Biol.* 103:62–70
1a. Barajas, L., Salido, E. C., Powers, K. V. 1988. Anatomical basis of the tubuloglomerular feedback mechanism: The juxtaglomerular apparatus. In *The Juxtaglomerular Apparatus and the Tubuloglomerular Feedback Mechanism. The Erik K. Fernstrom Symposium*, ed. A. E. G. Persson, U. Bobert. pp. 7–26. Amsterdam: Elsevier
2. Beer, D. G., Zweifel, K. A., Simpson, D. P., Pitot, H. C. 1987. Specific gene expressing during compensatory renal hypertrophy in the rat. *J. Cell. Physiol.* 131:29–35

2a. Bell, G. I., Fong, N. M., Stempien, M. M., Wormsted, M. A., Caput, D., et al. 1986. Human epidermal growth factor precursor: cDNA sequence, expression in vitro and gene organization. *Nucleic Acids Res.* 14:8427–46
3. Bosch, F., Bouscarel, B., Slaton, J., Blackmore, P. F., Exton, J. H. 1986. Epidermal growth factor mimics insulin effects in rat hepatocytes. *Biochem. J.* 239: 523–30
3a. Breyer, J., Harris, R. 1988. EGF binds to specific EGF receptors and stimulates mitogenesis in renal medullary interstitial cells. *Kidney Int.* 33:255 (Abstr.)
3b. Breyer, M. D., Jacobson, H. R., Breyer, J. 1988. Epidermal growth fac-

tor inhibits both chlorophenylthio-cyclic AMP and vasopressin stimulated hydraulic conductivity in the rabbit cortical collecting tubule. *Kidney Int.* 33:255 (Abstr.)

4. Bynny, R. L., Orth, D. N., Cohen, S. 1972. Radioimmunoassay of epidermal growth factor. *Endocrinology* 90:1261–66

5. Callegari, C., Laborde, N. P., Buenaflor, G., Nascimento, C. G., Brasel, J. A., Fisher, D. A. 1988. The source of urinary epidermal growth factor in humans. *Eur. J. Appl. Physiol.* In press

6. Cohen, S., Carpenter, G. 1975. Human epidermal growth factor: isolation and chemical and biological properties. *Proc. Natl. Acad. Sci. USA* 72:1317–21

7. Cohen, S., Taylor, J. M. 1974. Recent studies on the chemistry and biology of epidermal growth factor. *Rec. Prog. Horm. Res.* 30:551–74

8. Deuel, T. F. 1987. Polypeptide growth factor: roles in normal and abnormal cell growth. *Ann. Rev. Cell Biol.* 3:443–92

9. Doolittle, R. R., Feng, D. F., Johnson, M. S. 1984. Computer based characterization of epidermal growth factor precursor. *Nature* 320:558–60

10. Fine, L. 1986. The biology of renal hypertrophy. *Kidney Int.* 26:619–34

11. Frati, L., Cenci, G., Sbaraglia, G., Venzateti, D., Covelli, I. 1976. Levels of epidermal growth factor in mice tissues measured by a specific radioreceptor assay. *Life Sci.* 18:905–12

11a. Freemark, M., Comer, M. 1987. Epidermal growth factor (EGF)-like transforming growth factor (TGF) activity and EGF receptors in ovine fetal tissues. Possible role for TGF in ovine fetal development. *Pediatr. Res.* 22:609–15

12. Gospodarowicz, D. 1981. Epidermal and nerve growth factor in mammalian development. *Ann. Rev. Physiol.* 43:251–63

13. Gray, A., Dull, T. J., Ullrich, A. 1983. Nucleotide sequence of epidermal growth factor cDNA predicts a 128,000 molecular weight precursor. *Nature* 303:722–25

14. Gregory, H. 1975. The isolation and structure of urogastrone and its relationship to epidermal growth factor. *Nature* 257:325–27

15. Gubits, R. M., Shaw, P. A., Gresik, E. W., Onetti-Muda, A., Barka, T. 1986. Epidermal growth factor gene expression is regulated differently in mouse kidney and submandibular gland. *Endocrinology* 119:1382–87

16. Hayslett, J. P., Kashgarian, M., Ep-

stein, F. H. 1968. Functional correlates of compensatory renal hypertrophy, *J. Clin. Invest.* 47:774–82

17. Hessian, C., Decker, J. M., Sherblom, A. P., Kumar, S., Yue, C. C., et al. 1987. Uromodulin (Tamm Horsfall Glycoprotein): a renal ligand for lymphokines. *Science* 237:1474–84

18. Hirata, Y., Orth, D. N. 1979. Epidermal growth factor (urogastrone) in human tissues: *J. Clin. Endocr. Metab.* 48:667–72

19. Hirata, Y., Orth, D. N. 1979. Epidermal growth factor (urogastrone) in human fluids: size heterogeneity. *J. Clin. Endocr. Metab.* 48:673–79

20. Hofmann, G. E., Rao, C. V., Brown, M. J., Murray, L. F., Schultz, G. S., Siddiqi, T. A. 1988. Epidermal growth factor in urine of nonpregnant women throughout pregnancy and at delivery. *J. Clin. Endocr. Metab.* 66:119–23

21. Jennische, E., Andersson, G., Hansson, H. A. 1987. Epidermal growth factor is expressed by cells of the distal tubles during postnephrectomy renal growth. *Acta Physiol. Scand.* 129:449–50

22. Jennische, E., Andersson, G., Skottner, A., Hansson, H. A. 1986. Expression of IGF-I in the kidney of normal rats after nephrectomy. *Acta Physiol. Scand.* 129:A58–80

23. Kashimata, M., Hiramatsu, M., Minami, N., Ninami, N. 1987. Biochemical properties of epidermal growth factor in mouse kidney. *Comp. Biochem. Physiol.* 86:651–53

24. Kasselberg, A. G., Orth, D. N., Gray, M. E., Stahlman, M. T. 1985. Immunocytochemical localization of human epidermal growth factor/urogastrone in several human tissues. *J. Histochem. Cytochem.* 33:315–22

25. Kurnick, N. B., Lindsay, P. A. 1968. Nucleic acids in compensatory renal hypertrophy. *Lab. Invest.* 18:700–8

26. Larsson, L., Aperia, A., Wilton, P. 1980. Effect of normal developmental on compensatory renal growth. *Kidney Int.* 18:29–35

26a. Lee, D. C., Rochford, R., Todaro, G. J., Villarreal, L. P. 1985. Development expression of rat transforming growth factor alpha mRNA. *Mol. Cell. Biol.* 5:3644–46

27. Louvard, D. 1980. Apical membrane amino peptidase appears at site of cell contact in cultured kidney epithelial cells. *Proc. Natl. Acad. Sci. USA* 77:4132–36

27a. Maratos-Flier, E., Kao, C. Y. Y., Verdin, E. M., King, G. L. 1987. Receptor mediated vectorial transcytosis of epidermal growth by Madin-Darby canine kidney cells. *J. Cell Biol.* 105:1595–1601

27b. Marquardt, H., Hunkapiller, M. W., Hood, L. E., Todaro, G. J. 1984. Rat transforming growth factor type 1: structure and relation to epidermal growth factor. *Science* 233:1079–81

27c. Marquardt, H., Hunkapiller, M. W., Hood, L. E., Twardzik, D. R., De-Larco, J. E., et al. 1983. Transforming growth factors produced by retrovirus-transformed rodent fibroblasts and human melanoma cells: amino acid sequence homology with epidermal growth factor. *Proc. Natl. Acad. Sci. USA* 80:4684–88

27d. Massague, J. 1983. Epidermal growth factor-like transforming growth factor. II interaction with epidermal growth factor receptor in human placenta membranes and A 431 cells. *J. Biol. Chem.* 258:13614–20

27e. Massague, J., Czech, M. P., Iwaka, K., Delarco, J. E., Todaro, G. J. 1982. Affinity labeling of a transforming growth factor receptor that does not interact with epidermal growth factor. *Proc. Natl. Acad. Sci. USA* 79:6822–26

28. Mattila, A. L. 1986. Human urinary epidermal growth factor: effects of age, sex and female endocrine status. *Life Sci.* 39:1879–84

29. Mattila, A. L., Pasternack, A., Viinikka, L., Perheentupa, J. 1986. Subnormal concentrations or urinary epidermal growth factor in patients with kidney disease. *J. Clin. Endocr. Metab.* 62:1180–83

30. Mattila, A. L., Perheentupa, J., Persönen, K., Viinikka, L. 1985. Epidermal growth factor in human urine from birth to puberty. *J. Clin. Endocr. Metab.* 61:997–1000

31. Mount, C., Lukas, T. J., Orth, D. N. 1985. Purification and characterization of epidermal growth factor (β-urogastrone) and epidermal growth factor fragments from large volumes of human urine. *Arch. Biochem. Biophys.* 240:33–42

31a. Nexo, E., Hollenberg, M. D., Figueroa, A., Pratt, R. M. 1980. Detection of epidermal growth factor-urogastrone and its receptor during fetal mouse development. *Proc. Natl. Acad. Sci. USA* 77:2782–85

32. Nexo, E., Lamberg, S. I., Hollenberg, M. D. 1981. Comparison of a receptor binding assay with a radioimmunoassay for measuring human epidermal growth factor–urogastrone in urine. *Scand. J. Clin. Lab. Invest.* 41:577–82

33. Norman, J., Badie-Dezfooly, B., Nord, E. P., Kurtz, I., Schlosser, J., et al. 1987. EGF-induced mitogenesis in proximal tubular cells: potentiation by angiotensin II. *Am. J. Physiol.* 22:F299–F309

34. Oka, Y., Orth, D. N. 1983. Human plasma epidermal growth factor urogastrone is associated with blood platelets. *J. Clin. Invest.* 72:249–59

35. Olsen, P. S., Nexo, E., Poulsen, S. S., Hansen, H. F., Kirkegaard, P. 1984. Renal origin of rat urinary epidermal growth factor. *Regul. Pept.* 10:37–45

35a. Partanen, A. M., Thesloff, I. 1987. Localization and quantitation of ^{125}I-epidermal growth factor binding in mouse embryonic tooth and other embryonic tissues at different development stages. *Dev. Biol.* 120:186–97

36. Perheentupa, J., Lakshmanan, J., Fisher, D. A. 1984. Epidermal growth factor in neonatal mouse urine: Maturative effect of thyroxine. *Pediatr. Res.* 18:1080–84

37. Perheentupa, J., Lakshmanan, J., Fisher, D. A. 1985. Urine and kidney epidermal growth factor: Ontogeny and sex difference in the mouse. *Pediatr. Res.* 19:428–32

38. Perheentupa, J., Lakshamanan, J., Fisher, D. A. 1987. Epidermal growth factor in mouse urine: Non-blood origin and increase by sialoadenectomy and T4 therapy. *Acta Endocrinol.* 108:428–32

39. Perheentupa, J., Lakshmanan, J., Hoath, S. B., Beri, U., Kim, H., et al. 1985. Epidermal growth factor measurements in mouse plasma: method, ontogeny and sex difference. *Am. J. Physiol.* 11:E391–E396

40. Perheentupa, J., Lakshamanan, J., Macaso, T., Fisher, D. A. 1984. Growth hormone increases neonatal mouse urine epidermal growth factor. *Acta Endocrinol.* 106:184–87

41. Pfeiffer, S., Ullrich, A. 1985. Epidermal growth factor. Is the precursor a receptor? *Nature* 313:184

41a. Pike, L. J., Marquardt, H., Todaro, G. J., Gallis, B., Casnellie, J. E., et al. 1982. Transforming growth factor and epidermal growth factor stimulate the phosphorylation of a synthetic tryosine-containing peptide in a similar manner. *J. Biol. Chem.* 257:14628–31

42. Pollack, P. F., Goda, T., Colony, P. C., Edmond, J., Thornburg, W., et al. 1987. Effects of internally fed epidermal growth factor on the small and large in-

testine on the suckling rat. *Regul. Pept.* 17:121–32

43. Popliker, M., Shatz, A., Avini, A., Ullrich, A., Schlessinger, J., Webb, C. G. 1987. Onset of endogenous synthesis of epidermal growth factor in neonatal mice. *Dev. Biol.* 119:38–44

44. Rall, L. B., Scott, J., Bell, G. I., Crawford, R., Penschow, J. D., et al. 1985. Mouse prepro-epidermal growth factor synthesis by the kidney and other tissues. *Nature* 313:228–31

45. Roger, P. R., Dumont, J. E. 1982. Epidermal growth factor controls the proliferation and expression of differentiation in canine thyroid cells in primary culture. *FEBS Lett.* 144:209–12

46. Rozengurt, E. 1986. Early signals in the mitogenic response. *Science* 234:161–234

47. Rozengurt, E., Heppel, L. 1975. Serum rapidly stimulates ouabain-sensitive 86 Rb+ influx in quiescent 3T3 cells. *Proc. Natl. Acad. Sci. USA* 72:4492–95

48. Russell, D. W., Schneider, W. J., Yamamoto, T., Luskey, K. L., Brown, M. S., Goldstein, J. L. 1984. Domain map of the LDL receptor: sequence homology with the epidermal growth factor precurser. *Cell* 37:577–85

49. Salido, E. C., Barajas, L., Lechago, J., Laborde, N. P., Fisher, D. A. 1986. Immunocytochemical localization of epidermal growth factor (EGF) in mouse kidney. *J. Histochem. Cytochem.* 34:1155–60

50. Salido, E. C., Fisher, D. A., Barajas, L. 1986. Immunoelectron microscopy of epidermal growth factor in mouse kidney. *J. Ultrastruct. Mol. Struct. Res.* 91:105–13

51. Salido, E. C., Laborde, N. P., Buenaflor, G., Grodin, M., Barajas, L., Fisher, D. A. 1988. Renal EGF after unilateral nephrectomy. *Clin. Res.* 36:245A (Abstr.)

52. Scheving, L. A., Scheving, L. E., Tsai, T. H., Vesely, D. L. 1985. Epidermal growth factor enchances guanylate cyclase activity in vivo and in vitro. *Endocrinology* 116:332–36

53. Scoggins, B. D., Butkus, A., Coghlan, J. P., Fei, D. T. W., McDougall, J. G., et al. 1984. In *Endocrinology*, ed. F. Labrie, L. Proulx, p. 573. New York: Elsevier

54. Scott, J., Urdea, M., Quiroga, M., Sanchez-Pescador, R., Fong, N., et al.

1983. Structure of a mouse submaxillary messenger RNA encoding epidermal growth factor and seven related proteins. *Science* 221:236–40

55. Starkey, R. H., Cohen, S., Orth, D. N. 1975. Epidermal growth factor: Identification of a new hormone in human urine. *Science* 189:800–2

56. Starkey, R. H., Orth, D. N. 1977. Radioimmunoassay of human epidermal growth factor. *J. Clin. Endocr. Metab.* 45:1144–53

57. Stiles, A. D., Sosenko, I. R. S., D'Ercole, A. J., Smith, B. T. 1985. Relation of kidney tissue somatomedin C/insulin like growth factor I to postnephrectomy renal growth in the rat. *Endocrinology* 117:2397–2401

58. Thorburn, G. D., Waters, M. J., Young, I. R., Dolling, M., Buntine, D., Hopkins, P. S. 1981. Epidermal growth factor: a critical factor in fetal maturation. In *The Fetus and Independent Life.* Ciba Found. Symp., 86:172–98

59. Tsukumo, K., Nakamura, H., Sakamoto, S. 1987. Purification and characterization of high molecular weight human epidermal growth factor from human urine. *Biochem. Biophys. Res. Commun.* 145:126–33

60. Van Zoelen, E. J. J., Van Oostwaard, T. M. J., DeLatt, S. W. 1986. Transforming growth factor B and retinoic acid modulate phenotypic transformation of normal rat kidney cells induced by epidermal growth factor and platelet derived growth factor. *J. Biol. Chem.* 261:5003–9

61. Wilson, P. D., Horster, M. F. 1983. Differential response to hormones of defined distal nephron epithelia in culture. *Am. J. Physiol.* 13:C166–C174

62. Wirthensohn, G., Lefrank, S., Guder, W. G. 1984. Phospholipid metabolism in rat kidney cortical tubules II effects of hormones on 32p incorporation. *Biochim. Biophys. Acta* 795:401–10

63. Yamamoto, T., Davis, C. G., Brown, M. S., Schneider, W. J., Casey, M. L., et al. 1984. The human LDL receptor: a cysteine rich protein with multiple A1U sequences in its mRNA. *Cell* 39:27–38

64. Yeh, Y. C., Scheving, L. A., Tsai, T. H., Scheving, L. W. 1981. Circadian stage dependent effects of epidermal growth factor on deoxyribonucleic acid synthesis in ten different organs of the adult male mouse. *Endocrinology* 109:644–51

GASTROINTESTINAL PHYSIOLOGY

Introduction, George Sachs *Section Editor*

The focus of this year's reviews in the GI tract is regulation of transport. Two reviews cover $[Ca]_i$ in hepatocytes and pancreas, another relates recent data on Cl transport regulation. A review on dietary regulation of Na cotransport systems in the gut provides insight into a rapidly growing area of investigation whereas regulation of bile acid transport by nonmembrane bound proteins in the liver rounds off this series.

Ca signalling and homeostasis in epithelial cells has a complexity equal to that of excitable cells. Perhaps only the ryanodine receptor, responsible for excitation-contraction coupling, is absent from epithelial cells. Ca release from intracellular stores is due to the release of IP_3 from PIP_2 due to the activation of membrane bound PLC. Coupling of receptors to PLC varies, in some instances because of G proteins, in others via tyrosine kinases. The action of IP_3 is to activate a Ca channel intracellularly thus releasing Ca from intracellular stores. The IP_3 concentration rises rapidly to a peak and then falls to a new steady-state level. This time dependence is a function of at least three enzymes, PLC, IP_3 kinase (making IP_4), and a 5' phosphatase. In addition, the action of IP_3 may be regulated by $[Ca]_i$ with high levels inactivating the IP_3 receptor. The combination of these events may account for a recently discovered phenomenon, the oscillation of $[Ca]_i$ in individual cells. To explain this a feedback must be present with a delay with respect to the original signal. For example, inhibition of the effect of IP_3 by increasing $[Ca]_i$ could produce such an effect. Other mechanisms could also be postulated and regulation of these oscillations is an important new area of research. The site of storage of intracellular Ca some years ago moved from mitochondria to rer. More recently a new organelle, perhaps connecting to the rer, the calciosome,

81

has been postulated to be the target of IP_3. The presence of two possible compartments for Ca release may explain some puzzling features of Ca homeostasis, such as inability to release all intracellular Ca, the action of GTP that seems to connect two compartments and the quantal action of IP_3.

Entry of Ca across the plasma membrane is by voltage-activated or hormone-activated pathways. The former are seen as channels, the latter mostly as Ca conductance. The latter are regulated by a variety of mechanisms, including direct receptor coupling, a combination of IP_3 and IP_4, and G proteins. The consequence of changes in cell Ca and PLC action producing diacyl glycerol is activation of protein kinases. These kinases also feed back to the Ca signalling pathways. These different aspects of Ca regulation for liver and pancreas form the subject of two of the reviews.

Changes in intracellular signals alter transport. Epithelial Cl transport regulation appears to be affected in cystic fibrosis and is reviewed in depth. A general model for Cl transport appears to be emerging. Cl concentration in cells is raised above net (taking into account both basal and apical surfaces) electrochemical equilibrium either by $NaKCl_2$ cotransport or by coupled $Na/H,Cl/HCO_3$ exchange. A Cl channel on the contralateral surface allows for this secondary active secretion, coupled to Na moving paracellularly. How this channel is regulated, by insertion and/or phosphorylation, may be crucial to understanding the defect of cystic fibrosis.

Dietary regulation of Na cotransporters in the gut is apparently universal and is a way to understanding complicated adaptive mechanisms. For example, the signals are not necessarily the substrates of the cotransporter being up regulated. Fructose is better than glucose as a signal for synthesis of the Na/glucose symporter. The regulation of expression by dietary changes allows for simple experimental manipulations with which to study transcriptional or translational regulation. This rather new field is reviewed by one of its pioneers.

Transport of bile acids involves both membrane processes and intracellular transport. Cytosolic bile acid binding proteins are thought to provide a shielded transcellular transport pathway that also minimizes backdiffusion across the sinusoidal membrane. Presumably it is the bound bile acids that are the donor to the canalicular transporter. There are several classes of these binding proteins, glutathione s-transferases, γ' binders, and fatty acid binding proteins. How these interact to catalyse transhepatocellular transport of bile acids forms the substance of the last review in this section.

Annu. Rev. Physiol. 1989. 51:83–105

CALCIUM TRANSPORT PATHWAYS OF PANCREATIC ACINAR CELLS

S. Muallem

Laboratory of Membrane Biology, Research Institute, Department of Medicine, Cedars-Sinai Medical Center and University of California at Los Angeles, School of Medicine, Los Angeles, California 90048

INTRODUCTION

The involvement of Ca^{2+} ions in digestive enzyme secretion by pancreatic acinar cells has been documented in many studies. Ca^{2+} ions serve as messengers in enzyme secretion stimulated by the hormones cholecystokinin, bombesin, substance P, and the neurotransmitter acetylcholine. Early observations showed that omission of Ca^{2+} from the incubation medium impaired hormonal stimulation of enzyme secretion (3, 8, 19, 39, 53, 99). Subsequently, it was shown that an increase in the concentration of free cytosolic Ca^{2+}, $[Ca^{2+}]_i$, is sufficient to trigger enzyme secretion (29, 89, 135). Ca^{2+} ions also augment secretion triggered by an increase in cellular cAMP levels (16, 33) and by stimulation of protein kinase C (17, 85).

The messenger and effector roles of Ca^{2+} ions necessitate that the acinar cells, as other cells, regulate $[Ca^{2+}]_i$ at rest and during stimulation. Ca^{2+} ions are unique messengers because they must be regulated by compartmentalization either across the plasma or organelle membranes or by binding sites, rather than by synthesis and breakdown. Thus, the cells have an extensive and flexible network of Ca^{2+}-transporting pathways that maintain large Ca^{2+} gradients across cellular membranes while allowing fluctuations in $[Ca^{2+}]_i$ upon demand. Our understanding of the components of this network and their relative contribution to the regulation of $[Ca^{2+}]_i$ is based on measurements of ^{45}Ca fluxes in intact (25, 31, 55, 64, 84, 103) and permeabilized cells (74, 104, 116), and isolated subcellular vesicles (5, 7, 91). A major advance in our understanding of $[Ca^{2+}]_i$ regulation by cells was made with the development of Ca^{2+}-sensitive fluorescent dyes, which can be incorporated into small cells

0066-4278/89/0315-0083$02.00

in a nondisruptive manner (35, 126). These dyes permit the direct measurement of $[Ca^{2+}]_i$ in intact resting and stimulated cells. Thus, it is possible to recognize the initial and continuous receptor-mediated changes in $[Ca^{2+}]_i$ and to define the sources of Ca^{2+} and the pathways responsible for the observed changes in $[Ca^{2+}]_i$.

A second important development was made when the link between receptor occupation, inositol-containing lipid hydrolysis, and changes in $[Ca^{2+}]_i$ was established. Hokin & Hokin (41) observed that cholinergic stimulation of pancreatic fragments increased the turnover of phosphatidylinositol (PI) in these cells. This observation, which was confirmed and extended to other cells, led Michell (69) to the suggestion that the increased PI turnover is linked to changes in Ca^{2+} fluxes across cellular membranes and thus to changes in $[Ca^{2+}]_i$. Subsequently, using a kinetic approach, Berridge (9) found that the event immediately following receptor occupation is the hydrolysis of phosphatidylinositol 4,5-bisphosphate (PIP$_2$) and the release of inositol 1,4,5-trisphosphate (IP$_3$) to the cytosol. Streb et al (115) then demonstrated that IP$_3$ and hormonal stimulation release Ca^{2+} from the same intracellular, nonmitochondrial pool, which probably is a component of or associated with the endoplasmic reticulum (ER).

Our ability to measure $[Ca^{2+}]_i$ and the effect of inositol phosphates on cellular Ca^{2+} pathways resulted in considerable clarification of the regulation of $[Ca^{2+}]_i$ by pancreatic acinar and other cells. There is an intimate relationship between the metabolism of the inositol-containing lipids and the regulation of Ca^{2+} transport pathways in cells. The current knowledge of inositol lipid metabolism has been reviewed recently (10, 40, 62). The details of the role of Ca^{2+} ions in enzyme secretion by the acinar cells have been summarized in several previous reviews (33, 42, 106, 132). The present review describes the Ca^{2+} transporting pathways in the acinar cells and their role in regulating $[Ca^{2+}]_i$. However, the available knowledge of the mechanisms of Ca^{2+} transport by the different pathways in pancreatic acinar cells is limited. Therefore, the results available from other cellular systems are refered to in the context of their relevance to Ca^{2+} transport by the pancreatic acinar cells.

CELLULAR Ca^{2+} BUFFERS

Resting pancreatic acinar cells maintain $[Ca^{2+}]_i$ at approximately 150 nM (15, 68, 82–85, 125), while the total calcium content of the cells is approximately 12 nmoles/mg protein (25, 31). Of the total intracellular calcium content, about 3 nmoles/mg protein can be released to the cytosol by hormonal stimulation (25, 79) and are, therefore, sequestered in a hormone mobilizable pool. The release of Ca^{2+} from the pool to the cytosol (3–6 μl/mg/

protein) should increase $[Ca^{2+}]_i$ from 150 nM to 0.5–1.0 mM. However, the measured hormone-evoked increase of $[Ca^{2+}]_i$ is only to 1.0–1.5 μM (76, 79, 80, 82–85, 125). Further, exposure of cells suspended in Ca^{2+}-free medium to high concentrations of Ca^{2+} ionophores also resulted in a micromolar increase in $[Ca^{2+}]_i$ (68, 80). Therefore, the cytosol of pancreatic acinar cells, as that of other cells, must contain millimolar concentrations of Ca^{2+} buffering capacity, and most of this Ca^{2+} buffer should be free of Ca^{2+} in the resting cell. Estimation of Ca^{2+} buffering capacity in human neutrophils shows that these cells contain approximately 0.76 mM Ca^{2+} buffer with an apparent single dissociation constant of 0.55 μM. Approximately 20% of the buffer is occupied with Ca^{2+} in the resting cells (128). There is virtually no information available as to the nature of the cytosolic Ca^{2+} buffer in pancreatic acinar cells. Phosphate-containing molecules such as nucleoside phosphates may provide some Ca^{2+} buffering power to the cytosol. The different types of high-affinity Ca^{2+} binding proteins described in other cells (21, 70, 108, 119, 120) may also exist in pancreatic acinar cells and may contribute to the Ca^{2+} buffering capacity of the cytosol. In addition, it is possible that acidic phospholipids, which have considerable Ca^{2+} binding capacity (27), also participate in Ca^{2+} buffering.

It is believed that most of the hormone mobilizable Ca^{2+} is stored in a distinct fraction associated with the ER (see below). The total Ca^{2+} concentration in this organelle (3 nmoles/mg cell protein) is several millimolar. The only available estimation of ionized, free Ca^{2+} concentration in this pool in intact smooth muscle cells shows it to be approximately 0.5 μM (134). Thus, it is likely that Ca^{2+} is stored in the ER as buffered Ca^{2+}.

A possible ER Ca^{2+} buffer is a protein similar to the Ca^{2+} binding protein, calsequestrin (22). Calsequestrin is present in large amounts in the inner space of the terminal cisternae of sarcoplasmic reticulum (61, 117). Recent studies (22) reported the presence of an intraluminal, Ca^{2+} binding protein in rat liver ER, immunologically related to calsequestrin.

If the reported low, free Ca^{2+} concentration in the ER of smooth muscle cells can be established in other cells, it suggests that the Ca^{2+} gradient across the ER membrane is only about 4 while that across the plasma membrane is approximately 10^4. Rapid kinetic measurements in parotid acinar cells showed that upon hormonal stimulation the rates of Ca^{2+} flux across both membranes are similar (65, 66). However, if the Ca^{2+} electrochemical gradient is the driving force for both processes (see below), the rate of Ca^{2+} flux across the plasma membrane should be faster than that across the ER membrane. It is, therefore, conceivable that upon cell stimulation, the Ca^{2+} binding properties of the ER Ca^{2+} buffer change so that the free Ca^{2+} concentration in the ER rapidly increases, thus allowing the rapid flow of Ca^{2+} from the ER to the cytosol.

CALCIUM FLUXES ACROSS THE PLASMA MEMBRANE

Calcium Efflux

As indicated above, pancreatic acinar cells, like other cells, maintain a large inwardly directed Ca^{2+} gradient across the plasma membrane (15, 68, 76, 79, 80, 82–85, 125). The presence of an active Ca^{2+} efflux mechanism in the plasma membrane of acinar cells has been suspected on the basis of ^{45}Ca efflux measurements. Stimulation of the cells with Ca^{2+} mobilizing hormones resulted in net loss of Ca^{2+} from the cells (19, 25, 31, 55, 64, 76, 79, 80, 84, 96, 133). Subsequently, two active Ca^{2+} efflux mechanisms have been described in pancreatic acinar cells, a plasma membrane Ca^{2+} pump (2, 5, 57) and a Na^+-Ca^{2+} exchange system (6). Isolated plasma membrane–enriched fractions were used to partially characterize these transport systems.

The enzymatic activities of the plasma membrane Ca^{2+} pump were followed by measurements of Ca^{2+} uptake and ATPase activity. Both the hydrolysis of ATP and ATP-dependent Ca^{2+} uptake require Mg^{2+} ions (2, 5, 57). The apparent affinity for Ca^{2+} of these activities is in the range of 0.2–0.8 μM. ATP is the only high energy substrate that can support Ca^{2+} transport (5). Unlike Ca^{2+} uptake into ER vesicles (90, 91), Ca^{2+} uptake into plasma membrane vesicles could not be augmented by oxalate or other Ca^{2+} precipitating ions (5, 57). The Ca^{2+} pump can form a hydroxylamine-sensitive, acid stable phosphorylated intermediate with an apparent molecular weight on SDS-polyacrylamide gel of 115,000 Daltons (2). Ca^{2+} uptake can be blocked by VO_4^{2-} with an apparent K_I of approximately 5 μM (57).

Another feature of this pump is its sensitivity to the Ca^{2+} binding protein, calmodulin, and acidic phospholipids. Kribben et al (57) reported no effect of calmodulin or trifluoperazine in doses up to 100 μM on ATP-dependent Ca^{2+} uptake into basolateral membrane vesicles. However, it is likely that these vesicles were not stripped of endogenous calmodulin, and thus the pump was probably saturated with calmodulin. When calmodulin-stripped membranes were used, calmodulin stimulated the Ca,Mg-ATPase activity, while trifluoperazine, chlorpromazine, and compound 48/80 (calmodulin antagonists) inhibited only the fraction of calmodulin-stimulated ATPase activity (2). The pancreatic plasma membrane Ca-ATPase can also be stimulated by acidic phospholipids. Acidic phospholipids mimic the effect of calmodulin on the Ca^{2+} pump (2, 100). Similar to the effect of calmodulin on the red blood cell Ca^{2+} pump (78, 100), calmodulin increased the apparent affinity for Ca^{2+} and the maximal rate of the pancreatic Ca^{2+} pump (2). Based on cation and anion requirements and the effect of an imposed membrane potential on ATP-dependent Ca^{2+} uptake into basolateral membrane vesicles, it was suggested that the plasma membrane Ca^{2+} pump of acinar cells is electrogenic (5). Thus, the available data suggests that the plasma membrane Ca^{2+}

pump of pancreatic acinar cells is similar to the better characterized Ca^{2+} pump of red blood cells (100).

A Na^+-Ca^{2+} exchange system in plasma membrane vesicles derived from pancreatic acini was reported in one study (6). Although the exchanger shows high apparent affinity for Ca^{2+} (0.62 μM), the maximal capacity of Ca^{2+} transport by the exchanger was approximately 10-fold lower than that by the ATP-dependent Ca^{2+} pump in the same vesicles. Indeed, incubation of acinar cells in K^+-free medium and in the presence of ouabain, which collapsed both the Na^+ gradient and thus the potential across the plasma membrane, increased $[Ca^{2+}]_i$ from 136 to 206 nM (76). Similar treatment of proximal tubules, a nonexcitable tissue with potent Na^+-Ca^{2+} exchange activity, increased $[Ca^{2+}]_i$ from 82 to 835 nM (137). Furthermore, the rates of hormone-stimulated ^{45}Ca efflux (76, 131) and the reduction in $[Ca^{2+}]_i$ that follows the initial increase in $[Ca^{2+}]_i$ (76) were not affected by removal of Na^+ from the incubation medium. All this evidence suggests that the Na^+-Ca^{2+} exchanger plays a minor role in Ca^{2+} efflux from pancreatic acinar cells.

Indirect evidence from intact cells studies argue that the plasma membrane Ca^{2+} pump of the pancreatic acinar cells is activated by Ca^{2+}-mobilizing hormones. ^{45}Ca influx measurements demonstrated that the hormones increase the plasma membrane permeability to Ca^{2+} by approximately 7-fold (25, 55, 56, 76, 79, 80, 84, 104, 118), and that this increased Ca^{2+} permeability persists as long as the cells are stimulated (25, 79, 80, 84). In view of persistent plasma membrane Ca^{2+} permeability, acinar cells reduce $[Ca^{2+}]_i$ back to near resting levels within 3–5 minutes of stimulation and maintain $[Ca^{2+}]_i$ at this level (15, 68, 76, 79, 80, 82–85). Since steady-state $[Ca^{2+}]_i$ is determined by pump-leak turnover rates, the findings described above suggest that stimulation of the cells increased the rate of Ca^{2+} efflux (i.e. Ca^{2+} pumping across the plasma membrane). However, measurements of ATP-dependent Ca^{2+} uptake failed to demonstrate an increased rate of Ca^{2+} pumping by basolateral membrane vesicles isolated from stimulated pancreatic acinar cells compared to resting cells (98). It is possible, though, that during vesicles isolation, the stimulating effect of the pump was lost. More direct evidence for plasma membrane Ca^{2+} pump stimulation was obtained in platelets and neutrophils by testing the effect of Ca^{2+} ionophores on $[Ca^{2+}]_i$ of resting and stimulated cells. Exposure of cells to Ca^{2+} ionophore resulted in an increased $[Ca^{2+}]_i$ to a new steady-state level. In prestimulated cells, the same concentration of Ca^{2+} ionophore increased $[Ca^{2+}]_i$ to lower steady-state level (97). Furthermore, stimulation of cells exposed to Ca^{2+} ionophore resulted in reduction of $[Ca^{2+}]_i$ (88). This effect could be mimicked by stimulation of protein kinase C with phorbol esters (88, 97). Similar observations were made with stimulated pancreatic acinar cells (S. Muallem et al, unpublished observations). In addition, stimulation of protein kinase C increased the rate and extent of ATP-dependent Ca^{2+} uptake into plasma membrane vesicles isolated from neutrophils (58). Thus, it appears that stimulation of cells is followed by activation of the plasma membrane Ca^{2+} pump, and pump activation is mediated, at least in part, by protein kinase C. Such activation is probably required to prevent large and sustained increases in $[Ca^{2+}]_i$ in stimulated cells in the face of a persistent increase in plasma membrane Ca^{2+} permeability.

Calcium Influx

Hormone-activated Ca^{2+} influx pathways in the plasma membrane of pancreatic acinar cells have been suspected for a long time. Sustained enzyme secretion by these cells is absolutely dependent on the presence of medium Ca^{2+} (32, 101, 132). Sustained activation of the Ca^{2+}-activated K^+ channel requires the presence of Ca^{2+} in the incubation medium (86). Hormones also increase the rate of ^{45}Ca influx (25, 79, 80, 84) when $[Ca^{2+}]_i$ is constant and at near resting levels (79, 80, 82–85). The nature of the hormone-activated Ca^{2+} entry pathway is unknown. It has been suggested that the large Ca^{2+} electrochemical gradient across the plasma membrane may be the driving force for Ca^{2+} entry, and therefore Ca^{2+} enters the cells through channels. Accordingly, depolarization of lacrimal (71) and parotid (67) acinar cells by elevation of medium K^+ eliminated the sustained, hormone-mediated increase in $[Ca^{2+}]_i$ that is dependent on the presence of Ca^{2+} in the incubation medium. However, there is no direct electrophysiological evidence for a specific hormone-stimulated Ca^{2+} channel in the plasma membrane of acinar cells. A nonselective channel that can conduct K^+, Na^+, and Ca^{2+} was described in pancreatic acinar cells (63) and neutrophils (129). Petersen & Maruyama (87) suggested that this channel may provide the Ca^{2+} entry pathways observed in stimulated cells.

Recently, evidence relating Ca^{2+} entry to inositol phosphates has been obtained. Irvine & Moor (49, 50) showed that injection of inositol 1,3,4,5-tetrakisphosphate (IP_4) together with 2,4,5-IP_3 into sea urchin eggs results in the formation of the fertilization membrane. This effect required the two inositol phosphates and the presence of Ca^{2+} in the incubation medium. A very similar phenomenon was observed in lacrimal acinar cells. Morris et al (72) followed the activity of the Ca^+-activated K^+ channel in these cells. Perfusion of the cell interior with either IP_3 or IP_4 failed to activate the K^+ channel, whereas combined perfusion of IP_3 and IP_4 evoked a sustained increase in K^+ current that was dependent on extracellular Ca^{2+}. However, Ca^{2+} release from intracellular stores and an increase in $[Ca^{2+}]_i$ produced by Ca^{2+} ionophore could not substitute IP_3 in facilitating the IP_4-mediated effects (50). Thus, it appears that a specific release of Ca^{2+} from intracellular stores by IP_3 or by the presence of IP_3 in the cytosol was required for activation of the plasma membrane Ca^{2+} entry pathway by IP_4. Stimulation of pancreatic acinar cells results in increased levels of IP_3 and IP_4 (125). Therefore, it is likely that the IP_4-mediated Ca^{2+} entry pathway also operates in pancreatic acinar cells.

The Ca^{2+} entry pathway in pancreatic acinar cells was localized to a site separate from the hormone-receptor site (121). A similar observation was made in neutrophils (129). When the agonist was applied locally through the patch-clamp pipette, it failed to activate a nonselective Ca^{2+} permeating channel. Addition of agonist to the medium of the same cell resulted in activation of the channel. These observations are consistent with the findings that activation of Ca^{2+} entry requires the action of IP_3 on internal Ca^{2+} stores and is mediated by IP_4.

An important function of the plasma membrane Ca^{2+} entry pathway in all cells is to allow Ca^{2+} reloading of the intracellular stores. Reloading of intracellular stores takes place when cell stimulation is terminated and is absolutely dependent on medium Ca^{2+} (67, 77, 79, 80, 84). Reloading can be blocked by low concentrations of La^{3+} (84). Changing medium Ca^{2+} concentration affects the reloading time but not the extent of Ca^{2+} reloading (84, 95). Once the reloading Ca^{2+} pathway is activated by hormonal-mediated release of Ca^{2+} from intracellular stores, it remains activated even when the agonist is withdrawn (4, 67, 84, 95). Hence, continuous stimulation is not required to keep the reloading Ca^{2+} entry pathway activated.

The properties of Ca^{2+} influx across the plasma membrane evoked by IP_4 or hormonal stimulation suggest a close relationship between the Ca^{2+} content of the ER and Ca^{2+} entry. It is not clear yet whether the IP_4-activated Ca^{2+} entry pathway is the Ca^{2+} reloading pathway. If IP_4-evoked Ca^{2+} entry provides the route for Ca^{2+} reloading, then IP_3 (the precursor for IP_4) and IP_4 levels should remain elevated when the agonist is removed, while the intracellular pool is kept depleted of Ca^{2+}. Preliminary evidence (75) argues that Ca^{2+} entry during reloading may differ from the IP_4-mediated Ca^{2+} entry. Thus, the addition of antagonist to stimulated cells suspended in Ca^{2+}-free medium reduces the levels of inositol polyphosphates to control values, but did not prevent reloading of internal stores when Ca^{2+} was subsequently added to the medium. However, further experimental evidence is necessary to determine whether more than one hormone-activated Ca^{2+} entry pathway in pancreatic acinar cells exists.

As originally observed in gastric cells (77), Ca^{2+} reloading of the ER of pancreatic (79, 80, 84) and parotid (67) acinar cells occurs without a change in $[Ca^{2+}]_i$. Such observations, together with the relationship betweeen ER Ca^{2+} and Ca^{2+} entry discussed above, led to the suggestion that the reloading Ca^{2+} entry pathway is located in a region where there is morphological association between the plasma and ER membranes (93, 94). The release of Ca^{2+} from the ER relieves the inhibition of the plasma membrane Ca^{2+} entry pathway and allows the flow of Ca^{2+} from the medium directly into the ER. The most appealing feature of this model is that it can explain the intimate relationship between the Ca^{2+} content of the ER and Ca^{2+} entry across the plasma membrane. However, several recent experiments argue against the presence of a Ca^{2+} pathway that connects the ER interior to the extracellular medium. Ca^{2+} release from the ER by IP_3 (49, 72) or Ca^{2+} ionophore (50) is insufficient to activate Ca^{2+} entry across the plasma membrane. The ER reloads with Ca^{2+} by Ca^{2+} uptake from the cytosol (77, 80). Reloading of the ER can be blocked by inhibition of Ca^{2+} entry from medium into the cytosol (84). The extent of Ca^{2+} reloading is similar at medium Ca^{2+} concentrations between 0.5–2.0 mM (84, 95). Finally, during the reloading period, the rate of Ca^{2+} influx into the ER is at least 12-fold faster than the rate of Ca^{2+} efflux from the ER (80). Hence, during reloading, Ca^{2+} uptake and Ca^{2+} efflux across the ER membrane appear to occur through separate pathways. Therefore, it seems that the Ca^{2+} entry pathway in the plasma membrane provides a route for Ca^{2+} influx from the medium into the cytosol, and then Ca^{2+} is incorporated into the ER. This path of Ca^{2+} reloading does not exclude a possible role for an association region of the plasma and ER membrane in controlling Ca^{2+} entry across the plasma membrane.

CALCIUM FLUXES ACROSS THE ENDOPLASMIC RETICULUM MEMBRANE

The ER Ca^{2+} Pump

The mechanism of Ca^{2+} transport by the ER has received much attention in recent years, when it was discovered that Ca^{2+} mobilizing hormones can release Ca^{2+} from the ER or an organelle associated with the ER. (10, 94, 115). Although hormonal stimulation may result in Ca^{2+} release from part of the ER or an organelle associated with the ER, we assume that the properties of Ca^{2+} uptake into isolated ER or permeabilized cells also reflect those of the hormone-mobilizable intracellular pool. Ca^{2+} uptake into the ER is mediated by a Ca^{2+} pump that resembles the better studied sarcplasmic reticulum (SR) Ca^{2+} pump of skeletal and cardiac muscles (45, 122). The details of Ca^{2+} uptake by the ER and the turnover cycle of the ER Ca^{2+} pump are only partially known.

Ca^{2+} uptake into isolated ER vesicles (7) or permeabilized pancreatic acinar cells (116, 130) requires ATP and Mg^{2+} ions. The apparent affinity of the pump for Ca^{2+} is between 0.1–0.2 μM (7, 74, 130). Ca^{2+} uptake into the ER can be augmented by Ca^{2+} precipitating anions such as oxalate (90, 91, 116, 130) and phosphate (7). Ca^{2+} uptake into the ER can be blocked by VO_4^{3-} ions (74, 116). The apparent affinity for VO_4^{3-} is increased by pre-incubation of the ER with VO_4^{3-} (34) and is decreased by elevation of

Ca^{2+} concentration in the uptake medium (74). The platelet ER Ca^{2+} pump was purified to near homogeneity and reconstituted into artificial phospholipid liposomes (23). This system was used to measure the Ca^{2+}: ATP stoichometry, which was found to be 2:1 (23).

Ca^{2+} uptake into the ER depends on the presence of a membrane permeable cation and anion in the incubation medium (7, 54, 81). The cation requirement can be substituted by a conductive protonophore (81). The highest rate of Ca^{2+} uptake was measured in the presence of K^+ ions (7, 81). In isolated liver ER vesicles equilibrated with KCl, the initiation of Ca^{2+} uptake was followed by K^+ efflux (81). These observations were interpreted as evidence for the electrogenic nature of the ER Ca^{2+} pump. Hence, to compensate for the charge gradient generated by the transport of Ca^{2+}, K^+ leaves the ER through a separate, conductive pathway. Accordingly, a K^+ conductive pathway was demonstrated in isolated ER vesicles (81).

The dependence of Ca^{2+} uptake on the presence of permeable anions is less clear. An anion transport pathway must exist in the ER membrane to allow the movement of K^+. In ER vesicles from pancreatic acinar cells, substituting Cl^- with impermeant anions inhibited Ca^{2+} uptake (54) and (Ca^{2+} + Mg^{2+})-dependent ATP hydrolysis in intact but not permeabilized vesicles (54). However, the substituting anions did not support Ca^{2+} uptake acccording to their membrane permeability. In isolated ER from liver, Cl^- ions also enhance the uptake of K^+ when the K^+ conductive pathway is blocked (81). This was considered evidence for the existence of a KCl cotransport pathway in the ER membrane. The inhibition of IP$_3$-mediated Ca^{2+} release from the ER by Cl^- suggested the presence of a Cl^- conductive pathway in the ER membrane (52). The currently available experimental evidence is not sufficient to determine the nature of the Cl^- pathway in the ER membrane.

An acid stable phosphoprotein of approximately 100 kDa was identified in the ER membrane of pancreatic acinar cells (43, 54). Formation of the phosphoprotein required Ca^{2+} but not Mg^{2+} ions. The rate of phosphoprotein formation is increased with an increase in the incubation temperature. Phosphoprotein formation was inhibited by VO_4^{2-}. These data were taken to suggest that the Ca^{2+} and ATP-dependent phosphoprotein is a phosphorylated intermediate in the turnover cycle of the ER Ca^{2+} pump. An important criteria for a phosphorylated intermediate of this type of pump is its sensitivity to hydroxylamine. Hydroxylamine cleaved only part of the phosphoprotein formed in the presence of Ca^{2+} and ATP, and similar cleavage was obtained by incubating the phosphoprotein at pH 5.4 (43). In addition, steady-state levels of the phosphoprotein formed in permeabilized pancreatic ER vesicles was partially inhibited by removal of Cl^- from the medium while Ca,Mg-ATPase activity of the same membranes was independent of Cl^- (54). Reduction of the steady-state level of the phosphoenzyme may result from inhibition of the overall phosphorylation rate, which should inhibit the Ca,Mg-ATPase, or stimulation of the overall dephosphorylation rate, which should stimulate the Ca,Mg-ATPase. The dissociation between the effects of Cl^- on phosphoenzyme levels and Ca,Mg-ATPase suggest that at least part of the phosphoenzyme measured is not a phosphorylated intermediate in the turnover cycle of the ER Ca^{2+} pump.

Further details of the turnover cycle of the ER Ca^{2+} pump were obtained in ER membranes isolated from rat and human liver (38, 111). In the presence of Ca^{2+} and ATP, an acid stable phosphorylated protein of molecular mass 116–118 kDa is formed. This phosphorylated protein was cleaved by hydroxylamine but not by reducing the pH to 5.2, which indicate the formation of an acylphosphate bond. The dephosphorylation rate of the phosphoenzyme was increased by Mg^{2+} ions. Both MgATP and CaATP can be utilized by the pump as substrates for the catalytic, phosphorylating site. In the presence of Ca^{2+} and ATP, most of the phosphorylated enzyme is sensitive to ADP. Addition of ADP resulted in quantitative disappearance of the phosphoenzyme and appearance of ATP. This indicates that the turnover cycle of the ER Ca^{2+} pump is reversible. Removal of Ca^{2+} after the phosphorylation reaction is completed resulted in conversion of the ADP-sensitive phosphoenzyme to an ADP-insensitive phosphoenzyme. The details of the turnover cycle of the ER Ca^{2+} pump are very similar to those described for the SR Ca^{2+} pump (45). Further similarities between the two pumps are their dependence on ATP and their existence in two conformational states. The dependence of Ca^{2+} uptake into ER vesicles isolated from platelets on MgATP concentration shows a negative cooperativity behavior with K_m for the catalytic site of 9.5 μM and the regulatory site of 0.6 mM (1). The effect of Ca^{2+} concentration on the inhibition of Ca^{2+} uptake into the ER by VO_4^{2-} (74) indicates that the pump exists in VO_4^{2-} sensitive (E_2) and Ca^{2+} sensitive (E_1) forms.

The results from the different studies suggest that a minimal turnover cycle of the ER Ca^{2+} pump is as shown in Figure 1. The pump exists in two nonphosphorylated (E_1, E_2) and two phosphorylated (E_1P, E_2P) conformational states. The E_1 form of the pump possesses high affinity Ca^{2+} binding sites and binds two Ca^{2+} ions. Then E_1Ca_2 binds and hydrolyses MgATP (or CaATP) to release ADP and to form the high energy phosphoenzyme $E_1P(Ca_2)$. $E_1P(Ca_2)$ can react with ADP to form ATP and release Ca^{2+} to the ER exterior. $E_1P(Ca_2)$ undergoes a conformational transition to $E_2P(Ca_2)$, which is the low energy, ADP-insensitive phosphoenzyme. This is probably the stage where Ca^{2+} ions are transfered to the ER interior. Ca^{2+} ions now dissociate from the low Ca^{2+} affinity sites of the pump, which results in the appearance of E_2P. E_2P interacts with H_2O to release the Pi (phosphate) from the pump. E_2 is the form that interacts with VO_4^{2-} ions. This interaction results in pump inhibition. E_2 undergoes another conformational transition to E_1 to complete the cycle. The steps in the turnover cycle of the ER Ca^{2+} pump that are accelerated by ATP and Mg^{2+} ions are unknown. By analogy with the SR Ca^{2+} pump, it is likely that ATP accelerates both conformational transitions. Mg^{2+} ions accelerate one of the partial reactions in the dephosphorylation sequence.

There is growing evidence that the ER Ca^{2+} pump is stimulated by hormones. Stimulation of pancreatic acinar cells results in Ca^{2+} release from the ER to the cytosol and then Ca^{2+} efflux from the cells. Subsequently, the cells take up part of the released Ca^{2+} (25, 31, 118). Recently it was shown that this reuptake represent Ca^{2+} uptake back into the ER (79, 80). Ca^{2+} uptake into the ER of stimulated cells occurs despite the high Ca^{2+} permeability of the ER membrane (80). Similar Ca^{2+} reuptake into the ER of stimulated cells was observed in muscle cells and hepatocytes (12, 13, 110). In the latter studies Ca^{2+} content of the ER was determined in vivo by electron probe microanalysis. Ca^{2+} uptake into the ER of stimulated cells takes place when the $[Ca^{2+}]_i$ is reduced and maintained at near resting levels (79, 80, 84) and IP_3 level is elevated (24, 125). These observations indicate that the ER of stimulated cells partially reload with Ca^{2+} and provide indirect evidence that the ER Ca^{2+} pump is stimulated during continuous hormonal stimulation. The first direct evidence for stimulation of the pancreatic acinar cells ER Ca^{2+} pump was obtained by Ponappa & Williams (90). Stimulation of the cells with cholecystokinin octapeptide (CCK-OP) or carbachol increased the rate of Ca^{2+} uptake into isolated ER vesicles by approximately 60% in a dose dependent manner. Using isolated vesicles, it was reported that the ER Ca^{2+} pump of stimulated cells has higher V_{max} than the pump of resting cells, but has the same apparent affinity for Ca^{2+} (90, 98). Permeabilized pancreatic acinar cells were also used to compare the properties of the ER Ca^{2+} pump in resting and prestimulated cells (74). Stimulation of the cells resulted in up to a fourfold increase in the rate of Ca^{2+} uptake into the ER. The stimulated pumps show higher V_{max} and higher apparent affinity for Ca^{2+}. Furthermore,

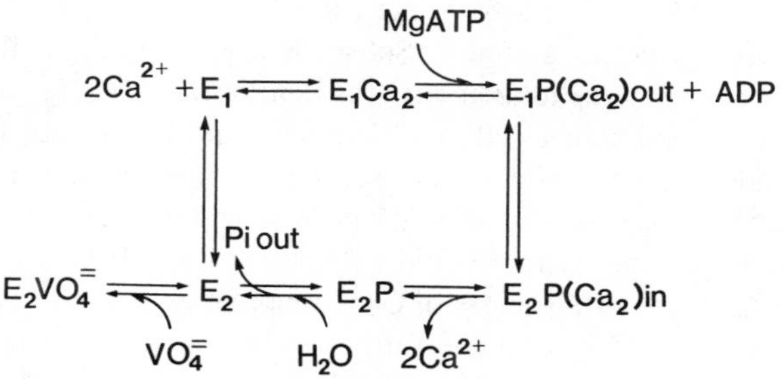

$$2Ca^{2+} + E_1 \rightleftharpoons E_1Ca_2 \xrightarrow{MgATP} E_1P(Ca_2)out + ADP$$

$$E_2VO_4^= \rightleftharpoons E_2 \rightleftharpoons E_2P \rightleftharpoons E_2P(Ca_2)in$$

Pi out

$VO_4^=$ H_2O $2Ca^{2+}$

Figure 1   Minimal turnover cycle of the ER Ca^{2+} pump. See text for details.

the ER Ca^{2+} pump of stimulated cells displayed lower apparent affinity for VO_4^{2-} ions. These observations were interpreted to suggest that stimulation of the Ca^{2+} pump results in acceleration of the rate of the conformational transition $E_2 \rightarrow E_1$.

The biochemical mechanism of pump activation is still unclear. The platelet ER Ca^{2+} pump can be activated by cAMP-dependent protein kinase (60) and protein kinase C (138) mediated phosphorylation. The cardiac SR Ca^{2+} pump can be activated by the same mechanisms (73, 123) and also by Ca^{2+} and calmodulin-dependent protein kinase (59). CCK-OP and carbachol increase $[Ca^{2+}]_i$ and activate protein kinase C in pancreatic acinar cells. Therefore, it is possible that activation of the ER Ca^{2+} pump in pancreatic acinar cells is mediated by a protein kinase-dependent phosphorylation reaction. In this context, it is useful to note that stimulation of the cardiac SR Ca^{2+} pump by protein kinases is not by direct phosphorylation of the pump. The SR of cardiac and smooth muscle contain a hydrophobic proteolipid called phospholamban (123). Phospholamban is a complex of five identical subunits. Each has a molecular mass of 6080 daltons (30). The nonphosphorylated phospholamban is attached to the pump and reduces its activity. Phosphorylation of phospholamban at serine -16 or threonine -17 leads to dissociation of the proteolipid from the Ca^{2+} pump and activation of Ca^{2+} transport (46). It remains to be determined whether the ER in different cells contain a protein analogous to phospholamban that regulates pump activity.

Calcium Efflux From the ER

Considerable evidence indicates that Ca^{2+} mobilizing hormones release Ca^{2+} from the ER or an organelle associated with the ER. Early studies with ^{45}Ca fluxes (104, 118) and chlorotetracycline fluorescence (20) implicated Ca^{2+} bound to the plasma membrane or stored in mitochrondria as hormone mobilizable intracellular pool. However, these studies did not exclude the ER as the organelle responding to hormonal stimulation. Evidence that the ER is the major source of Ca^{2+} released by hormones was obtained from analysis of hormone-induced changes in Ca^{2+} content of subcellular organelles (26). Hormones induced Ca^{2+} loss from the ER without altering Ca^{2+} content of mitochondria or zymogen granules. Subsequently, when the ability of IP_3 to release Ca^{2+} from intracellular stores was demonstrated (115), it was shown that in permeabilized acinar cells the hormones and IP_3 release Ca^{2+} from a nonmitochondrial pool. IP_3 also released Ca^{2+} from isolated ER, and IP_3-mediated Ca^{2+} release correlated very well with marker enzymes of the rough endoplasmic reticulum (114). IP_3 did not release Ca^{2+} from isolated plasma membrane vesicles (114). The use of Ca^{2+} ionophores, which do not mobilize membrane bound Ca^{2+}, provide further evidence that hormones do not mobilize membrane bound Ca^{2+}. Incubation of acinar cells with Ca^{2+}

ionophores, specifically mobilized Ca^{2+} from the hormone sensitive pool (79) and prevented the hormone-evoked increase in $[Ca^{2+}]_i$ (80).

The localization of the hormone-mobilizable Ca^{2+} pool within acinar cells was studied by cytochemical method. Haase et al (37) demonstrated the presence of Ca^{2+} storage sites along the plasma membrane. CCK and car-bachol stimulation reduced the Ca^{2+} content of these sites by approximately 80%. Termination of cell stimulation resulted in the reappearance of Ca^{2+} in the storage sites. Measurements of subcellular Ca^{2+} content in intact smooth muscle cells revealed that agonists release Ca^{2+} from a pool located close to the plasma membrane (11). In *Xenopus* oocytes, the injection of IP_3 close to the plasma membrane has a greater effect than that of IP_3 injected deep within the oocyte (18). Thus, it appears that the hormone sensitive pool is located close to the plasma membrane. Such localization may be important for a rapid rate of Ca^{2+} release and reuptake into the pool.

Several aspects of the mechanism by which Ca^{2+} is released from the ER have been clarified in recent years. A role for IP_3 in mediating the hormone-evoked Ca^{2+} release from intracellular stores has been obtained in a variety of cells. The biochemical pathway leading to IP_3 formation and metabolism and the effects of IP_3 on ER Ca^{2+} and cell function have been reviewed recently (10). Only some aspects of the IP_3-mediated Ca^{2+} release are discussed here.

Ca^{2+} release by IP_3 involves the binding of IP_3 to a specific site in the ER membrane. A saturable binding site for IP_3 was described in permeabilized hepatocytes and neutrophils (112) and in ER membrane fractions isolated from adrenal cortex (36) and liver (113). The specificity of these binding sites for IP_3 was high because the relative potency of different inositol phosphates to release Ca^{2+} from the ER was identical to their potency to displace IP_3 from its receptor (36, 112).

IP_3 probably does not bind to the ER Ca^{2+} pump, and the IP_3-mediated Ca^{2+} release from the ER is not due to inhibition of the ER Ca^{2+} pump. Inhibition of the ER Ca^{2+} pump by VO_4^{2-} or by removal of ATP did not inhibit IP_3-mediated Ca^{2+} release (92). Ca^{2+} pump activity and IP_3-mediated Ca^{2+} fluxes across the ER membrane could be separated (81). Additionally, IP_3-mediated Ca^{2+} release can be observed at 0°C and 37°C (14, 81, 109). Thus, the ER membrane appears to have separate pathways for Ca^{2+} uptake and Ca^{2+} release.

The IP_3-mediated Ca^{2+} release is a conductive pathway. Using isolated ER from liver (81) and permeabilized hepatocytes (52), it was shown that IP_3-mediated Ca^{2+} release required the presence of a permeable cation in the medium bathing the ER. Furthermore, a K^+ electrochemical gradient was sufficient to drive Ca^{2+} flux through the IP_3-mediated Ca^{2+} pathway (81). According to the direction of the K^+ electrochemical gradient, both IP_3-mediated Ca^{2+} efflux and influx were observed (81). Thus, not only is the

IP_3-mediated Ca^{2+} flux reversible, but the electrochemical potential across the ER membrane appears to be the driving force for Ca^{2+} fluxes across the IP_3-activated Ca^{2+} pathway. The cationic conductive pathway in the ER membrane has been identified as a K^+ conductance (81). Inhibition of this K^+ conductance resulted in inhibition of IP_3-mediated Ca^{2+} fluxes (81). Such properties are consistent with the IP_3-activated Ca^{2+} pathway having a channel rather than carrier properties.

It is not clear whether IP_3 is the only physiological mediator of Ca^{2+} release from the ER. In some cells, a GTP mediated Ca^{2+} release from a nonmitochondrial pool has been described (28, 127). GTP induced Ca^{2+} release by a mechanism different from that of IP_3 (127). The nonhydrolyzable analogue of GTP, GTPγS, does not induce Ca^{2+} release and inhibits the GTP-mediated Ca^{2+} release (127). The ability of GTP to release Ca^{2+} from the ER of pancreatic acinar cells was not tested. However, it was shown that 50 μM GTPγS does not inhibit, but rather augments the CCK-OP evoked Ca^{2+} release from the ER of permeabilized acinar cells (105). This finding suggests that, at least in pancreatic acinar cells, GTP-mediated Ca^{2+} release does not occur during hormonal stimulation. Furthermore, it is likely that GTP does not regulate the IP_3-activated Ca^{2+} conductance in these cells.

Another possible mediator of Ca^{2+} release from the ER that may have physiological relevance is 1,2-cyclic-4,5 inositol trisphosphate (IcP_3). Sekar et al (107) showed that stimulation of pancreatic acinar cells with carbachol results in the appearance of both IP_3 and IcP_3 in the cytosol. However, the time courses for IP_3 and IcP_3 levels are different. Following cell stimulation, the level of IP_3 reaches a maximum within less than 10 seconds, then decays to approximately 50% of maximum, and remains at this level for at least 20 minutes of stimulation. The IcP_3 level increases slowly, reaches a maximum after approximately 5 minutes and is maintained at this level for at least 20 minutes of stimulation (24). Although the time courses of the inositol phosphates were not studied in as much detail, stimulation of platelets with thrombin also results in the generation of IP_3 and IcP_3 (51, 124). Similar to IP_3, IcP_3 is capable of Ca^{2+} release from a nonmitochondrial pool (48, 136). The potency of IcP_3 to release Ca^{2+} from permeabilized Swiss 3T3 cells (48) and platelets (136) is similar to that of IP_3. In *Limulus* photoreceptor cells, IcP_3 was about five times more potent than IP_3 in eliciting Ca^{2+} release and membrane depolarization (136). The studies of Dixon & Hokin (24) in pancreatic acinar cells, therefore, suggest that hormone-mediated Ca^{2+} release may have two components, an IP_3- and an IcP_3-mediated components. Sustained high levels of IP_3 and IcP_3 during cell stimulation should keep the ER membrane permeable to Ca^{2+} for as long as the cells are stimulated. This is supported by ^{45}Ca flux studies (25, 56, 79, 84). From the time courses of the appearance of each inositol trisphosphate, it was suggested that the initial hormone-evoked increase in $[Ca^{2+}]_i$ is mediated by IP_3. IcP_3 may affect $[Ca^{2+}]_i$ at a subsequent stimulation period (24). However, the evidence implicating IcP_3 as a possible mediator of hormone-evoked Ca^{2+} release is meager and further studies are required to determine whether IP_3 and IcP_3 have separate or complimentary roles in the process of Ca^{2+} release.

SUMMARY

The control of $[Ca^{2+}]_i$ in resting and stimulated pancreatic acinar cells is achieved by at least four Ca^{2+} transporting pathways. Conductive pathways in the plasma and ER membranes allow Ca^{2+} influx into the cytosol while ATP-fueled Ca^{2+} pumps remove Ca^{2+} from the cytosol. The contribution of these Ca^{2+} pathways to cytosolic Ca^{2+} is illustrated in the Figure 2.

In the resting cells, $[Ca^{2+}]_i$ is determined by the rates of Ca^{2+} influx and efflux across the plasma membrane. Cytosolic Ca^{2+} is buffered to approximately 150 nM. The rate of Ca^{2+} pumping across the plasma membrane is equal to the rate of Ca^{2+} influx, which keeps $[Ca^{2+}]_i$ at a constant level. The buffering of cytosolic Ca^{2+} prevents large fluctuations in $[Ca^{2+}]_i$. The ER contains about 3 nmoles calcium/mg of cell protein. ER calcium is probably also buffered, which results in low free Ca^{2+} concentration in the ER interior. The Ca^{2+} permeability of the ER membrane is very low. The low ER free

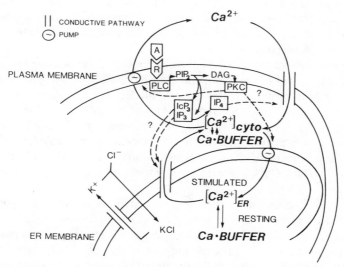

Figure 2   A model of Ca^{2+} influx and efflux from the cytosol of resting and stimulated cells. See text for details.

Ca^{2+} concentration and Ca^{2+} permeability result in a low rate of Ca^{2+} pumping by the ER Ca^{2+} pump. The low pump-leak turnover rate of Ca^{2+} across the ER membrane minimizes the contribution of the ER to $[Ca^{2+}]_i$ in the resting cells.

When the cells are stimulated, a sequence of events is initiated, the end result of which is a transient increase in $[Ca^{2+}]_i$. To produce the transient increase in $[Ca^{2+}]_i$, the activity of the four Ca^{2+} pathways is modified. The sequence of activation of each Ca^{2+} pathway has not been completely re-solved. It is, however, likely that binding of agonist to a receptor is followed by activation of phospholipase C (PLC). PLC catalizes the breakdown of PIP_2 to IP_3 and diacylglycerol (DAG). In subsequent stimulation periods PIP_2 is also hydrolyzed to IcP_3. At the onset of stimulation, the properties of the Ca^{2+} buffer in the ER may be changed so that free Ca^{2+} concentration in the ER interior is increased. IP_3 binds to specific receptors in the ER membrane and activates a Ca^{2+} conductance. This leads to Ca^{2+} efflux from the ER to the cytosol and K^+ influx from the cytosol to the ER through a K^+ conductive pathway. It is unclear if K^+ influx is sufficient to balance the charge released as Ca^{2+}. In the case of muscle SR, it was suggested that K^+, Mg^{2+}, and H^+ influx are required to balance the charge released as Ca^{2+} (110).

Kinetic studies in parotid acinar cells suggest that the plasma membrane Ca^{2+} entry is activated at the same time or before Ca^{2+} release from the ER (65, 66). If IP_4 is the mediator of the plasma membrane Ca^{2+} entry pathway, then some of the IP_3 is phosphorylated to IP_4 within the first 300 milliseconds of cell stimulation. Ca^{2+} efflux from the ER and Ca^{2+} influx across the plasma membrane results in a $[Ca^{2+}]_i$ increase. The $[Ca^{2+}]_i$ increase reaches a maximum within 1–2 seconds and is maintained at maximal levels for approx-imately 10–15 seconds.

The generation of DAG and the increase in $[Ca^{2+}]_i$ can activate two protein kinases, Ca^{2+}, and calmodulin-dependent protein kinase and protein kinase C. One or both protein kinases activate the ER and the plasma membrane Ca^{2+} pumps. Thus, $[Ca^{2+}]_i$ is reduced due to Ca^{2+} efflux out of the cells and reuptake of Ca^{2+} back into the ER. The plasma and ER membrane Ca^{2+} pathways remain activated for as long as the cells are stimulated. Ca^{2+} entry across the plasma membrane and uptake into the ER partially reload the ER with Ca^{2+}. Thus, Ca^{2+} is continuously circulated across the plasma and ER membranes.

When cell stimulation is terminated, the activity of the four Ca^{2+} pathways sequentially decays to that in resting cells. The first event appears to be a rapid reduction in the Ca^{2+} permeability of the ER membrane, and possibly a rapid change in the Ca^{2+} buffering property of the ER. Whether the hydroly-sis of IP_3 and IcP_3 is required for the reduction in ER Ca^{2+} permeability is unclear. Upon termination of cell stimulation, the change in ER permeability appears to occur within a few seconds (80) while IP_3 hydrolysis seems to require approximately 2–3 minutes (44, 47). It is, therefore, possible that the ER membrane becomes refractory to IP_3 during the reloading period. The Ca^{2+} that was incorporated into the ER during the stimulation period is then trapped in the ER. The plasma membrane Ca^{2+} entry mechanism remains activated until the ER is completely reloaded with Ca^{2+}. To prevent a large increase in $[Ca^{2+}]_i$ during the reloading period, the plasma membrane and ER Ca^{2+} pumps also remain activated until ER reloading is completed. With the progress of ER reloading, the activities of Ca^{2+} entry through the plasma membrane, Ca^{2+} efflux through the plasma membrane Ca^{2+} pump, and Ca^{2+} uptake into the ER by the ER Ca^{2+} pump are decreased in a synchronous manner. With the completion of Ca^{2+} reloading, the cells are reprimed for further stimulation to release Ca^{2+} from the ER.

ACKNOWLEDGMENT

I thank Rita Kaz for her skillful preparation of the manuscript. Work from the author's laboratory was funded by National Institutes of Health grant DK 38938 and a grant from the National Osteoporosis Foundation. S. Muallem is an established investigator of the American Heart Association.

Literature Cited

1. Adunyah, S. E., Dean, W. L. 1986. Ca^{2+} transport in human platelet membranes: Kinetics of active transport and passive release. *J. Biol. Chem.* 261:3122–27
2. Ansah, T. A., Molla, A., Katz. 1984. Ca^{2+}-ATPase activity in pancreatic acinar plasma membranes: Regulation by calmodulin and acidic phospholipids. *J. Biol. Chem.* 259:13442–50
3. Argent, B. E., Case, R. M., Scratcherd, T. 1973. Amylase secretion by the perfused cat pancreas in relation to the secretion of calcium and other electrolytes and as influenced by the external ionic environment. *J. Physiol.* 230:575–93
4. Aub, D. L., McKinney, J. S., Putney, J. W. 1982. Nature of the receptor-regulated calcium pool in the rat parotid gland. *J. Physiol.* 331:557–65
5. Bayerdorffer, E., Eckhardt, L., Haase, W., Schulz, I. 1985. Electrogenic calcium transport in plasma membrane of rat pancreatic acinar cells. *J. Membr. Biol.* 84:45–60
6. Bayerdorffer, E., Haase, W., Schulz, I. 1985. Na^+/Ca^{2+} countertransport in

plasma membrane of rat pancreatic acinar cells. *J. Membr. Biol.* 87:107–19
7. Bayerdorffer, E., Streb, H., Eckhardt, L., Haase, W., Schulz, I. 1984. Characterization of calcium uptake into rough endoplasmic reticulum of rat pancreas. *J. Membr. Biol.* 81:69–82
8. Benz, L., Eckstein, B., Matthews, E. K., Williams, J. A. 1972. Control of pancreatic amylase release in vitro: Effect of ions, cyclic AMP and colchicine. *Br. J. Pharmacol.* 46:66–77
9. Berridge, M. J. 1983. Rapid accumulation of inositol trisphosphate reveals that agonists hydrolyze polyphosphoinositides instead of phosphatidylinositol. *Biochem. J.* 212:849–58
10. Berridge, M. J. 1987. Inositol trisphosphate and diacylglycerol: Two interacting second messengers. *Annu. Rev. Biochem.* 56:159–93.
11. Bond, M., Kitazawa, T., Somlyo, A. P., Somlyo, A. V. 1984. Release and recycling of calcium by the sarcoplasmic reticulum in guinea pig portal vein smooth muscle. *J. Physiol.* 355:677–95
12. Bond, M., Shuman, H., Somlyo, A. P., Somlyo, A. V. 1984. Total cytoplasmic

calcium in relaxed and maximally contracted rabbit protal vein smooth muscle. *J. Physiol.* 357:185–201

13. Bond, M., Vadasz, G., Somlyo, A. V., Somlyo, A. P. 1987. Subcellular calcium and magnesium mobilization in rat liver stimulated in vivo with vasopressin and glucagen. *J. Biol. Chem.* 262: 15630–36

14. Brass, L. F., Joseph, S. K. 1985. A role for inositol trisphosphate in intracellular Ca^{2+}-mobilization and granule secretion in platelets. *J. Biol. Chem.* 260:15172–79

15. Bruzzone, R., Pozzan, T., Wollheim, C. B. 1986. Caerulein and carbamylcholine stimulate pancreatic amylase release at resting cytosolic free Ca^{2+}. *Biochem. J.* 235:139–43

16. Burnham, D. B., McChesney, D. J., Thurston, K. C., Williams, J. A. 1984. Interaction of cholecystokinin and vasoactive intestinal polypeptide on function of mouse pancreatic acini in vitro. *J. Physiol.* 349:475–82

17. Burnham, D. B., Munowitz, P., Hootman, S. R., Williams, J. A. 1985. Regulation of protein phosphorylation in pancreatic acini. Distinct effects of Ca^{2+} ionophore A23187 and 12-0-tetradecanoylphorbol 13-acetate. *Biochem. J.* 235:125–31

18. Busa, W. B., Ferguson, J. E., Joseph, S. K., Williamson, J. R., Nuccitelli, R. 1985. Activation of frog *(Xenopus laevis)* eggs by inositol trisphosphate I. Characterization of Ca^{2+} release from intracellular stores. *J. Cell Biol.* 101:677–82

19. Case, R. M., Clausen, T. 1973. The relationship between calcium exchange and enzyme secretion in the isolated rat pancreas. *J. Physiol.* 235:75–102

20. Chandler, D. E., Williams, J. A. 1978. Intracellular divalent cation release in pancreatic acinar cells during stimulus-secretion coupling. II. Subcellular localization of the fluorescent probe chlorotetracycline. *J. Cell Biol.* 76:386–99

21. Cruetz, C. E., Dowling, L. G., Sando. J. J., Villar-Palasi, C., Whipple, J. H., Zaks, W. J. 1983. Characterization of the chromobindins. Soluble proteins that bind to the chromaffin granule membrane in the presence of Ca^{2+}. *J. Biol. Chem.* 258:14664–74

22. Damian, E., Spamer, C., Heilmann, C., Salvatori, S., Margreth, A. 1988. Endoplasmic reticulum of rat liver contains two proteins closely related to skeletal sarcoplasmic reticulum Ca^{2+}-

ATPase and calsequestrin. *J. Biol. Chem.* 263:340–43

23. Dean, W. L. 1984. Purification and reconstitution of a Ca^{2+} pump from human platelets. *J. Biol. Chem.* 259:7343–48

24. Dixon, J. F., Hokin, L. E. 1987. Inositol 1,2-cyclic 4,5-trisphosphate concentration relative to inositol 1,4,5-trisphosphate in pancreatic minilobules on stimulation with carbamylcholine in the absence of lithium. *J. Biol. Chem.* 262:13892–95

25. Dormer, R. L., Poulsen, J. H., Licko, W., Williams, J. A. 1981. Calcium fluxes in isolated pancreatic acini: Effects of secretagogues. *Am. J. Physiol.* 240:G38–G43

26. Dormer, R. L., Williams, J. A. 1981. Secretagogue-induced changes in subcellular Ca^{2+} distribution in isolated pancreatic acini. *Am. J. Physiol.* 240: G130–G140

27. Dowson, R. M. C. 1965. Phosphatidopeptide like complexes formed by the interaction of calcium triphosphoinositide with protein. *Biochem. J.* 97:134–38

28. Dowson, A. P., Comerford, J. G., Fulton, D. V. 1986. The effect of GTP on inositol 1,4,5-trisphosphate-stimulated Ca^{2+} efflux from a rat liver microsomal fraction. Is a GTP-dependent protein phosphorylation involved? *Biochem. J.* 234:311–15

29. Eimerl, S., Savion, N., Heichal, O., Selinger, Z. 1974. Induction of enzyme secretion in rat pancreatic slices using the ionophore A23187 and calcium. An experimental bypass of the hormone receptor pathway. *J. Biol. Chem.* 249: 3991–93

30. Fujii, J., Kadoma, M., Tada, M., Toda, H., Sakiyawa, F. 1986. Characterization of structural unit of phospholamban by amino acid sequencing and electrophorectic analysis. *Biochem. Biophys. Res. Commun.* 138:1044–50

31. Gardner, J. D., Conlon, D. T. P., Klaereman, H. L., Adams, T. D., Ondetti, M. A. 1975. Action of cholecystokinin and cholinergic agents on calcium transport in isolated pancreatic acinar cells. *J. Clin. Invest.* 56:366–75

32. Gardner, J. D., Costenbader, C. L., Uhlemann, E. R. 1979. Effect of extracellular calcium on amylase release from dispersed pancreatic acini. *Am. J. Physiol.* 236:E754–E762

33. Gardner, J. D., Jensen, R. T. 1981. Regulation of pancreatic enzyme secre-

tion in vitro. In *Physiology of the Gastrointestinal Tract*, ed. L. R. Johnson, pp. 831–71. New York: Raven

34. Gill, D. L., Chueh, S. H. 1985. An intracellular (ATP + Mg)-dependent calcium pump within the N1E-115 neuronal cell line. *J. Biol. Chem.* 260:9289–97

35. Grynkiewicz, G., Poenie, M., Tsien, R. Y. 1985. A new generation of Ca^{2+} indicators with greatly improved fluorescence properties. *J. Biol. Chem.* 260: 3440–50

36. Guillemette, G., Balla, T., Baukal, A., Spat, A., Catt, K. 1987. Intracellular receptors for inositol 1,4,5-trisphosphate in angiotensin II target tissues. *J. Biol. Chem.* 262:1010–15

37. Haase, W., Friese, W., Heitman, R. 1984. Electron-microscopic demonstration of the distribution of calcium deposits in the exocrine pancreas of the rat after application of carbachol, atropine, cholecystokinin, and procaine. *Cell Tissue Res.* 235:683–90

38. Heilmann, C., Spamer, C., Gerok, W. 1985. Reaction mechanism of the calcium-transport ATPase in endoplasmic reticulum of rat liver: Demonstration of different reactive forms of the phosphorylated intermediate. *J. Biol. Chem.* 260:788–94

39. Hokin, L. E. 1966. Effects of calcium omission on acetylcholine-stimulated amylase secretion and phospholipid synthesis in pigeon pancreas slices. *Biochim. Biophys. Acta* 115:219–21

40. Hokin, L. E. 1985. Receptors and phosphoinositide-generated second messengers. *Annu. Rev. Biochem.* 54:205–35

41. Hokin, M. R., Hokin, L. E. 1953. Enzyme secretion and the incorporation of ^{32}P into phospholipids of pancreas slices. *J. Biol. Chem.* 203:967–77

42. Hootman, S. R., Williams, J. A. 1987. Stimulus-secretion coupling in the pancreatic acinus. See Ref. 33, pp. 1129–46

43. Imaura, K., Schulz, I. 1985. Phosphorylated intermediate of $(Ca^{2+} + K^+)$-stimulated Mg^{2+}-dependent transport ATPase in endoplasmic reticulum from rat pancreatic acinar cells. *J. Biol. Chem.* 260:11339–47

44. Imbaden, J. B., Weiss, A. 1987. The T-cell antigen receptor regulates sustained increase in cytoplasmic free Ca^{2+} through extracellular Ca^{2+} influx and ongoing intracellular Ca^{2+} mobilization. *Biochem. J.* 247:695–700

45. Inesi, G. 1985. Mechanism of calcium transport. *Annu. Rev. Physiol.* 47:573–601

46. Inoui, M., Chamberlain, B. K., Saito, A., Fleischer, S. 1986. The nature of the modulation of Ca^{2+} transport as studied by reconstitution of cardiac sarcoplasmic reticulum. *J. Biol. Chem.* 261:1794–800

47. Irvine, R. F., Anggard, E. E., Letcher, A. J., Downes, P. C. 1985. Metabolism of inositol 1,4,5-trisphosphate and inositol 1,3,4-trisphosphate in rat parotid glands. *Biochem J.* 229:505–11

48. Irvine, R. F., Letcher, A. J., Lander, D. J., Berridge, M. J. 1986. Specificity of inositol phosphate-stimulated Ca^{2+} mobilization from Swiss-mouse 3T3 cells. *Biochem. J.* 240:301–4

49. Irvine, R. F., Moore, R. B. 1986. Micro-injection of inositol 1,3,4,5-tetrakisphosphate activates sea urchin eggs by a mechanism dependent on external Ca^{2+}. *Biochem. J.* 240:917–20

50. Irvine, R. F., Moor, R. M. 1987. Inositol (1,3,4,5) tetrakisphosphate-induced activation of sea urchin eggs requires the presence of inositol trisphosphate. *Biochem. Biophys. Res. Commun.* 146:284–90

51. Ishii, H., Connolly, T. M., Bross, T. E., Majerus, P. W. 1986. Inositol cyclic trisphosphate [inositol 1,2-(cyclic)-4,5-trisphosphate] is formed upon thrombin stimulation of human platelets. *Proc. Natl. Acad. Sci. USA* 83:6397–6401

52. Joseph, S., Williamson, J. R. 1986. Characteristics of inositol trisphosphate-mediated Ca^{2+} release from permeabilized hepatocytes. *J. Biol. Chem.* 261:14658–64

53. Kanno, T. 1972. Calcium-dependent amylase release and electrophysiological measurements in cells of the pancreas. *J. Physiol.* 226:353–71

54. Kemmer, T. P., Bayerdorffer, E., Will, H., Schulz, I. 1987. Anion dependence of Ca^{2+} transport and $(Ca^{2+} + K^+)$-stimulated Mg^{2+}-dependent transport ATPase in rat pancreatic endoplasmic reticulum. *J. Biol. Chem.* 262:13758–64

55. Kondo, S., Schulz, I. 1976. Calcium ion uptake in isolated pancreas cells induced by secretagogues. *Biochim. Biophys. Acta* 419:76–92

56. Kondo, S., Schulz, I. 1976. Ca^{2+} fluxes in isolated cells of rat pancreas: Effect of secretagogues and different Ca^{2+} concentrations. *J. Membr. Biol.* 29:185–203

57. Kribben, A., Tyrakowski, T., Schulz, I. 1983. Characterization of Mg-ATP-dependent Ca^{2+} transport in cat pancreatic microsomes. *Am. J. Physiol.* 244: G480–90

58. Lagast, H., Pozzan, T., Waldragel, F.

A., Lew, D. P. 1984. Phorbol myristate acetate stimulates ATP-dependent calcium transport by the plasma membrane of neutrophils. *J. Clin. Invest.* 73:878–83

59. LePeuch, C. J., Haiech, J., Demaille, J. G. 1979. Concerted regulation of cardiac sarcoplasmic reticulum calcium transport by cyclic-AMP-dependent and calcium-calmodulin-dependent phosphorylation. *Biochemistry* 18:5150–57

60. LePeuch, C. J., LePeuch, D. A. M., Katz, S., Demaille, J. G., Hincke, M. T., et al. 1983. Regulation of calcium accumulation and efflux from platelet vesicles. Possible role for cyclic-AMP-dependent phosphorylation and calmodulin. *Biochim. Biophys. Acta* 731:456–64

61. MacLennan, D. H., Wong, P. T. S. 1971. Isolation of a calcium-sequestering protein from sarcoplasmic reticulum. *Proc. Natl. Acad. Sci. USA* 68:1231–35

62. Majerus, P. W., Connolly, T. M., Deckmyn, H., Ross, T. S., Bross, T. E., et al. 1986. The metabolism of phosphoinositide-derived messenger molecules. *Science* 234:1519–26

63. Maruyama, Y., Petersen, O. H. 1982. Single-channel currents in isolated patches of plasma membrane from basal surface of pancreatic acini. *Nature* 299:159–61

64. Mattews, E. K., Petersen, O.H., Williams, J. A. 1973. Pancreatic acinar cells: Acetylcholine-induced membrane depolarization, calcium efflux and amylase release. *J. Physiol.* 234:689–701

65. Merritt, J. E., Rink, T. J. 1987. Rapid increases in cytosolic free calcium in response to muscarinic stimulation of rat parotid acinar cells. *J. Biol. Chem.* 262:4958–60

66. Merritt, J. E., Rink, T. J. 1987. The effects of substance P and carbachol on inositol tris- and tetrakisphosphate formation and cytosolic free calcium in rat parotid acinar cells. *J. Biol. Chem.* 262:14912–16

67. Merritt, J. E., Rink, T. J. 1987. Regulation of cytosolic free calcium in Fura-2 loaded rat parotid acinar cells. *J. Biol. Chem.* 262:17362–69

68. Merritt, J. E., Rubin, R. P. 1985. Pancreatic amylase secretion and cytoplasmic free calcium: Effect of ionomycin, phorbol dibutyrate and diacylglycerols alone and in combination. *Biochem. J.* 230:151–59

69. Michell, R. H. 1975. Inositol phospholipids and cell surface receptor function. *Biochim. Biophys. Acta* 415:81–147

70. Moore, P. B., Dedman, J. R. 1982. Calcium-dependent protein binding to phenothiazine columns. *J. Biol. Chem.* 257:9663–67

71. Morris, A. P., Fuller, C. M., Gallacher, D. V. 1987. Cholinergic receptors regulate a voltage-insensitive but Na^+-dependent calcium influx pathway in salivary acinar cells. *FEBS Lett.* 211:195–99

72. Morris, A. P., Gallacher, D. V., Irvine, R. F., Petersen, O. H. 1987. Synergism of inositol trisphosphate and tetrakisphosphate in activating Ca^{2+}-dependent K^+ channels. *Nature* 330:653–55

73. Mousesian, M. A., Nishikawa, M., Adelstein, R. S. 1984. Phosphorylation of phospholamban by calcium-activated, phospholipid-dependent protein kinase. *J. Biol. Chem.* 259:8029–32

74. Muallem, S., Beeker, T. G., Fimmel, C. J. 1987. Activation of the endoplasmic reticulum Ca^{2+} pump of pancreatic acini by Ca^{2+} mobilizing hormones. *Biochim. Biophys. Res. Commun.* 149:213–20

75. Muallem, S., Beeker, T. G., Fimmel, C. J., Pandol, S. 1987. Inositol phosphate levels during Ca^{2+} reloading of the ER. In *Cellular Calcium and Phosphate Transport in Health and Disease*, ed. F. Bronner, M. Peterlik, pp. 183–89. New York: Liss

76. Muallem, S., Beeker, T. G., Pandol, S. J. 1988. The role of Na^+/Ca^{2+} exchange and the plasma membrane Ca^{2+} pump in hormone mediated Ca^{2+} efflux from pancreatic acini. *J. Membr. Biol.* 102:153–62

77. Muallem, S., Fimmel, C. J., Pandol, S. J., Sachs, G. 1986. Regulation of free cytosolic Ca^{2+} and secretion in parietal and peptic cells. *J. Biol. Chem.* 261:2660–67

78. Muallem, S., Karlish, S. J. D. 1980. Studies on the mechanism of regulation of the red cell Ca^{2+}-pump by calmodulin and ATP. *Biochim. Biophys. Acta* 647:73–86

79. Muallem, S., Schoeffield, M. S., Fimmel, C. J., Pandol, S. J. 1988. The agonist-sensitive calcium pool in the pancreatic acinar cell, I. Permeability properties. *Am. J. Physiol.* 255:G221–28

80. Muallem, S., Schoeffield, M. S., Fimmel, C. J., Pandol, S. J. 1988. The agonist-sensitive calcium pool in the pancreatic acinar cell, II. Reloading during and at the termination of stimulation. *Am. J. Physiol.* 255:G229–35

81. Muallem, S., Schoeffield, M. S., Pandol, S. J., Sachs, G. 1985. Inositol trisphosphate modification of ion transport in rough endoplasmic reticulum. *Proc. Natl. Acad. Sci. USA* 82:4433–37

82. Ochs, D. L., Korenbrot, J. I., Williams, J. A. 1983. Intracellular free calcium concentration in isolated pancreatic acini: Effects of secretagogues. *Biochem. Biophys. Res. Commun.* 117:122–28

83. Ochs, D. L., Korenbrot, J. I., Williams, J. A. 1985. Relationship between agonist-induced changes in the concentration of free intracellular calcium and the secretion of amylase by pancreatic acini. *Am. J. Physiol.* 249:G389–G398

84. Pandol, S. J., Schoeffield, M. S., Fimmel, J. C., Muallem, S. 1987. The agonist-sensitive calcium pool in the pancreatic acinar cell: Activation of plasma membrane Ca^{2+} influx mechanism. *J. Biol. Chem.* 262:16963–68

85. Pandol, S. J., Schoeffield, M. S., Sachs, G., Muallem, S. 1985. The role of free cytosolic calcium in secretagogues stimulated amylase release from dispersed acini from guinea pig pancreas. *J. Biol. Chem.* 260:10081–86

86. Petersen, O. H. 1986. Calcium-activated potassium channels and fluid secretion by exocrine glands. *Am. J. Physiol.* 251:G1–G13

87. Petersen, O. H., Maruyama, Y. 1983. What is the mechanism of the calcium influx to pancreatic acinar cells evoked by secretagogues. *Pflüegers Arch.* 396:82–84

88. Pollock, W. K., Sage, S. O., Rink, T. J. 1987. Stimulation of Ca^{2+} efflux from Fura-2-loaded platelets activated by thrombin or phorbol myristate acetate. *FEBS Lett.* 210:132–36

89. Ponappa, B. C., Williams, J. A. 1980. Effects of ionophore A23187 on calcium flux and amylase release in isolated mouse pancreatic acini. *Cell Calcium* 1:267–78

90. Ponappa, B. C., Williams, J. A. 1981. Comparison of $^{45}Ca^{2+}$ uptake activity by microsomes from control and stimulated mouse pancreatic acini. *Life Sci.* 28:2395–2402

91. Preissler, M., Williams, J. A. 1983. Localization of ATP-dependent calcium transport activity in mouse pancreatic microsomes. *J. Membr. Biol.* 73:137–44

92. Prentki, M., Wollheim, C. B., Lew, P. D. 1984. Ca^{2+} homeostasis in permeabilized human neutrophils. Characterization of Ca^{2+}-sequestering pools and the action of inositol 1,4,5-trisphosphate. *J. Biol. Chem.* 259:13777–82

93. Putney, J. W. 1986. A model for receptor-regulated calcium entry. *Cell Calcium* 7:1–12

94. Putney, J. W. 1987. Formation and actions of calcium-mobilizing messenger, inositol 1,4,5-trisphosphate. *Am. J. Physiol.* 252:G149–G157

95. Reinhart, P. H., Taylor, W. M., Bygrave, F. L. 1984. The role of calcium ions in action of α-adrenergic agonists in rat liver. *Biochem. J.* 223:1–13.

96. Renckens, B. A. M., Schrijen, J. J., Swarts, H. G. P., DePont, J. J. H. H. M., Bonting, S. L. 1978. Role of calcium in exocrine pancreatic secretion. IV. Calcium movements in isolated acinar cells of rabbit pancreas. *Biochim. Biophys. Acta* 544:338–50

97. Richard, J. E., Sheterline, P. 1985. Evidence that phorbol ester interferes with stimulated Ca^{2+} redistribution by activating Ca^{2+} efflux in neutrophil leucocytes. *Biochem. J.* 231:623–28

98. Richardson, A. E., Dormer, R. L. 1984. Calcium-ion-transporting activity in two microsomal subfractions from rat pancreatic acini: Modulation by carbamylcholine. *Biochem. J.* 219:679–86

99. Robberecht, P., Christophe, J. 1971. Secretion of hydrolases by perfused fragments of rat pancreas: Effect of calcium. *Am. J. Physiol.* 220:911–17

100. Schatzmann, H. J. 1982. The plasma membrane calcium pump of erythrocytes and other animal cells. In *Membrane Transport of Calcium*, ed. E. Carafoli, pp. 41–108. London: Academic

101. Scheele, G., Haymorits, A. 1979. Cholinergic and peptide-stimulated discharge of secretory protein in guinea pig pancreatic lobules. Role of intracellular and extracellular calcium. *J. Biol. Chem.* 254:10346–53

102. Deleted in proof

103. Schulz, I. 1980. Messenger role of calcium in function of pancreatic acinar cells. *Am. J. Physiol.* 239:G335–G347

104. Schulz, I., Kimura, T., Wakasugi, H., Hasse, W., Kribben, A. 1981. Analysis of Ca^{2+} fluxes and Ca^{2+} pools in pancreatic acini. *Philos. Trans. R. Soc. Lond. Ser. B* 296:105–13

105. Schulz, I., Schnefel, S., Banfic, F., Trevenod, F., Kemmer, T., Eckhardt, L. 1987. The role of phosphatidylinositides in stimulus-secretion coupling in the exocrine pancreas. In *Cell Calcium and the Control of Membrane Transport*, ed. L. J. Mandel, D. C. Eaton, 42:117–131. New York: Rockefeller Univ. Press

106. Schulz, I., Stolze, H. H. 1980. The

exocrine pancreas: The role of secretagogues, cyclic nucleotides, and calcium in enzyme secretion. *Annu. Rev. Physiol.* 42:127–56

107. Sekar, C. M., Dixon, J. F., Hokin, L. E. 1987. The formation of inositol 1,2-cyclic 4,5-trisphosphate and inositol 1,2-cyclic 4-bisphosphate on stimulation of mouse pancreatic minilobules with carbamylcholine. *J. Biol. Chem.* 262:340–44

108. Shadle, P. J., Gerke, V., Weber, K. 1985. Three Ca^{2+} binding proteins from porcine liver and intestine differ immunologically and physiochemically and are distinct in Ca^{2+} affinities. *J. Biol. Chem.* 260:16354–60

109. Smith, J. B., Smith, L., Higgins, B. L. 1985. Temperature and nucleotide dependence of calcium release by myoinositol 1,4,5-trisphosphate in cultured vascular smooth muscle cells. *J. Biol. Chem.* 260:14413–16

110. Somlyo, A. V., Gonzalez-Serratos, H., Shuman, H., McClelland, G., Somlyo, A. P. 1981. Calcium release and ionic changes in the sarcoplasmic reticulum of tetanized muscle. An electron-probe study. *J. Cell Biol.* 90:577–94

111. Spamer, C., Heilmann, C., Gerok, W. 1987. Ca^{2+}-activated ATPase in microsomes from human liver. *J. Biol. Chem.* 262:7782–89

112. Spat, A., Bradford, P. G., McKinney, J. G., Rubin, R. P., Putney, J. W. 1986. A saturable receptor for ^{32}P-inositol-1,4,5-trisphosphate in hepatocytes and neutrophils. *Nature* 319:514–16

113. Spat, A., Fabiato, A., Rubin, R. P. 1986. Binding of inositol trisphosphate by a liver microsomal fraction. *Biochem. J.* 233:929–32

114. Sterb, H., Bayerdorffer, E., Haase, W., Irvine, R. F., Schulz, I. 1984. Effect of inositol-1,4,5-trisphosphate on isolated subcellular fractions of rat pancreas. *J. Membr. Biol.* 81:241–53

115. Streb, H., Irvine, R. F., Berridge, M. J., Schulz, I. 1983. Release of Ca^{2+} from a nonmitochondrial intracellular store in pancreatic acinar cells by inositol-1,4,5-trisphosphate. *Nature* 306:67–69

116. Streb, H., Schulz, I. 1983. Regulation of cytosolic free Ca^{2+} concentration in acinar cells of rat pancreas. *Am. J. Physiol.* 245:G347–G357

117. Stewart, P. S., MacLennan, D. H. 1974. Surface particles of sarcoplasmic reticulum membranes. Structural features of the adenosine trisphosphatase. *J. Biol. Chem.* 249:985–93

118. Stolze, H., Schulz, I. 1980. Effect of

atropine, ouabain, antimycin A, and A23187 on "trigger Ca^{2+} pool" in exocrine pancreas. *Am. J. Physiol.* 238:G338–G348

119. Sudhof, T. C., Ebbecke, M., Walker, J. H., Fritche, V., Bonstead, C. 1984. Isolation of mammalian calelectrins: A new class of ubiquitous Ca^{2+}-regulated proteins. *Biochemistry* 23:1103–9

120. Sugden, M. C., Christie, M. R., Ashcroft, S. J. 1979. Presence and possible role of calcium-dependent regulator (calmodulin) in rat islets of langerhans. *FEBS Lett.* 105:95–100

121. Suzuki, K., Petersen, C. C. H., Petersen, O. H. 1985. Hormonal activation of single K^+ channels via internal messenger in isolated pancreatic acinar cells. *FEBS Lett.* 192:307–12

122. Tada, M., Katz, A. 1982. Phosphorylation of the sarcoplasmic reticulum and sarcolemma. *Annu. Rev. Physiol.* 44:401–23

123. Tada, M., Kirchberger, M. A., Katz, A. M. 1975. Phosphorylation of a 22,000-Dalton component of the cardiac sarcoplasmic reticulum by adenosine 3':5'-monophosphate-dependent protein kinase. *J. Biol. Chem.* 250:2640–47

124. Tarver, A. P., King, W. G., Rittenhause, S. E. 1987. Inositol 1,4,5-trisphosphate and inositol 1,2-cyclic 4,5-trisphosphate are minor components of total mass of inositol trisphosphate in thrombin-stimulated platelets. *J. Biol. Chem.* 262:17268–71

125. Trimble, E. R., Bruzzone, R., Meehan, C. J., Biden, T. J. 1987. Rapid increases in inositol 1,4,5 trisphosphate, inositol 1,3,4,5 tetrakisphosphate and cytosolic free Ca^{2+} in agonist-stimulated pancreatic acini of the rat. *Biochem. J.* 242:289–92

126. Tsien, R. Y., Pozzan, T., Rink, T. J. 1981. Calcium homeostasis in intact lymphocytes: Cytoplasmic free calcium monitored with a new intracellular trapped fluorescent indicator. *J. Cell Biol.* 94:325–34

127. Veda, T., Chueh, S. H., Noel, M. W., Gill, D. L. 1986. Influence of inositol 1,4,5-trisphosphate and guanine nucleotides on intracellular calcium release within the N1E-115 neuronal cell line. *J. Biol. Chem.* 261:3184–92

128. Von Tscharner, V., Deranleau, D. A., Baggiolini, M. 1986. Calcium fluxes and calcium buffering in human neutrophils. *J. Biol. Chem.* 261:10163–68

129. Von Tscharner, V., Prodhom, B., Baggiolini, M., Reuter, H. 1986. Ion channels in human neutrophils activated by a

rise in free cytosolic calcium concentration. *Nature* 324:369–72

130. Wakasugi, H., Kimura, T., Haase, W., Kribben, A., Kaufmann, R., Schulz, I. 1982. Calcium uptake into acini from rat pancreas: Evidence for intracellular ATP-dependent calcium sequestration. *J. Membr. Biol.* 65:205–20

131. Williams, J. A. 1980. Multiple effects of Na^+ removal on pancreatic secretion in vitro. *Cell Tissue Res.* 210:295–303

132. Williams, J. A. 1980. Regulation of pancreatic acinar cell function by intracellular calcium. *Am. J. Physiol.* 238:G269–G279

133. Williams, J. A., Chandler, D. 1975. Ca^{2+} and pancreatic amylase release. *Am. J. Physiol.* 228:1729–32

134. Williams, D. A., Fogarty, K. E., Tsien, R. Y., Fay, F. S. 1985. Calcium gradients in single smooth muscle cells revealed by the digital imaging microscope using Fura-2. *Nature* 318:558–61

135. Williams, J. A., Lee, M. 1974. Pancreatic acinar cells: Use of a calcium inophore to separate enzyme release from the earlier steps in stimulus-secretion coupling. *Biochem.Biophys. Res. Commun.* 60:542–48

136. Wilson, D. B., Connolly, T. M. Bross, T. E., Majerus, P. W., Sherman, W. R., et al. 1985. Isolation and characterization of the inositol cyclic phosphate products of polyphosphoinositide cleavage by phospholipase C. *J. Biol. Chem.* 260:13496–501

137. Windhager, E. E., Yang, J. M., Lee, C. O., Frindt, G., Palmer, L. G. 1987. Measurements of $^a Ca$, $^a Na$ and membrane potential and patch clamp studies of the effect of changes in $^a Ca$ on Na channel activity in renal tubules. See Ref. 75, pp. 203–7

138. Yoshida, K., Nachmias, V. T. 1987. Phorbol ester stimulated calcium sequestration in saponized human platelets. *J. Biol. Chem.* 262:16048–54

Annu. Rev. Physiol. 1989. 51:107–24

HORMONE EFFECTS ON CELLULAR Ca^{2+} FLUXES

John R. Williamson and Jonathan R. Monck

Department of Biochemistry and Biophysics, University of Pennsylvania School of Medicine, Philadelphia, Pennsylvania 19104

INTRODUCTION

The cytosolic free Ca^{2+} concentration functions as an important intracellular signaling mechanism whereby hormones and growth factors regulate many different cellular processes such as secretion, metabolism, neurotransmitter release, cell growth, and differentiation (for reviews see 9, 42, 113). Signal transduction by the ligand-activated receptor is mediated by specific guanine nucleotide binding proteins (G proteins), which activate phospholipase C–mediated hydrolysis of phosphatidylinositol 4,5-bisphosphate (PIP$_2$) in the plasma membrane (38, 96). The products of this reaction are 1,2-diacylglycerol, which is retained in the plasma membrane, and D-*myo*-inositol-1,4,5-trisphosphate (Ins1,4,5-P$_3$). Both compounds act as intracellular messengers with different functions. Diacylglycerol activates a Ca^{2+} and phospholipid dependent kinase, termed protein kinase C, and promotes its translocation to the plasma membrane (57, 73). Ins 1,4,5-P$_3$ is responsible for the mobilization of intracellular Ca^{2+}, thereby causing a rapid increase of cytosolic free Ca^{2+} (9, 112). In addition, receptor occupancy is associated with an enhanced influx of Ca^{2+}, which maintains the cytosolic free Ca^{2+} above resting levels for the duration of the agonist response (2, 81).

This review describes recent advances that have elucidated the mechanisms involved in the various steps of the signal transduction pathway resulting in Ca^{2+} mobilization. A marked heterogeneity in the protein components of the pathway, as well as the diversity of Ca^{2+} responses observed with single cells, suggests that a complex network of positive and negative feedback controls continuously regulates the agonist response, which can include oscillatory behavior of the cytosolic free Ca^{2+}.

0066-4278/89/0315-0107$02.00

GENERATION OF INTRACELLULAR SECOND MESSENGERS

In all cell types agonist-induced Ca^{2+} mobilization involves an interaction in the plasma membrane between three different types of proteins: receptors, G proteins, and phospholipase C. Most cells contain many different types of receptors in the plasma membrane, which upon stimulation by suitable agonists cause an increase of cytosolic free Ca^{2+} (for reviews see, 2, 9, 29). The number of receptors and their affinity determines the relative sensitivity of the cell to each agonist and the extent of phospholipase C activation. Moreover, since a particular agonist is often capable of interacting with several different receptor subtypes, the specificity of signal transduction is determined by the nature and properties of the G protein that interacts with a particular receptor subtype and effector system. The G proteins involved in signal transduction are heterotrimers composed of diverse α, β, and γ subunits; the GTP-binding α-subunit provides the functional specificity. The structure and molecular properties of various members of the G protein family have been reviewed recently (38, 96). These include G_s and G_i, which when activated lead to stimulation and inhibition of adenylate cyclase, respectively, and G_o, which is prevalent in brain but whose function has not been ascertained. Multiple forms of G_i- and G_o-like α-subunits with high sequence homology have been identified by cDNA cloning (46).

The Role of G Proteins in Activating Phospholipases

The original evidence leading to the conclusion that a G protein is involved in receptor coupling of Ca^{2+}-mobilizing agonists to PIP_2 breakdown has been reviewed recently (21, 96, 113). When G protein activating agents such as GTP, GTPγS, or A1F$_3$ (which mimics GTP binding) are added to permeabilized cells or plasma membrane preparations, they activate phospholipase C and decrease agonist binding affinity. Further evidence is provided by (*a*) the enhancement of phospholipase C activation by suboptimal concentrations of GTPγS in the presence of agonist, (*b*) an agonist-induced stimulation of GTPase activity, (*c*) the inhibition of phospholipase C activation by GDPβS, and (*d*) the retention of receptor–G protein complexes (31, 32, 79) or G protein–phospholipase C complexes (109) during purification. The receptor-mediated activation of phospholipase C can be inhibited by pertussis toxin in some, but not all, cells (see 21). In other cells, there appears to be heterogeneity since different receptors are coupled through pertussis toxin sensitive or insensitive G proteins. For example, in hepatocytes, epidermal growth factor (EGF) responses are pertussis toxin sensitive, whereas those to angiotensin II and vasopressin are not (49).

A number of novel G proteins that may be involved in coupling to phospholipase C have been identified in various cells. In neutrophils and human leukemia HL60 cells (36, 74, 79), a pertussis toxin sensitive 40-kDa α-subunit has been purified and shown to be immunologically distinct from the α-subunits of G_o and G_i. The copurification of this 40-kDa polypeptide with the chemoattractant receptor suggests that it is responsible for activation of phospholipase C (79). This same 40-kDa α-subunit from HL60 cells is also ADP-ribosylated by cholera toxin in the presence of the Ca^{2+} mobilizing chemotactic peptide fMet-Leu-Phe (35). A pertussis toxin sensitive 40-kDa α-subunit has also been isolated from brain (55) and shown to differ structurally and immunologically from two other pertussis toxin sensitive G proteins ($G_i\alpha_{41}$, and $G_o\alpha_{39}$) of brain and other tissues (46).

Reconstitution of G_i or G_o prepared from brain into plasma membranes from pertussis toxin treated HL60 cells showed that they were equally effective in restoring GTP-dependent fMet-Leu-Phe-stimulated formation of inositol phosphates (58). Furthermore, G_o or G_i stimulated the activity of partially purified phospholipase C from platelet membranes (4). These results suggest an apparent promiscuity of G protein coupling to phospholipase C, but since the preparations of G_o or G_i used in these experiments probably contained $G\alpha_{40}$, it is possible that this G protein, which also stimulates phospholipase C activity (4), provides specificity for pertussis toxin sensitive G protein–phospholipase C coupling. A different G protein that is pertussis toxin insensitive due to a difference in its primary structure (33) may mediate signal transduction in cases where receptor coupling to phospholipase C is not blocked by the toxin.

Several inositol lipid specific phospholipase C enzymes have been found in both the soluble and plasma membrane fractions of the cell. Membrane-bound phospholipase C has been purified after detergent solubilization from brain, with a molecular mass of 150–154 kDa (56, 63), while 100-kDa and 62-kDa enzymes have been purified from platelets (5) and uterus (8), respectively. Generally, these enzymes will hydrolyse phosphatidylinositol (PI), phosphatidylinositol4-phosphate (PIP), and PIP_2 at high Ca^{2+} concentrations, but are more active towards PIP and PIP_2 at Ca^{2+} concentrations below 10 μM. Forms of phospholipase C apparently specific for PI and not for polyphosphoinositides have also been recognized (65). A cDNA encoding a 148-kDa phosphatidylinositol-specific phospholipase C from brain has been cloned (97). The major effect of activated G protein on PIP_2-specific phospholipase C activity is to decrease the Ca^{2+} concentration required for enzyme activity to the physiological level of about 0.1 μM (91, 100).

Regulation of Ins 1,4,5-P_3 Production and Metabolism

In the intact cell, Ins 1,4,5-P_3 is formed together with small amounts of the 1,2 cyclic isomer only by phospholipase C–mediated hydrolysis of PIP_2 (see

64 for a review). The amount of PIP_2 that is available for hydrolysis is only sufficient to maintain Ins $1,4,5-P_3$ production for a few minutes. However, this hormone-sensitive PIP_2 pool is rapidly replenished from part of the much larger PI pool by the action of PI and PIP kinases (42, 113). These enzymes exist in multiple forms, and there is evidence that some types are activated by tyrosine kinases (111). The large PI pool and the high activity of the enzymes synthesizing PIP_2 mitigates against regulation of Ins $1,4,5-P_3$ production by substrate availability.

The production of Ins $1,4,5-P_3$ is subject to several kinds of feedback regulation. A rapid inhibition of agonist-induced Ins $1,4,5-P_3$ production and Ca^{2+} signaling is observed in many cell types by phorbol ester–induced activation of protein kinase C (for reviews see 9, 57, 113). Some receptors, notably α_1-adrenergic and EGF receptors, are phosphorylated by protein kinase C. This decreases agonist binding and prevents agonist-mediated signal transduction to the G proteins (see 89 for a review). An additional postreceptor site for protein kinase C–mediated interaction is suggested from studies with plasma membrane preparations. Pretreatment with phorbol ester had no effect on agonist binding affinity or the suppression of high affinity agonist binding by GTP analogues (92), but it did inhibit GTPγS-stimulated hydrolysis of PIP_2, which indicates that the site of postreceptor interaction is the G protein–phospholipase C complex (75, 92). Although several G protein α-subunits (notably $G_i\alpha_{41}$) have been shown to be phosphorylated by protein kinase C (23, 54), clear evidence for the phosphorylation of an α-subunit functionally coupled to phospholipase C is presently lacking.

Ins $1,4,5-P_3$ is rapidly metabolized to products that do not release Ca^{2+} from intracellular stores. Recent studies have shown that Ins $1,4,5-P_3$ is both dephosphorylated and further phosphorylated (reviewed in 64). Ins $1,4,5-P_3$ is degraded to Ins $1,4-P_2$ by both membrane-bound and soluble 5-phosphomonoesterases with K_m values of 3–18 μM (40) and is also metabolized by a calmodulin-dependent 3-kinase to Ins $1,3,4,5-P_4$. The purified rat brain 3-kinase has a K_m for Ins $1,4,5-P_3$ of 0.2–0.4 μM (48). Since the concentration of Ins $1,4,5-P_3$ in resting cells is about 0.1 μM and increases to 1–2 μM during agonist stimulation (99), the low K_m of the Ins $1,4,5-P_3$-kinase favors the formation of Ins $1,3,4,5-P_4$.

The accumulation of Ins $1,4,5-P_3$ in cells after agonist stimulation is typically biphasic, with a peak increase occurring within 10–15 s, whereas PIP_2 hydrolysis is maintained for several minutes (18). Two feedback effects increase the rate of Ins $1,4,5-P_3$ metabolism. The increased cytosolic free Ca^{2+} caused by Ins $1,4,5-P_3$-induced intracellular Ca^{2+} release promotes the formation of Ins $1,3,4,5-P_4$ by Ca^{2+} activation of the calmodulin-dependent Ins $1,4,5-P_3$ 3-kinase (10, 48, 83), while the 5-phosphomonoesterase has been shown to be activated by protein kinase C (22). However, the latter effect may not occur in the intact cell since inhibition of protein kinase C in platelets by staurosporine had no effect on thrombin-induced increases of inositol phosphates (110).

INTRACELLULAR Ca^{2+} MOBILIZATION

The Hormone-Sensitive Ca^{2+} Pool

Recent evaluations of the tissue distribution of total Ca^{2+} between the cytosol and the different organelles have led to the conclusion that the bulk of the sequestered Ca^{2+} is in endoplasmic reticular structures (11, 17). It is also generally accepted that this pool represents the source of the Ca^{2+} released by Ca^{2+} mobilizing agonists. The addition of agonists to intact cells or of Ins 1,4,5-P_3 to permeabilized cells and isolated microsomal preparations only releases a fraction of the sequestered Ca^{2+}, which indicates heterogeneity of the Ca^{2+} pools (9). Recent studies have, in fact, suggested that a morphologically discrete organelle termed the calciosome, which generally copurifies with endoplasmic reticulum membranes, may represent the source of hormone releasable Ca^{2+} (106). In some cells, such as smooth muscle and Limulus photoreceptors, the sites for Ca^{2+} release may be adjacent to the plasma membrane (2). In *Xenopus* oocytes, both shallow and deep injections of Ins 1,4,5-P_3 caused a local release of Ca^{2+}, which suggests that Ins 1,4,5-P_3-sensitive Ca^{2+} pools are distributed throughout the cell (15, 37). For most cell types, however, the distribution and morphology of Ins 1,4,5-P_3-sensitive Ca^{2+} pools have not been established. The mitochondria are not involved in Ins 1,4,5-P_3-mediated Ca^{2+} release, but respond to the increased cytosolic free Ca^{2+} by a net uptake of Ca^{2+} and an increase of the matrix free Ca^{2+} concentration with consequent activation of mitochondrial (e.g. α-ketogluturate dehydrogenase) dehydrogenases and respiration (27, 50).

Sequestration of Ca^{2+} by the endoplasmic reticulum occurs by an ATP-driven Ca^{2+} pump. A high affinity Ca^{2+}-ATPase with a molecular mass of 116-kDa and a K_m for Ca^{2+} of 0.1–0.2 μM has been purified from liver (95) and other tissues (17). This enzyme is biochemically, kinetically, and immunologically similar to that of skeletal muscle sarcoplasmic reticulum (25). In some cell types it is also calmodulin dependent (17). The rate of Ca^{2+} uptake into liver microsomes is inhibited by the intravesicular free Ca^{2+} concentration with an apparent K_i of 250–300 μM (13). The Ca^{2+} sequestered by the endoplasmic reticulum is in equilibrium between free and bound forms. It is of considerable interest that calsequestrin (the major Ca^{2+}-binding protein of sarcoplasmic reticulum, with a K_d for Ca^{2+} of 100 μM) or a similar protein has recently been detected in the endoplasmic reticulum of nonmuscle cells (25), including the calciosome (106). The total amount of Ca^{2+} binding protein in the vesicular compartments presumably provides a limit to the amount of Ca^{2+} that can be accumulated. The free Ca^{2+} concentration in the endoplasmic reticulum has not been measured directly, but is probably 2–3 orders of magnitude higher than that in the cytosol in order to provide a suitable electrochemical gradient for rapid Ca^{2+} efflux through the Ins 1,4,5-P_3-sensitive Ca^{2+} channel.

The endoplasmic reticulum Ca^{2+} pump of pancreatic acinar cells has been shown to be activated after hormonal stimulation with a twofold increase of V_{max} for Ca^{2+} uptake and a decrease of the K_d for Ca^{2+} from 0.26 to 0.09 μM (71). Evidence obtained with saponized platelets suggests that activation of protein kinase C may account for a similar stimulation of Ca^{2+} sequestration after thrombin addition (120). An activation of the Ca^{2+} pump by either a Ca^{2+}/calmodulin mechanism or by a protein kinase C–mediated phosophorylation may, therefore, augment the Ca^{2+} content of both Ins 1,4,5-P_3 sensitive and insensitive Ca^{2+} pools. Since activation of the Ca^{2+} pump by the protein kinase C mechanism could persist after the initial Ca^{2+} transient, the Ca^{2+} pools may be refilled from the extracellular Ca^{2+} pool without a simultaneous increase of the cytosolic free Ca^{2+}, as occurs when agonist is displaced from its receptor (51, 60, 67, 76).

Ins 1,4,5-P_3-Induced Ca^{2+} Release

The ability of Ins 1,4,5-P_3 to release Ca^{2+} from intracellular, nonmitochondrial, vesicular stores appears to be a ubiquitous property of cells. The amount of Ca^{2+} that can be released by Ins 1,4,5-P_3 is sufficient to raise the intracellular Ca^{2+} concentration to 200–500 μM (114). However, the increase of the cytosolic free Ca^{2+} is limited to about 1 μM because of the presence of a variety of Ca^{2+}-binding proteins in the cytosol (17). The Ca^{2+} buffering capacity in the cytosol of neutrophils, for instance, has been estimated to be 0.76 mM with an average dissociation constant of 0.55 μM (107). The peak increase of the cytosolic free Ca^{2+} occurs within a few seconds of its initiation. The formation of Ins 1,4,5-P_3 has been shown to occur prior to or simultaneously with the increase of cytosolic free Ca^{2+} after addition of agonists to intact cells (for reviews see 9, 133). It is important to note, however, that the density of certain receptor types in a given cell may be so high that agonist stimulation causes an accumulation of Ins 1,4,5-P_3 far in excess of the amount required for a maximal release of Ca^{2+}. Thus, the peak increase of Ins 1,4,5-P_3 accumulation occurs after the peak of the cytosolic free Ca^{2+} in vasopressin-stimulated hepatocytes (113), whereas in other cells (e.g. A431 carcinoma; 103), the accumulation of Ins 1,4,5-P_3 is more transitory and appears to correlate with a transient rise and fall of the cytosolic free Ca^{2+}. A lag of 100–200 ms before onset of the agonist-induced Ca^{2+} increase has been demonstrated using stopped-flow techniques in parotid acinar cells (66) and platelets (85). Measurement of Ca^{2+} changes in groups of single hepatocytes showed that individual cells responded to vasopressin or α_1-adrenergic stimulation only after a variable latent period of up to 45 s, which was diminished by higher agonist concentrations (69). These data are consistent with a requirement for the accumulation of a threshold concentration of a mediator in the signaling pathway, possibly determined by a variable density of receptors in each cell.

Investigations concerning the mechanism of Ins $1,4,5$-P_3-induced Ca^{2+} release have provided evidence in favor of a ligand-gated Ca^{2+} channel, with the charge imbalance associated with Ca^{2+} efflux from the vesicular pool compensated by an influx of K^+ through tetraethylammonium-sensitive K^+ channels (53, 72, 88). Further evidence for a Ca^{2+} channel rather than a cation exchange mechanism is provided by the temperature insensitivity of Ins $1,4,5$-P_3-activated Ca^{2+} efflux, as measured with permeabilized cells or microsomal fractions (19, 53, 94). More direct evidence for an Ins $1,4,5$-P_3-gated Ca^{2+} channel has been obtained from electrophysiological studies after incorporation of microsomal proteins into lipid bilayers at the tips of patch-clamped micropipettes (105). Studies with permeabilized basophilic leukemia cells, in which the rate of Ins $1,4,5$-P_3-mediated Ca^{2+} release was measured with fura-2, indicated that channel opening was sensitive to Ins $1,4,5$-P_3 at concentrations below 10 nM and was highly cooperative (68). Experiments with permeabilized cells have shown that the Ins $1,4,5$-P_3-mediated Ca^{2+} release does not become desensitized (80, 114).

The density and affinity of Ins $1,4,5$-P_3 binding sites have been characterized in membrane fractions derived from liver, adrenal cortex, macrophages, neutrophils, anterior pituitary, and brain (see references in 39, 119). Several reports indicate that plasma membrane–enriched fractions of liver (39) and platelets (82) contain a higher density of Ins $1,4,5$-P_3 binding sites than fractions derived from the endoplasmic reticulum. These findings are consistent with the proposal that Ins $1,4,5$-P_3 binding and Ca^{2+} release occur in specialized organelles (calciosomes) that are not physically or functionally part of either the plasma or endoplasmic reticular membranes. The ability of different inositol phosphates to displace radiolabeled Ins $1,4,5$-P_3 from these binding sites is similar to their relative potency in causing Ca^{2+} release, namely Ins $1,4,5$-P_3 > Ins. $2,4,5$-P_3 > Ins $4,5$-P_2 > Ins $1,4$-P_2, Ins P_5, Ins P_6. Other inositol phosphates such as Ins $1,3,4$-P_3 and Ins $1,3,4,5$-P_4 were 1–5% as effective as Ins $1,4,5$-P_3 in causing displacement of bound Ins $1,4,5$-P_3. The number of binding sites for Ins $1,4,5$-P_3 is higher in cerebellum compared with other parts of the brain (118) and is about 100 times greater than that observed in peripheral tissues. In addition, the half maximum binding affinity (40–80 nM) in cerebellar membranes (119) is lower than values of 1–10 nM reported in other tissues (39). The discrepancy between these low values for half maximum Ins $1,4,5$-P_3 binding and the half maximum concentration of Ins 1,4,5-P_3 (0.1–2 μM) required to release Ca^{2+} from permeabilized cells or isolated microsomes (9) has not been resolved.

The Ins 1,4,5-P_3 receptor has recently been purified from rat cerebellum using a heparin affinity column (98). This solubilized membrane protein was shown to have a molecular mass of 260 kDa by SDS-PAGE and to bind Ins 1,4,5-P_3 with a K_d of 100 nM at pH 8.3. In contrast to studies with cerebellar membrane fractions where Ca^{2+} was shown to inhibit Ins 1,4,5-P_3 binding with a half maximal effect at 300 nM (119), the binding of Ins 1,4,5-P_3 to the purified receptor was unaffected by Ca^{2+} (98). The Ca^{2+} sensitivity is apparently conferred by a separate protein present in solubilized brain membranes that has an estimated M_r of 300,000 by gel filtration (26). The effect of Ca^{2+} in cerebellar membranes is to decrease the affinity of Ins 1,4,5-P_3 binding to the receptor (51a). An increase of extravesicular Ca^{2+} in the range from 1–10 μM has been shown to inhibit Ins 1,4,5-P_3-induced Ca^{2+} release in permeabilized neuronal cells and microsomes (19, 47). In studies with cerebellar microsomes, the concentration of Ca^{2+} required for inhibition was lower at suboptimal Ins 1,4,5-P_3 concentrations (51a). Feedback inhibition by Ca^{2+} to decrease the affinity of Ins 1,4,5-P_3 binding to the receptor might provide a mechanism for generating oscillations in cytosolic Ca^{2+} concentration without changing Ins 1,4,5-P_3 concentration.

Ca^{2+} Efflux from the Cell

An early event following stimulation of cells by Ca^{2+} mobilizing agonists is an increased efflux of Ca^{2+}, with a consequent fall in the total cellular Ca^{2+} content (29, 81, 112) Evidence with hepatocytes has indicated that the onset of net Ca^{2+} efflux is delayed by 5–10 s after agonist addition, which indicates that there is an initial inhibition of the plasma membrane Ca^{2+} efflux pump (52). Subsequently, however, this inhibition is overcome so that Ca^{2+} efflux is stimulated above the resting rate. This can be attributed partly to the Ins 1,4,5-P_3-induced increase of cytosolic free Ca^{2+}, which stimulates the calmodulin-dependent plasma membrane Ca^{2+}-ATPase and the electrogenic Na^+-Ca^{2+} exchanger. The latter system is present in the plasma membrane of many cells (6), and removal of extracellular Na^+ has been shown to inhibit agonist-stimulated Ca^{2+} efflux in some cells, such as arterial smooth muscle (93), but not in others, such as platelets (84). However, efflux of Ca^{2+} by the Ca^{2+}-ATPase probably predominates in most cells. A net loss of Ca^{2+} from the cell occurs over the first few minutes until there is a balance between the rate of Ca^{2+} efflux and the agonist-stimulated rate of Ca^{2+} influx.

The Ca^{2+} efflux rate is not solely dependent on the cytosolic free Ca^{2+} concentration since the rate of exchange of CA^{2+} across the plasma membrane is increased two to fourfold during the sustained phase of the Ca^{2+} transient when the cytosolic free Ca^{2+} is only slightly elevated above control levels (81). Studies in a variety of cells have indicated that activation of protein kinase C by phorbol esters stimulates Ca^{2+} efflux (28, 84). The mechanism of this effect has been investigated by studies with the erythrocyte Ca^{2+}-ATPase, which showed that calmodulin increased the V_{max} 14-fold, with a 4-fold decrease of the K_m to 0.3 μM, while addition of activated protein kinase C independently increased the V_{max} 5 to 7 fold without changing the K_m (90). A prolonged, Ca^{2+}-independent activation of the Ca^{2+}-ATPase by protein kinase C may thus account for the higher Ca^{2+} efflux rate compared with control cells. This dual regulation of the Ca^{2+}-ATPase by Ca^{2+}/calmodulin and by protein kinase C, together with different contributions of the Na^{+}-Ca^{2+} exchanger to Ca^{2+} efflux probably accounts for the many differences in the relative duration and shape of the Ca^{2+} transient observed upon addition of different agonists to various cell types.

EXTRACELLULAR Ca^{2+} MOBILIZATION

A sustained hormonal response requires an influx of extracellular Ca^{2+} to maintain an elevated cytosolic free Ca^{2+} concentration. Evidence for an agonist-dependent stimulation of Ca^{2+} influx is based on the dependence of the sustained phase upon extracellular Ca^{2+} and an increase of unidirectional $^{45}Ca^{2+}$ influx (81, 112). The temporal relationship between intracellular Ca^{2+} release and stimulated influx appears cell specific since rapid kinetic measurements show that the onset of stimulated Ca^{2+} influx occurs at least as rapidly as intracellular Ca^{2+} release in parotid cells (66) and platelets (85), whereas in A10 smooth muscle cells (69) and GH_3 pituitary cells (1), stimulated Ca^{2+} influx occurs after the transient intracellular Ca^{2+} release.

The 10,000-fold concentration gradient of Ca^{2+} across the plasma membrane requires strict regulation of its permeability to Ca^{2+}. Several types of voltage-sensitive Ca^{2+} channels that open upon membrane depolarization have been well characterized (104), and in some secretory cells, notably GH_3 pituitary (1) and adrenal glomerulosa cells (60), Ca^{2+} entry by voltage-sensitive Ca^{2+} channels may contribute toward the sustained phase of the agonist-induced Ca^{2+} transient. However, membrane depolarization is not obligatory for the response of most cells to Ca^{2+} mobilizing agonists and a hyperpolarization may be observed due to a secondary Ca^{2+} activation of K^{+} and Cl^{-} channels (e.g. 30). Alternatively, agonist-induced Ca^{2+} entry is considered to be regulated by a process usually referred to as a receptor-operated Ca^{2+} channel, which is inhibited by agents that block voltage-sensitive Ca^{2+} channels at only very high concentrations (51, 67). In fact, several types of mechanisms may mediate activation of Ca^{2+} channels by receptor occupation. One is by direct ligand activation, which appears to occur with the ATP-activated high conductance cation channel in smooth muscle (7). Another is by receptor-activated G proteins, which have been demonstrated to regulate several types of K^+ and Ca^{2+} channels in a variety of cells (reviewed in 14). Evidence consistent with a role for a G protein in activating receptor-operated Ca^{2+} channels is suggested from the observations that pretreatment with pertussis toxin inhibited Ca^{2+} influx induced by vasopressin in hepatocytes (43) and by angiotensin II in adrenal glomerulosa cells (59), but did not affect intracellular Ca^{2+} mobilization. A nonselective cation channel activated by a rise of cytosolic free Ca^{2+} has been reported (78, 108), but in most cells the onset of Ca^{2+} influx does not lag behind intracellular Ca^{2+} mobilization. Stimulated Ca^{2+} influx persists after the initial Ca^{2+} transient and is dependent on receptor occupancy rather than on the cytosolic free Ca^{2+} concentration (43, 51, 67, 76).

An attractive possibility that has generated considerable attention is that Ins 1,4,5-P_3 itself or one of its metabolic products may be responsible for agonist-stimulated Ca^{2+} influx. Ins 1,4,5-P_3-induced Ca^{2+} release has been demonstrated in Na^+-loaded plasma membrane vesicles from platelets (82). Mitogenic stimulation of T-lymphocytes has been shown to be associated with activation of a low conductance voltage-independent Ca^{2+} channel in the cell attached patch, which could be directly activated by Ins 1,4,5-P_3 after excision of the patch (62). An involvement of Ins 1,3,4,5-P_4 in mediating Ca^{2+} influx was suggested from microinjection experiments with sea urchin eggs (45 but also see 22a). Ins 1,3,4,5-P_4 injection alone produced no activation, but required the coinjection of Ins 2,4,5-P_3 to induce intracellular Ca^{2+} release. Unlike injection of Ins 1,4,5-P_3, injection of Ins 2,4,5-P_3 alone produced no response, and since it is a poor substrate for further phosphorylation by the inositol phosphate 3-kinase, it was hypothesized that Ins 1,3,4,5-P_4-induced Ca^{2+} entry required a depleted Ins 1,4,5-P_3-sensitive Ca^{2+} pool. Experiments with *Xenopus* oocytes showed that injection of Ins 1,3,4,5-P_4 activated a voltage-sensitive Ca^{2+} channel, particularly after a "priming" injection of Ins 1,4,5-P_3 (77). Measurements of whole-cell current with voltage-clamped lacrimal acinar cells (70), where acetylcholine in the presence of extracellular Ca^{2+} evokes a sustained hyperpolarization of the plasma membrane by increasing an outward Ca^{2+}-activated K^+ current, showed that the sustained response required the presence of both Ins 1,4,5-P_3 and Ins 1,3,4,5-P_4 as well as extracellular Ca^{2+}. In other studies, an inward current due to nonspecific cation channels was evoked by injection of Ins 1,3,4,5-P_4 or Ins 1,3,4-P_3 into NG108-15 neuronal cells, but unlike Ins 1,4,5-P_3 injection, these compounds failed to elicit the outward Ca^{2+}-activated K^+ current (41). In contrast, studies with NIE-115 neuronal cells showed that injection of Ins 1,3,4-P_3, but not Ins 1,3,4,5-P_4, produced a membrane depolarization in 50% of the cells tested (101).

In summary, it must be concluded that there is insufficient evidence to deduce the mechanism for receptor-dependent Ca^{2+} entry into cells, although it is likely that different mechanisms predominate in different cell types. Whether Ins 1,3,4,5-P_4 or another inositol phosphate are involved remains an open question. Specific Ins 1,3,4,5-P_4 binding sites have been demonstrated in membranes of several tissues that are distinct from Ins 1,4,5-P_3 binding sites, but their function has not yet been ascertained (12, 102).

OSCILLATIONS IN CYTOSOLIC FREE Ca^{2+}

In contrast to the many studies with bulk cell suspensions, where agonist-induced Ca^{2+} transients are typically biphasic, the development of methods for measuring changes of Ca^{2+} in single cells has revealed that the response may be oscillatory. Measurements with the bioluminescent protein aequorin in single hepatocytes stimulated with agonist showed a series of periodic increases in cytosolic free Ca^{2+} to about 600 nM, each returning to resting levels within 7 s (115, 116). The frequency of these oscillations was a function of phenylephrine concentration, with a period varying from 20–240 s. Low concentrations of vasopressin and angiotensin II caused similar oscillations, which suggests that the occurrence of Ca^{2+} oscillations is favored when tissue Ins 1,4,5-P_3 concentrations are low (cf 113). In contrast, fura-2 loaded hepatocytes rarely exhibit Ca^{2+} oscillations after addition of agonists (69). However, in other cell types, oscillations of the cytosolic free Ca^{2+} in a proportion of cells have been observed using fura-2 as the Ca^{2+} indicator. For example, BC3H-1 cells stimulated with phenylephrine exhibited a burst of Ca^{2+} spikes that ceased after several minutes (3), and macrophages induced to spread onto a suitable substratum (frustrated phagocytosis) showed similar oscillations (61). In general, measurements of Ca^{2+} with fura-2 show a more transient, irregular pattern of Ca^{2+} fluctuations than those obtained with aequorin and with a smaller proportion of cells generating oscillations.

The difference between the data obtained with aequorin and fura-2, even in the same cell type, suggest that they may arise from the different properties of the Ca^{2+} indicators. Since fura-2 is a Ca^{2+} chelator, it is possible that it diminishes the peak rise of the Ca^{2+} transients, which may be part of a negative feedback interaction responsible for generating the oscillations. On the other hand, the nonlinear relationship between aequorin bioluminescence and Ca^{2+} concentration may amplify spatially localized oscillations of Ca^{2+}. It is interesting to note, however, that sustained Ca^{2+} oscillations have been observed in oocytes after fertilization using either Ca^{2+} selective microelectrodes (44) or aequorin to measure the Ca^{2+} changes (24).

Indirect evidence for oscillations of the cytosolic free Ca^{2+} in response to Ca^{2+} mobilizing hormones has been obtained from electrophysiological measurements of the oscillatory behavior of Ca^{2+}-activated K^+ and Cl^- channels. In HeLa cells, histamine stimulated a pattern of Ca^{2+}-dependent channel activation characterized by a series of bursts separated by silent periods, which correlated with membrane potential oscillations and occurred in the absence of extracellular Ca^{2+} (86). Similarly, α_1-adrenergic stimulation of voltage clamped guinea pig hepatocytes induced oscillatory membrane conductance increases to K^+ and Cl^-, which were attributed to Ca^{2+} activated K^+ and Cl^- channels (16). A close correlation between oscillatory Ca^{2+}-activated K^+ channel activity and intracellular Ca^{2+} has been reported in hamster oocytes (44).

Mechanisms for generation of Ca^{2+} oscillations appear to fall into two categories: oscillations that occur secondary to spontaneous action potentials as in some secretory cells (87) and oscillations induced by Ca^{2+}-mobilizing hormones. The latter can be initiated in the absence of extracellular Ca^{2+}; thus, intracellular Ca^{2+} release is the primary source of Ca^{2+} although extracellular Ca^{2+} is required for maintenance of Ca^{2+} oscillations (3, 16, 61, 86). A minimum oscillating system requires a feedback loop, and for sustained oscillations some delay step is necessary to generate the periodicity (34). Theoretically, oscillations in Ins $1,4,5$-P_3 concentration could be produced by a negative feedback effect on the receptor or the G protein coupled to activation of phospholipase C by protein kinase C. The delay step could be caused by a slow rate of activation of the G protein or of protein kinase C by diacylglycerol. This mechanism was proposed to explain variations in the shape of the individual aequorin spikes seen in liver with different agonists (20). However, such a mechanism involving a periodically activated protein kinase C is difficult to reconcile with the decrease in the frequency of the Ca^{2+} oscillations observed by addition of exogenous diacylglycerol or phorbol ester to hepatocytes (117). Furthermore, in guinea pig hepatocytes, oscillations in Ca^{2+}-dependent ion conductances could be induced by injection of Ins $1,4,5$-P_3, which suggests that changes in the Ins $1,4,5$-P_3 concentration are not required (16). As suggested earlier, a possible mechanism for negative feedback is provided by the inhibitory effect of Ca^{2+} on Ins $1,4,5$-P_3 binding to its receptor, while the time required for reaccumulation of Ca^{2+} into the Ins $1,4,5$-P_2-sensitive pool could provide the delay to generate a characteristic periodicity.

SUMMARY

The involvement of inositol lipid metabolism in agonist-mediated Ca^{2+} signaling by Ins $1,4,5$-P_3 has become firmly established. Recent advances have led to a better understanding of the proteins associated with signal transduction in the plasma membrane. A number of specific receptors (G proteins, phospholipases and inositol lipid kinases) have now been purified and characterized. An Ins 1,4,5-P_3 receptor has also been purified which is presumably involved in mediating Ca^{2+} efflux from intracellular stores. The morphological site of the hormone-sensitive Ca^{2+} pool has been tentatively identified as discrete, specialized intracellular structures (calciosomes), but further studies are required to demonstrate that these contain Ins 1,4, 5-P_3-gated Ca^{2+} channels and their possible functional relationship to the plasma membrane. Receptor occupancy by Ca^{2+} mobilizing agonists also stimulates Ca^{2+} entry into the cell, but the mechanism for activation of voltage insensitive Ca^{2+} channels and the possible involvement of Ins 1, 4,5-P_3, Ins 1,3,4,5-P_4 and/or G proteins in this process has not been established.

The Ca^{2+} signaling pathway is subject to multisite feedback regulation by Ca^{2+} itself and by a diacylglycerol-mediated activation of protein kinase C. Potential sites for Ca^{2+} interaction are displacement of Ins 1,4,5-P_3 from its receptor by a Ca^{2+}-dependent mechanism, promotion of Ins 1,3,4,5-P_4 formation by the Ca^{2+}/calmodulin-regulated Ins 1,4,5-P_3 3-kinase, and efflux of Ca^{2+} from the cell or sequestration into intracellular Ca^{2+} stores by Ca^{2+}/calmodulin-regulated Ca^{2+}-ATPases. Protein kinase C activation potentially affects the rate of generation of Ins 1,4,5-P_3 by negative feedback to the receptor–G protein–phospholipase C transduction system and possibly also the rate of Ins 1,4,5-P_3 degradation by activation of an inositol polyphosphate 5-phosphomonoesterase. It may also attenuate the Ca^{2+} transient directly by increasing the activity of Ca^{2+}-ATPases associated with the plasma membrane and the endoplasmic reticulum. Cell-to-cell heterogeneity in the relative control strengths of these different mechanisms may explain the differences in the Ca^{2+} signal in different tissues and even in different cells within a population. The ability of Ca^{2+} and protein kinase C to provide negative feedback at various points in the signal transduction pathway suggests that a complex mechanism involving multiple feedback loops is likely to regulate the generation of Ca^{2+} oscillations seen in some cells. The precise interactions between these feedback mechanisms and the crosstalk with other intracellular signaling pathways enables each cell to respond with an appropriate and unique response.

ACKNOWLEDGMENTS

This work was supported by grants from the National Institutes of Health (DK-15120 and HL-14461) and from the Juvenile Diabetes Foundation.

120　　WILLIAMSON & MONCK

Literature Cited

1. Albert, P. R., Tashjian, A. H., 1984. Relationship of thyrotropin-releasing hormone-induced spike and plateau phases in cytosolic free Ca^{2+} concentrations to hormone secretion. *J. Biol. Chem.* 259:15350–63
2. Alkon, D. L., Rasmussen, H. 1988. A spatial-temporal model of cell activation. *Science* 239:998–1005
3. Ambler, S. K., Poenie, M., Tsien, R. Y., Taylor, P. 1988. Agonist-stimulated oscillations and cycling of intracellular free calcium in individual cultured muscle cells. *J. Biol. Chem.* 263:1952–59
4. Banno, Y., Nagao, S., Katada, T., Nagata, K., Ui, M., et al. 1987. Stimulation by GTP-binding proteins (G_i, G_o) of partially purified phospholipase C activity from human platelet membranes. *Biochem. Biophys. Res. Commun.* 146:861–69
5. Banno, Y., Nozawa, Y. 1987. Characterization of partially purified phospholipase C from human platelet membranes. *Biochem. J.* 248:95–101
6. Bayerdöffer, E., Haase, W., Schulz, I. 1985. Na^+/Ca^{2+} countertransport in plasma membrane of rat pancreatic acinar cells. *J. Membr. Biol.* 87:107–19
7. Benham, C. D., Tsien, R. W. 1987. A novel receptor-operated Ca^{2+}-permeable channel activated by ATP in smooth muscle. *Nature* 328:275–78
8. Bennett, C. F., Crooke, S. T. 1987. Purification and characterization of a phosphoinositide-specific phospholipase C from guinea pig uterus. *J. Biol. Chem.* 262:13789–97
9. Berridge, M. J. 1987. Inositol trisphosphate and diacylglycerol: two interacting second messengers. *Annu. Rev. Biochem.* 56:159–93
10. Biden, T. J., Comte, M., Cox, J. A., Wollheim, C. B. 1987. Calcium-calmodulin stimulates inositol 1,4,5-trisphosphate kinase activity from insulin-secreting RINm5F cells. *J. Biol. Chem.* 262:9437–40
11. Bond, M., Vadasz, G., Somlyo, A. V., Somlyo, A. P. 1987. Subcellular calcium and magnesium mobilization in rat liver stimulated *in vivo* with vasopressin and glucagon. *J. Biol. Chem.* 262:15630–36
12. Bradford, P. G., Irvine, R. F. 1987. Specific binding sites for [^{3}H]inositol(1,3,4,5)tetrakisphosphate on membranes of HL-60 cells. *Biochem. Biophys. Res. Commun.* 149:680–85
13. Brattin, W. J., Waller, R. L. 1983. Calcium inhibition of rat liver microsomal calcium-dependent ATPase. *J. Biol. Chem.* 258:6724–79
14. Brown, A. M., Birnbaumer, L. 1988. Direct G-protein gating of ion channels. *Am. J. Physiol.* 254:H401–10
15. Busa, W. B., Ferguson, J. E., Joseph, S. K., Williamson, J. R., Nuccitelli, R. 1985. Activation of frog *(Xenopus laevis)* eggs by inositol trisphosphate. I. Characterization of Ca^{2+} release from intracellular stores. *J. Cell. Biol.* 101:677–82
16. Capiod, T., Field, A. C., Ogden, D. C., Sanford, C. A. 1987. Internal perfusion of guinea-pig hepatocytes with buffered Ca^{2+} or inositol 1,4,5-trisphosphate mimics noradrenaline activation of K^+ and Cl^- conductances. *FEBS Lett.* 217:247–52
17. Carafoli, E. 1987. Intracellular calcium homeostasis. *Annu. Rev. Biochem.* 56:395–433
18. Chahwala, S. B., Fleischman, L. F., Cantley, L. 1987. Kinetic analysis of guinosine 5'-O-(3-thiotriphosphate effects on phosphatidylinositol turnover in NRK cell homogenates. *Biochemistry* 26:612–22
19. Cheuh, S. H., Gill, D. L. 1986. Inositol 1,4,5-trisphosphate and guanine nucleotides activate calcium release from endoplasmic reticulum via distinct mechanisms. *J. Biol. Chem.* 261:13883–86
20. Cobbold, P., Cuthbertson, R., Woods, N. 1988. The generation of repetitive free calcium transients in a hormone-stimulated hepatocyte. In *Hormones and Cell Regulation, Proc. 12th Eur. Symp,* ed. J. Libbey. In press
21. Cockcroft, S. 1987. Polyphosphoinositide phosphodiesterase: regulation by a novel guanine nucleotide binding protein, G_p. *Trends Biochem. Sci.* 12:75–78
22. Connolly, T. M., Lawing, W. J., Majerus, P. W. 1986. Protein kinase C phosphorylates human platelet inositol trisphosphate 5'-phosphomonoesterase, increasing the phosphatase activity. *Cell* 46:951–58
22a. Crossley, I., Swann, K., Chambers, E., Whitaker, M. 1988. Activation of sea urchin eggs by inositol phosphates is independent of external calcium. *Biochem. J.* 252:257–62
23. Crouch, M. F., Lapetina, E. G. 1988. A role for G_i in control of thrombin recep-

tor-phospholipase C coupling in human platelets. *J. Biol. Chem.* 263:3363–71

24. Cuthbertson, K. S. R., Cobbold, P. H. 1985. Phorbol ester and sperm activate mouse oocytes by inducing sustained oscillations in cell Ca^{2+}. *Nature* 316:541–42

25. Damiani, E., Spamer, C., Heilmann, C., Salvatori, S., Margreth, A. 1988. Endoplasmic reticulum of rat liver contains two proteins closely related to skeletal sarcoplasmic reticulum Ca-ATPase and calsequestrin. *J. Biol. Chem.* 263:340–43

26. Danoff, S. K., Supattapone, S., Synder, S. H. 1988. Characterization of a membrane protein from brain mediating the inhibition of inositol 1,4,5-trisphosphate receptor by calcium. *Biochem. J.* In press

27. Denton, R. M. 1985. Ca^{2+} transport by mammalian mitochondria and its role in hormone action. *Am. J. Physiol.* 249:E543–54

28. Drummond, A. H. 1985. Bidirectional control of cytosolic free calcium by thyroptropin-releasing hormone in pituitary cells. *Nature* 315:752–55

29. Exton, J. H. 1988. Role of phosphoinositides in the regulation of liver function. *Hepatology* 8:152–66

30. Field, A. C., Jenkinson, D. H. 1987. The effect of noradrenaline on the ion permeability of isolated mammalian hepatocytes, studied by intracellular recording. *J. Physiol.* 392:493–512

31. Fishman, J. B., Dickey, B. F., Fine, R. E. 1987. Purification and characterization of the rat liver vasopressin (V1) receptor. *J. Biol. Chem.* 262:14049–55

32. Fitzgerald, T. J., Uhing, R. J., Exton, J. H. 1986. Solubilization of the vasopressin receptor from rat liver plasma membranes. *J. Biol. Chem.* 261:16871–77

33. Fong, H. K. W., Yoshimoto, K. K., Eversole-Cire, P., Simon, M. I. 1988. Identification of a GTP-binding protein α-subunit that lacks an apparent ADP-ribosylation site for pertussis toxin. *Proc. Natl. Acad. Sci. USA* 85:3066–70

34. Friesen, W. O., Block, G. D. 1984. What is a biological oscillator? *Am. J. Physiol.* 246:R847–51

35. Gierschik, P., Jakobs, K. H. 1987. Receptor-mediated ADP-ribosylation of a phospholipase C-stimulating G protein. *FEBS Lett.* 224:219–23

36. Gierschik, P., Sidiropoulos, D., Spiegel, A., Jakobs, K. H. 1987. Purification and immunochemical characterization of the major pertussis-toxin-sensitive guanine-nucleotide-binding protein of bovine-neutrophil membranes. *Eur. J. Biochem.* 165:185–94

37. Gillo, B., Lass, Y., Nadler, E., Oron, Y. 1987. The involvement of inositol 1,4,5-trisphosphate and calcium in the two-component response to acetylcholine in *Xenopus* oocytes. *J. Physiol.* 392:349–61

38. Gilman, A. G. 1987. G-proteins: transducers of receptor-genetated signals. *Annu. Rev. Biochem.* 56:615–49

39. Guillemette, G., Balla, T., Baukal, A. J., Catt, K. J. 1988. Characterization of inositol 1,4,5-trisphosphate receptors and calcium mobilization in a hepatic plasma membrane fraction. *J. Biol. Chem.* 263:4541–48

40. Hansen, C. A., Johanson, R. A., Williamson, M. T., Williamson, J. R. 1987. Purification and characterization of two types of soluble inositol phosphate 5-phosphomonoesterases from rat brain. *J. Biol. Chem.* 262:17319–26

41. Higashida, H., Brown, D. A. 1986. Membrane current responses to intracellular injections of inositol 1,3,4,5-tetrakisphosphate and inositol 1,3,4-trisphosphate in NG108-15 hybrid cells. *FEBS Lett.* 208:283–86

42. Hokin, L. E. 1985. Receptors and phosphoinositide-generated second messengers. *Annu. Rev. Biochem.* 54:205–35

43. Hughes, B. P., Crofts, J. N., Auld, A. M., Read, L. C., Barritt, G. J. 1987. Evidence that a pertussis-toxin-sensitive substrate is involved in the stimulation by epidermal growth factor and vasopressin of plasma-membrane Ca^{2+} inflow in hepatocytes. *Biochem. J.* 248: 911–18

44. Igusa, Y., Miyazaki, S.-I. 1986. Periodic increase of cytoplasmic free calcium in fertilized hamster eggs measured with calcium-sensitive electrodes. *J. Physiol.* 377:193–205

45. Irvine, R. F., Moor, R. M. 1986. Micro-injection of inositol 1,3,4,5-tetrakisphosphate activates sea urchin eggs by a mechanism dependent on external Ca^{2+}. *Biochem. J.* 240:917–20

46. Itoh, H., Katada, T., Ui, M., Kawasaki, H., Suzuki, K., et al. 1988. Identification of three pertussis toxin substrates (41, 40 and 39 kDa proteins) in mammalian brain. *FEBS Lett.* 230:85–89

47. Jean, T., Klee, C. B. Calcium modulation of inositol 1,4,5-trisphosphate-induced calcium release from neuroblastoma x glioma hybrid (NG108-15) microsomes. *J. Biol. Chem.* 261:16414–20

48. Johanson, R. A., Hansen, C. A., Williamson, J. R. 1988. Purification of D-*myo*-inositol 1,4,5-trisphosphate 3-ki-

nase from rat brain. *J. Biol. Chem.* 263:7465–71

49. Johnson, J. D., Garrison, J. C. 1987. Epidermal growth factor and angiotensin II stimulates formation of inositol 1,4,5- and inositol 1,3,4-trisphosphate in hepatocytes. *J. Biol. Chem.* 262:17285–93

50. Johnston, J. D., Brand, M. D. 1987. Stimulation of the respiration rate of rat liver mitochondria by sub-micromolar concentrations of extramitochondrial Ca^{2+}. *Biochem. J.* 245:217–22

51. Joseph, S. K., Coll, K. E., Thomas, A. P., Rubin, R., Williamson, J. R. 1985. The role of extracellular Ca^{2+} in the response of the hepatocyte to Ca^{2+}-dependent hormones. *J. Biol. Chem.* 260:12508–15

51a. Joseph, S. K., Rice, H. L., Williamson, J. R. 1988. The effect of external calcium and pH on inositol trisphosphate-mediated calcium release from cerebellum microsomes. *Biochem. J.* In press

52. Joseph, S. K., Williamson, J. R. 1983. The origin, quantitation, and kinetics of intracellular calcium mobilization by vasopressin and phenylephrine in hepatocytes. *J. Biol. Chem.* 258:10425–32

53. Joseph, S. K., Williamson, J. R. 1986. Characteristics of inositol trisphosphate-mediated Ca^{2+} release from permeabilized hepatocytes. *J. Biol. Chem.* 261:14658–64

54. Katada, T., Gilman, A. G., Watanabe, Y., Bauer, S., Jakobs, K. H. 1985. Protein kinase C phosphorylates the inhibitory guanine-nucleotide-binding regulatory component and apparently suppresses its function in hormonal inhibition of adenylate cyclase. *Eur. J. Biochem.* 151:431–37

55. Katada, T., Oinuma, M., Kusakabe, K., Ui, M. 1987. A new GTP-binding protein in brain tissues serving as the specific substrate of islet-activating protein, pertussis toxin. *FEBS Lett.* 213:353–58

56. Katan, M., Parker, P. J. 1987. Purification of phosphoinositide-specific phospholipase C from a particulate fraction of bovine brain. *Eur. J. Biochem.* 168:413–18

57. Kikkawa, U., Nishizuka, Y. 1986. The role of protein kinkase C in transmembrane signalling. *Annu. Rev. Cell Biol.* 2:149–78

58. Kikuchi, A., Kozawa, O., Kaibuchi, I., Katada, K., Ui, M., et al. 1986. Direct evidence for involvement of a guanine nucleotide-binding protein in chemotactic peptide-stimulated formation of inositol bisphosphate and trisphosphate in

differentiated human leukemic (HL-60) cells. *J. Biol. Chem.* 261:11558–62

59. Kojima, I., Shibata, H., Ogata, E. 1986. Pertussis toxin blocks angiotensin II-induced calcium influx but not inositol trisphosphate production in adrenal glomerulosa cell. *FEBS Lett.* 204:347–51

60. Kojima, I., Shibata, H., Ogata, E. 1987. Time-dependent restoration of the trigger pool of calcium after termination of angiotensin II action in adrenal glomerulosa cells. *J. Biol. Chem.* 262:4557–63

61. Kruskal, B. A., Maxfield, F. R. 1987. Cytosolic free calcium increases before and oscillates during frustrated phagocytosis in macrophages. *J. Cell Biol.* 105:2685–93

62. Kuno, M., Gardner, P. 1987. Ion channels activated by inositol 1,4,5-trisphosphate in plasma membrane of human-T-lymphocytes. *Nature* 326:301–4

63. Lee, K. Y., Ryu, S. H., Suh, P. G., Choi, W. C., Rhee, S. G. 1987. Phospholipase C associated with particulate fractions of bovine brain. *Proc. Natl. Acad. Sci. USA* 84:5540–44

64. Majerus, P. W., Connolly, T. M., Bansal, V. S., Inhorn, R. C., Ross, T. S., et al. 1988. Inositol phosphates: synthesis and degradation. *J. Biol. Chem.* 263:3051–54

65. Manne, V. 1987. Indentification of polyphosphoinositide-specific phospholipase C and its resolution from phosphoinositide-specific phospholipase C from human platelet extract. *Oncogene* 2:49–54

66. Merritt, J. E., Rink, T. J. 1987. Rapid increases in cytosolic free calcium in response to muscarinic stimulation of rat parotid acinar cells. *J. Biol. Chem.* 262:4958–60

67. Merritt, J. E., Rink, T. J. 1987. Regulation of cytosolic free calcium in fura-2-loaded rat parotid acinar cells. *J. Biol. Chem.* 262:17362–69

68. Meyer, T., Holowka, D., Stryer, L. 1988. Highly cooperative opening of calcium channels by inositol 1,4,5-trisphosphate. *Science* 240:653–6

69. Monck, J. R., Reynolds, E. E., Thomas, A. P., Williamson, J. R. 1988. Novel kinetics of single cell Ca^{2+} transients in stimulated hepatocytes and A10 cells measured using fura-2 and video microscopy. *J. Biol. Chem.* 263:4569–75

70. Morris, A. P., Gallacher, D. V., Irvine, R. F., Peterson, O. H. 1987. Synergism of inositol trisphosphate and tetrakisphosphate in activating Ca^{2+}-dependent K^+ channels. *Nature* 330:653–55

71. Muallem, S., Beeker, T. G., Fimmel, C. J. 1987. Activation of the endoplasmic reticulum Ca^{2+} pump of pancreatic acini by Ca^{2+} mobilizing hormones. *Biochem. Biophys. Res. Commun.* 149:213–20

72. Muallem, S., Schoeffield, M., Pandol, S., Sachs, G. 1985. Inositol trisphosphate modification of ion transport in rough endoplasmic reticulum. *Proc. Natl. Acad. Sci. USA* 82:4433–37

73. Nishizuka, Y. 1986. Studies and perspectives of protein kinase C. *Science* 233:305–12

74. Oinuma, M., Katada, T., Ui, M. 1987. A new GTP-binding protein in differentiated human leukemic (HL-60) cells serving as the specific substrate of islet-activating protein, pertussis toxin. *J. Biol. Chem.* 262:8347–53

75. Orellana, S., Solski, P. A., Brown, J. H. 1987. Guanosine 5'-O- (thiotriphosphate)-dependent inositol trisphosphate formation in membranes is inhibited by phorbol ester and protein kinase C. *J. Biol. Chem.* 262:1638–43

76. Pandol, S. J., Schoeffield, M. S., Fimmel, C. J., Muallem, S. 1987. The agonist-sensitive calcium pool in the pancreatic acinar cell. *J. Biol. Chem.* 262:16963–68

77. Parker, I., Miledi, R. 1987. Injection of inositol 1,3,4,5-tetrakisphosphate into *Xenopus* oocytes generates a chloride current dependent upon intracellular calcium. *Proc. R. Soc. Lond. B* 232:59–70

78. Petersen, O. H., Maruyama, Y. 1983. What is the mechanism of the calcium influx to pancreatic acinar cells evoked by secretagogues? *Pflügers Arch.* 396:82–84

79. Polakis, P. G., Uhing, R. J., Snyderman, R. 1988. The formylpeptide chemoattractant receptor copurifies a GTP-binding protein containing a distinct 40-kDa pertussis toxin substrate. *J. Biol. Chem.* 263:4969–76

80. Prentki, M., Corkey, B. E., Matschinsky, F. M. 1985. Inositol 1,4,5-trisphosphate and the endoplasmic reticulum Ca^{2+} cycle of a rat insulinoma cell line. *J. Biol. Chem.* 260:9185–90

81. Rasmussen, H., Barrett, P. Q. 1984. Calcium messenger system: an integrated view. *Physiol. Rev.* 64:938–84

82. Rengasamy, A., Feinberg, H. 1988. Inositol 1,4,5-trisphosphate-induced calcium release from platelet plasma membrane vesicles. *Biochem. Biophys. Res. Commun.* 150:1021–26

83. Rhu, S. H., Lee, S. Y., Lee, K. Y., Rhee, S. G. 1987. Catalytic properties of inositol trisphosphate kinase: activation by Ca^{2+} and calmodulin. *FASEB J.* 1:388–93

84. Rink, T. J., Sage, S. O. 1987. Stimulated calcium efflux from fura-2-loaded human platelets. *J. Physiol.* 393:513–24

85. Sage, S. O., Rink, T. J. 1987. The kinetics of changes in intracellular calcium concentration in fura-2-loaded human platelets. *J. Biol. Chem.* 262:16364–69

86. Sauvé, R., Simoneau, C., Parent, L., Monette, R., Roy, G. 1987. Oscillatory activation of calcium-dependent potassium channels in HeLa cells induced by histamine H_1 receptor stimulation: a single-channel study. *J. Membr. Biol.* 96:199–208

87. Schlegel, W., Winiger, B. P., Mollard, P., Vacher, P., Wuarin, F., et al. Oscillations of cytosolic Ca^{2+} in pituitary cells due to action potentials. *Nature* 329:719–21

88. Shah, I., Pant, H. C. 1988. Potassium-channel blockers inhibit inositol trisphosphate-induced calcium release in the microsomal fractions isolated from the rat brain. *Biochem. J.* 250:617–20

89. Sibley, D. R., Benovic, J. L., Caron, M. G., Lefkowitz, R. J. 1987. Regulation of transmembrane signaling by receptor phosphorylation. *Cell* 48:913–22

90. Smallwood, J. I., Gügi, B., Rasmussen, H. 1988. Regulation of erythrocyte Ca^{2+} pump activity by protein kinase C. *J. Biol. Chem.* 263:2195–2202

91. Smith, C. D., Cox, C. C., Snyderman, R. 1986. Receptor-coupled activation of phosphoinositide-specific phospholipase C by an N protein. *Science* 232:97–100

92. Smith, C. D., Uhing, R. J., Snyderman, R. 1987. Nucleotide regulatory protein-mediated activation of phospholipase C in human polymorphonuclear leukocytes is disrupted by phorbol esters. *J. Biol. Chem.* 262:6121–27

93. Smith, J. B., Smith, L. 1987. Extracellular Na^+ dependence of changes in free Ca^{2+}, $^{45}Ca^{2+}$ efflux, and total cell Ca^{2+} produced by angiotensin II in cultured arterial muscle cells. *J. Biol. Chem.* 262:17455–60

94. Smith, J. B., Smith, L., Higgins, B. L. 1985. Temperature and nucleotide dependence of calcium release by *myo*-inositol 1,4,5-trisphosphate in cultured vascular smooth muscle cells. *J. Biol. Chem.* 260:14413–16

95. Spamer, C., Heilmann, C., Gerok, W. 1987. Ca^{2+}-activated ATPase in microsomes from human liver. *J. Biol. Chem.* 262:7782–89

96. Spiegel, A. M. 1987. Signal transduction by guanine nucleotide binding proteins. *Mol. Cell. Endocrinol.* 49:1–16

97. Stahl, M. L., Ferenz, C. R., Kelleher,

K. L., Kriz, R. W., Knopf, J. L. 1988. Sequence similarity of phospholipase C with the non-catalytic region of src. *Nature* 332:269–72

98. Supattapone, S., Worley, P. F., Baraban, J. M., Snyder, S. H. 1988. Solubilization, purification, and characterization of an inositol trisphosphate receptor. *J. Biol. Chem.* 263:1530–34

99. Tarver, A. P., King, W. G., Rittenhouse, S. E. 1987. Inositol 1,4,5-trisphosphate and inositol 1,2-cyclic 4,5-trisphosphate are minor components of total mass of inositol trisphosphate in thrombin-stimulated platelets. *J. Biol. Chem.* 262:17268–71

100. Taylor, S. J., Exton, J. H. 1987. Guanine-nucleotide and hormone regulation of polyphosphoinositide phospholipase C activity of rat liver plasma membranes. *Biochem. J.* 248:791–99

101. Tertoolen, L. G. J., Tilly, B. C., Irvine, R. F., Moolenaar, W. H. 1987. Electrophysiological responses to bradykinin and microinjected inositol polyphosphates in neuroblastoma cells. *FEBS Lett.* 214:365–69

102. Theibert, A. B., Supattapone, S., Worley, P. F., Baraban, J. M., Meek, J. L., et al. 1987. Demonstration of inositol 1,3,4,5,-tetrakisphosphate receptor binding. *Biochem. Biophys. Res. Commun.* 148:1283–89

103. Tilly, B. C., van Paridon, P. A., Verlann, I., Wirtz, K. W. A., de Laat, S. W., et al. 1987. Inositol phosphate metabolism in bradykinin-stimulated human A431 carcinoma cells. *Biochem. J.* 244:129–35

104. Tsien, R. W., Hess, P., McClesky, E. W., Rosenberg, R. L. 1987. Calcium channels: mechanisms of selectivity, permeation, and block. *Annu. Rev. Biophys. Chem.* 16:265–90

105. Vassilev, P. M., Kanazirska, M. P., Tien, H. T. 1987. Ca^{2+} channels from brain microsomal membranes reconstituted in patch-clamped bilayers. *Biochim. Biophys. Acta* 897:324–30

106. Volpe, P., Krause, K.-H., Hashimoto, S., Zorzato, F., Pozzan, T., et al. 1988. "Calciosome," a cytoplasmic organelle: the inositol 1,4,5-trisphosphate-sensitive Ca^{2+} store of nonmuscle cells? *Proc. Natl. Acad. Sci. USA* 85:1091–95

107. von Tscharner, V., Deranleau, D. A., Baggiolini, M. 1986. Calcium fluxes and calcium buffering in human neutrophils. *J. Biol. Chem.* 261:10163–68

108. von Tscharner, V., Prod'hom, B., Baggiolini, M., Reuter, H. 1986. Ion channels in human neutrophils activated by a rise in free cytosolic calcium concentra-tion. *Nature* 324:369–72

109. Wang, P., Toyoshima, S., Osawa, T. 1987. Physical and functional association of cytosolic inositol-phospholipid-specific phospholipase C of calf thymocytes with a GTP-binding protein. *J. Biochem.* 102:1275–87

110. Watson, S. P., McNally, J., Shipman, L. J., Godfrey, P. P. 1988. The action of protein kinase C inhibitor, staurosporine, on human platelets. *Biochem. J.* 249:345–50

111. Whitman, M., Kaplan, D., Roberts, T., Cantley, L. 1987. Evidence for two distinct phosphatidylinositol kinases in fibroblasts. *Biochem. J.* 247:165–74

112. Williamson, J. R., Cooper, R. H., Joseph, S. K., Thomas, A. P. 1985. Inositol trisphosphate and diacylglycerol as intracellular second messengers in liver. *Am. J. Physiol.* 248:C203–16

113. Williamson, J. R., Hansen, C. A. 1987. Signalling systems in stimulus-response coupling. In *Biochemical Actions of Hormones,* ed. G. Litwack, 14:29–80. New York: Academic.

114. Williamson, J. R., Joseph, S. K., Coll, K. E., Thomas, A. P., Verhoeven, A., et al. 1986. Hormone-induced inositol lipid breakdown and calcium-mediated cellular responses in liver. In *New Insights into Cell and Membrane Transport Processes,* ed. G. Poste, S. T. Crooke, pp. 217–47. New York: Plenum

115. Woods, N. M., Cuthbertson, K. S. R., Cobbold, P. H. 1986. Repetitive transient rises in cytoplasmic free calcium in hormone-stimulated hepatocytes. *Nature* 319:600–2

116. Woods, N. M., Cuthbertson, K. S. R., Cobbold, P. H. 1987. Agonist-induced oscillations in cytoplasmic free calcium concentration in single rat hepatocytes. *Cell Calcium* 8:79–100

117. Woods, N. M., Cuthbertson, K. S. R., Cobbold, P. H. 1987. Phorbol-ester-induced alterations of free calcium ion transients in single rat hepatocytes. *Biochem. J.* 246:619–23

118. Worley, P. F., Baraban, J. M., Colvin, J. S., Snyder, S. H. 1987. Inositol trisphosphate receptor localization in brain: variable stoichiometry with protein kinase C. *Nature* 325:159–61

119. Worley, P. F., Baraban, J. M., Supattapone, S., Wilson, V. S., Snyder, S. H. 1987. Characterization of inositol trisphosphate receptor binding in brain. *J. Biol. Chem.* 262:12132–36

120. Yoshida, K. I., Nachmias, V. T. 1987. Phorbol ester stimulates calcium sequestration in saponized human platelets. *J. Biol. Chem.* 262:16048–54

Annu. Rev. Physiol. 1989. 51:125–41

SPECIFIC REGULATION OF INTESTINAL NUTRIENT TRANSPORTERS BY THEIR DIETARY SUBSTRATES

Ronaldo P. Ferraris and Jared M. Diamond

Physiology Department, University of California Medical School, Los Angeles, California 90024-1751

INTRODUCTION

Studies of bacteria provide most information on the regulation of protein synthesis. Since bacteria are unicellular organisms living in media whose composition they cannot control, they are exposed to wide variations in substrate levels. Thus, it makes sense that levels of many bacterial enzymes and transporters are regulated by levels of their substrates or products.

Cells of multicellular organisms, on the other hand, are bathed in an internal milieu whose composition is maintained constant by the organism itself. Hence, levels of most eukaryotic enzymes are not regulated by substrate levels. The few exceptions mainly involve enzymes of the gastrointestinal (GI) tract, which are exposed to a luminal milieu that varies with diet, or of liver, pancreas, and adipocytes, which are exposed to plasma nutrient levels that also vary with diet.

Examples of adaptive enzymes in the GI tract have long been known; in fact, pancreatic amylase and chymotrypsin, which are regulated by dietary carbohydrate and protein, were among the first adaptive enzymes discovered in any organism. Yet little attention has been paid to the regulation of intestinal nutrient transporters despite the vast literature on the transport mechanisms themselves. This chapter summarizes the evidence that levels of most intestinal nutrient transporters are regulated by their substrates. This phenomenon is interesting for at least four reasons: It is physiologically

125

0066-4278/89/0315-0125$02.00

important in overcoming a potential digestive bottleneck; the observed regulatory patterns are diverse and functionally significant; the state of enterocyte maturation at which regulation occurs is still unsolved; and differences exist between bacteria and enterocytes in the speed and amplitude of regulation.

In this review we are concerned with specific and reversible regulation of individual transporters, mainly by dietary levels or body stores of their substrates (see 19, 39, 40 for previous reviews). We do not discuss nonspecific regulation of many transporters that can occur in parallel with specific regulation, especially during pregnancy and other conditions associated with simultaneously altered need for many nutrients, and that are mediated by changes in quantity of intestinal mucosa (see 39 for a review). We also do not discuss irreversible regulation during ontogenetic development, which is instead treated in a companion review (see Buddington & Diamond, this volume). We consider regulation of both brush-border and basolateral membrane transporters, but most of our examples involve the former since they are experimentally more accessible and better studied.

First, we contrast the time course and peak-to-base activity ratio of regulation in enterocytes and bacteria. We next outline four functions of regulation and the varied regulatory patterns that these considerations predict. We then compare these predictions with observed regulatory patterns for four classes of transporters: those for sugars, minerals, vitamins, and amino acids and peptides. Next we synthesize findings about the patterns, signals, sites, and mechanisms of regulation. Finally, we show how finely transporter levels are regulated so that they neither pose digestive bottlenecks nor waste biosynthetic resources.

SCOPE AND AMPLITUDE OF REGULATION

To a bacterial geneticist, two features of the regulation of intestinal nutrient transporters are striking. First, for virtually all intestinal transporters studied to date, the peak-to-base activity ratio is less than 10, often less than 2, while values of several thousand are common in bacteria. For example, the ratio for the glucose transporter of mouse intestine is only about 2, i.e. transporter activity even on a carbohydrate-free diet is fully half of the maximal activity attainable on a high-carbohydrate diet (18). Second, the time required to reach a steady-state is relatively slow: Up-regulation of the glucose and proline transporters of mouse intestine occurs after 1 day, down-regulation after 3 days (18). (The functional significance and mechanism of this asymmetry are unknown.) Even when the transit time of food from mouth to intestine is short-circuited by intravenous substrate administration (46) or by vitamin D stimulation of calcium transport (65), regulation of intestinal transporters involves lags of at least 0.5–4 hr. In contrast, bacterial enzyme activities often respond to altered substrate levels within minutes. Other adaptive eukaryotic enzymes also exhibit these two distinctive characteristics of slow and modest regulation compared to bacterial enzymes (72).

Given that regulation of intestinal transporters is (for whatever reason) slow, we suggest two functions of modest peak-to-base activity ratios. First, since regulatory delays are on the order of meal transit times from mouth to anus, significant basal activities of transporters must be maintained in the absence of substrate in order that ingested substrates be utilized at all. Regulation serves to match transporter activity to a running average of diet composition over many days; it does not switch transporters on and off with each meal. Second, nutrients enter the intestinal lumen constantly, even in the absence of dietary inputs, as a result of diffusion down concentration gradients from plasma or as a result of sloughed enterocytes. Moderate basal activities serve to recapture these endogenous nutrients, which would otherwise be lost via the feces. The fact that the bulk of these recycled nutrients is protein may explain why basal activities are especially high (peak-to-base activity ratios low) for amino acid transporters, particularly the transporters of essential amino acids (See section on amino acids and peptides).

PREDICTED PATTERNS OF REGULATION

Do substrates stimulate, repress, or nonmonotonically affect their transporters? At least four functional considerations bear on this question (19, 39):

1. Biosynthetic and other costs of synthesizing and maintaining any protein (17). A transporter should be repressed if those costs exceed the benefits that the transporter provides; the benefits could be either metabolizable calories or an essential nutrient.
2. Caloric payoff. Since metabolizable nutrients yield calories in proportion to the amount of nutrient, a transporter for a nutrient that yields calories should tend to be up-regulated by its substrate.
3. Fixed daily requirements for essential nutrients that the body cannot synthesize and that must be obtained from the diet. Transporters of such nutrients should tend to be down-regulated by their substrates since the transporter would be most needed at low dietary substrate levels, while at high levels the fixed requirement could be extracted by fewer transporters or even by passive diffusion down a concentration gradient.
4. Toxicity. Toxic nutrients should tend to repress their transporters, so as to protect the organism against risk of intoxication at high dietary substrate levels.

All four considerations predict that nonessential, nontoxic nutrients used as a source of calories (e.g. aldohexoses, fructose, nonessential amino acids, and short-chain fatty acids) should up-regulate their transporters (curve A of Figure 1). All considerations also predict that essential substrates that are toxic in large quantities and are not used for calories (e.g. vitamins and trace minerals) should down-regulate their transporters (curve B of Figure 1). For nutrients that are essential and potentially toxic but also yield calories (e.g. essential amino acids), the considerations yield conflicting predictions that make more complex patterns likely (curves C and D of Figure 1).

We now compare these predictions with experimental results.

OBSERVED PATTERNS OF REGULATION

Sugars

EFFECT OF DIETARY CARBOHYDRATE ON BRUSH-BORDER ALDOHEXOSE UPTAKE   Numerous studies (see 18, 40, 66 for citations) have shown that dietary carbohydrate stimulates brush-border aldohexose uptake. The effect is observed in intestines of mice, rats, and carp, which are omnivores, and of mink, which is a carnivore belonging to an omnivorous family, but not of trout, leopard frog, and cats, which are carnivores belonging to strictly carnivorous families (7). Thus, sugar uptake is regulated only in those species or families that encounter significant and varying carbohydrate levels in their

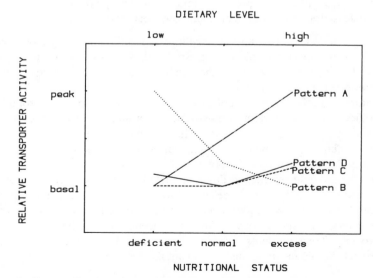

Figure 1 Four predicted regulatory patterns for activities of intestinal nutrient transporters (ordinate) as a function of the dietary levels or body stores of their substrates (abscissa). See text for basis of the different predictions.

natural diet. In the steady state, sugar uptake of mouse intestine increases monotonically with dietary carbohydrate level from 0 to 68% (Figure 2). Aldohexoses for which stimulation of uptake has been documented include D-glucose, D-galactose, and 3-O-methylglucose.

The intestinal brush-border has at least two different aldohexose transporters, which differ in V_{max} and K_m for glucose uptake, affinity for phlorizin, relative affinities for different sugars, distribution along the crypt/villus gradient, distribution along the length of the intestine, uptake as a function of temperature, and ontogenetic development (6, 24, 28, 42, 64, 66). The transporters also appear to differ in their regulatory responses to dietary carbohydrate and fasting (6, 24). In mouse intestine, in situ phlorizin binding studies (24) have shown that most of the observed increase in D-glucose uptake on a high-carbohydrate ration is due to increased numbers of sites with

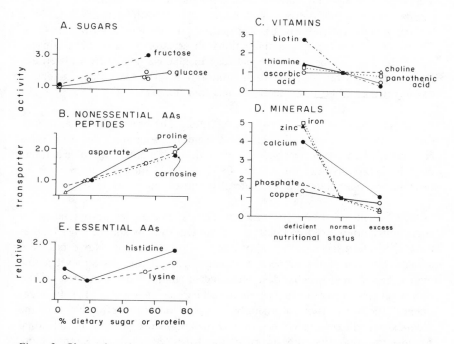

Figure 2 Observed regulatory patterns for activities of intestinal nutrient transporters (ordinate) as a function of dietary levels or body stores of their substrates (abscissa). (*A*) Glucose and fructose transporters of mouse intestine (41, 66). (*B*) Aspartate, proline, and peptide (carnosine) transporters of mouse intestine (25, 41). (*C*) Transporters for biotin, choline, thiamine, ascorbate, and pantothenic acid in intestine of rat, rat, rat, guinea pig, and mouse respectively (H. Said, personal communication; 37a, 55, 61, 69, respectively). (*D*) Iron, zinc, calcium, phosphate, and copper transporters of rat intestine (14, 53, 67, 70, 75). (*E*) Transport of the AAs lysine and histidine by mouse intestine (41). Modified from Ref. 19.

a high capacity and a low affinity for D-glucose, but with a high affinity for phlorizin (System 1 of Ref. 64).

EFFECT OF HYPERGLYCEMIA ON BASOLATERAL ALDOHEXOSE TRANS-PORT   Intravenous infusion of glucose produces a stimulation of basolateral glucose transport that is blocked by cycloheximide (an inhibitor of protein synthesis) and is inhibited by phloretin but not by phlorizin (12, 38, 46, 47). The effect appears within 4 hr, at a time when brush-border uptake is still unchanged. The mechanism appears to involve not only a change in the number of basolateral membrane transporters, but also a modulation of transporters already in the membrane (47). This effect of acute experimental hyperglycemia is the best studied example of regulation of a basolateral nutrient transporter. From this observation one cannot automatically assume that high-carbohydrate rations also up-regulate the basolateral glucose transporter since the hyperglycemia induced in humans by a meal is brief (< 2 hr) and modest ($< 50\%$ increase in plasma glucose level). However, C. I. Cheeseman's (personal communication) observation of a cytochalasin B– inhibitable, phlorizin-insensitive increase in glucose uptake by isolated en-terocytes of rats fed a high-carbohydrate ration for 1 week does indicate a dietary effect on the basolateral glucose transporter.

REGULATION OF FRUCTOSE TRANSPORTERS   The brush-border has a fruc-tose transporter, which is distinct from the aldohexose transporters (it is not a Na^+-coupled cotransporter) but whose activity also increases in mice and rats on a high-carbohydrate ration (2, 66) (Figure 2). Intravenous infusion of fructose also stimulates the basolateral fructose transporter (13).

SIGNALS FOR REGULATION   Earlier dietary studies on up-regulation of sugar transporters used complex carbohydrates such as starch; other studies have used the disaccharides sucrose and maltose (18, 66). However, these solutes need not be the immediate signals for regulation since they become hydrolyzed to monosaccharides. More recent studies have compared regula-tory potencies of various dietary monosaccharides themselves (16). In mice, dietary fructose is (not surprisingly) considerably more effective than the aldohexoses glucose, galactose, or 3-O-methylglucose at inducing intestinal fructose transport (66). It is surprising that fructose may also be slightly more effective than these aldohexoses at inducing brush-border aldohexose trans-port (66). [However, ileal perfusion of glucose, but not galactose or fructose, stimulated jejunal glucose absorption in rat intestine in vivo, possibly by a humoral mechanism (16).] In contrast, the basolateral fructose and aldohex-ose transporters are each regulated by plasma levels of their own substrates (12, 13).

There appear to be at least two brush-border aldohexose transporters that have different substrate specificities and for which the various dietary monosaccharides differ in their relative potencies as regulatory signals, as shown by differences in the ratio of galactose to glucose uptake depending on the dietary sugar used as an inducer (66). The effectiveness of dietary 3-O-methylglucose (not metabolized) and galactose (metabolized by liver but not by enterocytes) shows that metabolism is not a prerequisite for regulatory potency.

The simplest interpretation for the site at which the regulatory signal is perceived, is that plasma sugar levels regulate basolateral transporters, while luminal or intracellular sugar levels regulate brush-border transporters. Studies of hyperglycemia produced by acute infusions of glucose generally reveal up-regulation only of the basolateral glucose transporter, not of the brush-border transporter. However, such experiments with acute infusion have generally been brief (< 12 hr), while observed regulatory responses of the brush-border glucose transporter are slow (> 1 day). Animals made chronically hyperglycemic by drugs that cause experimental diabetes do up-regulate their brush-border glucose transporters after 3 or more days (e.g. 21, 71). Thus, it is possible (but not proven) that plasma sugar levels contribute to regulation of brush-border as well as basolateral glucose transporters.

SUMMARY OF PATTERNS FOR SUGARS   Sugars up-regulate the brush-border and basolateral glucose and fructose transporters, as predicted for nonessential, nontoxic nutrients used as a source of calories.

Minerals

Iron absorption is greater in iron-deficient rats or humans than in normal subjects and is greater in normal rats than in iron-loaded rats (8, 10, 75; see Figure 2). This regulation applies to both inorganic iron and hemoglobin iron, which appear to be absorbed by different mechanisms (9). Both iron uptake from lumen to enterocyte and iron transport from enterocyte to body are enhanced in iron deficiency (75). The up-regulation of uptake mainly involves an increase in V_{max}, with little or no change in K_m (10, 56).

Dietary calcium (Ca^{2+}) deficiency stimulates active Ca^{2+} uptake in proximal intestine (Figure 2) by regulating the level of an enterocyte cytosolic protein called Ca^{2+} binding protein (CaBP). That regulation is in turn mediated by 1,25-dihydroxy vitamin D_3 (DOH) (see 5). The chain of events is as follows: Low dietary Ca^{2+} is reflected in low serum Ca^{2+}, and low levels of both stimulate DOH production (3). DOH causes a dose-dependent increase in the amount of CaBP; CaBP linearly increases the rate of intestinal Ca^{2+} transport (59). CaBP levels increase within a day of a switch from a high-Ca^{2+} to a low-Ca^{2+} ration (29). In addition to stimulating CaBP, vitamin D also regulates Ca^{2+} absorption by stimulating brush-border Ca^{2+} entry (52, 57), by increasing basolateral Ca^{2+}/Mg^{2+}-ATPase activity and hence Ca^{2+} extrusion (30), and by stimulating Ca^{2+} binding by isolated cells or organelles (5, 73, 74). Walters & Weiser (73) showed that the effect of vitamin D in stimulating basolateral Ca^{2+} extrusion, as measured by basolateral membrane vesicles, is exerted on differentiating enterocytes in the mid-villus region, not on mature enterocytes on the tips of intestinal villi.

Regulation of intestinal phosphate absorption, which involves Na^+-coupled carriers in both the brush-border (4, 48, 52) and basolateral (31) membranes, has been demonstrated in rats, rabbits, chickens, and pigs. Absorption increases on a low-phosphate ration and decreases on a high-phosphate ration (14, 45). Whether the basolateral step is regulated remains unknown, but brush-border uptake increases 4 hr after a low-phosphate meal (14) (Figure 2). The V_{max} and possibly the affinity for phosphate increase, but the affinity for Na^+ remains unchanged. Regulation of phosphate transport, as of Ca^{2+} transport, involves vitamin D: Phosphate deficiency increases DOH levels in plasma and in the intestinal mucosa (1); DOH stimulates phosphate absorption and brush-border uptake (4, 48, 52); injections of ethane-1-OH-1,1-diphosphonate (EHDP) that decrease plasma DOH also decrease brush-border phosphate uptake (35); and phosphate deprivation fails to enhance absorption in vitamin D deficient rats (45).

Zinc deficiency increases zinc absorption fivefold (Figure 2) and increases V_{max} of brush-border zinc uptake twofold, while K_m remains unchanged (67). Feeding rats dietary zinc leads within 6 hr to increased mRNA for metallothionein, an enterocyte zinc-binding protein whose increased synthesis then leads to raised mucosal zinc levels and decreased zinc absorption (50).

The mechanism, principal site, and regulation of copper absorption are uncertain (27). Copper absorption tends to decrease with increasing dietary copper in rats (54, 70) (Figure 2).

In summary, iron, calcium, zinc, and phosphate down-regulate their transporters, as predicted for essential, toxic nutrients that do not yield calories (Figure 2). For copper the evidence is uncertain. We lack information about the regulation of manganese, selenium, magnesium, and cobalt absorption.

Vitamins

Among the vitamins discussed below, intestinal absorption of biotin (62), thiamine (37), ascorbate (61), and pantothenic acid (22, 69) involves separate Na^+-dependent transporters (see 60 for a review).

Biotin-deficient rations increase V_{max} of biotin uptake in brush-border vesicles of rat intestine by 2.5–2.8-fold compared to control rations, which in turn yield uptakes 2.8-fold greater than rations with high biotin levels (Figure

2: H. Said, personal communication). However, the K_m of uptake is independent of dietary biotin level.

Rats fed thiamine-deficient rations have higher transepithelial transport rates (Figure 2) and higher thiamine levels in intestinal tissue than pair-fed controls (55).

Rose & Nahrwold (61) found that ascorbate uptake in ileum is reduced 30–50% by rations with ascorbate levels 5–25 times above control levels (Figure 2); W. Karasov (personal communication) observed a similar reduction (involving a reduction in V_{max}) in ileum but not in other intestinal regions. Uptake on an ascorbate-deficient ration was the same as in control guinea pigs (61).

Cobalamin absorption involves binding in the gut lumen to intrinsic factor (IF) and R protein, followed by binding of the IF-cobalamin complex to an ileal receptor (20). Dietary regulation of cobalamin uptake has not been studied, but uptake is specifically stimulated in pregnant mice as a result of a doubling of ileal receptor number (58).

Stein & Diamond (69) found no significant differences in pantothenic acid (PA) uptake between mice on rations with normal, excessive, or deficient PA levels, even in mice exhibiting severe clinical symptoms of PA deficiency (Figure 2).

V_{max} and K_m of the choline transporter were the same in control rats and in rats fed a ration with choline levels 7.6 times control values for 7 days (37a) (Figure 2).

Pyridoxine absorption appears to occur by simple diffusion rather than by a specific transporter (60). Not surprisingly, pyridoxine transfer in rat and chicken intestine is independent of dietary pyridoxine levels (33).

Let us now summarize and interpret these patterns for vitamins. Diamond & Karasov (19) predicted that vitamin transporters would be down-regulated by their substrates since they are essential, often toxic at high levels, and not used for calories. This prediction has been tested for five of the seven vitamins discussed above, and it proved to be true for ascorbate, biotin, and thiamine, but not for choline and pantothenic acid, for which transporter activity is independent of dietary levels (Figure 2). (Pyridoxine has no transporter, while the cobalamin transporter is specifically up-regulated in pregnancy, but regulation by its substrate has not been studied.)

Why is the prediction sustained for only three out of five vitamins? We note that the ratio of carrier-mediated uptake to the diffusional (nonsaturable) uptake component at a concentration equal to the transporter's K_m is high for the regulated vitamins (17, ≥ 10, ≥ 4 for ascorbic acid, biotin, and thiamine, respectively; 32, 37, 49, 62), but low for the nonregulated vitamins (2.0–2.5 and 2.0–2.3 for choline and pantothenic acid respectively; 22, 34, 63, 69). Perhaps, then, vitamin transporters are regulated only if they make the dominant contribution to uptake.

Amino Acids and Peptides

EFFECT OF DIETARY NITROGEN ON BRUSH-BORDER UPTAKE   As far as we
are aware, all earlier studies (reviewed in Table 6 in Ref. 41) of the effect of
low-nitrogen rations on amino acid (AA) transporters used low-protein rations. Unfortunately, by in effect reducing the dietary content of all AAs
equally, this procedure yielded a deficiency not only in total nitrogen but also
in every essential AA, and the animals' condition quickly deteriorated.
Hence, we confine our conclusions on the effects of low-nitrogen rations to a
study by Karasov et al (41), who devised a nitrogen-deficient ration (equivalent to 4% casein) that lacked all nonessential AAs but contained all essential
AAs at the same level as in casein. On this ration animals remain in good
condition even after 2 weeks.

The brush border has separate transporters for acidic AAs, basic AAs,
neutral AAs, imino acids (such as proline), and peptides; there may also be
multiple transporters within some of these solute classes. Figure 2 illustrates
the various regulatory patterns observed. Activities of the acidic AA transporter (probed by aspartate uptake), imino acid transporter (probed by proline
uptake), and possibly of a peptide transporter (probed by carnosine uptake)
increase monotonically with dietary nitrogen level (level of AAs or protein).
Nonmonotonic patterns are observed for the AAs leucine, lysine, methionine,
histidine, and alanine: Below the maintenance level (0–18% dietary nitrogen),
uptake decreases or remains constant with increasing dietary nitrogen. Above
the maintenance level (> 18%), uptake increases with increasing dietary
nitrogen.

Thus, transporters for the nonessential, nontoxic acidic AAs and imino
acids follow the regulatory pattern for other nonessential, nontoxic nutrients
used for calories, such as sugars. Essential, toxic AAs conveyed by the basic
and neutral AA transporters exhibit a hybrid regulatory pattern: At low
concentrations they display the same pattern as essential, toxic nutrients not
used for calories (vitamins and minerals); at high concentrations their pattern
is the same as that of sugars used for calories, but up-regulation occurs by a
more modest factor, befitting the toxicity of essential AAs. The regulatory
pattern for the nonessential, nontoxic alanine resembles that for essential
rather than nonessential AAs, because alanine shares the brush-border
transporter for neutral essential AAs.

REGULATION OF BASOLATERAL TRANSPORTERS   AAs are transported
across the basolateral membrane by Na^+-independent transporters (15),
whose regulation by dietary nitrogen or plasma AA levels has not been
studied. However, Lawless et al (44) observed that basolateral lysine transport is stimulated twofold by very low (0.1 μM!) concentrations of leucine.
The functional significance (if any) and mechanism of this observation are
uncertain.

SIGNALS FOR REGULATION   Mice adapted to a ration based on either whole casein, a partial hydrolysate of casein, or a free-AA mixture approximating a complete hydrolysate of casein do not differ in their activities of any AA or peptide transporter studied (25, 26). Thus, whole proteins, peptides, and AAs are similar in potency as regulatory signals for these transporters; it is not the case that each transporter is regulated mainly by dietary levels of the class of hydrolysis products that it transports. Furthermore, comparisons of rations with raised levels of individual AAs show that AAs conveyed by a given transporter do not necessarily act as potent regulatory signals for that transporter, and conversely that AAs acting as potent regulatory signals are not necessarily transported effectively (68). For example, while dietary aspartate proves (not surprisingly) to be the best inducer of the acidic AA transporter, and while valine is among the best inducers of the neutral AA transporter, it is surprising that the basic AA arginine is the second-best inducer of the acidic AA transporter, that the acidic AA aspartate is in turn the best inducer of the basic AA transporter, and that proline is not especially effective at inducing the imino acid transporter.

SIGNIFICANCE OF THE PATTERNS AND SIGNALS OF REGULATION

The observed patterns of regulation agree well with those predicted from the straightforward functional considerations set out in the section on predicted patterns of regulation. The prediction that nonessential nontoxic solutes utilized for calories up-regulate their transporters is supported for the transporters of glucose, fructose, acidic AAs, imino acids, and perhaps peptides. The prediction that essential toxic solutes not utilized for calories down-regulate their transporters is supported for all trace mineral transporters studied (those for iron, calcium, phosphate, zinc, and possibly copper) and for three vitamin transporters (those for biotin, thiamine, and ascorbic acid). These simple functional considerations yield conflicting predictions for transporters of essential, toxic AAs that can also be utilized for calories. In practice, the observed patterns for transporters of essential AAs combine the observed pattern for essential, toxic, nonmetabolized solutes at low dietary levels (i.e. down-regulation) with the observed pattern for nonessential, nontoxic, metabolized solutes at high dietary levels (i.e. up-regulation).

The observed signals of regulation do not agree so neatly with functionally based predictions. The simplest prediction would have been for each transporter to be regulated by dietary levels of its preferred substrate(s). This prediction appears to hold for mineral and vitamin transporters plus the fructose and acidic AA transporters. However, dietary solutes that are not transported substrates appear to be the best regulators of the glucose, basic AA, and imino acid transporters. Furthermore, AAs are as potent as peptides at regulating a peptide transporter, and the converse is also true for all AA transporters studied. Equally paradoxical discrepancies between regulatory signals and substrates have been reported for numerous eukaryotic and bacterial transporters and enzymes (see 41 and 68 for a summary). This paradox remains one of the unsolved problems of regulatory biology.

MECHANISM AND SITE OF REGULATION

Specific changes in a single transporter could occur by various mechanisms; the two most direct mechanisms are increased transporter number and increased activity per transporter. Increased transporter number has been demonstrated for the brush-border glucose transporter (assayed as glucose-inhibitable phlorizin binding sites; 21, 24), the basolateral glucose transporter (assayed as glucose-inhibitable cytochalasin B binding; 47), the iron transporter (assayed as iron binding to brush-border membranes; 43, 51), the cobalamin transporter (assayed as its ileal receptor; 58), and the calcium binding protein (59, 65). Hyperglycemia causes a 4-fold increase in the V_{max} of the basolateral glucose transporter but only a 1.5-fold increase in transporter number, which suggests that activity of existing transporters, in addition to transporter number, increased (47).

Increased transporter number could in turn result from increased synthesis (regulated at the level either of transcription or translation), decreased degradation, or increased insertion of preformed cytoplasmic transporters into membranes. Little information on this question is available. Zinc deficiency was shown to lead to increased mRNA and synthesis of a zinc-binding protein (50). Cycloheximide inhibits up-regulation of both calcium binding protein (65) and the basolateral glucose transporter (12), which suggests a role of increased synthesis of new transporters.

Enterocytes are continually turning over: New enterocytes form in intestinal crypts, mature as they migrate up the villi, and slough off at the villus tips around 2 or 3 days later. Can mature enterocytes be "reprogrammed" at any time by regulation of their transporters, or does regulation instead take place only in the crypt cells, whose functions are fixed there irreversibly for the remainder of their cell life-times? Marked up-regulation of calcium binding protein (65), phosphate transport (14), and basolateral glucose transport (12, 47) is detectable within 4 hr of alteration of substrate or vitamin D levels. This response is far too quick to be explained by maturation of irreversibly regulated crypt cells and thus seemingly proves that regulation of mature enterocytes is reversible. However, dietary regulation of brush-border glucose and AA transporters requires 1–3 days and thus is compatible with regulation only at the level of crypt cells. This possibility awaits testing.

DIGESTIVE BOTTLENECKS AND THE SIGNIFICANCE OF REGULATION

Based on Holdsworth & Dawson's (36) long-superceded estimate of V_{max} for glucose uptake by human jejunum in vivo, Crane (11) calculated that the daily uptake capacity of human small intestine for glucose is 5.4 kilograms (!!!), an enormous value exceeding even the most unreasonably high possible values of daily glucose intake. This calculation of excess intestinal absorptive capacity has often been uncritically repeated in the literature. If it were true, there would be no need for dietary substrates to up-regulate their transporters, and all the examples discussed in this chapter would be unexpected. In fact, the concept of excess absorptive capacity is not only wrong, but it violates biological common sense: Since all parts of an organism (including intestinal transporters) require energy for synthesis and maintenance, organisms manufacture only enough of each part to cover their needs by a modest safety margin. The error arose because Holdsworth & Dawson's (36) values were grossly inflated in three respects: They used glucose concentrations of up to 278 mM (50 times physiological concentrations); their calculated K_m (220 mM) exceeds values of other authors (even in vivo values) by 1–3 orders of magnitude; and their calculated V_{max} (equivalent to 0.024 g min^{-1} cm^{-1} intestine) exceeds other values by more than 100-fold.

The following example illustrates that limited intestinal absorptive capacity nearly imposes a bottleneck on nutrient processing. Mice on a high-carbohydrate ration consume 2.2 g glucose per day. One can calculate the glucose uptake capacity of the entire length of the small intestine by measureing uptake per cm as a function of intestinal position and then integrating over length (18). If glucose transporter activity on a high-carbohydrate ration were as low as that on a carbohydrate-free ration, a mouse's glucose uptake capacity would be only 50% or 120% of that needed to absorb its daily glucose intake, depending on whether the average luminal glucose concentration were 5 or 50 mM respectively. In reality, because dietary carbohydrate up-regulates the glucose transporter, uptake capacity is 80% or 180% of intake.

Corresponding calculations for five other transporters, as well those for fructose and the four main classes of AAs, show that the ratio of uptake capacity to dietary intake is similarly modest. On rations with high substrate levels, the capacities of all five transporters is approached or exceeded if the transporters retain the capacities that they have on a low-substrate ration and if they are not up-regulated. Thus, the function of regulation is to match uptake capacity to requirements, i.e. to provide enough transporters to process the substrates being ingested, but not to waste energy on unnecessary transporters. Buddington & Diamond (this volume) demonstrate that this conclusion applies not only to adult mammals but also to all other life-cycle stages from birth through weaning.

SUMMARY AND OUTLOOK

Most intestinal nutrient transporters studied to date are regulated by dietary levels of their substrates. With increasing substrate levels, transporters for glucose, fructose, two classes of nonessential amino acids, and peptide are up-regulated; transporters for trace minerals and for some vitamins (perhaps mainly those with little passive uptake) are down-regulated; transporters for essential AAs exhibit minimal activity at intermediate substrate levels. Compared to bacterial proteins, intestinal transporters show modest peak-to-base activity ratios (< 10) and slow responses (hours or days) in their regulation. The regulatory signals are in only some cases transported substrates. Regulation of numerous transporters involves changes in transporter number. Since the intestine's absorptive capacities are (contrary to widespread belief) closely matched to dietary intakes, the function of regulation is to provide just enough absorptive capacity, without wasting biosynthetic energy on unneeded transporters.

This area of research has exploded recently and is full of important unsolved problems. Regulatory patterns remain unknown for most basolateral transporters, bile acids, short-chain fatty acids, and numerous trace minerals and vitamins. Regulatory patterns for multiple transporters of the same nutrient (e.g. multiple transporters for glucose or for neutral AAs) are only beginning to be resolved (6). Why the regulatory signals are so often seemingly "inappropriate" remains unknown. As yet, there has been no detailed study of intestinal transporter regulation at the molecular level. The possibility that activities of some transporters are irreversibly fixed at the crypt-cell state by the prevailing substrate levels remains to be tested. We anticipate that intestinal nutrient transporters, which among the eukaryotic enzymes are most directly exposed to a changing environment, will furnish suitable material for studying many questions of regulatory biology.

ACKNOWLEDGMENTS

It is a pleasure to record our debt to many colleagues who generously provided manuscripts, data, and suggestions. Our work was supported by NIH grants GM 14772 and AM 17328 (UCLA Center for Ulcer Research and Education).

Literature Cited

1. Bar, A., Hurwitz, S. 1986. Reduced affinity of intestinal receptors for 1,25-dihydroxycholecalciferol in phosphorus-deficient chicks. *J. Endocrinol.* 110:217–23
2. Bode, Ch., Eisenhardt, J. M., Haberich, F. J., Bode, J. Ch. 1981. Influence of feeding fructose on fructose and glucose absorption in rat jejunum and ileum. *Res. Exp. Med.* 179:163–68
3. Boyle, I. T., Gray, R. W., Deluca, H. F. 1971. Regulation by calcium of *in vivo* synthesis of 1,25-dihydroxychole-calciferol and 21,25-dihydroxycholecal-ciferol. *Proc. Natl. Acad. Sci. USA* 68:2131–34
4. Brandis, M., Harmeyer, J., Kaune, R., Mohrmann, M., Murer, H., Zimolo, Z. 1987. Phosphate transport in brush-border membranes from control and rachitic pig kidney and small intestine. *J. Physiol.* 384:479–90
5. Bronner, F. 1987. Calcium absorption. In *Physiology of the Gastrointestinal Tract,* ed. L. R. Johnson, pp. 1419–35. New York: Raven. 1780 pp. 2nd ed.
6. Brot-Laroche, E., Dao, M. T., Alcalde, A. I., Delhomme, B., Triadou, N., Alvarado, F. 1988. Independent modulation by food supply of two distinct sodium-activated D-glucose transport systems in the guinea pig intestinal brush border membrane. *Proc. Natl. Acad. Sci. USA* 85:6370–73
7. Buddington, R. K., Chen, J. W., Diamond, J. M. 1987. Evolutionary constraints on the adaptive flexibility of nutrient transport by vertebrate intestine. *The Physiologist* 30:190
8. Callender, S. T., Mallett, B. J., Smith, M. D. 1957. Absorption of haemoglobin iron. *Br. J. Haematol.* 3:186–92
9. Conrad, M. E. 1987. Iron absorption. See Ref. 5, pp. 1437–53
10. Cox, T. M., Peters, T. J. 1980. Cellular mechanisms in the regulation of iron absorption by the human intestine: studies in patients with iron deficiency before and after treatment. *Br. J. Haematol.* 44:75–86
11. Crane, R. K. 1975. The physiology of the intestinal absorption of sugars. In *Physiological Effects of Food Carbohydrates,* ed. A. Jeanes, J. Hodges, pp. 1–19. Washington, D. C.: Am. Chem. Soc. 355 pp.
12. Csaky, T. Z., Fischer, E. 1981. Intestinal sugar transport in experimental diabetes. *Diabetes* 30:568–74
13. Csaky, T. Z., Fischer, E. 1984. Effects of ketohexosemia on the ketohexose transport in the small intestine of rats. *Biochim. Biophys. Acta* 772:259–63
14. Danisi, G., Caverzasio, J., Bonjour, J.-Ph., Murer, H., Straub, R. W. 1986. Mechanism of phosphate transport adaptation in rat intestinal and renal brush border membranes. *Adv. Exp. Med. Biol.* 208:223–26
15. Davies, S., Maenz, D. D., Cheeseman, C. I. 1987. A novel imino-acid carrier in the enterocyte basolateral membrane. *Biochim. Biophys. Acta* 896:247–55
16. Debnam, E. S. 1985. Adaptation of hexose uptake by the rat jejunum induced by the perfusion of sugars into the distal ileum. *Digestion* 31:25–30
17. Diamond, J. M. 1986. How to gamble on physiological requirements. *News Physiol. Sci.* 1:208–10
18. Diamond, J. M., Karasov, W. H. 1984. Effect of dietary carbohydrate on monosaccharide uptake by mouse small intestine in vitro. *J. Physiol.* 349:419–40
19. Diamond, J. M., Karasov, W. H. 1987. Adaptive regulation of intestinal nutrient transporters. *Proc. Natl. Acad. Sci. USA* 84:2242–45
20. Donaldson, R. M. 1987. Intrinsic factor and the transport of cobalamin. See Ref. 5, pp. 959–73
21. Fedorak, R. N., Change, E. B., Madara, J. L., Field, M. 1987. Intestinal adaptation to diabetes. *J. Clin. Invest.* 79:1571–78
22. Fenstermacher, D. K., Rose, R. C. 1986. Absorption of pantothenic acid in rat and chicken intestine. *Am. J. Physiol.* 250:G155–60
23. Ferraris, R. P., Diamond, J. M. 1986. A method for measuring apical glucose transporter site density in intact intestinal mucosa by means of phlorizin binding. *J. Membr. Biol.* 94:65–75
24. Ferraris, R. P., Diamond, J. M. 1986. Use of phlorizin binding to demonstrate induction of intestinal glucose transporters. *J. Membr. Biol.* 94:77–82
25. Ferraris, R. P., Diamond, J. M., Kwan, W. W. 1988. Dietary regulation of intestinal transport of the dipeptide carnosine. *Am. J. Physiol.* 255:G143–50
26. Ferraris, R. P., Kwan, W. W., Diamond, J. M. 1988. Regulatory signals for intestinal amino acid transporters and peptides. *Am. J. Physiol.* 255:G151–57
27. Fields, M., Craft, N., Lewis, C., Holbrook, J., Rose, A., et al. 1986. Con-

trasting effects of the stomach and small intestine of rats on copper absorption. *J. Nutr.* 116:2219–28

28. Freeman, H. J., Johnston, G., Quamme, G. A. 1987. Sodium-dependent D-glucose transport in brush-border membrane vesicles from isolated rat small intestine villus and crypt epithelial cells. *Can. J. Physiol. Pharmacol.* 65:1213–19

29. Freund, T., Bronner, F. 1975. Regulation of intestinal calcium-binding protein by calcium intake in the rat. *Am. J. Physiol.* 228:861–69

30. Ghijsen, W. E. J. M., De Jong, M. D., Van Os, C. H. 1982. ATP-dependent calcium transport and its correlation with Ca^{2+}-ATPase activity in basolateral plasma membranes of rat duodenum. *Biochim. Biophys. Acta* 689:327–36

31. Ghishan, F. K., Kikuchi, K., Arab, N. 1987. Phosphate transport by rat intestinal basolateral-membrane vesicles. *Biochem. J.* 243:641–46

32. Gore, J., Hoinard, C. 1987. Evidence for facilitated transport of biotin by hamster enterocytes. *J. Nutr.* 117:527–32

33. Heard, G. S., Annison, E. F. 1986. Gastrointestinal absorption of vitamin B-6 in the chicken (*Gallus domesticus*). *J. Nutr.* 116:107–20

34. Herzberg, G. R., Lerner, J. 1973. Intestinal absorption of choline in the chick. *Biochim. Biophys. Acta* 307:234–42

35. Hildmann, B., Storelli, C., Danisi, G., Murer, H. 1982. Regulation of Na^+-P_i cotransport by 1,25-dihydroxy vitamin D_3 in rabbit duodenal brush-border membrane. *Am. J. Physiol.* 242:G533–39

36. Holdsworth, C. D., Dawson, A. M. 1964. The absorption of monosaccharides in man. *Clin. Sci.* 27:371–79

37. Hoyumpa, A. M. Jr., Middleton, H. M. III, Wilson, F. A., Schenker, S. 1975. Thiamine transport across the rat intestine. *Gastroenterology* 68:1218–27

37a. Karasov, W. H., Darken, B. W., Bottum, M. C. 1987. Tests for nonspecific and specific adaptation of intestinal choline transport. *Physiologist* 30:191

38. Karasov, W. H., Debnam, E. S. 1987. Rapid adaptation of intestinal glucose transport: a brush-border or basolateral phenomenon? *Am. J. Physiol.* 253:G54–61

39. Karasov, W. H., Diamond, J. M. 1983. Adaptive regulation of sugar and amino acid transport by vertebrate intestine. *Am. J. Physiol.* 245:G443–62

40. Karasov, W. H., Diamond, J. M. 1987. Adaptation of intestinal nutrient transport. See Ref. 5, pp. 1489–97

41. Karasov, W. H., Solberg, D. H., Diamond, J. M. 1987. Dependence of intestinal amino acid uptake on dietary protein or amino acid levels. *Am. J. Physiol.* 252:G614–25

42. Keljo, D. J., MacLeod, R. J., Perdue, M. H., Butler, D. G., Hamilton, J. R. 1985. D-glucose transport in piglet jejunal brush-border membranes: insights from a disease model. *Am. J. Physiol.* 249:G751–60

43. Kimber, C. L., Mukherhee, T., Deller, D. J. 1973. In vitro iron attachment to the intestinal brush border. *Dig. Dis. Sci.* 18:81–91

44. Lawless, K., Maenz, D. D., Cheeseman, C. I. 1987. Is leucine an allosteric modulator of the lysine transporter in the intestinal basolateral membrane? *Am. J. Physiol.* 253:G637–42

45. Lee, D. B. N., Walling, M. W., Brautbar, N. 1986. Intestinal phosphate absorption: influence of vitamin D and non–vitamin D factors. *Am. J. Physiol.* 250:G369–73

46. Maenz, D. D., Cheeseman, C. I. 1986. Effect of hyperglycemia on D-glucose transport across the brush border and basolateral membranes of rat small intestine. *Biochim. Biophys. Acta* 860:277–85

47. Maenz, D. D., Cheeseman, C. I. 1988. Rapid regulation of Na^+ independent D-glucose transport in the basolateral membrane of rat jejunum. *Am. J. Physiol.* In press

48. Matsumoto, T., Fontaine, O., Rasmussen, H. 1980. Effect of 1,25-dihydroxyvitamin D-3 on phosphate uptake into chick intestinal brush border membrane vesicles. *Biochim. Biophys. Acta* 599:13–23

49. Mellors, A. J., Nahrwold, D. L., Rose, R. C. 1977. Ascorbic acid flux across mucosal border of guinea pig and human ileum. *Am. J. Physiol.* 233:E374–79

50. Menard, M. P., McCormick, C. C., Cousins, R. J. 1981. Regulation of intestinal metallothionein biosynthesis in rats by dietary zinc. *J. Nutr.* 111:1353–61

51. Muir, W. A., Hopfer, U., King, M. 1984. Iron transport across brush-border membranes from normal and iron-deficient mouse upper small intestine. *J. Biol. Chem.* 259:4896–4903

52. Murer, H., Hildmann, B. 1981. Transcellular transport of calcium and inorganic phosphate in the small intestinal

epithelium. *Am. J. Physiol.* 240:G409–16

53. Nellans, H. N., Kimberg, D. V. 1978. Cellular and paracellular calcium transport in rat ileum: effect of dietary calcium. *Am. J. Physiol.* 235:E726–37

54. Oestreicher, P., Cousins, R. J. 1985. Copper and zinc absorption in the rat: mechanism of mutual antagonism. *J. Nutr.* 115:159–66

55. Patrini, C., Cusaro, G., Ferrari, G., Rindi, G. 1981. Thiamine transport by rat small intestine "in vitro": influence of endogenous thiamine content of jejunal tissue. *Acta Vitaminol. Enzymol.* 3:17–26

56. Raja, K. B., Simpson, R. J., Peters, T. J. 1987. Comparison of $^{59}Fe^{3+}$ uptake in vitro and in vivo by mouse duodenum. *Biochim. Biophys. Acta* 901:52–60

57. Rasmussen, H., Fontaine, O., Max, E. E., Goodman, D. B. P. 1979. The effect of 1-α-hydroxyvitamin D_3 administration on calcium transport in chick intestine brush border vesicles. *J. Biol. Chem.* 254:2993–99

58. Robertson, J. A., Gallagher, N. D. 1979. Effect of placental lactogen on the number of intrinsic factor receptors in the pregnant mouse. *Gastroenterology* 77:511–17

59. Roche, C., Bellaton, C., Pansu, D., Miller, A. III, Bronner, F. 1986. Localization of vitamin D–dependent active Ca^{2+} transport in rat duodenum and relation to CaBP. *Am. J. Physiol.* 251:G314–20

60. Rose, R. C. 1987. Intestinal absorption of water-soluble vitamins. See Ref. 5, pp. 1581–96

61. Rose, R. C., Nahrwold, D. L. 1978. Intestinal ascorbic acid transport following diets on high or low ascorbic acid content. *Int. J. Vitam. Nutr. Res.* 48:382–86

62. Said, H. M., Redha, R. 1987. A carrier-mediated system for transport of biotin in rat intestine in vitro. *Am. J. Physiol.* 252:G52–55

63. Sanford, P. A., Smyth, D. H. 1971. Intestinal transfer of choline in rat and hamster. *J. Physiol.* 215:769–88

64. Semenza, G., Kessler, M., Hosang, M., Weber, J., Schimdt, U. 1984. Biochemistry of the Na^+, D-glucose cotransporter of the small-intestinal brushborder membrane. *Biochim. Biophys. Acta* 779:343–79

65. Singh, R. P., Bronner, F. 1982. Duodenal calcium binding protein: induction by 1,25-dihydroxy vitamin D_3 in in vivo and in vitro. *Indian J. Exp. Biol.* 20:107–11

66. Solberg, D. H., Diamond, J. M. 1987. Comparison of different dietary sugars as inducers of intestinal sugar transporters. *Am. J. Physiol.* 252:G574–84

67. Steel, L., Cousins, R. J. 1985. Kinetics of zinc absorption by luminally and vascularly perfused rat intestine. *Am. J. Physiol.* 248:G46–53

68. Stein, E. D., Chang, S. D., Diamond, J. M. 1987. Comparison of different dietary amino acids as inducers of intestinal amino acid transport. *Am. J. Physiol.* 252:G626–35

69. Stein, E. D., Diamond, J. M. 1989. Activity of the intestinal transporter for pantothenic acid is independent of dietary substrate levels. *Proc. Natl. Acad. Sci. USA.* In press

70. Stuart, M. A., Johnson, P. E. 1986. Copper absorption and copper balance during consecutive periods for rats fed varying levels of dietary copper. *J. Nutr.* 116:1028–36

71. Thomson, A. B. R. 1981. Uptake of glucose into the intestine of diabetic rats. *Diabetes* 30:247–55

72. Walker, R. 1983. *The Molecular Biology of Enzyme Synthesis.* New York: Wiley. 381 pp.

73. Walters, J. R. F., Weiser, M. M. 1987. Calcium transport by rat duodenal villus and crypt basolateral membranes. *Am. J. Physiol.* 252:G170–77

74. Weiser, M. M., Bloor, J. H., Dasmahapatra, A., Freedman, R. A., MacLaughlin, J. A. 1981. Vitamin D–dependent rat intestinal Ca^{2+} transport. Ca^{2+} uptake by Golgi membranes and early nuclear events. In *Calcium and Phosphate Transport Across Biomembranes*, ed. F. Bronner, M. Peterlik, pp. 264–73. New York: Academic. 300 pp.

75. Wheby, M. S., Jones, L. G., Crosby, W. H. 1964. Studies on iron absorption. Intestinal regulatory mechanisms. *J. Clin. Invest.* 43:1433–42

Annu. Rev. Physiol. 1989. 51:143–60

REGULATION OF CHLORIDE TRANSPORT IN EPITHELIA

Carole M. Liedtke

The Cystic Fibrosis Center, Departments of Pediatrics and Developmental Genetics & Anatomy, Case Western Reserve University, Cleveland, Ohio 44106

INTRODUCTION

In a number of epithelia, overall electrolyte absorption and secretion are highly regulated (8, 25, 66). The absorptive and secretory states are characterized by the movement of fluids and electrolytes toward the serosa or toward the lumen, respectively. Although most epithelia are not thought of primarily as secretory, secretion plays a critical role in the normal functioning of epithelia and in the pathophysiology of disease affecting such physiologically distinct tissues as large airways, sweat gland, pancreas, and intestinal tract. Transport processes involved in secretion and absorption are regulated short-term by neurohormones, mediators, and local hormones, or long-term by steroid hormones, such as mineralocorticoids (25). This discussion focuses on short-term regulatory agents and looks specifically at second messenger systems that regulate Cl^- secretion in epithelia affected by the genetic disease Cystic Fibrosis (CF) and by secretory diarrhea. Recent excellent reviews provide details on trachea (99) and intestine (8, 25); hence, in this article, current reports on epithelial Cl^- transport regulation are reviewed.

Role of Abnormal Regulation in Pathophysiology

CF is the most common single gene, fatal disease in the Caucasion population, occurring in about 1 in 2000 live births (88). Although the disease is expressed over a wide spectrum of pathophysiology, CF fits an autosomal recessive model involving a single mutation. As a generalized exocrinopathy, CF severely affects sweat glands, pancreas, and airway epithelium of tracheo-bronchial tree and nasal passages, as well as the intestinal tract (4, 88). In sweat glands, ducts absorb less salt from primary secretory coil secretions, which results in elevated sweat NaCl content, or the diagnostic feature of CF. Deficient fluid secretion in the pancreas leads to inspissation of ductal secretions and atrophy of acinar cells. In the airways, dysfunctional electrolyte transport is thought to contribute to the thick, dehydrated tracheobronchial secretions that apparently impair mucociliary transport and lead to plugging of the airways. Underlying abnormal epithelial electrolyte transport in trachea and sweat glands is an impermeability to Cl^- associated with defective regulation of Cl^- channels in apical membranes (6, 7, 16, 29, 44, 49, 81, 100). In the airways, increased Na^+ absorption also contributes to the phenotypic expression of the CF defect (10).

In the small intestine, secretory diarrhea provides evidence for the capacity of this normally absorptive organ to secrete large amounts of fluids. Normally, villus and crypt cells participate in absorption and secretion, respectively (25). The two processes occur simultaneously unless disturbed by toxins or endogeneous agents, such as VIP (vasoactive intestinal peptide) that cause net secretion in the upper gastrointestinal tract. The secretion results in the accumulation of fluid and electrolytes in the lumen of the small intestine. When the volume of the secretions leaving the ileum exceed the reabsorptive capacity of the colon, diarrhea results. Dehydration develops due to loss of Na^+ and K^+ and hypokalemic acidosis due to secretion of K^+ and HCO_3^- by the colon.

Models of Cl^- Transport in Epithelia

The fundamental source of energy for ion transport is the Na, K-ATPase located in the basolateral plasma membrane of epithelial cells. The Na, K-ATPase mediates an electrogenic exchange of Na^+ for K^+ that results in a significant Na^+ electrochemical gradient across the basolateral membrane. The energy from this gradient drives Cl^- into the cell against its electrochemical gradient. During absorption (Figure 1), Cl^- enters the cell across the apical plasma membrane via two electrically dissimilar pathways. First, a conductance pathway in jejuneum and sweat duct (5–7, 52) mediates Cl^- uptake against its electrochemical gradient (Figure 1 *top*). Na^+ enters the cell by flowing down its electrochemical gradient via a conductive pathway as either organic solute-independent or solute-dependent transport. Because of the nature of the anion and cation conductance pathways, Cl^- entry is electrically coupled to Na^+ entry. In the ileum (Figure 1 *bottom*), electrically silent Na^+-H^+ and Cl^--HCO_3^- exchange pathways mediate NaCl uptake, with a pH gradient across the membrane serving as the coupling factor for the two exchangers (52). In both models of Na^+ absorption, the basolateral Na, K-ATPase pumps Na^+ from the cell. Although intracellular Ca^{2+} modulates the activity of the exchangers (25), the molecular site of action is not known.

During secretion (Figure 2), Cl^- enters the cell against its electrochemical

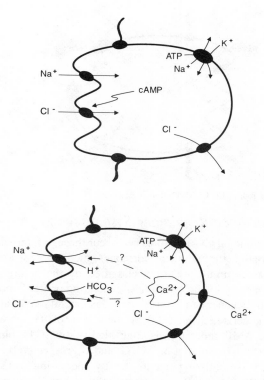

Figure 1 (top) General model for Cl⁻ absorption in epithelia where Na⁺ pathway may be nonelectrolyte coupled, as in small intestine, or a single conductance, as in sweat and pancreatic ducts. *(bottom)* Model for Cl⁻ absorption accomplished by two exchangers, as in mammalian ileum. Cl⁻ transport pathway in the basolateral membrane is speculative.

gradient coupled to Na⁺ by a Na⁺-K⁺-2Cl⁻ cotransporter that is sensitive to loop diuretics. Cl⁻ accumulates in the cell and then exits at the apical membrane via a conductance pathway or channel down its electrochemical gradient. In many epithelia, apical Cl⁻ channels are regulated by cAMP, an intracellular messenger for hormones that activate adenylate cyclase (AC). Na⁺ that is pumped out of the cell diffuses to the lumen by a paracellular route. K⁺ that enters the cell diffuses across the basolateral membrane by a Ca²⁺-regulated channel (32, 65, 99), thus providing the electrical driving force for Cl⁻ exit across the apical membrane. During secretion, apical Cl⁻ and basolateral K⁺ channel activities increase in order to prevent a prolonged depolarization of the cell voltage, which would prevent Cl⁻ exit through the apical Cl⁻ channel, and in order to prevent accumulation of K⁺, which would increase the intracellular K⁺ activity and cell volume.

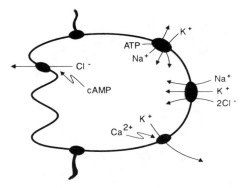

Figure 2   General model for Cl⁻ secretion in epithelia.

Major Intracellular Regulatory Systems

Regulation of epithelial Cl⁻ transport can occur through internal stimuli, such as pH, or externally, through neurohormones, mediators, or local hormones. In the latter case, stimuli are often classified by the predominant cellular biochemical response: cyclic nucleotide–generating or Ca^{2+}-mobilizing stimuli. Cyclic AMP is generated from ATP by basolateral membrane-bound AC, and cGMP is generated from GTP by the action of the enzyme guanylate cyclase. Cyclic AMP generation is controlled by two GTP binding proteins that act on the catalytic subunit of AC: G_s and G_i, respectively, stimulate and inhibit AC. Ca^{2+}-mobilizing agents act by increasing intracellular Ca^{2+} levels through the release of stored intracellular Ca^{2+} or the influx of extracellular Ca^{2+}. In the former case, stimuli activate a membrane bound phospholipase C (PLC) and thus promote the cleavage of phosphatidylinositol-4,5-bisphosphate (PIP_2) in the cell membrane to diacylglycerol (DG) and inositol-1,4,5-trisphosphate (IP_3) and other metabolites, including cyclic forms of the inositol phosphates (IP) esters (56, 69, 82). IP_3 triggers the release of Ca^{2+} from nonmitochondrial Ca^{2+} pools. DG associates with protein kinase C (PK-C) in a Ca^{2+}-dependent manner in the cell membrane. PK-C functions in many cell types to regulate electrolyte transport processes. Because Ca^{2+}-mobilizing stimuli apparently act indirectly on intracellular Ca^{2+} pools, one may consider phosphatidylinositol (PI) metabolites as second messengers in signal transduction and Ca^{2+} as a link between cyclic nucleotide (cAMP and cGMP) and PI metabolism.

The cyclic nucleotide and PI messenger systems share several salient features: transient elevation in intracellular messenger levels, role for Ca^{2+} in metabolism of the messenger, signal transduction modulation by GTP binding proteins, and activation of a protein kinase (69, 72, 87). How the intracellular second messengers produce their effects is an area of intense investigation. In some epithelia, the cyclic nucleotide–binding proteins and substrate proteins for protein phosphorylation have been localized to the apical or basolateral membrane, but overall, this area of research requires considerable attention.

TRACHEA

Transport Pathways

In the trachea and large airways, lining epithelial cells maintain a fluid layer on their surface, within which beating cilia move an overlying mucoid material cephalad to expel trapped foreign particles and bacteria. Maintenance of the fluid layer is achieved by absorption of electrolytes if excess fluid is detected or produced, or secretion of electrolytes if the fluid layer shrinks. Mammalian trachea absorb Na^+ via an apical amiloride-sensitive pathway. Cl^- secretion can be elicited by application of amiloride to rabbit, human, sheep, cat, and ferret trachea (99), and nasal airway epithelium (43, 44). In canine trachea, Cl^- secretion accounts for most of the short circuit current (99). Lower segmental regions of canine airways more closely resemble other mammalian airways in the overall net absorption of Na^+ (9).

Different second messengers regulate transport pathways operative during Cl^- secretion. In dog and human tracheal epithelium, β-adrenergic agonists and cAMP-generating agents activate the Cl^- channel (96, 99). Indeed, cAMP is a sufficient signal for activation of the apical Cl^- channel (96). Cl^- secretion in airway epithelium is not dependent on extracellular Ca^{2+} (99) yet there is evidence that elevation of cytosolic Ca^{2+} levels with A23187 stimulates Cl^- secretion and activates Cl^- channels (29, 98). Because prostaglandin synthesis and release may mediate effects of the ionophore (98), and there is a time lag between increasing Ca^{2+} concentration and increasing channel opening, Ca^{2+} may exert an indirect or secondary effect on Cl^- channel opening. Future research is needed to clarify the role of Ca^{2+} in apical Cl^- channel regulation.

Steady state stimulation of Cl^- secretion causes increased basolateral K^+ movement through a Ba^{2+}-sensitive conductance pathway (97). The intracellular second messenger required for K^+ channel activation is cytosolic Ca^{2+} (96, 101). Electrophysiological studies of intact tissue and cultured airway epithelial cells indicate the presence of a cotransporter (99). Using radiolabeled ions to quantitate electrolyte transport, we recently demonstrated loop diuretic-sensitive coupled transport of Na^+ and Cl^- in airway epithelial cells isolated from rabbit trachea, human trachea, and nasal polyps (53). Furosemide did not affect baseline Na^+ and Cl^- transport, but did block epinephrine-stimulated electrolyte transport, which indicates specific activation of coupled NaCl cotransport. Antagonist to α-adrenergic, but not to

β-adrenergic receptors blocked the stimulatory effects of epinephrine. It was concluded from these results that an airway epithelial Na^+-K^+-$2Cl^-$ cotransporter mediates the movement of at least two electrolytes, Na^+ and Cl^-, and undergoes α-adrenergic regulation.

In CF, the airway epithelium has Cl^- channels that share the kinetic and conductive properties of normal human airway cells, but are not activated by β-adrenergic agonists or cAMP-generating agents, which indicates defective regulation of the Cl^- channel (29, 100). Because β-adrenergic agents caused a similar dose-dependent increase in cAMP levels in CF and normal airway epithelial cells, it was concluded that the site of the defect was distal to the membrane receptor and AC (100), possibly at the site of protein phosphorylation. Recently, researchers tested this hypothesis and found that the purified catalytic subunit of cAMP-dependent protein kinase (PK-A) in the presence of ATP activated Cl^- channels in normal, but not CF, airway epithelial cells (49, 81). These results suggest a defect in the channel itself or in a regulatory protein associated with the Cl^- channel

Regulation of Tracheal Cl^- Transport

ADRENERGIC COMPONENT   Both α- and β-adrenergic agonists exert considerable control over Cl^- transport in airway epithelium. Two α-adrenergic receptor subtypes are typically classed as Ca^{2+} mobilizing (α_1-adrenergic) or AC inhibiting (α_2-adrenergic). The functional role of α_2-adrenergic receptors has expanded, however, to include regulation of Na^+-H^+ exchange (40, 62) and Ca^{2+} channels (35). In airway epithelium, α-adrenergic receptors modulate fursemide-sensitive coupled Na^+ and Cl^- transport, with α_1-adrenergic subtype effective in human airway epithelial cells and α_2-adrenergic subtype in rabbit tracheal epithelial cells (55). α_1-Adrenergic agonists also mediate K^+ channel activation in canine airway epithelium (96). There is evidence that Ca^{2+}, cAMP, and PI metabolites may act as second messengers in the α-adrenergic stimulation of electrolyte transporters: (a) α-Adrenergic agonists cause a transient increase in intracellular Ca^{2+} levels (55, 98). (b) In rabbit tracheal epithelial cells, α_2-adrenergic agonists stimulate prostaglandin E_2 (PGE_2) generation and release (50). PGE_2 causes a dose- and time-dependent elevation in cAMP levels in rabbit cells (50). (c) α-Adrenergic agonists stimulate PI metabolism to cause a rapid and transient accumulation of IP_3 and IP_2 before a detectable increase in inositol monophosphate levels (55). Because IP_3 is linked with Ca^{2+} mobilization from intracellular stores, α-adrenergic agonists may stimulate mobilization of Ca^{2+} by activating PLC. Also associated with PLC activation is the generation of the second messenger DG. At physiological Ca^{2+} levels, activation of PK-C with phorbol esters stimulates Cl^- secretion in a cAMP-independent manner although to a lower maximal rate than that induced by cAMP (3, 98).

Although β-adrenergic modulation of Cl⁻ secretion is dependent on intracellular cAMP (99, 100), only a few studies have focused on the mechanism of signal transduction. Stimulation of airway epithelial cells with β-adrenergic agonists causes a dose- and time-dependent accumulation of cAMP and occupancy of cAMP binding proteins by endogeneously generated cAMP (50, 51, 54, 55, 100). Indeed, in rabbit tracheal epithelial cells, the time dependent increase in cAMP levels is also manifest as decreased photoaffinity labeling of cAMP binding proteins with 8-N$_3$-[^{32}P]cAMP (Figure 3). Photoaffinity occupancy of two epithelial proteins (M_r-54,000 and 50,000) in rabbit tracheal epithelial cells decreases after incubation for 1 min with β-adrenergic agonist and reaches a minimum after 5 min, followed by a return to basal levels (55). The time course of cAMP occupancy of the binding proteins contrasts to the time dependence of cAMP accumulation, which reaches maximal levels after incubation for 10 min. with β-adrenergic agonist (55). The difference may indicate activation of PK-A at cAMP levels that are considerably lower than maximal levels. The 54-kDa and 50-kDa cAMP binding proteins correspond in electrophoretic mobility to the regulatory subunits of Type I and Type II PK-As, respectively. As recent evidence from studies on human airway epithelial cells indicate (49, 81), PK-A may play a pivotal role in cAMP induction of Cl⁻ secretion. The finding of a 36-kDa protein hyperphosphorylated in a cAMP-dependent manner in a cystic fibrosis nasal epithelial cell extract (7) suggests a link between PK-A and the defect in Cl⁻ channel regulation that must be explored more thoroughly.

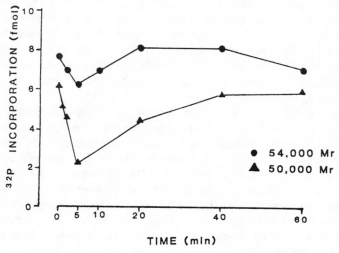

Figure 3 Occupancy of tracheocyte cAMP binding proteins as a function of incubation with β-adrenergic agonists (55).

NONADRENERGIC, NONCHOLINERGIC COMPONENT   Several lines of evidence indicate that prostaglandins, which are produced and released by the surface epithelial cells, modulate electrolyte transport: (*a*) Cyclooxygenase inhibitors block the basal rate of Cl^- secretion in canine trachea, the basal and stimulated cAMP levels in rabbit and canine tracheas, and prostaglandin production in rabbit and canine trachea, and (*b*) PGEs stimulate Cl^- secretion and increase intracellular cAMP levels (28, 45, 50, 99). Release of endogeneous prostaglandins may be induced by neurohormones (50) and local mediators (46–48), as well as exogeneously added agents such as A23187 (28, 99). PGE_2 and $PGF_{2\alpha}$ stimulate Cl^- secretion through the second messengers cAMP and Ca^{2+}, respectively (99). Leukotrienes are also produced and released from arachidonic acid by oxidative metabolism through the lipoxygenase pathway (28, 34, 37).

The local mediator adenosine stimulates Cl^- secretion in canine trachea, as does its analogue 2-Cl-adenosine, through apical receptors (68). Elevation of cAMP levels by 2-Cl-adenosine indicates a role for cAMP as the second messenger for the adenosine effects (51, 68).

SWEAT DUCT

Secretory Coil

Fluid secretion by the secretory coil is stimulated by cholinergic agonists, which produce a maximal sweat rate, and by β-adrenergic and α-adrenergic agonists, which effect successive lower sweat rates (73). The ionic basis for secretion of isotonic fluid by the secretory coil has yet to be firmly established. Electrophysiologically, secretory coil basolateral membrane is conductive to K^+ and Cl^-, with K^+ conductance 2.8 times greater than Cl^- conductance (74). Yet, cholinergic alterations in the potential difference across the basolateral membrane are consistent with Na^+ channel activation in the basolateral membrane and, from equivalent circuit analysis, a depolarization of the luminal membrane (74).

Details on signal transduction in secretory coils are still limited. Cyclic AMP apparently mediates the β-adrenegric and VIP control of sweat secretion (75, 78). Cholinergic-induced sweat secretion depends on extracellular, but not intracellular, Ca^{2+} (75). Cholinergics induce significant increases in IP esters and cGMP levels in cultured cells (41) and potentiate the biochemical response to a β-adrenergic stimulus without augmenting the physiological response (76). However, in isolated sweat gland cells, ionophore-mediated elevations in cytosolic Ca^{2+} are not sufficient to trigger secretion nor is activation of PK-C by phorbol esters likely to play a direct role in stimulus secretion coupling (80).

In CF, the secretory coil fails to respond to β-adrenergic and VIP stimulation and other cAMP-generating agents, such as forskolin. Yet, at the same time, cAMP levels are greater than those observed in control glands, which indicates an error in regulation distal to the two receptors (77, 79). The link, though, between the β-adrenergic receptor and stimulated sweat secretion has yet to be established.

Absorptive Duct

Normal intact sweat duct segments display a low resistance due to a conductance pathway for Cl^- that is likely transcellular and may involve Cl^- channels in apical and basolateral plasma membranes (5, 6, 70). The apical plasma membrane is also permeable to Na^+, as is the basolateral membrane to K^+ (6). β-Adrenergic stimulation of intact sweat duct induces absorption of HCO_3^- from the luminal fluid (70) and alterations in intracellular pH and cAMP levels (17). The latter finding suggests autonomic regulation of cytosolic pH through basolateral electrolyte exchange processes, such as Na^+-H^+ and HCO_3^--Cl^- (17). The role of the exchange transporters in ductal Cl^- transport is unclear, as is the intracellular second messenger and signal transduction pathway.

Cultured sweat duct segments retain the bioelectric properties of intact tissue and sensitivity to β-adrenergic agents (63, 71). Forskolin mimics the β-adrenergic-mediated response, which indicates a role for cAMP as the intracellular messenger (63). Pedersen reports a cholinergic-mediated increase in Cl^- flux and a short circuit current in cultured sweat glands that is not observed in sweat duct in vitro (64). This response is mimicked by the Ca^{2+} ionophore A23187 (64) and apparently stimulates PI metabolism (27).

In cultured CF sweat duct, a Cl^- conductance pathway, although present in the apical membrane (7), functions improperly (5, 6) to prevent uptake of NaCl from precursor sweat. Cl^- transport in these cells is insensitive to β-adrenergic agents (63, 71) and Ca^{2+}-mobilizing agents (7).

PANCREAS

Pancreatic Acinus

In the pancreatic acinar cell, regulation of electrolyte transport, measured with electrophysiological techniques, differs markedly from that in ductal cells (65). First, receptors linked to AC have little effect on acinar electrophysiological properties (66). Second, activation of K^+ channels is pivotal to the stimulation of NaCl secretion by pancreatic acinus (65, 67). K^+ channel activation is mediated by agents with receptors that are linked to PLC, such as cholecystokinin (CCK), and cause mobilization of Ca^{2+}, thus evoking the opening of Ca^{2+}-activated K^+ channels (66). Electrophysiologically, K^+ exit is matched by a luminal Cl^- exit. Sustained rates of Cl^- secretion require extracellular Ca^{2+}.

While a role for IP_3 in mobilizing intracellular Ca^{2+} stores is well documented (66), other PI metabolites may also regulate acinar electrolyte transport. One PI metabolite, inositol-1,3,4,5-tetrakisphosphate, may regulate Ca^{2+} influx across the plasma membrane (39). Similarly, inactivation of G_i regulatory proteins with pertussis toxin allows stimulation of AC by CCK without affecting Ca^{2+} mobilization (102). Because pertussis toxin interacts with G_i proteins linked to other receptors, additional investigations are needed to explore possible mechanisms underlying the CCK effects.

The acinar cell membrane is permeable to Cl^-, but properties of the conductance pathways have yet to be discerned. Whole-cell recordings in pig pancreatic acinar cells reveal agonist-induced activation of a Cl^- conductance pathway not localized in the basolateral membrane. It has been suggested that a Cl^- conductance pathway present in secretory granule membrane may be inserted into the luminal membrane during exocytosis (20). Indeed, in intact pancreas, physiologically relevant secretogogues, such as secretin and CCK, apparently activate granule Cl^- and K^+ conductance pathways prior to the fusion of granule and luminal membranes (30). These findings support the view that regulation of exocrine pancreatic secretion by two intracellular pathways involves Ca^{2+}-mobilizing agents and cAMP (36). Cyclic AMP acts as the second messenger for secretin-mediated effects and probably exerts its effects through activation of cAMP-dependent protein kinase (30).

Pancreatic Duct

In intact pancreatic duct, secretin acts via the intracellular second messenger cAMP to produce a HCO_3^--rich secretion that serves to neutralize the acid chyme entering the duodenum (11). Although various models have been proposed to explain the effects of secretin on Cl^- and HCO_3^- transport, uncertainty concerning the mechanism whereby pancreatic duct cells produced the HCO_3^--rich fluid has made it difficult to discern the intracellular mechanism of cAMP action. Recent studies on anion transport in the luminal membrane of rat pancreatic duct cells suggest a specific site of action for cAMP (60, 61). Cl^- channel blockers and the stilbene 4-acetamido-4'-isothiocyanatostilbene-2,2'-disulfonic acid (SITS), when applied to the luminal surface, blocked HCO_3^--induced depolarization of the basolateral membrane of duct cells. Dibutyryl cAMP also induced depolarization of the basolateral membrane but in a HCO_3^--independent manner, which suggests that cAMP mediates activation of a Cl^- channel in the luminal membrane of pancreatic duct cells. A model for pancreatic ductal anion transport that explains these data depicts a Cl^- channel in parallel with a $Cl^--HCO_3^-$ exchange in the luminal membrane. Cyclic AMP is thought to act by opening

Cl^- channels and thus stimulating Cl^- efflux. HCO_3^- secretion is then achieved by reuptake of Cl^- by the anion exchanger.

INTESTINAL TRACT

Small Intestine

In the small intestine, the cyclic nucleotides, Ca^{2+}, PK-C and arachidonic acid metabolites act as intracellular second messengers (25) to hormones and neurotransmitters (such as VIP, substance P, acetylcholine, and epinephrine), and substances involved in an inflammatory response (such as prostaglandins and bradykinin). The agents interact at the basolateral surface of enterocytes to activate or inhibit intracellular second messenger systems that produce their effects on the apical and basolateral membranes.

CYCLIC NUCLEOTIDES   Cyclic AMP and toxin-induced cGMP block electroneutral Na^+-Cl^- transport in absorptive villus cells and open Cl^- channels in crypt cells. Yet, the actual site of action and details on intracellular mechanisms of action are not yet elucidated. *Escherichia coli* heat-stable toxin promotes as increase in cGMP levels through activation of guanylate cyclase localized in the brush-border membrane (93). Intestinal crypt cells, but not absorptive villus cells, utilize cGMP as an activator of Cl^- channels, in addition to cAMP and DG, through respective kinases (18, 19). In toxin-induced secretory diarrhea, the Al-subunit of cholera toxin and *E. coli* heat-labile toxin irreversibly activate AC through ADP ribosylation of G_s (31). Several findings support the brush-border membrane as a site of cyclic nucleotide action: (*a*) Binding proteins for cAMP and cGMP are associated with Type II PK-A and with PK-G, respectively, and are localized in the interior surface of the brush-border membrane (18). (*b*) The amounts of high-affinity microvillus cAMP- and cGMP-binding sites are equal and display a disproportionate saturation of cAMP receptor sites in the absence of hormonal stimulation (92). (*c*) Treatment of intact intestine with cholera or *E. coli* heat-stable toxin causes increased receptor binding of cAMP and cGMP to respective receptor sites only (92).

Cyclic AMP mediates its effects in many cell systems through the phosphorylation of protein(s). Substrate proteins for small intestinal PK-A include three high molecular weight proteins (M_r = 105,000, 135,000, and 180,000) localized in the brush-border membrane, a cytosolic protein (M_r = 60,000) and a protein (M_r = 54,000) now identified as the phosphorylated regulatory subunit of Type II PK-A (93). In addition, a protein (M_r = 25,000) in the brush-border membrane serves as a substrate for both PK-A and cGMP-dependent protein kinase (PK-G) (18). The role of these proteins in inducing secretory diarrhea is highly speculative and remains to be elucidated.

CALCIUM   Cytosolic Ca^{2+} may regulate intestinal electrolyte transport through high-affinity binding sites (25). The nature of the binding sites for Ca^{2+} and of the mechanism whereby Ca^{2+} effects are mediated is, however, not clear. Recent studies have approached some of these questions. The sensitivity of Na^+, Cl^-, K^+, and fluid uptake by brush-border membrane vesicles to internal Ca^{2+} suggests that Ca^{2+} binding sites at the inner surface of the microvillus membrane may affect cation or anion channels or multiple channels (89). A cycle of Ca^{2+}-calmodulin dependent phosphorylation/ dephosphorylation may also be important in the modulation of ileal NaCl transport (15, 26). Thus, the Ca^{2+}-calmodulin antagonists, trifluoperazine and phenothiazine, stimulate Na^+ and Cl^- absorption in rabbit ileum at the same inhibitor concentration that blocks phosphorylation of microvillus membrane proteins ranging from $M_r = 50,000$ to $137,000$ (14). These results are consistent with a Ca^{2+}-calmodulin stimulated protein phosphorylation involved in basal suppression of NaCl absorption and in dephosphorylation of a protein ($M_r = 116,000$) involved in the regulation of NaCl absorption.

The interaction of cyclic nucleotides with Ca^{2+} to regulate electrolyte transport remains poorly defined. Recent studies present new information in cAMP-Ca^{2+} interaction, but do not allow general conclusions to be made. First, two low molecular weight ($M_r = 53,000$ and $32,000$) microvillus proteins apparently undergo phosphorylation when intracellular Ca^{2+} or cyclic nucleotides are increased (85). Second, in isolated chicken enterocytes, an 8-Br-cAMP-evoked increase in cytosolic Ca^{2+} and decrease in intracellular pH was independent of extracellular Ca^{2+}, which suggests a role for cAMP in the mobilization of Ca^{2+} stores (83).

PHOSPHOINOSITIDES   Evidence that metabolites of polyphosphoinositides (PPI) act as intracellular second messengers in the regulation of intestinal salt and water transport comes from several sources. (a) In enterocytes permeabilized with saponin or ethylenediaminetetraacetic acid (EDTA), addition of IP_3 causes a rapid and transient release of Ca^{2+} from nonmitochondrial stores (38, 84). (b) Intracellular Ca^{2+} stores in chicken (12, 83) and rat (91, 94) enterocytes and HT-29 and T84 colonocytes (2, 22, 90) are mobilized in response to agonists that stimulate Cl^- secretion. Indeed, carbachol, serotonin, and neurotensin cause a parallel increase in IP ester formation (2, 13). (c) Phorbol esters potentiate the action of Ca^{2+} by activation of PK-C, presumably by inhibiting a Na^+-H^+ exchanger in the apical membrane (1). (d) Recent studies localized enzymes involved in PI metabolism to the brush-border membrane (90). Ca^{2+} and nonhydrolysable GTP analogues trigger a pertussis toxin–insensitive release of IP_3 from the brush-border membrane, which suggests regulation by a GTP-binding protein other than G_i. How the generation of DG and IP_3 at the small intestinal brush border membrane is linked to physiological activators, which have receptors in the basolateral membrane, and affects brush border Cl^- and/or Na^+ transport is not clear.

Colon

Mammalian colon normally absorbs water, Na^+, and Cl^- while secreting K^+ and HCO_3^-. As in the small intestine, secretion of fluid is attributed to crypt cells and absorption to surface columnar cells (25). Colonic absorption of Na^+ and Cl^- is mainly attributed to apical electroneutral transport as either coupled Na,Cl(K) cotransport or dual ion exchangers (8, 42). Catecholamines and certain peptide hormones regulate NaCl absorption through cAMP- or Ca^{2+}-dependent mechanisms (8, 25). Evidence for at least two mechanisms of signal transduction have been proposed. First, serotonin inhibits NaCl absorption by a Ca^{2+}-dependent process that requires serosal, but not intracellular, Ca^{2+} (8, 25). Second, phorbol ester–induced inhibition of Na^+ and Cl^- absorption suggests a role for PK-C in the regulation of apical coupled Na^+ and Cl^- transporters (24).

Crypt, or secretory cells, possess apical Cl^- channels that are activated by cAMP-generating neurohormonal agents, such as VIP and PGE_1 (21, 23, 26, 33, 58, 86) and basolateral Na^+, K^+, $2Cl^-$ cotransporters (33). Ca^{2+} and cAMP have not yet been shown to regulate the intestinal cotransporter. Accompanying the secretory effect of VIP is the phosphorylation of four soluble proteins ($M_r = 17,000-37,000$; 14). Stimulation of Cl^- secretion in crypt cells can be dissociated from K^+ secretion by A23187 (58, 86). In T84 cells, carbachol, histamine, and A23187 increase Ba^{2+}-insensitive K^+ efflux (22, 57, 59, 95). At low doses, A23187 produces its effects without inducing Cl^- secretion, which suggests Ca^{2+} activation of basolateral K^+ channels (22). Histamine acting through an H_1 receptor evoked a rapid and transient increase in short circuit current that is similar to corresponding changes in K^+ efflux (95). The results are consistent with a role for Ca^{2+} as an activator of K^+ channels but only indirectly linked to Cl^- channel activation. One way that Ca^{2+} could exert its effects is through PK-C. Indeed, PI turnover in the human colonic cell line HT29 is stimulated by neurotensin, with feedback inhibition by phorbol esters (2). A role for PI metabolism in signal transduction in the colon is, however, not clearly evident. For example, in rat colon, phorbol ester–induced Cl^- secretion depended on arachidonic acid metabolism, which indicates a mechanism of signal transduction different from that involved in inhibition of Cl^- absorption (24).

SUMMARY AND FUTURE DIRECTIONS

The secretory process in the epithelia discussed above share the requirement for Cl^- as the actively secreted ion, with cAMP as the major intracellular second messenger in the signal transduction pathway. Cl^- becomes available for secretion through the activation of a Na^+, K^+, $2Cl^-$ cotransporter with Ca^{2+} and/or PI esters as the intracellular second messengers. Decreased Na^+ absorption in trachea and intestinal tract may accompany activation of epithelial Cl^- secretion. Ca^{2+}-dependent inactivation of apical Na^+ transporters or Cl^--HCO_3^- exchange could produce these effects. Because neurohormones and circulating hormones can produce their effects directly by interacting with membrane receptors or indirectly by stimulating the release of local mediators that interact with epithelial cells, future research is needed to define the physiologically relevant stimuli and intracellular second messengers that regulate Cl^- transport carriers. In particular, studies are needed to determine the link between Ca^{2+} and cAMP in the activation of Cl^- channels. Progress in understanding the regulation of epithelial Cl^- transport will require information at the molecular level on the intracellular mechanisms of signal transduction involving Ca^{2+}, cyclic nucleotides, and PI esters, and biochemical characterization of the transporters.

ACKNOWLEDGMENTS

The author thanks Dr. I Novak for access to manuscripts in press and Drs. U. Hopfer, D. Dearborn, and M. Welsh for helpful discussion. This work is supported by grants from the NIH Cystic Fibrosis Core Center (DK 27651) and from the Cystic Fibrosis Foundation.

Literature Cited

1. Ahn, J., Chang, E. B., Field, M. 1985. Phorbol ester inhibition of Na-H exchange in rabbit proximal cells. *Am. J. Physiol.* 249:C527–C530
2. Amar, S., Kitabgi, P., Vincent, J.-P. 1986. Activation of phosphatidylinositol turnover by neurotensin receptors in the human colonic adenocarcinoma cell line HT29. *FEBS Lett.* 201:31–36
3. Barthelson, R. A., Jacoby, D. B., Widdicombe, J. H. 1987. Regulation of chloride secretion in dog tracheal epithelium by protein kinase C. *Am. J. Phsyiol.* 253:C802–C808
4. Berschneider, H., Azizkhan, R. G., Knowles, M., Boucher, R., Powell, D. N. 1987. Intestinal electrolyte transport in cystic fibrosis. *Gastroenterology* 92: 1315 (Abstr.)
5. Bijman, J., Fromter, E. 1986. Direct demonstration of high transepthelial chloride-conductance in normal sweat duct which is absent in cystic fibrosis. *Pflüegers Arch.* 407:S123–S127
6. Bijman, J., Quinton, P. 1987. Permeability properties of cell membranes

and tight junctions of normal and cystic fibrosis sweat ducts. *Pflüegers Arch.* 408:505–10
7. Bijman, J., Scholte, B., de Jonge, H. R., Hoogeveen, A. T., Kansen, M., et al. 1988. Chloride transport in cystic fibrosis: chloride channel regulation in cultured sweat duct and cultured nasal polyp epithelium. In *Cellular and Molecular Basis of Cystic Fibrosis*, ed. G. Mastella, P. M. Quinton, pp. 133–40. San Francisco Press
8. Binder, H. J. 1988. Electrolyte absorption and secretion in the mammalian colon. In *Physiology of the Gastrointestinal Tract*, ed. L. R. Johnson, pp. 1389–1418. New York: Raven. 2nd ed.
9. Boucher, R. C., Stutts, M. J., Gatzy, J. T. 1981. Regional differences in bioelectric properties and ion flow in excised canine airways. *J. Appl. Physiol.* 51:706–14
10. Boucher, R. C., Stutts, M. J., Knowles, M. R., Cantlye, L. Gatzy, J. T. 1986. Na^+ transport in cystic fibrosis respiratory epithelia: abnormal basal rate and

Cl TRANSPORT REGULATION 157

response to adenylate cyclase activation. *J. Clin. Invest.* 78:1245–52

11. Case, R. M., Argent, B. E. 1986. Bicarbonate secretion by pancreatic acinar cell: Mechanism and control. In *The Exocrine Pancreas: Biology, Pathobiology, and Disease,* ed. V. L. W. Go, J. D. Gardner, F. P. Brooks, E. Lebenthel, E. P. DiMango, G. A. Sheele, pp. 213–43. New York: Raven

12. Chang, E. B., Brown, D. R., Wang, N. S. Field, M. 1986. Secretogague-induced changes in membrane calcium permeability in chicken and chinchilla ileal mucosa-selective inhibition by loperamide. *J. Clin. Invest.* 78:281–87

13. Chang, E. B., Wang, N. S., Musch, M. W. 1987. Cellular mechanism for Ca^{2+} activation in isolated enterocytes. *Gastroenterology* 90:1370 (Abstr.)

14. Cohen, J. A. 1987. Vasoactive intestinal peptide stimulates protein phosphorylation in a colonic epithelial cell line. *Am. J. Physiol.* 253:G420–G424

15. Cohen, M. E., Sharp, G. W. G., Donowitz, M. 1986. Suggestion of a role for calmodulin and phosphorylation in regulation of rabbit ileal electrolyte transport: effects of promethazine. *Am. J. Physiol.* 251:G710–G717

16. Cotton, C. U., Stutts, M. J., Knowles, M. R., Gatzy, J. T., Boucher, R. C. 1987. Abnormal apical cell membrane in cystic fibrosis respiratory epithelium. *J. Clin. Invest.* 79:80–85

17. Dearborn, D., Waller, R. L., Yike, I. 1988. The human sweat duct: cytosolic pH changes in response to autonomic agents. See Ref. 7, pp. 141–49

18. De Jonge, H. R. 1984. Cyclic nucleotide-dependent protein phosphorylation in intestinal epithelium. In *Mechanisms of Intestinal Electrolyte Transport and Regulation,* ed. M. Donowitz, G. W. G. Sharp, pp. 263–86. New York: Liss

19. De Jonge, H. R., Bijman, H., Sinaasappel, M. 1987. Relation of regulatory enzyme levels to chloride transport in intestinal epithelial cells. *Ped. Pulmonol. Suppl.* 1:54–57

20. DeLisle, R.C., Hopfer, U. H. 1986. Electrolyte permeabilities of pancreatic zymogen granules: implications for pancreatic secretion. *Am. J. Physiol.* 250: G489–G496

21. Dharmsathaphorn, K., Mandel, K. G., Masui, H., McRoberts, J. A. 1985. Vasoactive intestinal polypeptide-induced chloride secretion by a colonic epithelial cell line. *J. Clin. Invest.* 75: 462–71

22. Dharmsathaphorn, K., Pandol, S. J.

1986. Mechanism of chloride secretion induced by carbachol in a colonic epithelial cell line. *J. Clin. Invest.* 77:348–54

23. Dharmsathaphorn, K., Weymer, A., McRoberts, J. A. 1985. Chloride secretion induced by prostaglandin E (PGE) and participation of NaKCl cotransport, Cl channels and K channels. *Gastroenterology* 88:1364

24. Donowitz, M., Cheng, H. Y., Sharp, C. W. G. 1986. Effect of phorbol esters on sodium and chloride transport in rat colon. *Am. J. Physiol.* 251:G509–G517

25. Donowitz, M., Welsh, M. J. 1987. Regulation of mammalian small intestinal electrolyte secretion. See Ref. 8, pp. 1351–86

26. Donowitz, M., Wicks, J., Madara, J., Sharp, G. W. G. 1985. Studies on role of calmodulin in Ca^{2+} regulation of rabbit ileal Na and Cl absorption. *Am. J. Physiol.* 248:G726–G740

27. Doughney, C., Pederson, P. S., McPherson, M. A., Dormer, R. L. 1987. Autonomic regulation of inositol phosphate formation in cultured human sweat duct cells. *Ped. Pulmonol. Suppl.:* 119A

28. Eling, T. E., Danilowicz, R. M., Henke, D. C., Sivarajah, K., Yankaskas, J. R., Boucher, R. C. 1986. Arachidonic acid metabolism by canine tracheal epithelial cells. Product formation and relationship to chloride secretion. *J. Biol. Chem.* 261:12841–49

29. Frizzell, R. A., Rechkemmer, G., Shoemaker, R. L. 1986. Altered regulation of airway epithelial cell chloride channels in Cystic Fibrosis. *Science* 233:558–60

30. Gasser, K. W., DiDomenico, J., Hopfer, U. 1988. Secretagogues activate chloride transport pathways in pancreatic zymogen granules. *Am. J. Physiol.* 254:G93–G99

31. Gill, D. M., Woolkalis, M. 1985. Toxins which activate adenylate cyclase. *Ciba Found. Symp.* 112:57–73

32. Hardcastle, J., Hardcastle, P. T. 1986. The involvement of basolateral potassium channels in the intestinal response to secretagogues in the rat. *J. Physiol. (London)* 379:331–45

33. Heintze, K., Stewart, C. P., Frizzell, R. A. 1983. Sodium-dependent chloride secretion across rabbit descending colon. *Am. J. Physiol.* 244:G357–G365

34. Holtzman, M., Aizawa, J. H., Nadel, J. A., Goetzl, E. J. 1983. Selective generation of leukotriene B$_4$ by tracheal epithelial cells from dogs. *Biochem. Biophys. Res. Commun.* 114:1071–76

35. Homaidan, F. R., El-Sabban, M. W.,

Wicks, J., Cusolito, S., Donowitz, M., Sharp, G. W. G. 1986. Calcium channel blockers interact with the α_2-adrenergic receptor in basolateral membrane of rabbit ileum. *J. Gen. Physiol.* 88:28a

36. Hootman, S. R., Williams, J. A. 1987. Stimulus-secretion coupling in the pancreatic acinus. See Ref. 8, pp. 1129–46

37. Hunter, J. A., Finkbeiner, W. E., Nadel, J. A., Goetzl, E. J., Holtzman, M. J. 1985. Predominant generation of 15-lipoxygenase metabolites of arachidonic acid by epithelial cells from human trachea. *Proc. Natl. Acad. Sci. USA* 82:4633–37

38. Ilundain, A., O'Brien, J. A., Burton, K. A., Sepulveda, F. V. 1987. Inositol trisphosphate and calcium mobilisation in permeabilised enterocytes. *Biochim. Biophys. Acta* 896:113–16

39. Irvine, R. F., Moor, R. M. 1986. Micro-injection of inositol (1,3,4,5) tetrakisphosphate activates sea urchin eggs by promoting Ca^{2+} entry. *Biochem. J.* 240:917–20

40. Isom, L. L., Cragoe, E. J. Jr., Limbird, L. E. 1987. α_2-adrenergic receptors accelerate Na^+/H^+ exchange in neuroblastoma X glioma cells. *J. Biol. Chem.* 262:6750–57

41. Kealey, T. 1988. Phosphorylation studies on human eccrine sweat gland. See Ref. 7, pp. 150–54

42. Knauf, H., Haag, K. 1986. Modelling of colonic Cl^- and K^+ transport under resting and secreting conditions. *Pflüegers Arch.* 407(Suppl. 2):S85–S89

43. Knowles, M. R., Carson, J. L., Collier, A. M., Gatzy, J. T., Bouchers, R. C. 1981. Measurements of nasal transepithelial electric potential differences in normal human subjects in vivo. *Am. Rev. Respir. Dis.* 124:484–90

44. Knowles, M. R., Stutts, M. J., Spock, A., Fischer, N., Gatzy, J. T., Boucher, R. C. 1983. Abnormal ion permeation through cystic fibrosis respiratory epithelium. *Science* 221:1067–70

45. Lazarus, S. C., Basbaum, C. B., Gold, W. M. 1984. Prostaglandins and intracellular cyclic AMP in respiratory secretory cells. *Am. Rev. Respir. Dis.* 130:262–66

46. Lazarus, S. C., McCabe, L. J., Nadel, J. A., Gold, W. M., Leikauf, G. D. 1986. Effects of mast cell-derived mediators on epithelial cells in canine trachea. *Am. J. Physiol.* 251:C387–C394

47. Leikauf, G. D., Ueki, I. F., Nadel, J. A., Widdicombe, J. H. 1985. Bradykinin stimulates Cl secretion and prostaglandin E_2 release by canine tracheal epithelium. *Am. J. Physiol.* 248:F48–F55

48. Leikauf, G. D., Ueki, I. F., Widdicombe, J. H., Nadel, J. A. 1986. Alteration of chloride secretion across canine tracheal epithelium by lipoxygenase products of arachidonic acid. *Am. J. Physiol.* 250:F47–F53

49. Li, M., McCann, J. D., Liedtke, C. M., Nairn, A. C., Greengard, P., Welsh, M. J. 1988. Cyclic AMP-dependent protein kinase opens chloride channels in normal but not cystic fibrosis airway epithelium. *Nature* 331:358–60

50. Liedtke, C. M. 1986. Interaction of epinephrine with isolated rabbit tracheal epithelial cells. *Am. J. Physiol.* 251:C209–C215

51. Liedtke, C. M., Boat, T. F., Rudolph, S. A. 1982. Neurohormonal receptors and cyclic AMP-binding proteins in rabbit tracheal mucosa-submucosa. *Biochem. Biophys. Acta* 719:169–77

52. Liedtke, C. M., Hopfer, U. 1982. Mechanism of Cl^- translocation across small intestinal brush border membrane. I. Absence of Na^+-Cl^- cotransport. *Am. J. Physiol.* 242:G263–G271

53. Liedtke, C. M., Romero, M., Hopfer, U. 1988. Adrenergic control of the Na,K,2Cl cotransporter in airway epithelial cells. See Ref. 7, pp. 307–13

54. Liedtke, C. M., Rudolph, S. A., Boat, T. F. 1983. β-adrenergic modulation of mucin secretion in cat trachea. *Am. J. Physiol.* 244:C391–C398

55. Liedtke, C. M., Tandler, B. 1984. Physiological responsiveness of isolated rabbit tracheal epithelial cells. *Am. J. Physiol.* 247:C441–C449

56. Majerus, P. W., Connolly, T. M., Deckmyn, H., Ross, T. S., Bross, T. E., et al. 1986. The metabolism of phosphoinositide-derived messenger molecules. *Science* 234:1519–26

57. Mandel, K. G., Dharmsathaphorn, K., McRoberts, J. A. 1986. Characterization of a cyclic AMP-activated Cl^- transport pathway in the apical membrane of a human colonic epithelial cell line. *J. Biol. Chem.* 261:704–12

58. McCabe, R. D., Smith, P. L. 1985. Colonic potassium and chloride secretion: role of cAMP and calcium. *Am. J. Physiol.* 248:G103–G109

59. McRoberts, J. A., Beurlem, G., Dharmasthaphorn, K. 1985. Cyclic AMP and Ca^{++}-activated K transport in a human colonic epithelial cell line. *J. Biol. Chem.* 200:14160–72

60. Novak, I., Greger, R. 1988. Electrophysiological study of transport systems in isolated perfused pancreatic ducts:

properties of the basolateral membrane. *Pfluegers Arch.* 411:58–68

61. Novak, I., Greger, R. 1988. Properties of the luminal membrane of isolated perfused rat pancreatic ducts. Effect of cyclic AMP and blockers of chloride transport. *Pflüegers Arch.* 411:546–72

62. Nunnari, J. M., Repaske, M. G., Brandon, S., Cragoe, E. J. Jr., Limbird, L. E. 1987. Regulation of porcine brain α_2-adrenergic receptors by Na^+, H^+ and inhibitors of Na^+/H^+ exchange. *J. Biol. Chem.* 262:12387–92

63. Pedersen, P. S. 1987. Transepithelial ion transport in sweat duct cell cultures derived from normals and patients with cystic fibrosis. *Med. Sci. Res.* 17:1009–16

64. Pedersen, P. S. 1987. Cholinergic influence on chloride permeability in sweat duct cell cultures from normals and patients with cystic fibrosis. *Med. Sci. Res.* 15:769–70

65. Petersen, O. H. 1986. Calcium-activated potassium channels and fluid secretion by exocrine glands. *Am. J. Physiol.* 251:G1–G13

66. Petersen, O. H. 1987. Electrophysiology of the pancreas. *Physiol. Rev.* 67:1054–1116

67. Petersen, O. H., Maruyama, Y. 1984. Calcium-activated potassium channels and their role in secretion. *Nature* 307:693–96

68. Pratt, A.D., Clancy, G., Welsh, M. J. 1986. Mucosal adenosine stimulates chloride secretion in canine tracheal epithelium. *Am. J. Physiol.* 251:C167–C174

69. Rasmussen, H. 1986. The calcium messenger system. *N. Engl. J. Med.* 314:1164–70

70. Reddy, M. M., Quinton, P. M. 1988. Chloride and bicarbonate transport in the human sweat duct. See Ref. 7, pp. 125–32

71. Reddy, M. M., Riordan, J. R., Quinton, P. M. 1988. Electrical properties of cultured reabsorptive sweat duct cells from normal and cystic fibrosis subjects: intracellular microelectrode analysis. See Ref. 7, pp. 383–93

72. Ryu, S. H., Lee, S. Y., Lee, K.-Y., Rhee, S. G. 1987. Catalytic properties of inositol trisphosphate kinase: activation by Ca^{2+} and calmodulin. *FASEB. J.* 1:388–93

73. Sato, K. 1982. Mechanism of eccrine sweat secretion. In *Fluid and Electrolyte Abnormalities in Exocrine Glands in Cystic Fibrosis*, ed. P. M. Quinton, J. R. Martinez, U. Hopfer, pp. 35–52. San Francisco Press

74. Sato, K. 1986. Effect of methacholine on ionic permeability of basal membrane of the eccrine secretory cell. *Pflüegers Arch.* 407:S100–S106

75. Sato, K., Saga, K., Sato, F. 1988. Membrane transport and intracellular events in control and cystic fibrosis eccrine sweat glands. See Ref. 7, pp. 171–85

76. Sato, K., Sato, F. 1983. Cholinergic potentiation of isoproterenol-induced cAMP level in sweat gland. *Am. J. Physiol.* 245:C189–C195

77. Sato, K., Sato, F. 1984. Defective beta adrenergic response of Cystic Fibrosis sweat glands in vivo and in vitro. *J. Clin. Invest.* 73:1763–71

78. Sato, K., Sato, F. 1987. Effect of VIP on sweat secretion and cAMP accumulation in isolated simian eccrine glands. *Am. J. Physiol.* 253:R935–R941

79. Sato, K., Sato, F. 1987. Absence of cAMP mediated sweating response in cystic fibrosis sweat glands in the face of normal cAMP accumulation in the sweat secretory cells. *Clin. Res.* 35:714A

80. Sato, K., Sato, F. 1988. Dissociation between quin 2-determined cytosolic $[Ca^{2+}]$ and sweat secretion. *Am. J. Physiol.* 254:C310–C317

81. Schoumacher, R. A., Shoemaker, R. L., Halm, D. R., Tallant, E. A., Wallace, R. W., Frizzell, R. A. 1987. Phosphorylation fails to activate chloride channels from cystic fibrosis airway cells. *Nature* 330:752–54

82. Sekar, M. C., Hokin, L. E. 1986. The role of phosphoinositides in signal transduction. *J. Membr. Biol.* 89:193–210

83. Semrad, C. E., Change, E. B. 1987. Cellular mechanisms for Ca-activation in isolated enterocytes. *Am. J. Physiol.* 252:C315–C322

84. Sepulveda, F. V., Smith, S. M. 1987. Calcium transport by permeabilised rabbit small intestinal epithelial cells. *Pflüegers Arch.* 408:231–38

85. Sharp, G. W., Hannah-White, C., El-Sabban, M., Cohen, M. E., Donowitz, M. 1987. Effects of Ca^{2+}, theophylline and promethazine on protein phosphorylation in intact cells of rabbit ileum. Correlation with active Na and Cl absorption. *FEBS Lett.* 221:309–14

86. Smith, P. L., McCabe, R. 1984. A23187-induced changes in colonic K and Cl transport are mediated by separate mechanisms. *Am. J. Phys.* 247:G695–G707.

87. Speigel, A. M. 1987. Signal transfuction by guanine nucleotide binding proteins. *Mol. Cell. Endocrinol.* 40:1–6

88. Taussig, L. M., ed. 1984. *Cystic Fibrosis.* New York: Thieme-Stratton. 498 pp.
89. Vaandrager, A., Ploemacher, M. C., De Jonge, H. R. 1986. Modulation of salt permeabilities of intestinal brush-border membrane vesicles by micromolar levels of internal calcium. *Biochim. Biophys. Acta* 856:325–36
90. Vaandrager, A. B. 1987. *Ion transport regulation in intestinal brush border membranes.* PhD thesis. Erasmus University, Rotterdam, The Netherlands. 160 pp.
91. Van Corven, E. J. J. M., Verbost, P. M., de Jong, M. D., van Os, C. H. 1987. Kinetics of ATP-dependent Ca^{2+} uptake by permeabilized rat enterocytes. Effects of inositol 1,4,5-trisphosphate. *Cell Calcium* 8:197–206
92. van Dommelen, F. S., De Jonge, H. R. 1986. Local changes in fractional saturation of cGMP- and cAMP-receptors in intestinal microvilli in response to cholera toxin and heat-stable *Escherichia coli* toxin. *Biochim. Biophys. Acta* 886:135–42
93. van Dommelen, F. S., De Jonge, H. R. 1984. Cyclic-GMP and cyclic-AMP-induced intestinal ion secretion: analysis at the level of brush border membrane vesicles. In *Advances in Cyclic Nucleotide and Protein Phosphorylation Research,* ed. P. Greengard, G. A. Robison, R. Paoletti, S. Nicosia, 17:303–13, New York: Raven
94. Velasco, G., Shears, S. B., Michell, R. H., Lazo, P. S. 1986. Calcium uptake by intracellular compartments in permeabilized enterocytes. Effect of inositol 1,4,5-trisphosphate. *Biochem. Biophys. Res. Commun.* 139:612–18
95. Wasserman, S. I., Barrett, K. E., Huott, P. A., Beuerlein, G., Kagnoff, M. F., Dharmsathaphorn, K. 1988. Immune-related intestinal Cl^- secretion. I. Effect of histamine on T84 cell line. *Am. J. Physiol.* 254:C53–C62
96. Welsh, M. J. 1986. Adrenergic regulation of ion transport by primary cultures of canine tracheal epithelium: cellular electrophysiology. *J. Membr. Biol.* 91: 121–28
97. Welsh, M. J. 1983. Barium inhibition of basolateral membrane potassium conductance in tracheal epithelium. *Am. J. Physiol.* 244:F639–F645
98. Welsh, M. J. 1987. Effects of phorbol ester and calcium ionophore on chloride secretion in cultured canine tracheal epithelium. *Am. J. Physiol.* 253:C828–C837
99. Welsh, M. J. 1987. Electrolyte transport by airway epitheliua. *Physiol. Rev.* 67:1143–84
100. Welsh, M. J., Liedtke, C. M. 1986. Chloride and potassium channels in cystic fibrosis airway epithelia. *Nature* 322: 467–70
101. Welsh, M. J., McCann, J. D. 1985. Intracellular calcium regulates basolateral potassium channels in a chloride secreting epithelium. *Proc. Natl. Acad. Sci. USA* 82:8823–26
102. Willems, P. H. G. M., Lilly, R. H. J., DePont, J. J. H. H. M. 1987. Pertussis toxin stimulates cholecystokinin-induced cyclic AMP formation but is without effect on secretogogue-induced calcium mobilization in exocrine pancrease. *Biochim. Biophys. Acta* 928: 179–85

Annu. Rev. Physiol. 1989. 51:161–76

THE ROLE OF CYTOPLASMIC PROTEINS IN HEPATIC BILE ACID TRANSPORT[1]

Andrew Stolz, Hajime Takikawa, Murad Ookhtens, and Neil Kaplowitz

Liver Research Laboratory, Wadsworth Veterans Administration Hospital Center and the UCLA School of Medicine, Los Angeles, California 90073

INTRODUCTION

Bile acids play a crucial role in the promotion of bile flow and in the intestinal absorption of fatty acids via micellization. In addition, bile acids are the end product of cholesterol and constitute 50% of the excretable cholesterol pool in man. Hepatocytes in the liver efficiently extract bile acids from the portal venous system through the sinusoidal membrane and rapidly excrete them via the canalicular membrane into bile. This vectorial transport involves membrane carriers at each pole. However, the mechanism of the intracellular translocation is less apparent (10, 43, 45, 64, 66). In parallel with the characterization of membrane transport of bile acids, recent research has identified and characterized the cytosolic bile acid binding proteins present in rat and human liver and has begun to determine their physiological role. This chapter focuses on the intracellular bile acid binding proteins and reviews their biochemical characteristics and physiological role. We particularly focus on studies from our own laboratory during the past five years, and therefore do not intend to present a complete or encompassing historical review.

---

[1]The U.S. Government has the right to retain a nonexclusive royalty-free license in and to any copyright covering this paper.

ENTEROHEPATIC CIRCULATION

Bile acids serve a variety of important functions, some of which depend on an enterohepatic circulation. Thus, a small pool of bile acids (stored in the gall bladder) recycles from the intestine to the liver to the intestine many times during each meal, thereby insuring sufficient concentrations both in the intestinal lumen to solubilize fat and in the canaliculus to drive osmotic bile flow. For such a system to exist, two loci of transport for bile acids are necessary, namely the liver and the ileum (37, 85). At each location, vectorial transfer of bile acids from one surface of an epithelium to the other occurs. Therefore, membrane transport processes occur at each pole of the cell, and bile acids are transferred from one pole of the epithelial cell to the other.

BILE ACID TRANSPORT IN THE LIVER

Physiological bile acids enter the hepatocyte mainly via a $Na+$ cotransport process (3, 10, 26, 27, 79). So far, this transporter has not been exactly identified although affinity probes suggest that 48-kDa protein in the basolateral membrane is involved (1, 2, 36, 40, 81, 82, 84). The more hydrophilic bile acids, such as trihydroxy amidates and taurine conjugated dihydroxy bile acids, seem to share this uptake mechanism (7, 79). The more hydrophobic bile acids, such as unconjugated or glycine conjugated dihydroxy and monohydroxy bile acids, alternatively may enter hepatocytes by passive diffusion or by a facilitated carrier-mediated transport that also transports organic anions (82, 84). In addition, the existence of a cholate-hydroxyl exchanger has been suggested but remains controversial (9). Regardless of whether bile acids enter the hepatocyte by carrier-mediated transport or passive diffusion, the mechanism by which these molecules remain within the hepatocyte and are transferred to the canalicular pole for excretion, as opposed to refluxing into plasma (reverse transport or back-diffusion), is still not known. The latter would be especially likely since the bile acids are bound by plasma albumin with a high affinity.

The following three mechanisms may explain how bile acids are retained in the hepatocyte and are translocated across the cell: lateral diffusion through membranes, vesicular transport, and retention or transport by cytosolic binding proteins. Lateral membranous diffusion would explain the access of lipophilic substrates to relatively inaccessable microsomal enzymes, such as glucuronyl transferase, but would not be a logical and efficient vectorial transfer mechanism (12, 88). One would predict a general lack of organelle selectivity for diffusion. Indeed, bile acids then might be detoured from vectorial transport and accumulate in various loci within the cell. More likely, this does not occur and vectorial transfer dominates at physiological concentrations of bile acids in the hepatocytes. Some evidence for vesicular transport has been published (10, 39, 57, 65). Although inconclusive, bile acids and other cholephilic substances may accumulate in pericanalicular vesicles (21, 31) and then may be excreted into bile by exocytosis. Bile acids clearly do not enter the cell by endocytosis; therefore, if vesicular transport exists, it would be a more distal event in the transcellular translocation process. A 100-kDa protein has been identified in the canalicular membrane, which may participate in transport of bile acids into bile (27, 46, 54). Its relation to a vesicular mechanism, however, is unclear. Regardless of whether the transport of bile acids from hepatocytes into bile occurs via transport across the plasma membrane (canaliculus) or transport into pericanalicular vesicles (which undergo subsequent exocytosis), we have hypothesized that access to these excretory transporters most likely occurs via cytosol. Therefore, we have hypothesized that cytosolic proteins may play a key role in vectorial bile acid transport in at least two ways: (*a*) minimization of back diffusion at the sinusoidal pole, thereby affecting net extraction by the liver, and (*b*) retention of bile acids in the cytosolic compartment, thereby preventing distribution into an abyss of membranous compartments. Our work has been aimed at testing these hypotheses by identifying, purifying, and characterizing the binding properties of cytosolic proteins that exhibit specificity for bile acids and then by designing studies to test the physiological significance of some of these interactions.

CYTOPLASMIC BILE ACID BINDING PROTEINS

Within rat and human liver cytosol, three distinct groups of bile acid binding proteins with different molecular weight have been identified: (*a*) glutathione S-transferases (45–50 kDa), (*b*) Y' binders (33 kDa), and (*c*) fatty acid binding protein (FABP) (14 kDa). The major characteristics of each of these groups are reviewed and compared below.

Glutathione S-Transferases

The glutathione S-transferases are a family of dimeric proteins (homodimers and heterodimers) that catalyze the reaction of glutathione (GSH) and various endogenous and exogenous electrophilic substrates (32). In addition to the enzymatic activity, these proteins are capable of binding a wide variety of nonsubstrate ligands (11, 23, 24, 33, 34, 66, 76, 80). Recent molecular biological studies identified a supergene family with highly conserved individual families of subunit genes with great homology (35). A detailed discussion is beyond the scope of this review.

The rat transferases have been most extensively studied. The Y_a and Y_c subunits (also known as subunits 1 and 2) constitute one family, Y_b and Y_b'

(subunits 3 and 4) constitute the other major family (35). Although these are the most abundant subunits in rat liver, at least 10 distinct gene products have been identified (35). The Y_a subunit exhibits an unique nonsubstrate binding site that binds bilirubin, lithocholate, and some other ligands with very high affinity (66, 71, 76). The high affinity for these lipophilic substances is the basis for the designation of these transferases (Y_aY_a and Y_aY_c) as ligandins (24, 32). Wolkoff et al demonstrated, using indicator dilution techniques in the perfused rat liver, that the initial rate of bilirubin uptake is independent of hepatic ligandin content whereas the rate of release (back diffusion) is inversely related to ligandin content (86). This finding was the first direct demonstration of a cytosolic protein affecting net extraction by the liver and is consistent with our subsequent work and hypothesis with respect to bile acids and cytosolic proteins. In the case of ligandins, bilirubin back diffusion from cytosol to plasma is prevented by minimizing its free concentration through binding to the high affinity nonsubstrate site on the Y_a-containing GSH S-transferases.

As for bile acids other than lithocholate, rat transferases of the Y_a and Y_b group bind bile acids with comparable affinity in our studies (71, 76). However, there is some disagreement with regard to the selectivity of various transferases for bile acids (41, 42, 47). We have also found that binding of bile acids is inhibited in the presence of GSH by what appears to be an allosteric effect (71, 77). GSH S-transferases from human liver do not exhibit high affinity binding of bilirubin or bile acids (75, 77, 78). Thus, GSH S-transferases may only serve a ligandin role for bilirubin and lithocholate in the rat. However, heme binding is highly conserved. Human transferases retain the property of high affinity binding of heme seen with rat transferases (32, 33, 78). Thus, the major "ligandin" role of the GSH S-transferases may be the intracellular transport of tetrapyrroles such as heme and bilirubin.

Binding properties of this family of proteins for bile acids have been extensively examined using equilibrium or flow dialysis with radiolabeled bile acids and competitive displacement of the fluorescent binding probe, 1-anilino-8-naphthalene sulfonate. In addition, others have used inhibition of enzyme activity by bile acids to probe these interactions. Table 1 compares the dissociation constants in rat and man of the glutathione S-transferases with the other two major classes of binding proteins using approximate values from our own studies (69–71, 75–77).

Y' Bile Acid Binder

After the identification of the glutathione S-transferases as ligandins (32, 34), an additional group of organic anion binding proteins were identified in the rat liver cytosol. This 30-35 kDa molecular weight fraction, designated as the Y' fraction, could be clearly separated from the glutathione S-transferases (Y

Table 1 Summary of dissociation constants for binding of bile acids by three classes of cytoplasmic proteins from rat and human liver GSH S-transferase[a].

Bile Acids	GST[b]		Human	FABP[c]		Y' binder	
	Rat		Human	Rat	Human	Rat	Human
	Y_a class	Y_b class					
Lithocholate	0.5	5	10	5	10	1–2	.05
Lithocholate amidates[d]	5	—	20	5	10	1–2	.05
Chenodeoxycholate and amidates[d]	10–20	10–20[e]	100	20	20	1–2	0.1
Cholate and amidates[d]	20[e]	20[e]	1000	500	100	100	1.0

[a]All values in μmol/l.
[b]GST refers to GSH S-transferases.
[c]FABP refers to fatty acid binding protein.
[d]Amidates refers to glycine and taurine conjugates.
[e]Double with GSH.

proteins) by high resolution gel filtration chromatography (68, 69). Within this Y' fraction, a number of distinct proteins, which either bind or metabolize lipophilic compounds, were identified and purified to homogeneity. These proteins included: (a) organic anion binding protein, a 34 kDa tetrameric protein that binds organic anions such as heme and thyroid hormones with moderate affinity (63, 68), (b) bile acid binding proteins, 33 kDa proteins (69) that have been identified recently as being 3α-hydroxysteroid dehydrogenase (see below) (61, 62), (c) phenolic steroid sulfotransferase, a 32.5-kDa monomeric sulfotransferase (67, 73) that sulfates estradiol, estrone, and bile acids at the 3-OH position, and (d) tocopherol binding protein, a 32-kDa protein that selectively binds tocopherol (53) and is believed to mediate the transfer of tocopherol between membrane fractions in cells (13, 14).

The Y' bile acid binders in rat liver cytosol originally were identified by their capacity to bind bile acids (69). Two forms were identified, designated binders I and II (69). Subsequently, with improved resolution, binder II was separated into II and III (60–62). Binder I is the predominant form (61, 62). The binding properties of rat binder I can be compared to rat transferases by examining Table 1. The Y' binder exhibits somewhat lower affinity for unconjugated lithocholic acid than the Y_a-containing transferases. However, the Y' binder exhibits higher affinity for conjugated lithocholate and conjugated and unconjugated dihydroxy bile acids and somewhat lower affinity for trihydroxy bile acids. The latter difference, however, is minimized in the presence of GSH, which lowers the affinity of the rat transferases for most bile acids (69, 71, 76).

Further characterization of the Y' bile acid binders by a specific radioimmunoassay revealed that the liver contains the greatest concentration and the female rat liver contains a greater concentration of the proteins than the male

(58, 60). Ontogenic studies in both male and female rats demonstrated a parallel development of the Y' bile acid binder content with the development of bile acid metabolizing enzymes, such as the sulfotransferases (4, 60). Unfortunately, the presence of intestinal proteases prevented accurate measurement of these Y' bile acid binders in the small intestine. However, a 33-kDa protein band was identified on immunoblotting of small intestinal cytosol, which indicates the presence of a Y' bile acid binderlike protein in small intestinal cytosol (own unpublished observations). Further work will be required to determine the longitudinal and the villus distribution of the Y' bile acid binder in the small intestine. The GSH S-transferases are most abundant in the proximal intestine (52). It will be of interest to see if the Y' binder is more abundant in the distal intestine in parallel with localization of membrane transport.

Within human liver cytosol, a Y' molecular weight fraction similar to that of the rat was identified (59). From this Y' fraction, a 36-kDa bile acid binding protein was purified to homogeneity (59). This protein exhibited remarkably high binding affinities for the bile acids (75, 77) listed in Table 1. Thus, the species differences in binding properties are striking. GSH S-transferases exhibit much lower binding affinity in human than in rat whereas the Y' binder exhibits much higher binding affinity in human. The difference in human Y' binder and human GSH S-transferase, therefore, is greatly magnified (2–3 orders of magnitude difference).

Fatty Acid Binding Protein

Fatty acid binding protein is a 14.3-kDa monomeric protein that avidly binds fatty acids (5, 44). The precise function of this protein is unknown, but presumably it facilitates the transfer of fatty acids and other precursors required for lipid synthesis and metabolism. FABP exists in multiple organs, including the heart, intestine, brain, and kidneys (6, 17, 18, 56) Recently, the genes encoding both the intestinal and hepatic form were identified (6, 22) and are now being intensively studied. Bile acids are capable of binding to the hepatic form (70). The dissociation constants for bile acid binding, listed in Table 1, are higher in the rat than those for the other two groups of bile acid binding proteins (62, 69, 76). In view of their lower affinity for bile acids and their high affinity for abundant fatty acids, a role for FABP in bile acid transport is less likely.

STUDIES WITH AFFINITY PROBES OF BILE ACIDS

Many studies have attempted to identify the subcellular localization of bile acids in liver using fractionation techniques. However, redistribution during homogenization largely invalidates this approach. The association of bile acids with subcellular fractions during their translocation from the sinusoidal to the canalicular pole of the cell also has been examined with radiolabeled bile acid affinity probes. Radiolabeled, azido photo affinity bile acid probes have been extensively utilized by workers in Kurz' laboratory to identify the proteins that bind bile acids during uptake, translocation, and excretion by the liver (1, 2, 36, 38, 84). Ziegler performed similar work with chemical affinity probes with comparable results (89). The uptake and excretion of these bile acid probes and covalent labeling were competitively inhibited by native bile acids, which indicates that they share the same physiological mechanisms of handling. Therefore, under appropriate conditions, these probes covalently, and presumably specifically, bind to proteins. In addition to membrane proteins, as noted above, Abberger et al identified labeling mainly of a 33-kDa protein in cytosol (1, 2). No evidence of significant labeling of GSH S-transferase subunits or FABP was found when intact cells were labeled (1, 2).

In contrast, cytosol treated in vitro with bile acid probes demonstrated labeling of the subunits of the glutathione S-transferases (1, 2). Although the reason for the lack of binding to the individual subunits of the glutathione S-transferases in the intact cell is uncertain, it may be due to the inhibitory effect of GSH within the intact cell or competition by other ligands such as bilirubin or heme. These results indicate that these bile acid probes are preferentially associated with a 33-kDa cytosolic protein that is remarkably similar to the Y' bile acid binder. However, one can only speculate on a role for the 33-kDa protein or the Y' binder in the vectorial transport of bile acids, based on these results, which do not directly address the dynamics of translocation.

IDENTITY OF Y' BILE ACID BINDER AND 3α-HYDROXYSTEROID DEHYDROGENASES

The high binding affinity for bile acids by the rat Y' bile acid binders suggests that these proteins may catalyze reactions that utilize bile acids. This suspicion was confirmed by the copurification of 3α-hydroxysteroid dehydrogenase activity and bile acid binding activity within the rat Y' fraction (61, 62). The relationship between the human Y' binder and 3α-hydroxysteroid dehydrogenase is currently under investigation in our laboratory. 3α-Hydroxysteroid dehydrogenase stereospecifically reduces the 3-oxo group to the corresponding 3α-hydroxy group on sterols (or vice versa) and preferentially utilizes the NADP(H) (nicotinanide adenine dinucleotide phosphate) nucleotide cofactor. Purification of the 3α-hydroxysteroid dehydrogenase led to the identification of one major and two minor forms in rat liver (61, 62). The K_m for mono, di, and tri hydroxy bile acids of the major form (61, 62) were comparable to the dissociation constants for binding of bile acids seen in the absence of cofactors (69) (Table 1). The enzyme's optimum pH for reductions is 7 and for dehydrogenation is 9, and the enzyme shows a marked preference for NADP(H), which is predominantly in the reduced form under physiological conditions, over NAD+. Thus, the enzyme would be expected to catalyze net reduction of 3-oxo to 3α-OH steroids but not vice versa (74). This prediction was confirmed in intact hepatocytes (74). Nevertheless, 3α-OH bile acids can competitively inhibit the enzyme, which indicates that binding to the substrate site can occur without net conversion to 3-oxo-bile acid (61). Therefore, a dual role for 3α-hydroxysteroid dehydrogenase as a bile acid binder and 3-oxo steroid reductase seemed plausible.

In addition to metabolizing bile acids, 3α-hydroxysteroid dehydrogenase catalyzes the metabolism of bile acid precursors, dihydrodiol carcinogens, and steroid hormones (8, 19, 20, 25, 30). The 3α-hydroxysteroid dehydrogenase reduces the 3-oxo position of the cholestane precursors of chenodeoxycholic and cholic acid and thus plays a role in the synthesis of bile acids (55).

It was recently discovered that multiple nonsteroidal anti-inflammatory agents are nonsubstrate, competitive inhibitors of the steroid substrate binding site of the 3α-hydroxysteroid dehydrogenase (48–51, 58). These investigators speculated that the 3α-hydroxysteroid dehydrogenase may participate in the inflammatory response, possibly by metabolizing certain prostaglandins. Penning & Sharp recently demonstrated that the prostaglandins are in fact substrates for this enzyme (49). The nonsteroidal anti-inflammatory agent, indomethacin, demonstrated a K_i of 1–2 μM for the competitive inhibition of this enzymatic activity (50, 51). This fortuitous discovery provided a means of inhibiting bile acid binding to the 3α-hydroxysteroid dehydrogenases in both isolated hepatocytes and in the single-pass-perfused rat liver model, enabling us to examine the role of this cytosolic protein in the extraction and excretion of bile acids by the liver.

ROLE OF 3α-HYDROXYSTEROID DEHYDROGENASE IN BILE ACID TRANSPORT

Having determined that the Y' binder and 3α-hydroxysteroid dehydrogenase are identical and that the enzyme acts as a 3-oxo-steroid reductase under physiological conditions, we considered the possibility that the enzyme substrate site could also serve as a cytosolic binding site for 3α-OH–bile acids that would not undergo net conversion to 3-oxo-bile acids. Competitive inhibition of the reductase activity by 3α-OH bile acids with K_i values comparable to the K_d for binding of these same bile acids was consistent with this view (61). However, to address this problem directly in intact cells and liver, we utilized 3-β-^{3}H,C$_{24}$-^{14}C-labeled bile acids. ^{3}H loss from these bile acids was shown to be catalyzed only by 3α-hydroxysteroid dehydrogenase in cytosol and to be inhibited competitively by indomethacin (74). In the presence of a mixture of NAD(H) and NADP(H) that mimics the physiological redox condition, the purified enzyme catalyzed the loss of ^{3}H without net formation of 3-oxo bile acid (74). This indicates that equilibrium cyclical oxidation-reduction of bile acids can be catalyzed by the enzyme. We also showed that this ^{3}H loss exhibited the same K_m for the enzyme as dehydrogenation of bile acids by the enzyme in the presence of NADP+ alone. Therefore, we were able to use this reaction to probe specifically the interaction between 3α-OH bile acids and this cytosolic protein and the effect of its competitive inbhition by indomethacin in intact cells and the perfused liver.

In studies with isolated hepatocytes, progressive loss of ^{3}H from the 3β position was observed in incubations with various bile acids and was inhibited by indomethacin (74). In conjunction, with inhibition of the interaction of bile acids with 3α-hydroxysteroid dehydrogenase, bile acids were displaced from the cells into the incubation buffer (74). These data suggested that bile acids extensively interact with cytosolic proteins that may be important in their retention by cells.

Indomethacin (100 μM) did not alter the initial uptake rate for chenodeoxycholic acid or taurocholic acid in isolated hepatocytes (74), nor did it inhibit bile acid uptake by sinusoidal and canalicular enriched plasma membrane fractions as determined by rapid filtration technique (own unpublished observations). Thus, although indomethacin inhibited the interaction of bile acids with cytosolic 3α-hydroxysteroid dehydrogenase, as evidenced by decreased tritium loss, it did not inhibit bile acid carriers in either the sinusoidal or canalicular membrane. Indomethacin does inhibit the activity of the GSH S-transferases (87). We have found that it has an order of magnitude less potency in inhibiting the binding of bile acids by GSH S-transferases than 3α-hydroxysteroid dehydrogenase (unpublished observations).

Isolated hepatocytes lose polarity and therefore may not be the best model to study vectorial transport. However, it is of interest that the canalicular 100-kDa bile acid transporter is not expressed on the surface of isolated rat hepatocytes (54). Therefore, it is tempting to speculate that changes in the distribution of bile acids between cells and medium, as seen in our studies with indomethacin, reflect the equivalent of changes in net sinusoidal extraction. Thus, in the presence of indomethacin, displacement of bile acids from the cells became apparent soon after initial uptake (which was unaffected) and may reflect increased efflux of bile acids as a result of an increased unbound cytosolic concentrations of bile acid available for reverse transport.

To test this hypothesis, studies of vectorial transport were performed in the in situ perfused liver. Tracer bolus doses of double labeled bile acids were rapidly excreted in bile along with extensive loss of the ^{3}H-label (72). Thus, during one pass through the liver, bile acids extensively interacted with cytosolic 3α-hydroxysteroid dehydrogenase. Indomethacin inhibited the loss of ^{3}H and the excretion of bile acids in bile (72). In the absence of indomethacin, bile acids were rapidly and completely excreted. In the presence of indomethacin, the recovery of bile acid in bile during the 60 min interval following intraportal bolus administration was incomplete ($\sim$50%) and was not accounted for by recovery in the perfusate. Thus, indomethacin caused an increased retention of bile acid in the liver. The inhibition of cumulative loss of ^{3}H in bile acids recovered in bile was not simply due to inhibition of excretion. Loss of ^{3}H from bile acids in the control circumstance was accounted for by the very rapid appearance of ^{3}H$_2$O in the perfusate (72). Indomethacin also inhibited the rate of appearance of ^{3}H$_2$0 in the effluent perfusate. Thus, in parallel with its effect on bile acid excretion, indomethacin inhibited loss of ^{3}H and therefore the interaction of bile acids with 3α-hydroxysteroid dehydrogenase.

To avoid complicated interpretations of the additional metabolism of unconjugated bile acids, we have performed similar experiments with tracer bolus [^{14}C]glycocholic acid in the perfused liver. During the 30 min following administration, indomethacin caused a decrease in excretion in bile and an increased recovery in the perfusate. However, approximately 40% of the label remained in the liver (own unpublished observations).

To further define and confirm the mechanism of action of indomethacin in inhibiting overall bile acid transport, its effect as a step infusion was determined during the constant infusion of [^{14}C]glycocholic acid at three different concentrations, namely 50 μM, 5 μM and 0.007 μM (Figure 1). The effects of indomethacin were very rapid in onset and were rapidly reversible (72). At the highest glycocholate concentration, indomethacin inhibited steady-state extraction but not excretion. At this concentration, the capacity for excretion was maximal, and despite inhibition of extraction, sufficient bile acid uptake occurred, presumably to provide cytosolic concentrations of bile acids to maintain T_m (transport maximum) excretion. As the concentration of bile acid administered was decreased, a progressively and significantly greater inhibition of excretion and somewhat smaller inhibitory effect of indomethacin on extraction was observed (Figure 2). The effects of indomethacin are crucial to the interpretation of these data. Clearly, indomethacin inhibits the interaction of bile acids with 3α-hydroxysteroid dehydrogenase which, based on our binding studies and the affinity probe studies of others, is the most important cytosolic bile acid binder. Our cell studies and membrane vesicle studies support the view that at the concentrations used (up to 100 μM), indomethacin has no direct effect on sinusoidal or canalicular transport of bile acids. Therefore, inhibitory effects

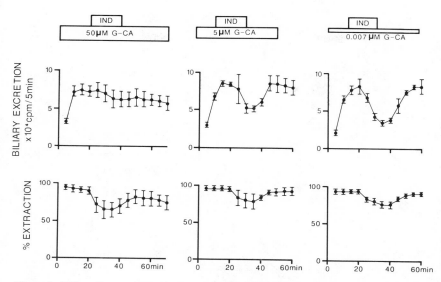

Figure 1   Effect of indomethacin on the steady state extraction and excretion of [^{14}C]glycocholic acid. Three concentrations of glycocholic acid (G-CA) were employed and a step infusion of 50 μM indomethacin (Ind) as noted by horizontal bars at the top. Each value is the mean $\pm$ s.e. of three experiments using the in situ perfused rat liver. These data appeared in part in Ref. 72.

of indomethacin observed on extraction or excretion can be interpreted as a consequence of inhibition of binding to cytosolic protein.

With the above as a working hypothesis, a model can be proposed (depicted in Figure 3). The central aspect of the model is that cytosolic bile acid binding, especially by 3α-hydroxysteroid dehydrogenase, retains bile acids in the cytoplasm after entry across the sinusoidal membrane and minimizes free concentrations available for reflux back into plasma or redistribution to other compartments in the hepatocyte from which excretion is delayed. Stated alternatively, for canalicular excretion to occur, bile acids must have access to the excretory mechanism (either canalicular membrane carrier or per-icanalicular vesicular carrier) from the cytosol. The effects of indomethacin can then be explained in relationship to the bile acid load (Figure 3). At high bile acid loads that far exceed T_m for excretion, despite displacement of bile acids from the cytosolic protein by indomethacin, sufficient concentration of bile acids remain available in the cytosol to maintain maximum excretion. However, the displacement affects net extraction by increasing the free concentration of bile acid in the cytosol available for back diffusion or counter-transport. In addition, there may be accumulation of bile acid in extracytosolic sites that may or may not become saturated. At low bile acid

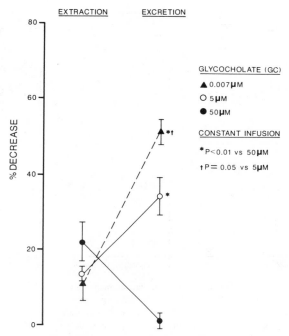

Figure 2 Inhibition by indomethacin of steady state extraction and excretion of glycocholate. See legend to Figure 3 for details. Inhibition is expressed as percent decrease.

loads, displacement of bile acids from the cytosolic compartment may also lead to apparent inhibition of excretion. This may occur because of both increased sinusoidal reflux and redistribution within the cell. The latter appears to make a quantitatively greater contribution as the bile acid load is diminished. The contribution of reflux versus intracellular redistribution at any free bile acid concentration in cytosol depends on the relative affinities and capacities of the two mechanisms. Below T_m either sinusoidal reflux (decreased net extraction) or redistribution with the cell results in apparent inhibition of bile acid excretion.

CONCLUSIONS

Hepatic cytosol of rat and man contain three classes of proteins that bind bile acids, namely GSH S-transferase, fatty acid binding protein, and 3α-hydroxysteroid dehydrogenase. Comparison of binding properties and the results of affinity labeling studies suggest that 3α-hydroxysteroid dehydrogenase plays a prominent role in cytosolic binding of bile acids. Recent studies

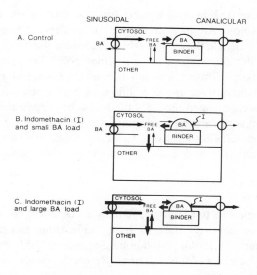

Figure 3 Model for the putative role of cytosolic bile acid (BA) binder in hepatic bile acid transport. Under control conditions the binder minimizes reflux at the sinusoidal pole of the hepatocyte and redistribution in the cell to other compartments from which excretion is delayed. Retention of bile acids in the cytosol then permits excretion in bile. Indomethacin (I) displaces bile acids from the cytosolic binder. At a small bile acid load, the bile acids redistribute in the cell and also reflux into plasma, thus limiting availability of bile acid for excretion into bile. At a large bile acid load, the bile acids that are displaced from the binder reflux into plasma but also redistribute in the cell. The latter may or may not become saturated. However, sufficient bile acid levels remain in the cytosol with the large load to maintain maximum excretion into bile.

have begun to clarify the physiological significance of cytosolic binders and strongly suggest that compartmentation of bile acids in the cytosol upon uptake by hepatocytes is crucial for the ultimate excretion of bile acids into bile. Binding to cytoplasmic proteins retains bile acids in the cytoplasm, minimizing their reflux into plasma or redistribution to other compartments in the cell. This view of cytosolic proteins is analogous to the role of albumin in plasma. Many lipophilic drugs and endogenous metabolites are bound in albumin. This minimizes their volume of distribution, keeping these substances in plasma and permitting specific transport processes in the liver and/or kidney to remove and excrete them. When competitively displaced from albumin or in states of severe hypoalbuminemia, these substances distribute widely outside the plasma volume and their excretion by the liver and/or kidney is markedly delayed (28, 29).

Many questions remain to be answered with regard to this hypothesis of the role of cytoplasmic binding of bile acids. Especially uncertain is the precise mechanism of cytoplasmic translocation. Do bile acid–protein complexes diffuse as a unit or do bile acids transfer from the binding site on one protein to the next and so on? Are there concentration gradients of free or bound bile acids or of the binders in the cytosol which determine the translocation of bile acids between the sinusoidal and canalicular pole? Do cytosolic proteins mediate the export of bile acids into bile in an analogous fashion to that proposed for albumin in the uptake of bile acids by the cell (15, 16, 83)? The work thus far accomplished provides the basis for suggesting that cytosolic binding and compartmentation are important in influencing net extraction and excretion of bile acids by the liver. However, much remains to be learned about the process(es) by which bile acids are translocated through the hepatocyte.

ACKNOWLEDGMENTS

The authors would like to acknowledge the secretarial help of Anita Starlight and technical contributions made by John Kuhlenkamp and Irv Lyon. Also Yuichi Sugiyama, Ph.D. and Motonobu Sugimoto, M.D. made important contributions. Veterans Administration Research Funds and NIH grant DK30312 supported this work.

Literature Cited

1. Abberger, H., Bickel, U., Buscher, H., Fuchte, K., Gerok, W., et al. 1981. In *Bile Acids and Lipids,* ed. G. Paumgartner, A. Stiehl, W. Gerok, pp. 233–46. Lancaster, England: MTP

2. Abberger, H., Buscher, H., Fuchte, K., Gerok, W., Giese, U., et al. 1983. In *Bile Acid and Cholesterol in Health and Disease,* ed. G. Paumgartner, A. Stiehl, W. Gerok, pp. 77–87. Lancaster, England: MTP

3. Anwer, M., Megner, D. 1978. *Hoppe-Seyler's Z. Physiol. Chem.* 359:181–92

4. Balistreri, W. F., Zimmer, L., Suchy, F. J., Bove, K. E. 1984. *J. Lipid Res.* 25:228–35

5. Bass, N. 1985. *Chem. Phys. Lipid* 38:95–114

6. Bass, N., Manning, J., Ockner, R., Gordon, J., Seetharam, S., et al. 1985. *J. Biol. Chem.* 260:1432–36

7. Bellentani, S., Hardison, W., Marchegiano, P., Zansi, G., Manenti, F. 1987. *Am. J. Physiol.* 15:G339–44

8. Bertics, S. J., Bertics, P. J., Clarke, J. L., Kavavolas, M. J. 1987. *J. Steroid Biochem.* 26:321–28

9. Blitzer, B., Terzakis, C., Scott, K. 1986. *J. Biol. Chem.* 261:12042–46

10. Boyer, J. 1980. *Physiol. Rev.* 60:303–26

11. Boyer, T. D., Vessey, D. A., Holcomb,

C., Saley, N. 1984. *Biochem. J.* 217:179–85

12. Boyer, T. D., Zakim, D., Vessey, D. A. 1980. *J. Biol. Chem.* 255:627–31

13. Catignani, G. L. 1980. *Methods Enzymol.* 67:117–22

14. Catignani, G. L., Bieri, T. G. 1977. *Biochim. Biophys. Acta* 497:349–57

15. Fleischer, A. B., Shurmantine, W. O., Luxon, B. A., Forker, E. L. 1987. *J. Clin. Invest.* 77:964–70

16. Forker, F. L., Luxon, B. A. 1981. *J. Clin. Invest.* 67:1517–22

17. Fournier, N., Rahim, M. 1985. *Biochemistry* 24:2387–96

18. Fujii, S., Kawaguchi, H., Yasuda, H. 1987. *Arch. Biochem. Biophys.* 254:552–58

19. Glath, H. R., Cooper, C. S., Grover, P. L., Sims, P. Bentley, P., et al. 1982. *Science* 215:1507–8

20. Glath, H. R., Vogel, K., Bentley, P., Oesch, F. 1979. *Nature* 277:319–20

21. Goldsmith, M., Huling, S., Jones, A. 1983. *Gastroenterology* 84:978–86

22. Gordon, J., Elshourbagy, N., Lowe, J., Liao, W., Alpers, D., et al. 1984. *J. Biol. Chem.* 25:1995–98

23. Hayes, J., Strange, R., Percy-Robb, I. W. 1980. *Biochem. J.* 185:83–87

24. Hayes, J., Strange, R., Percy-Robb, I. W. 1981. *Biochem. J.* 197:491–502

25. Hudson, R. W. 1982. *J. Steroid. Biochem.* 16:373–77
26. Inoue, M., Kinne, R., Tran, T., Arias, I. 1982. *Hepatology* 2:572–79
27. Inoue, M., Kinne, R., Tran, T., Arias, I. 1984. *J. Clin. Invest.* 73:659–63
28. Inoue, M., Okajima, K., Itoh, K., Ando, Y., Watanabe, N., et al. 1987. *Kidney Int.* 32:198–302
29. Inoue, M., Okajima, K., Nagase, S., Morino, Y. 1983. *Proc. Natl. Acad. Sci. USA* 80:7654–58
30. Jarrell, J., Robaire, B. 1982. *J. Steroid. Biochem.* 16:725–30
31. Jones, A., Schmucker, D., Mooney, J., Ockner, R., Adler, R. 1979. *Lab. Invest.* 40:512–17
32. Kaplowitz, N. 1980. *Am. J. Physiol.* 239:G439–44
33. Kaplowitz, N., Stolz, A., Sugiyama, Y. 1985. In *Enterohepatic Circulation of Bile Acids and Sterol Metabolism*, ed. G. Paumgartner, A. Stiehl, W. Gerok, pp. 67–76. Lancaster, England: MTP
34. Ketley, J., Habig, W., Jakoby, W. 1975. *J. Biol. Chem.* 250:8670–73
35. Ketterer, B. 1986. *Xenobiotic* 16:957–73
36. Kramer, W., Bickel, U., Buscher, H.-P., Gerok, W., Kurz, G. 1982. *Eur. J. Biochem.* 129:13–24
37. Kramer, W., Burckhardt, G., Wilson, F., Kurz, G. 1983. *J. Biol. Chem.* 258:3623–27
38. Kramer, W., Buscher, H., Gerok, W., Kurz, G. 1979. *Eur. J. Biochem.* 102:1–9
39. Lamri, Y., Roda, A., Dumont, M., Feldmann, G., Erlinger, E. 1987. *Hepatology* 7(5):1037 (Abstr.)
40. Levy, D., Ananthanarayanan, M., Von Dippe, P. 1987. In *Bile Acids and the Liver*, ed. G. Paumgartner, A. Stiehl, W. Gerok, pp. 79–87. Lancaster, England: MTP
41. Maruyama, H., Arias, I., Listowsky, I. 1984. *J. Biol. Chem.* 259:12444–48
42. Maruyama, H., Listowsky, I. 1984. *J. Biol. Chem.* 259:12449–55
43. Matern, S., Gerok, W. 1979. *Rev. Physiol. Biochem. Pharmacol.* 85:126–204
44. McCormack, M., Brecher, P. 1987. *Biochem. J.* 244:717–23
45. Meier, P., St. Meier-Abt, A., Barrett, C., Boyer, J. 1984. *J. Biol. Chem.* 259:10614–22
46. Meier, P., St. Meier-Abt, A., Boyer, J. 1987. *Biochem. J.* 242:465–69
47. Pattinson, N. R. 1981. *Biochim. Biophys. Acta* 667:70–76
48. Penning, T. M., Mukharji, I., Barrow, S., Talalay, P. 1984. *Biochem. J.* 222:601–11

49. Penning, T. M., Sharp, R. B. 1987. *Biochem. Biophys. Res. Commun.* 148:646–52
50. Penning, T. M., Smithgall, T., Askonas, L., Sharp, R. B. 1986. *Steroid* 47:221–47
51. Penning, T. M., Talalay, P. 1983. *Proc. Natl. Acad. Sci. USA* 80:4504–8
52. Pinkus, L. M., Ketley, J. N., Jakoby, W. B. 1977. *Biochem. Pharmacol.* 26:2359–63
53. Ren, I., Stolz, A., Sugiyama, Y., Takikawa, H., Kaplowitz, N. 1987. *Clin. Res.* 35(1):127 A (Abstr.)
54. Ruetz, S., Fricker, G., Hugentobler, G., Winterhalter, K., Kurz, G., et al. 1987. *J. Biol. Chem.* 262:11324–30
55. Salen, G., Shefer, S. 1983. *Ann. Rev. Physiol.* 45:674–85
56. Senjo, M., Ishibashi, T., Imai, Y., Takahashi, K., Ono, T. 1985. *Archiv. Biochem. Biophys.* 236:662–68
57. Simion, F., Fleischer, B., Fleischer, S. 1984. *J. Biol. Chem.* 259:10814–22
58. Smithgall, T., Penning, T. 1985. *Cancer Res.* 45:4946–49
59. Stolz, A., Sugiyama, Y., Kuhlenkamp, J., Kaplowitz, N. 1984. *FEBS Lett.* 177:31–35
60. Stolz, A., Sugiyama, Y., Kuhlenkamp, J., Osadchey, B., Yamada, T., et al. 1986. *Hepatology* 6:433–39
61. Stolz, A., Takikawa, H., Sugiyama, Y., Kaplowitz, N. 1987. See Ref. 40, pp. 125–37
62. Stolz, A., Takikawa, H., Sugiyama, Y., Kuhlenkamp, J., Kaplowitz, N. 1987. *J. Clin. Invest.* 79:427–34
63. Stolz, A., Yamada, T., Sugiyama, Y., Belknap, B., Kaplowitz, N. 1984. *Biochem. Biophys. Acta* 800:171–77
64. Strange, R. 1981. *Biochem. Soc. Trans.* 9:170–74
65. Strange, R. 1984. *Physiol. Rev.* 64:1055–1102
66. Sugiyama, Y., Stolz, A., Sugimoto, M., Kaplowitz, N. 1984. *J. Lipid Res.* 25:1173–83
67. Sugiyama, Y., Stolz, A., Sugimoto, M., Kuhlenkamp, J., Yamada, T., et al. 1984. *Biochem. J.* 224:947–53
68. Sugiyama, Y., Yamada, T., Kaplowitz, N. 1982. *Biochim. Biophys. Acta* 709:342–52
69. Sugiyama, Y., Yamada, T., Kaplowitz, N. 1983. *J. Biol. Chem.* 258:3602–7
70. Takikawa, H., Kaplowitz, N. 1986. *Arch. Biochem. Biophys.* 251:385–92
71. Takikawa, H., Kaplowitz, N. 1988. *J. Lipid Res.* 29:279–86
72. Takikawa, H., Ookhtens, M., Stolz, A., Kaplowitz, N. 1987. *J. Clin. Invest.* 80:861–66

73. Takikawa, H., Stolz, A., Kaplowitz, N. 1986. *FEBS Lett.* 207:19397
74. Takikawa, H., Stolz, A., Kaplowitz, N. 1987. *J. Clin. Invest* 80:852–60
75. Takikawa, H., Stolz, A., Sugimoto, M., Sugiyama, Y., Kaplowitz, N. 1986. *J. Lipid Res.* 27:652–57
76. Takikawa, H., Sugiyama, Y., Kaplowitz, N. 1986. *J. Lipid Res.* 27:955–66
77. Takikawa, H., Sugiyama, Y., Kaplowitz, N. 1988. *Biochem. Biophys. Acta* 954:37–43
78. Takikawa, H., Sugiyama, Y., Stolz, A., Sugimoto, M., Kaplowitz, N. 1986. *Biochem. Pharmacol.* 35:354–56
79. Van Dyke, R., Stephens, J., Scharschmidt, B. 1982. *Am. J. Physiol.* 243:G484–92
80. Vessey, D., Zakim, D. 1981. *Biochem. J.* 197:321–25
81. Von Dippe, P., Ananthanarayanan, A., Levy, D. 1986. *Biochem. Biophys. Acta* 862:352–60
82. Von Dippe, P., Levy, D. 1983. *J. Biol. Chem.* 258:8896–8901
83. Weisiger, R. 1985. *Proc. Natl. Acad. Sci. USA* 82:1563–67
84. Wieland, T., Nassal, M., Kramer, W., Fricker, G., Bickel, U., et al. 1984. *Proc. Natl. Acad. Sci. USA* 81:5232–36
85. Wilson, F., 1981. *Am. J. Physiol.* 241:G83–92
86. Wolkoff, A., Goresky, C., Sellin, J., Gatmaitan, Z., Arias, I. 1979. *Am. J. Physiol.* 236:E638–48
87. Wu, C., Mathews, K. P. 1983. *Biochem. Biophys. Res. Commun.* 112:980–85
88. Zakim, D., Vessey, D. A. 1977. *J. Biol. Chem.* 252:7534–37
89. Ziegler, K. 1985. *Biochem. Biophys. Acta* 819:37–44

CARDIOVASCULAR PHYSIOLOGY

Introduction, Howard E. Morgan, *Section Editor*

The focus of basic cardiovascular research has broadened in the past few years to include studies at the cellular and molecular level as well as more classical physiological and pharmacological investigations using organs, tissues, and whole animals. All of these approaches are vital to obtain an understanding of overall bodily function. Specific topics such as mechanisms of cardiac development, control of heart and vessel function by hormones, intracellular signalling that links hormonal and mechanical stimuli with changes in cardiac function, and control of cardiac growth are particularly amenable to studies using cellular and molecular techniques. The series of papers that follows is representative of these new approaches.

In the first paper, Drs. Wade & Kedes present recent work dealing with developmental regulation of contractile protein gene transcription. Appearance of these proteins is coordinated during muscle development, and maturation involves both transcriptional and posttranscriptional processes. Multiple DNA regions are involved in control of gene expression by *cis*-acting elements within the 5' flanking region and by *trans*-acting factors that may be common to many tissues or be muscle specific.

The next three papers describe structure, function, and genetic regulation of hormone receptors and guanine nucleotide binding proteins (G-proteins) of the heart and vascular system. Lefkowitz and associates present new information derived from cloning of the genes for β-adrenergic receptors. The amino acid sequences deduced from the DNA sequences indicate a characteristic seven-membrane spanning topography as the model for this class of receptors. Schimerlik describes the purification and reconstitution into defined lipid membranes of the muscarinic signal transduction system. The genes for four distinct muscarinic receptors have been cloned, sequenced, and expressed. These receptors also contain seven transmembrane segments and along with β-receptors are structurally similar to rhodopsin. The next step in the signal transduction pathway, the G-proteins, is described by Robishaw and Foster. These proteins contain multiple α, β, and γ subunits and the genes for several of these subunits have been cloned. G-proteins are the site of ADP-ribosylation by bacterial toxins, and they link hormone receptors to membrane effector molecules such as adenylate cyclase, phospholipase C, and ion-channels.

Simpson presents a new approach to discovering the specific signals that initiate and maintain myocyte hypertrophy. This approach is to view growth regulation in terms of growth factors and their receptors, intracellular transducers, and proteins that directly regulate RNA transcription. Proto-oncogenes are normal cellular genes that code for these regulatory proteins. Cardiac hypertrophy is associated with markedly enhanced proto-oncogene expression.

The realization that acute myocardial infarction is due to formation of a thrombus in a narrowed coronary vessel and that the clot can be removed with thrombolytic agents has resulted in widespread interest in the fibrinolytic system. Tissue plasminogen activator (t-PA) is an important component of the thrombolytic pathway. The gene encoding t-PA has been cloned, and genetically-engineered t-PA is used in patients for thrombolysis during acute myocardial infarction. Gerard and Meidell describe studies that established t-PA as a normal component of endothelial cells of both arteries and veins. In patients without an obvious reason for venous thrombosis, t-PA is reduced in about one-third.

Finally, an interesting problem in cell:cell interaction is described by Brutsaert. He suggests that the endocardial endothelium acts as a sensor of the superfusing blood and produces a signal that modulates the mechanical performance of the subjacent myocardium. The possibilities that this signal involves an electrochemical potential or release of a chemical messenger are discussed.

This group of seven papers demonstrate the successful application of cellular and molecular approaches to studies of cardiovascular function. These approaches provide detailed molecular mechanisms that could not be derived by earlier methods.

Annu. Rev. Physiol. 1989. 51:179–88

DEVELOPMENTAL REGULATION OF CONTRACTILE PROTEIN GENES

Robert Wade and Larry Kedes

Department of Medicine, Stanford University and Veterans Administration Medical Center, (151-M) 3801 Miranda Avenue, Palo Alto, California 94304

Introduction

The developmental regulation of the contractile proteins of the muscle sarcomere is well orchestrated. The proteins appear in concert during differentiation and accumulate to stoichiometric levels, and their induction can be examined both in vivo and in vitro. These properties make myofibrillogenesis an ideal model for the examination of coordinate gene expression during a complex ontogenetic event. In recent years, cDNAs and genes encoding many of the contractile proteins have been isolated from a variety of species. This has permitted direct examination of the structural elements that are important for the developmental regulation of these genes and has revealed the contributions of both transcriptional and posttranscriptional processes to their expression. In addition, such studies have provided insights about *trans*-acting factors that may mediate the coordinate expression of muscle-specific genes. The knowledge gained from the cloning of contractile protein genes is the focus of this review. Because of space limitations, we concentrate on the study of mammalian contractile protein genes, but we also consider some particularly relevant studies of contractile protein genes from other vertebrate species.

Contractile Protein Multi-Gene Families

The primary components of the muscle sarcomere can be divided into thick filament proteins [myosin heavy chain (MHC), alkali myosin light chains, (MLC1, MLC3), and regulatory myosin light chains (MLC2)] and thin filament proteins [actin, α- and β-tropomyosin, and the troponin complex: troponin T (TnT), troponin C (TnC), and troponin I(TnI)]. These contractile proteins are members of complex muscle gene families, many of which

179

contain separate striated muscle fiber–type isoforms, smooth muscle isoforms, and nonmuscle isoforms. As muscle differentiation proceeds, multigene family switching events occur in which muscle-specific isoforms are induced and the nonmuscle isoforms are suppressed (12). We limit our discussion to the induction of the striated muscle isoforms.

Table 1 lists examples of contractile protein isoforms of adult striated muscle whose corresponding genes or cDNAs have been cloned. The various contractile protein isoform genes exhibit several different patterns of striated muscle fiber–type expression: expression in (a) all striated muscle fiber types (such as skeletal α-actin), (b) separate fast-twitch skeletal, slow-twitch skeletal, and cardiac muscle isoforms (such as TnI and TnT), (c) separate fast-twitch and slow-twitch skeletal muscle genes with the slow-twitch skeletal muscle gene also expressed in the cardiac ventricle (such as MHC, MLC1, MLC2, MLC2', and TnC), (d) separate slow-twitch and fast-twitch skeletal muscle genes with the fast-twitch skeletal muscle gene also expressed in ventricular muscle (such as α-tropomyosin). This extraordinary diversity in

Table 1 Representative contractile protein isoform sequences cloned as genes or cDNAs.[a]

Protein	Skeletal		Cardiac	
	Type I fibers (slow)	Type II fibers (fast)	Ventricle	Atria
Actin	α-Skeletal (8)	α-Skeletal	α-Cardiac	α-Cardiac
	α-Cardiac (8)		α-Skeletal	α-Skeletal
Myosin heavy chain	MHC-β (13)	MHC$_{Fast\ IIA}$ (13)	MHC-α (13)	MHC-α
		MHC$_{Fast\ IIB}$ (13)	MHC-β	
Alkali myosin light chain	MLC1$_{Sa}$[b]	MLC1$_F$/3$_F$ (3)	MLC1$_{Sb}$	MLC1$_A$ (3)
	MLC1$_{Sb}$ (38)		(=MLC$_V$)	
Regulatory myosin light chain	MLC2$_S$ (39)	MLC2$_F$ (3)	MLC2$_S$	—
	MLC2$_S$' (39)		MLC2$_S$'	
Troponin T	TnT$_S$ (15)	TnT$_F$ (7)	TnT$_{card}$ (10)	?
Troponin C	TnC$_S$ (16)	TnC$_F$ (16)	TnC$_V$	?
			(=TnC$_S$)	
Troponin I	TnI$_S$ (38)	TnI$_F$ (23)	TnI$_{card}$[c]	TnI$_{card}$?
Tropomyosin	Tmα_S (25)	Tmα_F (25)	Tmα_F	?
	Tmβ (26)	Tmβ		

[a]Isoform classification is based on a revision of reference 8. For purposes of clarity, only the major adult isoforms are listed. Neonatal, embryonic, and extraocular isoforms of myosin heavy chain are not listed (13), nor are the recently cloned sequences corresponding to other sarcomere associated proteins such as C-protein, titin, nebulin, and dystrophin (35a). Isoform distribution may also vary with different species. Many of these sequences have been cloned from a variety of different species and in numerous laboratories, but only a single reference is given for each. However, many of these representative references cite the other studies. — = no cloned sequences available; ? = classification of isoform not available or uncertain.
[b]D. Hailstones & P. Gunning, personal communication.
[c]R. Gahlmann & R. Wade, unpublished data.

the distribution of contractile protein isoforms in different types of adult striated muscle adds to the complexity of the mechanisms that are responsible for their coordinate regulation. For example, the troponin C isoform TnC_S is coexpressed with two different troponin I isoform genes: TnI_S in slow-twitch skeletal muscle, and TnI_{card} in cardiac ventricular muscle.

Furthermore, during mammalian muscle development, the first isoform expressed in a given muscle is often not the isoform found in the adult tissue. For instance, cardiac isoform genes encoding contractile proteins such as TnT_{card} and $MLC1_A$ ($= MLC1_{emb}$) are ephemerally expressed during embryonic skeletal muscle development (3, 10). Perhaps the most dramatic example of isoform switching during embryonic muscle development is found with the myosin heavy chain genes. During skeletal muscle development, a series of embryonic and neonatal isoforms of myosin heavy chain are sequentially expressed. The precise developmental timing and selection of myosin heavy chain isoforms is determined by cell lineage, muscle innervation, and hormonal regulation. A full discussion of this area of muscle gene regulation is beyond the scope of this review, but has recently been considered extensively (13, 36).

The mechanism underlying the coordinate expression of contractile protein genes must be multifarious in order to accomodate the complex, mosaic pattern of isoform coexpression in adult and embryonic striated muscle tissues.

Evidence For Muscle-Specific Trans-Acting Factors

Some of the clearest evidence for the involvement of *trans*-acting factors in muscle differentiation has come from studies of heterokaryons formed by the fusion of nonmuscle cells with cultures of myotubes. When human fibroblasts are fused with differentiated cultures of mouse myotubes, previously dormant human muscle genes are activated (5). Remarkably, examination of the patterns of mouse and human muscle-specific transcript accumulation suggests that the human nuclei are induced to produce their own muscle regulatory factors, which in turn contribute to the modulation of expression of the mouse muscle genes (18). Other heterokaryon studies presented evidence that some cell types may contain negative *trans*-acting factors, which repress the expression of muscle genes in heterokaryons (23, 43).

What types of factors mediate the establishment of a myogenic phenotype from cells that previously were not commited myoblasts? Recent work with an embryonic mouse cell line C3H10T1/2 has offered the opportunity to address such a question directly (11, 34). The C3H10T1/2 cells are a clonal fibroblast line that converts to differentiated chondrocytes, adipocytes, or myocytes upon exposure to 5-azacytidine. It is likely that the conversion to a myogenic lineage promoted by 5-azacytidine is mediated by the demethylation of one or a few closely linked critical loci (20). Indeed, transfection of total genomic DNA from muscle-committed C3H10T1/2 cells into uncommitted C3H10T1/2 cells promotes the conversion to muscle cells in the absence of treatment with 5-azacytidine (24). Davis et al (11) exploited the differences between committed and noncommitted C3H10T1/2 cells in order to isolate MyoD, a cDNA encoding a sequence that appears to mediate the conversion to muscle cells. When the MyoD cDNA was placed in an expression vector and transfected into noncommitted C3H10T1/2 cells, a high percentage of the transfected cells converted to myogenic cells. Transfection of the MyoD expression vector into other, but not all, fibroblast cell lines also led to the establishment of a muscle phenotype in a small percentage of the cells.

While the mode of action of the MyoD gene product is not known, the protein encoded by MyoD shares a region of limited sequence similarity with a portion of the c-*myc* gene product. Interestingly, this same region of the MyoD protein also shares sequence similarity with the gene product of the aschaete-scute locus, a gene involved in the establishment of neurogenic cell lineages in *Drosophila*. The MyoD gene product alone is probably not sufficient to establish a complete myogenic phenotype since not every cell line that was transfected with the MyoD expression vector responded, and of those cell lines that did respond, only a percentage of the transfected cells exhibited muscle gene expression. In addition, while the MyoD mRNA is present in fetal and adult skeletal muscle, continuous MyoD expression is not required for the expression of contractile protein genes since it is not detected in adult cardiac muscle.

Gene Activation and Modulation

Recent experiments suggest that muscle gene expression may depend upon two dissociable stages: activation of the genes and the subsequent modulation of their level of expression. Gunning et al (17) examined the pattern of transcript accumulation for a large variety of human muscle genes and found a striking difference in the modulation of transcript accumulation during differentiation. Minty et al (29) demonstrated that a chimeric human cardiac actin gene is expressed at high levels following transient transfection of proliferating cultures of C2 myoblasts while the endogenous mouse gene remains silent. This suggests that the factors necessary for cardiac actin gene expression are present in myoblasts, but the endogenous gene is not accessible to these factors until a subsequent activation event occurs. However, temporal separation of endogenous gene activation from the prior establishment of factors capable of modulating their high level expression is not always evident. For example, another rodent cell line, L8, does not support the high level activity of the human cardiac actin gene promoter until after the onset of differentiation, when the endogenous gene is also active, and transfected copies of the quail TnI gene are not expressed at high levels in myogenic 10T1/3 cells until after the initiation of myotube formation (21).

Attempts have been made to assess the physical state of contractile protein genes prior to and after myogenesis. Active genes have often been associated with a chromatin conformation, which renders them particularly sensitive to mild digestion with DNAse I. Several studies have indicated that muscle-specific genes are not sensitive to mild DNAse I treatment in proliferating myoblasts, but become sensitive upon the onset of in vitro differentiation (1, 9). In adult tissues, DNAse I sensitivity has been noted for a contractile protein gene in striated muscle versus nonmuscle tissues (42).

A role for DNA modification in contractile protein gene expression has been suggested by recent studies. Winter & Arnold (42) found that a chick MLC2 gene is hypomethylated in heart tissue as compared with liver tissue. Yisraeli et al (44) transfected in vitro methylated skeletal α-actin constructs into myoblasts and fibroblasts. They found that the methylation significantly inhibited expression of the constructs in fibroblasts but not myoblasts, and were able to correlate the expression in myoblasts with a demethylation activity in the myogenic cells.

Chromosome mapping studies have indicated that with the exception of myosin heavy chain genes, which have been found to be present in two tandemly repeated clusters (13), contractile protein isoform genes that have been mapped are not closely linked and coordinate regulation cannot be explained by a simple model of regional chromosomal activation of a cluster of coexpressed muscle genes.

Transcriptional Regulation

Early studies of muscle differentiation demonstrated that myotube formation is accompanied by the appearance of an abundant class of muscle-specific mRNAs, which suggests that transcriptional regulation plays a central role in muscle differentiation. However, the direct demonstration of positive transcriptional regulation by nuclear run off experiments has been limited to myosin heavy chain and an isoform of troponin I (22, 27). The cloning of several of the genes encoding contractile protein isoforms has offered the opportunity to examine cis-acting sequences that confer the tissue-specific and developmentally modulated expression of muscle genes. The regulatory elements of the two coexpressed sarcomeric actin isoforms, cardiac and skeletal α-actin, are among the most thoroughly characterized muscle gene promoters (4, 28, 30, 35).

Transient expression assays of chimeric gene constructs containing the 5' flanking region of the human cardiac actin gene adjacent to the coding region of the bacterial chloramphenicol acetyltransferase (CAT) gene demonstrated that as little as 122 base pairs of the cardiac actin gene promoter sequence are sufficient to confer tissue-specific expression (30). Promoter sequence ablation analysis identified two regions within the first kilobase of the 5' flanking sequence whose removal results in the lowering of CAT activity. Removal of the distal region (about −443 to −395 bases upstream of the transcriptional start site) resulted in a 40–50% decrease in activity, while removal of the proximal segment (between −177 and −47 bases upstream) resulted in the near complete loss of activity (30, 32). Both of these regions were found to contain one or more copies of a sequence motif $CC(A/T-rich)_6GG$ that has been dubbed a "CArG box." The CArG sequence motif is a conserved feature of the promoters of actin genes from many vertebrate species, and it has also been found in the 5' flanking regions of several other contractile protein genes. The importance of the CArG sequence motif in the tissue-specific expression of muscle genes has been confirmed by similar analyses of both the human and chicken skeletal α-actin genes (4, 33).

The CArG box motifs have been shown to serve as core binding sites for putative positive *trans*-acting factors in muscle cells on the basis of in vivo competition studies and in vitro protein binding assays with muscle cell nuclear extracts (6a, 17a, 31, 40). Recent experiments have shown that the CArG sequence motifs present in the human cardiac and skeletal α-actin genes interact with common *trans*-acting factors and can compete with each other for the binding of these factors (32a).

Is the CArG box binding facor (CBF) the common *trans*-acting muscle-specific factor directly responsible for the coordinate modulation of multiple contractile protein genes? Surprisingly, the in vitro protein binding studies cited above have also demonstrated that a CArG binding factor is also present in a variety of nonmuscle cells. In addition, nonmuscle-specific genes such as c-*fos* have been shown to contain CArG motifs that act as core binding sites for factors that play an important role in transcriptional regulation (37). It is not known if the CBFs detected in muscle and nonmuscle cells are identical proteins, but they are indistinguishable on the basis of currently available data (discussed in 6a). If the muscle and nonmuscle CArG box binding factors are identical ubiquitous proteins, how can they mediate muscle-specific gene expression? Perhaps the CBF interacts with accessory proteins that are muscle-specific and in this way mediates tissue-specific expression. Alternatively, the limiting step in muscle gene expression may be the accessibility of muscle-gene CArG sequences to the binding factors. Much work will be required before the role of these factors in muscle gene expression can be clearly delineated.

Recently, the role of *cis*-acting sequences required for the high level tissue-specific expression of several other contractile protein genes have begun to be elucidated. These studies have highlighted the variety of mechanisms utilized in the regulation of muscle gene expression. For example, the rat embryonic myosin heavy chain gene has been found to contain both positive and negative 5' regulatory elements (6). The proper regulation of the quail fast-fiber skeletal muscle troponin I gene requires several *cis*-acting regulatory elements. One or more elements located within the 500 bases upstream of the transcription start site are necessary for the high level expression of the gene, while another large region within the first intron is required for proper developmental regulation (22).

Posttranscriptional Regulation

The generation of contractile protein isoforms is accomplished by two general methods: the differential expression of members of multi-gene families (Table 1) and for some contractile proteins, the generation of multiple isoforms from individual genes by alternative mRNA splicing. Alternative splicing is a mechanism utilized by a variety of genes in a variety of cell types, but it is particularly prevalent among muscle genes. The topic was the focus of a recent review (2).

One of the striking features of alternative splicing in muscle is the variety of modes of splicing utilized by different contractile protein genes. An early example of a contractile protein gene found to exhibit alternative splicing was the fast-fiber isoform of the alkali myosin light chain MLC1/MLC3 (3). MLC1 and MLC3 transcripts originate from a single gene with two separate promoters. The splicing pattern of the first several exons is determined by which promoter is utilized, and the choice of exons is mutually exclusive. In contrast, alternative splicing in the fast-fiber TnT gene occurs from a single gene that exhibits combinatorial splicing, consisting of a series of five sequential exons that may be spliced in any one of 32 possible combinations plus the mutually exlusive splicing of another pair of exons, which raises the total possible number of isoforms to 64(2). The cardiac and slow-fiber skeletal isoform genes of TnT exhibit patterns of alternative splicing that differ from that of the fast-fiber gene (10, 15).

In contrast to the alkali MLC and TnT genes, at least one α-tropomyosin gene is transcribed from a single promoter that is active in both muscle and nonmuscle cells, and the generation of muscle-specific α-tropomyosin isoforms is accomplished entirely by alternative splicing (41). The generation of muscle-specific isoforms by alternative splicing of a gene expressed in both muscle and nonmuscle cells suggests that muscle-specific factors may mediate the splicing process. Indeed, analysis of the splicing of TnT minigene constructs transfected into muscle and nonmuscle cells has implicated muscle-specific factors in the regulation of alternative splicing (7). Why is alternative splicing so prevalent in muscle genes? One possibility is that alternative splicing is faster and more efficient than gene switching between members of large multigene families in order to produce subtly altered gene products in response to the changing needs of an active muscle cell. Translational control is a level of posttranscriptional gene regulation whose role, if any, in normal muscle development remains ill defined. Translational control of contractile protein gene expression has been demonstrated in cultured muscle cells. When cultures of a rat myogenic cell line are blocked from fusing by the addition of Ethyleneglycol-bis-(β-aminoethyl Ether) N, N, N'-Tetraacetic Acid (EGTA) to the differentiation media, the cells produce muscle-specific mRNAs. However, these mRNAs are not loaded onto polysomes, and muscle-specific proteins are not produced (14). Experiments with RNA isolated from chick muscle tissue have implicated a small species of RNA, dubbed tcRNA, in the inhibition of the in vitro translation of muscle-specific transcripts (19). A possible role for translational control during mammalian in vivo muscle differentiation has not been clearly established, but it has been suggested that translational control may explain the discrepancy in the apparent absence of MLC3 protein in rodent soleus muscle despite the significant levels of its mRNA in this tissue (3).

Concluding Remarks

The primary insight that has been gleaned from the cloning and analysis of contractile protein genes is that the coordinate appearance of these proteins during muscle development and maturation is a superimposition of richly orchestrated transcriptional and posttranscriptional processes. It is clear that multiple DNA regions are involved in the tissue-specific and developmental regulation of contractile protein gene transcription. These *cis*-acting elements may be located within the 5' flanking or intragenic regions, and they may mediate positive or negative modulation of expression. It is not clear whether these elements are binding sites for different or common *trans*-acting factors or how many of these putative factors are actually muscle specific. As more contractile protein genes are cloned and their regulatory regions defined, it will be possible to test directly whether these genes are regulated by common *trans*-acting factors.

Literature Cited

1. Affara, N. A., Robert, B., Jacquet, M., Buckingham, M. E., Gros, F. 1980. Changes in gene expression during myogenic differentiation. I. Regulation of messenger RNA sequences expressed during myotube formation. *J. Mol. Biol.* 140:441–58

2. Andreadis, A., Gallego, M. E., Nadal-Ginard, B. 1987. Generation of protein isoform diversity by alternative splicing. *Annu. Rev. Cell Biol.* 3:207–42

3. Barton, P. J., Buckingham, M. E. 1985. The myosin alkali light chain proteins and their genes. *Biochem. J.* 231:249–61

4. Bergsma, D. J., Grichnick, J. M., Gosset, M. A., Schwartz, R. J. 1986. Delimitation and characterization of *cis*-acting DNA sequences required for the regulated expression and transcriptional control of the chicken α-skeletal actin gene. *Mol. Cell. Biol.* 6:2462–75

5. Blau, H. B., Pavlath, G. K., Hardeman, E. C., Chiu, C.-P., Silberstein, L., et al. 1985. Plasticity of the differentiated state. *Science* 230:758–66

6. Bouvagnet, P. F., Strehler, E. E., White, G. E., Strehler-Page, M.-A., Nadal-Ginard, B., Mahdavi, V. 1987. Multiple positive and negative 5' regulatory elements control the cell-type expression of the embryonic skeletal myosin heavy-chain gene. *Mol. Cell. Biol.* 7:4377–89

6a. Boxer, L. M., Miwa, T., Gustafson, T. A., Kedes, L. 1988. Identification and characterization of a factor that binds to two human sarcomeric actin promoters. *J. Biol. Chem.* Submitted for publication

7. Breitbart, R. E., Nadal-Ginard, B. 1987. Developmentally induced, muscle-specific trans factors control the differential splicing of alternative and constitutive troponin T exons. *Cell* 49:793–803

8. Buckingham, M. E., Minty, A. J. 1983. Contractile protein genes. In *Eukaryotic Genes*, ed. N. MacLean, S. P. Gregory, A. Flavell, pp. 365–97. London: Butterworth

9. Carmon, Y., Czosnek, H., Nudel, U., Shani, M., Yaffe, D. 1982. DNAse I sensitivity of genes expressed during myogenesis. *Nucleic Acids Res.* 10:3085–98

10. Cooper, T. A., Ordahl, C. P. 1984. A single troponin T gene regulated by different programs in cardiac and skeletal muscle development. *Science* 226:979–82

11. Davis, R. L., Weintraub, H., Lassar, A. B. 1988. Expression of a single transfected cDNA converts fibroblasts to myoblasts. *Cell* 51:987–1000

12. Deponti-Zilli, L., Seiler-Tuyns, A., Paterson, B. M. 1988. A 40 base pair sequence in the 3' end of the β-actin gene regulates β-actin mRNA transcription during myogenesis. *Proc. Natl. Acad. Sci. USA* 85:1389–93

13. Emerson, C. P. Jr., Bernstein, S. I. 1987. Molecular genetics of myosin. *Annu. Rev. Biochem.* 56:695–726

14. Endo, T., Nadal-Ginard, B. 1987. Three types of muscle-specific gene expression in fusion-blocked rat skeletal muscle cells: Translational control in EGTA-treated cells. *Cell* 49:515–26

15. Gahlmann, R., Troutt, A. B., Wade, R. P., Gunning, P., Kedes, L. 1987. Alternative splicing generates variants in important functional domains of human slow skeletal troponin T. *J. Biol. Chem.* 262:16122–26

16. Gahlmann, R., Wade, R., Gunning, P., Kedes, L. 1988. Differential expression of slow and fast skeletal muscle troponin C: Slow skeletal muscle troponin C is expressed in human firbroblasts. *J. Mol. Biol.* 201:379–91

17. Gunning, P., Hardeman, E., Wade, R., Ponte, P., Bains, W., et al. 1987. Differential patterns of transcript accumulation during human myogenesis. *Mol. Cell. Biol.* 7:4100–14

17a. Gustafson, T. A., Miwa, T., Boxer, L. M., Kedes, L. 1988. Interaction of nuclear proteins with muscle-specific regulatory sequences of the human cardiac α-actin promoter. *Mol. Cell. Biol.* In press

18. Hardeman, E. C., Chiu, A., Minty, A., Blau, H. 1986. The pattern of actin gene expression in human fibroblast X mouse muscle heterokaryons suggests that human muscle regulatory factors are produced. *Cell* 47:123–30

19. Heywood, S. M., Thibault, M. C., Siegel, E. 1983. Control of gene expression in muscle development. In *Cell and Muscle Motility*, ed. R. M. Dowben, J. W. Shay, 3:157–93. New York: Plenum. 297 pp.

20. Konieczny, S. F., Emerson, C. P. 1984. 5-Azacytidine induction of stable mesodermal stem cell lineages from 10T1/2 cells: Evidence for regulatory genes controlling determination. *Cell* 38:791–800

21. Konieczny, S. F., Emerson, C. P. 1985. Differentiation, not determination, regulates muscle gene activation: Transfection of troponin I genes into multipotential and muscle lineages of 10T1/2 cells. *Mol. Cell. Biol.* 5:2423–32

22. Konieczny, S. F., Emerson, C. P. 1987. Complex regulation of the muscle-specific contractile protein (troponin I) gene. *Mol. Cell. Biol.* 7:3065–75

23. Konieczny, S. F., Lawrence, J. B., Coleman, J. R. 1983. Analysis of muscle protein expression in polyethylene glycol-induced chicken:rat myoblast heterokaryons. *J. Cell Biol.* 97:1348–55

24. Lassar, A. B., Paterson, B. M., Weintraub, H. 1986. Transfection of a DNA locus that mediates the conversion of 10T1/2 fibroblasts to myoblasts. *Cell* 47:649–56

25. MacLeod, A. R., Gooding, C. 1988. Human hTMα gene: Expression in muscle and nonmuscle tissue. *Mol. Cell. Biol.* 8:433–40

26. MacLeod, A. R., Houlker, C., Reinach, F. C., Smillie, L. B., Talbot, K., et. al. 1985. A muscle-type tropomyosin in human fibroblasts: Evidence for ex-

pression by an alternative RNA splicing mechanism. *Proc. Natl. Acad. Sci. USA* 82:7835–39

27. Medford, R. M., Nguyen, H. T., Nadal-Ginard, B. 1983. Transcriptional and cell cycle-mediated regulation of myosin heavy chain expression during muscle cell differentiation. *J. Biol. Chem.* 258:11063–73

28. Melloul, D. B., Aloni, J., Calvo, D., Yaffe, D., Nudel, U. 1984. Developmentally regulated expression of chimeric genes containing muscle actin sequences in transfected myogenic cells. *EMBO J.* 3:883–90

29. Minty, A., Blau, H., Kedes, L. 1986. Two level regulation of cardiac actin gene transcription: Muscle-specific modulating factors can accumulate before gene activation. *Mol. Cell. Biol.* 6:2137–48

30. Minty, A., Kedes, L. 1986. Upstream regions of the human cardiac actin gene that modulate its transcription in muscle cells: Presence of an evolutionary conserved repeated motif. *Mol. Cell. Biol.* 6:2125–36

31. Miwa, T., Boxer, L. M., Kedes, L. 1987. CArG boxes in the human cardiac α-actin gene are core binding sites for positive trans-acting regulatory factors. *Proc. Natl. Acad. Sci. USA* 84:6702–6

32. Miwa, T., Kedes, L. 1987. Duplicated CArG box domains have positive and mutually dependent regulatory roles in expression of the human α-cardiac actin gene. *Mol. Cell. Biol.* 7:2803–13

32a. Muscat, G. E. O., Gustafson, T. A., Kedes, L. 1988. A common factor regulates skeletal and cardiac α-actin gene transcription in muscle. *Mol. Cell. Biol.* In press

33. Muscat, G., Kedes, L. 1987. Multiple 5'-flanking regions of the human α-skeletal actin gene synergistically modulate muscle-specific expression. *Mol. Cell. Biol.* 7:4089–99

34. Pinney, D. F., Konieczny, S. F., Latham, K. E., Pearson-White, S., Emerson, C. P. Jr. 1988. Myogenic determination of the multipotential 10T1/2 Cell Line by a cloned human DNA locus, myd. *J. Cell. Biochem. Suppl.* 12C:332

35. Seiler-Tuyns, A., Eldridge, J. D., Paterson, B. M. 1984. Expression and regulation of chicken actin genes introduced into mouse myogenic and nonmyogenic cells. *Proc. Natl. Acad. Sci. USA* 81:2980–84

35a. Stockdale, F., Kedes, L. 1988. *Cellular and Molecular Biology of Muscle Development. UCLA Symposia on Molecular and Cellular Biology (NS),* Vol. 93. New York: Liss. In press

36. Stockdale, F. E., Miller, J. B. 1987. The cellular basis of myosin heavy chain isoform expression during development of avian skeletal muscles. *Dev. Biol.* 123:1–9

37. Treisman R. 1986. Identification of a protein-binding site that mediates transcriptional response of the c-*fos* gene to serum factors. *Cell* 46:567–74

38. Wade, R., Feldman, D., Gunning, P., Kedes, L. 1988. Sequence and expression of human myosin alkali light chain isoforms. *Mol. Cell. Biochem.* In press

39. Wade, R., Gunning, P., Hardeman, E., Gahlmann, R., Blau, H., Kedes, L. 1987. Distinctive patterns of muscle-specific mRNA accumulation during human myogenesis. *J. Cell. Biochem. Suppl.* 11C:96

40. Walsh, K., Schimmel, P. 1987. Two nuclear factors compete for the skeletal muscle actin promoter. *J. Biol. Chem.* 261:1838–43

41. Wieczorek, D. F., Smith, C. W. J., Nadal-Ginard, B. 1988. The rat α-tropomyosin gene generates a minimum of six different mRNAs coding for striated, smooth, and nonmuscle isoforms by alternative splicing. *Mol. Cell. Biol.* 8:679–94

42. Winter, B. B., Arnold, H. H. 1987. Tissue-specific DNAse I-hypersensitive sites and hypomethylation in the chicken cardiac myosin light chain gene (L2-A). *J. Biol. Chem.* 262:13750–57

43. Wright, W. E. 1984. Induction of muscle genes in neural cells. *J. Cell. Biol.* 98:427–35

44. Yisraeli, J., Adelstein, R. S., Melloul, D., Nudel, U., Yaffe, D., Cedar, H. 1986. Muscle-specific activation of a methylated chimeric actin gene. *Cell* 46:409–16

Annu. Rev. Physiol. 1988. 51:189–202

PROTO-ONCOGENES AND CARDIAC HYPERTROPHY[1]

Paul C. Simpson

Cardiology Section (111-C), Veterans Administration Medical Center, Department of Medicine and Cardiovascular Research Institute, University of California, San Francisco, California 94121

INTRODUCTION

Generalized or focal myocardial hypertrophy is a component of most types of cardiac disease. Abnormalities of this growth process, which include inadequate, idiopathic, and pathological hypertrophy, have great clinical significance. Postnatal heart enlargement is produced largely by increased size of striated muscle cells (hypertrophy) and increased number of the other cell types in the heart (hyperplasia) (96). Cardiac myocyte hypertrophy appears to be a heterogeneous process qualitatively, as well as quantitatively, as deduced by selective expression of muscle genes in different forms of hypertrophy (35, 36, 65, 68). The specific signals that initiate and maintain different types of myocyte hypertrophy, the intracellular mechanisms that transduce these signals, and the reason(s) for the postnatal failure of myocyte hyperplasia have resisted elucidation. Two recent technical advances provide the foundation to begin to resolve these issues: (*a*) the development of new model systems, particularly those employing isolated or cultured myocytes; and (*b*) the application to these and other models of new techniques in cell and molecular biology. A major tenet of this chapter is that work with proto-oncogenes provides a useful paradigm for application of these technical advances to the study of myocyte growth. The paradigm visualizes cell growth regulation in terms of a limited number of critical regulatory proteins, comprising growth factors and their receptors, intracellular transducers, and proteins that directly

---

regulate RNA transcription and/or DNA replication. The proto-oncogene model and its application to myocyte hypertrophy are summarized briefly.

PROTO-ONCOGENES

Proto-oncogenes (or cellular oncogenes, c-*oncs*) are normal cellular genes encoding critical regulatory proteins. C-*oncs* were defined originally as genes with the potential to become oncogenes or transforming genes (7). They were identified in two major ways: (*a*) most commonly, as the normal progenitors of the mutated viral oncogenes (v-*oncs*) responsible for the acute transforming activity of certain retroviruses (82); and (*b*) less frequently, as the normal homologues of mutationally activated transforming genes isolated by transfection of tumor DNA into recipient cells (69). The transforming ability of these structurally altered or abnormally expressed genes implied strongly that c-*oncs,* the normal counterparts, might have a physiological role in growth regulation. Correlation of c-*onc* expression with stimulated growth provided additional support for this idea. The importance of c-*oncs* in growth regulation has been documented in two general ways: (*a*) by discovery of homology with known growth factors and growth factor receptors; and (*b*) by manipulation of cell levels of c-*onc* proteins using transfection of the cloned gene, microinjection of the proteins or antibodies to them, and introduction of anti-sense mRNA (39). All of these techniques have limitations in the study of mechanism (28, 90), but they do show that these genes are important in growth regulation. "New" c-*oncs* continue to appear as the sequences of v-*oncs* and of oncogenes identified by the transfection assay are compared with those of known cellular proteins, such as fibroblast growth factor (FGF) (19), the platelet derived growth factor (PDGF) receptor (95), phospholipase C (50), and the mRNA transcription factor, AP-1 (10). Conversely, transfection has been used to show that protein kinase C (PKC) has transforming potential (32, 56). Much correlative evidence related this enzyme to growth regulation, but it had not been identified previously as a c-*onc*.

Over 50 oncogenes and proto-oncogenes had been identified as of mid-1987 (48). The cognate proteins appear to fall within a relatively limited number of functional groups: growth factors and growth factor receptors, protein kinases, guanine nucleotide binding proteins, and RNA transcription factors (Table 1). This observation has prompted the view that "in principle, any gene encoding a growth factor, a receptor, an intracellular signalling molecule, or a protein which regulates transcription, may be considered as a proto-oncogene" (39, p. 4). This view broadens the original concept of c-*onc* since the transforming potential of all such proteins has not been shown. However, this view may be valid and useful. A multitude of biochemical processes are activated during growth; only some of them may be regulatory

Table 1 Major proto-oncogenes: functional groups and myocardial expression

Proto-oncogene[a]	Discovery[b]	Protein[c]	Myocardial expression[d]	References[e]
Growth factors				
sis	V	PDGF B chain	+/−	16, 43, 59
hst (int-2)	T	FGF		
?		TGF β		
?		NGF	+	55
Growth factor receptors				
erb-A	V	Thyroid (steroid, retinoic acid)	+/−	16, 25, 27, 43, 86
erb-B (neu)	V (T)	EGF (TGF α)	+/−	43, 58
fms	V	CSF-1	+	16
kit	V	PDGF	+/−	
ros (met, trk)	V	Insulin (IGF-I)	+	14
?		Angiotensin II	+	1
?		α_1-Adrenergic	+	72
?		Cytokines (ILs, IFNs, TNFs)	+	9
Protein-tyrosine kinases				
src	V	60	+	15, 16, 77
abl	V	150	+	15, 16
fps/fes	V	98/92	+	16
Protein-serine/threonine kinases				
mos	V			
raf	V	75	+	16
?		Protein kinase C	+	30
Guanine nucleotide binding proteins				
ras	V and T	21	+	16, 23, 43, 53, 78
Phospholipase C				
crk	V		+	1, 11
Nuclear proteins (transcription factors)				
myc	V and T	50–60	+	4, 15, 16, 43, 54, 64, 66, 81, 97
fos	V	55–65	+	2, 4, 15, 16, 36, 40, 43, 66
jun	V	AP-1		

Table 1 (*continued*)

Proto-oncogene[a]	Discovery[b]	Protein[c]	Myocardial expression[d]	References[e]
myb	V	75	−	16
ets	V	56		
ski	V		+	16
RB		110		
p53	T	53		

[a]Major representative c-*oncs* grouped according to their functional activity. A "?" means no c-*onc* has been identified by v-*onc* homology or by tumor DNA transfection. Activity as a growth factor or receptor is considered to define a c-*onc*. In some cases, e.g. *neu*, more is known about the oncogene than the progenitor c-*onc*. *Erb*-A, protein kinase C, *ras*, *myc*, and *jun* are multigene familities, and this may be true in other cases. Genes in parentheses are closely related.
[b]Discovered by v-*onc* homology (V) or transfection (T).
[c]Named or homologous protein encoded, or apparent molecular weight of protein product in kDa. Proteins in parentheses are closely related.
[d]In myocardial tissue, isolated cells, or cultures. In some cases the mRNA only has been studied; in others only the protein and/or its activity (see text). +, detected; −, not detected; +/− contradictory or unpublished evidence; blank, not studied.
[e]References are to myocardial expression. For general references see 6, 7, 26, 29, 33, 38, 39, 48, 89–92.

as opposed to permissive (3, 61). The classes of proteins represented by c-*oncs* clearly have an important regulatory role in growth.

Functions of Proto-Oncogenes and Role in Hypertrophy

A biological role in growth regulation has been confirmed as above for many c-*oncs*, but not all. For example c-*src*, does not transform normal cells (7). Furthermore, it has become apparent that c-*onc* proteins also regulate cellular differentiation and acute function. These diverse roles appear to be accomplished by a relatively limited number of biochemical functions (Table 1). However, the mechanisms responsible for normal growth or differentiation and the alterations causing transformation remain major areas for study (7).

About 20 peptide growth factors alone have been defined (13). The physiological effects of growth factors are considerably broader than their names might imply. First, diverse types of cells can respond to a given growth factor, and individual cell types can respond to multiple growth factors. These growth factors can originate from the target cell (autocrine), adjacent cells (paracrine), or distant tissues (endocrine). Second, growth factors can modulate cell growth, cell differentiation, or acute cell functions, such as contraction or secretion, and can do so either positively or negatively (5, 26, 49, 79, 92, 94). These varied effects may not be mutually exclusive and appear to depend on the total growth factor environment of a given cell and its stage of development. Thus, growth factors have been likened to individual characters in an alphabet or code (79). Major questions include exactly how surface receptors alter growth and differentiation, whether the transduction of these nuclear effects differs qualitatively or quantitatively from transduction of acute cytoplasmic responses such as contraction or secretion, the implication of the redundancy of signals to which a given cell responds, and the mechanisms of integration of these signals. Regulation of growth and differentiation by cytoplasmic receptors of the thyroid/steroid class (*erb*-A family) is best understood. Each receptor possesses individual domains responsible for hormone binding, nuclear translocation, DNA binding, and transcriptional activation (57). In the case of surface membrane receptors for polypeptides and amines, these functions may be distributed among various members of a postreceptor intracellular cascade of phosphorylated proteins (33). However, there is a possible role for the ligand and/or receptor in the nucleus (12) and for intracellular mechanisms yet to be discovered.

Several c-*oncs* encode proteins that localize in the nucleus and may modulate RNA transcription. Transcription factors bind directly to regulatory DNA sequences of the transcribed gene (promoters and enhancers) or to other proteins that bind DNA. They can stimulate or inhibit RNA polymerase II activity (20, 47). Like growth factors and receptors, the transcription factors may also be characters in an alphabet or code. Certain of the *trans*-acting proteins (*erb*-A, *jun*) appear to be present in the basal state and to be activated somehow by growth factors rather than being newly synthesized. Members of the *erb*-A family bind both hormone and DNA and modulate transcription through distinct domains. The DNA binding and transcriptional regulatory functions of proteins of the *jun* family can be activated by a PKC-activating phorbol ester, phorbol myristate acetate (PMA) (10, 46). The mechanism of *trans*-factor activation may involve phosphorylation of the protein or of an inhibitor of it (91). *Jun* may also be synthesized in response to growth factors (62). There is evidence that the *fos* and *myc* proteins are transcription factors (44, 90). The *fos* and *myc* mRNAs, and proteins in some cases, are rapidly induced in response to a wide variety of stimuli (91). Major questions include the mechanisms of *myc* and *fos* induction and the genes regulated by the *myc* and *fos* proteins, if they are indeed *trans*-factors.

There is no direct evidence by reconstitution in an in vitro assay that these nuclear c-*onc* proteins regulate DNA replication, whereas mRNA transcription is regulated in vitro (10). However, one DNA-binding protein can activate both RNA transcription and DNA replication (37). Thus, other transcription factors may also have a dual role. Alternately, the *myc* or *fos* proteins may regulate transcription of the mRNAs encoding other proteins involved in DNA replication.

The link between membrane receptors and transcription factors is thought to involve the cytoplasmic c-*oncs,* protein kinases and the guanine nucleotide binding *ras* proteins (Table 1). A few of the more common kinases that phosphorylate serine or threonine residues have been shown to have transforming potential, e.g. *raf* and PKC. Most potentially oncogenic kinases phosphorylate on tyrosine. Several receptors have tryosine kinase activity [epidermal growth factor (EGF), PDGF, colony stimulating factor-1 (CSF-1), insulin, and insulinlike growth factor I (IGF-I), but not α_1-adrenergic, interleukin-2 (IL-2), or nerve growth factor (NGF)] (13, 70). There are also membrane-associated cytoplasmic tyrosine kinases that do not bind ligands (6, 33). These cytoplasmic kinases may share regulation with phosphoinositide phospholipase C (PI-PLC). *V-crk* is structurally similar to the possible regulatory domains of PI-PLC and of *src*, the prototypic cytoplasmic tyrosine protein kinase (41, 50, 80). Physiologically important substrates of the various kinases remain uncertain although receptor auto-phosphorylation may be important (70). Proteins of the *ras* family have been postulated to couple growth factor receptors to effectors, in analogy with other G proteins. However, it is not clear whether coupling to receptors is direct or through a GTPase-activating or other protein (71). Similarly, the effectors to which *ras* may couple are unknown (28). Whatever the mechanisms, *ras* proteins can variably modulate growth or differentiation in different types of cells (28).

Cell hypertrophy and differentiation can be visualized as resulting from transcriptional regulation. Growth of all cells can be dissociated into component parts: increase in size, DNA replication, mitosis, and cytokinesis (3). Growth in size and DNA replicaton can be independently regulated by different growth factors (3). The same growth factor can modulate hypertrophy, hyperplasia, or both, depending on the other growth factors present (22). The orderly postnatal loss in cardiac myocytes of cytokinesis, mitosis, and DNA synthesis (17) may be produced by loss of stimulatory growth factors or transducers, or acquisition of inhibitory ones. Hypertrophy is of critical interest to cardiac myocyte biologists, but is not analyzed separately in most studies on proliferating cells. Growth in size is produced largely by and can be defined by an increase in cell proteins (3). Protein expression is most commonly regulated at the level of mRNA transcription (18). Thus, hypertrophy can be postulated to reflect the end result of transcription of various RNA species. Work in a cultured cardiac myocyte model supports this postulate (45; C. S. Long et al, unpublished observations). Diverse normal or abnormal types of hypertrophy, perhaps akin to varied degrees of differentiation, may be produced by different sets of growth factors that activate transcription of different sets of genes.

PROTO-ONCOGENES IN THE MYOCARDIUM AND IN MYOCYTES

Several c-*oncs* are constitutively expressed and/or induced in the myocardium or in myocytes. There is direct and indirect evidence for additional growth factors or receptors. Much of the available data is preliminary, and was obtained in intact myocardium or in heterogenous populations of isolated cells. Thus myocyte specificity of expression is uncertain for many studies. This overview begins outside the cell and works inward (Table 1).

Studies of *sis* mRNA (PDGF B chain) and the PDGF receptor raise the possibility of an autocrine or paracrine heart cell growth factor system. Expression of *sis* mRNA was detected in neonatal and adult rat myocardium and in isolated cells in one study (16), but not in adult rat myocardium in another (43). *Sis* is possibly induced in pressure-loaded rat myocardium (59). The PDGF receptor is present in cultures containing neonatal rat myocytes (L. T. Williams, personal communication) although exogenous PDGF does not induce c-*myc* expression in cultured myocytes (81). C-*fms* mRNA (CSF-1 receptor) is present in neonatal and adult rat tissue, but only in neonatal isolated cells (16). The PDGF receptor and c-*fms* are in the same family (95). Cultured heart cells also produce NGF (55).

Several other growth factor receptors have been detected. A member of the *erb*-A family (thyroid/steroid receptors) (93) was detected in neonatal and adult rat tissue and isolated cells (16). In fact, brain and heart share novel thyroid and steroid hormone receptor genes (25, 86). It is unclear whether thyroid hormone regulates myocyte growth directly or indirectly (31, 42), but thyroid hormone regulates myosin gene expression in cultured myocytes (27). This implies the presence of an *erb*-A gene. Other members of the thyroid/steroid/retinoic acid superfamily (60) may have biological effects in myocytes as well (67). Thus, one study's failure to detect *erb*-A in adult rat myocardium is surprising (43). *Erb*-B mRNA (EGF receptor) also was not found in the same study (43). However, there is an acute chronotropic response to EGF in embryonic chick myocyte aggregates, consistent with the presence of the receptor (58). Angiotensin II regulates growth of certain cells (24) although there is as yet no conclusive evidence for this in cardiac myocytes. Angiotensin II does elicit a contractile response in cultured myocytes and activates a PI-PLC (1). The insulin receptor-related c-*oncs* (*ros, met, trk*) (33) have not been studied in heart, but insulin receptors are present on myocytes (14). An interferon (IFN), one of the cytokine group [IFNs, interleukins (ILs), tumor necrosis factors (TNFs)], increases beating rate of cultured myocytes (9).

The α_1-adrenergic receptor is the first, and so far only, well-documented growth factor receptor for cardiac myocytes (72). Stimulation of this receptor on cultured neonatal rat myocytes increases cell size (total protein content, cell volume, and surface area) (72, 73), total and myofibrillar protein synthesis (52), total RNA content (which is largely rRNA) (8), c-*myc* mRNA content (81), and the per cell contents of several contractile protein mRNAs, in particular those encoding fetal/neonatal isoforms, that are up-regulated during pressure-load hypertrophy in vivo, skeletal α-actin, and β-myosin heavy chain (8; L. E. Waspe et al, unpublished observations). The increases in steady-state levels of mRNA and total RNA appear to be due at least in part to augmented transcription (45, C. S. Long et al, unpublished observations). The myocyte hypertrophic response to α_1 stimulation is not accompanied by DNA synthesis, mitosis, or cytokinesis (45, 76; C. S. Long et al, unpublished observations). In contrast, α_1 stimulation induces hyperplasia of a variety of other types of cultured cells. In some cases, but not all, co–growth factors are required (see 75). α_1-Mediated myocyte growth can be dissociated from α_1-mediated positive contractile effects, i.e. contractile activity is not necessary for increase in size or for mRNA transcription (73). It is not known whether the intracellular transduction mechanisms of growth and contractility differ quantitatively or qualitatively. The α_1 receptor in myocytes is coupled to cytoplasmic transducing proteins PI-PLC (11) and PKC (30). There is insufficient data to evaluate whether all receptors coupled to these transducers in myocytes induce growth. It is still unclear whether the α_1 receptor remains coupled to growth in cultured normal adult myocytes (see 74, 75). There is a directional change in a low-dose α_1 contractile response concomitant with innervation and/or maturation of rat myocytes (83).

In addition to PI-PLC and PKC, several other cytoplasmic signal-transducing c-*oncs* have been studied in myocardium. *Raf,* which encodes a serine/threonine protein kinase, is strongly expressed in neonatal and adult rat tissue and cells (16). Tyrosine protein kinase genes are present in isolated neonatal cells, including *src, abl,* and *fps/fes* (16). *Src* kinase activity is also detectable in adult heart (77). Treatment with PMA induces *abl* and *src* mRNA in cultured adult rat myocytes (15). *Ras* family genes are expressed at the mRNA and protein level in human and rodent myocardium and isolated cells. No major *ras* developmental change has been found (16, 23, 43, 53, 78). There is a delayed increase in a *ras* mRNA after aortic constriction in adult rat heart (43).

Among the nuclear c-*oncs, ski* mRNA was seen in neonatal and adult rat myocardium and cells, whereas *myb* was not (16). Studies of *fos* suggest that apparent nonexpression can be a function of technique. Constitutive expression of *fos* was not detected in total RNA of neonatal and adult rat myocardium (2, 16, 36, 66), but was found in both when mRNA was analyzed (43). *Fos* was also seen in neonatal mouse total RNA (40). Interestingly, *fos* mRNA increases with age in the rat myocardium (43). *Fos* appears to be regulated by multiple factors, in myocytes as in other cells. Thus *fos* mRNA in the myocardium is increased (*a*) by high coronary flow or pressure, or contractility in the isolated rat heart (4); (*b*) by myocyte isolation (16); (*c*) by ascending or abdominal aortic coarctation (36, 43); (*d*) by α- or β-adrenergic stimulation, the latter independent of calcium channel antagonists (2); and (*e*) by histamine H_1 and prostaglandin E_1 (PGE$_1$) (2). PMA increases *fos* mRNA in cultured adult rat myocytes (15). It is unknown whether the *fos* protein is also expressed in these diverse circumstances and what the signal(s) and role(s) might be.

There is general agreement that rodent myocardial expression of the *myc* family decreases during development (16, 43, 64, 66, 97) although it can be detected in adult tissue and cells (16, 97). As with *fos,* c-*myc* mRNA is induced in the isolated rat heart (4), by aortic constriction (36, 43, 54), and by PMA in cultured adult rat myocytes (15).

α_1-Adrenergic stimulation of noncontracting neonatal rat myocytes in serum-free culture increases c-*myc* mRNA content by five- to ten-fold over control (81). This response is rapid (onset within 30 min), transient, dose-related, and muscle cell specific. Among three other agents that elicit hypertrophy in this model, serum and PMA induce c-*myc* (81), whereas thyroid hormone does not (N. F. Starksen et al, unpublished observations). Thus *myc* expression may not be characteristic of all forms of hypertrophy. The translated *myc* exons 2 and 3 and the *myc* protein were not assayed in this study. Transcription of exons 2 and 3 is increased by α_1 stimulation, although possible anti-sense synthesis has not been evaluated (C. S. Long et al, unpublished observations). The pathway(s) from the α_1 receptor to *myc* expression is unknown. Also unknown is the function and role of the *myc* protein in myocytes, assuming it is translated from the mRNA. The hearts of mice expressing a *myc* transgene (84) are grossly enlarged, due either to myocyte hypertrophy or hyperplasia (J. L. Swain, personal communication).

SUMMARY AND FUTURE DIRECTIONS

The data summarized above indicate that a large number of genes or gene products known to regulate growth are constitutively expressed and/or induced in the myocardium. Although in many cases the responsible cell type has not been carefully studied, the implication is that cardiac myocyte growth, like that of other cells, is regulated by c-*onc* products. This is, perhaps, not surprising. The α_1-adrenergic receptor modulates myocyte hypertrophy and RNA transcription in one model system. Myocyte α_1 receptor numbers and activity may be increased in a genetic model for hypertrophy (75, 87).

The total number of c-*oncs* is likely greater than the 50+ recognized at present. Thus, work on c-*oncs* in heart is in its infancy. The biological effects produced by c-*oncs* appear to be highly dependent on cell type even though the biochemical functions of the proteins (growth factor, receptor, transducer, or transcription factor) may be the same in all cells. This argues for specific study of cardiac myocytes. Studies of c-*onc* expression in vivo may be useful, e.g. for asking whether different patterns of c-*onc* induction characterize various types of hypertrophy. Assays in these models can and should be done on well-characterized isolated myocytes (14) or with cell-specific methods (e.g. in situ hybridization or immunocytology). If myocytes are like other cells, additional myocyte growth factors probably await discovery. Given the potential for multiple paracrine and autocrine growth factors, well-defined culture systems would seem to be essential for defining new growth factors (75). Additional models are also needed, particularly for myocyte DNA replication. Animals expressing oncogenic proteins in the myocardium may be valuable new models (21, 64, 84).

It has been suggested in this review that the hypertrophic stage of growth, in myocytes and other cells, could be produced by transcriptional activation of multiple RNA species. Different types of hypertrophy may reflect the actions of various combinations of growth factors on particular myocyte-specific genes or set of genes. Regulation at other levels, such as translation, may be important in addition to transcription or instead of it (51). Definition of the level of regulation requires study of specific genes and provides the foundation to study intracellular transduction mechanisms. The total number of transduction systems and how they operate and are integrated are not known for any cell type.

Emphasis on growth factors should not obscure the fact that physical stimuli can activate cell transduction pathways, as exemplified by light in the retina. The effects of mechanical stimuli (such as stretch) on synthesis of heart total and specific proteins, the level of regulation, and pathways activated, and integration with other growth factors can now be studied in culture models (85). Possible "receptors" for mechanical stimuli include ion channels (63) and receptors for extracellular matrix proteins (34). There is evidence for an important interaction between mechanical and soluble growth factors in one model system (88).

CONCLUSIONS

The regulation of cardiac myocyte growth can be conceived as resulting from the actions of c-*onc* products: growth factors, receptors, intracellular signaling proteins, and transcription factors. Initial data on these genes and gene products in myocytes and myocardium suggest great potential for future progress. The ability to manipulate myocyte growth would have major clinical impact. However, some of the important questions are just now becoming apparent.

ACKNOWLEDGMENTS

My work is supported by the Veterans Administration Research Service and the National Institutes of Health (HL31113 and HL35561). I am a Clinical Investigator of the Veterans Administration. Charles P. Ordahl, Carlin S. Long, and Lawrence E. Waspe made major contributions to the new work described on the α_1-adrenergic receptor.

Literature Cited

1. Allen, I. S., Cohen, N. M., Dhallan, R. S., Gaa, S. T., Lederer, W. J., Rogers, T. B. 1988. Angiotensin II increases spontaneous contractile frequency and stimulates calcium current in cultured neonatal rat heart myocytes: insights into the underlying biochemical mechanisms. *Circ. Res.* 62:524–34

2. Barka, T., van der Noen, H., Shaw, P. A. 1987. Proto-oncogene *fos* (c-*fos*) expression in the heart. *Oncogene* 1:439–43

3. Baserga, R. 1985. *The Biology of Cell Reproduction*. Cambridge, Mass.: Harvard Univ. Press. 245 pp.

4. Bauters, C., Moalic, J. M., Bercovici, J., Mouas, C., Enanoil-Ravier, R., et al. 1988. Coronary flow as a determinant of c-myc and c-fos protooncogene expression in an isolated adult rat heart. *J. Mol. Cell Cardiol.* 20:97–101

5. Berk, B. C., Alexander, R. W., Brock, T. A., Gimbrone, M. A. Jr., Webb, R. C. 1986. Vasoconstriction: a new activity for platelet-derived growth factor. *Science* 232:87–90

6. Bishop, J. M. 1985. Viral oncogenes. *Cell* 42:23–38

7. Bishop, J. M. 1987. The molecular genetics of cancer. *Science* 235:305–11

8. Bishopric, N. H., Simpson, P. C., Ordahl, C. P. 1987. Induction of the skeletal α-actin gene in α_1 adrenoceptor-mediated hypertrophy of rat cardiac myocytes. *J. Clin. Invest.* 80:1194–99

9. Blalock, J. E., Stanton, J. D. 1980. Common pathways of interferon and hormonal action. *Nature* 283:406–8

10. Bohmann, D., Bos, T. J., Admon, A., Nishimura, T., Vogt, P. K., et al. 1987. Human proto-oncogene c-*jun* encodes a DNA binding protein with structural and functional properties of transcription factor AP-1. *Science* 238:1386–92

11. Brown, J. H., Buxton, I. L., Brunton, L. L. 1985. α_1-adrenergic and muscarinic cholinergic stimulation of phosphoinositide hydrolysis in adult rat cardiomyocytes. *Circ. Res.* 57:532–37

12. Burwen, S. J., Jones, A. L. 1987. The association of polypeptide hormones and growth factors with the nuclei of target cells. *Trends Biochem. Sci.* 12:259–62

13. Carpenter, G. 1987. Receptors for epidermal growth factor and other polypeptide mitogens. *Annu. Rev. Biochem.* 56:881–914

14. Clark, W. A., Decker, R. S., Borg, T. K., eds. 1988. *Biology of Isolated Adult Cardiac Myocytes*. New York: Elsevier. 441 pp.

15. Claycomb, W. C. 1988. "Dedifferentiation" of the cultured adult cardiac muscle cell by TPA. In *Biology of Isolated Adult Cardiac Myocytes*, ed. W. A. Clark, R. S. Decker, T. K. Borg, pp. 284–87. New York: Elsevier

16. Claycomb, W. C., Lanson, N. A. Jr. 1987. Proto-oncogene expression in-proliferating and differentiating cardiac and skeletal muscle. *Biochem. J.* 247:701–6

17. Clubb, F. J. Jr., Bishop, S. P. 1984. Formation of binucleated myocardial cells in the neonatal rat: an index for growth hypertrophy. *Lab. Invest.* 50: 571–77

18. Darnell, J. E. Jr. 1982. Variety in the level of gene control in eukaryotic cells. *Nature* 297:365–71

19. Delli Bovi, P., Curatola, A. M., Kern, F. G., Greco, A., Ittmann, M., Basilico, C. 1987. An oncogene isolated by transfection of Kaposis sarcoma DNA encodes a growth factor that is a member of the FGF family. *Cell* 50:729–37

20. Dynan, W. S., Tjian, R. 1985. Control of eukaryotic messenger RNA synthesis by sequence-specific DNA-binding proteins. *Nature* 316:774–78

21. Field, L. J. 1988. Atrial natriuretic factor–SV40 T antigen transgenes produce tumors and cardiac arrhythmias in mice. *Science* 239:1029–33

22. Fine, L. G., Holley, R. W., Nasri, H., Badie-Dezfooly, B. 1985. BSC-1 growth inhibitor transforms a mitogenic stimulus into a hypertrophic stimulus for renal proximal tubular cells: relationship to Na^+/H^+ antiport activity. *Proc. Natl. Acad. Sci. USA* 82:6163–66

23. Furth, M. E., Aldrich, T. H., Cordon-Cardo, C. 1987. Expression of ras proto-oncogene proteins in normal human tissues. *Oncogene* 1:47–58

24. Geisterfer, A. A. T., Peach, M. J., Owens, G. K. 1988. Angiotensin II induces hypertrophy, not hyperplasia, of cultured rat aortic smooth muscle cells. *Circ. Res.* 62:749–56

25. Giguere, V., Yang, N., Segui, P., Evans, R. M. 1988. Identification of a new class of steroid hormone receptors. *Nature* 331:91–94

26. Goustin, A. S., Leof, E. B., Shipley, G. D., Moses, H. L. 1986. Growth factors and cancer. *Cancer Res.* 46:1015–29

27. Gustafson, T. A., Markham, B. E., Bahl, J. J., Morkin, E. 1987. Thyroid hormone regulates expression of a transfected α-myosin heavy chain fusion

gene in fetal heart cells. *Proc. Natl. Acad. Sci. USA* 84:3122–26

28. Hanley, M. R., Jackson, T. 1987. The *ras* gene: transformer and transducer. *Nature* 328:668–69

29. Heldin, C.-H., Westermark, B. 1984. Growth factors: mechanism of action and relation to oncogenes. *Cell* 37:9–20

30. Henrich, C. J., Simpson, P. C. 1987. Activation of protein kinase C in hypertrophy of cultured rat heart myocytes. *Circulation* 76:IV–235 (Abstr.)

31. Hinkle, P. M., Kinsella, P. A. 1986. Thyroid hormone induction of an autocrine growth factor secreted by pituitary tumor cells. *Science* 234:1549–52

32. Housey, G. M., Johnson, M. D., Hsiao, W. L. W., O'Brian, C. A., Murphy, J. P. 1988. Overproduction of protein kinase C causes disordered growth control in fibroblasts. *Cell* 52:343–54

33. Hunter, T. 1987. A thousand and one protein kinases. *Cell* 50:823–29

34. Hynes, R. O. 1987. Integrins: a family of cell surface receptors. *Cell* 48:549–54

35. Izumo, S., Lompre, A. M., Matsuoka, R., Koren, G., Schwartz, K. 1987. Myosin heavy chain messenger RNA and protein isoform transitions during cardiac hypertrophy: interaction between hemodynamic and thyroid hormone-induced signals. *J. Clin. Invest.* 79:970–77

36. Izumo, S., Nadal-Ginard, B., Mahdavi, V. 1988. Protooncogene induction and reprogramming of cardiac gene expression produced by pressure overload. *Proc. Natl. Acad. Sci. USA* 85:339–43

37. Jones, K. A., Kadonaga, J. T., Rosenfeld, P. J., Kelly, T. J., Tijan, R. 1987. A cellular DNA-binding protein that activates eukaryotic transcription and DNA replication. *Cell* 48:79–89

38. Kaczmarek, L. 1986. Biology of disease—protooncogene expression during the cell cycle. *Lab. Invest.* 54:365–76

39. Kahn, P., Graf, T. 1986. *Oncogenes and Growth Control.* Berlin: Springer-Verlag. 369 pp.

40. Kasik, J. W., Wan, Y.-J. Y., Ozato, K. 1987. A burst of c-*fos* gene expression in the mouse occurs at birth. *Mol. Cell. Biol.* 7:3349–52

41. Katan, M., Parker, P. J. 1988. Oncogenes and cell control. *Nature* 332:203

42. Klein, I., Hong, C. 1986. Effects of thyroid hormone on cardiac size and myosin content of the heterotopically transplanted rat heart. *J. Clin. Invest.* 77:1694–98

43. Komuro, I., Kurabayashi, M., Takaku, F., Yazaki, Y. 1988. Expression of cellular oncogenes in the myocardium during the developmental stage and pressure-overloaded hypertrophy of the rat heart. *Circ. Res.* 62:1075–79

44. Lech, K., Anderson, K., Brent, R. 1988. DNA-bound fos proteins activate transcription in yeast. *Cell* 52:179–84

45. Lee, H. R., Henderson, S. A., Meidell, R. S., Yuan, D., Chien, K. R. 1986. Alpha adrenergic regulation of cardiac gene transcription during hypertrophy in cultured myocardial cells. *Circulation* 74:II–156 (Abstr.)

46. Lee, W., Mitchell, P., Tijan, R. 1987. Purified transcription factor AP-1 interacts with TPA-inducible enhancer elements. *Cell* 49:741–52

47. Maniatis, T., Goodbourn, S., Fischer, J. A. 1987. Regulation of inducible and tissue-specific gene expression. *Science* 236:1237–45

48. Marx, J. L. 1987. Oncogene action probed. *Science* 237:602–3

49. Massagué, J. 1987. The TGF-β family of growth and differentiation factors. *Cell* 49:437–38

50. Mayer, B. J., Hamaguchi, M., Hanafusa, H. 1988. A novel viral oncogene with structural similarity to phospholipase C. *Nature* 332:272–75

51. McDermott, P., Whitaker-Dowling, P., Klein, I. 1987. Regulation of cardiac myosin synthesis: studies of RNA content in cultured heart cells. *Exp. Cell Res.* 173:183–92

52. Meidell, R. S., Sen, A., Henderson, S. A., Slahetka, M. F., Chien, K. R. 1986. α_1-adrenergic stimulation of rat myocardial cells increases protein synthesis. *Am. J. Physiol.* 251:H1076–84

53. Muller, R., Slamon, D. J., Adamson, E. D., Tremblay, J. M., Muller, D., et al. 1983. Transcription of c-*onc* genes c-*ras*^{ki} and c-*fms* during mouse development. *Mol. Cell. Biol.* 3:1062–69

54. Mulvagh, S. L., Michael, L. H., Perryman, M. B., Roberts, R., Schneider, M. D. 1987. A hemodynamic load in vivo induces cardiac expression of the cellular oncogene, c-*myc*. *Biochem. Biophys. Res. Commun.* 147:627–36

55. Norrgren, G., Ebendal, T. 1986. Nerve growth factor in medium conditioned by embryonic chicken heart cells. *Int. J. Dev. Neurosci.* 4:41–49

56. Persons, D. A., Wilkison, W. O., Bell, R. M., Finn, O. J. 1988. Altered growth regulation and enhanced tumorigenicity of NIH-3T3 fibroblasts transfected with

protein kinase C-I cDNA. *Cell* 52:447–58

57. Picard, D., Yamamoto, K. R. 1987. Two signals mediate hormone-dependent nuclear localization of the glucocorticoid receptor. *EMBO J.* 6:3333–40

58. Rabkin, S. W., Sunga, P., Myrdal, S. 1987. The effect of epidermal growth factor on chronotropic response in cardiac cells in culture. *Biochem. Biophys. Res. Commun.* 146:889–97

59. Re, R. N. 1987. Cellular mechanisms of growth in cardiovascular tissue. *Am. J. Cardiol.* 60:104I–109I

60. Robertson, M. 1987. Retinoic acid receptor: towards a biochemistry of morphogenesis. *Nature* 330:420–21

61. Rozengurt, E. 1986. Early signals in the mitogenic response. *Science* 234:161–66

62. Ryder, K., Lau, L. F., Nathans, D. 1988. A gene activated by growth factors is related to the oncogene v-*jun*. *Proc. Natl. Acad. Sci. USA* 85:1487–91

63. Sachs, F. 1986. Biophysics of mechanoreception. *Membr. Biochem.* 6:173–95

64. Saule, S., Merigaud, J. P., Al-Moustafa, A.-E. M., Ferre, F., Rong, P. M., et al. 1987. Heart tumors specifically induced in young avian embryos by the v-*myc* oncogene. *Proc. Natl. Acad. Sci. USA* 84:7982–86

65. Schaibel, T. F., Ciambrone, G. J., Capasso, J. M., Scheuer, J. 1984. Cardiac conditioning ameliorates cardiac dysfunction associated with renal hypertension in rats. *J. Clin. Invest.* 73:1086–94

66. Schneider, M. D., Payne, P. A., Ueno, H., Perryman, M. B., Roberts, R. 1986. Dissociated expression of c-*myc* and a *fos*-related competence gene during cardiac myogenesis. *Mol. Cell. Biol.* 6:4140–43

67. Scheuer, J., Malhotra, A., Schaible, T. F., Capasso, J. 1987. Effects of gonadectomy and hormone replacement on rat hearts. *Circ. Res.* 61:12–19

68. Schwarz, F., Schaper, J., Kittstein, D., Flameng, W., Walter, P., et al. 1981. Reduced volume fraction of myofibrils in myocardium of patients with decompensated pressure overload. *Circulation* 63:1299–1304

69. Shih, C., Shilo, B.-Z., Goldfarb, M. P., Dannenberg, A., Weinberg, R. A. 1979. Passage of phenotypes of chemically transformed cells via transfection of DNA and chromatin. *Proc. Natl. Acad. Sci. USA* 76:5714–18

70. Sibley, D. R., Benovic, J. L., Caron, M. G., Lefkowitz, R. L. 1987. Regulation of transmembrane signaling by receptor phosphorylation. *Cell* 48:913–22

71. Sigal, I. S. 1988. The *ras* oncogene: a structure and some function. *Nature* 332:485–86

72. Simpson, P. 1983. Norepinephrine-stimulated hypertrophy of cultured rat myocardial cells is an α_1-adrenergic response. *J. Clin. Invest.* 72:732–38

73. Simpson, P. 1985. Stimulation of hypertrophy of cultured neonatal rat heart cells through an α_1-adrenergic receptor and induction of beating through an alpha$_1$- and β_1-adrenergic receptor interaction: evidence for independent regulation of growth and beating. *Circ. Res.* 56:884–94

74. Simpson, P. 1988. Comments on "Load regulation of the properties of adult feline cardiocytes: The role of substrate adhesion" which appeared in *Circ. Res.* 58:692–703. *Circ. Res.* 62:864–66

75. Simpson, P. C. 1989. α_1-Adrenergic stimulated hypertrophy in neonatal rat heart muscle cells. In *Hypertrophic Cardiomyopathy*, ed. H. Toshima, B. J. Maron. Tokyo: Univ. Tokyo Press. In press

76. Simpson, P., McGrath, A., Savion, S. 1982. Myocyte hypertrophy in neonatal rat heart cultures and its regulation by serum and by catecholamines. *Circ. Res.* 51:787–801

77. Sorge, J. P., Sorge, L. K., Maness, P. F. 1985. pp60$^{c\text{-}src}$ is expressed in human fetal and adult brain. *Am. J. Pathol.* 199:151–57

78. Spandidos, D. A., Dimitrov, T. 1985. High expression levels of ras p21 protein in normal mouse heart. *Biosci. Rep.* 5:1035–39

79. Sporn, M. B., Roberts, A. B. 1988. Peptide growth factors are multifunctional. *Nature* 332:217–19

80. Stahl, M. L., Ferenz, C. R., Kelleher, K. L., Kriz, R. W., Knopf, J. L. 1988. Sequence similarity of phospholipase C with the non-catalytic region of src. *Nature* 332:269–72

81. Starksen, N. F., Simpson, P. C., Bishopric, N., Coughlin, S., Lee, W. M. F. et al. 1986. Cardiac myocyte hypertrophy is associated with c-*myc* proto-oncogene expression. *Proc. Natl. Acad. Sci. USA* 83:8348–50

82. Stehelin, D., Varmus, H. E., Bishop, J. M., Vogt, P. K. 1976. DNA related to the transforming gene(s) of avian sarcoma viruses is present in normal avian DNA. *Nature* 260:170–73

83. Steinberg, S. F., Drugge, E. D., Bilezikian, J. P., Robinson, R. B. 1985.

Acquisition by innervated cardiac myocytes of a pertussis toxin–specific regulatory protein linked to the α_1 receptor. *Science* 230:186–88

84. Swain, J. L., Stewart, T. A., Leder, P. 1987. Parental legacy determines methylation and expression of an autosomal transgene: a molecular mechanism for parental imprinting. *Cell* 50:719–27

85. Terracio, L., Miller, B., Borg, T. K. 1988. Effects of cyclic mechanical stimulation of the cellular components of the heart: in vitro. *In Vitro Cell Dev. Biol.* 24:53–58

86. Thompson, C. C., Weinberger, C., Lebb, R., Evans, R. M. 1987. Identification of a novel thyroid hormone receptor expressed in the mammalian central nervous system. *Science* 237:1610–14

87. Toshima, H., Nakata, M., Nohara, M., Chiba, M., Koga, Y. 1987. Increased adrenergic receptor activity and hypertrophic response to norepinephrine in cultured SHR myocardial cell. *Circulation* 76(Suppl. IV):IV–534 (Abstr.)

88. Vandenburgh, H. H. 1983. Cell shape and growth regulation in skeletal muscle: exogenous versus endogenous factors. *J. Cell. Physiol.* 116:363–71

89. Varmus, H. E. 1984. The molecular genetics of cellular oncogenes. *Annu. Rev. Genet.* 18:553–612

90. Varmus, H. E. 1987. Oncogenes and transcriptional control. *Science* 238:1337–39

91. Verma, I. M., Sassone-Cors, P. 1987. Proto-oncogene *fos*: complex but versatile regulation. *Cell* 51:513–14

92. Weinberg, R. A. 1985. The action of oncogenes in the cytoplasm and nucleus. *Science* 230:770–76

93. Weinberger, C., Thompson, C. C., Ong, E. S., Lebo, R., Gruol, D. J., Evans, R. M. 1986. The c-*erb*-A gene encodes a thyroid hormone receptor. *Nature* 324:641–46

94. Woodland, H., Jones, L. 1988. Growth factors in amphibian cell differentiation. *Nature* 332:113–15

95. Yarden, Y., Escobedo, J. A., Kuang, W. J., Yang-Feng, T. L., Daniel, T. O., et al. 1986. Structure of the receptor for platelet-derived growth factor helps define a family of closely related growth factor receptors. *Nature* 323:226–32

96. Zak, R., ed. 1984. *Growth of the Heart in Health and Disease.* New York: Raven. 480 pp

97. Zimmerman, K. A., Yancopoulos, G. D., Collum, R. G., Smith, R. K., Kohl, N E., et al. 1986. Differential expression of *myc* family genes during murine development. *Nature* 319:780–83

Annu. Rev. Physiol. 1989. 51:203–15

GENETIC REGULATION OF β-ADRENERGIC RECEPTORS

Sheila Collins, Mark A. Bolanowski, Marc G. Caron, and Robert J. Lefkowitz

Departments of Medicine, Biochemistry and Physiology, Howard Hughes Medical Institute at Duke University Medical Center, Durham, North Carolina 27710

INTRODUCTION

Cell surface receptors for neurotransmitters that are coupled to guanine nucleotide binding proteins (G proteins) comprise a family of structurally related transmembrane molecules with structural analogies to the opsin visual pigments (1). The basic elements of these signalling systems, depicted in Figure 1A, illustrate the receptor coupled to a G protein, which transduces the hormonal signal to an effector molecule. In the last few years the genes for several of these receptors have been cloned (4, 8, 12, 15, 17, 23–26, 33, 35). These advances now permit a closer examination of the physical structure of these molecules; they also provide the opportunity to examine directly their genetic regulation.

RECEPTOR STRUCTURE REVEALED BY CLONING

Cloning of these receptors has revealed several general features. A comparison of the protein sequences deduced from the genes indicates that considerable sequence similarity exists between the members of this group and predicts that these receptors contain seven hydrophobic domains (Figure 1B) (14). Topographically, these transmembrane segments presumably form closely packed helical bundles traversing the membrane, by analogy with rhodopsin (21). This arrangement of receptors in the plasma membrane predicts that the amino terminus and the sequences connecting putative transmembrane segments II–III, IV–V, and VI–VII are located on the extracellular surface. On the cytoplasmic side of the membrane would be the

203

0066-4278/89/0315-0203$02.00

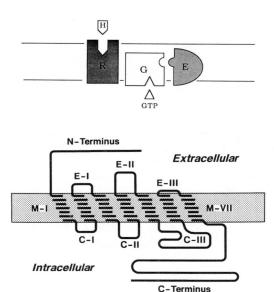

Figure 1 Model of G-protein coupled receptors. (A) Scheme for the organization of the signalling complex in the plasma membrane. R, receptor; G, G protein; E, effector enzyme (e.g. adenylate cyclase, phospholipase C). (B) Proposed topography for G-protein coupled receptors in the plasma membrane. Segments M-1 through M-VII are proposed as spanning the bilayer. With this arrangement, the amino terminus and the connecting loops E-1, E-II, and E-III would lie on the extracellular surface of the membrane. Connecting loops C-I, C-II, and C-III and the carboxyl terminus are represented as exposed to the cytoplasmic side of the plasma membrane.

carboxyl terminus of these proteins, as well as the segments connecting transmembrane helices I–II, III–IV, and V–VI, where the peptide segments can interact with other components of intracellular effector systems. Various features of this topographic organization have been validated for the hamster β_2-adrenergic receptor (β_2AR) (17).

GENE STRUCTURE

The genes for the vertebrate opsin visual pigments, to which the G protein coupled receptors are closely related both structurally and mechanistically, contain several introns separating major coding domains (1, 31). The genes encoding the β_2AR, α_2AR, and the muscarinic cholinergic receptor subtypes are unusual because they lack introns in their coding and 3'-untranslated regions. The muscarinic receptor genes do, however, contain a small intron in the 5'-untranslated sequences (4, 33). As a result, it has been suggested that this family of receptors evolved from a common ancestor by a gene processing event (23).

Promoter Structure

A schematic representation of the promoter regions of the human and hamster β_2AR genes is found in Figure 2. Analysis of these 5'-flanking sequences upstream from the gene reveals characteristic elements of eukaryotic promoters (27). The start site of transcription determined for the human gene (23) is at nucleotide position −219 relative to the start of translation (1 in Figure 2A). In the hamster gene, the equivalent sequence is found at position −228. About 30 base pairs (bp) upstream from the start site of transcription are two TATA box–like sequences (−238 and −252 in the human; −247 and −261 in the hamster, 2a and 2b in Figure 2A) and a reverse complement of the CAAT box located an additional ~50 bp upstream (3 in Figure 2A). These sequences encode positional specificity for RNA polymerase so that transcripts are initiated at the correct nucleotide (27). Also present in these genes, but not depicted in Figure 2A, are short clusters of sequence rich in guanine and cytosine residues. These clusters have been found in several eukaryotic genes that are expressed constitutively at a low level in the cell (27).

A major feature distinguishing the human from the hamster promoter region is the existence of an open reading frame (ORF) at −987 to −234 in the human β_2AR. Although this region does contain putative promoter ele-

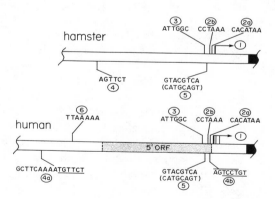

Figure 2 Organization of the promoter region for hamster and human β_2AR genes. Basic promoter elements: (*1*) site of initiation of transcription, (*2a, b*) TATA-box elements, (*3*) reverse complement of CAAT-box element, (*6*) TATA-like element flanking the 5' ORF. Potential regulatory elements: (*4*) consensus glucocorticoid regulatory element (GRE) in the hamster β_2AR, (*4a*) extended GRE sequence (16) in human β_2AR, with core sequence underlined, (*4b*) overlapping GRE sequences in human β_2AR indicated by overlining and underlining, (*5*) reverse complement of consensus cyclic AMP regulatory sequence.

ments (15, 23; 6 in Figure 2A), current evidence suggests it is devoid of functional promoter activity.

In addition to these basic elements, the promoter region of a gene may also contain sequences that specify tissue- or hormone-dependent regulation of expression. Such sequences appear to be binding sites for nuclear factors that participate in the process of transcriptional regulation (36, 42). Elements 4 and 5 in the hamster and human β_2AR gene of Figure 2A contain consensus sequences for transcriptional regulation by glucocorticoids (16, 36) and cyclic AMP (11, 30), respectively.

REGULATION OF ADRENERGIC RECEPTORS

Hormonal responsiveness of tissues can be regulated by several mechanisms, one of which is the dynamic regulation of the number of specific receptor sites on the cell surface. A wide variety of physiological and pathophysiological conditions can influence receptor number (39). Potential points of regulation for receptor-mediated processes include desensitization and uncoupling of the receptor from the effector, down-regulation and loss of receptors from the cell surface in response to long-term agonist exposure, and alterations in the rates of synthesis and degradation of both the receptor protein and its mRNA. Much attention has been focused upon desensitization of adrenergic receptor responsiveness, which involves receptor phosphorylation and uncoupling from G proteins. Recent developments in understanding the regulation of the receptor protein itself have been reviewed (2). Here we review regulatory processes that have recently been shown to occur at the level of expression of the receptor gene.

Receptor Subtypes

The subtypes of adrenergic receptors, α_1, α_2, β_1, and β_2 were originally defined by their distinct physiological actions in specific tissues and by differences in the rank order of potency of pharmacologically specific ligands. From the perspective of developmental regulation, the expression of subtypes in predominantly one tissue type or another is an important genetic question. For example, while β_1AR and β_2AR subtypes bind similar agonist ligands and stimulate adenylate cyclase via coupling to G_s, they have characteristic tissue distributions. β_1AR generally tends to be more abundant in the central nervous system, while β_2AR tends to be localized in nonneuronal tissues. We now know from molecular cloning that the β_1AR and β_2AR are the products of different genes (17). This subtype distribution is reflected in the relative abundance of the mRNAs for β_1AR and β_2AR in different tissues (Figure 3). For the α_2AR, subtypes that were predicted to exist based upon ligand binding

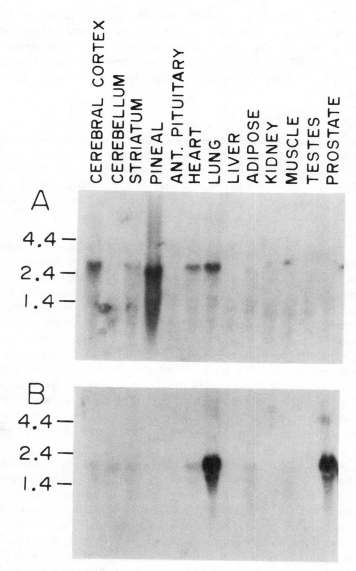

Figure 3 Northern blot hybridization analysis of rat tissue RNA. Total cellular RNA was isolated from each tissue by the cesium chloride gradient method, and forty mecrograms (except pineal, 26 μg) of RNA from each tissue were fractionated through 1.2% agarose gels for RNA blot hybridization analysis. Hybridizations were performed using (*A*) a ^{32}P-labeled human β_1AR cDNA probe or (*B*) a hamster β_2AR cDNA probe.

characteristics have been unequivocally demonstrated with the recent cloning and expression of the human platelet α_2AR (termed α_2A) and a human kidney α_2AR (termed α_2B) (24, 35). It is not known what developmental cues predispose a tissue to express predominantly one subtype or another, but these questions may now begin to be addressed as a result of the recent cloning of these genes.

Hormonal Regulation

Heterologous hormonal regulation of receptor-mediated processes refers to regulation of receptor responsiveness by hormones and drugs that are not specific ligands for the receptor. Heterologous hormonal regulation of adrenergic responsiveness has been a topic of considerable interest to both clinicians and basic researchers. The regulation of the adrenergic system by adrenal steroids has been of particular interest (10, 39).

GLUCOCORTICOIDS   Early studies demonstrated that regulation of adrenergic responsiveness can be achieved by the modulation of adrenergic receptor number. Additional studies in vivo and in vitro have shown that glucocorticoids increase β_2AR levels and agonist-stimulated adenylate cyclase activity (6, 32, 39). The major mechanism of action for most steroids appears to be direct changes in the expression of target genes. These changes are largely controlled by the rate of transcription although significant differences in message stability have also been described (36). For this reason, it has been suggested that the regulation of β_2AR by steroid hormones (glucocorticoids in particular) may occur at the level of transcription. The recent cloning of the β_2AR gene and the identification of several putative hormone response elements in the promoter region (Figure 2) has made it possible to extend these earlier findings and to address directly the role of β_2AR gene expression in this process.

The hamster smooth muscle cell line DDT_1MF-2 contains both adrenergic and glucocorticoid receptors. The density of β_2AR in these cells, assessed by radioligand binding, is doubled in response to glucocorticoids (6, 32). Rapid increases in the level of β_2AR mRNA (which precede the appearance of new receptors in the plasma membrane) have been observed (Figure 4A). During this period there was no detectable change in mRNA levels for actin, an unrelated cellular gene (Figure 4B). When expressed relative to actin (Figure 4C), β_2AR mRNA doubled in the first hour. The increase in β_2AR mRNA in response to glucocorticoids can also be blocked by the RNA polymerase inhibitor, actinomycin D. Together these data suggest that changes in β_2AR gene transcription are probably involved.

Nuclear run-off transcription assays provide a means of measuring the rate of transcription of a gene. Isolated nuclei, in the presence of radioactive

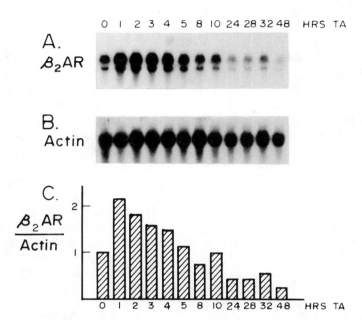

Figure 4 Effect of glucocorticoid treatment on β_2AR and actin mRNA levels in DDT$_1$MF-2 smooth muscle cells. Cells were harvested at indicated times after the addition of 100 nM triamcinolone acetonide, and total cellular RNA was prepared. RNA (20 μg) was fractionated on 1.2% agarose gels for blot hybridization analysis. Hybridizations were performed using a ^{32}P-labeled (A) hamster β_2AR cDNA probe or (B) actin cDNA probe. (C) Autoradiograms were quantitated by densitometric scanning to determine the fold increase in β_2AR mRNA relative to actin mRNA. The average maximal increase in β_2AR mRNA was 2.4 ± 0.4 fold (mean ± s.d., n = 6).

precursor nucleotides, are capable of elongating and completing transcripts synthesized at the time of isolation (19), but are unable to initiate new transcripts. These new transcripts can be quantitated by hybridization to excess, unlabeled complementary DNA for that gene. For the β_2AR gene, nuclear run-off transcription assays performed with DDT$_1$MF-2 nuclei following 30 min of glucocorticoid treatment indicated that the rate of β_2AR gene transcription was increased approximately threefold (6). These results are in agreement with the doubling of β_2AR mRNA levels observed by Northern blotting.

Recent investigations into the molecular nature of transcriptional control by steroid hormones have revealed the existence of sequences within target genes that appear to play a critical role in their regulation. Our understanding is best, although still not completely clarifed, in model systems developed for the glucocorticoid hormone receptor (GR) (16, 36). In cloned genes that are highly responsive to glucocorticoids, such as the mouse mammary tumor virus (MMTV), the core sequence motif (T/A)GT(T/C)CT has been identified as an element to which purified GR protein binds tightly and specifically. Such sequence elements have been termed glucocorticoid response elements (GRE) and are required for functional promoter activity in vitro. They can stimulate transcription over a wide range of distances from the start site of transcription and when placed in the forward or reverse orientation. This position and orientation independence is characteristic of so-called genetic enhancer elements (27). Since this 6-base core sequence is expected to appear at random once every 4096 bp, additional sequences may be required to confer specificity, either for the binding of the glucocorticoid receptor itself or for ancillary proteins that are involved in the transcriptional activation process. In fact, not all of the TGTTCT sequences found in a gene represent functional GREs (36, 42). Recently, an expanded sequence, GGTA-CANNNTGTTCT, has been defined (16). A twofold increase in β_2AR expression in response to hydrocortisone has been observed in cells transfected with a 12-kilobase (kb) segment of the human β_2AR gene (5' limit at −1500 bp from start of transcription). This finding suggests that the sequences responsible for glucocorticoid regulation are located within this fragment. In the human β_2AR gene, two candidates for GREs are the proximal element at position −248, adjacent to the TATA box ($\overline{\text{AGTCCTGT}}$, 4b in Figure 2A), or the distal element further upstream at position −1447 (TGTTCT, 4a in Figure 2A). This latter sequence at −1447, G̲CTTCAAAATGTTCT, is a close homologue of the expanded GRE sequence. In the hamster β_2AR gene a consensus sequence is found at position −1031 (AGTTCT, 4 in Figure 2A). While we do not know which, if any, of these putative GREs confer transcriptional enhancing properties, this is an obvious area for further study.

SEX STEROIDS   The effects of estrogen and progesterone on noradrenergic activity in the central and peripheral nervous system, and various reproductive functions have been established. In some cases, these effects on responsiveness have been associated with alterations in the density of various adrenergic subtypes. This work has been previously reviewed (39). More recent studies have examined the role of androgens in regulating the β_2AR and the activation of adenylate cyclase in the rat ventral prostate. This tissue has been a popular model for the study of androgen action, particularly in the area of gene expression. When compared to other tissues, the ventral prostate contains one of the highest densities of β_2AR and its 2.2-kb mRNA (Figure 3). While the biological significance of this is unclear, recent evidence indicates that both neurotransmitters and androgens participate in the development and function of the prostate and other sex accessory organs (22, 28, 29, 41). Thus, the study of β_2AR in this system is particularly attractive for understanding the biology of the prostate.

Prostatic adenylate cyclase and β_2AR number have been shown to be significantly affected by circulating androgens (34, 37). Shima et al (37) demonstrated a reduction both in isoproterenol-stimulated adenylate cyclase activity and in β_2AR number 7 days after castration; this reduction could be blocked by daily testosterone (T) supplementation. These receptors have also been shown to be exclusively of the β_2-subtype (34). With the cloned β_2AR gene as a probe to examine the regulation of β_2AR expression in the ventral prostate by T, β_2AR number and mRNA levels were monitored at frequent intervals following castration and T replacement (7). Following a steady decline in the number of β_2AR after castration to 50% of control by 4 days, a rapid and complete recovery of prostatic β_2AR was effected within 24 h of testosterone replacement (Figure 5A).

The decrease in prostatic β_2AR observed following castration was not

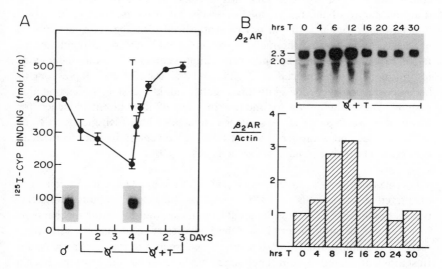

Figure 5   Effect of castration (δ) and testosterone treatment (δ + T) on the β_2AR and its mRNA in the rat ventral prostate. Male CD rats (250–300 g) were castrated via the scrotal route. Four days after castration, daily injections of testosterone propionate (T; 1.0 mg in 0.1 ml vegetable oil) were begun and animals were sacrificed at the indicated times. (A) Specific β_2AR binding in ventral prostate membranes with 400 pM [^{125}I]cyanopindolol. (*inset*) Northern blot analysis of ventral prostate β_2AR mRNA from intact (δ) and 4-day castrates (δ). (B) Northern blot analysis of β_2AR mRNA levels in rat ventral prostate after testosterone administration to 4-day castrates. Total cellular RNA (20 μg) was fractionated on 1.2% agarose gels and hybridized to a ^{32}P-labeled hamster β_2AR cDNA probe. The fold increase in β_2AR mRNA relative to actin mRNA was computed from densitometric tracings of the autoradiograms.

reflected in the steady-state mRNA levels analyzed by Northern blot hybridization (Figure 5A, inset). Equivalent amounts of β_2AR mRNA relative to total RNA were still detected 4 days after castration, which were not different from levels in intact animals. The process of receptor turnover may be sensitive to testosterone such that following castration the rate of degradation of the receptor was elevated. Alternatively, the efficiency of translation of the β_2AR message could have been influenced by hormonal status, as shown for a number of other proteins. Further work is necessary to distinguish between these various possibilities.

Testosterone replacement to 4-day castrates produced an increase in β_2AR mRNA levels that peaked 8 to 12 h after the initiation of hormone treatment (Figure 5B). However, this enhancement was not maintained, and it soon returned to the level of the untreated control. Similar findings of temporary transcriptional enhancement and mRNA accumulation have been reported for other hormone-regulated genes in vivo and is also remininiscent of glucocorticoid stimulation of β_2AR in DDT$_1$MF-2 cells. In some of these cases, the transient nature of the rise in mRNA levels has been ascribed to increased translational efficiency of the newly synthesized message. Further work is necessary to understand the mechanisms involved in the rapid regulation of β_2AR in ventral prostate by androgens. Improvements in culture techniques for hormone-dependent cells (22, 29) and the transfer and expression of hormone responsive genes into these cells should assist in dissecting this system. These studies are of interest in view of the current evidence for identical or overlapping DNA sequence elements with which glucocorticoid, progesterone, and androgen (but not estrogen) receptors interact to mediate transcriptional enhancement of target genes (5, 9).

THYROID HORMONE   An extensive review of the biochemical consequences of altered thyroid status on both α- and β-adrenergic receptors in several tissues has appeared (3). It is apparent from these studies that the mechanisms involved can be multifactorial, and these studies suggest that the adrenergic receptor complex itself is affected. Since many obvious clinical manifestations of altered thyroid function are cardiovascular, the heart has been a major focus of study. For example, in the heart, which contains predominantly β_1AR, receptor density is directly correlated with levels of circulating thyroid hormone and is thought to be responsible for the tachycardia associated with the hyperthyroid condition. The mechanism involved in this increase is unclear, but presumably involves new receptor synthesis. By contrast, in the liver, the changes in βAR number in response to altered thyroid function are opposite to those found in the heart. Recent studies in thyroidectomized-adrenalectomized rats have convincingly demonstrated that thyroid hormones indirectly regulate hepatic βAR through changes in corticosteroid levels (40).

The thyroid hormone receptor is a member of the steroid receptor gene family (16). Since genes known to be under the control of thyroid hormone, such as growth hormone (18), alpha-myosin (20), and thyrotropin (38), have been reported to display both transcriptional and posttranscriptional regulation, direct effects on adrenergic receptor gene expression may be expected. With the recent cloning of the human β_1AR cDNA, we are now in a position to establish a more complete mechanistic picture of thyroid hormone regulation of the adrenergic receptors, β_1AR in particular.

SUMMARY

Several members of the family of receptors coupled to G proteins have been cloned in recent years. From the primary sequence information furnished by these clones, a characteristic seven-membrane spanning topography has emerged as the prototype for this class of receptors, in analogy with the opsin visual pigments. Cloned genes for the various receptors provide important tools for probing the regulation of their expression. For example, the underlying genetic basis for the expression of adrenergic receptor subtypes can now be explored. The physiological regulation of receptors by heterologous hormones, such as steroids and thyroid hormones, has long been suspected to involve changes in the expression of the relevant adrenergic receptor genes. At least for the glucocorticoids, β_2AR expression is controlled at the level of transcription. The hormonal regulation of other adrenergic receptor subtypes is currently being explored.

ACKNOWLEDGMENTS

The authors wish to thank Donna Addison and Mary Holben for their skillful assistance in preparing this manuscript, and Linda Frejlach for artwork.

Literature Cited

1. Applebury, M. L., Hargrave, P. A. 1986. Molecular biology of the visual pigments. *Vision Res.* 26:1881–95
2. Benovic, J. L., Bouvier, M., Caron, M. G., Lefkowitz, R. J. 1988. Regulation of adenylyl cyclase–coupled β-adrenergic receptors. *Annu. Rev. Cell Biol.* 4:405–28
3. Bilezikian, J. P., Loeb, J. N. 1983. The influence of hyperthyroidism and hypothyroidism on α- and β-adrenergic receptor systems and adrenergic responsiveness. *Endocr. Rev.* 4:378–88
4. Bonner, T. I., Buckley, N. J., Young, A. C., Brann, M. R. 1987. Identification of a family of muscarinic acetylcholine receptor genes. *Science* 237:527–32
5. Cato, A. C. B., Henderson, D., Ponta, H. 1987. The hormone response element of the mouse mammary tumour virus DNA mediates the progestin and androgen induction of transcription in the proviral long terminal repeat region. *EMBO J.* 6:363–68
6. Collins, S., Caron, M. G., Lefkowitz, R. J. 1988. β_2-Adrenergic receptors in

hamster smooth muscle cells are transcriptionally regulated by glucocorticoids. *J. Biol. Chem.* 263:9067–70

7. Collins, S., Quarmby, V., French, F., Lefkowitz, R. J., Caron, M. G. 1988. Regulation of the β_2-adrenergic receptor in the rat ventral prostate by testosterone. *FEBS Lett.* 233:173–76

8. Cotecchia, S. Schwinn, D. A., Randall, R. R., Lefkowitz, R. J., Caron, M. G. et al. 1988. Molecular cloning and expression of the cDNA for hamster alpha$_1$-adrenergic receptor. *Proc. Natl. Acad. Sci.* In press

9. Darbre, P., Page, M., King, R. J. B. 1986. Androgen regulation by the long terminal repeat of mouse mammary tumor virus. *Mol. Cell. Biol.* 6:2847–54

10. Davies, A. O., Lefkowitz, R. J. 1984. Regulation of β-adrenergic receptors by steroid hormones. *Annu. Rev. Physiol.* 46:119–30

11. Deutch, P. J., Jameson, L. J., Habener, J. F. 1987. Cyclic AMP responsiveness of a human gonadotropin-α gene transcription is directed by a repeated 18-base enhancer. *J. Biol. Chem.* 262:12169–74

12. Dixon, R. A. F., Kobilka, B. K., Strader, D. J., Benovic, J. L., Dohlman, H. G., et al. 1986. Cloning of the gene and cDNA for mammalian β-adrenergic receptor and homology with rhodopsin. *Nature* 321:75–79

13. Dohlman, H. G., Bouvier, M., Benovic, J. L., Caron, M. G., Lefkowitz, R. J. 1987. The multiple membrane spanning topography of the β_2-adrenergic receptor. *J. Biol. Chem.* 262:14282–88

14. Dohlman, H. G., Caron, M. G., Lefkowitz, R. J. 1987. A family of receptors coupled to guanine nucleotide regulatory proteins. *Biochemistry* 26:2657–64

15. Emorine, L. J., Marullo, S., Delavier-Klutchko, C., Kaven, S. V., Durieu-Trautmann, O., Strosberg, A. D. 1987. Structure of the gene for human β_2-adrenergic receptor: Expression and promoter characterization. *Proc. Natl. Acad. Sci. USA* 84:6995–99

16. Evans, R. M. 1988. The steroid and thyroid hormone receptor superfamily. *Science* 240:889–95

17. Frielle, T., Collins, S., Daniel, K. W., Caron, M. G., Lefkowitz, R. J., Kobilka, B. K. 1987. Cloning of the cDNA for the human β_1-adrenergic receptor. *Proc. Natl. Acad. Sci. USA* 84:7920–24

18. Glass, C. K., Franco, R., Weinberger, C., Albert, V. R., Evans, R. M., Rosenfeld, M. G. 1987. A c-*erb*-A binding site in rat growth hormone gene mediates trans-activation by thyroid hormone. *Nature* 329:738–41

19. Groudine, M., Peretz, M., Weintraub, H. 1981. Transcriptional regulation of hemoglobulin switching in chicken embryos. *Mol. Cell. Biol.* 1:281–88

20. Gustafson, T. A., Bahl, J. J., Markham, B. E., Roeske, W. R., Morkin, E. 1987. Hormonal regulation of myosin heavy chain and α-actin gene expression in cultured fetal rat heart myocytes. *J. Biol. Chem.* 262:13316–22

21. Henderson, R., Unwin, P. N. T. 1975. Three-dimensional model of purple membrane obtained by electron microscopy. *Nature* 257:28–32

22. Kinghorn, E. M., Bate, A. S., Higgins, S. J. 1987. Growth of rat seminal vesicle epithelial cells in culture: Neurotransmitters are required for androgen-regulated synthesis of tissue-specific secretory proteins. *Endocrinology* 121:1678–88

23. Kobilka, B. K., Frielle, T., Dohlman, H. G., Bolanowski, M. A., Dixon, R. A. F., et al. 1987. Delineation of the intronless nature of the genes for the human and hamster β_2-adrenergic receptor and their putative promoter regions. *J. Biol. Chem.* 262:7321–27

24. Kobilka, B. K., Matsui, H., Kobilka, T. S., Yang-Feng, T. L., Francke, U., et al. 1987. Cloning, sequencing and expression of the gene coding for the human platelet α_2-receptor. *Science* 238:650–56

25. Kubo, T., Fukuda, K., Mikami, A., Maeda, A., Takahashi, H., et al. 1986. Cloning, sequencing and expression of complementary DNA encoding the muscarinic acetylcholine receptor. *Nature* 323:411–16

26. Kubo, T., Maeda, A., Sugimoto, K., Akiba, I., Mikami, A., et al. 1986. Primary structure of porcine cardiac muscarinic acetylcholine receptor deduced from the cDNA sequence. *FEBS Lett.* 209:367–72

27. Maniatis, T., Goodbourn, S., Fischer, J. A. 1987. Regulation of inducible and tissue-specific gene expression. *Science* 236:1237–45

28. Marchetti, B., Cioni, M., Badr, M., Follea, N., Pelletier, G. 1987. Ovarian adrenergic nerves directly participate in the control of luteinizing hormone-releasing hormone and β-adrenergic receptors during puberty: a biochemical and autoradiographic study. *Endocrinology* 121:219–26

29. Martikainen, P., Harkonen, P., Vanhala, T., Makela, S., Viljanen, M.,

Suominen, J. 1987. Multihormonal control of synthesis and secretion of prostatein in cultured rat ventral prostate. *Endocrinology* 121:604–11

30. Montminy, M. R., Bilezikian, L. M. 1987. Binding of a nuclear protein to the cyclic-AMP response element of the somatostatin gene. *Nature* 328:175–78

31. Nathans, J., Hogness, D. S. 1983. Isolation, sequence analysis, and intron-exon arrangement of the gene encoding bovine rhodopsin. *Cell* 34:807–14

32. Norris, J. S., Brown, P., Cohen, J., Cornett, L. E., Kohler, P. O., et al. 1987. Glucocorticoid induction of β-adrenergic receptors in DDT_1MF-2 smooth muscle cell line involves synthesis of new receptor. *Mol. Cell. Biochem.* 74:21–27

33. Peralta, E. G., Winslow, J. W., Peterson, G. L., Smith, D. H., Ashkenazi, A., et al. 1987. Primary structure and biochemical properties of an M_2 muscarinic receptor. *Science* 236:600–5

34. Poyet, P., Gagne, B., Labrie, F. 1986. Characteristics of the β-adrenergic stimulation of adenylate cyclase activity in rat ventral prostate and its modulation by androgens. *The Prostate* 9:237–45

35. Regan, J. W., Kobilka, T. S., Yang-Feng, T. L., Caron, M. G., Lefkowitz, R. J., et al. 1988. Cloning and expression of a human kidney cDNA for a novel α_2-adrenergic receptor. *Proc. Natl. Acad. Sci.* In press

36. Ringold, G. M. 1985. Steroid hormone regulation of gene expression. *Annu. Rev. Pharmacol. Toxicol.* 25:529–66

37. Shima, S., Kawashima, Y., Hirai, M., Asakura, M. 1980. Effects of androgens on isoproterenol-sensitive adenylate cyclase system of the rat prostate. *Mol. Pharmacol.* 18:45–48

38. Shupnik, M. A., Chin, W. W., Habener, J. F., Ridgway, E. C. 1985. Transcriptional regulation of the thyrotropin subunit genes by thyroid hormone. *J. Biol. Chem.* 260:2900–3

39. Stiles, G. L., Caron, M. G., Lefkowitz, R. J. 1984. β-Adrenergic receptors: Biochemical mechanisms of physiological regulation. *Physiol. Rev.* 64:661–743

40. Sundaresan, P. R., Banerjee, S. P. 1987. Differential regulation of beta-adrenergic receptor-coupled adenylate cyclase by thyroid hormones in rat liver and heart: possible role of cortisteroids. *Hormone Res.* 27:109–18

41. Thompson, T. C., Zhau, H., Chung, L. W. K. 1987. Catecholamines are involved in the growth and expression of prostatic binding protein by rat ventral prostatic tissues. In *Current Concepts and Approaches to the Study of Prostate Cancer*, eds. D. S. Coffey, W. A. Gardner Jr., N. Bruchovsky, M. I. Resnick, J. P. Karr, pp. 239–48. New York: Liss

42. Yamamoto, K. R. 1985. Steroid receptor regulated transcription of specific genes and gene networks. *Annu. Rev. Genetics.* 19:209–52

Annu. Rev. Physiol. 1989. 51:217–27

STRUCTURE AND REGULATION OF MUSCARINIC RECEPTORS

M. I. Schimerlik

Department of Biochemistry and Biophysics, Oregon State University, Corvallis, Oregon 97331

INTRODUCTION

Muscarinic receptor mediated responses have been demonstrated in the central and peripheral nervous system, smooth muscle, secretory glands, and the heart. Recently, muscarinic receptors have been purified and reconstituted into defined lipid mixtures with other purified components of the muscarinic signal transduction systems. The genes coding for four distinct muscarinic receptors have been cloned, sequenced, and expressed, which has allowed the identification of subtype specific biochemical properties. Finally, a combination of biochemical, pharmacological, and electrophysiological approaches has begun to elucidate the various pathways by which muscarinic receptor activation may be coupled to physiological responses. The reader is also referred to other recent reviews (67, 72).

COUPLING OF MUSCARINIC RECEPTORS TO PHYSIOLOGICAL EFFECTOR SYSTEMS

The coupling of muscarinic agonist binding to inhibition of adenylyl cyclase is mediated by guanine nucleotide binding proteins (G proteins) (30). These proteins are heterotrimers that can dissociate to yield differing α and similar $\beta\gamma$ subunits upon binding GTP or a nonhydrolyzable GTP analogue. The α subunit of G_s activates adenylyl cyclase, while G_i and G_o inhibit the enzyme. Pertussis toxin–catalyzed ADP-ribosylation of the α subunit of G_i or G_o functionally uncouples the muscarinic receptor and prevents the inhibition of adenylyl cyclase in several systems including rat heart (49). In 1321N1 astrocytoma cells (43), however, the decrease in cAMP concentration was the

217

result of the activation of a calmodulin stimulated phosphodiesterase (88). These results suggested that muscarinic receptors in 1321N1 cells may not be capable of interacting with G_i.

The initial event in the stimulation of inositol lipid turnover appears to be a G-protein mediated activation of phospholipase C (39). The protein that mediates this interaction (G_p) has not yet been isolated and characterized. Coupling of muscarinic receptors to inositol phospholipid metabolism in chick heart cells and in 1321N1 astrocytoma cells (40, 64) is not affected by pertussis toxin, which suggests that G_p is distinct from G_i and G_o in these systems. Muscarinic receptors in Flow 9000 cells stimulate inositol phospholipid metabolism through a cholera toxin sensitive G protein (59). These results, and data from other systems in which stimulation of inositol lipid metabolism is sensitive to pertussis toxin (71) or to either pertussis or cholera toxin (29), suggest that various receptors, receptor subtypes, and phospholipase C subtypes couple through different G proteins.

Both hydrolysis products of the phospholipase C catalyzed reaction serve as second messengers in the cell. Inositol 1,4,5-trisphosphate causes calcium release from the endoplasmic reticulum (87). The observed synergism between inositol 1,4,5-trisphosphate and inositol 1,3,4,5-tetrakisphosphate in promoting entry of extracellular calcium (69) indicates a possible physiological role for the latter compound. Diacylglycerol, in concert with calcium, activates protein kinase C, which may in turn phosphorylate specific proteins (73). Direct activation of protein kinase C by phorbol esters inhibited carbachol-induced, GTPγS-dependent inositol trisphosphate formation in 1321N1 astrocytoma cells (75). Thus, a feedback loop may exist where persistant activation of protein kinase C by diacylglycerol turns off the stimulation of phosphoinositide metabolism by modulating G_p interactions with phospholipase C. A calcium activated phospholipase, A_2, may further metabolize diacylglycerol to release arachidonate, a precursor of eicosanoid synthesis. Rapid incorporation of labeled arachidonate into eicosanoids occurs upon exposure of parotid acinar cells to carbachol (86).

Muscarinic stimulation of inositol lipid metabolism appears to be dependent on agonist structure since acetylcholine and carbachol activate the response to a much greater extent than oxotremorine, arecoline, or pilocarpine (12, 23). Oxotremorine activated muscarinic receptors are as effective in inhibiting adenylyl cyclase as receptors activated by carbachol (12). These data suggest that the receptor conformation is agonist dependent and that the mass action equilibria in the cell for receptor coupling to G_i or G_p are different.

Activation of muscarinic receptors has been shown to increase cGMP levels in several tissues including N1E-115 neuroblastoma cells, where drugs that block lipoxygenase metabolism of arachidonate (68) as well as phorbol esters

(52) attenuate muscarinic mediated increases in cGMP. Injection of cGMP into *Xenopus* oocytes causes a similar increase in membrane permeability to potassium ions as that evoked by acetylcholine (18). There appears to be a requirement for extracellular calcium for receptor mediated increases in cGMP (74) although calcium influx has not always been demonstrated (67).

The mechanism of cGMP signal transduction is unknown. Activation of a cGMP dependent cyclic nucleotide phosphodiesterase in heart cells decreases cAMP levels, reducing Ca^{2+} entry (38). Muscarinic agonists have been shown to stimulate cGMP dependent protein kinase in the heart (57) and to promote cGMP dependent phosphorylation of membrane bound proteins in vascular smooth muscle (13). Activation of muscarinic receptors also inhibits phosphorylation of proteins stimulated by β-adrenergic agonists (58).

Muscarinic agonists are capable of generating either hyperpolarizing or depolarizing responses, depending on the cell type (14). In heart (84) and central neurons (20), acetylcholine causes an increase in potassium conductance, which results in a hyperpolarization of the membrane potential. The hyperpolarization can inhibit action potentials or regulate neuronal firing patterns (66). M currents, potassium currents rapidly activated at potentials more positive than -60 mV, are reduced by activation of muscarinic receptors in several cell types including smooth muscle (85). Muscarinic agonists also affect calcium dependent potassium channels (62), as well as increase chloride permeabilities in *Xenopus* oocytes, an effect that can be mimicked by injection of inositol 1,4,5-trisphosphate or calcium (70). The discovery that either G_i or G_o mediated muscarinic activation of inward rectifying potassium channels in the heart arose from observations that treatment with pertussis toxin blocked receptor stimulated $^{86}Rb^+$ efflux in cultured chick heart cells (63) and that guanine nucleotides were required for channel activation (11, 80). Patch clamp studies indicated G_i was much more effective than G_o; G_s showed no effect (92). Results using resolved subunits of G_i have been highly controversial; one group identified the α subunit of G_i as the activating agent (15), and a second group presented evidence that the $\beta\gamma$ subunits are responsible for channel opening (60).

LIGAND INTERACTIONS WITH MUSCARINIC RECEPTORS

Binding studies using nonselective muscarinic antagonists showed competition for a single class of binding sites (44), while multiple noninteracting classes of agonist binding sites were present with low, high, and superhigh agonist affinity states (7). The observation that agents affecting G-protein coupling modulated the muscarinic receptor affinity for agonists (4, 22) led to a model in which the high affinity agonist state was assumed to be coupled to a G protein while the low affinity agonist state represented free receptor. Although more complex models of muscarinic interactions with ligands (65) have been presented, most binding data, as well as muscarinic-mediated inhibition of adenylyl cyclase (21), agree with a model in which noninteracting receptor subtypes are capable of interacting with various G proteins.

Kinetic studies of labeled antagonist binding to muscarinic receptors support a model in which a rapid binding step is followed by an isomerization step for both membrane bound (45) and detergent solubilized (41) preparations. Two kinetic phases were observed for acetylcholine binding (31), while the association of oxotremorine-M showed a single phase (36). The kinetics of cis-methyldioxolane binding were consistent with parallel independent reactions arising from interactions with the low and high affinity forms of the receptor (26). Agonist induced interconversion from low to high affinity receptor states has not been found (26, 83). The development of ligands such as pirenzepine (35), as well as other selective agonists and antagonists (28), resulted in the first unequivocal demonstration of muscarinic receptor heterogeneity.

SOLUBILIZATION, PURIFICATION, AND CHARACTERIZATION OF MUSCARINIC RECEPTORS

Solubilization using commercially available digitonin (3) or digitonin and cholate (16) results in uncoupling of receptors from G proteins and gives rise to an apparently homogeneous class of agonist binding sites (41); however, guanine nucleotide–sensitive high affinity agonist binding has been demonstrated (6). Highly purified preparations of active muscarinic receptors have been obtained from porcine atria (78) and cerebellum (32), rat forebrain (5), and chick heart (50). Properties of antagonist binding in purified preparations are similar to those of membrane bound receptors, while agonist dissociation constants are comparable to the low affinity agonist state for the membrane bound proteins (32, 82).

Affinity alkylation with labeled propylbenzilylcholine mustard (8), photoaffinity labeling by antagonist analogues (1, 17), and radiation inactivation analysis (90) indicated an apparent M_r of 70,000–90,000 for the polypeptide by SDS-polyacrylamide gel electrophoresis, with some variability for different cell types (42, 55). Detailed electrophoretic analysis of the purified atrial receptor led to an estimation of $M_r = 51,000$ for the protein portion of the molecule (79). The agreement of these results with hydrodynamic measurements suggests that the molecular weight of the protein plus carbohydrate is about 70,000; a compositional analysis indicated that the receptor is about 27% carbohydrate by weight (79).

CLONING AND EXPRESSION OF MUSCARINIC SUBTYPES

The complete amino acid sequences of muscarinic receptors have been deduced from DNA sequences of clones isolated from cDNA and genomic libraries (9, 46, 47, 76, 77). To date, four distinct muscarinic subtypes (M_1–M_4) have been identified (9, 76). Hydropathy analysis suggested that all four subtypes contain seven transmembrane segments and belong to the class of hormone receptors that are structurally similar to rhodospin (19). The amino terminus, which contains potential sites for glycosylation, is located extracellularly; the carboxyl terminus is located intracellularly. Peptide mapping studies of [^{3}H]propylbenzilylcholine affinity alkylated receptor from rat forebrain (91) indicated that an aspartate residue located in the second transmembrane segment is the most likely candidate for ion pairing with the quarternary ammonium group of muscarinic ligands. Regions of the highest amino acid identity for all rhodopsinlike receptors include the transmembrane regions and intracellular loops 1–2 and 3–4. Correspondence at the carboxyl and amino termini is low, and the similarity of amino acid sequences in the large intracellular loop 5–6 found in muscarinic receptors is very poor among the four subtypes, as well as for muscarinic receptors compared to other hormone receptors of this class.

M_1 and M_2 receptors expressed in *Xenopus* oocytes showed the appropriate pharmacological specificity for ligands (25). M_1 and M_2 receptors activate an oscillatory increase in chloride conductance, while M_2 receptors also activate a second class of ion channels in which current is carried by sodium and potassium ions. Expression of M_2 receptors at varying cellular concentrations in Chinese hampster ovary cells (2) showed that the protein activates inositol phospholipid metabolism and inhibits adenylyl cyclase. The inhibition of adenylyl cyclase couples more efficiently than activation of inositol phospholipid metabolism and is more sensitive to pertussis toxin, which suggests that different G proteins mediate the two responses. Expression of cloned M_1 receptors in A9 L cells (10) results in muscarinic activation of endogenous chloride channels preceeded by a lag phase, which suggests involvement of a second messenger.

In situ hybridization utilized to map muscarinic binding sites in brain (9) and northern blot analysis (76) appeared to indicate that expression of all four muscarinic receptor subtypes identified in mRNA from whole rat brain are tissue or cell line specific (76). Binding studies indicated that it may be difficult to differentiate between all four muscarinic subtypes using selective ligands such as pirenzepine (9, 76). Southern analysis of human and rat genomic DNA (9) indicated that there may be two additional human muscarinic subtypes and as many as five additional subtypes in rat.

RECONSTITUTION OF MUSCARINIC RECEPTORS WITH G PROTEINS

Bovine brain muscarinic receptors, resolved from G proteins and reconstituted with purified G_o and G_i, demonstrated guanine nucleotide–sensitive high affinity agonist binding (24). Addition of $G_{o\alpha}$ resulted in a small increase in affinity for agonists that was enhanced by addition of the $\beta\gamma$ subunits: $\beta\gamma$ alone had no effect. A preparation of reconstituted muscarinic receptors purified from porcine brain with G_i or G_o (33) displayed high affinity agonist binding that was inhibited by prior ADP-ribosylation of G_i. Preparations from porcine brain showed a 20–50% increase in the V_{max} for carbachol stimulated GTPase activity of G_i, with a slight increase in the K_m for GTP (48).

Reconstitution of purified muscarinic receptors and G_i from porcine atria (89) showed that the carbachol receptor complex increased the turnover number of G_i in the GTPase reaction 11-fold. Analysis of the kinetic data suggested that GDP release is the rate limiting step in the absence of muscarinic agonists and that the carbachol receptor complex accelerates this step to the point where it may no longer be solely rate determining. Both the atrial (89) and cerebral (34) muscarinic receptors interact with multiple G proteins to enhance the velocity of the GTPase reaction. When atrial G_i was ADP-ribosylated by pertussis toxin after reconstitution (89), complete uncoupling occurred only in the presence of muscarinic agonists plus GTP, which suggests that prior association with the receptor protected G_i from ADP-ribosylation.

The muscarinic receptor in rat heart is phosphorylated in vivo in the presence of agonists (50, 51). Muscarinic receptors purified from porcine cerebrum were phosphorylated in vitro by protein kinase C (34), but purified procine atrial receptors were not (34, 81). These results suggest a specificity of various kinases for particular muscarinic subtypes. Reconstituted atrial muscarinic receptors were phosphorylated by cAMP dependent protein kinase (81), and the apparent stoichiometry of phosphate incorporation was doubled in the presence of G_i plus a muscarinic agonist, but returned to control levels in the presence of GTPγS, which indicates that the agonist-occupied receptor exists in a unique conformation when associated with G_i. Phosphorylation of the receptor by protein kinase C (34) or by cAMP dependent protein kinase (81) did not appear to alter either the coupling to G proteins or the receptor affinity for ligands. Thus, the phosphorylated receptor may be recognized by yet other effector molecules that play a role in receptor metabolism.

REGULATION OF MUSCARINIC RECEPTORS

Persistant exposure to agonists in several systems has been shown to cause down regulation of muscarinic receptors (27, 51), which is thought to be mediated, at least in part, by rapid internalization of receptors from the cell surface (37). Treatment of neuroblastoma clone N1E-115 with phorbol ester induced a rapid internalization of receptors (56), which suggests the involvement of protein kinase C in receptor regulation for that cell line. Studies of the regulation of muscarinic receptors and G-protein subunits in embryonic chick heart have demonstrated specific developmental patterns for these proteins in atrial and ventricular tissue and have correlated the levels of these proteins with regulation of adenylyl cyclase activity (61). Developmental changes in muscarinic receptor isoelectric point (53) and glycosylation (54) have also been observed.

SUMMARY AND CONCLUSIONS

Our knowledge of muscarinic receptor structure, mechanism, and regulation has increased enormously over the past five years. At this time, expression of receptor subtype and coupling via signal transducing elements to specific effector systems seems to be cell or tissue specific events. Determining the specific detailed molecular mechanisms of interaction for the various permutations of receptors and effector proteins and how the effector systems initiate physiological responses are challenging areas for future research.

ACKNOWLEDGEMENTS

The author would like to acknowledge the expert typing of Barbara Hanson and the support of USPHS grants HL23632 and ES00210.

Literature Cited

1. Amitai, G., Avissar, S., Balderman, D., Sokolovsky, M. 1982. Affinity labeling of muscarinic receptors in rat cerebral cortex with a photolabile antagonist. *Proc. Natl. Acad. Sci. USA* 79:243–47
2. Ashkenazi, A., Winslow, J. W., Peralta, E. G., Peterson, G. L., Schimerlik, M. I., et al. 1987. An M2 muscarinic receptor subtype coupled to both adenylyl cyclase and phosphoinositide turnover. *Science* 238:672–74
3. Beld, A. J., Ariens, E. J. 1974. Stereospecific binding as a tool in attempts to localize and isolate muscarinic receptors. *Eur. J. Pharmacol.* 25:203–9
4. Berrie, C. P., Birdsall, N. J. M., Burgen, A. S. V., Hulme, E. C. 1979. Guanine nucleotides modulate muscarinic receptor binding in the heart. *Biochem. Biophys. Res. Commun.* 87:1000–5
5. Berrie, C. P., Birdsall, N. J. M., Dadi, H. K., Hulme, E. C., Morris, R. J., et al. 1985. Purification of the muscarinic

acetylcholine receptor from rat forebrain. *Biochem. Soc. Trans.* 13:1101–3
6. Berrie, C. P., Birdsall, N. J. M., Hulme, E. C., Keen, M., Stockton, J. M. 1984. Solubilization and characterization of guanine nucleotide-sensitive muscarinic agonist binding sites from rat myocardium. *Br. J. Pharmacol.* 82:853–61
7. Birdsall, N. J. M., Burgen, A. S. V., Hulme, E. C. 1978. The binding of agonists to brain muscarinic receptors. *Mol. Pharmacol.* 14:723–36
8. Birdsall, N. J. M., Burgen, A. S. V., Hulme, E. C. 1979. A study of the muscarinic receptor by gel electrophoresis. *Br. J. Pharmacol.* 66:337–42
9. Bonner, T. I., Buckley, N. J., Young, A. C., Brann, M. R. 1987. Identification of a family of muscarinic acetylcholine receptor genes. *Science* 237:527–32
10. Brann, M. R., Buckley, N. J., Jones, S.

V. P., Bonner, T. I. 1987. Expression of a cloned muscarinic receptor in A9 L cells. *Mol. Pharmacol.* 32:450–55

11. Breitwieser, G. E., Szabo, G. 1985. Uncoupling of cardiac muscarinic and β-adrenergic receptors from ion channels by a guanine nucleotide analogue. *Nature* 317:538–40

12. Brown, J. H., Brown, S. L. 1984. Agonists differentiate muscarinic receptors that inhibit cyclic AMP formation from those that stimulate phosphoinositide metabolism. *J. Biol. Chem.* 259:3777–81

13. Casnellie, J. E., Ives, H. E., Jamieson, J. D., Greengard, P. 1980. Cyclic GMP-dependent protein phosphorylation in intact medial tissue and isolated cells from vascular smooth muscle. *J. Biol. Chem.* 255:3770–76

14. Christie, M. J., North, R. A. 1988. Control of ion conductances by muscarinic receptors. *Trends Pharmacol. Sci. Suppl.* 8:30–33

15. Codina, J., Yatani, A., Grenet, D., Brown, A. M., Birnbaumer, L. 1987. The α subunit of the GTP binding protein G_k opens atrial potassium channels. *Science* 236:442–45

16. Cremo, C. R., Herron, G. S., Schimerlik, M. I. 1981. Solubilization of the atrial muscarinic receptor: A new detergent system and rapid assays. *Anal. Biochem.* 115:331–38

17. Cremo, C., Schimerlik, M. I. 1984. Photoaffinity labeling of the solubilized, partially purified muscarinic receptor from porcine atria by *p*-azidoatropine methyl iodide. *Biochemistry* 23:3494–3501

18. Dascal, N., Landau, E. M., Lass, Y. 1984. *Xenopus* oocyte resting potential, muscarinic responses and the role of calcium and guanosine 3', 5'-cyclic monophosphate. *J. Physiol.* 352:551–74

19. Dratz, E. A., Hargrave, P. A. 1983. The structure of rhodopsin and the rod outer segment disc membrane. *Trends Biochem. Sci.* 8:128–31

20. Egan, T. M., North, R. A. 1986. Acetylcholine hyperpolarizes central neurones by acting on an M2 muscarinic receptor. *Nature* 319:405–7

21. Ehlert, F. J. 1985. The relationship between muscarinic receptor occupancy and adenylate cyclase inhibition in the rabbit myocardium. *Mol. Pharmacol.* 28:410–21

22. Ehlert, F. J., Roeske, W. R., Yamamura, H. I. 1981. Muscarinic receptor: Regulation by guanine nucleotides, ions and *N*-ethylmaleimide. *Fed. Proc.* 40:153–59

23. Fisher, S. K., Klinger, P. D., Agranoff, B. W. 1983. Muscarinic agonist binding and phospholipid turnover in brain. *J. Biol. Chem.* 258:7358–63

24. Florio, V. A., Sternweiss, P. C. 1985. Reconstitution of resolved muscarinic cholinergic receptors with purified GTP-binding proteins. *J. Biol. Chem.* 260:3477–83

25. Fukuda, K., Kubo, T., Akiba, I., Maeda, A., Mishina, M., et al. 1987. Molecular distinction between muscarinic acetylcholine receptor subtypes. *Nature* 327:623–25

26. Galper, J. B., Haigh, L. S., Hart, A. C., O'Hara, D. S., Livingston, D. J. 1987. Muscarinic cholinergic receptors in the embryonic chick heart: Interaction of agonist; receptor, and guanine nucleotides studied by an improved assay for direct binding of the muscarinic agonist [^{3}H] Cismethyldioxolane. *Mol. Pharmacol.* 32:230–40

27. Galper, J. B., Smith, T. W. 1980. Agonist and guanine nucleotide modulation of muscarinic cholinergic receptors in cultured heart cells. *J. Biol. Chem.* 255:9571–79

28. Gardner, A. L., Darroch, S. A., Choo, L. K., Mitchelson, F. 1988. The effect of some selective agonists and antagonists on peripheral muscarinic receptors. *Trends Pharmacol. Sci. Suppl.* 8:40–43

29. Gierschik, P., Jakobs, K. H. 1987. Receptor-mediated ADP-ribosylation of a phospholipase C-stimulating G protein. *FEBS Lett.* 224:219–23

30. Gilman, A. G. 1987. G proteins: Transucers of receptor-generated signals. *Ann. Rev. Biochem.* 56:615–49

31. Gurwitz, D., Kloog, Y., Sokolovsky, M. 1984. Recognition of the muscarinic receptor by its endogenous neurotransmitter: Binding of [^{3}H] acetylcholine and its modulation by transition metal ions and guanine nucleotides. *Proc. Natl. Acad. Sci. USA* 81:3650–54

32. Haga, K., Haga, T. 1985. Purification of the muscarinic acetylcholine receptor from porcine brain. *J. Biol. Chem.* 260:7927–35

33. Haga, K., Haga, T., Ichiyama, A. 1986. Reconstitution of the muscarinic acetylcholine receptor, guanine nucleotide-sensitive high affinity binding of agonists to purified muscarinic receptors reconstituted with GTP-binding proteins (G_i and G_o). *J. Biol. Chem.* 261:10133–40

34. Haga, T., Haga, K., Berstein, G., Nishiyama, T., Uchiyama, H., et al. 1988. Molecular properties of muscarin-

ic receptors. *Trends Pharmacol. Sci. Suppl.* 8:12–18

35. Hammer, R., Berrie, C. P., Birdsall, N. J. M., Burgen, A. S. V., Hulme, E. C. 1980. Pirenzepine distinguishes between different subclasses of muscarinic receptors. *Nature* 283:90–92

36. Harden, T. K., Meeker, R. B., Martin, M. W. 1983. Interaction of radiolabeled agonist with cardiac muscarinic cholinergic receptors. *J. Pharmacol. Exp. Ther.* 227:570–77

37. Harden, T. K., Petch, L. A., Traynelis, S. F., Waldo, G. L. 1985. Agonist-induced alteration in the membrane form of muscarinic cholinergic receptors. *J. Biol. Chem.* 260:13060–66

38. Hartzell, H. C., Fischmeister, R. 1986. Opposite effects of cyclic GMP and cyclic AMP on Ca^{2+} current in single heart cells. *Nature* 323:273–75

39. Haslam, R. J., Davidson, M. M. L. 1984. Receptor-induced diacylglycerol formation in permeabilized platelets; possible role for a GTP-binding protein. *J. Recept. Res.* 4:605–29

40. Hepler, J. R., Harden, T. K. 1986. Guanine nucleotide-dependent pertussistoxin-insensitive stimulation of inositol phosphate formation by carbachol in a membrane preparation from human astrocytoma cells. *Biochem. J.* 239:141–46

41. Herron, G. S., Miller, S., Manley, W.-L., Schimerlik, M. I. 1982. Ligand interactions with the solubilized porcine atrial muscarinic receptor. *Biochemistry* 21:515–20

42. Hootman, S. R., Picado-Leonard, T. M., Burnham, D. B. 1985. Muscarinic acetylcholine receptor structure in acinar cells of mammalian exocrine glands. *J. Biol. Chem.* 260:4186–94

43. Hughes, A. R., Martin, M. W., Harden, T. K. 1984. Pertussis toxin differentiates between two mechanisms of attenuation of cyclic AMP accumulation by muscarinic cholinergic receptors. *Proc. Natl. Acad. Sci. USA* 81:5680–84

44. Hulme, E. C., Birdsall, N. J. M., Burgen, A. S. V., Mehta, P. 1978. The binding of antagonists to brain muscarinic receptors. *Mol. Pharmacol.* 14:737–50

45. Järv, J., Hedlund, B., Bartfai, T. 1979. Isomerization of the muscarinic receptor antagonist complex. *J. Biol. Chem.* 254:5595–98

46. Kubo, T., Fukuda, K., Mikami, A., Maeda, A., Takahashi, H., et al. 1986. Cloning, sequencing and expression of complementary DNA encoding the muscarinic acetylcholine receptor. *Nature* 323:411–16

47. Kubo, T., Maeda, A., Sugimoto, K., Akiba, I., Mikami, A., et al. 1986. Primary structure of porcine cardiac muscarinic acetylcholine receptor deduced from the cDNA sequence. *FEBS Lett.* 209:367–72

48. Kurose, H., Katada, T., Haga, T., Haga, K., Ichiyama, A., et al. 1986. Functional interactions of purified muscarinic receptors with purified guanine nucleotide regulatory proteins reconstituted in phospholipid vesicles. *J. Biol. Chem.* 261:6423–28

49. Kurose, H., Ui, M. 1983. Functional uncoupling of muscarinic receptors from adenylate cyclase in rat cardiac membranes by the active component of islet-activating protein, pertussis toxin. *J. Cyclic Nucleotide Protein Phosphorylation Res.* 9:305–18

50. Kwatra, M. M., Hosey, M. M. 1986. Phosphorylation of the cardiac muscarinic receptor in intact chick heart and its regulation by a muscarinic agonist. *J. Biol. Chem.* 261:12429–32

51. Kwatra, M. M., Leung, E., Maan, A. C., McMahon, K. K., Ptasienski, J., et al. 1987. Correlation of agonist-induced phosphorylation of chick heart muscarinic receptors with receptor desensitization. *J. Biol. Chem.* 262:16314–21

52. Lai, W. S., El-Fakahany, E. E. 1987. Phorbol ester-induced inhibition of cyclic GMP formation mediated by muscarinic receptors in murine neuroblastoma cells. *J. Pharmacol. Exp. Ther.* 241:366–72

53. Large, T. H., Cho, N. J., De Mello, F. G., Klein, W. L. 1985. Molecular alteration of a muscarinic acetylcholine receptor system during synaptogenesis. *J. Biol. Chem.* 260:8873–81

54. Large, T. H., Rauh, J. J., De Mello, F. G., Klein, W. L. 1985. Two molecular weight forms of muscarinic acetylcholine receptors in the avian central nervous system: Switch in predominant form during differentiation of synapses. *Proc. Natl. Acad. Sci. USA* 82:8785–89

55. Liang, M., Martin, M. W., Harden, T. K. 1987. [^{3}H]Propylbenzilylcholine mustard-labelling of muscarinic cholinergic receptors that selectively couple to phospholipase C or adenylate cyclase in two cultured cell lines. *Mol. Pharmacol.* 32:443–49

56. Liles, W. C., Hunter, D. D., Meier, K. E., Nathanson, N. M. 1986. Activation of protein kinases C induces rapid internalization and subsequent degradation of muscarinic acetylcholine receptors in neuroblastoma cells. *J. Biol. Chem.* 261:5307–13

57. Lincoln, T. M., Keely, S. L. 1981. Regulation of cardiac cyclic GMP-dependent protein kinase. *Biochim. Biophys. Acta* 676:230–44

58. Lindemann, J. P., Watanabe, A. M. 1985. Muscarinic cholinergic inhibition of β-adrenergic stimulation of phospholamban phosphorylation and Ca^{2+} transport in guinea pig ventricles. *J. Biol. Chem.* 260:13122–29

59. Lo, W. W. Y., Hughes, J. 1987. A novel cholera toxin-sensitive G-protein (G_c) regulating receptor-mediated phosphoinositide signalling in human pituitary clonal cells. *FEBS Lett.* 220:327–31

60. Logothetis, D. E., Kurachi, Y., Galper, J., Neer, E. J., Clapham, D. E. 1987. The $\beta\gamma$ subunits of GTP-binding proteins activate the muscarinic K^+ channel in heart. *Nature* 325:321–26

61. Luetje, C. W., Gierschik, P., Milligan, G., Unson, C., Spiegel, A., et al. 1987. Tissue-specific regulation of GTP-binding protein and muscarinic acetylcholine receptor levels during cardiac development. *Biochemistry* 26:4876–84

62. Madison, D. V., Lancaster, B., Nicoll, R. A. 1987. Voltage clamp analysis of cholinergic action in the hippocampus. *J. Neurosci.* 7:733–41

63. Martin, J. M., Hunter, D. D., Nathanson, N. M. 1985. Islet activating protein inhibits physiological responses evoked by cardiac muscarinic acetylcholine receptors. Role of guanosine triphosphate binding proteins in regulation of potassium permeability. *Biochemistry* 24:7521–25

64. Masters, S. B., Martin, M. W., Harden, T. K., Brown, J. H. 1985. Pertussis toxin does not inhibit muscarinic-receptor-mediated phosphoinositide hydrolysis or calcium mobilization. *Biochem. J.* 227:933–37

65. Mattera, R., Pitts, B. J., Entman, M. L., Birnbaumer, L. 1985. Guanine nucleotide regulation of a mammalian myocardial muscarinic receptor system. Evidence for homo- and heterotropic cooperativity in ligand binding analyzed by computer-assisted curve fitting. *J. Biol. Chem.* 260:7410–21

66. McCormick, D. A., Prince, D. A. 1986. Acetylcholine induces burst firing in thalamic reticular neurones by activating a potassium conductance. *Nature* 319:402–5

67. McKinney, M., Richelson, E. 1984. The coupling of the neuronal muscarinic receptor to responses. *Annu. Rev. Pharmacol. Toxicol.* 24:121–46

68. McKinney, M., Richelson, E. 1986. Blockade of N1E–115 murine neuroblastoma muscarinic receptor function by agents that affect the metabolism of arachidonic acid. *Biochem. Pharmacol.* 35:2389–97

69. Morris, A. P., Gallacher, D. V., Irvine, R. F., Petersen, O. H. 1987. Synergism of inositol trisphosphate and tetrakisphosphate in activating Ca^{2+}-dependent K^+ channels. *Nature* 330:653–55

70. Nadler, E., Gillo, B., Lass, Y., Oron, Y. 1986. Acetylcholine and inositol 1,4,5-trisphosphate-induced calcium mobilization in *Xenopus laevis* oocytes. *FEBS Lett.* 199:208–12

71. Nakamura, T., Ui, M. 1985. Simultaneous inhibitions of inositol phospholipid breakdown, arachidonic acid release, and histamine secretion in mast cells by islet-activating protein, pertussis toxin. A possible involvement of the toxin-specific substrate in the Ca^{2+}-mobilizing receptor-mediated biosignaling system. *J. Biol. Chem.* 260:3584–93

72. Nathanson, N. M. 1987. Molecular properties of the muscarinic acetylcholine receptor. *Annu. Rev. Neurosci.* 10:195–236

73. Nishizuka, Y. 1986. Studies and perspectives of protein kinase C. *Science* 233:305–12

74. Ohsako, S., Deguchi, T. 1984. Receptor-mediated regulation of calcium mobilization and cyclic GMP synthesis in neuroblastoma cells. *Biochem. Biophys. Res. Commun.* 122:333–39

75. Orellana, S., Solski, P., Brown, J. H. 1987. Guanosine 5′-O-(Thiotriphosphate)-dependent inositol trisphosphate formation in membranes is inhibited by phorbol ester and protein kinase C. *J. Biol. Chem.* 262:1638–43

76. Peralta, E. G., Ashkenazi, A., Winslow, J. W., Smith D. H., Ramachandran, J., et al. 1987. Distinct primary structures, ligand-binding properties and tissue specific expression of four human muscarinic acetylcholine receptors. *EMBO J.* 6:3923–29

77. Peralta, E. G., Winslow, J. W., Peterson, G. L., Smith, D. H., Ashkenazi, A., et al. 1987. Primary structure and biochemical properties of an M_2 muscarinic receptor. *Science* 236:600–5

78. Peterson, G. L., Herron, G. S., Yamaki, M., Fullerton, D. S., Schimerlik, M. I. 1984. Purification of the muscarinic receptor from porcine atria. *Proc. Natl. Acad. Sci. USA* 81:4993–97

79. Peterson, G. L., Rosenbaum, L. C., Broderick, D. J., Schimerlik, M. I.

1986. Physical properties of the purified cardiac muscarinic acetylcholine receptor. *Biochemistry* 25:3189–3202

80. Pfaffinger, P. J., Martin, J. M., Hunter, D. D., Nathanson, N. M., Hille, B. 1985. GTP-binding proteins couple cardiac muscarinic receptors to a K channel. *Nature* 317:536–38

81. Rosenbaum, L. C., Malencik, D. A., Tota, M. R., Anderson, S. R., Schimerlik, M. I. 1987. Phosphorylation of the porcine atrial muscarinic receptor by cAMP-dependent protein kinase. *Biochemistry* 26:8183–88

82. Schimerlik, M. I., Miller, S., Peterson, G. L., Rosenbaum, L. C., Tota, M. R. 1986. Biochemical studies on muscarinic receptors in porcine atrium. *Trends Pharmacol. Sci. Suppl.* 7:1–7

83. Schreiber, G., Henis, Y. I., Sokolovski, M. 1985. Rate constants of agonist binding to muscarinic receptors in rat brain medulla. Evaluation by competition kinetics. *J. Biol. Chem.* 260:8795–8802

84. Shibasaki, T. 1987. Conductance and kinetics of delayed rectifier potassium channels in nodal cells of the rabbit heart. *J. Physiol.* 387:227–50

85. Sims, S. M., Singer, J. J., Walsh, J. V. Jr. 1988. Antagonistic adrenergic-muscarinic regulation of M current in smooth muscle cells. *Science* 239:190–93

86. Söling, H.-D., Machado-De-Domenech, E., Kleineke, J., Fest, W. 1987. Early effects of β-adrenergic and muscarinic secretagogues on lipid and phospholipid metabolism in guinea pig

parotid acinar cells. Stimulation of 2,3-sn-Diacylglycerol formation by isoproterenol. *J. Biol. Chem.* 262:16786–92

87. Streb, H., Irvine, R. F., Berridge, M. J., Schultz, I. 1983. Release of Ca^{2+} from a nonmitochondrial intracellular store in pancreatic acinar cells by inositol-1,4,5-trisphosphate. *Nature* 306:67–68

88. Tanner, L. I., Harden, T. K., Wells, J. N., Martin, M. W. 1986. Identification of the phosphodiesterase regulated by muscarinic cholinergic receptors of 1321N1 human astrocytoma cells. *Mol. Pharmacol.* 29:455–60

89. Tota, M. R., Kahler, K. R., Schimerlik, M. I. 1987. Reconstitution of the purified porcine atrial muscarinic acetylcholine receptor with purified procine atrial inhibitory guanioe nucleotide binding protein. *Biochemistry* 26:8175–82

90. Venter, J. C. 1983. Muscarinic receptor structure. Receptor size, membrane orientation and absence of phylogenetic structural diversity. *J. Biol. Chem.* 258:4842–48

91. Wheatley, M., Hulme, E. C., Birdsall, N. J. M., Curtis, C. A. M., Eveleigh, P., et al. 1988. Peptide mapping studies on muscarinic receptors; Receptor structure and localization of the ligand binding site. *Trends Pharmacol. Sci. Suppl.* 8:19–24

92. Yatani, A., Codina, J., Brown, A. M., Birnbaumer, L. 1987. Direct activation of mammalian atrial muscarinic potassium channels by GTP regulatory protein G_K. *Science* 235:207–11

Annu. Rev. Physiol. 1989. 51:229–44

ROLE OF G PROTEINS IN THE REGULATION OF THE CARDIOVASCULAR SYSTEM

Janet D. Robishaw and Karen A. Foster

Weis Center for Research, Geisinger Clinic, Danville, Pennsylvania

INTRODUCTION

The G proteins are a family of GTP-binding proteins that play an obligatory role in the transduction of extracellular, receptor-detected signals across the cell membrane to intracellular effectors. These proteins have been the focus of a major research effort since 1971 when Rodbell and colleagues first demonstrated a GTP requirement for hormonal stimulation of adenylyl cyclase in liver (52). Based on this and other indirect observations, Rodbell et al (52) and Levitski (See 38 for a review) hypothesized that the site of action of GTP might be on a protein distinct from both the hormone receptor and the effector, adenylyl cyclase. This hypothesis was confirmed with the purification of a GTP-binding protein from liver (58). This protein was called G_s for G stimulatory protein. Shortly thereafter, a GTP requirement for hormonal inhibition of adenylyl cyclase was observed, and a second G protein, called G_i for G inhibitory protein, was purified from liver (4). Subsequently, using techniques nearly identical to those developed for G_s and G_i, a third G protein was purified from brain (59). Since the function of this protein was not known, the new protein was called G_o for G other protein. The discovery of G_o was important, because it suggested that G proteins might be involved in hormonal regulation of effectors other than adenylyl cyclase. Further support for this suggestion came with the purification of a fourth G protein from retina (20). This protein, called G_t for G transducin protein, is required for light activation of cGMP phosphodiesterase.

The purification and biochemical characterization of these four G proteins has allowed the formulation of a model, which describes some of the steps

229

involved in G protein transduction of receptor-detected signals (see 24 for a review). According to this model (described in detail below), the α subunit regulates the activity of a specific effector, whereas the $\beta\gamma$ subunits inhibit the interaction of the α subunit with its effector. Because the specificity of G protein function appears to reside with the α subunits, most research on these proteins has been focused on defining the number of α subunits that exist and determining their primary structures. As a result, cDNAs have been cloned and sequenced for the α subunits of G_s (50, 51), G_i (48), G_o (29), and G_t (46, 63, 68). In addition, cDNAs for three, previously-unknown, α subunits, G_{i2} (29), G_{i3} (30), and G_{t2} (39), have been sequenced. However, the specific functions of most of these α subunits are not known with precision.

While many excellent reviews on G proteins have appeared (11, 12, 24, 60), none have focused specifically on the role of G proteins in the regulation of the cardiovascular system. The purpose of this review is to highlight current knowledge of G proteins in general and to apply this knowledge to the structure and function of G proteins in the heart and vascular system. In addition, we present gaps in our knowledge of the subunit composition of the G proteins that must be addressed before detailed functions of the G proteins can be understood in any tissue, much less tissues under multi-hormonal control such as the heart and vasculature.

STRUCTURE OF G PROTEINS

Each G protein has been named on the basis of the function or suggested function of its α subunit. To date, eight different G proteins have been purified. The term purified is used to indicate that the G protein has been separated from most other cellular proteins; however, this does not necessarily mean that the different G protein types have been separated from each other. Molecular cloning has provided information on the primary sequences of all of the G proteins that have been purified, some of which were previously unknown because of an inability to resolve them from the other known G proteins.

Structure of α Subunits

α SUBUNITS OF G_s At least two forms of $G_{s\alpha}$ with apparent molecular masses of 52 and 45 kDa on SDS-polyacrylamide gels exist (58). The relative concentrations of the different $G_{s\alpha}$ forms vary among cells and tissues, which suggests that their functions may be tissue dependent, but functional differences have yet to be confirmed. Both the α_{45} and α_{52} subunits of G_s can be ADP-ribosylated by cholera toxin, which results in permanent activation of the α subunits by preventing their reassociation with the $\beta\gamma$ subunits. Cloning has revealed that the α_{45} subunit of $G_{s\alpha}$ differs from the α_{52} subunit by the substitution of 2 and the deletion of 14 amino acids (51). The two forms are produced from two different mRNAs, which arise from a single gene by alternative splicing of internal exons. In addition, two additional forms of $G_{s\alpha}$ may exist based on the presence of four mRNA species (6).

α SUBUNITS OF G_i Molecular cloning has revealed the existence of three distinct proteins with similar structures and apparent molecular weights, which have been called $G_{i\alpha1}$ (48), $G_{i\alpha2}$ (29), and $G_{i\alpha3}$ (30). Both $G_{i\alpha1}$ and $G_{i\alpha3}$ have molecular masses of 41 kDa, while $G_{i\alpha2}$ has a molecular mass of 40 kDa (46b). All three forms of $G_{i\alpha}$ appear to be substrates for N-myristoylation (10) and for ADP-ribosylation by pertussis toxin, which inactivates these proteins by preventing their association with receptors. At the present time, it is uncertain if all three forms of G_i are actually involved in receptor-mediated inhibition of adenylyl cyclase. Since inhibition of adenylyl cyclase may be mediated by the $\beta\gamma$ subunits of G_i as discussed below, any G protein containing common $\beta\gamma$ subunits may be responsible for this function. Thus, the G_i nomenclature can be confusing since it no longer appears to reflect a specific function as originally intended.

α SUBUNIT OF G_o This α subunit has a molecular mass of 39 kDa and is also a substrate for ADP-ribosylation by pertussis toxin (47, 59). The $G_{o\alpha}$ has been cloned recently (29). Although the function of G_o is still unclear, recent evidence (26a) suggests that G_o may be involved in regulation of Ca^{2+} channels.

α SUBUNIT OF G_t The α subunit of G_t has a molecular mass of 39 kDa and can be ADP-ribosylated by both cholera and pertussis toxins. Two different $G_{t\alpha}$ subunits have been cloned (39, 46, 63, 68). $G_{t\alpha1}$ is present only in rods and $G_{t\alpha2}$ is found only in cones (37).

STRUCTURAL COMPARISON OF THE α SUBUNITS   Comparison of the primary structures of the α subunits has provided insight into possible functional domains of these proteins (12, 24 for reviews). Presumably, the high degree of homology between the eight α subunits of the G proteins reflects properties that are shared by all α subunits, such as GTP binding and hydrolysis, interaction with the $\beta\gamma$ subunits, and ADP-ribosylation by bacterial toxins. However, at least three regions of the α subunits are notable for their lack of homology. One such area at the amino terminus is the proposed binding site for the $\beta\gamma$ subunits. The second variable section is a 30 amino acid region toward the middle of the protein, which is the suggested site for effector interaction (12, 24 for reviews). The carboxy terminus is the third difference region, which is the proposed receptor binding site. This region also contains the ADP-ribosylation site for pertussis toxin. The most significant differences between the G_is lie in the putative effector binding area, while the differences between the G_ts are in the putative receptor binding region (24). The variable regions of $G_{s\alpha}$ are adjacent to the G_s-specific inserts, which indicates that they may be involved in G_s-specific functions.

Structure of the β and γ Subunits

Although it is often ignored, each G protein contains β and γ subunits in addition to the α subunit. The β and γ subunits form a tightly associated complex. In spite of previous studies suggesting the existence of a single βγ subunit complex shared by all α subunits of G_s, G_i, and G_o, more recent studies have indicated the existence of multiple forms of both β and γ subunits in tissues such as the brain. However, the functional significance of the heterogeneity in the β and γ subunits is not known. Recently, Cerione et al (13) demonstrated that βγ subunits isolated from brain and retina do not have the same ability to inhibit $G_{s\alpha}$-stimulated adenylyl cyclase activity. Although this study showed very clearly that all βγ subunit complexes are not the same, it did not address the more interesting question as to whether differences exist between βγ subunit complexes in the same tissue.

Since it is now clear that several different forms of the α, β, and γ subunits exist, future studies must be directed toward determining the specific subunit composition of each G protein and the specific function of each subunit. With the availability of peptide antibodies to specific subunits, it is now possible for the first time to make a systematic effort to determine if there is specific association of individual forms of the α, β, and γ subunits in vivo, and if a specific composition of the βγ subunit complex is required to associate with and modify the function of a particular α subunit. Also, any function of the βγ subunits other than deactivation of the α subunit must be determined. This information will be important for a complete understanding of G protein function.

β AND γ SUBUNITS OF G_t Since G_t is the only G protein present in the retina in any significant amount, the subunit composition of G_t has been determined. The α subunit of G_t copurifies with a single β and a single γ subunit with apparent molecular masses of 36 and 8 kDa, respectively (60). Recently, cDNA clones encoding the β_{36} (19, 61) and γ_8 (27) subunits have been isolated from a retinal library.

β AND γ SUBUNITS OF G_s, G_i, AND G_o The subunit compositions of G_s, G_i, and G_o have not been determined. Two β subunits with apparent molecular masses of 36 and 35 kDa are present in most tissues other than the retina (58, 59). Recently, cDNA clones encoding the β_{36} (17) and the β_{35} (18, 21,

22) subunits have been isolated from liver and adrenal cDNA libraries, respectively. Based on deduced amino acid sequences, these subunits are highly homologous (sharing 90% identity). In addition, since the β_{36} cDNA clone has been found in both a liver and retinal library, it seems likely that the β_{36} subunit in retina is identical to that of other tissues.

Based on a limited amount of partial amino acid sequence information, the γ subunits of the G proteins appear to be more diverse than the β subunits. When purified preparations of brain G proteins are resolved on SDS-polyacrylamide gels, three proteins are observed in the 8–10-kDa range (59). Recently, partial amino acid sequences have been obtained for two of these proteins (own unpublished results). A comparison of these sequences to the sequence reported for the γ subunit of G_t (27) shows several regions of homology interspersed with regions that are clearly unique to each of the γ subunits. Overall, the partial sequences of the two γ subunits from brain are 70% identical to each other, but are only 42% identical to the γ subunit from retina. Although the complete amino acid sequences of the brain γ subunits have yet to be determined, it is clear that at least three different γ subunits exist. Preliminary results on the tissue distribution of these are intriguing. An antibody against the γ subunit of retinal G_t does not recognize γ subunits from other tissues (23, 53). Likewise, an antibody made to one of the brain γ subunits does not recognize the other γ subunit from brain, nor the γ subunits from retinal or liver G proteins (own unpublished results). Although further work is clearly needed, more than three γ subunits may exist with specific tissue distribution. As yet, it is not known if there is any specific association of particular γ and β subunits with the α subunits of G_s, G_i, and G_o.

ROLE OF G PROTEINS IN NEUROHORMONAL REGULATION OF THE CARDIOVASCULAR SYSTEM

Elucidation of the primary sequences of the G protein subunits has permitted the synthesis of peptides based on regions of the sequence unique or common to the various G protein subunits and the generation of region-specific antibodies. In comparison to the older, non specific, toxin labeling approach for identifying the α subunits of the G proteins (9, 25, 32, 55), the use of α subunit–specific antibodies represents a great advance in determining the tissue distribution of known G proteins. The development of α subunit–common antibodies may prove useful in discovering new G proteins. Using antibodies specific for various α and β subunits, Mumby et al (46a) demonstrated the presence of the α_{45} and α_{52} subunits of G_s, the α_{39} subunit of G_o, and the β_{36} subunit in membranes prepared from bovine heart tissue. Another study by Mumby et al (46b) revealed the presence of the α_{40} subunit of $G_{i\alpha2}$ in membranes prepared from rat heart tissue. More recently, we demonstrated the existence of the α_{45} and α_{52} subunits of G_s and the α_{40} and α_{41} subunits of G_i in membranes prepared from rat arterial smooth muscle cells (own unpublished results). In addition, both the β_{36} and β_{35} subunits are present in these cells. However, there is no information available on the number or type of γ subunits in either the heart or vasculature.

Although the results of these studies provide a good starting point, it is clear that further studies on G protein composition are needed to better understand neurohormonal control of the heart. For instance, it is not known whether there is a differential localization of specific G proteins within the heart. For example, the right atrium may have a different G protein profile than the left ventricle because these tissues are innervated differently and have different primary functions. Furthermore, previous immunoblotting studies were done on membranes prepared from heart tissue, not individual cell types. Thus, it is possible that a different complement of G proteins exists in each of the various cell types of the heart. The use of antibodies to localize individual G proteins within specific cell types may provide valuable clues to their functions.

Although much remains to be learned, some information is available on the roles of G proteins in regulation of the cardiovascular system, and even more roles have been speculated. We summarize the current knowledge in this review and attempt to point out areas where problems exist or data are too sparse to allow any integrated conclusions.

β-Adrenergic Receptor-Mediated Effects in Heart

The β-adrenergic stimulation of heart rate, force of contraction, and rate of relaxation are such well-known physiological effects that we mistakenly tend to believe that the detailed mechanisms by which activation of β-adrenergic receptors causes these effects are understood. The present belief is that the effects are mediated by an increase in the intracellular production of cAMP in a reaction catalyzed by adenylyl cyclase. An increase in the intracellular cAMP is known to occur and has been shown to activate cAMP-dependent protein kinase, which in turn phosphorylates many cellular proteins. Phosphorylation of proteins, such as phospholamban (62) and voltage-sensitive Ca^{2+} channel (1), has been suggested to increase Ca^{2+} uptake by the sarcoplasmic reticulum and to increase Ca^{2+} influx across the sarcolemmal membrane, thereby accounting for the increased rate of relaxation and the increased force of contraction. However, β-adrenergic effects on contractile activity of the heart are complex, and the critical proteins phosphorylated by cAMP-dependent protein kinase and their relative roles in causing these effects have not been explained adequately. This is particularly true in the case of the β-adrenergic receptor-mediated increase in heart rate.

ROLE OF G_s IN β-ADRENERGIC STIMULATION OF ADENYLYL CY-
CLASE   The most rigorous evidence for the involvement of G_s in stimulation
of adenylyl cyclase is the reconstitution of three purified proteins, β-
adrenergic receptor, G_s, and adenylyl cyclase, into artificial, phospholipid
vesicles to form a hormonally responsive pathway (45). The ability to recon-
stitute purified proteins into phospholipid vesicles has provided a large
amount of data, which has allowed the formulation of a model delineating
some of the steps involved in β-adrenergic stimulation of adenylyl cyclase by
G_s (see 24 for a review). According to this model, G_s exists as a complex of
α, β, and γ subunits with GDP bound to α subunits in the membrane. In
response to agonist binding to the β-adrenergic receptor on the outer surface
of the membrane, activation of G_s occurs in a process involving the release of
GDP and the subsequent binding of GTP to the α subunit, and the dissociation
of this $\alpha \cdot$ GTP subunit from the $\beta\gamma$ subunit complex. Once activated, the $\alpha \cdot$
GTP subunit of G_s interacts with adenylyl cyclase to stimulate the intracellular
production of cAMP. This interaction is terminated by deactivation of G_s, a
process involving the hydrolysis of GTP and the reassociation of the α and $\beta\gamma$
subunits.

Since the α subunit interacts with adenylyl cyclase, it is interesting that
both known forms of $G_{s\alpha}$ appear to be capable of stimulating the activity of
adenylyl cyclase although subtle differences in the relative abilities of the two
α subunits to support hormone-stimulated adenylyl cyclase activity have been
suggested. Sternweis et al (58) reported that fractions enriched in the α_{52}
subunit appeared to stimulate adenylyl cyclase to a larger extent in response to
hormone than fractions enriched in the α_{45} subunit. Although intriguing, these
differences have yet to be confirmed using fully resolved α_{52} and α_{45} subunits. It is of interest, however, that the ventricle of the heart, which contains
mostly the α_{45} subunit of G_s, exhibits a much lower rate of hormone-
stimulated adenylyl cyclase activity than tissues, such as the brain, that
contain mostly the α_{52} subunit.

POSSIBLE ROLE OF G_s IN β-ADRENERGIC STIMULATION OF THE VOLTAGE-
SENSITIVE CA^{2+} CHANNEL   While it is clear that activation of β-adrenergic
receptors leads to an increase in the intracellular cAMP concentration, there is
some controversy as to whether the increase in cAMP concentration can
account for all β-adrenergic receptor-mediated effects. In this regard, Ingebretsen (28) suggested that β-adrenergic activation of voltage-sensitive
Ca^{2+} channels in the heart can occur independent of changes in cAMP. Using
membrane patches from guinea pig myocytes, Yatani et al (67) confirmed and
extended this observation by showing activation of cardiac Ca^{2+} channels
following the addition of preactivated G_s or its α subunit, but not by de-

activated G_s or by preactivated G_i. These results suggest a direct interaction between the α subunit of G_s and the Ca^{2+} channel. However, verification of this possibility will require the purification and reconstitution of the appropriate Ca^{2+} channel with individual α subunits of G_s. Maguire & Erdos (43) demonstrated that β-adrenergic inhibition of Mg^{2+} uptake by wild-type S49 cells can occur independent of changes in cAMP. Since this effect of β-adrenergic agonists was not present in cyc-S49 cells, which lack $G_{s\alpha}$ (5, 54), one or both of the α subunits of G_s may probably interact directly with an effector other than adenylyl cyclase. Although β-adrenergic inhibition of Mg^{2+} uptake by the heart has not been examined, it is interesting that changes in the intracellular Mg^{2+} concentration dramatically alter the activity of voltage-sensitive Ca^{2+} channels in the heart (65). Thus, a direct effect of β-adrenergic agonists on the influx of either Mg^{2+} or Ca^{2+} could explain the apparent effects of β-adrenergic agonists on both of these divalent ions.

Muscarinic Receptor-Mediated Effects in the Heart

The stimulation of muscarinic, cholinergic receptors has two primary effects in the heart: to decrease heart rate and to a lesser extent, to decrease β-adrenergic-stimulated force of contraction. Compared to the effects of β-adrenergic receptor stimulation, the detailed mechanisms by which activation of muscarinic receptors cause these effects on cardiac function are even less well understood. Among the mechanisms suggested are inhibition of adenylyl cyclase, activation of K^+ channels, and stimulation of phosphatidylinositol hydrolysis. The present belief is that muscarinic inhibition of adenylyl cyclase may account for the small decrease in β-adrenergic-stimulated force of contraction by lowering intracellular cAMP levels.

ROLE OF G_i IN MUSCARINIC INHIBITION OF ADENYLYL CYCLASE   The involvement of oligomeric G_i in receptor-mediated inhibition of adenylyl cyclase is based on its ability to restore this pathway (33) following reconstitution into membranes preinactivated with pertussis toxin (26). Given the apparent opposing roles of G_i and G_s in the regulation of adenylyl cyclase, it was fully expected that the mechanisms by which hormonal activation of G_i and G_s regulate adenylyl cyclase, it was fully expected that the mechanisms by which hormonal activation of G_i and G_s regulate adenylyl cyclase activity would be similar, and to a certain extent, this expectation has been confirmed. Thus, similar to G_s, muscarinic agonists activate G_i by promoting the exchange of GDP for GTP bound to the α subunit and the dissociation of the α subunit of G_i from the $\beta\gamma$ subunits (see 24 for a review). Likewise, G_i is deactivated by hydrolysis of GTP to GDP and reassociation of α and $\beta\gamma$ subunits. However, in contrast to the α subunits of G_s, the α subunit(s) of G_i interacts only weakly with adenylyl cyclase to inhibit its activity (57).

Although direct interaction of the α subunit of G_i and adenylyl cyclase does occur, the limited ability of $G_{i\alpha}$ to cause inhibition of adenylyl cyclase suggests that this is not the most physiologically relevant mechanism. Instead, Gilman, Katada, and associates (24, 35) proposed that the $\beta\gamma$ subunits, released as the result of hormonal activation of G_i, can mediate inhibition of adenylyl cyclase by interacting with the α subunits of G_s, thereby reducing the amount of activated $G_{s\alpha}$ available to stimulate adenylyl cyclase. A number of observations support this mechanism (14, 35, 57). In addition, since G_i is present in 10–20-fold excess over G_s, deactivation of $G_{s\alpha}$ by the $\beta\gamma$ subunits of G_i would be favored, possibly by the formation of an $\alpha_s \cdot$ GTP $\beta\gamma$ complex with subsequent hydrolysis of bound GTP to GDP (31). Recently, Katada et al (34) suggested another mechanism for inhibition of adenylyl cyclase by the $\beta\gamma$ subunits of G_i as a result of their interaction with Ca^{2+}-calmodulin, thereby reducing the amount of Ca^{2+}-calmodulin available to stimulate adenylyl cyclase. A previous study by these investigators (36) purporting a direct interaction of the $\beta\gamma$ subunits with adenylyl cyclase to inhibit its activity has not been confirmed.

If indirect inhibition of $G_{s\alpha}$-stimulated adenylyl cyclase by the $\beta\gamma$ subunits of G_i is the physiologically relevant mechanism, what is the function of the α subunits of G_i? According to the model described above, one possible function of the α subunits of G_i is to act as a binding protein for the $\beta\gamma$ subunits of G_i, thereby preventing indirect inhibition of adenylyl cyclase. However, it is also possible that the α subunits of G_i may interact with an effector other than adenylyl cyclase to regulate some of the other muscarinic receptor-related functions. In this regard, the involvement of G_i in coupling muscarinic receptors to stimulation of cardiac K^+ channels has been suggested.

One of the major effects of muscarinic agonists in the heart is to decrease the heart rate set by specialized "pacemaker" cells in the right atrium. Muscarinic agonists appear to decrease the heart rate by activating a K^+ channel in "pacemaker" cells, thereby stimulating K^+ efflux and hyperpolarizing these cells. The activation of K^+ channels by muscarinic agonists requires GTP and can be attenuated by pretreatment with pertussis toxin (7, 49), which suggests the involvement of a G protein. One explanation of these results is that activation of K^+ channels is mediated by the decrease in the intracellular cAMP concentration that occurs in response to muscarinic agonists. Since muscarinic receptor-mediated inhibition of adenylyl cyclase involves the participation of a G protein as described in the previous section, the GTP requirement and the effect of pertussis toxin would be readily explained. However, a number of recent studies demonstrated that activation of K^+ channels in response to muscarinic agonists can occur even in the presence of elevated intracellular cAMP levels (66), ruling out changes in cAMP as the mediator of this effect.

ROLE OF G_i IN MUSCARINIC STIMULATION OF K^+ CHANNELS   While a great deal of evidence suggests the involvement of a G protein in muscarinic stimulation of K^+ channels in the heart, the exact identity of the G protein involved and the mechanism by which this G protein stimulates the opening of K^+ channels are unclear. Using the inside-out membrane patch technique, Yatani et al (66) demonstrated that cAMP-independent activation of K^+ channels by muscarinic agonists can be mimicked by the addition of pre-activated G_i oligomer from erythrocytes, but not by unactivated G_i oligomer or preactivated G_s oligomer, which suggests the possibility of direct interaction of G_i with the K^+ channel to stimulate its activity. Since G_i and G_s appeared to share the same $\beta\gamma$ subunits, these investigators assumed that the α subunit(s) of G_i was responsible for K^+ channel activation. On the other hand, Logothetis et al (40), using the same technique, but with separated α and $\beta\gamma$ subunits of G_i or G_o from brain, reported that the $\beta\gamma$ subunits, not the α subunits, are responsible for activating the $K+$ channel. More recently, Codina et al (16) observed activation of K^+ channels in pituitary cells by addition of the α subunit(s) of G_i from erythrocytes, but not by the $\beta\gamma$ subunits. However, the issue of whether the α or the $\beta\gamma$ subunits of G_i directly regulate the $K+$ channel in the heart that is responsible for changes in heart rate has yet to be resolved. Indeed, the basic hypothesis that either or both the α or the $\beta\gamma$ subunits of G_i interact directly with the K^+ channel has yet to be proven. These issues must be settled by purification and reconstitution of the appropriate K^+ channel from heart along with the α or $\beta\gamma$ subunits of G_i.

Although the reason for the apparently contradictory results mentioned above is not yet known, most investigators seem to favor the α subunits as the activator of K^+ channels based on presumed analogous roles for the α subunits of G_s and G_t as activators of adenylyl cyclase and cGMP phosphodiesterase respectively. If the α subunit(s) of G_i is responsible for muscarinic activation of the K^+ channel, the recently documented heterogeneity of the α subunits(s) of G_i must be considered. As discussed above, three distinct α subunits of G_i have now been described; these proteins have been designated α_{41} of G_{i1}, α_{40} of G_{i2}, and α_{41} of G_{i3} (see 24 for a review). Using antisera generated against peptides derived from sequences unique to the $G_{i\alpha}$ clones, Mumby et al (46b) demonstrated that erythrocyte membranes, the source of G_i used by Yatani et al (66) and Codina et al (16), contain both the α_{40} subunit of G_{i2} and the α_{41} subunit of G_{i3}, which suggests that one of these proteins may be responsible for activation of K^+ channels in heart. However, it will be necessary to resolve the various α subunits of G_i for use in future reconstitution experiments before the identity of the particular form of G_i responsible for activating cardiac K^+ channels can be established. In this regard, resolution of the α_{40} and the α_{41} subunits of brain G_i has been reported (46b).

Because both stimulation of K^+ channels and inhibition of adenylyl cyclase in response to muscarinic agonists are mediated by pertussis toxin–sensitive G proteins, it is tempting to speculate that both effects result from the activation of a single G protein, such as G_{i2} or G_{i3}. Thus, the α subunit of G_{i2} or G_{i3} may stimulate opening of K^+ channels to hyperpolarize atrial cells, thereby slowing the heart rate, while the $\beta\gamma$ subunits may mediate inhibition of adenylyl cyclase to decrease the intracellular cAMP concentration, thereby coordinating the activities of the two potentially opposing pathways.

ROLE OF $G_?$ in muscarinic stimulation of phospholipase c and pip_2 hydrolysis   In addition to inhibition of adenylyl cylcase and activation of K^+ channels in heart, muscarinic agonists have also been reported to cause stimulation of phospholipase C, the phosphodiesterase responsible for catalyzing the hydrolysis of phosphatidylinositol-4,5-bisphosphate (PIP_2) to myoinositol-1,4,5-triphosphate (IP_3) and diacylglycerol (DG). Based on results of studies on a number of different receptors in various cell types (see 2 for a review), stimulation of PIP_2 hydrolysis is generally thought to lead to an increase in the free cytosolic Ca^{2+} concentration. However, it seems unlikely that the physiological effects attributed to muscarinic stimulation, such as decreases in both heart rate and force of contraction, could result from an increase in the cytosolic Ca^{2+} concentration. Furthermore, as discussed below, the physiological effects of muscarinic and α_1-adrenergic receptor activation are very different although both receptors stimulate PIP_2 hydrolysis. One possible explanation for these results is that muscarinic receptor-mediated stimulation of PIP_2 hydrolysis occurs in nonmuscle cells in the heart. However, Brown et al (8) reported stimulation of PIP_2 hydrolysis by muscarinic agonists in cardiac muscle cell culture, which suggests that the pathway does exist in cardiac myocytes. Although the physiological effect(s) of stimulating PIP_2 hydrolysis is not known, coupling of muscarinic receptors to stimulation of phospholipase C appears to involve a G protein. The identity of this G protein and its relationship to the G protein involved in α_1-adrenergic stimulation of phospholipase C are not known. These issues are discussed further below.

α_1-Adrenergic Effects

In heart, activation of α_1-adrenergic receptors potentiates the force of contraction, while in vascular smooth muscle, stimulation of these receptors initiates contraction. Both of these effects are thought to be mediated by an increase in the free cytosolic Ca^{2+} concentration through its action on a number of Ca^{2+}- and Ca^{2+}/calmodulin-dependent proteins. The exact mechanism leading to the increase in the cytosolic Ca^{2+} concentration is still unclear; however, α_1-adrenergic stimulation of phospholipase C and PIP_2 hydrolysis to form IP_3

and DG may be involved (8). An increase in IP_3 is thought to trigger the release of Ca^{2+} from intracellular stores, while the increase in DG in combination with an elevated Ca^{2+} concentration may stimulate protein kinase C. Stimulation of protein kinase C is postulated to alter cell growth, which may account, at least in part, for the hypertrophic effect of α_1-adrenergic agonists in neonatal hearts (56).

ROLE OF $G_?$ in stimulation of phospholipase c   Recent evidence suggests that a G protein is involved in α_1-adrenergic receptor-mediated stimulation of phospholipase C. This evidence is based primarily on the observation that nonhydrolyzable GTP analogs (15) and AlF_4 (3), which are both known to activate other G proteins, can stimulate phospholipase C and PIP_2 hydrolysis independent of receptor activation. Although this observation is consistent with G protein involvement in stimulation of phospholipase C, the identity of this G protein and its relationship to known G proteins is still not clear. Complicating the identification of this G protein is the finding by a number of investigators that pertussis toxin treatment has different effects on receptor-mediated stimulation of phospholipase C depending on the cell type. In the heart (8, 44) and vasculature (64), for example, pertussis toxin has no effect on stimulation of phospholipase C and PIP_2 hydrolysis by either α_1-adrenergic or muscarinic agonists. Since all known G proteins for which specific functions have yet to be assigned (i.e. G_o, G_{i1}, G_{i2}, G_{i3}) are sensitive to pertussis toxin, either one of these known G proteins has been modified such that it is no longer a substrate for pertussis toxin–dependent ADP-ribosylation, or a previously unknown pertussis toxin–insensitive G protein is involved. Whether the same pertussis toxin–insensitive G protein is involved in stimulation of phospholipase C by both α_1-adrenergic and muscarinic agonists is not clear. Although it is tempting to speculate that the same G protein participates in both of these receptor-mediated signaling systems, Brown et al (8) demonstrated that the effects of α_1-adrenergic and muscarinic agonists on phospholipase C stimulation are additive, which suggests either that two separate pools of the same G protein exist in myocytes or that two different pertussis toxin–insensitive G proteins exist. Further work is needed to clarify this issue.

SUMMARY

A precise description of the involvement of G proteins in regulation of the cardiovascular system is not possible at the present time although it is clear that they do have important regulatory roles. The cardiovascular system is composed of a variety of cell types, which are subject to control by several different hormones, as well as by hormones that have several different effects in the same cell type. Although, historically, variations in the type and number of receptors located on each cell have been used to explain this diversity of hormonal responses, we must now consider the large number and diversity of G proteins in any effort to understand the coordinated hormonal regulation of cellular functions. Given that there are eight known G proteins and several others have been speculated, each of which is composed of three subunits, each of which has several different forms, the possible combinations of subunits into functionally distinct G proteins is enormous. To place this newly described family of G proteins into the appropriate hormone signaling pathways will require a continued research effort. However, with recent progress in producing specific antibodies to each of the G protein subunits, it may now be possible to determine the specific receptor-effector functions of each G protein and their individual subunits.

ACKNOWLEDGMENTS

We thank J. R. Neely for his helpful comments on the text and D. McCaffery for her invaluable secretarial assistance.

Literature Cited

1. Azuma, J., Sawamura, A., Harada, H., Tanimoto, T., et al. 1981. Cyclic adenosine monophosphate modulation of contractility via slow Ca^{2+} channels in chick heart. *J. Mol. Cell. Cardiol.* 13: 577–87

2. Berridge, M. J. 1987. Inositol triphosphate and diacylglycerol: two interacting second messengers. *Annu. Rev. Biochem.* 56:159–93

3. Blackmore, P. F., Bocckino, S. B., Waynick, L. E., Exton, J. H. 1985. Role of a guanine nucleotide-binding regulatory protein in the hydrolysis of hepatocyte phosphatidylinositol 4,5-bisphosphate by calcium-mobilizing hormones and the control of cell calcium. Studies utilizing aluminum fluoride. *J. Biol. Chem.* 260:14477–83

4. Bokoch, G. M., Katada, T., Northup, J. K., Hewlett, E. L., Gilman, A. G. 1983. Identification of the predominant substrate for ADP-ribosylation by islet activating protein. *J. Biol. Chem.* 258:2072–75

5. Bourne, H. R., Coffino, P., Tomkins, G. M. 1975. Selection of a variant lymphoma cell deficient in adenylate cyclase. *Science* 187:750–52

6. Bray, P., Carter, A., Simons, C., Guo, V., et al. 1986. Human cDNA clones for alpha subunits of G_s. *Proc. Natl. Acad. Sci. USA* 23:8893–97

7. Breitwieser, G. E., Szabo, G. 1985. Uncoupling of cardiac muscarinic and beta-adrenergic receptors from ion channels by a guanine nucleotide analogue. *Nature* 317:538–40

8. Brown, J. H., Buxton, I. L., Brunton, L. L. 1985. α_1-adrenergic and muscarinic cholinergic stimulation of phosphoinositide hydrolysis in adult rat cardiomyocytes. *Circ. Res.* 57:532–37

9. Bruns, C., Marmé, D. 1987. Pertussis toxin inhibits the angiotensin II and serotonin-induced rise of free cytoplasmic calcium in cultured smooth muscle cells from rat aorta. *FEBS Lett.* 212:40–44

10. Buss, J. E., Mumby, S. M., Casey, P. J., Gilman, A. G., Sefton, B. M. 1987. Myristoylated alpha subunits of guanine nucleotide-binding regulatory proteins. *Proc. Natl. Acad. Sci USA* 84:7493–97

11. Casey, P. J., Gilman, A. G. 1988. G protein involvement in receptor-effector coupling. *J. Biol. Chem.* 263:2577–80

12. Casperson, G. F., Bourne, H. R. 1987. Biochemical and molecular genetic analysis of hormone-sensitive adenylyl cyclase. *Annu. Rev. Pharmacol. Toxicol.* 27:371–84

13. Cerione, R. A., Gierschik, P., Staniszewski, C., Benovic, J., et al. 1987. Functional differences in the beta gamma complexes of transducin and the in-

hibitory guanine nucleotide regulatory protein. *Biochemistry* 26:1485–91

14. Cerione, R. A., Staniszewski, C., Gierschik, P., Codina, J., Somers, R., et al. 1986. Mechanism of guanine nucleotide regulatory protein-mediated inhibition of adenylate cyclase. Studies with isolated subunits of transducin in a reconstituted system. *J. Biol. Chem.* 261:9514–20

15. Cockcroft, S., Gomperts, B. D. 1985. Role of guanine nucleotide binding protein in the activation of polyphosphoinositide phosphodiesterase. *Nature* 314:534–36

16. Codina, J., Grenet, D., Yatani, A., Birnbaumer, L., Brown, A. 1987. Hormonal regulation of pituitary GH_3 cell K^+ channels by G_k is mediated by its α subunit. *FEBS Lett.* 216:104–6

17. Codina, J., Stengel, D., Woo, S. L., Birnbaumer, L. 1986. Beta-subunits of the human liver G_s/G_i signal-transducing proteins and those of bovine retinal rod cell transducin are identical. *FEBS Lett.* 207:187–92

18. Fong, H. K. W., Amatruda, T., Birren, B., Simon, M. I. 1987. Distinct forms of the beta subunit of GTP-binding regulatory proteins identified by molecular cloning. *Proc. Natl. Acad. Sci. USA* 84:3792–96

19. Fong, H. K. W., Hurley, J. B., Hopkins, R. S., Miake-Lye, R., et al. 1986. Repetitive segmental structure of the transducin beta subunit: homology with the CDC4 gene and identification of related mRNAs. *Proc. Natl. Acad. Sci. USA* 83:2162–66

20. Fung, B. K.-K., Hurley, J. B., Stryer, L. 1981. Flow of information in the light-triggered cyclic nucleotide cascade of vision. *Proc. Natl. Acad. Sci. USA* 78:152–56

21. Gao, B., Gilman, A. G., Robishaw, J. D. 1987. A second form of the β subunit of signal-transducing G proteins. *Proc. Natl. Acad. Sci. USA* 84:6122–25

22. Gao, B., Mumby, S., Gilman, A. G. 1987. The G protein β_2 complementary DNA encodes the β_{35} subunit. *J. Biol. Chem.* 262:17254–57

23. Gierschik, P., Codina, J., Simons, C., Birnbaumer, L., Spiegel, A. 1985. Antisera against a guanine nucleotide binding protein from retina cross-react with the beta subunit of the adenylyl cyclase-associated guanine nucleotide binding proteins, N_s and N_i. *Proc. Natl. Acad. Sci. USA* 82:727–31

24. Gilman, A. G. 1987. G proteins: Transducers of receptor-generated signals. *Annu. Rev. Biochem.* 56:615–49

25. Halvorsen, S. W., Nathanson, N. M. 1984. Ontogenesis of physiological responsiveness and guanine nucleotide sensitivity of cardiac muscarinic receptors during chick embryonic development. *Biochemistry* 23:5813–21

26. Hazeki, O., Ui, M. 1981. Modification by islet-activating protein of receptor-mediated regulation of cyclic AMP accumulation in isolated rat heart cells. *J. Biol. Chem.* 256:2856–62

26a. Hescheler, J., Rosenthal, W., Trautwein, W., Schultz, G. 1987. The GTP-binding protein, G_i regulates neuronal calcium channels. *Nature* 325:445–47

27. Hurley, J. B., Fong, H. K., Teplow, D. B., Dreyer, W. J., Simon, M. I. 1984. Isolation and characterization of a cDNA clone for the γ subunit of bovine retinal transducin. *Proc. Natl. Acad. Sci. USA* 81:6948–52

28. Ingebretsen, C. G. 1980. Interaction between alpha and beta adrenergic receptors and cholinergic receptors in isolated perfused rat heart: effects on cAMP-protein kinase and phosphorylase. *J. Cyclic Nucleotide Res.* 6:121–32

29. Itoh, H., Kozasa, T., Nagata, S., Nakamura, S., et al. 1986. Molecular cloning and sequence determination of cDNAs for alpha subunits of the guanine nucleotide-binding proteins G_s, G_i, and G_o from rat brain. *Proc. Natl. Acad. Sci. USA* 83:3776–80

30. Jones, D. T., Reed, R. R. 1987. Molecular cloning of five GTP-binding protein cDNA species from rat olfactory neuroepithelium. *J. Biol. Chem.* 262:14241–49

31. Kanaho, Y., Tsai, S.-C., Adamik, R., Hewlett, E. L., et al. 1984. Rhodopsin-enhanced GTPase activity of the inhibitory GTP-binding protein of adenylate cyclase. *J. Biol. Chem.* 259:7378–81

32. Kanaide, H., Matsumoto, T., Nakamura, M. 1986. Inhibition of calcium transients in cultured vascular smooth muscle cells by pertussis toxin. *Biochem. Biophys. Res. Commun.* 140:195–203

33. Katada, T., Bokoch, G. M., Northup, J. K., Ui, M., Gilman, A. G. 1984. The inhibitory guanine nucleotide-binding regulatory component of adenylate cyclase. Properties and function of the purified protein. *J. Biol. Chem.* 259:3568–77

34. Katada, T., Kusakabe, K., Oinuma, M., Ui, M. 1987. A novel mechanism for the inhibition of adenylate cyclase via inhibitory GTP-binding proteins. *J. Biol. Chem.* 262:11897–11900

35. Katada, T., Northup, J. K., Bokoch, G. M., Ui, M., Gilman, A. G. 1984. The inhibitory guanine nucleotide-binding regulatory component of adenylate cyclase. Subunit dissociation and guanine nucleotide-dependent hormonal inhibition. *J. Biol. Chem.* 259:3578–85

36. Katada, T., Oinuma, M., Ui, M. 1986. Mechanisms for inhibition of catalytic activity of adenylate cyclase by the guanine nucleotide-binding proteins serving as the substrate of islet-activating protein, pertussis toxin. *J. Biol. Chem.* 261:5215–21

37. Lerea, C. L., Somers, D. E., Hurley, J. B. 1986. Identification of specific transducin alpha subunits in retinal rod and cone photoreceptors. *Science* 234:77–80

38. Levitzki, A. 1985. Reconstitution of membrane receptor systems. *Biochem. Biophys. Acta* 892:127–53

39. Lochrie, M. A., Hurley, J. B., Simon, M. I. 1985. Sequence of the alpha subunit of photoreceptor G protein: homologies between transducin, ras, and elongation factors. *Science* 228:96–99

40. Logothetis, D. E., Kurachi, Y., Galper, J., Neer, E., Clapham, D. E. 1987. The βγ subunits of GTP-binding proteins activate the muscarinic K$^+$ channel in heart. *Nature* 325:321–26

41. Deleted in proof

42. Deleted in proof

43. Maguire, M. E., Erdos, J. J. 1980. Inhibition of magnesium uptake by beta-adrenergic agonists and prostaglandin E$_1$ is not mediated by cyclic AMP. *J. Biol. Chem.* 255:1030–35

44. Master, S. B., Martin, M. W., Harden, T. K., Brown, J. H. 1985. Pertussis toxin does not inhibit muscarinic-receptor-mediated phosphoinositide hydrolysis or calcium mobilization. *Biochem. J.* 227:933–37

45. May, D. C., Ross, E. M., Gilman, A. G., Smigel, M. D. 1985. Reconstitution of catecholamine-stimulated adenylyl cyclase activity using three purified proteins. *J. Biol. Chem.* 260:15829–33

46. Medynski, D. C., Sullivan, K., Smith, D., Van Dop, C., et al. 1985. Amino acid sequence of the alpha subunit of transducin deduced from the cDNA sequence. *Proc. Natl. Acad. Sci. USA* 82:4311–15

46a. Mumby, S. M., Kahn, R. A., Manning, D. R., Gilman, A. G. 1986. Antisera of designed specificity for subunits of guanine nucleotide-binding regulatory proteins. *Proc. Natl. Acad. Sci. USA* 83:265–69

46b. Mumby, S., Pang, I., Gilman, A. G., Sternweis, P. C. 1988. Chromatographic resolution and immunologic identification of the α$_{40}$ and α$_{41}$ subunits of guanine nucleotide-binding regulatory proteins from bovine brain. *J. Biol. Chem.* 263:2020–26

47. Neer, E. J., Lok, J. M., Wolf, L. G. 1984. Purification and properties of the inhibitory guanine nucleotide regulatory unit of brain adenylate cyclase. *J. Biol. Chem.* 259:14222–29

48. Nukada, T., Tanabe, T., Takahashi, H., Noda, M., et al. 1986. Primary structure of the alpha-subunit of bovine adenylate cyclase-inhibiting G-protein deduced from the cDNA sequence. *FEBS Lett.* 197:305–10

49. Pfaffinger, P., Martin, J., Hunter, D., Nathanson, N., Hille, B. 1985. GTP-binding proteins couple cardiac muscarinic receptors to a K channel. *Nature* 317:536–38

50. Robishaw, J. D., Russell, D. W., Harris, B. A., Smigel, M. D., Gilman, A. G. 1986. Deduced primary structure of the α subunit of the GTP-binding stimulatory protein of adenylate cyclase. *Proc. Natl. Acad. Sci. USA* 83:1251–55

51. Robishaw, J. D., Smigel, M. D., Gilman, A. G. 1986. Molecular basis for two forms of the G protein that stimulates adenylate cyclase. *J. Biol. Chem.* 261:9587–90

52. Rodbell, M., Krans, H. M., Pohl, S. L., Birnbaumer, L. 1971. The glucagon sensitive adenyl cyclase system in plasma membranes of rat liver. *J. Biol. Chem.* 246:1872–76

53. Roof, D. J., Applebury, M. L., Sternweis, P. C. 1985. Relationships within the family of GTP-binding proteins isolated from bovine central nervous system. *J. Biol. Chem.* 260:16242–49

54. Ross, E. M., Gilman, A. G. 1977. Resolution of some components of adenylate cyclase necessary for catalytic activity. *J. Biol. Chem.* 252:6966–69

55. Sasaguri, T., Hirata, M., Itoh, T., Koga, T., Kuriyama, H. 1986. Guanine nucleotide binding protein involved in muscarinic responses in the pig coronary artery is insensitive to islet-activating protein. *Biochem. J.* 239:567–74

56. Simpson, P. 1985. Stimulation of hypertrophy of cultured neonatal rat heart cells through an alpha$_1$-adrenergic receptor and induction of beating through an alpha$_1$- and beta$_1$-adrenergic receptor interaction. Evidence for independent regulation of growth and beating. *Circ. Res.* 56:884–94

57. Smigel, M. D. 1986. Purification of the catalyst of adenylate cyclase. *J. Biol. Chem.* 261:1976–82

58. Sternweis, P. C., Northup, J. K., Smigel, M. D., Gilman, A. G. 1981. The regulatory component of adenylate cyclase. *J. Biol. Chem.* 256:11517–26

59. Sternweis, P. C., Robishaw, J. D. 1984. Isolation of two proteins with high affinity for guanine nucleotides from membranes of bovine brain. *J. Biol. Chem.* 259:133806–13

60. Stryer, L. 1986. Cyclic GMP cascade of vision. *Annu. Rev. Neurosci.* 9:87–119

61. Sugimoto, K., Nukada, T., Tanabe, T., Takahashi, H., et al. 1985. Primary structure of the beta-subunit of bovine transducin deduced from the cDNA sequence. *FEBS Lett.* 191:235–40

62. Tada, M., Katz, A. M. 1982. Phosphorylation of the sarcoplasmic reticulum and sarcolemma. *Annu. Rev. Physiol.* 44:401–23

63. Tanabe, T., Nukada, T., Nishikawa, Y., Sugimoto, K., et al. 1985. Primary structure of the alpha-subunit of transducin and its relationship to ras proteins. *Nature* 315:242–45

64. Terman, B. I., Slivka, S. R., Hughes, R. J., Insel, P. A. 1987. α_1-adrenergic receptor-linked guanine nucleotide-binding protein in muscle and kidney epithelial cells. *Mol. Pharmacol.* 31:12–20

65. White, R. I., Hartzell, H. C. 1988. Effects of intracellular free magnesium on calcium current in isolated cardiac myocytes. *Science* 239:778–80

66. Yatani, A., Codina, J., Brown, A. M., Birnbaumer, L. 1987. Direct activation of mammalian atrial muscarinic potassium channels by GTP regulatory protein G_k. *Science* 235:207–11

67. Yatani, A., Codina, J., Imoto, Y., Reeves, J. P., et al. 1987. A G protein directly regulates mammalian cardiac calcium channels. *Science* 238:1288–92

68. Yatsunami, K., Khorana, H. G. 1985. GTPase of bovine rod outer segments: the amino acid sequence of the alpha subunit as derived from the cDNA sequence. *Proc. Natl. Acad. Sci. USA* 82:4316–20

Annu. Rev. Physiol. 1989. 51:245–62

REGULATION OF TISSUE PLASMINOGEN ACTIVATOR EXPRESSION

Robert D. Gerard and Robert S. Meidell

Departments of Internal Medicine and Biochemistry, University of Texas Southwestern Medical Center, Dallas, Texas

INTRODUCTION

Widespread interest in the biology of the fibrinolytic system has developed with the recognition of the role of intravascular thrombosis in the pathogenesis of human disease. The therapeutic application of thrombolytic agents is a result of the rapid evolution of our understanding of the biochemistry and physiological importance of this system. In reviewing the regulation of tissue plasminogen activator expression, we emphasize the role of this system in thrombolysis and include within regulated expression the control of enzymatic activity. No attempt is made to review comprehensively the literature concerning plasminogen, plasminogen activators, their respective inhibitors, or the array of biological processes in which these proteins are involved. Instead, the reader is referred to several prior reviews (13, 21, 26, 37, 78, 117) for detailed discussions of these topics.

Fibrin forms the structural skeleton of a thrombus, and enzymatic degradation of fibrin by the serine protease plasmin is the basis of thrombolysis. Plasmin is derived from the inactive circulating zymogen plasminogen by specific proteolytic cleavage of the single-chain precursor to a disulfide-linked, two-chain, catalytically active form in a process termed plasminogen activation. While several proteases are capable of activating plasminogen with low efficiency, specific plasminogen activators (PA), urinary PA (u-PA) and tissue PA (t-PA), have been identified.

Because of its high catalytic activity for the conversion of plasminogen to plasmin and the selectivity of this process for fibrin surfaces, t-PA appears to

245

be the principal physiological activator of the fibrinolytic system, and the local activity of t-PA at the site of thrombus formation the principal determinant of fibrinolytic activity. Since both the capacity to form a stable thrombus in the setting of a loss of vascular integrity and the capacity to prevent uncontrolled intravascular thrombosis are central to the maintenance of circulatory function, mechanisms for tightly controlled t-PA activity are critical.

REGULATION OF t-PA SYNTHESIS

Tissue Specificity

t-PA was initially identified as PA activity in extracts from a variety of animal and human tissues. Immunological cross-reactivity of the PA in tissue extracts and blood (101) identified the circulating PA as the tissue activator. Histochemical studies demonstrated t-PA in all tissues studied (reviewed in 26). In most cases, however, the specific cellular origins of t-PA have not been clearly determined.

Isolation of t-PA from medium conditioned by cultured melanoma cells (104, 131) led to the isolation of cDNA clones coding for human t-PA (28, 50, 63, 97, 111). t-PA synthesis by a variety of other transformed cell lines including HeLa (132), hepatoma (9, 10, 35), mammary carcinoma (16, 17), and fibrosarcoma (83) cells has also been reported.

Immunocytochemical studies have identified t-PA in endothelial cells of both veins and arteries (68). t-PA is secreted from primary cultures of bovine (74, 75) and human (76) endothelial cells, which suggests that vascular endothelium is the principal source of t-PA in blood. While endothelial cells cultured from human umbilical vein have been most frequently studied, comparative studies suggest that t-PA secretion from these cells is severalfold lower than from cells isolated from vena cava, large arteries, or microvasculature (124). In one study, t-PA could not be demonstrated in the endothelium of capillaries (68). Additionally, t-PA production by endothelial cells in culture has been observed to vary with growth state (75). While t-PA secretion in culture may not accurately reflect production in situ, these results suggest variability in t-PA synthesis by the endothelium of different vascular beds.

Effector Molecules That Alter t-PA Synthesis

A variety of effectors, both natural and synthetic, have been demonstrated to alter the rate of t-PA secretion from vascular endothelial cells or from one or more transformed cell types.

STEROID HORMONES   Both glucocorticoids and androgenic steroids alter t-PA production in selected cell lines. Incubation of the human mammary carcinoma cell line MDA-MB-231 in dexamethasone has been reported to decrease t-PA synthesis (17). This effect was apparently posttranscriptional as no associated change in the cellular content of mRNA coding for t-PA was detected. In contrast, HBL-100 mammary carcinoma cells have been reported to increase t-PA synthesis twofold in response to dexamethasone with an associated increase in t-PA mRNA (16). The accumulation of t-PA mRNA was not inhibited by cycloheximide, which suggests a direct effect on t-PA gene expression. Exposure of HTC rat hepatoma cells to glucocorticoids decreases secreted PA activity (9, 10, 35). This effect, however, results from an stimulated release of PA inhibitor (PAI) rather than diminished production of t-PA (9). Paradoxically, dexamethasone enhances 3', 5'-cyclic adenosine monophosphate (cAMP) mediated stimulation of t-PA synthesis by a glucocorticoid receptor-dependent mechanism. Production of t-PA by cultured bovine aortic endothelial cells is not affected by dexamethasone (75). Anabolic steroids, however, have been reported to increase synthesis and release of PA from blood vessel walls (89).

PROTEINS AND PEPTIDE EFFECTORS

Thrombin   Exposure of cultured human endothelial cells to thrombin stimulates secretion of t-PA (76). This effect is dose- and time-related, dependent upon the active site of thrombin, and follows an initial lag phase, consistent with de novo protein synthesis rather than secretion from a preformed pool. Thrombin-stimulated secretion is abolished by inhibitors of protein or RNA synthesis. Thrombin treatment does not increase net PA activity as increased secretion of PAI has also been demonstrated (49).

Cytokines and growth factors   Several cytokines and angiogenic growth factors alter expression of the fibrinolytic system, but in most cases alterations in the rates of PAI or u-PA production rather than t-PA synthesis have been observed. Cultured human endothelial cells exposed to interleukin-1 (IL-1) show reduced secretion of t-PA (12). Similarly, bacterial lipopolysaccharide (LPS), which stimulates endothelial release of IL-1 (119), has been demonstrated to inhibit t-PA release (12) although conflicting results have also been reported (49). Basic fibroblast growth factor (bFGF) stimulates secretion of t-PA, u-PA, and PAI-1 from bovine endothelial cells (109); this effect is antagonized by transforming growth factor beta (TGF β). Whether bFGF or TGF β affect PA synthesis by human endothelial cells has not been reported. Epidermal growth factor (EGF) stimulates t-PA secretion and t-PA mRNA accumulation in HeLa cells (73), but effects on endothelial t-PA secretion have yet to be identified.

Peptide hormones   The best characterized effect of peptide hormones on t-PA synthesis is that of gonadotropins on t-PA production by rat granulosa cells (93). Follicle stimulating hormone and leutenizing hormone, following a lag period of several hours, induce synthesis and secretion of t-PA more than 50-fold. This response correlated with cellular t-PA mRNA levels and required RNA synthesis, but accumulation of t-PA mRNA was not inhibited by cycloheximide, which suggests that gonadotropin induction of t-PA expression results from a direct effect on transcription of the t-PA gene.

BIOGENIC AMINES   Parenterally administered epinephrine increases blood PA activity (82). Correlations between serum catecholamine levels and PA activity, however, are poor (52). Histamine increases t-PA secretion from cultured endothelial cells in a dose dependent manner (49). In one study, only transient exposure of endothelial cells to histamine was required to increase t-PA secretion over 24 h, which suggests the induction of a stable intracellular mediator (113).

MISCELLANEOUS EFFECTORS   Retinoic acid, but not other retinoids, induces t-PA secretion from F9 teratocarcinoma cells (120). Parallel increases in the cellular content of t-PA suggest an increase in de novo t-PA synthesis. Biguanides have been reported to stimulate a sustained increase in t-PA release from vascular wall (88), and recently, sulfonylureas have been demonstrated to stimulate release of t-PA from vascular endothelial cells in culture (70).

Second Messengers in the Control of t-PA Synthesis

The effects of gonadotropins on granulosa cells are believed to be due to receptor-mediated stimulation of adenylate cyclase (93). In rat hepatoma cells, cAMP stimulation of t-PA synthesis has been demonstrated directly (9). When examined (93), cAMP-induced t-PA secretion has been dependent upon de novo RNA synthesis, which suggests that transcription of the t-PA gene is accelerated. There are no data directly implicating cAMP in the regulation of human t-PA gene expression in endothelial cells.

A variety of effectors, including thrombin, induce a receptor-mediated activation of inositol-specific phospholipase C with release of inositol phosphates and diacylglycerol (reviewed in 80, 81). Released inositol 1, 4, 5-trisphosphate functions as a second messenger to induce cytoplasmic release of calcium from intracellular pools, while diacylglycerol is a direct activator of protein kinase C. Consistent with a possible role for phosphoinositide hydrolysis in transducing effects on t-PA synthesis, the tumor promoting phorbol esters, structural analogs of diacylglycerol, and direct activators of protein kinase C, induce synthesis and secretion of t-PA from cultured HeLa (132), melanoma (94), and endothelial (51) cells. Concomitant accumulation of mRNA encoding t-PA has been demonstrated in melanoma and

HeLa cells. t-PA mRNA accumulation in response to phorbol esters is abolished by cycloheximide (132), implying a requirement for de novo synthesis of an intermediary protein. Cytosolic calcium accumulation in response to the calcium ionophore A23187 also increases PA secretion from HeLa cells (24), but the mechanism by which this occurs is uncertain.

Conflicting data exist on the role of prostenoids in modulating t-PA synthesis. Thrombin, which stimulates t-PA synthesis by endothelial cells, also induces release of prostacyclin (133), but inhibition of prostenoid synthesis with indomethacin does not affect t-PA synthesis (49). Moreover, IL-1, which inhibits t-PA release from endothelial cells (12), and histamine, which stimulates this activity (49), each stimulate prostacyclin synthesis (12, 133). Determination of whether prostenoids play a significant role in regulating t-PA expression must await more direct experimental study.

Molecular Mechanisms Regulating t-PA Synthesis

Little information is available concerning the molecular mechanisms that regulate t-PA synthesis. While both cAMP and diacylglyerol have been implicated as second messengers, and changes in t-PA mRNA levels have been demonstrated in response to gonadotropins, IL-1, and phorbol esters, the cellular machinery linking these observations remains unidentified. In theory, changes in cellular mRNA levels could result from effects on t-PA gene transcription, posttranscriptional processing, or message stability.

Direct evidence demonstrating transcriptional control of t-PA gene expression is limited. Inhibition of RNA synthesis with actinomycin D abolishes stimulated secretion of t-PA in response to thrombin (76) or phorbol esters (6); the limitations to interpreting such experiments have been highlighted previously (26). The effects of gonadotropins on t-PA synthesis appear to result from cAMP-mediated effects on gene transcription (93), but direct assessment of transcriptional activity is unavailable. More recently, nuclear run-off transcription studies have shown that dexamethasone increases transcription of the t-PA gene in HT1080 fibrosarcoma cells (83). The observations that cycloheximide both causes a transient increase in t-PA mRNA levels in HT1080 cells (83) and prolongs the increase in t-PA mRNA levels caused by gonadotropins (93) suggest that an unstable protein factor affecting message stability may also contribute to regulation of t-PA synthesis.

The molecular mechanisms regulating transcription of the human t-PA gene could, in principal, operate on promoter mediated transcriptional initiation or attenuation of t-PA gene transcription. Genomic clones of the human t-PA gene have been isolated by several groups (33, 34, 91) and sequenced (34). The transcriptional initiation site has been identified (33) and is located 29 nucleotide pairs downstream from a typical TATA box. Nucleotide sequence comparison of the 5'-flanking region reveals no identifiable homology with other eukaryotic promoters (33) or with consensus binding sequences for known eukaryotic transcription factors. A recombinant construct containing a 475-nucleotide fragment of the human t-PA gene upstream of the cap site was expressed when injected into *Xenopus laevis* oocytes (33). Similarly, fusion genes containing 424 nucleotide pairs of the 5'-flanking region are sufficient for expression after introduction into HeLa, HepG2, and endothelial cells (84). The limits of the human t-PA gene promoter and those sequences required for regulated expression have not been identified.

REGULATION OF t-PA ACTIVITY

Plasmin can degrade both fibrin and fibrinogen. Generalized activation of plasminogen produces a systemic fibrinolytic state, rapid depletion of circulating fibrinogen, and a resulting hemorrhagic tendency (reviewed in 78). The specificity of the endogenous fibrinolytic system results from tight physiological control of plasminogen activation, and several different mechanisms regulate the activity of t-PA.

Conversion of Single- to Two-Chain t-PA

Most serine proteases are synthesized and secreted as inactive zymogens that are activated by specific proteolytic cleavage. Similarly, t-PA is secreted as a single polypeptide chain and is cleaved at the Arg_{275}-Ile_{276} peptide bond to yield a disulfide-linked two-chain form (99). There is universal agreement that the two-chain form of t-PA is catalytically active, but considerable disagreement regarding the catalytic activity of the single-chain precursor. Single-chain t-PA has been variably reported to show no PA activity (1), diminished PA activity (103), catalytic activity indistinguishable from the two-chain form (106), or diminished activity except in the presence of physiological concentrations of fibrinogen (121). Interpretation is complicated by the various assay methods and the distinct possibility that contaminating proteases catalyze one-chain to two-chain cleavage. Recently, the activity of a mutant t-PA molecule in which the sequence of the cleavage site was altered by site-directed mutagenesis has demonstrated that the single-chain form possesses PA activity, but a three to five fold lower V_{max} for plasminogen activation (14, 97a).

Small quantities of plasmin generated by single-chain t-PA at the surface of a thrombus catalyze (*a*) conversion of glu-plasminogen to lys-plasminogen, rendering the precursor more susceptible to activation (56, 102) and (*b*) conversion of single-chain to two-chain t-PA, increasing PA activity and creating an amplification loop.

Fibrin Binding and Stimulation

In purified systems, t-PA is a poor activator of plasminogen. In the presence of fibrin, however, the catalytic activity of t-PA is dramatically increased (56,

102). Considerable data now exist on the biochemical basis of this finding. In the absence of fibrin, the K_m for activation of glu-plasminogen and lys-plasminogen by t-PA are 65 μM and 19 μM, respectively (56). Binding of t-PA to partially degraded fibrin lowers the K_m for plasminogen activation to 0.16 μM and 0.02 μM for the two plasminogens, respectively. Because plasminogen circulates at a concentration of 2 μM, plasminogen activation on the surface of a clot proceeds several orders of magnitude more efficiently than in free circulation, which accounts for substantial clot-selectivity.

Conflicting data exist on the structural basis for the fibrin-binding and activation properties of t-PA. Several groups have approached the issue of fibrin binding and activation through the expression of recombinant t-PA molecules from which one or more structural domains have been deleted. Having constructed t-PA muteins using native restriction sites in the t-PA cDNA, van Zonneveld et al (127) reported that t-PA molecules lacking the kringle II domain show diminished fibrin-stimulated PA activity, while loss of both the finger and kringle II domains abolishes fibrin stimulation. The muteins were also examined for binding to lysine-Sepharose (128). Kringle II, but not the finger domain, showed evidence of a high-affinity lysine binding site. It appears that the finger domain mediates the initial binding to intact fibrin, but that subsequent digestion of fibrin exposes carboxyterminal lysine residues that bind to kringle II (57, 128). This model is supported by observations that mutant t-PAs lacking the finger domain show diminished binding to fibrin clots but normal stimulation by fibrinogen fragments (72, 129) and by chemical modification studies demonstrating a critical role for fibrin lysine residues in stimulation of PA activity (100). Kalyan et al (62) presented conflicting data on the expression of a mutant t-PA molecule lacking the finger and EGF domains with both diminished fibrin binding and fibrin-stimulated PA activity. Recent data concerning deletion mutants constructed to conform precisely to intron-exon boundaries by oligonucleotide-directed mutagenesis have demonstrated that either kringle or t-PA is capable of mediating fibrin stimulation, and that a mutant lacking only the finger domain retains fibrin-stimulated PA activity (39). Studies on hybrid plasminogen activators linking the heavy-chain of t-PA to the catalytic domain of u-PA have demonstrated that an interaction between the heavy and light chains of t-PA is required to confer fibrin stimulation, while the heavy chain alone conveys fibrin affinity (40, 86).

Inhibition of t-PA Activity

The proteolytic activity of t-PA, like other serine proteases, is subject to regulation by plasma serine protease inhibitors (serpins). The current model for the inhibition of t-PA postulates that the inhibitor serves as a suicide substrate, analogous to α_1-antitrypsin inhibition of elastase (123). A loop of amino acid residues in the serpin molecule that resemble the normal substrate (the reactive center) fits into the active site. With proteolytic cleavage of the serpin, a covalent bond forms between the activator and inhibitor molecules and stably blocks the active site. t-PA is subject to inactivation both by serpins whose primary targets are other serine proteases and by specific PAI molecules. C1-esterase inhibitor, α_1-antitrypsin, α_2-antiplasmin, α_2-macroglobin, and protease nexin all can form stable 1:1 complexes with t-PA, with first-order rate constants between 10^0–10^5 M^{-1} sec^{-1} (44, 66, 107, 112, 122). PAI-2, a specific PA inhibitor found in plasma during pregnancy is also a relatively slow inhibitor of t-PA (59). Inhibition of t-PA by these serpins, therefore, is of secondary importance to inhibition by PAI-1, which exhibits rapid (10^8 M^{-1} sec $^{-1}$), specific inhibition of plasminogen activators (reviewed in 117).

PAI-1 was originally identified as the inhibitory factor present in serum (19, 122, 134). Subsequent characterization revealed a glycoprotein ($M_r =$ 52,000) capable of rapidly forming SDS-stable 1:1 complexes with t-PA (126). Molecular cloning and characterization of the cDNA encoding PAI-1 has been accomplished (41, 92, 95). The deduced amino acid sequence reveals a mature protein of 379 residues preceded by a 23–amino acid signal peptide. High sequence homology with α_1-antitrypsin, antithrombin III, and ovalbumin identify PAI-1 as a member of the serpin superfamily. The plasminogen activator cleavage site has been identified as the Arg$_{346}$-Met$_{347}$ peptide bond (3).

TISSUE SPECIFICITY OF PAI-1 EXPRESSION   PAI-1 is synthesized by platelets (15, 31, 116), vascular endothelial cells (30, 79, 98), and by both cultured hepatocytes (118) and hepatoma cell lines (25, 118). Reports that severe hepatic dysfunction (54) and surgical hepatectomy (42) are associated with a marked fall in serum PAI-1 levels suggest that hepatic synthesis may contribute significantly to the circulating PAI-1 pool. Other cell types including vascular smooth muscle (65) and HT1080 fibrosarcoma cells (2, 87) have also been demonstrated to synthesize and secrete PAI-1.

REGULATION OF PAI-1 SYNTHESIS AND RELEASE   In platelets, PAI-1 is stored in alpha granules and released essentially quantitatively during aggregation (69). Thus, the local concentration of PAI-1 at the site of thrombus formation may be substantially higher than in the general circulation, effectively suppressing premature clot lysis.

In vascular endothelial cells and several other cell types, secretion of PAI-1 is responsive to a variety of physiological stimuli and appears to reflect synthesis of the protein rather than release from cytoplasmic stores. Tumor necrosis factor (TNF) (38), IL-1 (12, 29), LPS (23, 29, 49), and thrombin (36, 49) have all been shown to increase PAI-1 secretion from cultured endothelial cells. In vivo induction of PAI-1 by LPS and IL-1 also occurs (22, 29). Stimulated secretion of PAI-1 by dexamethasone has been demonstrated in hepatoma (20, 25, 35) and fibrosarcoma (2) cells. Most studies have examined PAI-1 expression at the protein level, but more recently increases in PAI-1 expression have been associated with accumulation of mRNA encoding PAI-1. Both TNF and LPS increase PAI-1 mRNA severalfold in endothelial cells (38) because of both an increase in the rate of transcription of the PAI-1 gene and increased stability of PAI-1 mRNA. Increased PAI-1 gene transcription has also been observed in HT1080 cells stimulated with dexamethasone (83). PAI-1 mRNA stability may be regulated in a manner analogous to that of mRNAs for several cytokines by a *cis*-acting "message instability" sequence in the 3'-untranslated region, and a sequence motif similar to that mediating message stability in granulocyte/macrophage colony stimulating factor (114) is found in the 3.2-kilobase mRNA for PAI-1. However, the molecular mechanisms of signal transduction regulating PAI-1 mRNA levels remain unknown.

REGULATION OF PAI-1 ACTIVITY   PAI-1 exists in multiple forms that differ in their capacity to inhibit t-PA: (*a*) free, active PAI-1, (*b*) PAI-1 complexed to t-PA, (*c*) latent PAI-1, and (*d*) PAI-1 bound to extracellular matrix or cell surfaces.

Latent vs active PAI-1   PAI-1 is present in blood in both active and inactive (latent) forms (77). Latent PAI-1, accounting for more than 90% of circulating PAI-1, can be activated in vitro by protein denaturants (53) and negatively charged phospholipid vesicles (71). Reactivation of latent PAI-1 through binding to phospholipid membranes may be an important mechanism for regulating PAI-1 activity in vivo.

Binding to extracellular matrix   PAI-1 is specifically bound to extracellular matrix (ECM) in an active form and can be released as a PA:PAI-1 complex by exposure to plasminogen activator (65, 85). Matrix-bound PAI-1 may thus serve a dual purpose: (*a*) protecting extracellular matrix from plasminogen activator-induced degradation and (*b*) serving as an extracellular pool of active PAI-1.

The concept that ECM may serve as reservoir of PAI-1 is important to the therapeutic use of thrombolytic agents. The high doses of t-PA required for effective thrombolytic therapy may reflect a requirement to saturate PAI-1 stores before thrombolysis is initiated. Such doses of t-PA are two orders of magnitude higher than the pool of free, active PAI-1 present in blood and suggest rapid neutralization of t-PA by the reservoir of matrix-bound PAI-1.

Proteolytic inactivation   PAI-1 can also be inactivated by proteolytic degradation. In vitro, thrombin (65, 125) catalyzes cleavage of PAI-1, rendering the inhibitor inactive, but the physiological significance of this observation is uncertain. Activated protein C stimulates fibrinolysis (125), is generated at the endothelial cell surface by thrombin/thrombomodulin complexes (32), and has been shown to form SDS-stable 1:1 complexes with PAI-1 (108). If the presumption (27) that protein C cleaves the Arg_{336}-Met_{337} bond of coagulation factor VIII is correct, then cleavage of PAI-1 by protein C may occur at the reactive center Arg-Met peptide bond, with protein C functioning to competively antagonize PAI-1 inactivation of t-PA.

REGULATION OF t-PA RELEASE AND CLEARANCE

In response to more effectors, increased secretion of t-PA follows cellular accumulation of t-PA mRNA and a gradual increase in cellular t-PA content, consistent with de novo synthesis rather than release from presynthesized stores. Physiological stimuli such as venous occlusion and exercise (reviewed in 18), or the systemic administration of catecholamines (82) or vasopressin (89, 130), increase blood PA activity within minutes and cannot reflect new synthesis. In theory, rapid increases in blood PA activity could result from stimulated secretion of t-PA from intracellular stores, displacement of t-PA from cell surface or extracellular matrix binding sites, or inactivation of PAI-1 with resulting release or accumulation of free t-PA. Direct studies of the transport of t-PA along the secretory pathway have not been reported, nor have significant cellular stores been demonstrated. Binding of t-PA to a variety of cell surface (11, 55) and extracellular (110, 115) sites has been reported, but evidence of specific, inducible displacement from these sites is lacking. Inactivation of PAI-1 has been demonstrated, but the role of this process in mediating physiological increases in PA activity requires further investigation.

t-PA is cleared rapidly from the circulation, with an in vivo half-life of 2–6 min (67, 105). Organ distribution studies show rapid accumulation in the liver (67), and interruption of hepatic blood flow (105) or surgical hepatectomy (42) produce marked increases in half-life and circulating concentrations, and identify the liver as the principal site of clearance. Isolated rat hepatocytes possess a specific uptake mechanism for t-PA (half-maximal concentration 10 μM) that is distinct from the asialoglycoprotein and mannose/N-acetylglucosamine receptors (8). Specific cell surface binding of t-PA by cultured fibroblasts (55) and endothelial cells (11, 45) has also been reported, but the physiological significance of these observations needs to be addressed.

Limited information is available concerning the structural basis for hepatic clearance of t-PA. The single-chain and two-chain forms of the enzyme appear to have similar biological half-lives (105). Irreversible blockade of the active site of t-PA does not alter hepatic clearance in animals (67). A specific cell surface receptor for u-PA in U-937 monocytic cells has been identified (4), and peptide competition experiments suggest that a segment of the growth factor domain mediates receptor binding. Recently, the biological half-life of a mutant t-PA molecule lacking the finger and EGF domains has been determined to be 50 min, which suggests that clearance of t-PA from the circulation may be similarly mediated by EGF domain-receptor binding (62).

EXPRESSION OF t-PA IN CLINICAL DISORDERS

Alterations in blood PA activity have been reported in association with several clinical disorders. In patients lacking an apparent cause for venous thrombosis, roughly one third have diminished PA activity. In the majority of these patients, elevated levels of PAI-1 have been found, but diminished t-PA release after venous occlusion has been consistently observed in a smaller fraction (61, 90). PAI-1 appears to behave as an acute phase reactant, with elevated levels associated with a variety of illnesses (60), or following surgery or trauma (64). Venous thrombosis is common during pregnancy, and progressive increases in PA inhibitor activity throughout gestation have been described (43, 59). A family with decreased t-PA release and recurrent venous thrombosis has also been described (58).

Diminished PA activity and increased PAI-1 levels have been observed in a fraction of patients with acute myocardial infarction (46, 48, 96) and in young survivors three years after myocardial infarction, which suggests that disordered regulation of the fibrinolytic system may convey independent risk. Elevated PAI-1 levels have also been correlated with the risk of recurrent myocardial infarction (47) and with the risk of graft occlusion following coronary bypass surgery (5).

In contrast, increased blood PA activity and t-PA antigen levels with associated hemorrhagic tendencies have been reported both on a familial basis (7) and in patients with hepatic cirrhosis (54).

FUTURE DIRECTIONS

Additional studies of the relationship between structure and function of the t-PA and PAI-1 proteins should clarify the molecular mechanisms controlling the enzymatic activity of t-PA. These studies should include (*a*) specific definition of the structural basis in t-PA for fibrin binding and stimulation; (*b*) delineation of the sequences in t-PA involved in binding to PAI-1; (*c*) determination of the tertiary structures of both molecules to elucidate their molecular interaction, determine the molecular basis for the phenomenon of latency, and promote understanding of protease/serpin interactions; and (d) evaluation of the physiological significance of matrix associated PAI-1. Definition of the structural basis for the enzymatic properties of t-PA may prompt the development of strategies to therapeutically manipulate fibrinolytic activity.

If t-PA and PAI-1 protein levels can be causally related to the formation and lysis of blood clots, then elucidation of the physiological and molecular controls over the synthesis and secretion of the proteins at the systemic and local levels may ultimately permit pharmacological intervention to prevent thrombotic disorders. Alternatively, manipulation of the t-PA:PAI-1 molecular interaction may accomplish the same goal.

Considerable progress in our understanding of the biology of the thrombolytic system suggests these goals may be achievable in the near future.

ACKNOWLEDGMENT

R. D. G. is the recipient of an Established Investigatorship from the American Heart Association and R. S. M. is the recipient of an American Heart Association Clinician-Scientist Award. This work was supported in part by a Bugher Foundation center grant to the University of Texas Southwestern Medical Center, and by grants from the American Heart Association, Texas Affiliate.

Literature Cited

1. Andreasen, P. A., Nielsen, L. S., Grondahl-Hansen, J., Skriver, L., Zeuthen, J., et al. 1984. Inactive proenzyme to tissue-type plasminogen activator from human melanoma cells, identified after affinity purification with a monoclonal antibody. *EMBO J.* 3:51–56

2. Andreasen, P. A., Pyke, C., Riccio, A., Kristensen, P., Nielsen, L. S., et al. 1987. Plasminogen activator inhibitor type 1 biosynthesis and mRNA level are increased by dexamethasone in human fibrosarcoma cells. *Mol. Cell. Biol.* 7: 3021–25

3. Andreasen, P. A., Riccio, A., Welinder, K. G., Douglas, R., Sartorio, R., et al. 1986. Plasminogen activator inhibitor type-1: reactive center and amino-terminal heterogeneity determined by protein and cDNA sequencing. *FEBS Lett.* 209:213–18

4. Apella, E., Robinson, E. A., Ullrich, S. J., Stoppelli, M. P., Corti, A., et al. 1987. The receptor-binding sequence of urokinase. *J. Biol. Chem.* 262:4437–40

5. Arnesen, H., Semb, G., Hol, R., Karlsen, H. 1983. Fibrinolytic capacity after venous stasis in patients undergoing aorto-coronary by-pass surgery: relation to shunt occlusion. *Scand. J. Haematol.* 30(Supp 39):43–46

6. Ashino-Fuse, H., Opdenakker, G., Fuse, A., Billian, A. 1984. Mechanism of the stimulatory effect of phorbol 12-myristate 13-acetate on cellular production of plasminogen activator. *Proc. Soc. Exp. Biol. Med.* 176:109–18

7. Aznar, J., Estelles, A., Vila, V., Reganon, E., Espana, F., et al. 1984. Inherited fibrinolytic disorder due to an enhanced plasminogen activator level. *Thromb. Haemostas.* 52:196–200

8. Bakhit, L., Lewis, D., Billings, R., Malfroy, B. 1987. Cellular catabolism of recombinant tissue-type plasminogen activator: identification and characterization of a novel high affinity uptake system on rat hepatocytes. *J. Biol. Chem.* 262:8716–20

9. Barouski-Miller, P. A., Gelehrter, T. D. 1982. Paradoxical effects of glucocorticoids on regulation of plasminogen acti-

vator activity of rat hepatoma cells. *Proc. Natl. Acad. Sci. USA* 79:2319–22

10. Barouski-Miller, P. A., Gelehrter, T. D. 1984. Paradoxical effects of glucocorticoids on regulation of plasminogen activator activity. *J. Steroid Biochem.* 20: 533–37

11. Beebe, D. J. 1987. Binding of tissue plasminogen activator to human umbilical vein endothelial cells. *Thromb. Res.* 46:241–54

12. Bevilacqua, M. P., Schleef, R. R., Gimbrone, M. A., Loskutoff, D. J. 1986. Regulation of the fibrinolytic system of cultured human vascular endothelium by interleukin-1. *J. Clin. Invest.* 78:587–91

13. Blasi, F., Riccio, A., Sebastio, G. 1986. Human plasminogen activators. Genes and proteins structure. In *Human Genes and Diseases*, ed. F. Blasi, pp. 377–414. London: Wiley

14. Boose, J. A., Kuismanen, E., Gerard, R. D., Sambrook, J. F., Gething, M.-J. 1988. The single-chain form of tissue-type plasminogen activator has catalytic activity: studies with a mutant enzyme that lacks the cleavage site. *Biochemistry* In press

15. Booth, N. A., Anderson, J. A., Bennett, B. 1985. Platelet release protein which inhibits plasminogen activators. *J. Clin. Pathol.* 38:825–30

16. Busso, N., Belin, D., Failly-Crepin, C., Vassalli, J.-D. 1986. Plasminogen activators and their inhibitors in a human mammary cell line (HBL-100): modulation by glucocorticoids. *J. Biol. Chem.* 261:9309–15

17. Busso, N., Belin, D., Failly-Crepin, C., Vassalli, J.-D. 1987. Glucocorticoid modulation of plasminogen activators and one of their inhibitors in the human mammary carcinoma cell line MDA-MB-231. *Cancer Res.* 47:364–70

18. Cash, J. D. 1978. Control mechanisms of activator release. In *Progress in Chemical Fibrinolysis and Thrombolysis*, ed. J. F. Davidson, M. M. Samama, P. C. Desnoyers, 3:65–75. New York: Raven

19. Chmielewska, J., Ranby, M., Wiman, B. 1983. Evidence for a rapid inhibitor to tissue plasminogen activator in plasma. *Thromb. Res.* 31:427–36

20. Coleman, P. L., Barouski, P. A., Gelehrter, T. D. 1982. Dexamethasone-induced inhibitor of fibrinolytic activity in hepatoma cells: a cellular product which specifically inhibits plasminogen activation. *J. Biol. Chem.* 257:4260–64

21. Collen, D. 1980. On the regulation and control of fibrinolysis. *Thromb. Haemostas.* 43:77–89

22. Colucci, M., Paramo, J. A., Collen, D. 1985. Generation in plasma of a fast-acting inhibitor of plasminogen activator in response to endotoxin stimulation. *J. Clin. Invest.* 75:818–24

23. Crutchley, D. J., Conanan, L. B. 1986. Endotoxin induction of a inhibitor of plasminogen activator in bovine pulmonary artery endothelial cells. *J. Biol. Chem.* 261:154–59

24. Crutchley, D. J., Maynard, J. R. 1983. Induction of plasminogen activator by 12-O-tetradecanoylphorbol 13-acetate and calcium ionophore. *Biochem. Biophys. Acta* 762:76–85

25. Cwickel, B. J., Barouski-Miller, P. A., Coleman, P. L., Gelehrter, T. D. 1984. Dexamethasone induction of an inhibitor of plasminogen activator in HTC hepatoma cells. *J. Biol. Chem.* 259:6847–51

26. Dano, K., Andreasen, P. A., Grondahl-Hansen, J., Kristensen, P., Nielsen, L. S., et al. 1985. Plasminogen activators, tissue degradation and cancer. *Adv. Cancer Res.* 44:139–266

27. Eaton, D., Rodriguez, H., Vehar, G. A. 1986. Proteolytic processing of human factor VIII: correlation of specific cleavages of thrombin, factor Xa, and activated protein C with activation and inactivation of factor VIII coagulant activity. *Biochemistry* 25:505–12

28. Edlund, T., Ny, T., Ranby, M., Heden, L. O., Palm, G., et al. 1983. Isolation of cDNA sequences coding for a part of human tissue plasminogen activator. *Proc. Natl. Acad. Sci. USA* 80:349–52

29. Emeis, J. J., Kooistra, T. 1986 Interleukin 1 and lipopolysaccharide induce an inhibitor of tissue-type plasminogen activator in vivo and in cultured endothelial cells. *J. Exp. Med.* 163:1260–66

30. Emeis, J. J., van Hinsbergh, V. W. M., Verheijen, J. H., Wijngaards, J. 1983. Inhibition of tissue-type plasminogen activator by conditioned medium from cultured human and porcine vascular endothelial cells. *Biochem. Biophys. Res. Commun.* 110:392–98

31. Erickson, L. A., Ginsberg, M. H., Loskutoff, D. J. 1984. Detection and partial characterization of an inhibitor of plasminogen activator in human platelets. *J. Clin. Invest.* 74:1465–72

32. Esmon, C. T., Esmon, N. L., Harris, K. W. 1982. Complex formation between thrombin and thrombomodulin inhibits both thrombin-catalyzed fibrin formation and factor V activation. *J. Biol. Chem.* 257:7944–47

33. Fisher, R., Waller, E. K., Grossi, G., Thompson, D., Tizard, R., et al. 1985. Isolation and characterization of the human tissue-type plasminogen activator structural gene including its 5'-flanking region. *J. Biol. Chem.* 260:11223–30
34. Friezner-Degen, S., Rajput, B., Reich, E. 1986. The human tissue plasminogen activator gene. *J. Biol. Chem.* 261: 6972–85
35. Gelehrter, T. D., Barouski-Miller, P. A., Coleman, P. L., Cwickel, B. J. 1983. Hormonal regulation of plasminogen activator in rat hepatoma cells. *Mol. Cell. Biochem.* 53/54:11–21
36. Gelehrter, T. D., Sznycer-Laszuk, R. 1986. Thrombin induction of plasminogen activator-inhibitor in cultured human endothelial cells. *J. Clin. Invest.* 77:165–69
37. Gerard, R. D., Chien, K. R., Meidell, R. S. 1986. Molecular biology of tissue plasminogen activator and endogenous inhibitors. *Mol. Biol. Med.* 3:449–57
38. Gerard, R. D., Riedo, F. X., Chien, K., Munford, R. 1988. Expression of plasminogen activator inhibitor-1 in cultured human vascular endothelial cells. *J. Cell. Biochem. Suppl.* 12B:291
39. Gething, M.-J., Adler, B., Boose, J.-A., Gerard, R. D., Madison, E. L., et al. 1988. Variants of human tissue-type plasminogen activator that lack specific structural domains of the heavy chain. *EMBO J.* 7:2731–40
40. Gheysen, D., Linjen, R., Pierard, L., de Foresta, F., Denarsin, E., et al. 1987. Characterization of a recombinant fusion protein of the finger domain of tissue-type plasminogen activator with a truncated single chain urokinase-type plasminogen activator. *J. Biol. Chem.* 262:11779–84
41. Ginsberg, D., Zeheb, R., Yang, A. Y., Rafferty, A. M., Andreasen, P. A., et al. 1986. cDNA cloning of human plasminogen activator inhibitor from endothelial cells. *J. Clin. Invest.* 78:1673–80
42. Glas-Greenwalt, P., Gruppo, R. A., Ryckman, F. C., Fischer, C. G. 1987. Accelerated fibrinolysis in liver transplantation. *Blood* 70(Suppl.):402a
43. Gore, M. J., Eldon, S., Trofatter, K. F., Soong, S.-J., Pizzo, S. V. 1987. Pregnancy-induced changes in the fibrinolytic balance: evidence for defective release of tissue plasminogen activator and increased levels of the fast acting tissue plasminogen activator inhibitor. *Am. J. Obstet. Gynecol.* 156:674–80
44. Haggroth, L., Mattsson, Ch., Friberg, J. 1984. Inhibition of human tissue plas-
minogen activator in plasma from different species. *Thromb. Res.* 33:583–94
45. Hajjar, K. A., Hamel, N. M., Harpel, P. C., Nachman, R. L. 1987. Binding of tissue plasminogen activator to cultured human endothelial cells. *J. Clin. Invest.* 80:1712–19
46. Hamsten, A., Blomback, M., Wiman, B., Svensson, J., Szamosi, A., et al. 1986. Haemostatic function in myocardial infarction. *Br. Heart J.* 55:58–66
47. Hamsten, A., de Faire, U., Walldins, G., Dahlen, G., Szamosi, A., et al. 1986. Plasminogen activator inhibitor in plasma: risk factor for recurrent myocardial infarction. *Lancet* 2(8549):3–9
48. Hamsten, A., Wiman, B., de Faire, U., Blomback, M. 1985. Increased plasma levels of a rapid inhibitor of tissue plasminogen activator in young survivors of myocardial infarction. *N. Engl. J. Med.* 313:1557–63
49. Hanss, M., Collen, D. 1987. Secretion of tissue-type plasminogen activator and plasminogen activator inhibitor by cultured human endothelial cells: modulation by thrombin, endotoxin, and histamine. *J. Lab. Clin. Med.* 109:97–108
50. Harris, T. J. R., Patel, T., Marston, F. A. O., Little, S., Emstage, S., et al. 1986. Cloning of a cDNA coding for human tissue-type plasminogen activator and its expression in *Escherichia coli*. *Mol. Biol. Med.* 3:279–92
51. Hatzakis, H., Sanduja, S. K., Wu, K. K. 1987. Stimulation of endothelial cell production of tissue plasminogen activator and eicosanoids by phorbol ester. *Blood* 70(Suppl. 1):404a
52. Hawkey, C. M., Britton, B. J., Wood, W. G., Peele, M., Irving, M. H. 1975. Changes in blood catecholamine levels and blood coagulation and fibrinolytic-activity in response to graded exercise in man. *Br. J. Haematol.* 29:377–84
53. Hekman, C. M., Loskutoff, D. J. 1985. Endothelial cells produce a latent inhibitor of plasminogen activators that can be activated by denaturants. *J. Biol. Chem.* 260:11581–87
54. Hersch, S. L., Kunelis, T., Francis, R. B. 1987. The pathogenesis of accelerated fibrinolysis in liver cirrhosis: a critical role for tissue plasminogen activator inhibitor. *Blood* 69:1315–19
55. Hoal, E. G., Wilson, L., Dowdle, E. B. 1983. The regulation of tissue plasminogen activator activity by human fibroblasts. *Cell* 34:273–79
56. Hoylaerts, M., Rijken, D. C., Lijnen, H. R., Collen, D. 1982. Kinetics of activation of plasminogen by human tis-

sue-type plasminogen activator: role of fibrin. *J. Biol. Chem.* 257:2912–19

57. Ichinose, A., Takio, K., Fujikawa, K. 1986. Localization of the binding site of tissue-type plasminogen activator to fibrin. *J. Clin. Invest.* 78:163–69

58. Johansson, L., Hedner, U., Nilsson, I. M. 1978. A family with thromboembolic disease associated with deficient fibrinolytic activity in vessel wall. *Acta Med. Scand.* 203:477–80

59. Jorgensen, M., Philips, M., Thorsen, S., Selmer, J., Zeuthen, J. 1987. Plasminogen activator inhibitor-1 is the primary inhibitor of tissue-type plasminogen activator in pregnancy plasma. *Thromb. Haemostas.* 58:872–78

60. Juhan-Vague, I., Moerman, B., de Cock, F., Aillaud, M. F., Collen, D. 1984. Plasma levels of a specific inhibitor of tissue-type plasminogen activator (and urokinase) in normal and pathological conditions. *Thromb. Res.* 33:523–30

61. Juhan-Vague, I., Valadier, J., Alessi, M. C., Aillaud, M. F., Ansaldi, J., et al. 1987. Deficient t-PA release and elevated PA inhibitor levels in patients with spontaneous or recurrent deep venous thrombosis. *Thromb. Haemostas.* 57: 69–72

62. Kalyan, N. K., Lee, S. G., Wilhelm, J., Fu, K. P., Hum, W.-T., et al. 1988. Structure-function analysis with tissue-type plasminogen activator: effects of deletion of NH_2-terminal domains on its biochemical and biological properties. *J. Biol. Chem.* 263:3971–78

63. Kaufman, R., Wasley, L. D., Spiliotes, A. J., Gossels, S. D., Lat, S. A., et al. 1985. Co-amplification and co-expression of human tissue-type plasminogen activator and murine dihydrofolate reductase in Chinese hamster ovary cells. *Mol. Biol. Med.* 5:1750–59

64. Kluft, C., Verheijen, J. H., Jie, A. F. H., Rijken, D. C., Preston, F. E., et al. 1985. The postoperative fibrinolytic shutdown: a rapidly reverting acute phase pattern for the fast-acting inhibitor of tissue-type plasminogen activator after trauma. *Scand. J. Clin. Lab. Invest.* 45:605–10

65. Knudsen, B. S., Harpel, P. C., Nachman, R. L. 1987. Plasminogen activator inhibitor is associated with the extracellular matrix of cultured bovine smooth muscle cells. *J. Clin. Invest.* 80:1082–89

66. Korninger, C., Collen, D. 1981. Neutralization of human extrinsic (tissue-type) plasminogen activator in human plasma: no evidence for a specific

inhibitor. *Thromb. Haemostas.* 46:662–65

67. Korninger, C., Stassen, J. M., Collen, D. 1981. Turnover of human extrinsic (tissue-type) plasminogen activator in rabbits. *Thromb. Haemostas.* 46:658–61

68. Kristensen, P., Larsson, L. I., Nielsen, L. S., Grondahl-Hansen, J., Andreasen, P. A., et al. 1984. Human endothelial cells contain one type of plasminogen activator. *FEBS Lett.* 168:33–37

69. Kruithof, E. K. O., Tran-Thang, C., Bachmann, F. 1986. Studies on the release of plasminogen activator inhibitor by human platelets. *Thromb. Haemostas.* 55:201–5

70. Kuo, B.-S., Korner, G., Bjornsson, T. D. 1988. Effects of sulfonylureas on the synthesis and secretion of plasminogen activator from bovine aortic endothelial cells. *J. Clin. Invest.* 81:730–37

71. Lambers, J. W. J., Cammenga, M., Konig, B. W., Mertens, K., Pannekoek, K., et al. 1987. Activation of human endothelial cell-type plasminogen activator inhibitor (PAI-1) by negatively charged phospholipids. *J. Biol. Chem.* 262:17492–96

72. Larsen, G. R., Henson, K., Blue, Y. 1988. Variants of human tissue-type plasminogen activator: fibrin binding, fibrinolytic, and fibrinogenolytic characterization of genetic variants lacking the fibronectin finger-like and/or the epidermal growth factor domains. *J. Biol. Chem.* 263:1023–29

73. Lee, L. S., Weinstein, I. B. 1978. Epidermal growth factor, like phorbol esters, induces plasminogen activator in HeLa cells. *Nature* 274:696–97

74. Levin, E. G., Loskutoff, D. J. 1982. Cultured bovine endothelial cells produce both urokinase and tissue-type plasminogen activators. *J. Cell Biol.* 94:631–36

75. Levin, E. G., Loskutoff, D. J. 1982. Regulation of plasminogen activator production by cultured endothelial cells. *Ann. NY Acad. Sci.* 401:184–94

76. Levin, E. G., Marzec, U., Anderson, J., Harker, L. A. 1984. Thrombin stimulates tissue plasminogen activator release from cultured human endothelial cells. *J. Clin. Invest.* 74:1988–95

77. Levin, E. G., Santell, L. 1987. Conversion of active to latent plasminogen activator inhibitor from human endothelial cells. *Blood* 70:1090–98

78. Lijnen, H. R., Collen, D. 1986. Molecular mechanisms of thrombolytic therapy. *Haemostasis* 16(Supp 3):3–15

79. Loskutoff, D. J., van Mourik, J. A.,

Erickson, L. A., Lawrence, D. 1983. Detection of an unusually stable fibrinolytic inhibitor produced by bovine endothelial cells. *Proc. Natl. Acad. Sci. USA* 80:2956–60

80. Majerus, P. W., Connolly, T. M., Deckmyn, H., Ross, T. S., Bross, T. E., et al. 1986. The metabolism of phosphoinositide-derived messenger molecules. *Science* 234:1519–26
81. Majerus, P. W., Neufeld, E. J., Wilson, D. B. 1984. Production of phosphoinositide derived messengers. *Cell* 37:701–3
82. Markwardt, F., Klocking, H. P. 1976. Studies on the release of plasminogen activator. *Thromb. Res.* 8:217–23
83. Medcalf, R. L., Van den Berg, E., Schleuning, W.-D. 1988. Glucocorticoid-mediated gene expression of tissue- and urinary-type plasminogen activator and plasminogen activator inhibitor 1 and 2. *J. Cell Biol.* 106:971–78
84. Meidell, R. S., Gerard, R. D., Chien, K. R., Sambrook, J. F. 1987. Transcriptional regulation of human tissue-type plasminogen activator gene expression. *J. Mol. Cell. Cardiol.* 19:S13
85. Mimuro, J., Schleef, R. R., Loskutoff, D. J. 1987. Extracellular matrix of cultured bovine aortic endothelial cells contains functionally active type 1 plasminogen activator inhibitor. *Blood* 70:721–28
86. Nelles, L., Lijnen, R., Collen, D., Holmes, W. E. 1987. Characterization of a fusion protein consisting of amino acids 1 to 263 of tissue-type plasminogen activator and amino acids 144 to 411 of urokinase-type plasminogen activator. *J. Biol. Chem.* 262:10855–62
87. Nielsen, L. S., Andreasen, P. A., Grondahl-Hansen, J., Huang, J. Y., Kristensen, P., et al. 1986. Monoclonal antibodies to human 54,000 molecular weight plasminogen activator inhibitor from fibrosarcoma cells- inhibitor neutralization and one-step affinity purification. *Thromb. Haemostas.* 55:206–12
88. Nilsson, I. M. 1975. Phenformin and ethylestrenol in recurrent venous thrombosis. See Ref. 18, 1:1–12
89. Nilsson, I. M. 1978. Effect of drugs on activator synthesis and release. See Ref. 18, 3:77–89
90. Nilsson, I. M., Ljungner, H., Tengborn, L. 1985. Two different mechanisms in patients with venous thrombosis and defective fibrinolysis: low concentration of plasminogen activator or increased concentration of plasminogen activator inhibitor. *Br. Med. J.* 290:1453–56

91. Ny, T., Elgh, F., Lund, B. 1984. The structure of the human tissue-type plasminogen activator gene: correlation of intron and exon structures to functional and structural domains. *Proc. Natl. Acad. Sci. USA* 81:5355–59
92. Ny, T., Sawdey, M., Lawrence, D., Millan, J. L., Loskutoff, D. J. 1986. Cloning and sequencing of a cDNA coding for the human beta-migrating endothelial-cell-type plasminogen activator inhibitor. *Proc. Natl. Acad. Sci. USA* 83:6776–80
93. O'Connell, M. L., Canipari, R., Strickland, S. 1987. Hormonal regulation of tissue plasminogen activator secretion and mRNA levels in rat granulosa cells. *J. Biol. Chem.* 262:2339–44
94. Opdenakker, G., Ashino-Fuse, H., van Damme, J., Billian, A., de Somer, P. 1983. Effects of 12-O-tetradecanoylphorbol 13-acetate on the production of mRNAs for human tissue-type plasminogen activator. *Eur. J. Biochem.* 131:481–87
95. Pannekoek, H., Veerman, H., Lambers, H., Diergaarde, P., Verweij, C. L., et al. 1986. Endothelial plasminogen activator inhibitor (PAI): a new member of the serpin gene family. *EMBO J.* 5:2539–44
96. Paramo, J. A., Colucci, M., Collen, D. 1985. Plasminogen activator inhibitor in the blood of patients with coronary artery disease. *Br. Med. J.* 291:573–74
97. Pennica, D., Holmes, W. E., Kohr, W. J., Harkins, R. N., Vehar, G. A., et al. 1983. Cloning and expression of human tissue-type plasminogen activator cDNA in E. coli. *Nature* 301:214–21
97a. Petersen, L. C., Johannesen, M., Foster, D., Kumar, A., Mulvihill, E. 1988. Effect of polymerised fibrin on the catalytic activities of one-chain, tissue-type plasminogen activator as revealed by an analogue resistant to plasmin cleavage. *Biochim. Biophys. Acta* 952:245–54
98. Philips, M., Juul, A.-G., Thorsen, S. 1984. Human endothelial cells produce a plasminogen activator inhibitor and a tissue-type plasminogen activator-inhibitor complex. *Biochim. Biophys. Acta* 802:99–110
99. Pohl, G., Kallstrom, M., Bergsdorf, N., Wallen, P., Jornvall, H. 1984. Tissue plasminogen activator: peptide analyses confirm an indirectly derived amino acid sequence, identify the active site serine residue, establish glycosylation sites, and localize variant differences. *Biochemistry* 23:3701–7
100. Radcliffe, R. 1983. A critical role of

lysine residues in the stimulation of tissue plasminogen activator by denatured proteins and fibrin clots. *Biochem. Biophys. Acta* 743:422–30

101. Radcliffe, R., Heinze, T. 1978. Isolation of plasminogen activator from human plasma by chromatography on lysine-Sepharose. *Arch. Biochem. Biophys.* 189:185–94

102. Ranby, M. 1982. Studies on the kinetics of plasminogen activation by tissue plasminogen activator. *Biochem. Biophys. Acta* 704:461–69

103. Ranby, M., Bergdorf, N., Nilsson, T. 1982. Enzymatic properties of the one- and two-chain form of tissue plasminogen activator. *Thromb. Res.* 27:175–83

104. Rijken, D. C., Collen, D. 1981. Purification and characterization of the plasminogen activator secreted by human melanoma cells in culture. *J. Biol. Chem.* 256:7035–41

105. Rijken, D. C., Emeis, J. J. 1986. Clearance of the heavy and light polypeptide chains of tissue-type plasminogen activator in rats. *Biochem. J.* 238:643–46

106. Rijken, D. C., Hoylaerts, M., Collen, D. 1982. Fibrinolytic properties of one-chain and two-chain human extrinsic (tissue-type) plasminogen activator. *J. Biol. Chem.* 257:2920–25

107. Rijken, D. C., Juhan-Vague, I., Collen, D. 1983. Complexes between tissue-type plasminogen activator and proteinase inhibitiors in human plasma, identified with an immunoradiometric assay. *J. Lab. Clin. Med.* 101:285–94

108. Sakata, Y., Loskutoff, D. J., Gladson, C. L., Hekman, C. M., Griffin, J. H. 1986. Mechanism of protein C-dependent clot lysis: role of plasminogen activator inhibitor. *Blood* 68:1218–23

109. Saksela, O., Moscatelli, D., Rifkin, D. B. 1987. The opposing effects of basic fibroblast growth factor and transforming growth factor beta on the regulation of plasminogen activator activity in capillary endothelial cells. *J. Cell Biol.* 105:957–63

110. Salonen, E. M., Saksela, O., Vartio, T., Vaheri, A., Nielsen, L. S., et al. 1985. Plasminogen and tissue-type plasminogen activator bind to immobilized fibronectin. *J. Biol. Chem.* 260:12302–7

111. Sambrook, J., Hanahan, D., Rodgers, L., Gething, M.-J. 1987. Expression of human tissue-type plasminogen activator from lytic viral vectors and in established cell lines. *Mol. Biol. Med.* 3:459–81

112. Scott, R. W., Bergman, B. L., Bajpai, A., Hersh, R. T., Rodriguez, H., et al.

1985. Protease nexin: properties and a modified purification procedure. *J. Biol. Chem.* 260:7029–34

113. Shatos, M., Doherty, J., Hoak, J., Stump, D. 1987. Effect of oxygen free radicals on the fibrinolytic response of cultured human vascular endothelium. *Blood* 70(Suppl. 1):408a

114. Shaw, G., Kamen, R. 1986. Conserved AU sequence from the 3' untranslated region of GM-CSF mRNA mediates selective mRNA degradation. *Cell* 46:659–67

115. Silverstein, R. L., Leung, L. L. K., Harpel, P. C., Nachman, R. L. 1984. Complex formation of platelet thrombospondin with plasminogen: modulation of activation by tissue activator. *J. Clin. Invest.* 74:1625–33

116. Sprengers, E. D., Akkerman, J. W. N., Jansen, B. G. 1986. Blood platelet plasminogen activator inhibitor: two different pools of endothelial cell type plasminogen activator inhibitor in human blood. *Thromb. Haemostas.* 55:325–29

117. Sprengers, E. D., Kluft, C. 1987. Plasminogen activator inhibitors. *Blood* 69:381–87

118. Sprengers, E. D., Princen, H. M. G., Kooistra, T., van Hinsbergh, V. W. M. 1985. Inhibition of plasminogen activators by conditioned medium of human hepatocytes and hepatoma cell line HepG2. *J. Lab. Clin. Med.* 105:751–58

119. Stern, D. M., Bank, I., Nawroth, P. P., Cassimeris, J., Kisiel, W., et al. 1985. Self-regulation of procoagulant events on the endothelial cell surface. *J. Exp. Med.* 162:1223–35

120. Strickland, S., Mahdavi, V. 1978. The induction of differentiation in teratocarcinoma stem cells by retinoic acid. *Cell* 15:393–403

121. Tate, K. M., Higgins, D. L., Holmes, W. E., Winkler, M. E., Heyneker, H. L., et al. 1987. Functional role of proteolytic cleavage at Arginine 275 of human tissue plasminogen activator as assessed by site-directed mutagenesis. *Biochemistry* 26:338–43

122. Thorsen, S., Philips, M. 1984. Isolation of tissue-type plasminogen activator-inhibitor complexes from human plasma: evidence for a rapid plasminogen activator inhibitor. *Biochim. Biophys. Acta* 802:111–18

123. Travis, J., Salvensen, G. S. 1983. Human plasma proteinase inhibitors. *Ann. Rev. Biochem.* 52:655–709

124. van Hinsbergh, V. W., Binnema, D., Scheffer, M. A., Sprengers, E. D., Kooistra, T., et al. 1987. Production of plasminogen activators and inhibitors by

serially propogated endothelial cells from adult human vessels. *Arteriosclerosis* 7:389–400

125. van Hinsbergh, V. W. M., Bertina, R. M., van Wijngaarden, A., van Tilburg, N. H., Emeis, J. J., et al. 1985. Activated protein C decreases plasminogen activator-inhibitor activity in endothelial cell-conditioned medium. *Blood* 65: 444–51

126. van Mourik, J. A., Lawrence, D. A., Loskutoff, D. J. 1984. Purification of an inhibitor of plasminogen activator (antiactivator) synthesized by endothelial cells. *J. Biol. Chem.* 259:14914–21

127. van Zonneveld, A. J., Veerman, H., Pannekoek, H. 1986. Autonomous functions of structural domains on tissue-type plasminogen activator. *Proc. Natl. Acad. Sci. USA* 83:4670–74

128. van Zonneveld, A. J., Veerman, H., Pannekoek, H. 1986. On the interaction of the finger and kringle-2 domain of tissue-type plasminogen activator with fibrin. *J. Biol. Chem.* 261:14214–18

129. Verheijen, J. H., Caspers, M. P. M., Chang, G. T. G., de Monk, G. A. W., Pouwels, P. H., et al. 1986. Involvement of the finger domain and kringle-2 domain of tissue-type plasminogen activator in fibrin binding and stimulation of activity by fibrin. *EMBO J.* 5:3525–30

130. Wadhwa, N., Glas-Greenwalt, P., Kim, S., Ahn, C., Kant, K. S., et al. 1987. The response of the fibrinolytic system to desmopressin infusion. *Blood* 70(Suppl. 1):410a

131. Wallen, P., Pohl, G., Bergsdorf, N., Ranby, M., Ny, T., et al. 1983. Purification and characterization of a melanoma cell plasminogen activator. *Eur. J. Biochem.* 132:681–86

132. Waller, E. K., Schleuning, W.-D. 1985. Induction of fibrinolytic activity in HeLa cells by phorbol myristate acetate: tissue-type plasminogen activator antigen and mRNA augmentation require intermediate protein biosynthesis. *J. Biol. Chem.* 260:6354–60

133. Watanabe, K., Weksler, B. B., McCaffrey, T. M., Jaffe, E. A. 1987. Endotoxin stimulates prostacyclin production by human umbilical vein endothelial cells. *Blood* 70(Suppl. 1):412a

134. Wiman, B., Chmielewska, J., Ranby, M. 1984. Inactivation of tissue plasminogen activator in plasma. *J. Biol. Chem.* 259:3644–47

Annu. Rev. Physiol. 1989. 51:263–73

THE ENDOCARDIUM

Dirk L. Brutsaert

University of Antwerp, Antwerp, Belgium

> . . . Cinderella of the Heart! . . .
>
> Once upon a time, in a kingdom far away, there lived a lovely maiden named Endo. She had a sweet and gentle nature and always went about her chores with a song and a smile. Endo lived with her cruel stepmother, Cardia, and two ugly stepsisters, Myo and Peri. Cardia forced Endo to work as a maid for the family, doing all of the cooking and cleaning. Endo's stepsisters were jealous of her beauty and sweet disposition, and forced her to wear rags while they were dressed in fine gowns. But beautiful clothes could not hide their nasty natures and rags could not hide Endo's gentle grace. Through all of her hardships, she remained pleasant and kind . . .

The heart occupies a unique position in the cardiovascular system. All blood passes through its lumen and is continuously exposed to the endothelial cells of the endocardium. Brutsaert et al found that the endocardium may constitute an important modulator of the performance of the subjacent myocardium (13). Thus, the endocardium may theoretically be a feedback control for the heart through direct interaction with the superfusing blood. Yet, since the endocardium has long been considered a mere "watertight" interface with the superfusing blood, it is a much neglected subject and little is known about its functional role.

In the embryo, the endocardial endothelial monolayer forms the endocardial heart tube or, as in human embryos, the endocardial plexus, and constitutes the earliest structure of the future heart. Its development precedes that of the myocardium and of, later still, coronary vascularization, conducting fibers, and autonomic innervation (20, 24, 29, 30, 35, 37, 42, 47).

The internal surface of the ventricular chambers of the mature heart is extremely irregular, resembling Norwegian fjords; it consists of ridges and valleys produced by interlacing fiber bundles and crisscrossed arrays of trabeculae carneae and papillary muscles (45). Although this feature in general is more pronounced in the right than in the left ventricle, prominent left ventricular trabeculations are considered common variants of the normal

263

0066-4278/89/0315-0263$02.00

human heart. The prominent trabecular structure of the cavitary side of the ventricular wall and the surface characteristics of the endothelial cells, with their numerous microvilli and invaginations, offer an astonishingly high ratio of cavitary surface area to ventricular volume. At peak systole, trabecular muscles are squeezed together, and intertrabecular spaces are reduced in volume, displacing blood from the valleys and facilitating exchange of the endothelial monolayer with the superfusing blood both in systole and in diastole (17, 22, 36, 39, 45, 48).

Speculations on the physiological role of the endocardium, in particular the mural endocardium, have focused on a mechanical function of the fibro-musculo-elastic layer, for example, in preventing cardiac overdistension and in supporting elastic recoil during relaxation (9). The endocardium was also thought to act as an elastic buffer to prevent compression of the sub-endocardial vasculature and to control the patency of the Thebesian vessels (5). Apart from these speculations on the mechanical aspects, the mural endocardium has been attributed electrophysiological (4), anticoagulant, and fibrinolytic properties, as well as a possible role in water and ion exchange, and in ATP and glycogen metabolism (5). However, experimental data are scarce. Brutsaert et al found that the endocardial endothelium, in addition, modulates the mechanical performance of the subjacent myocardium (13), and that it may act as a cardiac sensor of the superfusing blood (32, 41) (A. L. Meulemans, L. J. Andries, D. L. Brutsaert, submitted for publication). We now briefly review some of these functions.

TRANSENDOCARDIAL TRANSPORT

In the primitive tubular heart, the endocardial monolayer and the underlying cardiac jelly are barriers separating the myocardium from the tubular lumen. Substances are exchanged with the primitive blood through these two media. Prior to the onset of myocardial vascularization in the embryo, the myocardium is characterized by extensive intercellular or intertrabecular spaces (sinusoids) through which substances can diffuse (20, 24, 29). Transport of substances by the sinusoidal circulation is subsequently replaced by the coronary circulation, whose development appears to accompany the formation of compact myocardium in the outer portion of the wall (20). A reminiscent developmental feature is present in Pisces and Reptilia, where capillaries were observed only in the epicardial and outer compact regions of the ventricular wall (26). However, in several other lower adult animals, such as the cyclostome (23) and the frog (20, 26), there is no coronary circulation in the myocardium, and exchange of substances between the luminal blood and the myocardium is accomplished exclusively through the endothelial cellular layer of the endocardium (43, 44). Interestingly, in Arthropoda the heart is a highly trabeculated, single-chambered organ with no capillaries and no endocardial lining; the only barrier to the blood is the external lamina of the myocardial cells (26). In higher animals, including man, the intertrabecular spaces regress as the coronary circulation develops; they are either reduced to strands of endothelium without lumen or give rise to capillaries in the central and inner portions of the ventricular wall, with persistence of ventricular communication through the Thebesian vessels (1, 7). However, a transendocardial path of supply and exchange may remain functional, in particular in the auricles, the right ventricle, and the trabeculated inner and central portion of the left ventricular wall (7, 20).

Most of our knowledge on transendothelial transport comes from studies on the vascular endothelium (15, 46). The cardiovascular endothelium, including that of the heart, is one continuous organ that shares various functions; the properties of vascular endothelial cells vary from organ to organ and even within a given microvascular bed. For example, despite ultrastructural similarities, permeability may vary considerably (2, 4).

Theoretically, although the contribution of the underlying basal lamina is still unknown (26), there are at least two ways substances can cross the endocardial endothelial monolayer: through transcellular transport and through the intercellular clefts. The presence of numerous vesicles in the cytoplasm of the thin endothelial cells was originally thought to indicate intense active fluid transport through pinocytosis across these cells. However, what first appeared to be isolated free vesicles are in reality elements of a complex and elaborate system of multiple vesicular invaginations with abundant microtubules from both cell surfaces that communicate directly with the cell interior and exterior (15, 19). Thus, function of these vesicular invaginations may be other than pinocytotic vesicular shuttling across the cell. Since a true endoplasmic reticulum is not well developed in endothelial cells, the vesicular invaginations in these cells could represent a system that is functionally analogous to the sarcoplasmic reticulum in muscle with respect to the regulation of $[Ca^{2+}]_i$ (15). Contractile elements have been found in various types of endothelial cells (6, 16, 21), including endocardial endothelial cells of the ventricles and the left atrium (6, 50), where actin bundles are abundant and are oriented parallel to the direction of blood flow. Changes in cell motility and shape of endocardial endothelial cells have been demonstrated (10, 18). It is tempting to suggest that some form of contraction or change in shape of these cells (6) could vary the hydraulic conductivity of the intercellular spaces or clefts (4, 33, 46). Endocardium appears permeable to tracers such as horseradish peroxidase (40,000-kDa), perhaps, via the intercellular junctions (4). The endothelial cells could thus be involved in the regulation of endocardial permeability through variations in size of the intercellular clefts.

Moreover, electron microscope studies have emphasized the existence of a few specialized membrane junctions, resembling true gap junctions, in the clefts between the closely apposed endothelial cells (4). Gap junctions are membrane specializations thought to be sites of low electric resistance pathways between adjacent cells. These gap junctions would thus provide indirect support for the presence of electric coupling between the cells of the endocardial endothelial monolayer. There is growing experimental evidence that voltage-dependent Ca^{2+} channels (49), Ca^{2+}-dependent K^+ channels (14, 40), and transmembrane potentials (34) exist in endothelial cells. However, a transcellular electric potential difference across the entire endocardial endothelial monolayer has not yet been demonstrated. A transcellular potential difference would require a strong electrochemical gradient for certain ions as well as a selective boundary barrier (basal lamina?) (26) to prevent flushing of the ionic gradients into a leaky postcapillary coronary venular sink. A transcellular electrochemical potential difference could, as in other multicellular membranes, contribute substantially to the functional role of the endocardium. This role could include both controlling transendocardial ion fluxes and establishing some electric coupling with the sarcolemmal membrane potentials throughout the myocardial wall. The possibility of an endocardial calcium-dependent transendothelial potassium gradient (12) is discussed below.

In summary, the endocardial endothelial monolayer with its basal lamina is a cellular membrane structure that may be subject to direct physiological regulation and acts as a finely tuned modulator of permeability between superfusing blood and myocardium. This adjustable physicochemical barrier with special morphological, biochemical and physiological properties may selectively regulate the exchange of neutral and charged particles between the superfusing blood and the interstitial microenvironment of the cardiac muscle cells; it probably also regulates the entry of hormones and other active macromolecules from the superfusing blood.

CONTROL AND MODULATION OF CARDIAC MUSCLE PERFORMANCE

Brutsaert et al recently demonstrated that the endocardium is an important modulator of the performance of the subjacent cardiac muscle (13). Damaging the endocardium immediately resulted in an irreversible abbreviation of cardiac muscle twitch with reduction of peak isometric tension, particularly at 37°C and physiologic $[Ca^{2+}]_o$ (1.25 mM). Maximal unloaded velocity of shortening, V_{max}, was not significantly different before and after damage. This rather unique modulation of mechanical performance ought to be distinguished from most inotropic interventions that also change V_{max}.

The mechanisms responsible for this modulation are not yet known. The effect of an intact endocardium on contraction and relaxation resembles and seems to reinforce an increase in initial muscle length along the ascending limb of the length-tension relationship. The similar pattern of changes induced by changing initial muscle length at any $[Ca^{2+}]_o$ and by the presence or absence of a functional endocardium suggests that the endocardium-mediated cascade of events, which controls and modulates cardiac performance, may be mediated through changes in the sensitivity of the contractile proteins to $[Ca^{2+}]_i$ (3, 25), and that such changes may be manifested as a modulation of the onset of early tension decline during relaxation with no change in V_{max}.

As for the different steps in the endocardium-mediated cascade of events from the endocardial endothelium to the contractile proteins, we can only speculate at present. The endocardium could possibly affect myocardial performance by electrochemical control or by the release of a chemical substance or messenger.

First, as an adjustable physical barrier with variable permeability, it could control homeostasis of the interstitial fluid surrounding the cardiac muscle cells, perhaps by establishing a delicate transendothelial electrochemical potential. Impairment of this active barrier could then cause a rapid change in concentration of neutral or charged particles in the interstitial fluid, with an immediate and dramatic effect on twitch contraction. This cannot be attributed to a sudden fall in $[Ca^{2+}]_o$ since the observed changes in twitch tension profile and V_{max}—after the removal of the endocardium—are not typical for a Ca^{2+} effect. Moreover, appropriately rising $[Ca^{2+}]_o$ compensated for the rate of rise and peak tension of the twitches, but not for the twitch duration, which irreversibly remained shorter. Extracellular potassium concentration, $[K^+]_o$, is another possible candidate. A sudden increase in $[K^+]_o$ in the interstitial fluid after damaging the endocardial surface would decrease the resting potential, shorten the action potential (27), and could lead to a decreased twitch peak and duration. Recent experiments have demonstrated that an intact endocardial endothelium somehow protects the mechanical performance of the subjacent myocardium against fluctuations in $[K^+]_o$ between 2.5 and 10 meq/l in the superfusing blood, and that a Ca^{2+}-dependent transendothelial K^+ efflux from the interstitial fluid to the superfusing blood could be the underlying mechanism (12). A high $[K^+]$-induced depression, most marked at high $[Ca^{2+}]_o$, of peak twitch tension with shortening of the twitch was observed only after damaging the endocardial surface. These observations suggest that an intact endocardium, at least regarding K^+ homeostasis, would be akin to the blood-brain barrier since the endocardium seems to maintain interstitial $[K^+]$ lower than in plasma. Whether this property is due to an active endothelial K^+ extrusion or to a selective barrier function of the basal lamina needs further investigation.

Secondly, by analogy with the as yet unidentified endothelium-derived relaxing factor (EDRF), which mediates relaxation of vascular smooth muscle via $[cGMP]_i$, one could propose the existence of an endocardially released factor that induces premature relaxation of the myocardium (myocardium relaxing factor). However, as the presence of a functional endocardium delays the onset of isometric tension decline and the removal of the endocardium irreversibly abolishes this effect, we may—by analogy with the recently isolated vasoconstrictor peptide (endothelin) produced by vascular endothelial cells (51)—rather speculate that the endocardium releases a factor that increases the sensitivity of the contractile proteins to $[Ca^{2+}]_i$ (myocardium contracting factor).

How these two mechanisms, an electrochemical control or the release of a chemical messenger, could participate in a cascade of events eventually leading to changes in the sensitivity of the contractile proteins to $[Ca^{2+}]_i$ is difficult to conceive at present. First, the rapidity of this control and its high temperature dependency (Q10 2.5–3; 1.5 for diffusion) indicate that it is not diffusion limited. This situation would favor an electrochemical potential control of the endocardial membrane rather than a control limited by the diffusion of substances unless these substances themselves affect an electrotonically mediated control of the subjacent myocardium. Second, how an adjustable electrochemical control or a chemical messenger could influence the cardiac cell is still open for speculation. Both the electrochemical properties of the myocardial sarcolemma through electric coupling with the transendocardial electric potential, with subsequent changes in resting and/or action potential, and a sarcolemmal receptor-mediated control could equally well be involved. Third, in order to function optimally, a transendocardial electrochemical control should somehow be functionally separated from the leaky postcapillary coronary bed. This important question, as well as the role of the basal lamina as a selective boundary barrier, requires further investigation. Preliminary experiments have demonstrated transient shortening of the sarcolemmal action potential after the endocardial surface is damaged (K. S. Sipido, P. R. Housmans, D. L. Brutsaert, unpublished observations). Ionic mechanisms, such as rapid changes in K^+ conductance, could underly this abbreviation of the sarcolemmal action potential. K^+-controlled electrotonic linkage through low-resistance junctions could, therefore, electrically couple the endocardium to the subjacent myocardium through most of the ventricular wall. Changes in action potential duration could be secondary, however, to changes in $[Ca^{2+}]_i$ as a result of changes in actin and myosin interaction by altered affinity of these proteins for Ca^{2+} (28).

In summary, the endocardium, as the most primitive structure of the heart, plays an important and essential role in controlling the performance of the heart by modulating peak contractile performance, relaxation, and filling of the heart, but without any direct changes in contractility (V_{max}) during the initial rising phase of the cardiac cycle. Modulation by the endocardium resembles and amplifies modulation by changes in muscle length, i.e. changes in volume of the intact ventricle. Hence, teleologically, the primitive endocardial tube, together with muscle length (or ventricular volume) could be considered as the first shortloop feedback control of the rhythmically pumping subjacent primitive myocardium. This control is still operative in the mature heart, but how it is mediated is largely unknown.

SENSORY FUNCTION

The endocardial endothelial cell surface occupies a special and unique position. Since it is continuously exposed to the superfusing blood, it could sense, transmit, and participate in regional and global adjustments of the subjacent myocardium to variations in homeostasis. Despite the vast contact surface of the cardiac chambers, we are still ignorant of most features of the interaction between the endocardium and the superfusing blood.

Meulemans et al recently demonstrated that atrial natriuretic peptide (ANP) has a direct effect on isolated cardiac muscle (32). Similar to the removal of a functional endocardium, ANP induced early tension decline with no changes in V_{max}. This effect was selectively mediated through the endocardial endothelium as it was abolished after previous impairment of the endocardial surface. The sensor function of the endocardium for ANP could be predicted already from the presence, in the ventricles of rat, of specific receptors for ANP on the endocardial endothelial cells (8). Early relaxation and filling of the heart with no effect on V_{max} could reinforce the ANP-induced unloading effect by natriuresis and vasodilation in conditions of cardiovascular overloading. This direct action of ANP on ventricular myocardium would constitute the shortest logical feedback loop for ANP, i.e. between its release in the atria and its action on the first organ it contacts, the ventricles. In vascular smooth muscle the action of ANP is accompanied by an increase in [cGMP]$_i$. The similarities between the effects on myocardial performance induced by the removal of a functional endocardium and those induced by dibutyryl-cGMP, and also by nitroprusside, which is known to increase [cGMP]$_i$, or by ANP (32) suggest that alterations in [cGMP]$_i$ might somehow be implicated in the endocardium-mediated control of cardiac performance.

Could circulating catecholamines be involved in the endocardium-mediated control in vivo? The abundance of contractile filaments in endocardial endothelial cells (50) and the presence of adrenergic-receptor-like sites in some endothelial cells (38) would indeed favor a direct regulatory action of catecholamines on the endocardial endothelial cells. Under beta-blockade, low concentrations (10^{-9}–10^{-7} M) of the α_1-agonist phenylephrine induced a marked positive inotropic response with typical prolongation of the twitches but no change in V_{max}; this response was opposite to the effect of ANP and akin to what would be expected from positive activation of the endocardium-mediated control of cardiac performance (A. L. Meulemans, L. J. Andries, D. L. Brutsaert, submitted for publication). The α-agonist positive inotropic effect was abolished after treatment with prazosin, but also after damaging the endocardial surface. Hence, cardiac α_1-agonist activity seems to be selectively mediated through the endocardial endothelium. Interestingly, higher concentrations (10^{-6}–10^{-5} M) of phenylephrine irreversibly destroyed the endocardial endothelial surface at $[Ca^{2+}]_o = 1.25$ mM, but not at high $[Ca^{2+}]_o$. Thus, catecholamines circulating in the superfusing blood could act through Ca^{2+}-modulated active variations of the adjustable clefts between the endocardial endothelial cells, possibly through contraction of the actin bundles with concomitant changes in the shape of these cells.

Could substances also act on the endocardium-mediated cascade downstream from the endocardial endothelial cells? Both angiotensin I and II increased peak twitch tension of isolated cardiac muscle, with typical slight twitch prolongation, but with no change in V_{max} (A. L. Meulemans, D. L. Brutsaert, unpublished observations). The response to angiotensin I, not to angiotensin II, was abolished after the addition of a converting enzyme inhibitor, captopril. Although the response to angiotensin I and II strikingly resembled the typical response after treatment with phenylephrine, it was not abolished after damaging the endocardial surface, which indicates that these substances act at some site along the endocardially mediated cascade downstream from the endothelial cell. Although these data do not exclude the presence of converting enzyme in the endocardial endothelial cells, a sufficient amount of the enzyme is also present downstream from the endothelial cells, and hence the effect of angiotensin I does not require an intact endocardial endothelium either for its conversion into its active form or for its actual inotropic response.

Finally, in recent experiments, aggregation of platelets increased contractile performance of isolated cat papillary muscle, and performance was significantly increased in the absence of an intact endocardium (41). Serotonin and ATP released from the aggregating platelets may partly account for this response. How the intact endocardium partly suppresses and slightly modifies the direct effect of the aggregating platelets on the subjacent myocardium is unknown; however, in the experiments by Shah et al (41), it could not be explained by the antiaggregation properties of the endocardial endothelium (11).

In summary, growing experimental evidence indicates that the endocardium-mediated control acts as a sensor for volume, either directly as outlined above or indirectly through ANP, and for various substances or cells circulating in the superfusing blood. The nature and localization of these specific sensor sites may differ for various stimuli. The sensor function may be localized either at the endocardial endothelial level itself, as for ANP and α_1-agonists, which are receptor-mediated, or at some intermediate step along the endocardium-mediated cascade of events, both eventually leading to changes in the sensitivity of the contractile proteins.

OTHER FUNCTIONS

As only a few papers directly relate to the endocardium, we are fairly ignorant about other possible functions. The endocardial endothelial monolayer is continuous with the endothelial lining cells of the vessels, and no major morphologic differences have been described. One may, therefore, be tempted to extend to endocardial endothelial cells some of our knowledge derived from vascular endothelial cells (2).

Yet, however helpful studies on the vascular endothelium may be, the functional differentiation of the various regions within the cardiovascular system makes extrapolation to the endocardial endothelium speculative. One of the few recent papers that directly relates to the endocardium attributes an important role to the conversion of arachidonate to prostaglandins (11). Although synthesis of prostacyclin is considerable in human cardiac tissue, the activity of tissue cyclooxygenase, which converts arachidonate into prostaglandins, was found to be about twice as high in the endocardium, and located specifically in the endothelial cell fraction rather than in the myocardium (11). By virtue of its ability to synthesize prostacyclin, a potent inhibitor of platelet aggregation, the endocardial endothelial surface may be antithrombogenic.

However, until there is more direct experimental evidence about other possible functions of the endocardial endothelium the fundamental role of the endocardium will not be fully appreciated.

CONCLUSIONS

The endocardium plays an important role in modulating peak systolic performance, relaxation, and rapid filling of the heart. The mechanisms and process of the endocardial interaction with the superfusing blood are largely unknown. The endocardium, along with chamber volume changes, may perhaps through similar underlying mechanisms constitute the two embryologically most primitive feedback regulations, which transform the developing contracting myocardium into a pumping system.

Literature Cited

1. Adyshirin-Zade, E. A., Gabain, L. I. 1984. Relief peculiarities of the internal surface of the cardiac ventricles and viessen-thebesian vessels. *Arch. Anat. Histol. Embryol.* 87:54–59
2. Albelda, S. M., Karnovsky, M. J., Fishman, A. P. 1987. Perspectives in endothelial cell biology. *J. Appl. Physiol.* 4:1345–48
3. Allen, D. G., Kentish, J. C. 1985. The cellular basis of the length-tension relation in cardiac muscle. *J. Mol. Cell. Cardiol.* 17:821–40
4. Anversa, P., Giacomelli, F., Wiener, J. 1975. Intercellular junctions of rat endocardium. *Anat. Rec.* 183:477–84
5. Becker, B. J. P. 1964. Studies of the human mural endocardium. *J. Pathol. Bacteriol.* 88:541–47
6. Becker, C. G., Murphy, G. E. 1969. Demonstration of contractile protein in endothelium and cells of the heart valves, endocardium, intima, arteriosclerotic plaques, and Aschoff Bodies of rheumatic heart disease. *Am. J. Pathol.* 55:1–37
7. Bellet, S., Gouley, B. A. 1932. Congenital heart disease with multiple cardiac anomalies. *Am. J. Med. Sci.* 183:458–65
8. Bianchi, C., Gutkowska, K., Thibault, G., Garcia, R., Genest, J., Cantin, M. 1985. Radioautographic localization of ^{125}I-atrial natriuretic factor (ANF) in rat tissues. *Histochemistry* 82:441–52
9. Black-Schaeffer, B. 1957. Infantile endocardial fibroelastosis. A suggested etiology. *Arch. Pathol.* 63:281–306
10. Bolender, D. L., Markwald, R. R. 1979. Epithelial-mesenchymal transformation in chick atrioventricular cushion morphogenesis. *Scan. Electron. Microsc.* 3:313–22
11. Brandt, R., Nowak, J., Sonnenfield, T. 1984. Prostaglandin formation from exogenous precursor in homogenates of human cardiac tissue. *Basic Res. Cardiol.* 79:135–41
12. Brutsaert, D. L., Meulemans, A. L. 1988. Transendothelial ionic exchange underlies endocardial control of myocardial performance. *Biophys. J.* 53:59a
13. Brutsaert, D. L., Meulemans, A. L., Sipido, K. R., Sys, S. U. 1988. Effects of damaging the endocardial surface on the mechanical performance of isolated cardiac muscle. *Circ. Res.* 62:358–66
14. Colden-Stanfield, M., Schilling, W. P., Ritchie, A. K., Eskin, S. G., Navarro, L. T., Kunze, D. L. 1987. Bradykinin-induced increases in cytosolic calcium and ionic currents in cultured bovine aortic endothelial cells. *Circ. Res.* 61:632–40
15. Crone, C. 1986. Modulation of solute permeability in microvascular endothelium. *Fed. Proc.* 45:77–83
16. Drenckhahn, D. 1983. Cell motility and cytoplasmic filaments in vascular endothelium. *Prog. Appl. Microcirc.* 1: 53–70
17. Edanaga, M. 1975. A scanning electron microscope study on the endothelium of vessels. II. Fine surface structure of the endocardium in normal rabbits and rats. *Arch. Histol. Jpn.* 37:301–12
18. Fitzharris, T. P. 1981. Endocardial shape change in the truncus during cushion tissue formation. In *Mechanisms of Cardiac Morphogenesis and Teratogenesis*, ed. T. Pexieder, pp. 227–35. New York: Raven
19. Frokjaer-Jensen, J. 1985. The vesicle controversy. *Prog. Appl. Microcirc.* 9: 21–42
20. Grant, R. T., Regnier, M. 1926. The comparative anatomy of the cardiac coronary vessels. *Heart* 13:285–317
21. Hammersen, F. 1980. Endothelial contractility—Does it exist? *Adv. Microcirc.* 9:95–134
22. Harasaki, H., Suzuki, I., Tanaka, J., Hanano, H., Torisu, M. 1975. Ultrastructure research of the endocardial endothelium of monkeys. *Arch. Histol. Jpn.* 38:71–84
23. Hardisty, M. W. 1979. *Biology of the Cyclostomes*, pp. 93–115. London: Chapman and Hall
24. Henningsen, B., Schiebler, T. H. 1969. Zur Fruehentwicklung der herzeigenen Strombahn. *Z. Anat. Entwicklungsgesch.* 130:101–14
25. Hibberd, M. G., Jewell, B. R. 1982. Calcium- and length-dependent force production in rat ventricular muscle. *J. Physiol.* 329:527–40
26. Howse, H. D., Ferrans, V. J., Hibbs, R. G. 1970. A comparative histochemical and electron microscopic study of the surface coatings of cardiac muscle cells. *J. Mol. Cell. Cardiol.* 1:157–68
27. Kavaler, F., Hyman, P. M., Lefkowitz, R. B. 1972. Positive and negative inotropic effects of elevated extracellular potassium level on mammalian ventricular muscle. *J. Gen. Physiol.* 60:351–65
28. Lab, M. J., Allen, D. G., Orchard, C. H. 1984. The effects of shortening on myoplasmic calcium concentration and

action potential in mammalian ventricular muscle. *Circ. Res.* 55:825–29

29. Manasek, F. J. 1971. The ultrastructure of embryonic myocardial blood vessels. *Dev. Biol.* 26:42–54

30. Manasek, F. J. 1981. Determinants of heart shape in early embryos. *Fed. Proc.* 40:2011–16

31. Deleted in proof

32. Meulemans, A. L., Sipido, K. R., Sys, S. U., Brutsaert, D. L. 1988. Atriopeptin III induces early relaxation of isolated mammalian papillary muscle. *Circ. Res.* 62:1171–72

33. Miller, F. N., Sims, D. E. 1986. Contractile elements in the regulation of macromolecular permeability. *Fed. Proc.* 45:84–88

34. Northover, B. J. 1980. The membrane potential of vascular endothelial cells. *Adv. Microcirc.* 9:135–60

35. Papp, J. G. 1988. Autonomic responses and neurohumoral control in the human early antenatal heart. *Basic Res. Cardiol.* 83:2–9

36. Peine, C. J., Low, F. N. 1975. Scanning electron microscopy of cardiac endothelium of the dog. *Am. J. Anat.* 142:137–58

37. Pexieder, T. 1981. Prenatal development of the endocardium: a review. *Scan. Electron. Mircrosc.* 2:223–53

38. Rubanyi, G. M., Vanhoutte, P. M. 1985. Endothelium-removal decreases relaxations of canine coronary arteries caused by beta-adrenergic agonists and adenosine. *J. Cardiovasc. Pharmacol.* 7:139–44

39. Sarphie, T. G., Allen, D. G. 1978. Scanning and transmission electron microscopy of normal and methotrexate-treated endocardial cell population in dogs. *J. Submicrosc. Cytol.* 10:15–25

40. Sauve, R., Parent, L., Simoneau, C., Roy, G. 1988. The role of external ATP in the activation process of calcium dependent potassium channels in bovine aortic endothelium cells: a single channel study. *Biophys. J.* 53:55a

41. Shah, A., Meulemans, A. L., Brutsaert, D. L. 1988. Aggregating platelets increase myocardial contractility. Submitted for publication

42. Sissman, N. J. 1970. Development landmarks in cardiac morphogenesis: comparative chronology. *Am. J. Cardiol.* 25:141–48

43. Staley, N. A., Benson, E. S. 1968. The ultrastructure of frog ventricular cardiac muscle and its relationship to mechanisms of excitation-contraction coupling. *J. Cell Biol.* 38:99–114

44. Stehbens, W. E., Meyer, E. 1965. Ultrastructure of endothelium of the frog heart. *J. Anat.* 99:127–34

45. Streeter, D. D. Jr. 1979. Gross morphology and fiber geometry of the heart. In *Handbook of Physiology*, eds. R. M. Berne, N. Sperelakis, S. R. Geiger, pp. 61–112. Bethesda, Maryland: Am. Physiol. Soc.

46. Svensjo, E., Grega, G. J. 1986. Evidence for endothelial cell-mediated regulation of macromolecular permeability by postcapillary venules. *Fed. Proc.* 45:89–95

47. Van Mierop, L. H. S. 1979. Morphological development of the heart. See Ref. 45, pp. 1–28

48. Wheeler, E. E., Gavin, J. B., Herdson, P. B. 1973. A study of endocardium endothelium using freeze-drying and scanning electron microscopy. *Anat. Rec.* 175:579–84

49. Williams, J. S., Whitmer, K. R., Izzo, N. J., Peach, M. J., Schwartz, A. 1987. Effects of calcium channel modulators in endothelial cells. *Biophys. J.* 51:429a

50. Wong, A. J., Pollard, T. D., Herman, I. M. 1983. Actin filament stress fibers in vascular endothelial cells in vivo. *Science* 219:867–69

51. Yanagisawa, M., Kurihara, H., Kimura, S., Tomobe, Y., Kobayashi, M., et al. 1988. A novel potent vasoconstrictor peptide produced by vascular endothelial cells. *Nature* 332:411–15

SPECIAL TOPIC: CONTRACTION IN SMOOTH MUSCLE CELLS

Richard A. Murphy, Section Editor

Department of Physiology, University of Virginia School of Medicine, Charlottesville, Virginia 22908

INTRODUCTION

Smooth muscle tissue is composed of mechanically and often electrically coupled contractile cells that may be unique to vertebrates (22). Smooth muscle is characterized by an extraordinary functional diversity associated with many extracellular regulatory systems. These include a wide variety of neurotransmitters, hormones, ions, metabolites, and responses mediated by other associated cells as well as nerves. The current interest in the intracellular mechanisms governing contraction and relaxation reflects the importance of smooth muscle in the function of all organ systems and as the target cells for many drugs.

There is a consensus among most workers that the sliding filament-crossbridge mechanism underlies contraction (11, 14, 15, 46, 47). Nevertheless, smooth muscle has properties not exhibited by skeletal muscle. Most importantly, Ca^{2+} does not regulate crossbridge interactions as a simple on/off switch. Both the number of crossbridges interacting with the thin filaments and their cycling rate are regulated (11, 24, 30). This remarkable property is associated with a covalent regulatory system: Ca^{2+}-stimulated crossbridge phosphorylation.

275

The objective of this special topic section is to summarize our current knowledge of contractile system regulation in smooth muscle cells and to address some broad questions. Do all smooth muscle cells share a common contractile apparatus? If so, functional diversity must largely arise from variations in the extracellular control systems and the membranes regulating myoplasmic Ca^{2+}. How are crossbridge cycling rates and thus the energetics of contraction regulated? Why does smooth muscle differ from striated muscle in this respect? Finally, why does smooth muscle have a covalent regulatory mechanism involving Ca^{2+}-dependent crossbridge phosphorylation, which necessarily increases ATP consumption and reduces the efficiency of contraction? Definitive answers are premature. However, these questions are related, and an explanation of how Ca^{2+} regulates crossbridge interactions with the thin filament will suggest some of the answers. One starting point is an examination of the physiology of smooth muscle.

THE FUNCTIONAL DIFFERENCE BETWEEN SMOOTH AND SKELETAL MUSCLE

Smooth and striated muscle are historically distinguished on anatomical grounds. However, structure subserves function, and Prosser (32) emphasized the physiological differences between contractile cells attached to a skeleton and those in the walls of hollow organs. Skeletal muscle cells bridge their attachment points, with the skeleton bearing most gravitational loads. The cells (as motor units) are recruited individually to perform work. By contrast, cells in hollow organs must contract in a coordinated fashion. While they develop force and perform work, smooth muscle tissues must also serve as a "skeleton" to stabilize organ dimensions against imposed loads. This difference fundamentally changes the energetic balance.

Skeletal muscle has a high efficiency in converting the energy of ATP hydrolysis into mechanical work. This minimizes the cost of contraction in muscles with a high power output. Smooth muscle is comparatively inefficient (30). This difference may be largely explicable in terms of the additional ATP consumption associated with the operation of a covalent regulatory mechanism (17). However, no work is done during tonic contractions where the efficiency is zero. This type of contraction often characterizes the muscle of hollow organs and the economy of force maintenance is important. In fact many smooth muscles require less than 1% of the ATP needed by a skeletal muscle to sustain a comparable force (30). Some insights into how these functional differences arise stem from investigations exploring the role of Ca^{2+}-stimulated crossbridge phosphorylation in the regulation of contraction.

CROSSBRIDGE PHOSPHORYLATION AND "LATCH"

Biochemical studies of smooth muscle myosin revealed a phosphorylation dependence of the actin-activated ATPase activity (1, 19, 24, 46). In skinned smooth muscle preparations force was typically observed to be proportional to myosin phosphorylation (50, 20). Such observations suggested that Ca^{2+}-stimulated phosphorylation of a crossbridge enabled it to interact with the thin filament (1, 19, 46). In this model phosphorylation is the switch that turns a crossbridge on.

Tests of the phosphorylation switch hypothesis required development of methods to estimate changes in myoplasmic $[Ca^{2+}]$ and crossbridge phosphorylation in tissues where the mechanical activation could be assessed. Both measurements are difficult and various artifacts played a role in numerous reported inconsistencies. However, smooth muscle from a variety of organs now appears to share the behavior illustrated in figure 1.

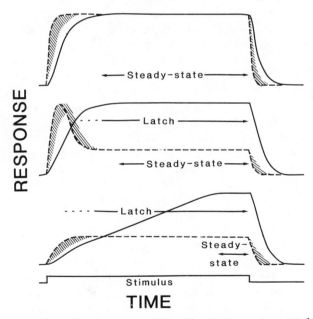

Figure 1 Responses of smooth muscle to stimulation. Changes in myoplasmic $[Ca^{2+}]$ (dashed lines) are followed by changes in myosin light chain kinase activity, crossbridge phosphorylation, and cycling rates as estimated by shortening velocity at zero load (V_0) (hatched areas), and force generation (solid lines). *(top)* response to a large sustained increase in $[Ca^{2+}]$ (unphysiological). *(middle)* typical response to agonists mobilizing intracellular Ca^{2+} stores. *(bottom)* response after depletion of intracellular Ca^{2+} pools or to agents that only increase plasma membrane Ca^{2+} permeability.

The phosphorylation switch hypothesis predicted the response illustrated in the top panel of Figure 1. The application of a maximal stimulus should produce a sustained increase in myoplasmic $[Ca^{2+}]$ followed by a rise in crossbridge phosphorylation to a high value. Steady-state force should be proportional to the fraction of the crossbridges that were phosphorylated. Removal of the stimulus should be followed by reductions in Ca^{2+}, phosphorylation, and relaxation.

In practice, the illustrated response is rarely observed because smooth muscles have powerful mechanisms to lower myoplasmic $[Ca^{2+}]$ rapidly to [agonist]-dependent sustained levels in the submicromolar range. The typical response to an agonist eliciting a strong contraction is shown in the middle panel of Figure 1. Stimulation elicits a transient in myoplasmic $[Ca^{2+}]$ (29, 37, 48, 49). These large initial transients appear to be the result of Ca^{2+} release from the sarcoplasmic reticulum (34, 49). The Ca^{2+} transient is associated with an increase and decrease in crossbridge phosphorylation to modest levels (37). Nevertheless, force rapidly develops to a sustained high level. The most striking experimental observation was that estimates of crossbridge cycling rates, such as shortening velocity with no load (V_0), changed in proportion to phosphorylation (2, 10, 25).

A behavior not predicted by the phosphorylation switch hypothesis was the "latch" state (Figure 1), which was initially defined as force maintenance without proportional phosphorylation and with reduced crossbridge turnover rates (10). Such behavior was appropriate for muscle in a hollow organ as it would contribute to force maintenance with reduced ATP consumption (J_{ATP}) and a high economy for tonic contractions. Nevertheless, it implied that smooth muscle, unlike skeletal muscle, has the ability to regulate crossbridge turnover rates and that Ca^{2+}-dependent phosphorylation is involved. Studies of skinned tissues suggested that induction of latch was dependent on initially high $[Ca^{2+}]$ and phosphorylation values and that another Ca^{2+}-dependent system was responsible for force maintenance (8, 27).

A better understanding of latch resulted from protocols in which the initial Ca^{2+} transient was largely abolished in intact tissues. This can be achieved with the same agonist after depletion of intracellular Ca^{2+} stores or through the use of other stimuli that apparently do not induce Ca^{2+} release from the sarcoplasmic reticulum. The result, (Figure 1, bottom) is a modest increase in $[Ca^{2+}]$ (C. M. Rembold & R. A. Murphy, unpublished data) and phosphorylation (34) to a sustained level, which is associated with the very slow development of high levels of force.

A definition of latch that is consistent with the observations illustrated in Figure 1 would be "a range of phosphorylation values in which parameters associated with crossbridge turnover (V_0, J_{ATP}) are lower than predicted by the parameters reflecting the number of attached crossbridges (steady-state force, stress, or stiffness and load bearing capacity)." The sliding filament-crossbridge paradigm is assumed in this definition. The rationale for this assumption is considered in the following section.

HYPOTHESES FOR CONTRACTION AND LATCH

The biochemical and biophysical evidence (11) supporting a sliding filament-crossbridge mechanism as the basis for force development in smooth muscle led to its general acceptance. Recent advances in imaging techniques are providing further structural support (4, 13, 15, 47). However, controversy remains over whether attached crossbridges or some other parallel mechanical linkages, possibly involving the cytoskeleton (33, 45), are responsible for latch. This is reminiscent of the long-standing argument about the basis for the catch state in certain molluscan muscles, which maintain shell closure with very low energy expenditure (39). Catch and latch are similar in mechanical and energetic comparisons if allowance is made for the very long thick filaments in molluscan catch muscles (5, 42). Three classes of explanations have been invoked to explain latch.

Cytoskeletal or Other Novel Linkages

Mechanical comparisons of smooth muscles that develop comparable forces under conditions giving high and low levels of phosphorylation show little difference with the exception of parameters related to turnover rates (3, 9, 25, 26, 42, 44). The observation that latch is characterized by slowed contraction rates favors attached crossbridges as the mechanistic basis for the observed force. Furthermore, the ability to slowly shorten in a latch state (Figure 1, bottom) is inconsistent with the concept that latch is the result of some "lock up" of the myofibrillar or cytoskeletal apparatus to sustain a preexisting force.

Variable Crossbridge Cycle Rate vs Two Crossbridge Population Models

In principle, the observation of Ca^{2+} and/or phosphorylation-dependent variations in V_0 can be explained by either: (a) the statistical balance between two crossbridge populations with different turnover rates, or (b) a single crossbridge population with regulatory mechanisms providing for a more or less continuous variation in the individual turnover rate. My colleagues and I favored the former possibility in view of its simplicity. However, it appeared necessary to hypothesize that an attached, dephosphorylated "latchbridge" opposed and slowed the turnover of cycling phosphorylated crossbridges to explain the dependence of V_0 on phosphorylation (2, 10). A second Ca^{2+}-dependent mechanism was invoked to regulate the latchbridge population (8, 10).

The introduction of an internal load over and above any mechanical interactions characteristic of a uniform population of crossbridges has certain consequences. One prediction was that a decrease in the energy cost of force maintenance should occur with an increasing fraction of latchbridges. This was not detected experimentally (6, 7, 42). Consequently Siegman et al (42) proposed the single population, variable turnover model. This model is conceptually difficult as multiple regulatory mechanisms operating on each crossbridge must be invoked. However, some enzyme molecules exhibit more than two activity levels because of multiple regulatory events.

Independent evidence with a bearing on how crossbridge turnover rates might be regulated was obtained with the assay system developed by Sheetz et al (41), which allowed measurement of the rates of movement of myosin coated beads down actin cables from the algae, *Nitella*. In this in vitro system, Sellers et al (40) found that the rate of movement of beads coated with smooth muscle myosin was proportional to the fractional phosphorylation in the absence of Ca^{2+}. There are uncertainties in interpreting this result, but it suggests that phosphorylation, per se, can determine the average turnover rate of smooth muscle myosin with actin. Reiser et al (36) provided a direct demonstration of the effect of a mixture of fast and slow cycling crossbridges on V_0 in a cell. Rabbit soleus muscle fibers contain varying ratios of the slow and fast type skeletal myosin heavy chains. V_0 in single cells was directly proportional to the fractional content of the fast heavy chain, which showed that V_0 will vary in proportion to the relative amounts of fast and slow cycling crossbridges (36). Thus, a two crossbridge population model can explain regulation of V_0.

The "Latchbridge" Model: Two Regulatory Systems or Two Substrates?

Although Ca^{2+} was clearly necessary for force maintenance in the latch state, the concentrations required originally appeared to be lower than those necessary to produce statistically significant elevations in phosphorylation (2, 10). Other data supported the concept that latch requires low concentrations of Ca^{2+}. (a) Ca^{2+}-dependent resting resistance to stretch was associated with crossbridge interactions without cycling in the taenia coli (43). (b) Stress was maintained for some time in skinned fibers after a reduction in the $[Ca^{2+}]$ lowered phosphorylation to near basal levels (8, 27). (c) There were reports of contraction in the absence of detectable increases in phosphorylation (28, 31) or myoplasmic $[Ca^{2+}]$ (23).

An alternative interpretation of these studies is that the appreciable basal or resting levels of phosphorylation or $[Ca^{2+}]$ were artifactual and masked a steep dependence of stress on relatively low levels of phosphorylation (20, 35, 37, 38). Instead of an additional Ca^{2+}-dependent regulatory mechanism, the "latchbridge hypothesis" postulates two substrates for the myosin kinase–phosphatase system: free and attached crossbridges (12, 17, 18). This model appears to explain the behavior of smooth muscle reviewed above and potentially resolves a number of the problems discussed. Nevertheless, the model may be incomplete and additional actions of Ca^{2+} have been postulated in a more complex version (21).

CHAPTER TOPICS

In contrast to skeletal muscle, it is clear that regulation and crossbridge function are conceptually and experimentally related topics. A full understanding of the role of crossbridge phosphorylation depends on a quantitative knowledge of the relationship between agents acting on the cellular membrane systems, Ca^{2+} mobilization, crossbridge phosphorylation, and the crossbridge interactions underlying the mechanical response.

Hai & Murphy address the narrow question of whether Ca^{2+}-stimulated phosphorylation, per se, can explain contraction and latch. Although their analysis suggests that this may be true, this does not exclude a role for other systems. In fact, there is considerable inferential evidence for other Ca^{2+}-dependent or independent regulatory mechanisms in smooth muscle. Kamm & Stull assess these data and the role that such systems may play physiologically.

An important difference between skeletal and smooth muscle is that the latter must precisely regulate the myoplasmic $[Ca^{2+}]$ at submicromolar levels in an [agonist]-dependent manner. An additional requirement is the generation of the initial Ca^{2+} transients. van Breemen & Saida consider the role of the plasma membrane and the sarcoplasmic reticulum in Ca^{2+} mobilization and regulation. In conjunction with tissue specific extracellular control systems, membrane characteristics determining cellular Ca^{2+} metabolism may provide the functional diversity characteristic of smooth muscle tissues.

My prefatory thesis was that functional considerations and their energetic consequences underlie the distinctive properties of smooth muscle. The operation of a covalent regulatory mechanism adds a new dimension to an energetic analysis in smooth muscle because much of the ATP consumption during contraction is associated with phosphorylation and dephosphorylation. A rigorous test of any hypothesis for contractile system function is its energetic predictions. Paul reviews the current knowledge of smooth muscle energetics and outlines an agenda for research in this important, but little studied area.

ACKNOWLEDGMENTS

The research of the author and his colleagues was supported by the National Institute of Health (5 PO1 HL19242). I am indebted to Drs. Chi-Ming Hai and Christopher M. Rembold for their contributions in the preparation of this manuscript and for the assistance of Ms. Dana Hannum-Baugh.

282

Literature Cited

1. Adelstein, R. S., Pato, M.D., Conti, M. A. 1981. The role of phosphorylation in regulating contractile proteins. *Adv. Cyclic Nucleotide Res.* 14:361–73
2. Aksoy, M. O., Mras, S., Kamm, K. E., Murphy, R. A. 1983. Ca^{2+}, cAMP, and changes in myosin phosphorylation during contaction of smooth muscle. *Am. J. Physiol.* 245 (*Cell Physiol.* 14):C255–70
3. Arner, A., Hellstrand, P. 1983. Activation of contraction and ATPase activity in intact and chemically skinned smooth muscle of rat portal vein. *Circ. Res.* 53:695–702
4. Bagby, R. 1986. Toward a comprehensive three-dimensional model of the contractile system of vertebrate smooth muscle cells. *Int. Rev. Cytol.* 105:67–128
5. Butler, T. M., Siegman, M. J., Mooers, S. U. 1982. Chemical energetics of contraction in mammalian smooth muscle. In *Basic Biology of Muscles: A Comparative Approach*, ed. B. M. Twarog, R. J. C. Levine, M. M. Dewey, pp. 189–201. New York: Raven. 406 pp.
6. Butler, T. M., Siegman, M. J., Mooers, S. U. 1986. Slowing of crossbridge cycling in smooth muscle without evidence of an internal load. *Am. J. Physiol.* 251(*Cell Physiol.* 20):C945–50
7. Butler, T. M., Siegman, M. J., Mooers, S. U. 1987. Slowing of crossbridge cycling rate in mammalian smooth muscle occurs without evidence of an increase in internal load. In *Regulation and Contraction of Smooth Muscle*, ed. M. J. Siegman, A. P. Somlyo, N. L. Stephens, pp. 289–301. New York: Liss. 507 pp.
8. Chatterjee, M., Murphy, R. A. 1983. Calcium-dependent stress maintenance without myosin phosphorylation in skinned smooth muscle. *Science* 221:464–66
9. De Mey, J. G., Brutsaert, D. L. 1984. Mechanical properties of resting and active isolated coronary arteries. *Circ. Res.* 55:1–9
10. Dillon, P. F., Aksoy, M. O., Driska, S. P., Murphy, R. A. 1981. Myosin phosphorylation and the cross-bridge cycle in arterial smooth muscle. *Science* 211:495–97
11. Driska, S. P. 1984. Mechanical properties, contractile proteins, and regulation of contraction of vascular smooth muscle. In *Physiology and Pathophysiology in the Heart*, ed. N. Sperelakis, pp. 757–79. Boston: Nijhoff. 846 pp.
12. Driska, S. P. 1987. High myosin light

    chain phosphatase activity in arterial smooth muscle: can it explain the latch phenomenon" See Ref. 7, pp. 757–79
13. Fay, F. S., Fujiwara, K., Rees, D. D., Fogarty, K. E. 1983. Distribution of α-actinin in single isolated smooth muscle cells. *J. Cell Biol.* 96:783–95
14. Fay, F. S., Rees, D. D., Warshaw, D. M. 1980. Contractile mechanism of smooth muscle. In *Membrane Structure and Function*, ed. E. Bittar, pp. 79–130. New York: Wiley. 211 pp.
15. Gabella, G. 1984. Structural apparatus for force transmission in smooth muscles. *Physiol. Rev.* 64:455–77
16. Deleted in proof
17. Hai, C.-M., Murphy, R. A. 1988. Cross-bridge phosphorylation and regulation of latch state in smooth muscle. *Am. J. Physiol.* 254 (*Cell Physiol.* 23):C99–106
18. Hai, C.-M., Murphy, R. A. 1988. Regulation of shortening velocity by crossbridge phosphorylation in smooth muscle. *Am. J. Physiol.* 255 (*Cell Physiol.* 24). C86–94
19. Hartshorne, D. J. 1980. Biochemical basis for contraction of vascular smooth muscle. *Chest* 78 (Suppl.):140–49
20. Hoar, P. E., Kerrick, W. G. L., Cassidy, P. S. 1979. Chicken gizzard: relation between calcium-activated phosphorylation and contraction. *Science* 204:503–6
21. Hoar, P. E., Pato, M. D., Kerrick, W. G. L. 1985. Myosin light chain phosphatase. *J. Biol. Chem.* 260:8760–64
22. Hoyle, G. 1983. *Muscles and Their Neural Control*, p. 313. New York: Wiley. 689 pp.
23. Jiang, M. J., Morgan, K. G. 1987. Intracellular calcium levels in phorbol ester-induced contractions of vascular smooth muscle. *Am. J. Physiol.* 253 (*Heart Circ. Physiol.* 22):H1365–71
24. Kamm, K. E., Stull, J. T. 1985. The function of myosin and myosin light chain kinase phosphorylation in smooth muscle. *Annu. Rev. Pharmacol. Toxicol.* 25:593–620
25. Kamm, K. E., Stull, J. T. 1985. Myosin phosphorylation, force, and maximal shortening velocity in neurally stimulated tracheal smooth muscle. *Am. J. Physiol.* 249(*Cell Physiol.* 18):C238–47
26. Meiss, R. A. 1984. Nonlinear force response of active smooth muscle subjected to small stretches. *Am. J. Physiol.* 246(*Cell Physiol.* 15):C114–24
27. Moreland, R. S., Murphy, R. A. 1986.

Determinants of Ca^{2+}-dependent stress maintenance in skinned swine carotid media. *Am. J. Physiol.* 251(*Cell Physiol.* 20):C892–903

28. Moreland, S., Moreland, R. S. 1987. Effects of dihydropyridines on stress, myosin phosphorylation and V_0 in smooth muscle. *Am. J. Physiol.* 252(*Heart Circ. Physiol.* 21):H1049–58

29. Morgan, J. P., Morgan, K. G. 1984. Stimulus-specific patterns of intracellular calcium levels in smooth muscle of ferret portal vein. *J. Physiol.* 351:155–67

30. Murphy, R. A. 1988. The muscle cells of hollow organs. *News in Physiol. Sci.* 3:124–28

31. Park, S., Rasmussen, H. 1986. Carbachol-induced protein phosphorylation changes in bovine tracheal smooth muscle. *J. Biol. Chem.* 261:15734–39

32. Prosser, C. L. 1982. Diversity of narrow-fibered and wide-fibered muscles. See Ref. 5, pp. 381–97

33. Rasmussen, H., Takuwa, Y., Park, S. 1987. Protein kinase C in the regulation of smooth muscle contraction. *FASEB J.* 1:177–85

34. Ratz, P. H., Murphy, R. A. 1987. Contributions of intracellular and extracellular Ca^{2+} pools to activation of myosin phosphorylation and stress in swine carotid media. *Circ. Res.* 60:410–21

35. Ratz, P. H., Murphy, R. A. 1987. Agonist-, ionomycin-, and phorbol dibutyrate-induced stress in swine carotid media is dependent on myosin phosphorylation. *Fed. Proc.* 46:1098 (Abstr.)

36. Reiser, P. J., Moss, R. L., Giulian, G. G., Greaser, M. L. 1985. Shortening velocity in single fibers from adult rabbit soleus muscles is correlated with myosin heavy chain composition. *J. Biol. Chem.* 260:9077–80

37. Rembold, C. M., Murphy, R. A. 1988, Myoplasmic $[Ca^{2+}]$ determines myosin phosphorylation in agonist stimulated swine arterial smooth muscle. *Circ. Res.* 63:593–603

38. Rembold, C. M., Murphy, R. A. 1988. Myoplasmic $[Ca^{2+}]$ determines myosin phosphorylation and isometric stress in agonist stimulated swine arterial smooth muscle. *J. Cardiovasc. Pharmacol.* In press

39. Rüegg, J. C. 1986. *Calcium in Muscle Activation: A Comparative Approach*, pp. 155–64. Berlin: Springer-Verlag. 300 pp.

40. Sellers, J. R., Spudich, J. A., Sheetz, M. P. 1985. Light chain phosphorylation regulates the movement of smooth muscle myosin on actin filaments. *J. Cell Biol.* 101:1897–1902

41. Sheetz, M. P., Chasin, R., Spudich, J. A. 1984. ATP-dependent movement of myosin in vitro: characterization of a quantitative assay. *J. Cell Biol.* 99:1867–71

42. Siegman, M. J., Butler, T. M., Mooers, S. U. 1985. Energetics and regulation of crossbridge states in mammalian smooth muscle. *Experientia* 41:1020–25

43. Siegman, M. J., Butler, T. M., Mooers, S. U., Davies, R. E. 1976. Crossbridge attachment, resistance to stretch, and viscoelasticity in resting mammalian smooth muscle. *Science* 191:383–85

44. Singer, H. A., Kamm, K. E., Murphy, R. A. 1986. Estimates of activation in arterial smooth muscle. *Am. J. Physiol.* 251(*Cell Physiol.* 20):C465–73

45. Small, J. V., Fürst, D. O., De Mey, J. 1986. Localization of filamin in smooth muscle. *J. Cell Biol.* 102:210–20

46. Small, J. V., Sobieszek, A. 1980. The contractile apparatus of smooth muscle. *Int. Rev. Cytol.* 64:241–306

47. Somlyo, A. P., Somlyo, A. V. 1986. Smooth muscle structure and function. In *The Heart and Cardiovascular System*, ed. H. A. Fozzard, pp. 845–64. New York: Raven. 1694 pp.

48. Sumimoto, K., Kuriyama, H. 1986. Mobilization of free Ca^{2+} measured during contraction-relaxation in smooth muscle cells of the porcine coronary artery using quin2. *Pflügers Arch.* 406:173–80

49. Takuwa, Y., Takuwa, N., Rasmussen, H. 1987. Measurement of cytoplasmic free Ca^{2+} concentration in bovine tracheal smooth muscle using aequorin. *Am. J. Physiol.* 253(*Cell Physiol.* 22):C817–27

50. Tanner, J. A., Haeberle, J. R., Meiss, R. A. 1988. Regulation of glycerinated smooth muscle contraction and relaxation by myosin phosphorylation. *Am. J. Physiol.* 255(*Cell Physiol.* 24):C34–42

Annu. Rev. Physiol. 1989. 51:285–98

Ca²⁺, CROSSBRIDGE PHOSPHORYLATION, AND CONTRACTION

Chi-Ming Hai and Richard A. Murphy

Department of Physiology, School of Medicine, University of Virginia, Charlottesville, Virginia 22908

INTRODUCTION

Ca^{2+}-calmodulin dependent phosphorylation of the 20,000-dalton myosin light chain by myosin light chain kinase (MLCK) and dephosphorylation by myosin light chain phosphatase (MLCP) are important regulatory mechanisms for smooth muscle contraction (47, 55, 87, 91). This review attempts to answer a specific question: Can Ca^{2+}-calmodulin dependent MLCK activation, per se, explain the steady-state and transient changes in crossbridge phosphorylation, isometric stress, and isotonic shortening velocity during smooth muscle contraction? We address this question by first considering the experimental data. A rather simple hypothesis that predicts changes in phosphorylation, isometric stress, and isotonic shortening velocity using MLCK activity as the input is then discussed (36, 37).

EXPERIMENTAL RELATIONSHIPS BETWEEN PHOSPHORYLATION AND CONTRACTION

Experimental Issues

The role of crossbridge phosphorylation and the nature of crossbridge interactions with the thin filament in smooth muscle remains a contentious topic. Some issues arise from difficulties in experimentally estimating crossbridge attachment, cycling rate, and phosphorylation (60). Any interpretation

285

0066-4278/89/0315-0285$02.00

of mechanical data in terms of crossbridge properties is dependent on appropriate tissue preparations, measurement techniques, and data normalizations.

Steady-state force development by a muscle reflects the number of attached crossbridges according to the sliding filament-crossbridge paradigm (24, 42, 90). Isometric stress (force/cell cross-sectional area) at the optimal length for force generation (L_o) is probably the best estimate of steady-state crossbridge attachment (60). The normalization by cell cross-sectional area allows comparisons of the response of different tissues and gives an index of the viability of tissue preparations. Several types of smooth muscles develop stresses of $2-3 \times 10^5$ N/m^2 upon depolarization (14, 60). It is not known whether all smooth muscle cells have the same stress generating capacity. Isometric stress is a valid index only if the contractile state of the muscle is in a steady state, and the load-bearing capacity should be used as an index of crossbridge attachment at earlier times (60, 83). In general, simple correlations, or lack thereof, between phosphorylation and force (in grams) cannot be interpreted in terms of crossbridge interactions.

Isotonic shortening velocity of a muscle reflects crossbridge cycling rates. Maximum shortening velocity at zero load (V_o) expressed in L_o/time is probably the best index of average crossbridge cycling rate. V_o is commonly estimated by three methods. Isotonic afterload experiments provide force-velocity data that is used to calculate V_o by extrapolation (15). In the slack test method, a muscle is released to a slack length (zero force), and the time interval between a release and the reappearance of force is recorded. A linear regression line fitted to the slack length-time data allows calculation of the unloaded shortening velocity (V_{us}) of the contractile element (23). The third approach, the zero load-clamp method, requires more elaborate equipment (57). These methods do not always produce the same values (10, 57, 70). The slack test method is particularly prone to error, possibly due to shortening inactivation (31). All velocity measurements have artifacts if heterogeneity in activation is present. This is inevitable in agonist-induced contractions before diffusional equilibrium is attained. In contrast to skeletal muscle, V_o is a variable parameter that must be determined to fully characterize crossbridge properties.

Phosphorylation of the 20,000-dalton myosin light chain is commonly measured by two methods. Two-dimensional gel electrophoresis separates the light chains from other proteins by their molecular weight and charge differences, and further separates the phosphorylated and dephosphorylated light chains by their isoelectric pH differences (19). Urea-glycerol gel electrophoresis separates the phosphorylated and dephosphorylated light chains by their charge difference and also separates light chains from other proteins by molecular weight. The light chains are then assayed by radioimmunoblotting techniques using antibodies specific for the smooth muscle light chains

(38). The two methods have many common problems, such as artifactual changes in phosphorylation during tissue processing, charge modification (particularly during electrophoresis in the presence of commercial grade urea), multiple phosphorylation, and the presence of nonmuscle light chain isoforms (1, 19, 22, 26, 33). Phosphorylation values estimated by the two methods are similar (38). Analysis of the net effect of these artifacts with the direct visualization of proteins on two-dimensional gels shows that estimates will be high at low levels of phosphorylation (B. Gaylinn, unpublished observations). Error in measuring basal phosphorylation [0.04–0.15 mole phosphate (P_i)/mole light chain] in relaxed tissues is the major problem because small increases in phosphorylation have large effects on stress (see below). The following practices help reduce basal phosphorylation levels: (a) minimization of tissue dissection damage, (b) rapid tissue homogenization and denaturation, (c) prefocusing and the use of a narrower range of ampholyte (pI 4.5–5.4) for isoelectric focusing (22, 26), and (d) careful gel staining and destaining to improve background uniformity. Tissue phosphorylation measurements may underestimate initial rapid phosphorylation transients in situations where agonist diffusion delays yield nonuniform activation.

In summary, most of the measurements required to establish the role of phosphorylation pose difficulties in smooth muscle. This is particularly true for the initial transient changes, where most discrepancies are reported. Our approach in the following analysis is to emphasize steady-state observations that meet specific criteria in order to minimize experimental artifacts.

An extensive data base on a single tissue preparation is necessary to test a model. The most information is available on the swine carotid media. The carotid media is also unique as the object of experimental verification of the assumption that tissue measurements provide valid estimates of cell mechanics and thus crossbridge function (20, 21, 92).

Dependence of Phosphorylation on Sarcoplasmic [Ca²⁺]

If change in sarcoplasmic [Ca^{2+}] is the major determinant of MLCK activity and crossbridge phosphorylation, then a quantitative relationship should exist between these variables (53). Initial transients in both [Ca^{2+}] and phosphorylation were observed in most agonist-induced contractions, and steady-state stress development is associated with elevated [Ca^{2+}] or phosphorylation in most but not all studies (12, 59, 75–79, 95, 96). However, it is controversial whether there is an invariant relationship between steady-state isometric stress and sarcoplasmic [Ca^{2+}] for different agonists (12, 59). Time-matched measurements of sarcoplasmic [Ca^{2+}], phosphorylation, isometric stress, and isotonic shortening velocity in the swine carotid showed good steady-state correlations between [Ca^{2+}] and phosphorylation, and between phosphorylation and stress or V_o (75–77). It is plausible that sarcoplasmic $[Ca^{2+}]$ is the normal physiological determinant of phosphorylation, but verification requires extensive further work.

Dependence of Isometric Stress on Phosphorylation

The quantitative relationship between stress and phosphorylation has been difficult to establish in intact tissues because of high basal phosphorylation artifacts and the effects of non-steady-state conditions (1, 2, 13, 29, Murphy this volume). Recent studies show a steep dependence of steady-state stress on phosphorylation in swine carotid media activated by different agonists (74, 76, 77). Small increases in phosphorylation led to significant stress development, and stress approached maximum levels with approximately 35% phosphorylation in the carotid media. However, significant phosphorylation without comparable stress development was observed in tracheal smooth muscle under some circumstances (28). Thus, there may not be a unique dependence of stress on phosphorylation in all tissues.

Dependence of Isotonic Shortening Velocity on Phosphorylation

Crossbridge cycling rates, as measured by isotonic shortening velocity at small or zero external load, are consistently linearly proportional to crossbridge phosphorylation in a steady-state contraction in the swine carotid (1, 2, 15, 83). This is true in other smooth muscle types (29, 46, 94), with different types of activation (K^+ depolarization and receptor activation) (29, 75, 76) and at different temperatures (22° and 37°C) (58). Although the steady-state dependence of shortening velocity on phosphorylation appears to be invariant, temporal dissociation of shortening velocity from phosphorylation was reported (82). Dissociation of V_o and phosphorylation under non-steady-state conditions would be predicted by the nature of the errors in those two measurements (phosphorylation is a tissue average, while V_o is dominated by the most highly activated cells). Unlike skeletal muscle the stress-velocity relationship is not unique and smooth muscle exhibits a family of phosphorylation-dependent curves (15).

Definition of Latch State

Our analysis of the literature suggests that phosphorylation, per se, may determine the mechanical response of smooth muscle. The three steady-state data sets are related in Figure 1: (a) the steep dependence of stress on low values of phosphorylation (solid line in the x-y plane), (b) the linear dependence of V_o on phosphorylation (solid line in the x-z plane), and (c) the family of stress-velocity curves associated with different phosphorylation levels (y-z planes). The surface defines the parameters that mechanically describe the carotid media. The latch state can be defined only in the relative sense in terms of high stress, associated with low velocities and phosphorylation (Murphy, this volume).

LATCHBRIDGE HYPOTHESIS

The postulate that the latch state is associated with dephosphorylated, attached crossbridges (latchbridges) has considerable experimental support (Murphy, this volume). The maintenance of latchbridges is Ca^{2+} dependent: a smooth muscle in the latch state can be relaxed by the removal of extracellular Ca^{2+}. This does not necessarily imply that a latchbridge is directly regulated by Ca^{2+}. Nevertheless, some Ca^{2+}-dependent process(es) must be involved in the formation of latchbridges. The formation of latchbridges may be phosphorylation dependent because stress development and maintenance are correlated with increased phosphorylation levels in intact tissues. The key question is whether Ca^{2+}-dependent phosphorylation can explain both contraction and the latch state or whether another Ca^{2+}-dependent regulatory mechanism is involved in latchbridge regulation.

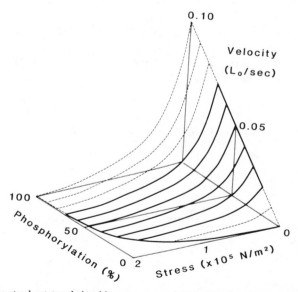

Figure 1 The steady-state relationships among crossbridge phosphorylation, stress, and velocity. Solid lines fit experimental measurements on the swine carotid media (37°C). Dashed lines are predicted behavior at levels of phosphorylation, which are difficult to measure accurately or cannot be sustained in the intact tissue. The axes are represented as dotted lines for 50% and 100% phosphorylation. This figure was generated by a model (36, 37).

Model

We took a minimalist approach by postulating that a latchbridge is formed by dephosphorylation of an attached phosphorylated crossbridge (Figure 2, *K5*) (36). In this model, latchbridge formation and detachment are assumed to be driven by mass action (18, 36). The only Ca^{2+}-dependent regulatory mechanism is crossbridge phosphorylation. The model is consistent with biochemical data that crossbridge phosphorylation is obligatory for crossbridge cycling and actin-activated myosin ATPase activity (47, 55). The novel feature in the model is the latchbridge species, which reflects the postulate that an attached crossbridge is also a substrate for MLCK and MLCP. The model has two crossbridge cycles: (*a*) the phosphorylated crossbridge cycle described by *K3* and *K4*, and (*b*) the latchbridge cycle described by *K1, K3, K5,* and *K7* (Figure 2). Note that two ATP molecules are hydrolyzed in the latchbridge cycle.

Rate constants in the model were resolved by fitting time-course data of myosin phosphorylation and stress during a fast contraction elicited by electrical stimulation of the carotid media (36, 84). Two constraints were necessary to resolve a unique set of rate constants (36). First, it was necessary to assume that MLCK and MLCP have equal affinities for free and attached crossbridges (i.e. *K1* = *K6* and *K2* = *K5*). Second, we assumed that the duty cycle of phosphorylated crossbridges was 4:1 (i.e. *K3/K4* = 4). Comparison of the rate constants shows that latchbridge detachment is the rate-limiting step. The only postulated difference between latchbridges (AM) and attached, phosphorylated crossbridges (AMp) is their detachment rates. This could be due to an increase in the ADP binding affinity of the dephosphorylated

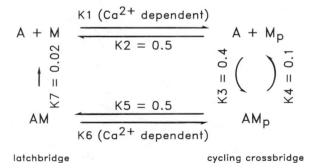

Figure 2   Structure of model. A, actin (thin filament); M, detached dephosphorylated crossbridge; Mp, detached phosphorylated crossbridge; AMp, attached phosphorylated crossbridge; AM, attached dephosphorylated crossbridge (latchbridge). The rate constants *K1* to *K7* were resolved from time-course data of myosin light chain phosphorylation and isometric stress development in fast contractions of the electrically stimulated swine carotid media at 37°C. The value of *K7* is higher than first estimated (36) as more data sets were modeled giving greater precision. Redrawn from Ref. 36 with permission from the American Physiological Society.

latchbridge (40, 80). Driska (18) derived a similar value for $K7$ in an examination of this model from data on dephosphorylation and relaxation in the swine carotid media.

Model Predictions

The steady-state phosphorylation-stress relationship can be predicted from the rate constants (Figure 3). The model predicts a steep dependence of stress on phosphorylation, with stress reaching 90% of maximum at 35% phosphorylation. This prediction was confirmed recently in the swine carotid (Figure 1; 74, 76, 77).

A. F. Huxley (42) showed that a two-state model consisting of free and attached crossbridges described by two first-order rate constants for attachment and detachment could predict the unique stress-velocity curve of skeletal muscle. We asked whether the four-state model (Figure 2) would predict the phosphorylation-dependent family of stress-velocity curves characteristic of smooth muscle (Figure 1; 37). We followed Huxley's approach, which postulates that the attachment and detachment rate constants depend on the position of a crossbridge relative to its equilibrium position. The four-state latchbridge model was transformed to resemble a two-state model by lumping the phosphorylated and unphosphorylated crossbridges. This was justified by the fact that AM and AMp have similar load-bearing capacities (83). Further-

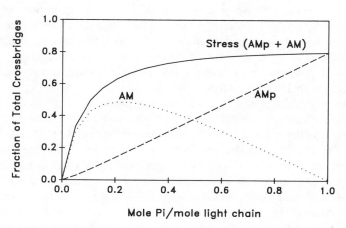

Figure 3   Model predictions of the steady-state dependence of stress (AMp + AM; solid line), attached phosphorylated crossbridges (AMp; dashed line), and latchbridges (AM; dotted line) on myosin phosphorylation for the swine carotid media (37°C). The relationships were generated by solving the system of differential equations describing the fractional content of each crossbridge species in terms of rate constants resolved from experimental data (Figure 2). The rate constants $K1$ and $K6$, representing Ca^{2+}-dependent myosin light chain kinase activity, were changed from 0.001 to 15 s^{-1}, which corresponded to phosphorylation levels up to 0.97 mole P$_i$/mole light chain. Modified from Ref. 36 with permission from the American Physiological Society.

more, the kinetics of phosphorylation and dephosphorylation are fast: at most times the phosphorylated and dephosphorylated crossbridges are in rapid equilibrium.

The steady-state exchange between the total free and total attached crossbridges are described by two apparent rate constants that represent the ratios of total flux per total number of crossbridges (37). For example, the apparent detachment rate constant is given by: (total flux along pathways labeled by *K4* and *K7*)/(AM + AMp). The model predicted a linear dependence of the apparent rate constants for overall attachment and detachment on phosphorylation. This was consistent with the experimental observation that V_o increased linearly with phosphorylation. Assuming a contractile unit length of 2.2 μm (3, 27) and structural similarities of the crossbridges in smooth and skeletal myosin (85, 90, 93), the model quantitatively predicts the linear relationship between V_o and phosphorylation and the family of stress-velocity curves associated with different phosphorylation levels (Figure 1; 37). Other model predictions may serve as additional tests for the hypothesis (36, 37).

The model also qualitatively predicts some non-steady-state experimental observations. First, a phosphorylation transient is predicted to increase only the rate of stress development, with no effect on the steady-state stress (36, 73 Murphy, this volume). A second prediction is that ATP consumption due to crossbridge phosphorylation and dephosphorylation is higher than that due to crossbridge cycling. This is consistent with the low efficiency of work production by smooth muscles, while a latchbridge could contribute to the high economy of force maintenance (7, 54, 81). Preliminary results (unpublished) also suggest that the model predicts time courses of dephosphorylation and stress during relaxation in the swine carotid media in agreement with Driska's analysis (18).

Data obtained from intact tissues are the primary focus of this review and analysis. However, chemically skinned tissue preparations have been used extensively in the study of smooth muscle physiology (4, 8, 9, 25, 32, 35, 39, 43, 48, 70, 78). Major differences between skinned and intact tissue preparations are temperature (22°C vs 37°C), concentrations of small molecules, and differential loss of proteins associated with the contractile apparatus (48, 52). There is some controversy on the steady-state relationship between stress and phosphorylation in Ca^{2+}-activated skinned smooth muscle. Most investigators report a linear dependence of stress on phosphorylation (90a). In contrast, Kenney et al (50) and Kerrick & Hoar (51) observed a steep dependence of stress on phosphorylation in skinned tissues similar to that seen in intact tissues (Figure 1). A difference in MLCP activity between Kerrick & Hoar's preparation and other preparations may account for the discrepancies. The model predicts that a decrease in MLCP activity (Figure 2, *K2, K5*) will change the steep stress-phosphorylation relationship to a more linear one with a smaller number of latchbridges for a given level of phosphorylation (Figure 3). This prediction is consistent with observed decreases in MLCP activity in some skinned tissues (6). There is more agreement on data obtained in contractions of thiophosphorylated skinned tissues (8). Since thiophosphorylated crossbridges are poor substrates for MLCP, only the phosphorylated crossbridge cycle is activated in a Ca^{2+}-free, thiophosphorylated skinned tissue. The model predicts linear dependence of stress on phosphorylation if K2 and K5 are very low in accordance with experimental observations.

MLCP is clearly an important enzyme involved in the regulation of smooth muscle contraction. Several different MLCPs in smooth muscle dephosphorylate the 20,000-dalton myosin light chain (16, 17, 65–69), probably because of the broad specificity of MLCPs in general (89). However, only the smooth muscle MLCP IV has a high enough affinity for heavy meromyosin (69). One MLCP is modulated by polycations (16, 17), but there is no evidence that a parameter that changes during contraction or relaxation can affect MLCP activity. The model assumes that MLCP is not regulated and that it apparently need not be regulated to explain the steady-state behavior of smooth muscle. Nevertheless, MLCP activity is a very important determinant of crossbridge interactions and the assumption that it is not regulated may reflect ignorance.

ASSESSMENT AND CONCLUSIONS

Merits

Other models of smooth muscle contraction have been proposed. However, these models either did not explain the latch state and the properties shown in Figure 1 (49, 71, 72) or did not explain the changes in crossbridge phosphorylation (30). The model described in this review is relatively simple and has a minimum number of ad hoc assumptions. The only novel element in the model is the postulate that attached, as well as free, crossbridges are substrates for MLCP and MLCK, which results in the latchbridge. The model shows that Ca^{2+}-calmodulin dependent myosin light chain phosphorylation may suffice to regulate force development and latch. The hypothesis generates specific predictions, which can be tested experimentally.

Is the Model Complete?

A unique relationship between sarcoplasmic $[Ca^{2+}]$ and phosphorylation of the MLCK-specific sites on the 20,000-dalton light chain must be demonstrated to completely establish the role of Ca^{2+} and MLCK in smooth muscle contraction (53). Myosin light chains can be phosphorylated by kinases other than MLCK, such as protein kinase C (5, 62, 63). This kinase has been proposed to be involved in the regulation of the latch state (72). However, a preliminary report suggests that only the MLCK-specific sites on the 20,000-dalton light chain are phosphorylated in activated tissues (45).

The model in this study was generated and tested on data obtained from the swine carotid media, a relatively slow tonic type of smooth muscle. Somewhat different rate constants can be resolved from the faster trachealis muscle (36), and it is probable that MLCK and MLCP contents or activities vary among tissue types and smooth muscle myosin isoforms may exist. It is also possible that additional regulatory mechanisms occur in the carotid and/or other smooth muscles with different functional specializations (28, 64, Kamm & Stull, this volume). This model described in this review serves as a framework for the integrative understanding of smooth muscle contraction in terms of the regulation of processes (rate constants). The model does not rule out other regulatory mechanisms (4, 11, 41, 43, 44, 56, 86, 88), which may not be manifested in the limited data sets. A Ca^{2+}-switch in the thin filament (56) or on myosin (4), which operates in parallel with crossbridge phosphorylation, is also consistent with the model.

Does the Model Have Wider Applicability?

Covalent modification of proteins by phosphorylation is a ubiquitous regulatory mechanism implicated in muscle contraction, nonmuscle motility, energy metabolism, carrier-mediated transport, and ion channels. However, because of the significant reduction in efficiency, it makes little sense to regulate crossbridges by phosphorylation if it acts simply as a switch. The four-state model, which depends on covalent regulation, allows control of both the rate and extent of a process, and the development of the latch state. This has significant energetic advantages for muscle in hollow organs, despite the fact that phosphorylation and dephosphorylation is a major source of ATP consumption. A four-state system may characterize other processes regulated by protein phosphorylation.

ACKNOWLEDGMENTS

This work was supported by NIH Grant 5-P01-HL19242, and a fellowship from the American Heart Association, Virginia Affiliate.

Literature Cited

1. Aksoy, M. O., Mras, S., Kamm, K. E., Murphy, R. A. 1983. Ca^{2+}, cAMP, and changes in myosin phosphorylation during contraction of smooth muscle. *Am. J. Physiol.* 245(*Cell Physiol.* 14):C255–70

2. Aksoy, M. O., Murphy, R. A., Kamm, K. E. 1982. Role of Ca^{2+} and myosin light chain phosphorylation in regulation of smooth muscle. *Am. J. Physiol.* 242(*Cell Physiol.* 11):C109–16

3. Ashton, F. T., Somlyo, A. V., Somlyo, A. P. 1975. The contractile apparatus of vascular smooth muscle: intermediate high voltage stereo electron microscopy. *J. Mol. Biol.* 98:17–29

4. Barsotti, R. J., Ikebe, M., Hartshorne, D. J. 1987. Effects of Ca^{2+}, Mg^{2+}, and myosin phosphorylation on skinned smooth muscle fibers. *Am. J. Physiol.* 252(*Cell Physiol.* 21):C543–54

5. Bengur, A. R., Robinson, E. A., Appel-

la, E., Sellers, J. R. 1987. Sequence of the sites phosphorylated by protein kinase C in the smooth muscle myosin light chain. *J. Biol. Chem.* 282:7613–17

6. Bialojan, C., Merkel, L., Rüegg, J. C., Gifford, D., DiSalvo, J. 1985. Prolonged relaxation of detergent-skinned smooth muscle involves decreased endogenous phosphatase activity. *Proc. Soc. Exp. Biol. Med.* 178:648–52

7. Butler, T. M., Seigman, M. J., Mooers, S. 1983. Chemical energy usage during shortening and work production in mammalian smooth muscle. *Am. J. Physiol.* 244(*Cell Physiol.* 13):C234–42

8. Cassidy, P., Hoar, P. E., Kerrick, W. G. L. 1979. Irreversible thiophosphorylation and activation of tension in functionally skinned rabbit ileum strips by [^{35}S]ATPδS. *J. Biol. Chem.* 254:11148–53

9. Chatterjee, M., Hai, C.-M., Murphy, R. A. 1987. Dependence of stress and velocity on Ca^{2+} and myosin phosphorylation in the skinned swine carotid media. In *Regulation and Contraction of Smooth Muscle,* ed. M. J. Siegman, A. P. Somlyo, N. L. Stephens, pp. 399–410. New York: Liss. 507 pp.

10. Claflin, D. R., Faulkner, J. A. 1985. Shortening velocity extrapolated to zero load and unloaded shortening velocity of whole rat skeletal muscle. *J. Physiol.* 359:357–63

11. Clark, T., Ngai, P. K., Sutherland, C., Gröschel-Stewart, U., Walsh, M. P. 1986. Vascular smooth muscle caldesmon. *J. Biol. Chem.* 261:8028–35

12. Defeo, T. T., Morgan, K. G. 1985. Calcium-force relationships as detected with aequorin in two different vascular smooth muscles of the ferret. *J. Physiol.* 369:269–82

13. Dillon, P. F., Aksoy, M. O., Driska, S. P., Murphy, R. A. 1981. Myosin phosphorylation and the cross bridge cycle in arterial smooth muscle. *Science* 211:495–97

14. Dillon, P. F., Murphy, R. A. 1982. High force development and crossbridge attachment in smooth muscle from swine carotid. *Circ. Res.* 50:799–804

15. Dillon, P. F., Murphy, R. A. 1982. Tonic force maintenance with reduced shortening velocity in arterial smooth muscle. *Am. J. Physiol.* 242(*Cell Physiol.* 11):C102–8

16. Di Salvo, J., Gifford, D., Kokkinakis, A. 1985. Properties and function of a bovine aortic polycation-modulated protein phosphatase. *Adv. Protein Phosphatases* 1:327–45

17. Di Salvo, J., Gifford, D., Kokkinakis,

A. 1985. Heat-stable regulatory factors are associated with polycation modulable phosphatases. *Adv. Enzyme Regul.* 23:103–22

18. Driska, S. P. 1987. See Ref. 9, pp. 387–98

19. Driska, S. P., Aksoy, M. O., Murphy, R. A. 1981. Myosin light chain phosphorylation associated with contraction in arterial smooth muscle. *Am. J. Physiol.* 240(*Cell Physiol.* 9):C222–33

20. Driska, S. P., Damon, D. N., Murphy, R. A. 1978. Estimates of cellular mechanics in an arterial smooth muscle. *Biophys. J.* 24:525–40

21. Driska, S. P., Murphy, R. A. 1978. Estimate of cellular force generation in an arterial smooth muscle with a high actin: myosin ratio. *Blood Vessels* 15:26–32

22. Eddinger, T. J., Gaylinn, B. D., Monical, P. L., Murphy, R. A. 1988. Evidence for non-muscle myosin in smooth muscle cells. *Biophys. J.* 53:579 (Abstr.)

23. Edman, K. A. P. 1979. The velocity of unloaded shortening and its relation to sarcomere length and isometric force in vertebrate muscle fibres. *J. Physiol.* 291:143–59

24. Eisenberg, E., Hill, T. L. 1985. Muscle contraction and free energy in biological systems. *Science* 227:999–1006

25. Endo, M., Iino, M. 1980. Specific perforation of muscle cell membranes with preserved SR functions by saponin treatment. *J. Muscle Res. Cell Motil.* 1:89–100

26. Erdodi, F., Bárány, M., Bárány, K. 1987. Myosin light chain isoforms and their phosphorylation in arterial smooth muscle. *Circ. Res.* 61:898–903

27. Fay, F. S., Fujiwara, K., Rees, D. D., Fogarty, K. E. 1983. Distribution of alpha-actinin in single isolated smooth muscle cells. *J. Cell Biol.* 96:783–95

28. Gerthoffer, W. T. 1987. Dissociation of myosin phosphorylation and active tension during muscarinic stimulation of tracheal smooth muscle. *J. Pharmacol. Exp. Ther.* 240:8–15

29. Gerthoffer, W. T., Murphy, R. A. 1983. Myosin phosphorylation and regulation of cross-bridge cycle in tracheal smooth muscle. *Am. J. Physiol.* 244(*Cell Physiol.* 13):C182–87

30. Gestrelius, S., Borgstrom, P. 1986. A dynamic model of smooth muscle contraction. *Biophys. J.* 50:157–69

31. Gunst, S. J. 1986. Effect of length history on contractile behavior of canine tracheal smooth muscle. *Am. J. Physiol.* 250(*Cell Physiol.* 19):C146–54

32. Haeberle, J. R., Hathaway, D. R.,

DePaoli-Roach, A. P. 1985. Dephosphorylation of myosin by the catalytic subunit of a type-2 phosphatase produces relaxation of chemically skinned uterine smooth muscle. *J. Biol. Chem.* 260:9965–68

33. Haeberle, J. R., Hott, J. W., Hathaway, D. R. 1984. Pseudophosphorylation of the smooth muscle 20,000 dalton myosin light chain: an artifact due to protein modification. *Biochim. Biophys. Acta* 790:78–86

34. Deleted in proof

35. Hai, C.-M., Murphy, R. A. 1987. Ba^{2+} induces contraction in swine carotid artery by mobilizing intracellular Ca^{2+}. *Am. J. Physiol.* 252(*Cell Physiol.* 21):C378–84

36. Hai, C.-M., Murphy, R. A. 1988. Cross-bridge phosphorylation and regulation of latch state in smooth muscle. *Am. J. Physiol.* 254(*Cell Physiol.* 23):C99–106

37. Hai, C.-M., Murphy, R. A. 1988. Regulation of shortening velocity by crossbridge phosphorylation in smooth muscle. *Am. J. Physiol.* 255(*Cell Physiol* 24):C86–94

38. Hathaway, D. R., Haeberle, J. R. 1985. A radioimmunblotting method for measuring myosin light chain phosphorylation levels in smooth muscle. *Am. J. Physiol.* 249(*Cell Physiol.* 18):C345–51

39. Hoar, P. E., Kerrick, W. G., Cassidy, P. S. 1979. Chicken gizzard: relation between calcium-activated phosphorylation and contraction. *Science* 204:503–6

40. Hoar, P. E., Mahoney, C. W., Kerrick, W. G. L. 1987. $MgADP^-$ increases maximum tension and Ca^{2+} sensitivity in skinned rabbit soleus fibers. *Pflügers Arch.* 410:30–36

41. Hoar, P. E., Pato, M. D., Kerrick, W. G. 1985. Myosin light chain phosphatase—effect on the activation and relaxation of gizzard smooth muscle skinned fibers. *J. Biol. Chem.* 260:8760–64

42. Huxley, A. F. 1957. Muscle structure and theories of contraction. *Prog. Biophys. Mol. Biol.* 7:255–318

43. Ikebe, M., Barsotti, R. J., Hinkins, S., Hartshorne, D. J. 1984. Effects of magnesium chloride on smooth muscle actomyosin adenosine-5'-triphosphatase activity, myosin conformation, and tension development in glycerinated smooth muscle fibers. *Biochemistry* 23:5062–68

44. Ikebe, M., Hinkins, S., Hartshorne, D. J. 1983. Correlation of enzymatic properties and conformation of smooth muscle myosin. *Biochemistry* 22:4580–87

45. Kamm, K. E., Colburn, J. C., Hsu, L.-C., Michnoff, C. H., Stull, J. T. 1988. Sites of myosin light chain phosphorylation in contracting smooth muscle. *Biophys. J.* 53:185 (Abstr.)

46. Kamm, K. E., Stull, J. T. 1985. Myosin phosphorylation, force and maximal shortening velocity in neurally stimulated tracheal smooth muscle. *Am. J. Physiol.* 249(*Cell Physiol.* 18):C238–47

47. Kamm, K. E., Stull, J. T. 1985. The function of myosin and myosin light chain kinase phosphorylation in smooth muscle. *Annu. Rev. Pharmacol. Toxicol.* 25:593–620

48. Kargacin, G. J., Fay, F. S. 1987. Physiological and structural properties of saponin-skinned single smooth muscle cells. *J. Gen. Physiol.* 90:49–73

49. Kato, S., Osa, T., Ogasawara, T. 1984. Kinetic model for isometric contraction in smooth muscle on the basis of myosin phosphorylation hypothesis. *Biophys. J.* 46:35–44

50. Kenney, R. E., Hoar, P. E., Kerrick, W. G. L. 1988. Myosin light chain phosphorylation and thiophosphorylation in skinned chicken gizzard at low Mg^{2+}. *Biophys. J.* 53:185 (Abstr.)

51. Kerrick, W. G. L., Hoar, P. E. 1985. Regulation of contraction in skinned smooth muscle cells by Ca^{2+} and protein phosphorylation. *Adv. Protein Phosphatases* 2:133–52

52. Kossmann, R., Fürst, D., Small, J. V. 1987. Structural and biochemical analysis of skinned smooth muscle preparations. *J. Muscle Res. Cell Motil* 8:135–44

53. Krebs, E. G., Beavo, J. A. 1979. Phosphorylation-dephosphorylation of enzymes. *Annu. Rev. Biochem.* 49:923–59

54. Krisanda, J., Paul, R. J. 1985. Energetics of isometric contraction in porcine carotid artery. *Am. J. Physiol.* 246(*Cell Physiol.* 15):C510–19

55. Marston, S. B. 1982. The regulation of smooth muscle contractile proteins. *Prog. Biophys. Mol. Biol.* 41:1–41

56. Marston, S. B., Lehman, W. 1985. Caldesmon is a Ca^{2+}-regulatory component of native smooth muscle. *Biochem. J.* 231:517–22

57. Mitchell, R. W., Stephens, N. L. 1983. Maximum shortening velocity of smooth muscle: zero load-clamp vs. afterloaded method. *J. Appl. Physiol.* 55:1630–33

58. Moreland, S., Moreland, R. S., Singer, H. A. 1986. Apparent dissociation between myosin light chain phosphoryla-

tion and maximal velocity of shortening in KCl depolarized swine carotid artery: effect of temperature and KCl concentration. *Pflügers Arch.* 408:139–45

59. Morgan, J. P., Morgan, K. G. 1984. Stimulus-specific patterns of intracellular calcium levels in smooth muscle of ferret portal vein. *J. Physiol.* 351:155–67

60. Murphy, R. A. 1980. Mechanics of vascular smooth muscle. In *Handbook of Physiology*, Vol. 2, Sect. 2, ed. D. F. Bohr, A. P. Somlyo, H. V. Sparks, Jr., 2:325–51. Bethesda, Md: Am. Physiol. Soc. Press. 686 pp.

61. Murphy, R. A. 1988. Special Topic: Contraction in smooth muscle cells. *Annu. Rev. Physiol.* 51:275–83

62. Nishikawa, M., Hidaka, H., Adelstein, R. S. 1983. Phosphorylation of smooth muscle heavy meromyosin by calcium-activated, phospholipid-dependent protein kinase. *J. Biol. Chem.* 258:14069–72

63. Nishikawa, M., Shirokawa, S., Adelstein, R. S. 1985. Phosphorylation of smooth muscle myosin light chain kinase by protein kinase C. *J. Biol. Chem.* 260:8978–83

64. Park, S., Rasmussen, H. 1986. Carbachol induces protein phosphorylation changes in bovine tracheal smooth muscle. *J. Biol. Chem.* 261:15734–39

65. Pato, M. D. 1985. Properties of the smooth muscle phosphatases from turkey gizzards. *Adv. Protein Phosphatases* 1:367–82

66. Pato, M. D., Adelstein, R. S. 1980. Dephosphorylation of the 20,000-dalton light chain of myosin by two different phosphatases from smooth muscle. *J. Biol. Chem.* 255:6535–38

67. Pato, M. D., Adelstein, R. S. 1983. Purification and characterization of a multisubunit phosphatase from turkey gizzard smooth muscle. *J. Biol. Chem.* 258:7047–54

68. Pato, M. D., Adelstein, R. S. 1983. Characterization of a Mg^{2+}-dependent phosphatase from turkey gizzard smooth muscle. *J. Biol. Chem.* 258:7055–60

69. Pato, M. D., Kerc, E. 1985. Purification and characterization of a smooth muscle myosin phosphatase from turkey gizzards. *J. Biol. Chem.* 260:12359–66

70. Paul, R. J., Doerman, G., Zeugner, C., Rüegg, J. C. 1983. The dependence of unloaded shortening velocity on Ca^{2+}, calmodulin, and duration of contraction in "chemically skinned" smooth muscle. *Circ. Res.* 53:342–51

71. Peterson, J. W. 1982. Simple model of

smooth muscle myosin phosphorylation and dephosphorylation as rate-limiting mechanism. *Biophys. J.* 37:453–59

72. Rasmussen, H., Takuwa, Y., Park, S. 1987. Protein kinase C in the regulation of smooth muscle contraction. *FASEB J.* 1:177–85

73. Ratz, P., Murphy, R. A. 1987. Contribution of intracellular and extracellular Ca^{2+} pools to activation of myosin phosphorylation and stress in swine carotid media. *Circ. Res.* 60:410–21

74. Ratz, P. H., Murphy, R. A. 1987. Agonist-, ionomycin-, and phorbol dibutyrate-induced stress in swine carotid media is dependent on myosin phosphorylation. *Fed. Proc.* 46:1098 (Abstr.)

75. Rembold, C. M., Murphy, R. A. 1986 Myoplasmic calcium, myosin phosphorylation, and regulation of the crossbridge cycle in swine arterial smooth muscle. *Circ. Res.* 58:803–15

76. Rembold, C. M., Murphy, R. A. 1988. Myoplasmic (Ca^{2+}) determines myosin phosphorylation and isometric stress in agonist stimulated swine arterial smooth muscle. *Circ. Res.* 63:593–603

77. Rembold, C. M., Murphy, R. A. 1988. Myoplasmic (Ca^{2+}) determines myosin phosphorylation and isometric stress in agonist stimulated swine arterial smooth muscle. *J. Cardiovasc. Pharmacol.* In press

78. Saida, K. 1982. Intracellular Ca release in skinned smooth muscle. *J. Gen. Physiol.* 80:191–202

79. Satoh, S., Itoh, T., Kuriyama, H. 1987. Actions of angiotensin II and noradrenaline on smooth muscle cells of the canine mesenteric artery. *Pflügers Arch.* 410:132–38

80. Schoenberg, M., Eisenberg, E. 1987. ADP binding to myosin crossbridges and its effect on the cross-bridge detachment rate constants. *J. Gen. Physiol.* 89:905–20

81. Siegman, M. J., Butler, T. M., Mooers, S. U., Davies, R. E. 1980. Chemical energetics of force development, force maintenance, and relaxation in mammalian smooth muscle. *J. Gen. Physiol.* 76:609–29

82. Siegman, M. J., Butler, T. M., Mooers, S. U., Michalek, A. 1984. Ca^{2+} can affect V_{max} without changes in myosin light chain phosphorylation in smooth muscle. *Pflügers Arch.* 401:385–90

83. Singer, H. A., Kamm, K. E., Murphy, R. A. 1986. Estimates of activation in arterial smooth muscle. *Am. J. Physiol.* 251(*Cell Physiol.* 20):C465–73

84. Singer, H. A, Murphy, R. A. 1987.

Maximal rates of activation in electrically stimulated swine carotid media. *Circ. Res.* 60:438–45

85. Small, J. V., Squire, J. M. 1972. Structural basis of contraction in vertebrate smooth muscle. *J. Mol. Biol.* 67:117–49

86. Smith, C. W., Pritchard, K., Marston, S. B. 1987. The mechanism of Ca^{2+} regulation of vascular smooth muscle thin filaments by caldesmon and calmodulin. *J. Biol. Chem.* 262:116–22

87. Sobieszek, A. 1985. Phosphorylation reaction of vertebrate smooth muscle myosin: an enzyme kinetic analysis. *Biochemistry* 24:1266–74

88. Sobue, K., Morimoto, K., Inui, M., Kanda, K., Kakiuchi, S. 1982. Control of actin-myosin interaction of gizzard smooth muscle by calmodulin- and caldesmon-linked flip-flop mechanism. *Biomed. Res.* 3:188–96

89. Sparks, J. W., Brautigan, D. L. 1986. Molecular basis for substrate specificity of protein kinases and phosphatases. *Int. J. Biochem.* 18:497–504

90. Squire, J. M. 1981. *The Structural Basis of Muscular Contraction.* New York: Plenum. 698 pp.

90a. Tanner, J. A., Haeberle, J. B., Meiss, R. A. 1988. Regulation of glycerinated smooth muscle contraction and relaxation by myosin phosphorylation. *Am. J. Physiol.* 255(*Cell Physiol.* 24):C34–42

91. Trybus, K. M., Lowey, S. 1985. Mechanism of smooth muscle myosin phosphorylation. *J. Biol. Chem.* 260: 15988–95

92. Walmsley, J. G., Murphy, R. A. 1987. Force-length dependence of arterial lamellar, smooth muscle, and myofilament orientations. *Am. J. Physiol.* 253(*Heart Circ. Physiol.* 22):H1141–47

93. Warrick, H. M., Spudich, J. A. 1987. Myosin structure and function in cell motility. *Ann. Rev. Cell Biol.* 3:379–421

94. Weisbrodt, N. W., Murphy, R. A. 1985. Myosin phosphorylation and contraction of feline esophageal smooth muscle. *Am. J. Physiol.* 249(*Cell Physiol.* 18):C9–14

95. Williams, D. A., Becker, P. L., Fay, F. S. 1987. Regional changes in calcium underlying contraction of single smooth muscle cells. *Science* 235:1644–48

96. Williams, D. A., Fay, F. S. 1986. Calcium transients and resting levels in isolated smooth muscle cells as monitored with quin 2. *Am. J. Physiol.* 250(*Cell Physiol.* 19):C779–91

Annu. Rev. Physiol. 1989. 51:299–313
Copyright © 1989 by Annual Reviews Inc. All rights reserved

REGULATION OF SMOOTH MUSCLE CONTRACTILE ELEMENTS BY SECOND MESSENGERS

Kristine E. Kamm and James T. Stull

Department of Physiology and Moss Heart Center, University of Texas Southwestern Medical Center at Dallas, Texas 75235

INTRODUCTION

In smooth muscle cells, development of force results from MgATP-dependent cyclic interactions of myosin in thick filaments with actin in thin filaments. The force of contraction, in turn, is regulated by the concentration of free Ca^{2+} surrounding these myofilaments. The purposes of the present chapter are to discuss (*a*) Ca^{2+}-dependent mechanisms other than myosin light chain phosphorylation by which contractile force in smooth muscle may be regulated, and (*b*) other second messenger mechanisms that regulate contractile elements or the myosin kinase/phosphatase system.

Since the discovery that phosphorylation of the 20-kDa light chains of myosin by Ca^{2+}/calmodulin-dependent myosin light chain kinase allows smooth muscle myosin MgATPase to be activated by actin, many investigators have studied the relationship between light chain phosphorylation and active force in smooth muscle (reviewed in 42; Hai & Murphy, this volume). It is generally accepted that myosin phosphorylation and dephosphorylation are sufficient to regulate contraction. While myosin phosphorylation/dephosphorylation may be the dominant regulatory pathway, the coexistence of thin-filament linked regulation is not ruled out (51).

OTHER Ca^{2+} REGULATORY SYSTEMS

The seminal observation by Dillon et al (17) precipitated interest in the idea that a second regulatory system may have a role in the maintenance of force

299

0066-4278/89/0315-0299$02.00

by vertebrate smooth muscle. These investigators found that while force was maintained in carotid arterial smooth muscle, both 20-kDa light chain phosphorylation and maximal velocity of shortening decreased to about one-third of their maximal values. It was proposed that the dephosphorylated myosin cross bridge (termed "latch bridge") cycled slowly or not at all, but was able to maintain force via a second, Ca^{2+}-dependent regulatory mechanism, which presumably had a higher sensitivity to activation by Ca^{2+} than the myosin light chain kinase. Similar observations have since been made in other types of smooth muscle (reviewed in 42; Hai & Murphy, this volume). Another line of evidence for force-bearing states with low values of light chain phosphorylation is found in studies of relaxing muscle. Myosin is dephosphorylated more rapidly than relaxation occurs (25, 43). After the light chains are dephosphorylated to resting levels, arterial muscle exhibits a slow phase of Ca^{2+}-dependent relaxation with a half-time on the order of 4 min (25). Mechanical perturbations that would detach cross bridges revealed that these dephosphorylated cross bridges could reattach and cycle slowly. Theories addressing the issue of force maintenance with low values of light chain phosphorylation include force maintenance by (a) attached cross bridges whose detachment rates are greatly slowed after dephosphorylation (18, 27), (b) unregulated cross bridges (90) interacting with regulated thin filaments (56, 64, 80), and (c) a cross-linking of filaments in the actomyosin domain (35) or in the intermediate filament domain of the cell (46, 74). The former two theories maintain that force results from cyclic interactions of myosin with actin, while the latter submits additionally that force may be maintained by structural alterations of the filamentous domains within the smooth muscle cell. The mechanical properties of smooth muscles during both the early and late phase of tonic contractions are consistent with a cross-bridge cycling model of contraction, i.e. muscles display a hyperbolic force-velocity relation, redevelop force following quick-release, and exhibit yielding at strains consistent with cross-bridge detachment (62). However, the ideas of active interaction of actin and myosin, and structural modifications of filaments are not mutually exclusive.

Ca^{2+} Binding to Myosin

Although there is evidence that Ca^{2+} may increase the actin-activated MgAT-Pase activity of phosphorylated smooth muscle myosin (39, 63), the Ca^{2+} concentrations are greater than those required to saturate calmodulin and to activate myosin light chain kinase (3, 32). Furthermore, these concentrations are much higher than those observed in smooth muscle cytoplasm. Therefore, the physiological relevance of this effect on myosin ATPase activity is questionable.

Caldesmon and Smooth Muscle Thin Filaments

Caldesmon, found in abundance in smooth muscle, is a calmodulin- and actin-binding protein of molecular weight 150,000 (82). Sobue and colleagues found that caldesmon bound to calmodulin in the presence of Ca^{2+} and bound to filamentous actin (F-actin) in the absence of Ca^{2+}, and thereby proposed a flip-flop mechanism for Ca^{2+} regulation of caldesmon binding to thin filaments (81). These observations coupled with the observation that caldesmon inhibits actomyosin MgATPase, and that Ca^{2+}/calmodulin can relieve this inhibition (56, 64, 81) led to a number of studies on the biochemical properties of caldesmon and thin filaments with the goal of elucidating a biological role for caldesmon in the regulation of smooth muscle contractility.

DISTRIBUTION AND LOCALIZATION   Caldesmon is widely distributed in smooth muscle and nonmuscle tissues and cells (7, 11, 65, 85). Immunocytochemical studies have shown that caldesmon is localized in the actomyosin domain and not the actin–intermediate filament domain within smooth muscle cells (22, 79). In cultured smooth muscle and nonmuscle cells (7, 69), caldesmon is colocalized in stress fibers, which also contain actin and myosin (47). Such studies show that caldesmon has a subcellular distribution that would be consistent with a role in smooth muscle contraction and nonmuscle motility.

Native thin filaments from smooth muscles are composed of actin, tropomyosin, and caldesmon in molar ratios of 28:4:1 (56). The composition of thin filaments isolated from smooth muscle corresponds to that described for the actomyosin filamentous domain, as defined immunocytochemically (49). Single caldesmon molecules observed in electron micrographs appear flexible and elongated; contour lengths of low-angle rotary-shadowed molecules may be as long as 150 nm (22, 50). This length would allow the extended caldesmon to span over 28 actin molecules. Marston et al (54) developed a model in which the elongated caldesmon molecule occupies the grooves between the actin double helix, with a head piece located in register with tropomyosin.

BIOCHEMICAL PROPERTIES   Immunologically related polypeptides can be divided into two general classes, termed h-caldesmon and l-caldesmon, based on relative mobilities on SDS-PAGE. h-Caldesmon (120–150 kDa) has been purified from avian (5, 53, 64, 82) and mammalian (11, 22, 55) smooth muscle tissues; l-caldesmon (70–80 kDa) is enriched in smooth muscle cells in culture (85) and in nonmuscle cells (11, 85).

The Ca^{2+}-dependent binding of calmodulin to caldesmon was first demonstrated by calmodulin-affinity chromatography (81, 82). The stoichiometry of calmodulin binding to caldesmon is 1 mol calmodulin per mol caldesmon

(82), with a concentration for half-maximal binding between 1 and 2 μM for the high affinity sites (56, 82). This is in contrast to a much lower value (1 nM) generally obtained with myosin light chain kinases (83). In the absence of Ca^{2+}/calmodulin, caldesmon binds F-actin (5, 11, 82). Caldesmon binds to actin/tropomyosin with a K_D value of 50 nM (56). Caldesmon has also been shown to cross-link or bundle actin filaments, but the functional relevance of this effect is uncertain (reviewed in 72). Recently, Ikebe & Reardon (35) showed that caldesmon also binds to smooth muscle myosin.

The Ca^{2+}-dependent regulatory effects of caldesmon were first demonstrated when purified caldesmon was found to inhibit ATP-dependent superprecipitation of desensitized chicken gizzard actomyosin, and when this inhibitory effect was reversed by Ca^{2+}/calmodulin. These effects were described as a flip-flop regulation where disinhibition resulted from Ca^{2+}/calmodulin-dependent removal of caldesmon from the thin filament (81). Many investigators demonstrated that caldesmon inhibits actin-activated myosin MgATPase using caldesmon and activated myosin from a number of sources (11, 14, 29, 48, 53, 64). However, Ca^{2+}/calmodulin is required in molar excess of caldesmon in order to dissociate caldesmon from actin-tropomyosin filaments (5, 14, 81). Other investigators (56, 80) noted that disinhibition of native thin filaments does not necessarily result in dissociation of caldesmon from actin-tropomyosin filaments. Smith and colleagues proposed a model whereby Ca^{2+} regulates thin filaments by converting the inhibited actin-tropomyosin-caldesmon-complex to active complexes of actin-tropomyosin-caldesmon-calmodulin-Ca^{2+} and actin-tropomyosin (80). These properties have raised the question whether caldesmon, together with tropomyosin, is a primitive form of the tropomyosin-troponin regulatory systems of striated muscle (6), with calmodulin or another Ca^{2+} binding protein (54, 56) as the Ca^{2+} receptor. A precise scheme for Ca^{2+}-dependent thin filament regulation by this mechanism must, however, accommodate results from skinned fibers where myosin light chain thiophosphorylation or phosphorylation by Ca^{2+}-independent kinase results in contraction in the absence of Ca^{2+} (28).

Caldesmon phosphorylation may provide an additional step in the regulation of thin filament function. Caldesmon is phosphorylated by a Ca^{2+}/calmodulin-dependent kinase (distinct from myosin light chain kinase), and only the dephosphorylated form is inhibitory (64, 66). Gizzard caldesmon has been shown to exhibit Ca^{2+}/calmodulin-dependent kinase activity and to undergo intermolecular autophosphorylation (75). The Ca^{2+}/calmodulin-dependent reversal of inhibition of actomyosin MgATPase is significantly more rapid, however, than phosphorylation of caldesmon in reconstituted or native thin filament preparations (29, 52). Caldesmon has also been shown to be phosphorylated by protein kinase C in vitro, but additional studies are required to establish a functional role (86).

FUNCTIONAL STUDIES   To date, only a few direct studies have been done to investigate the function of caldesmon in contractile or motile systems. In skinned gizzard smooth muscle fibers, addition of caldesmon induced relaxation of submaximal contractions without altering the level of myosin light chain phosphorylation (84). This effect was reversed by high molar excess of calmodulin over caldesmon in the presence of Ca^{2+}. Caldesmon also decreases tension in glycerinated skeletal muscle fibers whose intrinsic troponin regulatory system has been inactivated (54). Caldesmon inhibits the movement of myosin-coated beads along actin cables of Nitella, and this inhibition can be reversed by the addition of Ca^{2+}/calmodulin (77).

Some studies in smooth muscle indicate that Ca^{2+}-dependent myosin phosphorylation cannot always account for force and indirectly implicate caldesmon as a candidate regulatory element. Questions related to the latch state are discussed above. Wagner & Rüegg (89) showed that in freshly glycerinated gizzard fibers, force development was dependent on Ca^{2+}/calmodulin; however, no increase in myosin light chain phosphorylation was observed. Moreland and coworkers (61) showed that calmodulin antagonists inhibit latch bridges in detergent skinned carotid arterial muscle. A second category of dissociation between light chain phosphorylation and force is described by Gerthoffer (24), where reintroduction of Ca^{2+} to Ca^{2+}-depleted tracheal smooth muscle tissues in the presence of agonist causes significant phosphorylation without development of isometric force. This result indicates, in the event that the site is phosphorylated by myosin light chain kinase (see below), that the interaction of actin and myosin may be inhibited. Further investigations regarding the involvement of thin filament regulation in vertebrate smooth muscle contraction may clarify a number of such issues.

PROTEIN KINASE SUBSTRATES AND SECOND MESSENGER SYSTEMS

Second messengers such as cyclic AMP (cAMP), cyclic GMP (cGMP), and diacylglycerol (DAG) activate specific protein kinases including cAMP-dependent protein kinase, cGMP-dependent protein kinase, and protein kinase C, respectively (19). These second messenger systems may alter smooth muscle contraction by increasing or decreasing intracellular Ca^{2+} concentrations and, thus, indirectly affect the extent of myosin light chain phosphorylation. In this section we discuss the physiological importance of second messenger–mediated phosphorylation of specific proteins within the contractile elements.

Myosin Light Chain Kinase Phosphorylation

A number of protein kinases phosphorylate myosin light chain kinase. Myosin light chain kinase phosphorylates itself: it catalyzes an autophosphorylation reaction (67, 68). This reaction is slow relative to the rates of phosphorylation of myosin light chain kinase by other protein kinases. No functional significance for autophosphorylation has been identified.

cAMP-DEPENDENT PROTEIN KINASE   Adelstein and colleagues (reviewed in 76) reported that cAMP-dependent protein kinase phosphorylates myosin light chain kinase from gizzard smooth muscle. In the absence of Ca^{2+}/calmodulin, two sites (A and B) are phosphorylated, whereas in the presence of bound Ca^{2+}/calmodulin, only one site (B) is phosphorylated. Phosphorylation of site A decreases the affinity of myosin light chain kinase for Ca^{2+}/calmodulin. Similar results have been obtained with myosin light chain kinases from other smooth muscle tissues and provide a model by which smooth muscle relaxation could occur (42). An increase in cAMP results in a decrease in cytosolic Ca^{2+} concentrations (van Breeman & Saida, this volume); in addition, phosphorylation of myosin light chain kinase decreases the extent of kinase activation by decreasing the affinity of the enzyme for Ca^{2+}/calmodulin. Both of these events would decrease the extent of myosin light chain phosphorylation and cause relaxation.

For the past ten years, there has been considerable debate regarding the physiological importance of myosin light chain kinase phosphorylation by cAMP-dependent protein kinase; the reader may refer to recent reviews for detailed discussions (28, 42, 60). Experimental data both indirectly support and refute the physiological importance of myosin light chain kinase phosphorylation. However, only two reports deal directly with the effect of cAMP formation on myosin light chain kinase phosphorylation and Ca^{2+}/calmodulin activation. Miller et al (59) found that a β-adrenergic agonist stimulated cAMP formation and relaxation in bovine tracheal smooth muscle. However, there were no changes in the Ca^{2+}/calmodulin activation properties of myosin light chain kinase and, hence, no evidence for a decreased kinase activity due to phosphorylation. In another study, forskolin stimulation of cAMP formation increased phosphorylation from 1.0 to 1.7 mol ^{32}P per mol myosin light chain kinase, with a net incorporation of 0.7 mol ^{32}P per mol kinase (16). The high level of phosphorylation in control tissues is surprising and could, perhaps, be due to autophosphorylation. The sites of phosphorylation were not identified by peptide mapping nor were the Ca^{2+}/calmodulin activation properties analyzed. Thus, identification of phosphorylation sites and demonstration of decreased affinity for Ca^{2+}/calmodulin are needed to establish the physiological importance of myosin light chain kinase phosphorylation.

cGMP-DEPENDENT PROTEIN KINASE   In the absence of Ca^{2+}/calmodulin, purified gizzard myosin light chain kinase is phosphorylated on site B by cGMP-dependent protein kinase (67); however, when Ca^{2+}/calmodulin is bound to myosin light chain kinase, this phosphorylation is blocked. The phosphorylation has no known effect on Ca^{2+}/calmodulin activation properties. Thus, cGMP cannot promote smooth muscle relaxation via phosphorylation of myosin light chain kinase.

DIACYLGLYCEROL PROTEIN KINASE C   Diacylglycerol activates protein kinase C, which can also phosphorylate purified smooth muscle myosin light chain kinase. One group of investigators reported phosphorylation of two sites in the absence of Ca^{2+}/calmodulin. distinct from previously defined sites A and B (34). Others also found that two sites were phosphorylated, but one of the sites was site A, and its phosphorylation decreased the affinity of myosin light chain kinase for Ca^{2+}/calmodulin (68). When Ca^{2+}/calmodulin was bound to myosin light chain kinase, only one site was phosphorylated and it was distinct from the B site phosphorylated by cAMP-dependent protein kinase. Both groups found diphosphorylation of smooth muscle myosin light chain kinase by protein kinase C increased the concentration of Ca^{2+}/calmodulin required for activation. Hence, the biochemical effect is similar to phosphorylation of site A by cAMP-dependent protein kinase. However, no physiological studies on myosin light chain kinase phosphorylation by protein kinase C have been reported.

Myosin Light Chain Phosphorylation

Myosin light chain kinase phosphorylates a serine residue in the amino terminus of myosin light chain (83). This phosphorylation site originally led to a simple hypothesis by which smooth muscle contraction could be initiated (42, 62, 76). However, the possibility of a more complex system of regulation has arisen with the identification of other sites of phosphorylation in smooth muscle myosin light chain. Bárány & Bárány (2) first found evidence for diphosphorylated light chain in frog hearts. These studies were extended to uterine, vascular, and tracheal smooth muscle, where diphosphorylated myosin light chain was also obtained (12, 13, 20, 40, 71). Thus, multiple sites are phosphorylated in myosin light chain in smooth muscle cells.

Ca^{2+}/CALMODULIN MYOSIN LIGHT CHAIN KINASE   Studies have demonstrated the importance of basic residues 11–13 and 16 as primary determinants for catalysis by smooth muscle myosin light chain kinase, where phosphorylation of serine-19 leads to an increase in actin-activated myosin MgATPase activity. (41, 45, 57):

<pre>
          5   10   15   20
Ac S S K R A K A K T T <u>K K R</u> P Q <u>R</u> A T S (P) N V F,
</pre>

where abbreviations include: Ac, acetyl; S, serine; K, lysine; R, arginine; A, alanine; T, threonine; P, proline; Q, glutamine; (P), phosphate; N, aspartamine; V, valine; F, phenylanine.

Recently, another phosphorylation site in gizzard myosin light chain was described for myosin light chain kinase (31, 33). Threonine-18 is phosphorylated, but at a much slower rate than serine-19. Phosphorylation of the light chain at both sites is associated with a greater increase in the actin-activated MgATPase activity of myosin than that seen with phosphorylation of serine-19 alone.

Sites of light chain phosphorylation in smooth muscle tissues have been recently investigated. Specific sites phosphorylated in tracheal smooth muscle myosin light chain in response to short and prolonged periods of agonist stimulation were identified by peptide mapping and sequencing (12, 40). Monophosphorylated light chain contained phosphate in serine-19, whereas diphosphorylated light chain was phosphorylated in both serine-19 and threonine-18. The maximal amount of diphosphorylated light chain formed (5–10%) was substantially less than the amount of monophosphorylated light chain (60–70%). Arterial smooth muscle contains two isoforms of the 20-kDa myosin light chain (20). Each form can be monophosphorylated and diphosphorylated, but the amount of diphosphorylated forms is also substantially less than the amount of the monophosphorylated forms. High concentrations of Ca^{2+}/calmodulin in permeabilized porcine carotid artery lead to relatively high amounts of both monophosphorylated and diphosphorylated light chain (26). A serine residue can be thiophosphorylated, and subsequent phosphorylation with ATP occurs on threonine. Maximal isometric force and unloaded shortening velocity were found with 1 mol thiophosphate per mol light chain. There were no further changes in either parameter with additional phosphorylation. Thus, diphosphorylation of myosin light chain occurs at low levels in intact smooth muscles and is associated with no change in mechanical properties in permeabilized fibers. These findings indicate that multisite light chain phosphorylation by myosin light chain kinase is probably not physiologically significant in regulation of smooth muscle contractility.

DIACYLGLYCEROL PROTEIN KINASE C   A potential role exists for Ca^{2+}-activated, phospholipid-dependent protein kinase C in the regulation of smooth muscle contraction via myosin light chain phosphorylation. Protein kinase C phosphorylation of light chain in acto-heavy meromyosin, when subsequent to phosphorylation by myosin light chain kinase, results in a decrease in the myosin ATPase activity (68). Protein kinase C phosphorylation also inhibits the conformational change induced by myosin light chain kinase phosphorylation (87). The sites phosphorylated in myosin light chains by protein kinase C (serine-1, serine-2, threonine-9) are distinct from the two sites phosphorylated by myosin light chain kinase (threonine-18, serine-19) (4, 33).

Effects of protein kinase C activation on smooth muscle contractile properties have been described. Phorbol esters, activators of protein kinase C, appear either to stimulate or to inhibit smooth muscle contraction (1, 15, 21, 58, 73). Interpretations of these results are not straightforward due to the effects of protein kinase C activation on cytosolic Ca^{2+} concentrations (van Breeman & Saida, this volume) in addition to possible direct effects (phosphorylation) on contractile proteins. Recent investigations with phorbol esters in intact smooth muscles or skinned fiber preparations indicate that protein kinase C activation may increase the sensitivity of the contractile elements for Ca^{2+}. For example, phorbol esters may cause contraction without increasing cytosolic Ca^{2+} concentrations (37, 38). Furthermore, phorbol esters elicit contractions in detergent skinned arteries when the free Ca^{2+} concentration is maintained at 0.1 μM, a Ca^{2+} concentration that does not itself cause contraction (10, 58). In contrast to these results, the addition of purified protein kinase C to skinned contracted vascular smooth muscle results in a slow relaxation associated with phosphorylation of myosin light chain in sites phosphorylated by protein kinase C (36).

These contradictory results make it difficult to form a unifying hypothesis for the role of phosphorylation of smooth muscle myosin light chain by protein kinase C. Fundamental questions need to be answered regarding the occurrence of this phosphorylation in intact smooth muscle stimulated physiologically with neurotransmitters and hormones. If there is significant phosphorylation at protein kinase C sites, then additional investigations dealing with mechanical properties are necessary to establish the physiological function(s).

Myosin Heavy Chain Phosphorylation

The heavy chain of myosins from nonmuscle cells can be phosphorylated by protein kinase(s) other than myosin light chain kinase or protein kinase C (reviewed in 28, 76). Phosphorylation of nonmuscle myosin heavy chain diminishes the interaction of actin and myosin and decreases assembly of myosin filaments. Myosin associated in filaments is not phosphorylated.

Myosin from molluscan smooth muscle is phosphorylated in the rod portion of the heavy chain by an unidentified, endogenous kinase and the transition from the catch state to relaxation is correlated to myosin heavy chain phosphorylation (8, 9). Recently, Kawamoto & Adelstein (44) reported that myosin heavy chain was phosphorylated in aortic smooth muscle tissue or cells in culture. It will be of great interest to learn more about the regulation of heavy chain phosphorylation and to link this phosphorylation to specific contractile properties in smooth muscle tissues.

Intermediate Filaments

Intermediate filaments consist of a group of relatively insoluble proteins that may form a skeletal framework of the cytoplasm (cytoskeleton) of many different types of cells. Cytoskeletal and contractile proteins in smooth muscle cells appear to be distributed in two domains: (a) longitudinal intermediate filaments free of myosin, but containing filamin, actin, α-actinin, and desmin; and (b) contractile protein filaments containing actin, myosin, tropomyosin, and caldesmon (22, 78, 79). Questions have arisen as to possible unique functions for these two cellular domains in smooth muscle contraction.

The localization and abundance of filamin in smooth muscle cells led Small et al (79) to speculate that the intermediate filament domain may be involved in stress maintenance or tonic contractions, whereas the contractile protein domain would be involved in initiation of contraction. One way of modulating the intermediate filament domain is through protein phosphorylation/dephosphorylation reactions. Carbachol causes a transient phosphorylation of myosin light chain in tracheal smooth muscle, whereas desmin, synemin, and caldesmon are phosphorylated at a slower rate and maintained for a prolonged time (70). The phorbol ester, 12-deoxyphorbol 13-isobutyrate also caused a slow, but sustained contraction that was associated with incorporation of ^{32}P into desmin and synemin as well as caldesmon. A scheme whereby different phosphoproteins may be responsible for tension development (myosin light chain) and tension maintenance (desmin, synemin, etc) was proposed (74).

Phosphorylation of purified intermediate filament proteins affects assembly properties. For example, desmin phosphorylated by cAMP-dependent protein kinase or protein kinase C is not able to polymerize (23, 30). Thus, phosphorylation of these proteins could allow for dynamic regulation of assembly and turnover of intermediate filaments.

It is not yet clear if intermediate filaments play a functional role in smooth muscle contraction. Mechanical properties that provide unique descriptions for intermediate filament functions have yet to be defined. Importantly, the hypothesis that there is a unique relation between intermediate filament phosphorylation and sustained contractions needs to be tested.

CONCLUDING REMARKS

Ca^{2+} regulation of the contractile elements of smooth muscle is generally agreed to be conferred via specific phosphorylation of the 20-kDa light chain of myosin by Ca^{2+}/calmodulin-dependent myosin light chain kinase. Nevertheless, many experiments with both intact and permeabilized smooth muscle preparations have shown dissociations between light chain phosphorylation and contraction, which indicates that other regulatory elements may be involved. A substantial body of biochemical evidence has shown that smooth muscle thin filaments can be regulated in a Ca^{2+}-dependent manner, and that caldesmon and calmodulin confer this property. However, functional studies demonstrating that this system operates in smooth muscle cells are lacking at present.

The direct physiological regulation of contractile elements by second messenger systems also has not been established. Although phosphorylation of myosin light chain kinase by cAMP-dependent protein kinase has been a popular hypothesis for regulating smooth muscle contraction, direct experimental data for phosphorylation in vivo of the site that affects the affinity of myosin light chain kinase for Ca^{2+}/calmodulin are lacking. Although protein kinase C phosphorylates purified smooth muscle myosin light chain and myosin light chain kinase, the physiological importance of these observations need to be established.

Two new areas have emerged that could be important in smooth muscle contraction: phosphorylation of myosin heavy chains and of intermediate filament proteins. Additional biochemical and physiological data for the former is necessary in order to construct specific hypotheses related to smooth muscle contractility. A new hypothesis has been proposed for tonic force maintenance due to phosphorylation-mediated structural rearrangements of intermediate filament proteins following protein kinase C activation (74). Not only will additional physiological experiments be needed to test this hypothesis, but considerably more biochemical information will be required to define the specific mechanisms involved.

ACKNOWLEDGMENTS

We are grateful to Ms. Carrie DeLisse for her assistance in the preparation of this manuscript and to the National Institutes of Health for research support (HL26043 and HL32607).

Literature Cited

1. Baraban, J. M., Gould, R. J., Peroutka, S. J., Snyder, S. H. 1985. Phorbol ester effects on neurotransmission: interaction with neurotransmitters and calcium in smooth muscle. *Proc. Natl. Acad. Sci. USA* 82:604–7
2. Bárány, K., Bárány, M. 1982. Myosin light chain phosphorylation in frog heart. *Biochim. Biophys. Acta* 706:136–40
3. Barsotti, R. J., Ikebe, M., Hartshorne, D. J. 1987. Effects of Ca^{2+}, Mg^{2+}, and myosin phosphorylation on skinned smooth muscle fibers. *Am. J. Physiol.* 252:C543–54
4. Bengur, A. R., Robinson, E. A., Apella, E., Sellers, J. R. 1987. Sequence of the sites phosphorylated by protein kinase C in the smooth muscle myosin light chain. *J. Biol. Chem.* 262:7613–17
5. Bretscher, A. 1984. Smooth muscle caldesmon. *J. Biol. Chem.* 259:12873–80
6. Bretscher, A. 1986. Caldesmon: Thin filament regulatory proteins of smooth-

and non-muscle cells. *Nature* 321:726–27

7. Bretscher, A., Lynch, W. 1985. Identification and localization of immunoreactive forms of caldesmon in smooth and nonmuscle cells: a comparison with the distributions of tropomyosin and α-actinin. *J. Cell Biol.* 100:1656–63

8. Castellani, L., Cohen, C. 1987. Rod phosphorylation favors folding in a catch muscle myosin. *Proc. Natl. Acad. Sci. USA* 84:4058–62

9. Castellani, L., Cohen, C. 1987. Myosin rod phosphorylation and the catch state of molluscan muscles. *Science* 235:334–37

10. Chatterjee, M., Tejada, M. 1986. Phorbol ester-induced contraction in chemically skinned vascular smooth muscle. *Am. J. Physiol.* 251:C356–61

11. Clark, T., Ngai, P. K., Sutherland, C., Gröschel-Stewart, U., Walsh, M. P. 1986. Vascular smooth muscle caldesmon. *J. Biol. Chem.* 261:8028–35

12. Colburn, J. C., Michnoff, C. H., Hsu, L.-C., Slaughter, C. A., Kamm, K. E., Stull, J. C. 1988. Sites phosphorylated in myosin light chain in contracting smooth muscle. *Biol. Chem.* 263: In press.

13. Csabina, S., Mougios, V., Bárány, M., Bárány, K. 1986. Characterization of the phosphorylatable myosin light chain in rat uterus. *Biochim. Biophys. Acta* 871:311–15

14. Dabrowska, R., Goch, A., Galazkiewicz, B., Osinska, H. 1985. The influence of caldesmon on ATPase activity of the skeletal muscle actomyosin and bundling of actin filaments. *Biochim. Biophys. Acta* 842:70–75

15. Danthuluri, N. R., Deth, R. C. 1984. Phorbol ester-induced contraction of arterial smooth muscle and inhibition of α-adrenergic response. *Biochem. Biophys. Res. Commun.* 125:1103–9

16. deLanerolle, P., Nishikawa, M., Yost, D. A., Adelstein, R. A. 1984. Increased phosphorylation of myosin light chain kinase after an increase in cyclic AMP in intact smooth muscle. *Science* 223:1415–17

17. Dillon, P. F., Aksoy, M. O., Driska, S. P., Murphy, R. A. 1981. Myosin phosphorylation and the cross-bridge cycle in arterial smooth muscle. *Science* 211:495–97

18. Driska, S. P. 1987. High myosin light chain phosphatase activity in arterial smooth muscle: can it explain the latch phenomenon? *Prog. Clin. Biol. Res.* 245:387–98

19. Edelman, A. M., Blumenthal, D. K., Krebs, E. G. 1987. Protein serine/threonine kinases. *Annu. Rev. Biochem.* 56:567–613

20. Erdodi, F., Bárány, M., Bárány, K. 1987. Myosin light chain isoforms and their phosphorylation in arterial smooth muscle. *Circ. Res.* 61:898–903

21. Forder, J., Scriabine, A., Rasmussen, H. 1985. Plasma membrane calcium flux, protein kinase C activation and smooth muscle contraction. *J. Pharmacol. Exp. Ther.* 235:267–73

22. Fürst, D. O., Cross, R. A., DeMey, J., Small, J. V. 1986. Caldesmon is an elongated, flexible molecule localized in the actomyosin domains of smooth muscle. *EMBO J.* 5:251–57

23. Geisler, N., Weber, K. 1988. Phosphorylation of desmin in vitro inhibits formation of intermediate filaments: identification of three kinase A sites in the aminoterminal head domain. *EMBO J.* 7:15–20

24. Gerthoffer, W. T. 1987. Dissociation of myosin phosphorylation and active tension during muscarinic stimulation of tracheal smooth muscle. *J. Pharmacol. Exp. Ther.* 240:8–15

25. Gerthoffer, W. T., Murphy, R. A. 1983. Ca^{2+}, myosin phosphorylation, and relaxation of arterial smooth muscle. *Am. J. Physiol.* 245:C271–77

26. Haeberle, J. R., Sutton, T. A., Trockman, B. A. 1988. Phosphorylation of two sites on smooth muscle myosin. *J. Biol. Chem.* 263:4424–29

27. Hai, C. M., Murphy, R. A. 1988. Cross-bridge phosphorylation and regulation of latch state in smooth muscle. *Am. J. Physiol.* 254:C99–106

28. Hartshorne, D. J. 1987. Biochemistry of the contractile process in smooth muscle. In *Physiology of the Gastrointestinal Tract*, ed. L. R. Johnson, 2:423–82. New York: Raven

29. Horiuchi, K. Y., Miyata, H., Chacko, S. 1986. Modulation of smooth muscle actomyosin ATPase by thin filament associated proteins. *Biochem. Biophys. Res. Commun.* 136:962–68

30. Inagaki, M., Gonda, Y., Matsuyama, M., Nishizawa, K., Nishi, Y., Sato, C. 1988. Intermediate filament reconstitution *in vitro*. *J. Biol. Chem.* 263:5970–78

31. Ikebe, M., Hartshorne, D. J. 1985. Phosphorylation of smooth muscle myosin at two distinct sites by myosin light chain kinase. *J. Biol. Chem.* 260:10027–31

32. Ikebe, M., Hartshorne, D. J. 1985. Effects of Ca^{2+} on the conformation and

enzymatic activity of smooth muscle myosin. *J. Biol. Chem.* 260:13146–53

33. Ikebe, M., Hartshorne, D. J., Elzinga, M. 1986. Identification, phosphorylation, and dephosphorylation of a second site for myosin light chain kinase on the 20,000 Dalton light chain of smooth muscle myosin. *J. Biol. Chem.* 261:36–39

34. Ikebe, M., Inagaki, M., Kanamaru, K., Hidaka, H. 1985. Phosphorylation of smooth muscle myosin light chain kinase by Ca^{2+}-activated, phospholipid-dependent protein kinase. *J. Biol. Chem.* 260:4547–50

35. Ikebe, M., Reardon, S. 1988. Binding of caldesmon to smooth muscle myosin. *J. Biol. Chem.* 263:3055–58

36. Inagaki, M., Yokokura, H., Itoh, T., Kanmura, Y., Kuriyama, H., Hidaka, H. 1987. Purified rabbit brain protein kinase C relaxes skinned vascular smooth muscle and phosphorylates myosin light chain. *Arch. Biochem. Biophys.* 254:136–41

37. Itoh, H., Lederis, K. 1987. Contraction of rat thoracic aorta strips induced by phorbol 12-myristate 13-acetate. *Am. J. Physiol.* 252:C244–47

38. Jiang, M. J., Morgan, K. G. 1987. Intracellular calcium levels in phorbol ester-induced contractions of vascular muscle. *Am. J. Physiol.* 253:H1365–71

39. Kaminski, E. A., Chacko, S. 1984. Effects of Ca^{2+} and Mg^{2+} on the actin-activated ATP hydrolysis by phosphorylated heavy meromyosin from arterial smooth muscle. *J. Biol. Chem.* 259:9104–8

40. Kamm, K. E., Colburn, J. C., Hsu, L.-C., Michnoff, C. H., Stull, J. T. 1988. Sites of myosin light chain phosphorylation in contracting smooth muscle. *Biophys. J.* 53(2):185a (Abstr.)

41. Kamm, K. E., Leachman, S. A., Michnoff, C. H., Nunnally, M. H., Persechini, A., et al. 1987. Myosin light chain kinases and kinetics of myosin phosphorylation in smooth muscle cells. *Regul. Contraction Smooth Muscle,* 245:183–93

42. Kamm, K. E., Stull, J. T. 1985. The function of myosin and myosin light chain kinase phosphorylation in smooth muscle. *Annu. Rev. Pharmacol. Toxicol.* 25:593–620

43. Kamm, K. E., Stull, J. T. 1985. Myosin phosphorylation, force, and maximal shortening velocity in neurally stimulated tracheal smooth muscle. *Am. J. Physiol.* 249:6238–47

44. Kawamoto, S., Adelstein, R. S. 1988. The heavy chain of smooth muscle my-osin is phosphorylated in aorta cells. *J. Biol. Chem* 263:1099–1102

45. Kemp, B. E., Pearson, R. B. 1985. Spatial requirements for location of basic residues in peptide substrates for smooth muscle myosin light chain kinase. *J. Biol. Chem.* 260:3355–59

46. Kossmann, T., Fürst, D., Small, J. V. 1987. Structural and biochemical analysis of skinned smooth muscle preparations. *J. Muscle Res. Cell Motil.* 8:135–44

47. Langanger, G., Moeremans, M., Daneels, G., Sobieszek, A., DeBrabander, M., DeMey, J. 1986. The molecular organization of myosin in stress fibers of cultured cells. *J. Cell Biol.* 102:200–9

48. Lash, J. A., Sellers, J. R., Hathaway, D. R. 1986. The effects of caldesmon on smooth muscle heavy actomeromyosin ATPase activity and binding of heavy meromyosin to actin. *J. Biol. Chem.* 261:16155–60

49. Lehman, W., Sheldon, A., Madonia, W. 1987. Diversity in smooth muscle thin filament composition. *Biochim. Biophys. Acta* 914:35–39

50. Lynch, W. P., Riseman, V. M., Bretscher, A. 1987. Smooth muscle caldesmon is an extended flexible monomeric protein in solution that can readily undergo reversible intra- and intermolecular sulfhydryl cross-linking. *J. Biol. Chem.* 262:7429–37

51. Marston, S. B. 1982. The regulation of smooth muscle contractile proteins. *Prog. Biophys. Mol. Biol.* 41:1–41

52. Marston, S. B. 1986. Ca^{2+} can control vascular smooth-muscle thin filaments without caldesmon phosphorylation. *Biochem. J.* 237:605–7

53. Marston, S. B., Lehman, W. 1985. Caldesmon is a Ca^{2+}-regulatory component of native smooth-muscle thin filaments. *Biochem. J.* 231:517–22

54. Marston, S., Pritchard, K., Redwood, C., Taggart, M. 1988. Ca^{2+}-regulation of the thin filaments: biochemical mechanism and physiological role. *Biochem. Soc. Trans.* In press

55. Marston, S. B., Smith, C. W. J. 1984. Purification and properties of Ca^{2+}-regulated thin filaments and F-actin from sheep aorta smooth muscle. *J. Muscle Res. Cell Motil.* 5:559–75

56. Marston, S. B., Smith, C. W. J. 1985. The thin filaments of smooth muscles. *J. Muscle Res. Cell Motil.* 6:669–708

57. Michnoff, C. H., Kemp, B. E., Stull, J. T. 1986. Phosphorylation of synthetic peptides by skeletal muscle myosin light

chain kinases. *J. Biol. Chem.* 261:8320–26

58. Miller, J. R., Hawkins, D. J., Wells, J. N. 1986. Phorbol diesters alter the contractile responses of porcine coronary artery. *J. Pharmacol. Exp. Ther.* 239:38–42

59. Miller, J. R., Silver, P. J., Stull, J. T. 1983. The role of myosin light chain kinase phosphorylation in *Beta*-adrenergic relaxation of tracheal smooth muscle. *Mol. Pharmacol.* 24:235–42

60. Miller-Hance, W. C., Kamm, K. E., Stull, J. T. 1988. Role of calcium and myosin phosphorylation in arterial smooth muscle contraction. In *Essential Hypertension and Calcium*, ed. K. Aoki, E. D. Frohlich. Tokyo: Academic. In press

61. Moreland, S., Little, D. K., Moreland, R. S. 1987. Calmodulin antagonists inhibit latch bridges in detergent skinned swine carotid media. *Am. J. Physiol.* 252:C523–31

62. Deleted in press

63. Nag, S., Seidel, J. C. 1983. Dependence on Ca^{2+} and tropomyosin of the actin-activated ATPase activity of phosphorylated gizzard myosin in the presence of low concentrations of Mg^{2+}. *J. Biol. Chem.* 258:6444–49

64. Ngai, P. K., Walsh, M. P. 1984. Inhibition of smooth muscle actin-activated myosin Mg^{2+}-ATPase activity by caldesmon. *J. Biol. Chem.* 259:13656–59

65. Ngai, P. K., Walsh, M. P. 1985. Detection of caldesmon in muscle and nonmuscle tissues of the chicken using polyclonal antibodies. *Biochem. Biophys. Res. Commun.* 127:533–39

66. Ngai, P. K., Walsh, M. P. 1987. The effects of phosphorylation of smooth-muscle caldesmon. *Biochem. J.* 244:417–25

67. Nishikawa, M., deLanerolle, P., Lincoln, T. M., Adelstein, R. S. 1984. Phosphorylation of mammalian myosin light chain kinases by the catalytic subunit of cyclic AMP-dependent protein kinase and by cyclic GMP-dependent protein kinase. *J. Biol. Chem.* 259:8429–36

68. Nishikawa, M., Shirakawa, S., Adelstein, R. S. 1985. Phosphorylation of smooth muscle myosin light chain kinase by protein kinase C. Comparative study of the phosphorylated sites. *J. Biol. Chem.* 260:8978–83

69. Owada, M. K., Hakura, A., Iida, K., Yahara, I., Sobue, K., Kakiuchi, S. 1984. Occurrence of caldesmon (a calmodulin-binding protein) in cultured cells: comparison of normal and transformed cells. *Proc. Natl. Acad. Sci. USA* 81:3133–37

70. Park, S., Rasmussen, H. 1986. Carbachol-induced phosphorylation changes in bovine tracheal smooth muscle. *J. Biol. Chem.* 261:15734–39

71. Persechini, A., Kamm, K. E., Stull, J. T. 1986. Different phosphorylated forms of myosin in contracting tracheal smooth muscle. *J. Biol. Chem.* 261:6293–99

72. Pritchard, K., Moody, C. J. 1986. Caldesmon: a calmodulin-binding actin-regulatory protein. *Cell Calcium* 7:309–27

73. Rasmussen, H., Forder, J., Kojima, I., Scriabine, A. 1984. TPA-induced contraction of isolated rabbit vascular smooth muscle. *Biochem. Biophys. Res. Commun.* 122:776–84

74. Rasmussen, H. Takuwa, Y., Park, S. 1987. Protein kinase C in the regulation of smooth muscle contraction. *FASEB J.* 1:177–85

75. Scott-Woo, G. C., Walsh, M. P. 1988. Autophosphorylation of smooth muscle caldesmon. *Biochem. J.* In press

76. Sellers, J. R., Adelstein, R. S. 1987. Regulation of contractile activity. In *The Enzymes*, ed. P. D. Boyer, E. G. Krebs, 18B:381–418. New York: Academic. 512 pp.

77. Sellers, J. R., Shirinsky, V. P. 1987. Caldesmon inhibits movement of myosin-coated beads on nitella actin cables. *J. Cell Biol.* 150(4):194a (Abstr.)

78. Small, J. V. 1985. Geometry of actin-membrane attachments in the smooth muscle cell: the localizations of vinculin and α-actinin. *EMBO J.* 4:45–49

79. Small, J. V., Fürst, D. O., DeMey, J. 1986. Localization of filamin in smooth muscle. *J. Cell Biol.* 102:210–20

80. Smith, C. W. J., Pritchard, K., Marston, S. B. 1987. The mechanism of Ca^{2+} regulation of vascular smooth muscle thin filaments by caldesmon and calmodulin. *J. Biol. Chem.* 262:116–22

81. Sobue, K., Morimoto, K., Inui, M., Kanda, K., Kakiuchi, S. 1982. Control of actin-myosin interaction of gizzard smooth muscle by calmodulin- and caldesmon-linked flip-flop mechanism. *Biomed. Res.* 3:188–96

82. Sobue, K., Muramoto, Y., Fujita, M., Kakiuchi, S. 1981. Purification of a calmodulin-binding protein from chicken gizzard that interacts with F-actin. *Proc. Natl. Acad. Sci. USA* 78:5652–55

83. Stull, J. T., Nunnally, M. H., Michnoff, C. H. 1986. Calmodulin-dependent protein kinases. In *The Enzymes*, ed. E. G.

Krebs, P. D. Boyer, 17A:113–66. New York: Academic. 612 pp.

84. Szpacenko, A., Wagner, J., Dabrowska, R., Rüegg, J. C. 1985. Caldesmon-induced inhibition of ATPase activity of actomyosin and contraction of skinned fibres of chicken gizzard smooth muscle. *FEBS Lett.* 192:9–12

85. Ueki, N., Sobue, K., Kanda, K., Hada, T., Higashino, K. 1987. Expression of high and low molecular weight caldesmons during phenotypic modulation of smooth muscle cells. *Proc. Natl. Acad. Sci. USA* 84:9049–53

86. Umekawa, H., Hidaka, H. 1985. Phosphorylation of caldesmon by pro-tein kinase C. *Biochem. Biophys. Res. Commun.* 132:56–62

87. Umekawa, H., Naka, M., Inagaki, M., Onishi, H., Wakabayashi, T., Hidaka, H. 1985. Conformational studies of my-osin phosphorylated by protein kinase C. *J. Biol. Chem.* 260:9833–37

88. Deleted in press

89. Wagner, J., Rüegg, J. C. 1986. Skinned smooth muscle: calcium-calmodulin ac-tivation independent of myosin phosphorylation. *Pflügers Arch.* 407: 569–71

90. Wagner, P. D., Vu, N.-D. 1987. Actin-activation of unphosphorylated gizzard myosin. *J. Biol. Chem.* 262:15556–62

Annu. Rev. Physiol. 1989. 51:315–29

CELLULAR MECHANISMS REGULATING [Ca^{2+}]$_i$ SMOOTH MUSCLE

C. van Breemen

Department of Pharmacology, University of Miami School of Medicine, Miami, Florida 33101

K. Saida

Upjohn Pharmaceuticals, Tokyo, Japan

INTRODUCTION

The preceding chapters establish the primary role of Ca^{2+} in the activation of smooth muscle contractile proteins. In this chapter we discuss the Ca^{2+} transport mechanisms that determine the intracellular Ca^{2+} concentration ([Ca^{2+}]$_i$) and thus regulate smooth muscle contraction.

Two integrated membrane systems are involved in the control of smooth muscle [Ca^{2+}]$_i$: (*a*) the plasmalemma, which is under the control of the membrane potential (E_m) and agonists such as neurotransmitters hormones and autocoids, and (*b*) the sarcoplasmic reticulum, which is under the control of second messengers. Both membranes form a barrier to an approximately 10,000-fold concentration gradient; thus, an increase in permeability to Ca^{2+} leads to an increase in [Ca^{2+}]$_i$, while active ATP-fueled Ca^{2+} pumping and possibly Na$^+$-Ca^{2+} exchange leads to a decrease in [Ca^{2+}]$_i$. Plasmalemmal Ca^{2+} permeability is regulated by the voltage gated Ca^{2+} channels (VGCs) and by chemical gating of receptor operated channels (ROCs) (11, 83). In some cases, agonists also inhibit the Ca^{2+} extrusion pump (23). The membrane potential is determined by ionic concentration gradients and permeabilities according to the Goldman equation and is regulated close to the K$^+$ equilibrium potential by the opening or closing of K$^+$ channels (11).

315

0066-4278/89/0315-0315$02.00

Some of these K^+ channels are activated by $[Ca^{2+}]_i$ as described in the chapter by Latorre (this volume). The membrane potential is also affected by electrogenic ion pumps, e.g. activity of the ouabain sensitive Na^+-K^+ pump hyperpolarizes the plasmalemma (11). The Na^+-Ca^{2+} exchange carrier may also contribute to the membrane potential since during each transport cycle $3Na^+$ are transported for each Ca^{2+}. Although the Na^+-Ca^{2+} exchanger has been identified in smooth muscle plasmalemma (31), its relative contribution to Ca^{2+} transport is still debated and appears to vary from tissue to tissue (2, 52).

The membrane potential of smooth muscle often exhibits oscillatory behavior, with Ca^{2+} spikes superimposed at the peaks of depolarization. Several mechanisms may be involved. It has been proposed that for agonist-induced oscillations, Ca^{2+} entry through VGCs increases the $[Ca^{2+}]$ near the Ca^{2+}-activated K^+ channels, which then open and hyperpolarize the plasmalemma. The membrane potential will then be beyond the threshold for open VGCs; the VGCs will close, and the $[Ca^{2+}]$ near the K^+ channels will fall below their level of activation. This in turn will depolarize the cell membrane and activate the VGCs to initiate another oscillation (45). Acetylcholine induces electrical slow waves in intestinal smooth muscle by alternatively opening cation channels that allow Na^+ to enter and activating voltage sensitive K^+ channels (5, 16). Another type of pacemaker activity in the gut is related to the oscillatory behavior of the electrogenic Na^+-K^+ pump although the source of this activity may be within the interstitial cells of Cajal (16). In mesenteric arteries agonist-induced oscillations in sarcoplasmic reticulum (SR) Ca^{2+} release have been demonstrated (47) that might not be related to Em, but may originate in a negative feedback loop of diacylglycerol activated C kinase–inhibiting phospholipase C.

The spread of electrical depolarization, which activates the VGCs, originates either from adjacent cells through gap junctions or from agonist activation of relatively nonspecific cation channels (ROCs) that drive the Em towards the Na^+ equilibrium potential.

Agonists are also responsible for the generation of intracellular messengers besides Ca^{2+}. The cyclic nucleotides cAMP and cGMP stimulate Ca-ATPases in the plasmalemma and SR (23, 78). Inositol phosphates, especially inositol 1,4,5-trisphosphate and its cyclic derivative, release Ca^{2+} from the SR (9) while diacylglycerol activates C kinase (53). C kinase appears to activate some ionic channels and was postulated to increase the Ca^{2+} sensitivity of the myofilaments (see Kamm & Stull, this volume). In addition, C kinase activates the Na^+-H^+ exchanger, which prevents acidification of the cytoplasm caused by increased metabolic activity and H^+ influx through the stimulated Ca-ATPase (8).

Clearly, the regulation of $[Ca^{2+}]_i$ in smooth muscle is a complex process.

Furthermore the integration of the various Ca^{2+} transport mechanisms differs for various types of smooth muscle depending on both function and location.

Several general overviews of smooth muscle regulation have recently been published (38, 41, 69); the chapters by Bean Latorre, and Schatzmann (this volume) deal with the physiology of Ca^{2+}-channels, Ca^{2+}-activated K$^+$ channels, and ATP-dependent Ca^{2+} pumps. Due to limited space we focus on receptor-activated Ca^{2+} transport mechanisms, the sarcoplasmic reticulum, and the possible functional integration of the SR and plasmalemma.

Stimulation of Ca^{2+} Influx by Agonists

Agonists can induce tonic contractions in fully depolarized smooth muscle (22) and, under certain circumstances, in polarized cells without perturbation of the membrane potential (74). These facts, coupled to the observation that a number of agonists stimulate ^{45}Ca influx into smooth muscle cells, led to the hypothesis of receptor operated Ca^{2+} channels (11, 83). This hypothesis was recently verified by patch-clamp recording of single channel currents upon application of ATP to arterial smooth muscle cells (7). These ATP-activated cation channels have a low conductance (5–6 pico-siemens in 100 mM Ba^{2+}) and a permeability ratio ($P_{Ca}:P_{Na} = 3$), are voltage insensitive, are insensitive to nifedipine, and rapidly desensitize in the presence of ATP. Since these channels are not activated when ATP is added outside the patch pipette attached to the cell and are insensitive to the removal of Ca^{2+} from the cytoplasm, they may be considered directly coupled ROCs (7). In this type of ROC, the agonist induces a conformational change in the membrane-spanning receptor molecule in order to expose a hydrophilic ion-conducting pore, as described for the nicotinic acetylcholine receptor (42). Several observations suggest that other agonists, such as histamine, norepinephrine, vasopressin, and angiotensin, indirectly open ROCs in aortic smooth muscle cells. ^{45}Ca influx stimulated by these agents is much less sensitive to Ca^{2+} channel antagonists than depolarization-induced ^{45}Ca influx (14). Furthermore, maximal agonist-induced ^{45}Ca influx is additive to maximal high K$^+$-induced ^{45}Ca influx, but additivity is not seen when maximally effective doses of histamine, norepinephrine, vasopressin, and angiotensin are combined (93). (The improved kinetics of the ^{45}Ca fluxes measured in cultured smooth muscle cells remove the methodological reservations regarding the thicker aortic preparations.) The conventional pharmacological axiom is that significant differences in antagonist sensitivity indicate different types of receptors, in this case ion channels (these differences persisted in depolarized arteries). If so, these data suggest that in aortic cells the aforementioned agonists open a common set of ROCs through the intermediate action of a second messenger.

Although ion currents through indirectly coupled ROCs have not been recorded in smooth muscle cells, potentially relevant data have been obtained for blood and endothelial cells. In the latter, both thrombin and bradykinin stimulate Ca^{2+} influx by opening voltage insensitive, nonselective cation channels (39, 48). Since the channel characteristics are not dependent on the agonists applied, a common set of cation channels may be linked to different types of receptors via a second messenger. For thrombin activation of platelet Ca^{2+} channels, the intervention of a second messenger is suggested by a 200 msec delay between receptor activation and Ca^{2+} influx (58). This is supported by the recording of single channel currents through ROCs incorporated in the planar bilayer from microsomes derived from thrombin-activated platelets. These channels were again voltage insensitive, but did exhibit high Ca^{2+} selectivity for Ba^{2+} over Na^+ (94).

The nature of the second messenger that links the receptors to ROCs is still unresolved. It was recently reported that inositol 1,4,5-trisphosphate (IP_3) released Ca^{2+} from platelet-derived plasmalemmal vesicles that were Ca^{2+} loaded through the Na^+-Ca^{2+} exchange (66). Single cation channel activity has been recorded from T lymphocytes loaded with IP_3 (43). Inositol 1,3,4,5-tetrakisphosphate (IP_4) has also been proposed as the second messenger linking receptors to ROCs (36). Another possibility is that α subunits of GTP binding proteins (G proteins) are involved, as has been shown for muscarinic activation of K^+ channels and Ca^{2+} channels in other tissues (13). This type of coupling, though mediated by an intermediate transducing molecule, appears to be confined to the location of the activated receptor. A final candidate for indirect activation of at least some cation channels is cytoplasmic Ca^{2+} (87). Involvement of G proteins and phospholipase C in second messenger activation of ROCs also follows from the observation that thrombin-activated Ca^{2+} influx in platelets was inhibited by phorbol ester stimulated C kinase–mediated phosphorylation of α subunits of G_i and G_p (3). This type of negative feedback is also present in agonist stimulation of smooth muscle (30).

Figure 1 shows the various ways in which an extracellular agonist may activate Ca^{2+} entry into smooth muscle cells. Receptor activation opens ROCs directly or indirectly. The intracellular messengers responsible for the latter process may be α subunits of G proteins ($G\alpha$), IP_3, IP_4, or Ca^{2+}. Second messengers may also facilitate the opening of VGCs. Norepinephrine increases the probability of opening L and T type channels in vascular smooth muscle (see Bean, this volume). A similar action of acetylcholine in visceral smooth muscle has recently been ascribed to the intermediate activation of protein kinase C by diacylglycerol (15). VGCs can also be directly activated by the interaction of dihydropyridine Ca^{2+} agonists with their gating mechanism. A similar mechanism has been proposed for the potent, endothelium-derived contracting polypeptide, endothelin (92).

A final important mechanism of agonist activation of VGCs occurs through

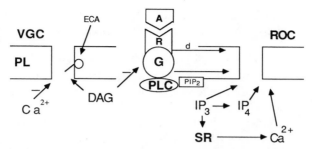

Figure 1 Putative mechanisms for activation of Ca^{2+} entry by agonists. Receptor activation may open ROCs directly or indirectly via the second messengers $G\alpha$, IP_3, IP_4, or Ca^{2+}. Agonists may also open VGCs directly, as for Bay K8644 and endogenous Ca^{2+} agonists, and indirectly through activation of protein kinase C by diacylglycerol (DAG). The latter process inhibits G protein activation and $[Ca^{2+}]_i$ has been shown to inactivate VGCs (54). (ECA = endogenous Ca^{2+} agonist, PLC = phospholipase C).

the depolarization that results from the opening of ROCs. In general, the latter are less selective, voltage insensitive cation channels capable of conducting an inward Na^+ and Ca^{2+} current. The degree of depolarization induced depends on their density and the number of Ca^{2+} sensitive K^+ channels activated.

The ratio of ROCs to VGCs activated by an agonist in a particular smooth muscle may be relevant to its physiological and pharmacological control. It is proposed that this ratio is high in the conduit arteries and efferent renal glomerular arterioles, whose norepinephrine-induced contractions have a low sensitivity to Ca^{2+} antagonists (14, 49). This ratio is low in most resistance arterioles, in which neurotransmitter-induced contraction is highly sensitive to Ca^{2+} antagonists (14).

Intracellular Ca^{2+} Stores

In the 1960s it became apparent that although in the narrow smooth muscle cells the time required for Ca^{2+} to diffuse from the surface to the interior presents no kinetic limitation on the rate of tension development, release of cellular Ca^{2+} is nevertheless involved in agonist induced contraction (10, 17, 33, 81). The Ca^{2+} release induced by high doses of agonists is transient and in the absence of extracellular Ca^{2+} exhausts the Ca^{2+} store (81, 85). The sequential application of various ligands to a smooth muscle bathed in Ca^{2+}-free medium shows that a number of physiological agonists, including norepinephrine, histamine, angiotensin, vasopressin, and prostaglandins, release Ca^{2+} from the same intracellular pool, which is also sensitive to caffeine (20, 21). This fact strongly implicated the SR as the intracellular Ca^{2+} source since caffeine acts directly on SR and has not been reported to release Ca^{2+} from any other organelle (24). The fact that norepinephrine releases Ca^{2+}

from vascular smooth muscle SR was finally proven by the electron microprobe determination of a decrease of in situ SR Ca^{2+} content (12) after the application of norepinephrine.

Plasmalemma bound Ca^{2+} has been suggested as an additional Ca^{2+} source (38). Hydrolysis of phosphatidylinositol phosphates during agonist stimulation can release this Ca^{2+} source (38), functioning perhaps to trigger further SR Ca^{2+} release (63). This hypothesis, however, lacks direct evidence. Isolated mitochondria and mitochondria in permeabilized smooth muscle cells do not take up significant quantities of Ca^{2+} unless the Ca^{2+} concentration exceeds 5 μM (73, 91). This is in agreement with their relatively high K_D for Ca^{2+} accumulation (10–17 μM) (27). Therefore, mitochondria become Ca^{2+} sinks only if locally high concentrations of Ca^{2+} are achieved, for example during SR Ca^{2+} release or if Ca^{2+} entry becomes abnormally high during some pathological states. In one study, 2,4-dinitrophenol-releasable Ca^{2+} was enhanced by high K^+-stimulated Ca^{2+} uptake in taenia coli (20). Minor fluctuations in mitochondrial Ca^{2+} content may accompany physiological activity (20), but the absence of a physiological Ca^{2+}-release mechanism in mitochondria precludes these fluctuations from being a Ca^{2+} source during cell activation.

SR Ca^{2+} Uptake

The SR consists of a continuous network of membrane bound tubules, of which a considerable fraction in smooth muscle cells is located peripherally (12). SR Ca^{2+} transport properties have been studied in intact and permeabilized smooth muscle and in isolated membrane vesicles. Similar to cardiac SR, Ca^{2+} uptake is accomplished by a 105,000-dalton Ca, Mg-ATPase that undergoes Ca^{2+} dependent phosphorylation (77) and is regulated through cAMP-mediated phosphorylation of phospholamban (23, 55). cGMP also stimulates the SR Ca^{2+} pump in vascular smooth muscle (78). The high capacity, low affinity Ca^{2+}-binding protein calsequestrin, which increases the Ca^{2+} storage capacity, has recently been demonstrated in smooth muscle SR preparations (89). The peripherally located SR has been reported to form special junctions with the plasmalemma, which are similar to the triadic junctions of skeletal muscle (72). Calsequestrin appears to be be localized in these junctional elements of the SR (72). The Ca^{2+} pump preserves its high Ca^{2+} affinity in muscle preparations permeabilized by saponin (61), half loading the SR at 0.4 μM Ca^{2+} and saturating at an ambient $[Ca^{2+}]$ of 1 μM (91).The apparent K_M is somewhat higher in SR vesicles, 1 μM Ca^{2+}, while that for ATP is 0.2 μM (76, 77). The rate of Ca^{2+} accumulation [i.e. 3 min to saturation in permeabilized mesenteric artery (64)] and the quantity of Ca^{2+} accumulated in the intact artery [76 $\mu moles/kg$ wet wt caffeine-releasable Ca^{2+} in the aorta and 52 $\mu moles/kg$ wet wt caffeine-releasable Ca^{2+} in mesenteric artery (46, 47)] are sufficient to support the role of SR as the major intracellular Ca^{2+} source for smooth muscle activation. Since the smooth muscle SR content varies between 2 and 7% of cell volume (69), the physiological SR Ca^{2+} concentration is estimated to be in the order of 5 mM (46). A similar value of 28 mmoles/kg dry wt ($\cong$ 6 mM) was obtained by electron microprobe analysis of the peripheral SR in the guinea pig portal vein (12).

Ca^{2+}-Induced Ca^{2+} Release (CICR)

As originally proposed, "the influx of a small amount of Ca^{2+} during excitation could release a much greater amount of Ca^{2+} from the ER" (80). CICR was shown to function in mechanically skinned skeletal (25, 28) and cardiac (26) muscle. The mechanism is now known to be due to the activation of large cation channels (75 pS in 100 mM Ba^{2+}) that are activated by μmolar Ca^{2+}, mmolar ATP, caffeine, and partially by ryanodine (67). Since insufficient Ca^{2+} for activation of contraction appeared to enter smooth muscle cells during action potentials, CICR was also proposed in this tissue (11, 37, 44). The use of saponin to permeabilize the plasmalemma while preserving SR function (61) allowed the direct demonstration of Ca^{2+}-induced Ca^{2+} release in smooth muscle (59, 60). The threshold for this process was estimated to be 3 μM Ca^{2+}, which could be raised by high [Mg^{2+}]. Procaine blocked CICR while cAMP potentiated it (64). Caffeine releases SR Ca^{2+} by facilitating CICR (24) and requires the presence of very low concentrations of ambient Ca^{2+} in smooth muscle (91). Since ryanodine also releases Ca^{2+} in smooth muscle (34), it is conceivable that Ca^{2+} channels similar to the ones described for skeletal muscle and associated with the ryanodine-binding junctional foot proteins may also be present in smooth muscle.

IP$_3$-Induced Ca^{2+} Release

The discovery that inositol 1,4,5-trisphosphate, the product of phospholipase C–mediated hydrolysis of phosphotidylinositol-4,5-bisphosphate, functions as the second messenger for Ca^{2+} release from the endoplasmic reticulum consitutes a major breakthrough in the quest to elucidate excitation-function coupling (9). IP$_3$ was subsequently also shown to activate Ca^{2+} release from smooth muscle SR (75). In cultured and freshly isolated permeabilized smooth muscle cells, IP$_3$-induced Ca^{2+} release was sufficiently large and rapid, and the half maximally effective concentration of approximately 1 μM IP$_3$ was low enough to account for transient smooth muscle activation (68, 75, 79, 90). In general these criteria were not convincingly met in permeabilized smooth muscle tissues (32, 35, 65, 70) until the introduction of caged IP$_3$ (88). Light activation of prediffused caged IP$_3$ showed that it rapidly released SR Ca^{2+} at submicromolar concentrations (88). A specific phosphatase, which rapidly inactivates IP_3 (57) in accordance with the requirement for its second messenger function, was also demonstrated to be present in smooth muscle (88).

The mechanism of IP_3-induced SR Ca^{2+} release relates to the section on ROCs (above). Accordingly, the interaction of IP_3 with its specific receptor (4) opens cation channels, which allow rapid discharge of SR Ca^{2+}. A guanine nucleotide regulatory mechanism also appears to be involved in this receptor-channel coupling system (18, 19, 29, 65). IP_3-induced Ca^{2+} release from permeabilized rabbit mesenteric smooth muscle is dependent on the presence of GTP (65) or its nonhydrolyzable analogue C_1ppNHp, and is inhibited by pertussis toxin (62).

Caffeine-induced Ca^{2+} release does not require GTP, is insensitive to pertussis toxin, and is more readily blocked by procaine than IP_3-induced Ca^{2+} release (86). Thus, it is clear that smooth muscle SR contains two separate types of Ca^{2+} release channels: IP_3- and Ca^{2+}-activated channels. The functional significance of having two types of SR Ca^{2+} release channels is not known. However, this may constitute a signal amplification system. IP_3-induced Ca^{2+} release may raise the $[Ca^{2+}]_i$ near the SR Ca^{2+} receptors above the threshold of 3×10^{-6} M and thus further activate Ca^{2+} release through the second set of channels. This possibility is supported by the observation that Ca^{2+} enhanced the IP_3-induced Ca^{2+} release from the SR in skinned smooth muscle (35).

Variability and Heterogeneity of Smooth Muscle SR

Ultrastructural studies have shown that a portion of the SR network is located close to the inner surface of the sarcolemma where it occasionally joins with the plasmalemma via special junctions, which contain structural "feet" separating the two membranes at these junctions (72). SR lying in the interior of the smooth muscle cells has been labeled "deep SR" (69). The lumen of all SR is probably contiguous even with the space between the double membrane of the nuclear envelope (72).

The volume of smooth muscle SR varies from 2–7.5% of the nucleus and mitochondria free volume (69) and is related to the muscle's capability to contract in Ca^{2+} free solution (71). In arterial smooth muscle, the relative contribution made by the SR to Ca^{2+} delivery during agonist-induced stimulation decreases as the lumen size becomes smaller (14). This decrease is associated with an increased sensitivity to Ca^{2+} antagonists.

Smooth muscle SR variability also extends to its functional heterogeneity. In the rabbit aorta, caffeine- and norepinephrine-induced release of isotopic Ca^{2+} into Ca^{2+}-free solution are similar, while in the mesenteric artery marked differences exist in the patterns of SR Ca^{2+} release

(46, 47, 63). In the latter, norepinephrine-induced release is distinctly biphasic, with an initial fast phase that is rapidly replenished (3 min) and a second portion with slow recovery (1 hr). Caffeine, on the other hand, exhibits only a single rapid phase of Ca^{2+} release, which is twice as large as the rapid norepinephrine-induced release phase. The loss and recovery of the caffeine-induced small mesenteric artery contraction upon removal of Ca^{2+} and replenishment is slower than that of the rapid norepinephrine-induced contraction (63). Similar differences between caffeine- and norepinephrine-induced Ca^{2+} release have been reported for cultured rat aorta (40). The above data may be best explained by the model depicted in Figure 2. As discussed in the previous section, the SR contains two types of Ca^{2+} channels, those sensitive to Ca^{2+}, ATP, and caffeine, and those activated by IP$_3$. Caffeine, which is not rapidly metabolized, discharges Ca^{2+} from all portions of the SR. IP$_3$ generated through agonist-induced stimulation of phospholipase C activates its Ca^{2+} channels in the superficial SR but may be hydrolyzed by a specific phosphatase before it reaches the deep SR. However, since the two portions are contiguous, a flow of Ca^{2+} from the deep to the superficial SR supports a slow Ca^{2+} release phase. The alternative model whereby part of the SR does not contain IP$_3$ receptors appears less likely due to the finding that 97% of SR Ca^{2+} is releasable by IP$_3$ in saponin-permeabilized cultured smooth muscle cells (90).

Functional Integration Between the Plasmalemma and the SR

It is clear from the above that smooth muscle SR is a membranous organelle located in the myoplasm from which it takes up Ca^{2+} to effect at least part of relaxation (the initial rapid phase) and to which it discharges Ca^{2+} during the initial phase of contraction. In addition to these functions it has been proposed that the peripheral SR also acts as a "superficial buffer barrier" to Ca^{2+} entry from the extracellular space into the myoplasm (82, 84).

A close functional relationship between the plasmalemma and SR is indicated by the following experimental observations: (a) As much as 200 μmoles of Ca^{2+}/kg smooth muscle may be transferred from the extracellular space to the SR within minutes without causing contraction (1). (b) The magnitude of contraction depends on the rate of net cellular Ca^{2+} gain rather than on the magnitude of this gain (82). (c) Any discharge of Ca^{2+} from the SR is always accompanied by stimulation of Ca^{2+} efflux into the extracellular space (47). (d) Tension development derived from activation of VGCs depends on the state of loading of the SR. A depleted SR will absorb all stimulated Ca^{2+} entry until it is repleted to near its physiological resting level before tension ensues (50). (e) Tonic aortic contractile tension depends on Ca^{2+} influx in a threshold type fashion and the Ca^{2+} influx threshold for

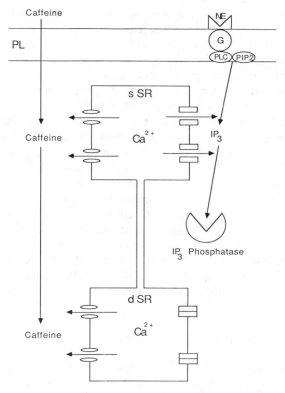

Figure 2 A two compartment model for vascular smooth muscle SR. IP_3 generated by norepinephrine (NE) activation of the α-adrenergic receptor opens Ca^{2+} channels in the superficial SR
(s SR) but is hydrolized by its specific phosphatase before it reaches the deep SR (d SR). After
release of the superficial SR, Ca^{2+} is replenished from the deep SR as well as from the
extracellular space. Caffeine causes a rapid release of Ca^{2+} from both SR compartments. (PL =
plasmalemma, G = G protein, PLC = phospholipase C).

tension development is decreased by opening SR Ca^{2+} channels and increased
by stimulating the Ca^{2+} ATPase, which is responsible for Ca^{2+} accumulation
(84). (*f*) SR Ca^{2+} depletion causes temporal dissociation of Ca^{2+} induced
luminescence of aquorin from tension and phosphorylation of the myosin light
chains when Ca^{2+} influx is stimulated (56). (*g*) Ca^{2+}-sensitive K^+ channels
of smooth muscle plasmalemma may be spontaneously activated without
contractile activity being apparent (6). (*h*) Ryanodine enhances tonic depolarization induced tension without affecting Ca^{2+} influx (34). (*i*) The
average $[Ca^{2+}]_i$ for a certain level of tone is higher in high potassium
depolarized artery than for the same contracted by norepinephrine (51).

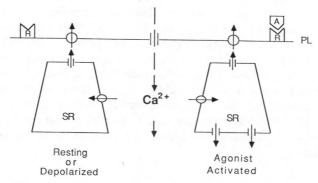

Figure 3 SR as a superficial buffer barrier. In the resting muscle or when activated by depolarization alone, Ca^{2+} that enters the cell though the leak and VGCs is partly pumped into the SR. It leaves the SR preferentially at the junctional surface (junction with plasmalemma, PL) possibly due to background IP$_3$ formation or calcium induced calcium release. From there it is transported into the extracellular space by way of the PL Ca-ATPase and the Na$^+$-Ca^{2+} exchange carrier. Receptor activation shunts this superficial Ca^{2+} cycle by the IP$_3$-mediated permeability increase of the SR membranes. See text for further details.

These data strongly suggest that (*a*) The superficial SR removes Ca^{2+} entering through the sarcolemma before it can activate myofilaments. (*b*) The state of the SR with respect to its permeability to Ca^{2+} and its rate of Ca-ATPase activity partly determines the steady state cellular Ca^{2+} concentration. (*c*) A variable Ca^{2+} gradient exists near the inner plasmalemmal surface, with Ca^{2+} activity increasing nearer that surface.

The schematic diagram in Figure 3 provides a plausible mechanism for the three postulates in the preceeding paragraph. At rest or during depolarization, which does not stimulate phospholipase C, part of the Ca^{2+} that enters the cell is taken up into the SR by its Ca^{2+} ATPase. It is then preferentially released towards the plasmalemma to be extruded into the extracellular space. The low background IP$_3$ production may be sufficient to open Ca^{2+} channels in the junctional SR membrane or locally higher [Ca^{2+}] may trigger vectorial Ca^{2+} release (84). The proposed higher [Ca^{2+}] near the inner surface of the membrane would allow extrusion via the Na$^+$-Ca^{2+} exchanger as well as via the Ca-ATPase. When receptors are activated by agonists the consequent IP$_3$ mediated permeability increase of the SR short circuits the Ca^{2+} cycle between the extracellular space and the SR. Ca^{2+} entry during the tonic phase of agonist-induced contraction would thus raise the level of activating Ca^{2+} more than would be true for the same Ca^{2+} entry during depolarization-induced tone.

The above model probably does not provide a complete explanation for all the experimental observations listed above (a-i). For example, the decrease affected by noradrenaline in the tension threshold for Ca^{2+} entry (e) and the lower $[Ca^{2+}]_i$ as measured by aquorin (i) could also reflect an increase in myofilament sensitivity to Ca^{2+} upon activation of α-adrenergic receptors (51). Such a shift in Ca^{2+} sensitivity was recently proven by the observation that $10^{-5}M$ norepinephrine reduced the $[Ca^{2+}]$ required for half maximally activating α-toxin permeabilized arterial smooth muscle from a control value of 890 ± 90 nM (n = 4) to 280 ± 50 nM (n = 3) (Nishimura, Kolber, and van Breemen, unpublished). However, the other observations, especially those related to the SR depletion paradigms (d,f,l), can not be explained by shifts in myofilament Ca^{2+} sensitivity and appear to depend on the proximity of SR and plasmalemma.

Literature Cited

1. Aaronson, P., van Breemen, C. 1981. Effects of Na gradient manipulation upon cellular Ca, ^{45}Ca fluxes and cellular Na in the guinea pig taenia coli. *J. Physiol.* 319:443–61
2. Ashida, T., Blaustein, M. P. 1987. Regulation of cell calcium and contractility in mammalian arterial smooth muscle: role of sodium-calcium exchange. *J. Physiol.* 392:617–35
3. Avdonin, P. V., Tkachuk, V. A. 1987. Properties of receptor-operated calcium channels in platelets. In *Receptors and Ion Channels,* ed. Y. A. Ovchinnikov, F. Hucho, pp. 193–202. Berlin: de Gruyter
4. Baukal, A. J., Gaetan, G., Rubin, R., Spat, A., Catt, K. J. 1985. Binding sites for inositol trisphosphate in the bovine adrenal cortex. *Biochem. Biophys. Res. Commun.* 113:532–38
5. Benham, C. D., Bolton, T. B. 1983. Patch clamp studies of slow potential sensitive potassium channels in longitudinal smooth muscle cells of rabbit jejunum. *J. Physiol.* 340:469–86
6. Benham, C. D., Bolton, T. B. 1986. Spontaneous outward currents in single visceral and vascular smooth muscle cells of the rabbit. *J. Physiol.* 381:385–406
7. Benham, C. D., Tsien, R. W. 1987. A novel receptor-operated Ca^{2+}-permeable channel activated by ATP in smooth muscle. *Nature* 328:275–78
8. Berk, B. C., Brock, T. A., Gimborne, M. A. Alexander, R. W. 1987. Early agonist mediated ionic events in cultured vascular smooth muscle. *J. Biol. Chem.* 262(11):5065–72
9. Berridge, M. J. Irvine, R. F. 1984. Inositol trisphosphate, a novel second

messenger in cellular signal transduction. *Nature* 312:315–21
10. Bohr, D. F. 1963. Vascular smooth muscle: dual effect of calcium. *Science* 139:597–99
11. Bolton, T. B. 1979. Mechanisms of action of transmitter and other substances on smooth muscle. *Physiol. Rev.* 59:606–718
12. Bond, M., Kitazawa, T., Somlyo, A. P, Somlyo, A. V. 1984. Release and recycling of calcium by the sarcoplasmic reticulum in guinea pig portal vein smooth muscle. *J. Physiol.* 355:677–95
13. Brown, A. M., Birnbaumer, L. 1988. Direct G protein gating of ion channels. *Am. J. Physiol.* 254:H401–H410
14. Cauvin, C., Loutzenhiser, R., van Breemen, C. 1983. Mechanisms of calcium antagonist-induced vasodilation. *Annu. Rev. Pharmacol. Toxicol.* 23:373–96
15. Clapp, L. H., Vivandon, M. B., Singer, J. J., Walsh J. V. Jr. 1987. A diacylglycerol analogue mimics the action of acetylcholine and substance P on calcium currents in freshly dissociated smooth muscle cells. *J. Gen. Physiol.* 90:13a
16. Dahms, V., Prosser, C. L., Suzuki, N. 1987. Two types of slow waves in intestinal smooth muscle of cat. *J. Physiol.* 392:51–69
17. Daniel, E. E. 1965. Attempted synthesis of data regarding divalent ions in muscle function. In *Muscle,* ed. W. M. Paul, E. E. Daniel, C. M. Kay, G. Monckton, pp. 295–313. Oxford: Pergamon
18. Dawson, A. P. 1985. GTP enhances inositol trisphosphate-stimulated Ca^{2+} release from rat liver microsomes. *FEBS Lett.* 185:147–50
19. Dawson, A. P., Hills, G., Comerford, J.

G. 1987. The mechanism of action of GTP on Ca^{2+} efflux from rat liver microsomal vesicles. *Biochem. J.* 244:87–92

20. Deth, R., Casteels, R. 1977. A study of releasable Ca fractions in smooth muscle cells of the rabbit aorta. *J. Gen. Physiol.* 69:401–16

21. Deth, R., van Breemen, C. 1977. Agonist induced release of intracellular Ca^{2+} in the rabbit aorta. *J. Memb. Biology* 30:363–80

22. Edman, K. A. P., Schild, H. O. 1962. The need for calcium in the contractile responses induced by acetylcholine and potassium in the rat uterus. *J. Physiol.* 161:424–41

23. Eggermont, J. A., Vrolix, M., Raeymaekers, L., Wuytack, F., Casteels, R. 1988. Ca^{2+}-transport ATPase of vascular smooth muscle. *Circ. Res.* 62:266–78

24. Endo, M. 1975. Mechanism of action of caffeine on the sarcoplasmic reticulum of skeletal muscle. *Proc. Jpn. Acad.* 51:479–84

25. Endo, M., Tanaka, M., Ogawa, Y. 1970. Calcium induced release of calcium from the sarcoplasmic reticulum of skinned skeletal muscle fibers. *Nature* 228:34–36

26. Fabiato, A., Fabiato, F. 1972. Excitation-contraction coupling of isolated cardiac fibers with disrupted or closed sarcolemma. Calcium-dependent cyclic and tonic contractions. *Circ. Res.* 31:293–301

27. Fiskum, G., Lehninger, A. L. 1982. Mitochondrial regulation of intracellular calcium. In *Calcium and Cell Function*, ed. W. Y. Cheung, 2:39–80. New York: Academic

28. Ford, L. E., Podolsky, R. J. 1970. Regenerative calcium release within muscle cells. *Science* 167:58–59

29. Gill, D. L., Veda, T., Chueh, S.-H., Noel, M. W. 1986. Ca^{2+} release from endoplasmic reticulum is mediated by a guanine nucleotide regulatory mechanism. *Nature* 320:461–64

30. Griendling, K. K., Rittenhouse, S. E., Brock, T. A., Ekstein, L. S., Gimbrone, M. A., Jr., Alexander, R. W. 1986. Sustained diacylglycerol formation from inositol phospholipids in angiotensin II-stimulated vascular smooth muscle cells. *J. Biol. Chem.* 261:5901–6

31. Grover, A. K., Kwan, C. Y., Rangachari, P. K., Daniel, E. E. 1983. Na-Ca exchange in smooth muscle plasma membrane enriched fraction. *Am. J. Physiol.* 244:C158–C165

32. Hashimoto, T., Hirata, M., Itoh, T.,

Kanmura, Y., Kuriyama, H. 1986. Inositol 1,4,5-trisphosphate activates pharmacomechanical coupling in smooth muscle of the rabbit mesenteric artery. *J. Physiol.* 370:605–18

33. Hinke, J. A. M. 1965. Calcium requirements for noradreanaline and high potassium ion contraction in arterial smooth muscle. See Ref. 17, pp. 269–84

34. Hwang, K., van Breemen, C. 1987. Ryanodine modulation of ^{45}Ca efflux and tension in rabbit aortic smooth muscle. *Pflügers Arch.* 408:343–50

35. Iino, M. 1987. Calcium dependent inositol trisphosphate-induced calcium release in the guinea-pig taenia coli. *Biochem. Biophys. Res. Commun.* 142:47–52

36. Irvine, R. F., Moor, R. M. 1986. Micro-injection of inositol 1,3,4,5-tetrakisphosphate activates sea urchin eggs by a mechanism dependent on external Ca^{2+}. *Biochem. J.* 240:917–20

37. Itoh, T., Kuriyama, H., Suzuki, H. 1981. Excitation-contraction coupling in smooth muscle cells of the guinea-pig mesenteric artery. *J. Physiol.* 321:513–35

38. Janis, R. A., Silver, P. J., Triggle, D. J. 1987. Drug action and cellular calcium regulation. *Adv. Drug Res.* 16:309–591

39. Johns, A., Lategan, T. W., Lodge, N. J., Ryan, U. S., van Breemen, C., Adams, D. J. 1987. Calcium entry through receptor-operated channels in boveine pulmonary artery endothelial cells. *Tissue & Cell* 19(6):733–45

40. Kanaide, H., Shogakiuchi, Y., Kakamura, M. 1987. The norepinephrine-sensitive Ca^{2+}-storage site differs from the caffeine-sensitive site in vascular smooth muscle of the rat aorta. *FEBS Lett.* 214(1):130–34

41. Khalil, R., Lodge, N., Saida, K., van Breemen, C. 1987. Mechanism of calcium activation in vascular smooth muscle. *J. Hypertens.* 5(Suppl. 4):S5–S17.

42. Kistler, J., Stroud, R. M., Klymkowsky, M. W., Lalancrette, R. A., Fariclough, R. H. 1982. Structure and function of an acetylcholine receptor. *Biophys. J.* 37:371–83

43. Kuno, M., Gardner, P. 1987. Ion channels activated by inositol 1,4,5-trisphosphate in plasma membrane of human T-lymphocytes. *Nature* 326:301–4

44. Kuriyama, H., Ito, Y., Suzuki, H., Kitamura, K., Itoh, T. 1982. Factors modifying contraction-relaxation cycle in vascular smooth muscles. *Am. J. Physiol.* 243:H641–H662

45. Lamb, F. S., Myers, J. H., Hanlin, M. N., Webb, R. C. 1985. Oscillatory con-

tractions in tail arteries from genetically hypertensive rats. *Hypertension* 7:125–130

46. Leijten, P. A. A., van Breemen, C. 1984. The effects of caffeine on the noradrenaline-sensitive calcium store in rabbit aorta. *J. Physiol.* 357:327–39

47. Leijten, P. A. A., van Breemen, C. 1986. The relationship between noradrenaline-induced contraction and ^{45}Ca efflux stimulation in rabbit mesenteric artery. *Br. J. Pharmacol.* 89:739–47

48. Lodge, N. J., Adams, D. J., Johns, A., Ryan, U. S., van Breemen, C. 1988. Ca^{2+} activation of endothelial cells. In *Proc. 2nd Int. Symp. Resistance Arteries,* ed. W. Halpern, Ithaca, New York: Perinatology. In press

49. Loutzenhiser, R., Epstein, M. 1985. Effects of calcium antagonists on renal hemodynamics. *Am. J. Physiol.* 249: F619–F629

50. Loutzenhiser, R., van Breemen, C. 1983. The influence of receptor occupation on Ca^{2+} influx mediated vascular smooth muscle contraction. *Circ. Res.* 52:I97–I103

51. Morgan, J. P., Morgan, K. G. 1984. Stimulus specific intracellular calcium levels in smooth muscle of ferret portal vein. *J. Physiol.* 351:155–67

52. Mulvany, M. J., Aalkjaer, C., Peterson, T. T. 1984. Intracellular sodium, membrane potential and contractility of rat mesenteric small arteries. *Circ. Res.* 54:740–49

53. Nishizuka, Y. 1984. The role of protein kinase C in cell surface signal transduction and tumor promotion. *Nature* 308:693–98

54. Ohya, Y., Kitamura, K., Kuriyama, H. 1987. Regulation of calcium current by intracellular calcium in smooth muscle cells of rabbit portal vein. *Circ. Res.* 62:375–83

55. Raeymaekers, L., Jones, L. R. 1986. Evidence for the presence of phospholamban in the endoplasmic reticulum of smooth muscle. *Biochim. Biophys. Acta* 882:258–65

56. Rembold, C., Murphy, R. H. 1988. Histamine induces mobilization of myoplasmic Ca from extracellular and intracellular stores in vascular smooth muscle. *Biophys. J.* 53:594A

57. Rossier, M. F., Capponi, A. M., Vallotton, M. B. 1987. Metabolism of inositol 1,4,5-trisphosphate in permeabilized rat aortic smooth-muscle cells. *Biochem. J.* 245:305–7

58. Sage, S. O., Rink, T. J. 1987. The kinetics of changes in intracellular calcium concentration in fura-2-loaded human platelets *J. Biol. Chem.* 262(34):16364–69

59. Saida, K. 1981. Ca^{2+}- and 'depolrization'-induced Ca^{2+} release in skinned smooth muscle fibers. *Biomed. Res.* 2:453–55

60. Saida, K. 1982. Intracellular Ca release in skinned smooth muscle. *J. Gen. Physiol.* 80:191–202

61. Saida, K., Nonomura, Y. 1978. Characteristics of Ca^{2+}- and Mg^{2+}-induced tension development in chemically skinned smooth muscle fibers. *J. Gen. Physiol.* 72:1–14

62. Saida, K., Twort, C., van Breemen, C. 1988. The specific GTP requirement for inositol 1,4,5-trisphosphate-induced Ca^{2+} release from skinned vascular smooth muscle. *J. Cardiovasc. Pharmacol.* In press

63. Saida, K., van Breemen, C. 1984. Characteristics of norepinephrine-sensitive Ca^{2+} store in vascular smooth muscle. *Blood Vessels* 21:43–52

64. Saida, K., van Breemen, C. 1984. Cyclic AMP modulation of adrenoreceptor-mediated arterial smooth muscle contraction. *J. Gen. Physiol.* 84:307–18

65. Saida, K., van Breemen, C. 1987. GTP requirement for inositol-1,4,5-trisphosphate-induced Ca^{2+} release from sarcoplasmic reticulum in smooth muscle. *Biochem. Biophys. Res. Commun.* 144:1313–16

66. Rengasamy, A., Feinberg, H. 1988. Inositol 1,4,5-trisphosphate-induced calcium release from platelet plasma membrane vesicles. *Biochem. Biophys. Res. Commun.* 150(3):1021–26

67. Smith, J. S., Coronado, R., Meissner, G. 1985. Sarcoplasmic reticulum contains adenine nucleotide-activated calcium channels. *Nature* 316:446–49

68. Smith, J. B., Smith, L. 1987. Extracellular Na^+ dependence of changes in free Ca^{2+}, $^{45}Ca^{2+}$ efflux, and total cell Ca^{2+} produced by angiotensin II in cultured arterial. *J. Biol. Chem.* 262: 17455–60

69. Somlyo, A. P. 1985. Excitation-contraction coupling and ultra structure of smooth muscle. *Circ. Res.* 57:497–507

70. Somlyo, A. V., Bond, M., Somlyo, A. P., Scarpa, A. 1985. Inositol trisphosphate-induced calcium release and contraction in vascular smooth muscle. *Proc. Natl. Acad. Sci. USA* 82:5231–35

71. Somlyo, A. P., Devine, C. E., Somlyo, A. V., North, S. R. 1971. Sarcoplasmic reticulum and the temperature-dependent contraction of smooth muscle

in calcium-free solutions. *J. Cell Biol.* 51:722–41

72. Somlyo, A. V., Franzini-Armstrong, C. 1985. New views of smooth muscle structure using freezing, deep-etching and rotary shadowing. *Experientia* 41: 841–56

73. Somlyo, A. P., Somlyo, A. V., Shuman, H., Endo, M. 1982. Calcium and monovalent ions in smooth muscle. *Fed. Proc.* 41:2883–90

74. Su, C., Bevan, J. A., Ursillo, R. C. 1964. Electrical quiescence of pulmonary artery smooth muscle during sympathomimetic stimulation *Circ. Res.* 15:20–27

75. Suematsu, E., Hirata, M., Hashimoto, T., Kuriyama, H. 1984. Inositol 1,4,5-trisphosphate releases Ca^{2+} from intracellular store sites in skinned single cells of porcine coronary artery. *Biochem. Biophys. Res. Commun.* 120: 481–85

76. Sumida, M., Hamada, M., Takenada, H., Hirata, Y., Nishgauchi, K., Okuda, H. 1986. Ca^{2+}, Mg^{2+}-ATPase of microsomal membranes from bovine aortic smooth muscle: Effects of Sr^{2+} and Cd^{2+} on Ca^{2+} uptake and formation of the phosphorylated intermediate of the Ca^{2+}, Mg^{2+}-ATPase. *J. Biochem.* 100: 765–72

77. Sumida, M., Okuda, H., Hamada, M. 1984. Ca^{2+}, Mg^{2+}-ATPase of microsomal membranes from bovine aortic smooth muscle. Identification and characterization of an acid-stable phosphorylated intermediate of the Ca^{2+}, Mg^{2+}-ATPasw. *J. Biochem.* 96:1365–74

78. Twort, C., van Breemen, C. 1988. Cyclic GMP-enhanced sequestration of of Ca^{2+} by sarcoplasmic reticulum in vascular smooth muscle. *Circ. Res.* 62:961–64

79. Ueno, H., Sumimoto, K., Hashimoto, T., Hirata, M., Kuriyama, H. 1987. Effects of procaine on pharmacomechanical coupling mechanisms activated by acetylcholine in smooth muscle cells of procine coronary artery. *Circ. Res.* 60:356–66

80. van Breemen, C. 1965. *Calcium distribution and exchange in rat uterus.* PhD thesis, University of Alberta. 110 pp.

81. van Breemen, C. 1969. Blockade of membrane calcium fluxes by lanthanum in relation to vascular smooth muscle contractility. *Int. Arch. Physiol. Biochem.* 77:710–17

82. van Breemen, C. 1977. Ca^{2+} requirement for activation of intact aortic smooth muscle. *J. Physiol.* 272:317–29

83. van Breemen, C., Aaronson, P., Loutzenhiser, R. 1979. Na$^+$, Ca^{2+} interactions in mammalian smooth muscle. *Pharmacol. Rev.* 30(2):167–208

84. van Breemen, C., Leyten, P., Yamamoto, H., Aaronson, P., Cauvin, C. 1986. Ca^{2+} activation of vascular smooth muscle. *Hypertension* 8(6):11:89–95

85. van Breemen, C., Farinas, C. B. R., Gerba, P., McNaughton, E. D. 1972. Excitation-contraction coupling in rabbit aorta studied by the lenthanum method for measuring cellular influx. *Circ. Res.* 30:44–54

86. van Breemen, C., Saida, K., Yamamoto, H., Hwang, K., Twort, C. 1988. Vascular smooth muscle sarcoplasmic reticulum. Function and Mechanisms of Ca^{2+} release. *Ann. NY Acad. Sci.* 522:60–73

87. von Tscharner, V., Prodhom, B., Baggiolini, M., Reuter, H. 1986. Ion channels in human neutrophils activated by a rise in free cytosolic calcium concentration. *Nature* 324:369–72

88. Walker, J. W., Somlyo, A. V., Goldman, Y. E., Somlyo, A. P., Trentham, D. R. 1987. Kinetics of smooth and skeletal muscle activation by laser pulse photolysis of caged inositol 1,4,5-trisphosphate. *Nature* 327:249–52

89. Wuytack, F., Raeymaekers, L., Verbist, J., Jones, L. R., Casteels, R. 1987. Smooth-muscle endoplasmic reticulum contains a cardiac-like form of calsequestrin. *Biochim. Biophys. Acta* 899: 151–58

90. Yamamoto, H., van Breemen, C. 1985. Inositol 1,4,5-trisphosphate releases calcium from skinned cultured smooth muscle cells. *Biochem. Biophys. Res. Commun.* 130:270–74

91. Yamamoto, H., van Breemen, C. 1986. Ca^{2+} compartments in saponin-skinned cultured vascular smooth muscle cells. *J. Gen. Physiol.* 87:369–89

92. Yanagisawa, M., Kurihara, H., Kimura, S., Tomobe, Y., Kobayashi, M., et al. 1988. A novel potent vasoconstrictor peptide produced by vascular endothelial cells. *Nature* 332:411–15

93. Zschauer, A., Scott-Burden, T., Buhler, F. R., van Breemen, C. 1987. Vasopressor Peptides and depolarization stimulated Ca^{2+}-entry into cultured vascular smooth muscle. *Biochem. Biophys. Res. Commun.* 148(1):225–31

Annu. Rev. Physiol. 1989. 51:331–49

SMOOTH MUSCLE ENERGETICS

R. J. Paul

Department of Physiology & Biophysics, University of Cincinnati, College of Medicine, Cincinnati, Ohio 45267–0576

INTRODUCTION

Muscle energetics now emcompasses several related areas. Historically, the approach of energetics was largely phenomenological and primarily involved quantitation of muscle heat production and mechanical output in order to define performance characteristics. Based heavily on thermodynamics, it was thus independent of any particular model, and importantly set limits to which any theory of muscle contraction must conform. With the development of techniques for the direct assessment of ATP breakdown during contraction, such as rapid freezing and NADH-linked fluorescent techniques, the emphasis has shifted in recent years to what may be termed the kinetics of the actomyosin ATPase in situ. The focus is on how mechanical constraints affect this reaction, with the ultimate goal of understanding the mechanochemical transduction events at the crossbridge level. In parallel with these studies, muscle energetics now encompasses metabolism, particularly energy metabolism, which focuses on the mechanisms underlying the coordination of metabolism and contractility. Excellent and comprehensive reviews of muscle energetics detailing these aspects for skeletal muscle are available (47, 97).

For smooth muscle, the coupling of energy utilization and supply is of necessity (see below) very close; thus, these two areas are closely intertwined and are the focus for this chapter. The metabolism and energetics of smooth muscle have been comprehensively reviewed in the past several years (8, 68, 75). I will thus only briefly summarize what is widely accepted, emphasizing what is controversial.

0066–4278/89/0315–0331$02.00

ENERGETICS STRATEGY: SKELETAL VS SMOOTH MUSCLE

Reflecting their different performance characteristics, skeletal and smooth muscles rely on different strategies for provision of ATP to meet contractile energy demands. For example, during contraction frog sartorius utilizes ATP approximately 100 times faster than its aerobic metabolism can resynthesize ATP. This large, step-change in energy demand is met primarily by a sizable (15–30 μmol/g) pool of preformed high energy phosphate in the form of phosphocreatine (PCr). This store is rapidly decreased during contraction, limiting the ability to maintain force, and is replenished on a time scale much longer than that of the contractile event. Vascular smooth muscle (VSM), at the other extreme, has relatively low levels of PCr (on the same order of magnitude as ATP; 1–3 μmol/g). Thus, the concept of the pool of PCr as a buffer for ATP is less meaningful in smooth muscle. In contrast to skeletal muscle, contractile activity in tonic VSM is associated with only a two to three fold increase in ATP utilization and virtually no change in the ATP + PCr content of the muscle as the ATP breakdown can be matched by the rate of its aerobic resynthesis. Tonic VSM, in fact, could not attain the peak of an isometric contraction if solely dependent on the preformed high energy phosphagen. Phasic smooth muscles are somewhat intermediate: PCr breakdown can be measured during contraction. However, these more rapidly contracting muscles are also able to attain steady states in which phosphagen content remains constant, with ATP utilization matched by aerobic resynthesis (37).

The techniques for measuring ATP utilization in intact smooth muscle reflect these different strategies (7, 65). For tonic muscles, measurement of steady state metabolic rates, usually oxygen consumption and/or lactate production, is often used to estimate ATP utilization. This method depends upon the assumption (largely verified) that during the measurement period [ATP] + [PCr] is constant. Alternatively, as is the case generally for skeletal muscle measurements, one can block ATP resynthesis (using oxygen- and substrate-free conditions and metabolic poisons) and measure directly the decline in ATP and PCr by rapid freezing of the muscle ("freeze-clamp") and analysis of extracts. Differences between the metabolite content of stimulated and unstimulated control muscles are then attributed to changes associated with contractile activity. This method has been successfully applied to some phasic smooth muscles although it is limited to time periods for which the decline in ATP and PCr is not severe and subject to the assumption that the metabolic poisons used do not affect performance. For further details and range of applicability see (7).

Recently two methodologies have begun to play a more significant role in smooth muscle energetics. The data base on heat measurements has considerably expanded (23, 24, 93, 96). This classical technique offers the greatest temporal resolution but is limited in terms of specificity. This can be a problem in smooth muscle studies since initial and recovery processes are not easily distinguishable, as is true for skeletal muscle. Nonetheless, these studies can fill in gaps inherent in other methodologies. Secondly, application of nuclear magnetic resonance (NMR) techniques is coming of age for smooth muscle studies (1, 15, 16, 18, 38, 48, 92, 98). Current levels of resolution have limited most studies to steady state results; however, this noninvasive method has given important confirmation to earlier freeze-clamp data. This methodology will likely play a more significant role since it is the only technique capable of unidirectional reaction rate measurements. These approaches have, in general, provided complementary results so that methodological differences and limitations do not appear to play a major role in the interpretation of smooth muscle energetics data.

THE RELATION BETWEEN CONTRACTILE ACTIVITY AND CHEMICAL UTILIZATION

Energetics of Isometric Contraction

Unstimulated VSM consumes ATP at rates between 0.5–1.0 μmol/(min·g) (7, 65, 68). Care must be taken in designating ATP utilization under unstimulated conditions as "basal" or "resting" utilization as smooth muscle often exhibits intrinsic levels of mechanical activity or tone. When mechanical activity is minimized, ATP utilization under unstimulated conditions shows little dependence on either length (or the consequent level of passive force) or bath calcium concentration (25, 44, 57, 87).

ATP utilization in stimulated smooth muscle, at lengths chosen to optimize isometric force, (L_0), is characterized by a biphasic pattern. A rapid increase in the rate of ATP utilization (J_{ATP}) to about three times the unstimulated rate is followed by a decrease to steady state rates of approximately twice the unstimulated rate. The time course and magnitude of changes are dependent on the tissue and stimulus studied, but this pattern has been observed in a variety of preparations (36, 65, 68, 75). The reported linear rate of heat production following stimulation under isometric conditions in the rabbit rectococcygeus (23, 24) appears to be the most notable exception to the biphasic energy utilization time course.

The challenge to smooth muscle energetics is to interpret these changes in terms of the kinetics of the actin-myosin ATPase. In addition to other ATP utilizing processes, such as ion pumping, which may be increased by stimulation, the level of the "basal" ATP utilizing processes may also be altered. Thus, separation of an actin-myosin dependent component from the total J_{ATP}

is not straightforward. Ideally, one could exploit the force-length characteristics of muscle to reduce or eliminate actin-myosin interaction and to ascribe the concomitant changes in J_{ATP} to the actin-myosin ATPase. This approach is dependent on two assumptions: (*a*) Changes in force with length are related to changes in actin-myosin interaction. (*b*) No other changes in J_{ATP} are dependent on length. For skeletal muscle, the first assumption can be verified for the descending limb of the force-length curve. Unfortunately, there is less theoretical justification for this in smooth muscle, and in practice, working at long muscle lengths is difficult due to the large passive forces and lack of reversibility (61, 74). With respect to the second assumption, it is known that the activation level of skeletal muscle can be dependent on length. There is little direct evidence to this point for smooth muscle. It has been reported that the sensitivity to pharmacological agonists can show length dependence (77, 78) and that the level of isometric force can be dependent on the previous history of length changes (28, 74). One might anticipate that activation by high KCl depolarization or supramaximal pharmacological stimulation, most often used in smooth muscle studies, would be less sensitive to length changes than electrical stimulation in skeletal muscle. However, whether changes in activation play a major role in shaping the force-length relation in smooth muscle remains an open question.

In general, under stimulated conditions the dependence of the steady state J_{ATP} on length does parallel that of isometric force, decreasing significantly at both short and long lengths. Approximately 20–50% of the suprabasal J_{ATP} remains at lengths at which no force is developed (8, 65). Under traditional partitioning schemes, this remaining J_{ATP} is designated activation energy, while the tension-dependent suprabasal J_{ATP}, some 80% in the case of hog carotid artery, is attributed to actin-myosin ATPase (75).

When reviewed earlier (65), the internal consistency (see below) and strong analogy to skeletal muscle energetics supported this interpretation. Recently, however, a model for smooth muscle contraction in which the largest fraction of steady state J_{ATP} is not attributed to the actin-activated myosin ATPase, but rather to the ATP utilization associated with the myosin light chain phosphorylation/dephosphorylation cycle has been proposed (63; see Murphy and Hai & Murphy, this volume). This model has refocused interest on the interpretation of length-dependent changes in J_{ATP}. Though the evidence is not extensive, myosin light chain phosphorylation does not appear to be strongly length dependent (2, 59). Thus, one would not anticipate appreciable changes in J_{ATP} with length if this theory were correct. In contrast to most reports of vascular smooth muscle, J_{ATP} in rabbit taenia coli did not decrease with force at short muscle lengths (85). This result was attributed to the misalignment of contractile filaments and/or cells at very short muscle lengths. An internal load arising from misalignment of filaments opposing force at short lengths could also be involved to explain this result. Nonetheless, one cannot unequivocally rule out myosin light chain phosphorylation/ dephosphorylation cycling as a major source of ATP utilization in all smooth muscle. I return to this interesting question following discussion of other methods of measurement of tension-dependent J_{ATP}.

At fixed lengths, graded levels of isometric force in intact smooth muscle can be produced by a variety of means including graded depolarization, and variation of agonist level and extracellular calcium. A hallmark of ATP utilization under these conditions is that it is linearly dependent on the level of isometric force (65). This also appears to be the case for studies on skinned smooth muscle in which force is varied by adjusting the level of calcium (4, 5). The total suprabasal J_{ATP} agrees with the total calculated ATPase activity based on that of isolated actin-activated myosin ATPase and estimates of the myosin content of the intact tissue (71). Alterations in force produced under conditions of maximal stimulation by changing length are also associated with a proportional change in J_{ATP}, though with a positive intercept at the origin. The difference in these linear relations between force and J_{ATP}, (fixed length with graded stimulation and fixed stimulation with varying length) imply that the tension-independent J_{ATP} ascribable to activation processes is proportional to the level of stimulation (65). These observations are consistent with the view that the tension-dependent J_{ATP} is related to the level of the actomyosin ATPase, with a small component of tension-independent J_{ATP} (approximately 20% of the total suprabasal J_{ATP} when measured at L_0) related to the degree of activation.

Could these observations also be consistent with the hypothesis that the major component of ATP utilization is related to myosin light chain phosphorylation/dephosphorylation? This is difficult to determine without reviewing the complete "latch" model (see next section). However, in addition to the data on the length dependence of J_{ATP}, which suggest that crossbridge ATP utilization is dominant, the strongest evidence against a major role for this phosphorylation-dephosphorylation cycle in steady state ATP utilization appears to be from skinned fiber energetics studies using ATPγS. This ATP analog is a substrate for myosin kinase but thiophosphorylated myosin is a poor substrate for myosin light chain phosphatase (84). Exposure of skinned fibers to ATPγS leads to a nearly irreversible thiophosphorylation of the myosin light chains. ATP utilization by skinned fibers after thiophosphorylation is about the same for fibers contracted by Ca^{2+}, in which myosin light chain phosphorylation/dephosphorylation can occur (34). Thus, at least in the skinned guinea pig taenia coli, this cycle does not appear to be a major contributor to the force-associated ATPase. However, one might argue that for skinned fibers, the relatively low temperatures and potential loss of kinase/phosphatase activity obscures the contribution of this ATPase relative to that of the actomyosin ATPase (Hai & Murphy, this volume).

These data are consistent with the relatively low estimates of ATP utilization attributable to myosin phosphorylation/dephosphorylation in intact smooth muscle. Using the rate of dephosphorylation during relaxation as an estimate of in vivo phosphatase activity, Butler et al (10) estimated that approximately 10% of J_{ATP} during steady state force maintenance is ascribable to myosin phosphorylation/dephosphorylation in rabbit taenia coli. In hog carotid artery, the myosin content is reported (64) to be about 5–10 mg/g media or 10–20 nmol/g media. A phosphatase rate constant of 0.13 s^{-1} has been estimated by Driska (17) from maximum in vivo dephosphorylation rates. Using an average steady state myosin light chain phosphorylation level of 0.2 mol P_i/mol P light chain, ATP utilization attributable to myosin light chain phosphorylation/dephosphorylation is estimated to be 0.13 s^{-1} × 0.2 mol P_i/mol P light chain 60 s/min × (10–20) nmol myosin/g media × 2 P light chain/myosin = 0.03–0.06 μmol/min·g. This value is between 1.5 and 15% of the reported steady state suprabasal J_{ATP} for hog carotid artery under various stimulus conditions (65) and is in reasonable agreement with that reported for the tension-independent component associated with activation. Clearly calculations alone will never be the final word. More direct evidence on the extent of the ATP utilization by myosin phosphorylation/dephosphorylation is needed.

Energetics and the Latch Hypothesis

One of the classical uses and strengths of muscle energetics is its ability, in some cases unique, to distinguish between various models of muscle contraction. The textbook example here is the Fenn Effect. The observation that energy utilization increased above the isometric rate in contractions in which work was produced led to the demise of the viscoelastic theory of muscle contraction (47). Currently, much attention in smooth muscle research is focused on the "latch" theory. As details have been given in this volume (see Murphy and Hai & Murphy) and elsewhere (63), I will only focus on the evidence obtained from studies of smooth muscle energetics. Briefly, the original observation that led to the latch theory is that while isometric force (F_0) increases monotonically to a plateau value following stimulation in intact preparations, both the maximum shortening velocity (V_m) and myosin light chain phosphorylation (MLC-P_i) attain maximal values early in the contraction and then decline. Importantly, MLC-P_i and V_m decline over time periods when F_0 is nearly constant or increasing. This led to the hypothesis that MLC-P_i, in addition to activating actin-myosin interaction, plays a role in modulation of crossbridge cycle rates, as suggested by the parallel behavior of V_m and MLC-P_i. It should be noted that there is debate over the universality of these observations, particularly the latter (8, 20–22, 44, 87).

In its current stage of evolution, the basis for this behavior put forth by the "latch" hypothesis is simple and elegant. Dephosphorylation of an attached crossbridge induces a noncycling "latch bridge," which has a slow detachment rate compared with a phosphorylated crossbridge. Dependent on the relative MLC kinase/phosphatase activity, this theory predicts two populations of crossbridges with different cycling rates and, consequently, different rates of ATP hydrolysis. Mathematical models based on this theory are consistent with the more notable characteristics of smooth muscle behavior, that of a modulable V_m and, in terms of energetics, the high economy of tension maintenance. An explanation of the ability of smooth muscle to maintain high levels of force (with lower levels of myosin than skeletal muscle) with J_{ATP} of up to 3 orders of magnitude less than skeletal muscle has been a driving force for studies of smooth muscle energetics for a long time (65).

What evidence can be obtained from smooth muscle energetics towards the validation of the "latch" theory? Initial studies focused on the time course of J_{ATP} during an isometric contraction. If the decrease in V_m with stimulus duration reflected a slowing of the crossbridge cycle rate, then one would predict that energy utilization should show a similar time course. This is based on the usual assumption that 1 ATP molecule is hydrolized during the crossbridge cycle. It should be noted that in the current interpretation of the latch hypothesis, 2 ATP are hydrolyzed per "latch" cycle, 1 by the actin-myosin cycle and 1 by myosin phosphorylation/dephosphorylation (Hai & Murphy, this volume). Energy utilization during development of tension in smooth muscle has long been known to be greater than that observed in the steady state (65). More recent, detailed studies of this time course of J_{ATP} after stimulation under isometric conditions indicate a maximal rate of some 2–4 times that measured in the steady state (37, 43, 86). If in the steady state the muscle is subjected to a rapid step shortening to discharge the force, the subsequent slower redevelopment of force is not associated with an increased J_{ATP} (43, 86). Thus, the increased J_{ATP} is not associated with force development per se, but is related to the time following stimulation or the rate of force development. This observation is consistent with the "latch" hypothesis since MLC-P_i declines following stimulation.

Whether this increase in J_{ATP} after stimulation is related to actin-myosin interaction or some other transient process(es) associated with stimulation, including an accelerated ATP utilization attributable to myosin phosphorylation/dephosphorylation, remains open. In one case, the transient increase in J_{ATP} following stimulation has been shown to be substantially reduced at short muscle lengths where little force was developed (43). However, interpretation of data at short muscle lengths in terms of a reduction of actin-myosin interaction is not unambiguous (8).

The time courses of V_m, J_{ATP}, and MLC-P_i are similar but not necessarily superimposable. Differences in the temporal resolution of these measurements precludes more definitive statements. However, recent studies comparing heat production and V_m argue more strongly for their similarity (93). The causal basis for the correlation between MLC-P_i and the mechanical and energetic parameters is less secure. Butler & Siegman (9) and Siegman et al (87) showed that in rabbit taenia coli, neither V_m nor J_{ATP} are uniquely correlated with MLC-P_i.

What can be said with certainty is that J_{ATP} does decline with duration of stimulation. The magnitude of this decrease (two to four fold), even when extrapolated to account for the maximum possible changes in MLC-P_i, cannot account for the differences in tension cost between smooth and skeletal muscle. At present, the largest component of this difference appears to reside in the intrinsic differences between the actin-activated myosin ATPases between skeletal and smooth muscle. Nonetheless, if the decline in J_{ATP} and V_m reflect a mechanism for modulating crossbridge cycle rates, this mechanism is of considerable physiological importance to smooth muscle function.

A second area of considerable research activity in smooth muscle energetics has been the dependence of J_{ATP} on calcium. The transients in MLC-P_i and V_m after stimulation are known to be paralleled by those of intracellular Ca^{2+} (60, 82; Murphy, this volume). The questions here are similar. Do changes in J_{ATP} parallel changes in MLC-P_i and Ca^{2+}? And what, if any, is the causal factor(s)? In contrast to skeletal muscle, in both intact and skinned fiber studies, F_o, V_m, and J_{ATP} all appear to be functions of calcium (4, 5, 44, 70, 82, 87). Furthermore, at high levels of calcium, increases in V_m and J_{ATP} tend to be larger than those of F_o, which suggests that the crossbridge cycle rate can be modified independently of force and thus presumably of crossbridge number (44, 87).

As calcium and MLC-P_i are known to be related, this evidence could be viewed as consistent with a major tenet of the latch hypothesis: MLC-P_i is a determinant of crossbridge cycle rate. However, there are a number of important exceptions to this straightforward interpretation. Siegman et al argued that at high levels of extracellular calcium ($[Ca^{2+}]_o$), large changes in V_m and J_{ATP} can occur in rabbit taenia coli with no significant changes in MLC-P_i or force (87). At the lower end of the Ca^{2+} range (0.15–1.6 mM), Krisanda & Paul argued that the reported levels of MLC-P_i for hog carotid artery in the steady state in many cases do not differ from baseline values, and yet changes in $[Ca^{2+}]_o$ in this range can be associated with substantial changes in V_m and J_{ATP} (44). Gerthoffer's laboratory as well provided substantial evidence that MLC-P_i, F_o, and V_m are not always related in a unique and/or proportional manner for dog tracheal smooth muscle (20–22). Thus, the only consensus appears to be that calcium is a major determinant of, and can potentially independently regulate, F_o, V_m, and J_{ATP}. The existence of mechanisms other than myosin phosphorylation for modulation of cross-bridge cycle rate and number remains open (41; Kamm & Stull, this volume).

The observation that both J_{ATP} and V_m are proportional to F_0, at least for $[Ca^{2+}]_o$ up to the physiological levels, is not consistent with the view, often used as a first approximation, that force reflects crossbridge number and V_m, the cycle rate. If this were the case, then J_{ATP}, which should reflect both number and cycle rate, would be proportional to the square of F_0, not linearly related as has been nearly the universal observation. Stiffness, a mechanical parameter also often used as an index of crossbridge number, is also proportional to F_0 under these conditions (73, 76). If one then accepts F_0 (and stiffness) as reflecting the number of bridges, then both J_{ATP} and V_m may not be ascribable to the same crossbridge cycle rate. It is possible, based on recent kinetic data in the skeletal muscle literature, that the rate limiting steps in the crossbridge cycle under isometric conditions differ from those limiting shortening (88).

One possible explanation for this paradox lies in the concept of an "internal load," which has recently received renewed interest in smooth muscle energetics. In this view, J_{ATP} measures the true cycle rate under isometric conditions, whereas V_m estimates a different cycle rate, one modulated by an internal load, which comes into play only during active shortening. Such an internal load could be a purely passive phenomenon, reflecting some structural compressive force inherent to filament sliding. On the other hand, in some views of the latch hypothesis, the putative slow or noncycling, dephosphorylated latchbridges themselves pose some form of load to the more rapidly cycling, phosphorylated bridges. Smooth muscle energetics is uniquely suited to testing such hypotheses.

Smooth Muscle Energetics: Work Producing Contractions

Though isometric conditions are the simplest and most extensively studied, contractions in which work is produced, as in the case of the Fenn Effect, have often led to more restrictive criteria for testing models of muscle contraction. In addition to imposing very different mechanical constraints on the in situ actin-myosin interaction, there is a thermodynamically well-defined parameter, efficiency; defined as the external work produced divided by the free energy change of the driving chemical reaction. Its theoretical maximum value is 1, permitting a test of the validity of the reaction scheme proposed. Such data for smooth muscle have only recently become available and are limited to relatively few muscles and conditions. Nonetheless, some cautious generalizations can be made. A Fenn Effect, i.e. an ATP utilization during work-producing contractions greater than that observed for isometric conditions, can be seen under some, but not all conditions (9, 72). This is true for skeletal muscle as well, and similarly, the significance of this observation is unclear (47, 80). More importantly, the efficiency of smooth muscle, in contrast to its economy of force maintenance, appears to be significantly lower than skeletal muscle. As the free energy associated with the hydrolysis of ATP in situ is subject to a degree of uncertainty, efficiency is often expressed as work produced per mole of the associated high energy phosphagen breakdown. For a variety of skeletal muscles this value is on the order of 20 kJ/mol. For the two cases reported for smooth muscle, this value is in the range of 5 kJ/mol (9, 72). If one assumes a free energy of ATP hydrolysis of 40 kJ/mol, the absolute thermodynamic efficiencies would be 0.50 and 0.12 for skeletal and smooth muscle respectively.

The bases underlying the relatively low efficiency and high economy of smooth muscle compared to that of skeletal muscle are not known with certainty. What is clear is that these are important constraints for models of smooth muscle contractility. Energetics can, in some cases, provide a unique test of hypotheses relating to this relatively low efficiency. An internal load is one case in point. If decreases in velocity were ascribable to the presence of an internal load, the prediction from energetics would be a concomitant decrease in the measured efficiency because work associated with an internal load would have an energetic cost in terms of ATP utilization, but the internal work would not contribute to the total work output of the tissue. If the energetic cost of internal work is the same as work against an external load, which is not unreasonable since the same crossbridge mechanism presumably underlies both, the measured efficiency (E_{meas}) of the whole muscle would be less than the true crossbridge efficiency (E_{true}) according to: $E_{meas} = E_{true} \times W_{obs}/(W_{obs} + W_{il})$, where W_{obs} and W_{il} are the observed work and the work attributable to the internal load, respectively. This can be further quantitated if one assumes that the magnitude of the internal load can be calculated from changes in velocity through the well characterized Hill force-velocity relation. For example, a two to three fold decrease in V_m would require an internal load of 0.1–0.2 F_0 for the hog carotid artery, using published values for its force-velocity relation. In the case of work performed under maximal power output ($F = 0.28 F_0$), one would predict a decrease in efficiency by 26% and 42% for internal loads of 0.1 and 0.2 F_0 respectively. Thus, if the velocity changes that occur with time or those associated with changes in [Ca^{2+}]$_o$ were ascribable to an internal load, significant decreases in efficiency would be anticipated.

However, in the limited literature on smooth muscle energetics efficiency does not appear to be a strong function of the external conditions. In taenia coli, conditions chosen to optimize the effects of an internal load were not found to have significant effects on efficiency (10). Krisanda & Paul have measured the efficiency of working contractions at maximum power output in hog carotid artery. Work was varied through a sevenfold range by altering stimulus and $[Ca]_o$. Though high levels of precision are difficult to obtain because of the low levels of chemical breakdown, efficiency was relatively constant in the range studied (72). Thus, while much research remains, these initial studies do not support the hypothesis that the changes in velocity are ascribable to an internal load. It should be noted that in the current interpretation of the latch hypothesis, an internal load is not explicitly proposed to explain the changes in velocity following stimulation though distinct populations of rapidly and slowly cycling crossbridges are operable (Hai & Murphy, this volume).

The present level of smooth muscle energetics does suggest that the absolute level of myosin phosphorylation per se does not play a strong role in terms of the efficiency of smooth muscle. However, if myosin phosphorylation/dephosphorylation is a substantial fraction of the ATP utilization associated with contractile activity, as suggested by Murphy and colleagues, this could account for the low efficiency of smooth muscle relative to skeletal muscle. Clearly, this is an area in which we anticipate considerable activity.

ENERGETICS: EVIDENCE FOR FUNCTIONAL COMPARTMENTATION OF METABOLISM

Up to this point we have focused on smooth muscle energetics in terms of ATP utilization. The other side of the energetics coin is the study of the processes involved in provision of ATP, and here too there has been significant activity in recent times. One intriguing development is the growing body of evidence that specific ATP-dependent functions may be underwritten by associated, compartmentalized metabolic pathways. The evidence and rationale for cytosolic compartmentation have been recently reviewed for many biological systems (40, 56) including smooth muscle. Thus, I summarize only the major features.

An unusual aspect of smooth muscle energy metabolism is that it is characterized by a substantial production of lactate under aerobic conditions. The basis for this aerobic glycolysis has been under investigation for some time (65). One clear consensus from recent studies is that oxidative metabolism and aerobic production of lactate in smooth muscle can vary independently, and often in opposite directions (12, 14, 35, 45, 49, 69, 90, 91). We have observed for tonic porcine carotid and coronary arteries, that the rate of oxygen consumption (J_{O_2}) is nearly universally correlated with the level of isometric force, whereas the rate of aerobic lactate production (J_{lac}) is more strongly correlated with the activity of the Na^+ pump (54, 66, 69). For example, in the presence of ouabain, J_{lac} is inhibited while isometric force and J_{O_2} increase in parallel. Based on many similar observations, Paul et al (69) suggested that metabolism in smooth muscle was functionally compartmentalized with suprabasal J_{O_2} associated primarily with the energy requirements of the actin-myosin ATPase and aerobic glycolysis linked to the energy requirements of membrane-related processes.

This hypothesis received further impetus from studies delineating the substrate underlying the aerobic production of lactate. Surprisingly, exogenous glucose is the sole substrate source for lactate production even though there can be substantial breakdown of glycogen (53). This observation implied the existence of at least two distinct enzyme cascades for glycolysis and glycogenolysis, and furthermore that the common metabolites of these two pathways do not freely mix. The latter does appear to hold at least for glucose-6-phosphate in hog carotid artery (55). Lynch & Paul (53) postulated that this functional compartmentation reflected enzymic localization, in particular with a glycolytic enzyme cascade associated with the plasma membrane and glycogenolysis linked to contractile filaments or cytosolic elements.

A major characteristic of smooth muscle metabolism is that this compartmentation of metabolism and function is never absolute. For example, normal ionic gradients can be maintained in smooth muscle by oxidative metabolism in the absence of glucose, or by glycolysis in the absence of oxygen (11, 81). Nonetheless under fully oxygenated conditions, when glucose is available, aerobic glycolysis with lactate as its end product appears to be the preferred source of ATP for supporting membrane pump function. Campbell et al recently attempted to quantitate the relation between aerobic lactate production and Na^+ pump activity in hog carotid artery (11). Though preliminary, the results indicate that for Na^+ pump rates in the physiological range, a stoichiometry near the theoretical value of $2K+$ per lactate, assuming 1 ATP per lactate, is observed. However, substantially larger pumping rates can be elicited for which oxidative metabolism can be the dominant source of ATP. The basis for this crossover from aerobic glycolysis to oxidative metabolism is unclear. However, these results are consistent with the hypothesis that a membrane associated glycolytic cascade is involved with maintenance of ion pump activity under physiological conditions.

This hypothesis has its origin in studies on the red blood cell (19, 79). The central observations from the red cell literature are the association of a glycolytic enzyme cascade with the plasma membrane (27) and the ability of glycolytic intermediates to support the Na^+ pump in red cell ghosts in the presence of an "ATP-trap" (58). This latter observation suggests that the ATP produced by membrane associated glycolysis may have preferential access to the Na^+ pump, potentially through a membrane bound ATP pool. Though again only preliminary, we have shown that glycolytic enzymes are present in a purified plasma membrane vesicle fraction prepared from pig antral smooth muscle (67). This glycolytic enzyme cascade can act in a concerted fashion, catabolizing fructose-1,6dP (fructose 1–6 diphosphate) to lactate, and importantly, can fuel Ca^{2+} uptake in this preparation (32). Moreover, initial experiments indicate that the endogenous glycolytic cascade can support Ca^{2+} uptake in the presence of an immobilized ATP-trap, which abolishes Ca^{2+} uptake supported by exogenous ATP (31). This simplified model further supports the hypothesis of a preferential coupling of membrane associated glycolysis and energy-dependent membrane function though clearly much research remains.

There is also evidence in the brain (50), kidney (51), and cardiac (33) literature that suggests the correlation of glycolysis and membrane function observed in smooth muscle may be representative of a more general phenomenon. Particularly notable to this end is a recent report (94) indicating that ATP-dependent K^+ channels in cardiac myocytes were more strongly linked to glycolytic than oxidative metabolism. Whether a similar coupling of membrane ion channel activity to glycolysis occurs in smooth muscle is not known at present, but based on the ability of glycolysis to support membrane ion pumps, such a hypothesis appears well worth investigating.

While it is becoming increasingly clear that the cytosol is not a single, uniform compartment (13), the physiological significance and the implications for energetics of cytosolic compartmentation remain to be elucidated. On the one hand, compartmentation has been predicted to lead to improved efficiency of enzymic reactions. This is ascribable to higher effective local metabolite concentrations or "substrate tunneling" models, and is supported by both theoretical models (46, 95) and simplified kinetic experiments (26). Direct in vivo tests of this hypothesis are difficult. A recent report indicates that the maximum velocity of the Na^+ pump in cultured kidney cells is increased some twofold when glycolytic rather than oxidative metabolism is the primary source of ATP, which suggests some type of kinetic advantage to compartmentation (52).

On the other hand, the major significance of compartmentation may lie in the requirement for independent regulation of various energy-dependent cellular functions. For example, during relaxation of contraction in smooth muscle, the actin-myosin ATPase would be reduced while that of Ca^{2+}-pumps activated. Compartmentation would permit the same metabolic signalling mechanism to be involved in the stimulation of ATP production in the environment where it was required. Here again the evidence is limited but intriguing. Adams & Dillon described conditions in which glucose is necessary for norepinephrine to elicit a contraction in hog carotid artery whereas control levels of force can be elicited by depolarization with KCl (1) in the absence of glucose. This mirrors an earlier study in which glucose depletion was shown to have agonist specific effects (3). The important contribution of the work of Adams & Dillon (1) is that the glucose-dependent effects were demonstrated under conditions in which no changes in ATP or PCr content from control were measured using NMR techniques. These results imply that the energy required for the cascade of events elicited by norepinephrine is in a compartment dependent on glycolysis or glycogenolysis. There is also complementary evidence that cyclic nucleotide effects may be consistent with some form of compartmentation (83). Thus, colocalization of the regulatory signal as well as the energy source with the specific function they subserve may play a role in the independent control of the various cytosolic processes.

COORDINATION OF METABOLISM AND FUNCTION

What then is the regulatory signal by which ATP demand and supply are matched? Similar to the behavior of isolated mitochondria, the most prevalent theory is based on acceptor- (or ADP)-limited respiration (47). In its simplest form, increased ATPase activity leads to a rise in ADP concentration, which in turn stimulates mitochondrial respiration. In muscle cells there is a large pool of bound ADP; thus, estimates of the free-ADP levels are most often based on the creatine kinase reaction and the assumption that it is at or near equilibrium. On the whole, the acceptor-limited theory does appear to be valid for fast skeletal muscle (47). However, for cardiac and smooth muscle in particular, there are major objections to its applicability. For the tonic hog carotid artery, Krisanda & Paul showed that when J_{O_2} is doubled on transition from rest to contraction, there is no apparent change in ATP and PCr and hence no change in the calculated free-ADP (42). The absence of changes in ATP and PCr under conditions when J_{O_2} is increased has also been seen for a number of smooth muscles using NMR techniques. Rat portal vein, which is characterized by rapid phasic contractions and relatively high ATPase activity, appears to be an exception in that changes in J_{O_2} can be correlated with ADP levels (37).

If the free-ADP calculated from ATP and PCr is not the signal regulating oxygen consumption in tonic smooth muscle, then what are the likely candidates? The available evidence may not, in fact, rule out free-ADP. The overall cellular levels of PCr and ATP may not be a reliable measure of free-ADP if compartmentation of these phosphagens is appreciable or if the creatine kinase reaction is not in equilibrium. I have summarized here the arguments that some form of compartmentation is likely, and the evidence concerning creatine kinase equilibrium in smooth muscle is limited (18, 39, 98).

Stronger arguments against ADP as the signal have been made in the cardiac muscle literature (6). Arising from these studies is the hypothesis that mitochondrial respiration is not "pulled" as in the acceptor limited theory, but rather is "pushed" at the substrate entry side, likely involving the NAD/NADH oxidation state (30). It has been suggested that intracellular Ca^{2+} may be the signal for the mobilization of substrates underlying this "push" hypothesis for the regulation of oxidative metabolism. Little evidence to this point is available for smooth muscle, though very recent data indicate that intracellular Ca^{2+} may independently activate carbohydrate metabolism and contractile elements (64a).

I have emphasized areas of uncertainty in smooth muscle energetics. I do not, however, want to leave the impression that little is known. In fact, substantial progress has been made. The available evidence, if anything, clearly indicates that our theories of smooth muscle energetics cannot simply be extrapolated from those generated from the more extensively studied skeletal muscle. Smooth muscle clearly differs in the areas of the independent regulation of crossbridge number and cycle rate, and this has wide ranging consequences to theories of control as well as to our understanding of its high economy and relatively low efficiency. Compartmentation of metabolism with specific function also appears more strikingly in smooth muscle and this cell may serve as a useful model for other cell types. The metabolite signals for the regulation and coordination of metabolism with function are not known with certainty. This is of particular interest in smooth muscle as glycolytic and oxidative components of metabolism appear to be independently regulated. These areas as well as those more traditionally associated with energetics appear to be essential for our understanding of smooth muscle.

ACKNOWLEDGMENTS

I would like to thank J. D. Campbell, C. Hardin, R. M. Lynch, R. A. Murphy, M. J. Siegman, and J. D. Strauss for their helpful comments on this manuscript, and P. S. Roth and A. Lutz for help in its preparation. Part of the work reported here was supported by NIH HL 23240, HL 22619, and NSF Belgian-American Cooperative Science Program.

Literature Cited

1. Adams, G. R., Dillon, P. F. 1988. Glucose dependence of sequential norepinephrine contractions of vascular smooth muscle. *Blood Vessels*. In press
2. Aksoy, M. O., Mras, S., Kamm, K. E., Murphy, R. A. 1983. Ca^{2+}, cAMP and changes in myosin phosphorylation during contraction of smooth muscle. *Am. J. Physiol.* 245 (*Cell Physiol.* 14):C255–C270
3. Altura, B. M., Altura, B. T. 1970. Differential effects of substrate depletion on drug-induced contraction of rabbit aorta. *Am. J. Physiol.* 219:1698–1705
4. Arner, A., Hellstrand, P. 1983. Activation of contraction and ATPase activity in intact and chemically skinned smooth muscle of rat portal vein. *Circ. Res.* 53:695–702
5. Arner, A., Hellstrand, P. 1985. Effects of calcium and substrate on force-velocity relation and energy turnover in skinned smooth muscle of the guinea-pig. *J. Physiol.* 360:347–65

6. Balaban, R. S., Kantor, H. L., Katz, L. A., Briggs, R. W. 1986. Relation between work and phosphate metabolites in the in vivo paced mammalian heart. *Science* 232:1121–23

7. Butler, T. M., Davies, R. E. 1980. High-energy phosphates in smooth muscle. In *Handbook of Physiology*, ed. D. F. Bohr, A. P. Somlyo, H. V. Sparks, 2:237–52. Bethesda, Md.: Am. Physiol. Soc.

8. Butler, T. M., Siegman, M. J. 1985. High-energy phosphate metabolism in vascular smooth muscle. *Ann. Rev. Physiol.* 47:629–43

9. Butler, T. M., Siegman, M. J., Mooers, S. U. 1983. Chemical energy usage during shortening and work production in mammalian smooth muscle. *Am. J. Physiol.* 244:C234–C242

10. Butler, T. M., Siegman, M. J., Mooers, S. U. 1986. Slowing of cross-bridge cycling in smooth muscle without evidence of an internal load. *Am. J. Physiol.* 251 (*Cell Physiol.* 20):C945–C950

11. Campbell, J. D., Agubosim, S., Paul, R. J. 1988. Compartmentation of metabolism and function in vascular smooth muscle: Quantitation of Na-pump activity and aerobic glycolysis. *FASEB J.* 2(4):A755

12. Casteels, R., Wuytack, F. 1975. Aerobic and anaerobic metabolism in smooth muscle cells of taenia coli in relation to active ion transport. *J. Physiol.* 250:203–20

13. Clegg, J. S. 1984. Properties and metabolism of aqueous cytoplasm and its boundaries. *Am. J. Physiol.* 246:R133

14. Davidheiser, S., Joseph, J., Davies, R. E. 1984. Separation of aerobic glycolysis from oxidative metabolism and contractility in rat anococcygeus muscle. *Am. J. Physiol.* 247(*Cell Physiol.* 16):C335–C341

15. Dawson, M. J., Wray, S. 1985. The effects of pregnancy and parturition on phosphorus metabolites in rat uterus studied by ^{31}P nuclear magnetic resonance. *J. Physiol.* 368:19–31

16. Degani, H., Shaer, A., Victor, T. A., Kaye, A. M. 1984. Estrogen-induced changes in high-energy phosphate metabolism in rat uterus: ^{31}P NMR studies. *Biochemistry* 23:2572–77

17. Driska, S. P. 1987. High myosin light chain phosphatase activity in arterial smooth muscle: Can it explain the latch phenomenon? In *Regulation and Contraction of Smooth Muscle*, ed. M. J. Siegman, A. P. Somlyo, N. L. Stephens, pp. 387–98. New York: Liss

18. Fisher, M. J., Dillon, P. F. 1987. Phenylphosphonate: a ^{31}P-NMR indicator of extracellular pH and volume in the isolated perfused rabbit bladder. *Circ. Res.* 60(4):472–77

19. Fossel, E. T., Solomon, A. K. 1977. Membrane mediated link between ion transport and metabolism in human red blood cells. *Biochim. Biophys. Acta* 464:82

20. Gerthoffer, W. T. 1986. Calcium dependence of myosin phosphorylation and airway smooth muscle contraction and relaxation. *Am. J. Physiol.* 250 (*Cell Physiol.* 19):C597–C604

21. Gerthoffer, W. T. 1986. Dissociation of myosin phosphorylation and active tension during muscarinic stimulation of tracheal smooth muscle. *J. Pharmacol. Exp. Ther.* 240:8–15

22. Gerthoffer, W. T., Murphey, K. A., McGinnis, M. 1987. Calcium-dependence of shortening velocity in canine tracheal smooth muscle. *Biophys. J.* 51:335

23. Gibbs, C. L., Kotsanas, G. 1984. Myothermic, polarographic and lactate production measurement on rabbit rectococcygeus muscle. In *Smooth Muscle Contraction*, ed. N. L. Stephens, pp. 259–69. New York: Dekker

24. Gibbs, C. L., Kotsanas, G., McCance, I. 1985. Effect of duration of stimulation and pH on energetics of rabbit rectococcygeus muscle. *Am. J. Physiol.* 248 (*Cell Physiol.* 17):C357–C364

25. Glück, E., Paul, R. J. 1977. The aerobic metabolism of porcine carotid artery and its relationship to isometric force: energy cost of isometric contraction. *Pflügers Arch.* 370:9–18

26. Goldman, R., Katchalski, E. 1973. Kinetic behavior of a two-enzyme membrane carrying out a consecutive set of reactions. *J. Theor. Biol.* 32:243

27. Green, D. E., Murer, E., Hultin, H. O., Richardson, S. H., Salmon, B., et al. 1965. Association of integrated metabolic pathways with membranes. I. Glycolytic enzymes of the red blood corpuscle and yeast. *Arch. Biochem. Biophys.* 112:635

28. Gunst, S. J. 1986. Effect of length history on contractile behavior of canine tracheal smooth muscle. *Am. J. Physiol.* 250(*Cell Physiol.* 19):C146–C154

29. Deleted in proof

30. Hansford, R. G. 1985. Relation between mitochondrial calcium transport and control of energy metabolism. *Rev. Physiol. Biochem. Pharmacol.* 102:1–72

31. Hardin, C., Raeymaekers, L., Wuytack, F., Casteels, R., Paul, R. J. 1988. Com-

parison of endogenous and exogenous sources of ATP in supporting Ca^{2+}-uptake in isolated smooth muscle plasma membrane vesicles (PMV). *Biophys. J.* 53(2,2):374a

32. Hardin, C., Raeymaekers, L., Wuytack, F., Casteels, R., Paul, R. J. 1987. An endogenous glycolytic cascade can preferentially fuel Ca^{2+}-uptake in a plasma membrane vesicle fraction (PMV) of smooth muscle. *Fed. Proc.* 46(4):1096

33. Hasin, Y., Doorey, A., Barry, W. H. 1984. Electrophysiologic and mechanical effects of metabolic inhibition of high-energy phosphate production in cultured chick embryo ventricular cells. *J. Mol. Cell. Cardiol.* 16:1009–21

34. Hellstrand, P., Arner, A. 1985. Myosin light chain phosphorylation and the crossbridge cycle at low substrate concentration in chemically skinned guinea pig taenia coli. *Pflügers Arch.* 405:323–28

35. Hellstrand, P., Jorup, C., Lydrup, M. L. 1984. O_2 consumption, aerobic glycolysis and tissue phosphagen content during activation of the Na^+/K^+ pump in rat portal vein. *Pflügers Arch.* 401:119–24

36. Hellstrand, P. G., Paul, R. J. 1982. Vascular smooth muscle: Relation between energy metabolism and mechanics. In *Vascular Smooth Muscle: Metabolic, Ionic and Contractile Mechanisms*, ed. M. F. Crass III, C. D. Barnes, pp. 1–36. New York: Academic

37. Hellstrand, P., Paul, R. J. 1983. Phosphagen content, breakdown during contraction and oxygen consumption in rat portal vein. *Am. J. Physiol.* 244:C250–C258

38. Hellstrand, P., Vogel, H. J. 1985. Phosphagens and intracellular pH in intact rabbit smooth muscle studied by ^{31}P-NMR. *Am. J. Physiol.* 248(*Cell Physiol.* 17):C320–C329

39. Ishida, Y., Paul, R. J. 1986. Lack of equilibrium between PCr and ATP in guinea pig taenia caecum: possible compartmentation of phosphagens. *Fed. Proc.* 45:766

40. Jones, D., 1988. Microcompartmentation. In *CRC Crit. Rev.* In press

41. Kamm, K. E., Stull, J. T. 1985. The function of myosin and myosin light chain kinase phosphorylation in smooth muscle. *Annu. Rev. Pharmacol. Toxicol.* 25:593–620

42. Krisanda, J. M., Paul, R. J. 1983. High energy phosphate and metabolite content during isometric contraction in porcine carotid artery. *Am. J. Physiol.* 244: C385–C390

43. Krisanda, J. M., Paul, R. J. 1984. Energetics of isometric contraction in porcine carotid artery. *Am. J. Physiol.* 246:C510–C519

44. Krisanda, J. M., Paul, R. J. 1988. The dependence of isometric force, unloaded shortening velocity and suprabasal O_2 consumption on extracellular Ca^{2+} in porcine carotid artery. *Am. J. Physiol.* In press

45. Kroeger, E. A. 1976. Effect of ionic environment on oxygen uptake and lactate production of myometrium. *Am. J. Physiol.* 230:158–62

46. Kurganov, B. I., Sugrobova, N. P., Mil'man, L. S. 1985. Supramolecular organization of glycolytic enzymes. *J. Theor. Biol.* 116:509

47. Kushmerick, M. J. 1983. Energetics of muscle contraction. In *Handbook of Physiology*, ed. L. D. Peachey, R. H. Adrian, S. R. Geiger, 10:189–236. Bethesda, Md.: Am. Physiol. Soc.

48. Kushmerick, M. J., Dillon, P. F., Meyer, R. A., Brown, T. R., Krisanda, J. M., Sweeney, H. L. 1986. ^{31}P NMR spectroscopy, chemical analysis, and free Mg^{2+} of rabbit bladder and uterine smooth muscle. *J. Biol. Chem.* 261: 14420–29

49. Kutchai, H., Geddis, L. M. 1984. Regulation of glycolysis in rat aorta. *Am. J. Physiol.* 247:C107–C114

50. Lipton, P., Robacker, K. 1983. Glycolysis and brain function: $[K^+]_0$ stimulation of protein synthesis and K^+ uptake require glycolysis. *Fed. Proc.* 42:2875–80

51. Lynch, R. M., Balaban, R. S. 1987. Energy metabolism of renal cell line A6 and MDCK: regulation by Na-K-ATPase. *Am. J. Physiol.* 252(*Cell Physiol.* 21):C225

52. Lynch, R. M., Balaban, R. S. 1987. Coupling of aerobic glycolysis and Na^+-K^+-ATPase in the renal cell line MDCK. *Am. J. Physiol.* 253 (*Cell Physiol.* 22):C269–76

53. Lynch, R. M., Paul, R. J. 1983. Compartmentation of glycolytic and glycogenolytic metabolism in vascular smooth muscle. *Science* 222:1344–46

54. Lynch, R. M., Paul, R. J. 1987. Compartmentation of carbohydrate metabolism in vascular smooth muscle: Effects of different energy loading conditions. *Am. J. Physiol.* 252:C328–C334

55. Lynch, R. M., Paul, R. J. 1986. Compartmentation of carbohydrate metabolism in vascular smooth muscle: evidence for at least two functionally independent pools of glucose-6-phosphate. *Biochim. Biophys. Acta* 887:315–18

56. Lynch, R. M., Paul, R. J. 1988. Functional compartmentation of carbohydrate metabolism. In *CRC Crit. Rev.* In press

57. McMahon, E. G., Paul, R. J. 1984. Metabolic and mechanical properties of aortas from aldosterone hypertensive rats. *Circ. Res.* 55:349–57

58. Mercer, R. W., Dunham, P. B. 1981. Membrane-bound ATP fuels the Na/K pump: Studies on membrane-bound glycolytic enzymes on inside-out vesicles from human red blood cell membranes. *J. Gen. Physiol.* 78:547

59. Moreland, R. S., Moreland, S., Murphy, R. A. 1988. Dependence of stress on length, Ca^{2+}, and myosin phosphorylation in skinned smooth muscle. *Am. J. Physiol.* In press

60. Morgan, J. P., Morgan, K. G. 1984. Stimulus-specific patterns of intracellular calcium levels in smooth muscle of ferret portal vein. *J. Physiol.* 351:155–67

61. Mulvany, M. J., Warshaw, D. M. 1979. The active tension-length curve of vascular smooth muscle related to its cellular components. *J. Gen. Physiol.* 74:85–104

62. Deleted in proof

63. Murphy, R. A. 1988. The muscle cells of hollow organs. *News Physiol. Sci.* 3:124–28

64. Murphy, R. A., Herlihy, J. T., Megerman, J. 1974. Force-generating capacity and contractile protein content of arterial smooth muscle. *J. Gen. Physiol.* 64:691–705

64a. Ozaki, H., Satoh, T., Karaki, H., Ishida, Y. 1988. Regulation of metabolisms and contraction by cytosolic calcium in the intestinal smooth muscle. *J. Biol. Chem.* 263: In press

65. Paul, R. J. 1980. The chemical energetics of vascular smooth muscle. Intermediary metabolism and its relation to contractility. See Ref. 7, pp. 201–35

66. Paul, R. J. 1983. Functional compartmentation of oxidative and glycolytic metabolism in vascular smooth muscle. *Am. J. Physiol.* 244(*Cell Physiol.* 13):C399

67. Paul, R. J. 1987. Smooth muscle energy metabolism: Cytosolic compartmentation of metabolism and function. *Adv. Physiol. Res.,* ed. H. McLennan, J. R. Ledsome, C. McIntosh, D. R. Jones, pp. 295–304. New York:Plenum

68. Paul, R. J. 1987. Smooth muscle: Mechanochemical energy conversion, relations between metabolism and contractility. In *Physiology of the Gastrointestinal Tract,* 1:483–506. New York: Raven. 2nd ed.

69. Paul, R. J., Bauer, M., Pease, W. 1979. Vascular smooth muscle: aerobic glycolysis linked to Na-K transport processes. *Science* 206:1414

70. Paul, R. J., Doerman, G., Zeugner, C., Rüegg, J. C. 1983. The dependence of unloaded shortening velocity on Ca^{2+}, calmodulin and the duration of contraction in "chemically-skinned" smooth muscle. *Circ. Res.* 53(3):342–51

71. Paul, R. J., Glück, E., Rüegg, J. C. 1976. Cross bridge ATP utilization in arterial smooth muscle. *Pflügers Arch.* 361:397–99

72. Paul, R. J., Strauss, J. D., Krisanda, J. M. 1987. The effects of calcium on smooth muscle mechanics and energetics. See Ref. 17, pp. 319–32

73. Peterson, J. W. 1977. Relation of stiffness, energy metabolism, and isometric tension in a vascular smooth muscle. In *Mechanisms of Vasodilatation,* ed. P. M. Vanhoutte, I. Leusen, pp. 79–88. Basel: Karger

74. Peterson, J. W., Paul, R. J. 1974. Effects of initial length and active shortening on vascular smooth muscle contractility. *Am. J. Physiol.* 227:1019–24

75. Peterson, J. W., Paul, R. J. 1988. Metabolism and energetics of vascular smooth muscle. In *Physiology and Pathophysiology of the Heart,* ed. N. Sperelakis. Boston, Mass.: Nijhoff

76. Pfitzer, G., Peterson, J. W., Rüegg, J. C. 1982. Length dependence of calcium-activated isometric force and immediate stiffness in living and glycerol-extracted vascular smooth muscle. *Pflügers Arch.* 394:174–81

77. Price, J. M., Davis, D. L., Knauss, E. B. 1981. Length-dependent sensitivity in vascular smooth muscle. *Am. J. Physiol.* 241(*Heart Circ. Physiol.* 10): H557–H563

78. Price, J. M., Davis, D. L., Knauss, E. B. 1983. Length-dependent sensitivity at lengths greater than L_{max} in vascular smooth muscle. *Am. J. Physiol.* 245(*Heart Circ. Physiol.* 14):H379–H384

79. Proverbio, F., Hoffman, J. F. 1977. Membrane compartmentalized ATP and its preferential use by the Na,K-ATPase in human red cell ghosts. *J. Gen. Physiol.* 69:605

80. Rall, J. A. 1982. Sense and nonsense about the Fenn effect. *Am. J. Physiol.* 242:H1–H6

81. Rangachari, P. K., Paton, D. M., Daniel, E. E. 1972. Aerobic and gly-

colytic support of sodium pumping and contraction in rat myometrium. *Am. J. Physiol.* 223:1009–15

82. Rembold, C. M., Murphy, R. A. 1986. Myoplasmic calcium, myosin phosphorylation, and regulation of the crossbridge cycle in swine arterial smooth muscle. *Circ. Res.* 58:803–15

83. Rubanyi, G., Galvas, P., Di Salvo, J., Paul, R. J. 1986. Eicosonoid metabolism and β-adrenergic mechanisms in coronary arterial smooth muscle: potential compartmentation of cAMP. *Am. J. Physiol.* 250(*Cell Physiol.* 19):C406–C412

84. Sherry, J.M.F., Gorecka, A., Aksoy, M. O., Dabrowska, R., Hartshorne, D. J. 1978. Roles of calcium and phosphorylation in the regulation of gizzard myosin. *Biochemistry* 17:4411–18

85. Siegman, M. J., Butler, T. M., Mooers, S. U. 1984. Energetic, mechanical, and ultrastructural correlates of the length-tension relationship in smooth muscle. See Ref. 23, pp. 189–98

86. Siegman, M. J., Butler, T. M., Mooers, S. U., Davies, R. E. 1980. Chemical energetics of force-development, force maintenance, and relaxation in mammalian smooth muscle. *J. Gen. Physiol.* 76:609–29

87. Siegman, M. J., Butler, T. M., Mooers, S. U., Michalek, A. 1984. Calcium can affect V_{max} without changes in myosin light chain phosphorylation in smooth muscle. *Pflügers Arch.* 401:385–90

88. Siemankowski, R. F., Wiseman, M. O., White, H. D. 1984. ADP dissociation from actomyosin subfragment 1 is sufficiently slow to limit the unloaded shortening velocity in vertebrate muscle. *Proc. Natl. Acad. Sci. USA* 82:658–62

89. Deleted in proof

90. Takai, A., Tomita, T. 1986. Glycolysis and oxidative phosphorylation during activation of the sodium pump in the taenia from guinea-pig caecum. *J. Physiol.* 381:65–75

91. Tomita, T., Takai, A., Tokuno, H. 1985. The physiology of the smooth muscle: an interdisciplinary review - Part II. *Experientia* 41:963–1088

92. Vogel, H. J., Lilja, H., Hellstrand, P. 1983. Phosphorus-31 NMR studies of smooth muscle from guinea pig taenia coli. *Biosci. Rep.* 3:863–70

93. Walker, J. S., Wendt, I. R., Gibbs, C. L. 1988. Heat production of the rat anococcygeus muscle during isometric contraction. *Am. J. Physiol.* 255 (*Cell Physiol.* 24). In press

94. Weiss, J. N., Lamp, S. T. 1987. Glycolysis preferentially inhibits ATP-sensitive K^+ channels in isolated guinea pig cardiac myocytes. *Science* 238:67–69

95. Welch, G. R. 1977. On the role of organized multienzyme systems in cellular metabolism: A general synthesis. *Prog. Biophys. Mol. Biol.* 32:103

96. Wendt, I. R., Gibbs, C. L. 1987. Energy expenditure of longitudinal smooth muscle of rabbit urinary bladder. *Am. J. Physiol.* 252 (*Cell Physiol.* 21):C88–C96

97. Woledge, R. C., Curtin, N. A., Homsher, E. 1985. *Energetic Aspects of Muscle Contraction.* New York: Academic. 360 pp.

98. Yoshizaki, K., Radda, G. K., Inubushi, T., Chance, B. 1987. ^{1}H- and ^{31}P-NMR studies on smooth muscle of bullfrog stomach. *Biochim. Biophys. Acta* 928:36–44

CELL AND MOLECULAR PHYSIOLOGY

DIVERSITY OF CHANNELS, CARRIERS, AND PUMPS

Introduction, Paul De Weer, *Section Editor*

The theme of this year's Cell and Molecular Physiology section is the molecular and functional diversity of the integral membrane protein molecules that mediate the passive or active passage of ions or small molecules across cell membranes. Until recently one would speak of "the" nicotinic acetylcholine receptor, "the" sodium channel, "the" sodium pump, and so on, with token allowance for species, developmental, or pharmacological variability. Today there is an almost bewildering proliferation of variants and homologs for each of these entities. Several developments are responsible for this circumstance: the further refinement of classical kinetic investigations and pharmacological characterizations; vastly improved purification and reconstitution methods; the availability of monoclonal antibodies; the advent of patch-clamp electrophysiology that allows the observation and analysis of a single channel molecule at a time; and the explosive growth in recombinant DNA techniques. A major dividend of the latter development has been, conversely, the discovery of unexpected homologies among functionally dissimilar and taxonomically distant molecules. In the eight chapters that follow, examples of this molecular and structural homology and diversity are reviewed. As always, the selections are somewhat arbitrary and subject to space constraints. However, it emerges that the molecular diversity of seemingly interchangeable transport-mediating membrane proteins is not a mere quirk of evolution or development, but often subserves a finely tuned and regulated functional diversity.

Annu. Rev. Physiol. 1989. 51:353–65

STRUCTURAL AND FUNCTIONAL DIVERSITY IN VERTEBRATE SKELETAL MUSCLE NICOTINIC ACETYLCHOLINE RECEPTORS

J. H. Steinbach

Department of Anesthesiology, Washington University School of Medicine, St. Louis, Missouri 63110

Introduction

Two aspects of vertebrate skeletal muscle nicotinic acetylcholine receptors are pursued in this review. First, the functional diversity of muscle nicotinic acetylcholine receptors (M-nAChR) expressed by a single cell type, which is not easily explained by our current understanding of M-nAChR structure, is discussed. Second, recent data on the functional properties of M-nAChR with different structures is compared. A number of recent reviews cover most aspects of this class of membrane receptors in greater detail (1, 9, 10, 13, 32, 46).

Before discussing diversity, it is worthwhile emphasizing the common features of these receptors. The channels are gated directly after the binding of ACh to binding sites (2 per receptor), which are contained in the same macromolecular complex as the membrane ion channel. The affinity of ACh is relatively low ($K_D > 10 \ \mu M$). The receptors show desensitization, i.e. they become unresponsive to ACh when exposed to a steady concentration for longer than a few hundred msec. The open channel is cation specific, but relatively nonselective among monovalent cations. The open channel passes inward and outward currents about equally. Structurally, the receptor is a multimer of related polypeptides. The vertebrate skeletal muscle nicotinic AChR is a pentamer of four distinct subunits with clear sequence homologies.

The discussion of receptor function emphasizes results obtained using patch clamp records of currents through single channels. The data were obtained

353

0066–4278/89/0315–0353$02.00

using cell-attached records, as the properties of the AChR appear essentially identical using this method or more traditional ones (see Table 1). Results obtained with isolated AChR reconstituted in lipid bilayers are not discussed (see 39). Some features of patch clamp data are summarized in Figure 1, and some frequently used terms are defined. Table 2 summarizes some structural features of muscle nAChR.

Structure and Function Correlated: Muscle γ and ϵ Subunits

Several years ago, it was found that mammals and frogs (but not chickens; 25) express two functionally distinct types of skeletal muscle nicotinic AChR: an

Table 1 "Simple" functional parameters

Muscle nAChR[a]	γ[b] pS	$\tau(-80$ mV)[c] msec	H[d] mV	γ/ϵ[e]	References
Electrophorus electroplax	—	1.2	86	?	47
	72	—	80	?	44
Torpedo electroplax (expressed in oocytes)	42	0.6	*	γ(?)	45
Frog junctional[f]	—	1.0	85	ϵ	41
Frog denervated extrajunctional	—	5.0	85	γ	41
Frog junctional	42	0.7	—	ϵ	14
Xenopus myocytes (i.c.)	60	1.0	—	ϵ	6
	40	3.5	—	γ	6
Rat junctional	—	1.2	109	ϵ	11
Rat denervated extrajunctional	—	3.6	—	γ	22
Rat innervated fibers	62	2.3	—	ϵ	59
	42	9.2	—	γ	59
Rat primary myotubes (i.c.)	54	2.3	—	ϵ	48
	35	14.7	156	γ	48
Bovine innervated fibers	60	6.0	83	ϵ	37
Bovine primary myotubes (i.c.)	40	11.0	105	γ	37
Chicken	—	4.5	100	?	25

[a]Values obtained for -100mV $< V_M < 0$ mV, with Na as the major charge carrier and comparable extracellular divalent ion concentrations (Ca : 1–2 mM, Mg 0–2 mM). Data on M-nAChR are from adult twitch fibers, or for embryonic cells in primary cultures "(i.c.)". [b]Single channel conductance from single channel current measurements. Values corrected to 20°C using Q_{10} of 1.4. [c]Mean burst duration (τ) at a membrane potential of -80 mV, obtained from postsynaptic current decays, from noise measurements or from single channel current measurements when a value for γ is also given (corrected to 20°C using Q_{10} of 3). [d]H is a measure of the voltage dependence for τ ($\tau(V) = \tau(0)$ exp $(-V_M/H)$; * indicates "very little" voltage sensitivity. Not corrected for temperature; obtained between 15°C and 25°C. [e]The likely subunit expressed (known for rat or bovine data). [f]Data for *Rana temporaria; R. pipiens* has a burst duration about two-fold longer (E. Neher & J. H. Steinbach, unpublished observations) and *Bufo marinus* an even longer burst duration (23).

Table 2 Some structural features of M-nAChR[a]

Subunit	MW[b] (kD)	N-linked[c] glycosylation	Phosphorylation sites[d]	
			PKA	PKC
α	~40	1 (1)	$-$T,C,X,M	$+$T,C,X,M
β	~46–48	1 (1)	$-$T,M	$-$T,M
γ	~53–60	2–4 (2)	$+$T,C,X;$-$M	$-$T,C,X,M
ϵ	?	3 $-$	$+$M	?M
δ	~60–65	2–3 (3)	$+$T,C,X,M	$+$T,C,X,M

[a]The complete M-nAChR has stoichiometry $\alpha_2\beta\gamma\delta$ or $\alpha_2\beta\epsilon\delta$ (the α subunit contains the ACh-binding site). [b]The apparent molecular weight on SDS PAGE (range for different tissues; see 10). [c] Number of potential N-linked glycosylation sites on each subunit (from nucleic acid sequences, see 10 for discussion). The numbers in parentheses are numbers of sugar chains determined for *Torpedo* M-nAChR (42). [d] Numbers of predicted potential phosphorylation sites (27) for cAMP-dependent protein kinase (PKA) and calcium-phospholipid-dependent protein kinase (PKC) (sequences reviewed in 55; for *Xenopus* see 7). The letter abbreviations are T: *Torpedo californica*, C: Chicken, M: Mammalian (cow, mouse, human), and X: *Xenopus laevis*. Not all subunits have been sequenced for all species (see 10). + means the site is present, $-$ means absent, 0 means that no sequence shows the site, and a ? means that the site is possibly present.

adult junctional type with a large conductance and a brief burst duration (see Figure 1) and a type found on developing fibers and denervated adult fibers, with a smaller conductance and a longer burst duration (Table 1). The question arose whether these functional classes were distinguished structurally by different subunit compositions or by one of the many possible posttranslational modifications. It is now clear that a single subunit of the muscle AChR has two forms that can substitute for each other. In adult junctional muscle AChR, the composition is $\alpha_2\,\beta\epsilon\delta$ (M-nAChRϵ) whereas in developing or denervated muscle, the predominant receptor type is $\alpha_2\,\beta\gamma\delta$ (M-nAChRγ; 29, 59). This conclusion has been reached by two main lines of research: a comparison of the functional properties of the AChR expressed on muscle fibers to those expressed in *Xenopus* oocytes injected with purified specific MRNAs and an analysis of the mRNA species present in muscles during development and after denervation. These results show that switching a single subunit can alter both the single channel conductance and the mean burst duration.

Functional Diversity: Kinetic Differences Within a Single Conductance Class

The studies of γ and ϵ subunits suggested that M-nAChR came in two functional classes with correlated kinetics and conductances: brief-lasting, large conductance M-nAChRϵ and longer-lasting, small conductance M-nAChRγ. However, it is clear that more kinetic diversity exists. For convenience, for the rest of this section M-nAChR is separated into two classes: low conductance (~40 pS) and high conductance (~60 pS).

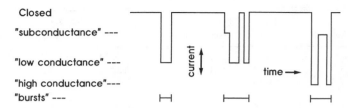

Figure 1   Some features of nAChR activity. At low agonist concentrations, channel openings occur in bursts of closely spaced openings separated from other bursts by long closed periods. There are often several sizes of currents in a record, referred to as main conductance states. In some preparations, a subconductance level can be associated with a main conductance opening.

Noninnervated *Xenopus* myotomal myocytes in cell culture express typical M-nAChRε and M-nAChRγ type receptors (5). At higher ACh concentrations, it becomes apparent that the low conductance class is kinetically complicated. At steady ACh concentrations above about 10 μM, these ACh receptors are usually desensitized. Rarely, a single receptor recovers and produces a long sequence of repeated openings and closings so that the behavior of a single AChR can be analyzed in some detail. Some AChR (about 15%) have brief openings and long closings (low probability of being open, or low P_o, whereas other have longer openings and briefer closings (high P_o; 5). The interpretation is that a low P_o AChR is relatively inefficient—closings are long because the effective channel opening rate is low, and openings are brief because the channel closing rate is high compared to a high P_o AChR. In some instances, a single AChR appears to change its behavior in the middle of a period of activity, but so few examples have been seen that the frequency of mode switching is not known. Two other systems studied have not shown this diversity:AChR at adult frog neuromuscular junctions (12) and AChR on young clonal mammalian BC3H1 cells (52) appear to produce only one pattern of activity.

There are other reports that the low conductance type of muscle AChR can show varying kinetic properties. In *Xenopus* myotomal myocytes, the burst duration for cells from very early embryos is two to four times longer than that seen 24 hours later (29, 31). Also, neonatal mouse muscle fibers express a low conductance M-nAChR, with a burst duration about threefold longer than denervated adult muscle (54), and myotubes formed in primary cultures of adult mouse muscle satellite cells show a low-conductance M-nAChR, with a mean burst duration about threefold shorter than myotubes formed from embryonic myoblasts (15).

The high conductance form of the M-nAChR also shows kinetic diversity. P_o values reveal at least two types on *Xenopus* myocytes in culture (5). A possibly related finding is that long-term (six week) denervated frog muscle fibers show both high and low conductance type M-nAChR, but the burst duration of the high conductance type is longer than that of the normal innervated neuromuscular junction and is actually close to that of the low conductance M-AChR (3). [Mouse muscle fibers denervated for up to three weeks do not show a change in burst duration for the high conductance M-nAChR (26).] Finally, a small proportion of the bursts recorded from frog junctional nAChR have a very long duration and statistically cannot belong to the normal long burst mode (14).

Tonic (nontwitch) fibers of both frog and snake muscles have slow AChR at the neuromuscular junction, with apparent burst durations three to five fold longer than on twitch fibers (19, 21, 35). These studies were made using analyses of endplate current decays and membrane current fluctuation analysis rather than single channel analysis so it is not yet clear what type of AChR is present at the junctions. The AChR appear to differ from the type expressed at nonjunctional regions of denervated fibers (35), but it is possible that junctional responses reflect the averaged behavior of several populations of receptors. Tonic and twitch fibers of chicken muscle do not show this difference (25).

Functional Diversity: Are There Additional Conductance Classes of Muscle AChR?

Most of the muscle AChR studied so far show subconductance states (Figure 1): The channel is open but less current flows through it. Subconductance states were identified because they are often directly connected to a main open state without an intervening closed state (see Figure 1; 24). The prevalence of subconductance states depends on the temperature (24), agonist used to activate the AChR (56), and preparation (50). In addition, there have been several reports of a very low conductance ($\sim$10–20 pS), ACh-activated channel in muscle cells; this channel does not show direct transitions to or from a main conductance opening and so differs from the subconductance levels originally described (4, 5, 15, 43). In *Xenopus* myocytes, these small channels show bursting behavior that is dependent on the ACh concentration (5; J. Owens, personal communication). This latter observation makes it more likely that these small channels actually do represent the activity of AChR. As yet, their functional properties, prevalence, or relationship to other functional forms of the AChR have not been characterized.

Summary of Simple Functional Diversity

So far, this discussion has concentrated on M-nAChR expressed by the same or comparable cells in a given species and on parameters for AChR function that do not require any kinetic scheme for interpretation. Kinetic diversity within a conductance class may be almost as large as between MnAChRε and

MnAChrγ forms, and additional conductance classes of MnAChR may exist. These conclusions imply that the simple picture of the γ/ε switch cannot explain the observed functional diversity. Some phenomena appear to be stable; for example, transitions between high and low conductance forms of the M-nAChR have not been observed. In these cases, the structure underlying the function is either permanent (e.g. subunit composition) or very stable. Other changes in function occur more rapidly (e.g. Po mode) and may reflect a posttranslational modification. The structural basis for much of this diversity is unclear; for example, do the changes in *Xenopus* low conductance channel kinetics during development reflect the presence of a novel subunit or a posttranslational effect?

Functional Diversity: A Closer Look at Bursts and Conductance

Analysis of single channel records shows that the behavior of individual M-nAChR is complicated. All M-nAChR studied at the single channel level show two types of bursts: very brief bursts (mean duration <0.5 msec) and long bursts (>1 msec; the values depend on experimental conditions, but the means are usually separated by 5- to 10-fold). The bursts discussed so far have been the latter class of bursts, which contribute the major portion of the cell response the ACh. Statistical arguments show that a single M-nAChR protein can produce both types of burst (50). Examination of the concentration dependence of burst duration histograms indicates that some brief bursts represent the openings of channels of an AChR with only one bound ACh molecule, whereas the long bursts result from diliganded AChR (14). However, brief bursts persist (10–30% of total) at high enough concentrations of ACh that it is impossible for all of them to reflect openings of monoliganded AChR (6, 14, 50, 52). Therefore, muscle AChR of either conductance class can make either type of burst, and the two types of burst cannot be explained solely on the basis of the state of ligation.

Furthermore, the current flowing during a main conductance opening shows greater noise than the baseline current. An analysis of the open channel current noise for low conductance channels led to the conclusion that the main conductance state actually is likely to be composed of several closely spaced (differing by less than 5%) conductance levels that interconvert on a time scale of a millisecond (49).

These observations demonstrate that while it may be appropriate to emphasize a normal or predominant functional mode in terms of burst duration or conductance, individual M-nAChR show more complex behavior. It is not clear how to view these phenomena: Do they reflect the fact that the M-nAChR is a very large protein and hence might be expected to show minor conformational states that are physiologically irrelevant? Or does some cellular process bias an M-nAChR to prefer one mode of behavior?

Posttranslational Modifications

Muscle nAChR undergo posttranslational covalent modifications, including acylation, glycosylation, and phosphorylation (33). Recent reports have suggested that receptor phosphorylation increases the rate of receptor desensitization of M-nAChR although the desensitization in the absence of ACh is unaltered (discussed in 55). cAMP-dependent protein kinase has been reported to phosphorylate mammalian and Torpedo M-nAChR (27, 36, 53). Treatment of rat muscle fibers with forskolin (an activator of adenylate cyclase) increases the rate of decline of ACh-evoked responses (2, 34) even using submicromolar concentrations of forskolin (2). However, care must be taken in the interpretation of this observation since forskolin and derivatives have a direct action on mammalian M-nAChR that resembles desensitization when used at concentrations above 10 μM (58). (Forskolin treatment of neuronal cells apparently reduces ACh responsiveness solely by a direct channel-blocking action on the neuronal nAChR; see 55.) Therefore, this question requires further study.

Some recent studies of M-nAChR expressed by clonal mammalian myocytes show that treatment of cells with drugs that alter carbohydrate processing can change receptor function (16). However, the effects do not include a change in channel conductance nor do they include major changes in burst duration (the effects are on the channel opening rate and agonist dissociation rate, and result in a lower overall P_o at a given ACh concentration).

Treatment of frog adult junctional M-nAChR by dithiothreitol results in a receptor with a reduced burst duration and reduced affinity for ACh (8) apparently because of the reduction of a disulfide bond on the extracellular surface of the α (agonist binding) subunit (see 10). Unfortunately, reduced receptors have not been studied extensively at the single channel level, and it is not known whether they are comparable to any class of normally expressed receptor nor whether cells normally express any receptors with a reduced disulfide (although labeling studies suggest that this is rare, see 17).

Thus, posttranslational modifications can alter M-nAChR function. However, none of the effects seen to date resemble the functional diversity described above.

More Detailed Analyses of M-nAChR Function

Several studies have used the increased resolution of single channel current records to obtain a more quantitative picture of M-nAChR function (Table 3). Any analysis of data on AChR function (even low concentration bursts) in terms of kinetic states requires the use of a kinetic scheme for the interpretation of the data. The favored linear scheme is able to account for the major features of receptor activation:

$$2A + R \underset{k_{-2}}{\overset{K_1}{\rightleftharpoons}} A + AR \underset{}{\overset{K_2}{\rightleftharpoons}} A_2R \underset{\alpha}{\overset{\beta}{\rightleftharpoons}} A_2R \text{ open}$$

When this particular scheme is used, the burst duration at low [ACh] is close to $(\beta + k_{-2})/(\alpha k_{-2})$.

The results show several common features: ACh binds with low affinity, the channel opening rate is comparable to the agonist dissociation rate (resulting in the production of bursts), and the channel opening rate is much larger than the closing rate. Rates for conformational changes (β and α) are significantly lower for M-nAChRγ receptors, but ACh affinity seems to be higher. The channel closing rate constant (α) decreases as the membrane potential (V_M) is made more negative for all of these receptors. However, the channel opening rate constant (β) increases with increasingly negative V_M for BC3H1 receptors but not frog junctional receptors. Finally, in describing the concentration dependence of activation, both frog junctional and *Xenopus* high-conductance AChR show essentially no signs of binding cooperativity. However, both BC3H1 and *Xenopus* low-conductance AChR are somewhat better described if some positive cooperativity in binding is assumed.

These more detailed analyses of function suggest that M-nAChRγ and M-nAChRϵ differ significantly and consistently in function. The correlation indicates that a change of a single subunit has global effects on all aspects of AChR function including agonist binding, which would simplistically be thought to reside largely in the agonist-binding (α) subunit.

However, there are interspecies differences in receptor function even between M-nAChR of the same type (see Tables 1 and 3). The structural basis for these differences is not known, although studies using hybrid receptors composed of subunits from various species suggest that at least some reflect differences in the primary amino acid sequences of the receptor subunits (see next section).

Modified Muscle nAChR: Expression Studies

The availability of cloned mRNA for M-nAChR subunits has made it possible to express functional nAChR in *Xenopus* oocytes. The functional properties of M-nAChR expressed in oocytes appear quite similar to those found in situ (bovine: 37; BC3H1: 52, 60, 61; Torpedo: 40, 45).

Chimeric M-nAChR have been made by combining mRNAs for subunits from different species, or mutated sequences, in order to determine the structural features of the M-nAChR that correlate with (and hence may determine) functional properties. The results do not yet show a clear pattern. The results for γ and ϵ subunits showed that this change can greatly affect both conductance and kinetics of M-nAChR. Studies of chimeric M-nAChR constructed of Torpedo and fetal bovine subunits showed that the δ subunit

Table 3 Calculated rate constants for M-NAChR activation

Cell	T °C	V_M mV	M-nAChR Type	β^a (sec^{-1})	$k_{-2}{}^b$ (sec^{-1})	α^c (sec^{-1})	$K_1{}^d$ (μM)	$K_2{}^d$ (μM)	$\dfrac{\beta^e}{\beta + \alpha}$	$\dfrac{\beta^f}{\beta + k_{-2}}$	$A_{50}{}^g$ (μM)	References
Rana[h]	10°	−130	ε	31,000	16,300	700	39	154	0.98	0.66	15	12, 14
Xenopus[i]	22°	−120	ε	38,200	12,000	3,960	24	96	0.92	0.90	23	6
Xenopus	22°	−120	γ	5,600	6,700	350	66	7	0.94	0.45	6	6
BC3H1[j]	10°	−70	γ	450	1,000	35	50	5	0.93	0.32	8	51, 52

[a]Channel opening rate constant. [b]Agonist dissociation rate constant. [c]Channel closing rate constant when two are bound (not corrected for statistical factors). [d]Equilibrium dissociation constants (not corrected for statistical factors). [e]The probability a channel will be open given it is doubly liganded (i.e. the fraction of time a channel is open at saturating [ACh]). [f]The probability a channel will open rather than lose ACh given it is doubly liganded and closed. [g]The concentration of ACh resulting in a 50% probability that a channel will be open. β and/or α depend on V_M, so the ratios and A_{50} also depend on membrane potential. [h]*Rana temporaria* junctional AChR. [i]Non-innervated embryonic *Xenopus* myocytes in primary culture. [j]BC3H1 clonal mammalian cells in cell culture.

has a major influence in determining the shape of the steady state current-voltage (IV) curve (45), but subsequent studies of all possible combinations of Torpedo and fetal mouse subunits demonstrate that the β subunit (in this set of subunits) has a stronger influence (60, 61). Earlier studies (20) indicate that the shape of the steady state IV curve is largely due to the voltage dependence of the channel opening and closing rates; thus, these data indicate that the voltage sensitivity of M-nAChR channel gating rates can be strongly influenced by subunits other than the α subunit.

An additional series of experiments with Torpedo and fetal calf subunits led to the conclusion that the net charge in a particular region of the δ subunit (between proposed hydrophic membrane spanning regions M2 and M3) has a major influence on single channel conductance (28). The difference in conductance may reflect the ability of negatively charged groups in the outer channel "vestibule" to concentrate permeant cations and hence increase conductance (18). Still, the γ/ϵ switch experiments show that the conductance clearly cannot be determined only by the δ subunit. An ambitious series of mutated torpedo α subunits has been generated (38, 57), but the functional properties of the chimeric AChR have not been characterized yet. Some alterations of the proposed hydrophobic membrane spanning region M4 result in reduced assembly but larger steady state currents per AChR (57), which indicates a change in either ion permeation or receptor activation.

It is not surprising that no clear picture has emerged from these studies since the M-nAChR is a large, multimeric protein with many intersubunit contacts. Our knowledge of secondary and tertiary structure is very limited, even of such basic features as the subunit folding pattern or the arrangement of subunits in the receptor (reviewed in 9, 10).

Expression studies show that functional receptors can be formed by only three subunits (which must include α), albeit with lowered efficiency both of assembly and function (30). No analysis of functional properties of receptors lacking one or more subunits has been published, and the subunit stoichiometry is unknown.

Summary

Overall, the data support the conclusion that the γ and ϵ subunits explain major features of the functional diversity of vertebrate muscle nAChR. They cannot account, however, for all observed functional diversity. It is not clear whether additional subunits exist or whether some posttranslational modifications produce the functional differences. Work is underway to correlate structural features of the muscle nicotinic AChR with functional properties. To date, the results demonstrate that each known subunit can affect receptor kinetic parameters and/or channel conductance.

Two remaining sets of questions must be answered. The first lies within the field of cell biology: What subunits are expressed, do posttranslational modifications underlie functional modifications, and what structural changes are associated with physiologically relevant changes in function? The second is more strictly of structure-function relationships: What are the functional parameters of structurally defined nAChRs and can structural features be correlated with function?

Literature Cited

1. Adams, P. R. 1987. Transmitter action at endplate membrane. In *The Vertebrate Neuromuscular Junction*, ed. M. Salpeter, 23:317–59. New York: Liss
2. Albuquerque, E. X., Deshpande, S. S., Aracava, Y., Alkondon, M., Daly, J. W. 1986. A possible involvement of cyclic AMP in the expression of desensitization of the nicotinic acetylcholine receptor. A study with forskolin and its analogs. *FEBS Lett.* 199:113–20
3. Allen, C. N., Albuquerque, E. X. 1986. Characteristics of acetylcholine-activated channels of innervated and chronically denervated skeletal muscles. *Exp. Neurol.* 91:532–45
4. Aracava, Y., Ikeda, S. R., Daly, J. W., Brookes, N., Albuquerque, E. X. 1984. Interactions of bupivacaine with ionic channels of the nicotinic receptor. *Mol. Pharmacol.* 26:304–13
5. Auerbach, A., Lingle, C. J. 1986. Heterogeneous kinetic properties of acetylcholine receptor channels in *Xenopus* myocytes. *J. Physiol.* 378:119–40
6. Auerbach, A., Lingle, C. J. 1987. Activation of the primary kinetic modes of large- and small-conductance cholinergic ion channels in *Xenopus* myocytes. *J. Physiol.* 393:437–66
7. Baldwin, T. J., Yoshihara, C. M., Blackmer, K., Kintner, C. R., Burden, S. J. 1988. Regulation of acetylcholine receptor transcript expression during development in *Xenopus laevis*. *J. Cell Biol.* 106:469–78
8. Ben-Haim, D., Dreyer, F., Peper, K. 1975. Acetylcholine receptor: modification of synaptic gating mechanism after treatment with a disulfide bond reducing agent. *Pflügers Arch.* 355:19–26
9. Changeux, J. P., Giraudat, J., Dennis, M. 1987. The nicotinic acetylcholine receptor: molecular architecture of a ligand-regulated ion channel. *Trends Pharmacol. Sci.* 8:459–65
10. Claudio, T. 1989. Molecular genetics of acetylcholine receptor-channels. In *Frontiers of Molecular Biology: Molecular Neurobiology*, ed. D. Glover, D. Hamer. London: IRL. In press
11. Colquhoun, D., Large, W. A., Rang, H. P. 1977. An analysis of the action of a false transmitter at the neuromuscular junction. *J. Physiol.* 266:361–95
12. Colquhoun, D., Ogden, D. C. 1988. Activation of ion channels in the frog end-plate by high concentrations of acetylcholine. *J. Physiol.* 395:131–59
13. Colquhoun, D., Ogden, D. C., Mathie, A. 1987. Nicotinic acetylcholine receptors of nerve and muscle: functional aspects. *Trends Pharmacol. Sci.* 8:465–72
14. Colquhoun, D., Sakmann, B. 1985. Fast events in single-channel currents activated by acetylcholine and its analogues at the frog muscle end-plate. *J. Physiol.* 369:501–57
15. Cossu, G., Eusebi, F., Grassi, F., Wanke, E. 1987. Acetylcholine receptor channels are present in undifferentiated satellite cells but not in embryonic myoblasts in culture. *Dev. Biol.* 123:43–50
16. Covarrubias, M., Kopta, C., Steinbach, J. H. 1989. Inhibition of N-linked oligosaccharide trimming affects gating of the nicotinic acetylcholine receptor in BC3H-1 cells. *J. Gen. Physiol.* In press
17. Damle, V. N., Karlin, A. 1980. Effects of agonists and antagonists on the reactivity of the binding site disulfide in acetylcholine receptor from *Torpedo californica*. *Biochemistry* 19:3924–32
18. Dani, J. A., Eisenman, G. 1987. Monovalent and divalent cation permeation in acetylcholine receptor channels. *J. Gen. Physiol.* 89:959–83
19. Dionne, V. E. 1981. The kinetics of slow muscle acetylcholine-operated channels in the garter snake. *J. Physiol.* 310:159–90
20. Dionne, V. E., Stevens, C. F. 1975. Voltage dependence of agonist effectiveness at the frog neuromuscular junction: resolution of a paradox. *J. Physiol.* 251:245–70
21. Fedorov, V. V., Magazanik, L. G., Snetkov, V. A., Zefirov, A. L. 1982. Postsynaptic currents in different types of frog muscle fibre. *Pflügers Arch.* 394:202–10

364   STEINBACH

22. Fischbach, G. D., Schuetze, S. M. 1980. A post-natal decrease in acetylcholine channel open time at rat endplates. *J. Physiol.* 303:125–37
23. Gage, P. W., Hamill, O. P. 1980. Lifetime and conductance of acetylcholineactivated channels in normal and denervated toad sartorius muscle. *J. Physiol.* 298:525–38
24. Hamill, O. P., Sakmann, B. 1981. Multiple conductance states of single acetylcholine receptor channels in embryonic muscle cells. *Nature* 294:462–64
25. Harvey, A. L., van Helden, D. 1981. Acetylcholine receptors in singly and multiple innervated skeletal muscle fibres of the chicken during development. *J. Physiol.* 317:397–411
26. Henderson, L. P., Lechleiter, J. D., Brehm, P. 1987. Single channel properties of newly synthesized acetylcholine receptors following denervation of mammalian skeletal muscle. *J. Gen. Physiol.* 89:999–1014
27. Huganir, R. L., Miles, K., Greengard, P. 1984. Phosphorylation of the nicotinic acetylcholine receptor by an endogenous tyrosine-specific protein kinase. *Proc. Natl. Acad. Sci. USA* 81:6968–72
28. Imoto, K., Methfessel, C., Sakmann, B., Mishina, M., Mori, Y., et al. 1986. Location of a δ-subunit region determining ion transport through the acetylcholine receptor channel. *Nature* 324:670–74
29. Kullberg, R., Owens, J. L., Brehm, P. 1986. Development of nicotinic acetylcholine receptor function. *Proc. IEEE* 8:948–50
30. Kurosaki, T., Fukuda, K., Konno, T., Mori, Y., Tanaka, K., et al. 1987. Functional properties of nicotinic acetylcholine receptor subunits expressed in various combinations. *FEBS Lett.* 214:253–58
31. Leonard, R. J., Nakajima, S., Nakajima, Y., Takahashi, T. 1984. Differential development of two classes of acetylcholine receptors in *Xenopus* muscle in culture. *Science* 226:55–57
32. Lindstrom, J., Schoepfer, R., Whiting, P. 1987. Molecular studies of the neuronal nicotinic acetylcholine receptor family. *Mol. Neurobiol.* 1:281–337
33. Merlie, J. P., Smith, M. M. 1986. Synthesis and assembly of acetylcholine receptor, a multisubunit membrane glycoprotein. *J. Membr. Biol.* 91:1–10
34. Middleton, P., Rubin, L. L., Schuetze, S. M. 1988. Desensitization of acetylcholine receptors in rat myotubes is enhanced by agents that elevate intracellular cAMP. *J. Neurosci.* In press
35. Miledi, R., Reiser, G., Uchitel, O. D. 1984. Characteristics of membrane channels induced by acetylcholine at frog muscle-tendon junctions. *J. Physiol.* 350:269–77
36. Miles, K., Anthony, D. T., Rubin, L. L., Greengard, P., Huganir, R. L., 1987. Regulation of nicotinic acetylcholine receptor phosphorylation in rat myotubes by forskolin and cAMP. *Proc. Natl. Acad. Sci. USA* 84:6591–95
37. Mishina, M., Takai, T., Imoto, K., Noda, M., Takahashi, T., et al. 1986. Molecular distinction between fetal and adult forms of muscle acetylcholine receptor. *Nature* 321:406–11
38. Mishina, M., Tobimatsu, T., Imoto, K., Tanaka, K., Fujita, Y., et al. 1985. Location of functional regions of acetylcholine receptor α-subunit by site-directed mutagenesis. *Nature* 313:364–69
39. Montal, M., Anholt, R., Labarca, P. 1986. The reconstituted acetylcholine receptor. In *Ion Channel Reconstitution*, ed. C. Miller, 1:157–204. New York: Plenum
40. Muller, D., Dunant, Y. 1987. Spontaneous quantal and subquantal transmitter release at the *Torpedo* nerve-electroplaque junction. *Neuroscience* 20:911–21
41. Neher, E., Sakmann, B. 1976. Noise analysis of drug induced voltage clamp currents in denervated frog muscle fibres. *J. Physiol.* 258:705–29
42. Nomoto, H., Takahashi, N., Nagaki, Y., Endo, S., Arata, Y., Hayashi, K. 1986. Carbohydrate structures of acetylcholine receptor from *Torpedo californica* and distribution of oligosaccharides among the subunits. *Eur. J. Biochem.* 257:233–42
43. Owens, J. L., Hartig, G. S., Laitinen, F. A., Kullberg, R. 1987. Multiple conductance classes of acetylcholine receptor channels in larval amphibian skeletal muscle. *Soc. Neurosci. Abstr.* 13:98
44. Pasquale, E. B., Udgaonkar, J. B., Hess, G. P. 1986. Single-channel current recordings of acetylcholine receptors in electroplax isolated from the *Electrophorus electricus* main and Sachs' electric organs. *J. Membr. Biol.* 93:195–204
45. Sakmann, B., Methfessel, C., Mishina, M., Takahashi, T., Takai, T., et al. 1985. Role of acetylcholine receptor subunits in gating of the channel. *Nature* 318:538–43

46. Schuetze, S. M., Role, L. W. 1987. Developmental regulation of nicotinic acetylcholine receptors. *Annu. Rev. Neurosci.* 10:403–57
47. Sheridan, R. E., Lester, H. A. 1977. Rates and equilibria at the acetylcholine receptor of *Electrophorus* electroplaques: a study of neurally evoked postsynaptic currents and of voltage-jump relaxations. *J. Gen. Physiol.* 70:187–219
48. Siegelbaum, S. A., Trautmann, A., Koenig, J. 1984. Single acetylcholine-activated channel currents in developing muscle cells. *Dev. Biol.* 104:366–79
49. Sigworth, F. J. 1985. Open channel noise. Noise in acetylcholine receptor currents suggests conformational fluctuations. *Biophys. J.* 47:709–20
50. Sine, S. M., Steinbach, J. H. 1984. Activation of a nicotinic acetylcholine receptor. *Biophys. J.* 45:175–85
51. Sine, S. M., Steinbach, J. H. 1986. Activation of acetylcholine receptors on clonal mammalian BC3H-1 cells by low concentrations of agonist. *J. Physiol.* 373:129–62
52. Sine, S. M., Steinbach, J. H. 1987. Activation of acetylcholine receptors on clonal mammalian BC3H-1 cells by high concentrations of agonist. *J. Physiol.* 385:325–59
53. Smith, M. M., Merlie, J. P., Lawrence, J. C. Jr. 1987. Regulation of phosphorylation of nicotinic acetylcholine receptors in mouse BC3H1 myocytes. *Proc. Natl. Acad. Sci. USA* 84:6601–5
54. Steele, J. A., Steinbach, J. H. 1986. Single channel studies reveal three classes of acetylcholine-activated channels in mouse skeletal muscle. *Biophys. J.* 49:361a
55. Steinbach, J. H., Zempel, J. 1987. What does phosphorylation do for the nicotinic acetylcholine receptor? *Trends Neurosci.* 10:61–64
56. Takeda, K., Trautmann, A. 1984. A patch-clamp study of the partial agonist actions of tubocurarine on rat myotubes. *J. Physiol.* 349:353–74
57. Tobimatsu, T., Fujita, Y., Fukuda, K., Tanaka, K., Mori, Y., et al. 1987. Effects of substitution of putative transmembrane segments on nicotinic acetylcholine receptor function. *FEBS Lett.* 222:56–62
58. Waggoner, P. K., Pallotta, B. 1988. Modulation of acetylcholine receptor desensitization does not involve cAMP. *Science* 240:1655–57
59. Witzemann, V., Barg, B., Nishikawa, Y., Sakmann, B., Numa, S. 1987. Differential regulation of muscle acetylcholine receptor γ- and ε-subunit mRNAs. *FEBS Lett.* 223:104–12
60. Yoshii, K., Yu, L., Mayne, K. M., Davidson, N., Lester, H. A. 1987. Equilibrium properties of mouse-*Torpedo* acetylcholine receptor hybrids expressed in *Xenopus* oocytes. *J. Gen. Physiol.* 90:553–73
61. Yu, L., Leonard, R. J., Labarca, C., Davidson, N., Lester, H. A. 1987. Channel duration mainly determines voltage sensitivity in mouse-*Torpedo* acetylcholine hybrids. *Soc. Neurosci. Abstr.* 13:97

Annu. Rev. Physiol. 1989. 51:367–84

CLASSES OF CALCIUM CHANNELS IN VERTEBRATE CELLS

Bruce P. Bean

Department of Neurobiology, Harvard Medical School, Boston, Massachusetts 02115

INTRODUCTION

Voltage-dependent Ca channels help regulate a wide range of cellular functions, including secretion, contraction, and excitability (56, 61, 73, 123). The diversity of Ca channels has long been clear, especially from comparative studies on invertebrates (see 55), which have included descriptions of multiple Ca channel types in single cells (57). This article summarizes a recent wave of papers describing multiple Ca channel types in vertebrate cells. Space limitations prevent inclusion of recent work on invertebrate Ca channels, receptor-operated Ca channels, or Ca channels of organelles.

VERTEBRATE CELLS WITH MULTIPLE TYPES OF Ca CHANNELS

Cardiac Muscle

Two types of Ca channels have been described in patch clamp recordings from guinea pig ventricular (92, 94), dog atrial (11), frog atrial (18), and rabbit sinoatrial (54) cells. There is excellent agreement between whole cell and single channel recordings. One type of channel has a small single channel conductance (~8 pico siemens (pS) with ~100 mM Ba), is activated by relatively small depolarizations (colloquially, "low threshold"), and inactivates relatively rapidly. These channels have been termed "T," "low threshold," and "fast" Ca channels (T channels in this article). The other type of Ca channel has a higher single channel conductance (15–25 pS with ~100 mM Ba) and requires larger depolarizations for activation. These channels (which have also been referred to as "slow" and "high threshold" channels) are called L channels in this article.

0066-4278/89/0315-0367$02.00

With Ba as the charge carrier, inactivation of L channels is much slower than that of T channels, and the two components of macroscopic Ca channel current are readily distinguished. However, because inactivation of L channels is promoted by Ca entry (e.g. 69), L channel inactivation is quite rapid (half-time 20–100 ms) with Ca as the charge carrier (belying the expectation that L currents are necessarily "long-lasting"), and distinct T and L components of macroscopic current are not so obvious from inactivation kinetics. With Ca as the charge carrier, the two components of current are most clearly distinguished by changes in holding potential: Holding at approximately −40 mV inactivates T channels with little effect on L channels.

T and L channels have different pharmacological properties. L channels are potently inhibited by dihydropyridine Ca channel blockers, such as nifedipine and nitrendipine, and are enhanced by dihydropyridine "Ca channel agonists" such as (−) BAY K 8644; T channels are unaffected by these drugs at concentrations below about 3 μM (11, 54, 92, 94). Verapamil and its methoxy derivative D600 also block L channels more potently than T channels (54, 92). In contrast, the insecticide tetramethrin completely inhibits T current at 100 nM without affecting L current (54).

Cardiac L and T channels evidently have different pore structures. In addition to their different unitary conductances, they have different ionic selectivity and different sensitivity to inorganic blockers. In L channels, Ba carries current twice as effectively as Ca, but in T channels, currents carried by Ba and Ca are nearly equal (11, 54, 94). L channels are more effectively blocked by low concentrations of Cd than are T channels (18, 92, 94; but see 54). In contrast, Ni is more effective in blocking T channels (18, 54; but see 92); with Ca as the charge carrier, 40 μM Ni completely blocks T current without affecting L current (54).

Cardiac Ca currents are enhanced by β-adrenergic stimulation, working through cAMP-dependent protein kinase (see 67). Four studies (11, 18, 54, 128a) reported that L but not T channels are affected by beta stimulation; a lone report of T current enhancement (92) may stem from the difficulty in distinguishing T from L currents when Ca is the charge carrier.

In all cardiac cell types examined so far, most of the macroscopic Ca channel current is carried by L channels. Some cell types (bullfrog ventricular cells, calf atrial and ventricular cells, rabbit atrial cells) appear to have no T current at all (own unpublished observations). In guinea pig ventricular cells (92, 94), frog atrial cells (18), canine atrial cells (11), and rabbit sinoatrial cells (54), peak T current is typically only 5–20% of the peak L current, even with ionic conditions that maximize the relative size of the T component (low external Ca).

Both the absolute density of T current and its density relative to L current are greater in rabbit sinoatrial cells than in atrial or ventricular cells, and the slowing of the later phase of diastolic depolarization by Ni suggests a possible role of T channels in sinoatrial pacemaking (54). The complete absence of T channels in many ventricular cells suggests that T channels do not play an important role in normal working myocardium.

Some ventricular cells may have a third type of Ca current (75), about which little is known.

Smooth Muscle

VASCULAR MUSCLE   Two types of calcium channels, which are very similar to the channels in heart muscle, have been found in cells from a variety of mammalian arteries (12, 14), veins (81, 113, 133), and aortic muscle cell lines (30, 46). A low-threshold, rapidly-inactivating T-type channel has a unitary current of ~8 pS in ~100 Ba (14, 133); it passes Ba and Ca equally well (113, 133, but see 46) and is relatively insensitive to dihydropyridines (14, 30, 46, 98, 133). A high-threshold L-type channel has a unitary current of 20–25 pS in ~100 Ba and inactivates more slowly; Ba is more permeant than Ca, and the channel is highly sensitive to dihydropyridine blockers and agonists. With Ba as the charge carrier, L current in vascular muscle inactivates with a time constant of 100s of ms (12, 14; but see 30) much like cardiac L current (69) and much faster than L current in neurons (44) or pituitary cells (29). L channels in cardiac and vascular muscle may not be precisely identical since those in vascular muscle are several times more sensitive to dihydropyridine blockers (12, 133). In excised patches of arterial muscle, two sizes of dihydropyridine-sensitive channels are seen (131); the smaller possibly represents a subconductance level of L channels. Two kinetic components of Ca current seen in voltage-clamped segments of cerebral arterioles (63) have not yet been clearly related to the channels studied in single cells.

Norepinephrine enhances the T current in portal vein cells (98) and the L current in rabbit ear artery cells (15); unlike enhancement of cardiac L current, the latter effect is apparently not mediated by β-adrenergic receptors.

OTHER SMOOTH MUSCLE   The predominant Ca current in visceral and myometrial smooth muscle cells is similar to L current in cardiac and vascular muscle, with a fairly high activation threshold, Ca-dependent inactivation, and sensitivity to dihydropyridines (e.g. 2, 40, 50). A component of low-threshold T-like current has recently been reported in toad stomach muscle cells (129), and two sizes of single channels are seen in guinea pig intestinal muscle cells (134); as in cardiac and vascular muscle, the lower conductance channel is insensitive to nifedipine.

Skeletal Muscle

Adult skeletal muscle also contains two types of Ca channels. However, they are quite different from those in cardiac and smooth muscle. The predominant

Ca current in skeletal muscle fibers has a voltage-dependence like that of L current in cardiac and smooth muscle, but activates more than an order of magnitude more slowly. The underlying channels, which also inactivate very slowly with a time constant (τ) of $\approx 1s$, have most often been referred to as slow Ca channels (see 13 for a review). They are blocked by dihydropyridines and D600 with a sensitivity much like that of cardiac L channels (87). And, like cardiac L current, slow Ca current in skeletal muscle is potentiated by β-adrenergic agonists or internal cAMP (6). However, unlike cardiac L channels (see 124), slow Ca channels in skeletal muscle can support currents carried by Mg (1), which suggests a somewhat different ionic selectivity.

Another component of Ca current has recently been recognized in muscle fibers (6, 33, 51). Like T current in cardiac muscle, it activates with a low threshold and very rapidly; unlike T current, however, it does not inactivate at all [at least over several seconds (33)]. This fast component of Ca current is not sensitive to dihydropyridines (6). Like slow Ca current, the fast Ca current is potentiated by adrenergic stimulation (6).

Ca currents in developing skeletal muscle are somewhat different. When embryonic or neonatal skeletal muscle is placed in culture, there is a low-threshold, rapidly-inactivating component of current that seems identical to T current in cardiac and smooth muscle (10, 28). This dihydropyridine-insensitive T current is also seen in muscle fibers from newborn rats (8) but disappears by three weeks (9); concurrently, the density of the dihydropyridine-sensitive slow Ca current grows.

Purified preparations of dihydropyridine-binding protein from skeletal muscle t tubules form functional Ca channels when reconstituted into lipid bilayers (43). So far, this is the best evidence that the skeletal muscle dihydropyridine receptor—the sequence of which is now known from molecular cloning (120)—is actually a Ca channel. The properties of the reconstituted channel—a conductance of 20 pS, sensitivity to dihydropyridines, and modulation by cAMP-dependent protein kinase (43)—are similar to those of cardiac L channels (108). For unknown reasons, dihydropyridine-sensitive channels reconstituted from native t-tubule preparations from skeletal muscles have lower conductances, with multiple subconductance states (82, 108).

The functions of skeletal muscle Ca channels are obscure. Ca entry through slow channels is not necessary to trigger contraction (13, 87). It has been proposed that slow Ca channels (or a closely related dihydropyridine-sensitive protein) might act as voltage sensors for excitation-contraction coupling (106), with Ca release from the sarcoplasmic reticulum somehow triggered by conformational changes associated with channel gating; muscles from mice with the muscular dysgenesis mutation, in which excitation-contraction coupling is disrupted, selectively lack slow Ca channels (10). No special functional role for fast Ca channels is yet known; a main role of both fast and slow channels might simply be long-term replenishment of internal Ca. The T channels present in developing muscle could help initiate spontaneous activity.

Neurons

SENSORY NEURONS   Defining the classes of Ca channels in neurons has been more difficult than in muscle. The most detailed studies have been done on sensory neurons. All recent reports agree on the presence of multiple Ca channel types, but while most groups have interpreted their data as reflecting two types of Ca channels, Nowycky et al (95) and Fox et al (44, 45) reported the existence of three types of Ca channels in chick sensory neurons.

All reports on chick (21–24, 44, 45, 68, 95, 117), rat (19–21, 23, 24, 41), and mouse (74) sensory neurons agree on the existence of a low-threshold, rapidly-inactivating Ca channel that seems nearly identical to the T-type channels later described in muscle cells. This channel is activated by depolarizations positive to about -60 mV, inactivates with a τ of about 20 ms at -20 mV, and has slowly decaying tail currents (23, 117). It has a single channel conductance of about 8 pS in 110 mM Ba (45, 95), passes Ba and Ca equally well (24, 41, 44, but see 20), and is blocked by $\sim$100 μM Ni (25, 44). It is not affected by dihydropyridines (17, 44, 95) or verapamil (17, 41).

Using a combination of single channel and whole cell recording, Nowycky et al (95) and Fox et al (44, 45) distinguished two types of high-threshold channels in chick dorsal root ganglion (DRG) neurons: a large conductance channel ($\sim$20 pS in 110 mM Ba), which they called the L channel, and a channel of intermediate size (13 pS), which they called the N channel. N channels activate at potentials more positive than T channels but slightly more negative than L channels, and have a midpoint of inactivation between those for T and L channels. In cell-attached patch recordings, N channels inactivate with a time constant of about 30 ms at 0 mV, slower than T channels but much faster than L channels. In whole cell recordings, N channels were considered to give rise to a high-threshold current component that inactivates fairly rapidly (but, for unexplained reasons, 2–5 times slower than in the patch recordings) and can be eliminated by holding at -60 to -40 mV. According to this picture, macroscopic current (in the absence of T current) can be separated into N and L components by either (a) identifying the decaying component of current during a 150–200 ms pulse as N current and the steady current at the end of the pulse as L current or (b) holding at -60 to -40 mV to inactivate N current and thereby eliciting L current in isolation.

SYMPATHETIC NEURONS   Rat and frog sympathetic neurons have little or no low-threshold T current (62, 77, 85, 130). Two single channel sizes are seen that are similar to N and L channels in sensory neurons: an 11–15 pS channel (in 110 mM Ba) that is insensitive to dihydropyridines and a 27–28 pS, dihydropyridine-sensitive channel (62, 77). However, the component of whole cell current identified as N current in sympathetic neurons inactivates much more slowly ($\tau \approx 500$–800 ms near 0 mV) than in chick DRG cells.

CENTRAL NEURONS   Distinct low-threshold and high-threshold Ca channels in vertebrate cells were first suggested by action potential recordings from guinea pig central neurons (66, 79). Recent voltage clamp and patch clamp recordings have confirmed the existence of multiple Ca channel types in central neurons; T-type, low-threshold, inactivating Ca currents have been described in hippocampal (16, 38, 58, 132), neocortical (115), cerebellar Purkinje (104), and motor neurons (89), usually together with a high-threshold component. Cell bodies of some hippocampal pyramidal neurons may have only high-threshold current (70). With little single channel (16, 132) or pharmacological data, it remains unclear just how closely the high-threshold channels resemble L and N channels in peripheral neurons.

NEURONAL CELL LINES   Neuroblastoma N1E-115 cells (93) have a low-threshold, rapidly-inactivating, T-type current and a high-threshold current that seems more L-like than N-like since it inactivates very little in 400 ms and is not reduced by a 5 s prepulse to −30 mV. Similar components are seen in N18 cells (121). In NG108-15 cells, there may be a third component of N-like current (inactivation time constant of 800 ms at +10 mV, similar to suggested N current inactivation in sympathetic neurons) that is preferentially blocked by gadolinium ions (37). In PC12 cells, the high-threshold current has both slowly inactivating and steady components (112), and two sizes of high-threshold single channels are seen, N-like (16–19 pS, not dihydropyridine sensitive) and L-like (23–27 pS, dihydropyridine sensitive) (101). PC12 cells also have T channels (47).

PHARMACOLOGY   One reason for believing that N- and L-type single channel events represent truly different channel types (rather than different conductance levels of a single type) is that L channel activity is blocked by nifedipine (45, 62) and enchanced by BAY K 8644 (45, 62, 96) while N channel activity is not (45, 62, 96). As in muscle, T channels in neurons have little or no sensitivity to dihydropyridines (17, 44, 95).

Effects of dihydropyridines on high-threshold macroscopic currents are highly variable from cell to cell, and the literature has been confused by reports generalizing results from only one or a few cells. In the most thorough study (68), nifedipine had no effect on currents in 28 of 56 chick DRG cells and reduced current by 5–50% in the others. Even when inhibition is maximized by eliciting current from depolarized holding potentials (see 103, 109), block is typically less than 50% complete (44, 103; own unpublished results) at concentrations that would wipe out L current in cardiac or smooth muscle (12, 109). This fact suggests either that neuronal L channels have a much lower sensitivity to dihydropyridines than muscle L channels or that the sustained current elicited from depolarized potentials is not completely L current. Increases in current by nifedipine (17) and decreases by BAY K 8644 (17, 68) are not completely shocking since even pure isomers of di-hydropyridines can both increase and decrease cardiac L current, depending on pulse protocol (see 72). However, the proposal that macroscopic N current is inhibited by BAY K 8644 (68) is surprising, though possibly supported by mild inhibition of N channels in patches (Figure 4 of Ref. 95).

The phenylalkylamine verapamil blocks high-threshold current but not low-threshold current in rat and chick DRG cells (17, 41). Since inhibition requires concentrations (20–400 μM) more than ten times higher than for block of L channels in cardiac muscle (109), it is possible that N as well as L channels are blocked.

ω-Conotoxin, a peptide from the marine snail *Conus geographus,* produces potent, largely irreversible inhibition of the high-threshold Ca current in many vertebrate neurons (68, 88, 97) but has little effect on current in cardiac, smooth, or skeletal muscle (88). Whether ω-conotoxin produces potent, irreversible block of both N and L channels (88) or only N channels (68) is disputed (both groups agree on weak, reversible block of T channels); ex-periments on clearly identified single channels [which are difficult since ω-conotoxin block is depressed at high divalent concentrations (88, 97)] are needed to clarify the issue. ω-Conotoxin does potently block high-threshold current in cultured anterior pituitary cells (116), a current that (by its very slow inactivation and high sensitivity to dihydropyridines; see 29) greatly resembles neuronal L current.

The insecticide tetramethrin blocks low-threshold but not high-threshold currents in N1E-115 neuroblastoma cells (125). Amiloride (121) and di-phenylhydantoin (128, 132) are also more effective blockers of low-threshold than high-threshold current. However, none of these drugs is likely to be a good pharmacological scalpel for T channels since all were first recognized for activity against Na channels or transporters. A more promising candidate is octanol, which is reported to block low-threshold Ca currents in inferior olivary neurons (80) at such low concentrations (submicromolar) that nonspecific effects may be unlikely.

MODULATION   Ca currents in many neurons can be inhibited by a variety of neurotransmitters (see 90). All three channel types may be susceptible to modulation. In sensory neurons, T current can be inhibited by norepinephrine (85; own unpublished results). Depression of high-threshold, inactivating

N-like current has been reported in sympathetic neurons by acetylcholine (130) and norepinephrine (78), in sensory neurons by κ-opiate (53) and GABA$_B$ agonists (35, 39), and in hippocampal cells by adenosine analogs (83). It seems likely that L channels can also be modulated since transmitters sometimes reduce a sustained component of current (35, 64); in N1E-115 cells, enkephalin and somatostatin reduce a sustained, L-like current but have no effect on T current (126). However, if some sustained current flows through N channels (discussed below), there may not yet be unambiguous evidence for L channel modulation (for example, showing that transmitter affects dihydropyridine-sensitive current), and there are several instances where N but not L current seems to be inhibited by transmitter (53, 78, 130). In many cases, GTP-binding proteins mediate transmitter effects on Ca currents (39, 60, 64, 130); activation of protein kinase C is implicated in some (84, 102), but not others (130; cf. 59), raising the possibility that transmitters inhibit different channel types by different pathways.

In hippocampal granule cells, β-adrenergic stimulation enhances Ca current (52). Although the affected channel has a conductance (15 pS) typical of an N channel, the similarity to β-adrenergic stimulation of cardiac L channels makes it important to use other kinetic and pharmacological criteria to define the channel affected, especially since β-adrenergic stimulation has been found to enhance current through L channels in bullfrog sympathetic neurons (78).

DISTRIBUTION AND FUNCTION   Despite suggestions that high-threshold channels may be preferentially localized in dendrites and low-threshold channels in cell bodies (66, 79), large high-threshold currents can be recorded from cell bodies of dissociated adult cells (104), and patch clamp and Ca influx experiments show the coexistence of T, L, and N channels throughout cell bodies, processes, and growth cones of cultured neurons (16, 77, 122). Depolarization of synaptosomal preparations induces a Ca influx that is resistant to dihydropyridine block (e.g. 105, but see 127) but is partially inhibited by ω-conotoxin (105), leading to suggestions that N channels preferentially mediate transmitter release from nerve terminals (see 91). Pharmacological studies of high potassium-induced transmitter release from cultured neurons implicate N channels [norepinephrine release from sympathetic cultures (62, 100)] or L channels [substance P release from DRG cultures (100, 103)], but such studies are of uncertain relevance to transmitter release at nerve terminals. Although ω-conotoxin blocks transmission at the frog neuromuscular junction (71), it does not block either of two components of Ca current in presynaptic terminals of the mouse neuromuscular junction (3, 99). Further pharmacological studies with ω-conotoxin, dihydropyridines, nickel, cadmium, and gadolinium may help identify channel types underlying transmitter release at other synapses.

As in cardiac muscle cells, the low threshold of neuronal T channels makes them well-suited for a role in pacemaking and bursting phenomena (see 66, 79). Further development of specific blockers will permit testing of their role in various cells.

SUMMARY AND CRITIQUE   The evidence for (at least) three distinct channel types in neurons is by now very convincing, especially from single channel recording; two distinct high-threshold channel types have been found in chick DRG neurons (45, 95), mouse DRG neurons (74), rat DRG neurons (34, 74), frog DRG neurons (own unpublished result), frog and rat sympathetic neurons (62, 77), hippocampal neurons (16), and PC12 cells (101).

However, exactly how N and L channels contribute to macroscopic currents is less clear. There are two problems with the prevailing view that N channels inactivate completely so that sustained current can be identified as L current. First, in chick DRG cells with both inactivating and steady components of high-threshold current, tail currents decay with the same monoexponential time course whether the depolarizing pulse is interrupted near peak current or after steady state is reached (117). Second, many rat DRG neurons have sustained current components that are not inhibited by dihydropyridine blockers (L. J. Regan, B. P. Bean, unpublished results). Most results could be explained if N channels were by far predominant in DRG cells, contributing most or (in some cells) all of the current (see 68). In this view, N channels would have complicated inactivation kinetics, with rapid, but incomplete, inactivation; N channels could contribute heavily to the sustained current presently identified as L current, as well as to the inactivating component. Without enhancement by dihydropyridine agonists, L current might be only a tiny fraction of N current, with most L channel openings brief and hard to resolve in single channel recordings.

Clear answers are needed to several key questions: Do N channels inactivate completely? Can current from N and L channels be distinguished by tail current kinetics? Are L channels as well as N channels irreversibly blocked by ω-conotoxin? Can L current be completely blocked by dihydropyridines? Are there perhaps multiple forms of N or L channels with distinct kinetic or pharmacological properties?

Other Tissues

PITUITARY CELLS   GH$_3$ and GH$_4$, clonal lines of anterior pituitary cells, have been studied extensively. Both have two components of Ca current (4, 5, 29, 86, 114, 116). One component is very similar to that from T channels in muscle cells and neurons: It is low-threshold, rapidly inactivating, and slowly deactivating (4, 29, 86). Ba and Ca carry current equally well (4, 86). Inactivation is voltage dependent, not Ca dependent (114). The other component has a higher threshold and fast deactivation kinetics (4, 29, 86). Ba currents are about twice as large as Ca currents (4, 86). Inactivation is extremely slow (little inactivation in many seconds) with Ba as charge carrier (29). Two types of single channels (5) are similar in size to T and L channels in other preparations, but they have not yet been systematically related to the whole cell current components.

The high-threshold current is potently blocked by dihydropyridines, while the low-threshold current is much less sensitive (29). The protein kinase C activator 1,2-oleylacetylglycerol inhibits both high-threshold and low-threshold current components (84), as in DRG neurons (84, 102). ω-Conotoxin irreversibly blocks the high-threshold but not the low-threshold component of current (116).

In its very slow inactivation and sensitivity to ω-conotoxin, the high-threshold current in GH3 cells more closely resembles L current in neurons than L current in muscle cells; there is (so far) no hint of an N-like current in GH3 cells. Two components of Ca current much like those in GH cells have also been recorded from normal rat pituitary cells (32, 36).

OTHER SECRETORY CELLS   Other types of secretory cells also have two types of Ca channels. Glucagon-secreting pancreatic alpha cells (107) and aldosterone-secreting adrenal glomerulosa cells (31, 59) both have two components of Ca current that seem similar to the currents through T and L channels of pituitary cells. Surprisingly, the T-type current in adrenal glomerulosa cells is somewhat depressed by submicromolar concentrations of nitrendipine when applied at depolarized holding potentials (31), which emphasizes that T channels should not be considered completely insensitive to dihydropyridines. Angiotensin II reportedly increases T current in adrenal glomerulosa cells (31) but in an aldosterone-secreting cell line, was found to increase an L-like current with no effect on T current (59).

Adrenal chromaffin cells are a rare case of a vertebrate cell type that has been well-investigated and has only a single class of Ca channels. High-threshold, slowly inactivating (42), and enhanced by BAY K 8644 (65), these channels seem similar to L channels in neurons and pituitary cells.

"NON-EXCITABLE" CELLS   A variety of cells once assumed to be electrically uninteresting have now been found to have Ca channels. Myeloma cells have a low-threshold, rapidly inactivating current (48) similar to T currents in other cells. Osteoblasts (27) and fibroblasts (26) have both L and T channels, with T channels selectively lacking in fibroblasts transformed by oncogenes (26). Even glial cells, once considered prototypic inexcitable cells, have recently been found to have a panoply of ionic channels; type 2 astrocytes from optic nerve have two types of Ca channels similar to T and L channels in neurons (7).

CLASSES OF Ca CHANNELS

T Channels

At least two fairly clearly defined classes of Ca channels emerge from these results. One consists of the low-threshold, rapidly inactivating T-type channels present in cardiac muscle, smooth muscle, developing skeletal muscle, pituitary and other secretory cells, fibroblasts, osteoblasts, astrocytes, and neurons. Although small differences are known, so far all of these channels seem to have very similar characteristics: low-threshold of activation, rapid inactivation ($\tau \approx 5$–50 ms), negative inactivation range, slow tail currents, single channel conductance of 5–10 pS in 100 Ba, Ba and Ca equally permeant, blocked potently by Ni, weakly blocked or not blocked by dihydropyridines, weakly blocked by ω-conotoxin. The main differences between cell types are the exact voltage-dependence and kinetics, which may arise from different lipids or surface charges in the membranes and not from different channel structures. (A few reports of Ba ions carrying less current than Ca (e.g. 20, 46) could reflect different levels of resting inactivation due to more effective screening of surface charge by Ca.)

The low threshold of T channels makes them well suited for participating in pacemaking, a role suggested in almost all cells. Also, T channel inactivation can be slow and incomplete for small depolarizations, leading to steady Ca influx that could underlie such functions as secretion or contraction, especially in tissues where a small depolarization need not produce a full-blown action potential (see 31). In skeletal muscle (9), smooth muscle (113), motor neurons (89), and hippocampal cells (132), T current is especially prominent in embryonic and immature cells, raising the possibility of some developmental role.

L Channels

A second fairly well-defined class of channels comprises the high-threshold, dihydropyridine-sensitive channels found in almost all tissues mentioned in this article. These share a similar voltage-dependence of activation, large single channel conductance, greater permeability to Ba than Ca, and high potency dihydropyridine block. Many are modulated by cAMP-dependent protein kinase. The similarities seem to justify considering this a class of closely related channels; in fact, high sensitivity to dihydropyridines can be taken as a convenient defining characteristic of an L channel. However, there is more variability between cell types than for T channels: Activation and inactivation kinetics vary widely (spanning orders of magnitude), and there are other special characteristics of L channels in various tissues, such as the possible ω-conotoxin sensitivity of neuronal channels, the Mg permeability of skeletal muscle channels, and the unusually high dihydropyridine sensitivity of vascular muscle channels.

Structural information supports the idea of a class of related dihydropyridine-sensitive Ca channels. The skeletal muscle dihydropyridine receptor consists of four polypeptides of 175, 170, 52, and 32 kd; the dihydropyridine binding site is on the 170 kd subunit, which has sequence homology with the voltage-dependent Na channel, and the 170- and 52-kd subunits are substrates for cAMP-dependent protein kinase (see 76, 111, 120). Dihydropyridine receptor complexes from brain and cardiac muscle are of similar size and show antigenic cross-reactivity with the skeletal muscle receptor (118, 119). It will be interesting to see whether dihydropyridine receptors in brain bind ω-conotoxin with high affinity.

Other Classes

Other classes of Ca channels are not yet so clearly defined. The evidence seems fairly good for a class of N channels, so far unique to neurons, that share similar single channel conductance, sensitivity to ω-conotoxin, and insensitivity to dihydropyridines, but which may differ from cell to cell in inactivation kinetics and perhaps voltage dependence. Whether the low-threshold but noninactivating channel in adult skeletal muscle might represent still another class is unclear.

Similarities Between Classes

All the classes of Ca channels share a steep voltage dependence and powerful selectivity for Ca over Na in physiological solutions. The open channel permeation pathway may be basically similar in all channels; T channels (e.g. 24, 49, 114), as well as L channels (see 124), become highly permeable to monovalent cations when external divalent cation concentrations are reduced to submicromolar levels, a phenomenon that has led to a model of selectivity arising from multiple high-affinity divalent binding sites in the permeation pathway (see 124). It will be interesting to see if N channels share this property. The known differences in selectivity between T and L channels could arise from small differences in the intra-channel binding sites.

There is also some pharmacological similarity between classes of Ca channels, along with the obvious differences; for example, though ω-conotoxin block of T channels is weak compared to that of N channels, it is strong compared with that of Na channels (97). (In other ways, T channels have close similarities with Na channels, both kinetically and in sensitivity to drugs like diphenylhydantoin.) Similarly, T channels may well be more sensitive to dihydropyridines than most non-Ca channels.

Now that the sequence of the dihydropyridine-binding peptide from skeletal muscle is known (along with those of voltage-dependent Na and K channels), the tools are at hand to make probes for other members of the Ca channel family. We will soon learn whether the various Ca channels are different gene products and what the structural relationships are between the various proteins. An interesting possibility is that some of the diversity of Ca channels may originate from different splicing of the same gene products, as for potassium channels coded for by the *Shaker* locus in *Drosophila* (110).

ACKNOWLEDGMENTS

I am grateful to Paul Ceelen for help with references, to Peter Hess, Jim Huettner, Laura Regan, and Dinah Sah for discussion, and to the American Heart Association, the National Institutes of Health, and the Rita Allen Foundation for support.

Literature Cited

1. Almers, W., Palade, P. T. 1981. Slow calcium and potassium currents across frog muscle membrane: measurements with a vaseline-gap technique. *J. Physiol.* 312:159–76
2. Amedee, T., Mironneau, C., Mironneau, J. 1987. The calcium channel current of pregnant rat single myometrial cells in short-term primary culture. *J. Physiol.* 392:253–72
3. Anderson, A. J., Harvey, A. L. 1987. ω-Conotoxin does not block the verapamil-sensitive calcium channels at mouse motor nerve terminals. *Neurosci. Lett.* 82:177–80
4. Armstrong, C. M., Matteson, D. R. 1985. Two distinct populations of calcium channels in a clonal line of pituitary cells. *Science* 227:65–66
5. Armstrong, D., Eckert, R. 1987. Voltage-activated calcium channels that must be phosphorylated to respond to membrane depolarization. *Proc. Natl. Acad. Sci. USA* 84:2518–22
6. Arreola, J., Calvo, J., Garcia, M. C., Sanchez, J. A. 1987. Modulation of calcium channels of twitch skeletal muscle fibres of the frog by adrenaline and cyclic adenosine monophosphate. *J. Physiol.* 393:307–30
7. Barres, B. A., Chun, L. L. Y., Corey, D. P. 1988. Ion channel expression by white matter glia. I. Type 2 astrocytes and oligodendrocytes. *Glia* 1:10–30
8. Beam, K. G., Knudson, C. M. 1988. Calcium currents in embryonic and neonatal mammalian skeletal muscle. *J. Gen. Physiol.* 91:781–98
9. Beam, K. G., Knudson, C. M. 1988. Effect of postnatal development on calcium currents and slow charge move-

ment in mammalian skeletal muscle. *J. Gen. Physiol.* 91:799–815
10. Beam, K. G., Knudson, C. M., Powell, J. A. 1986. A lethal mutation in mice eliminates the slow calcium current in skeletal muscle cells. *Nature* 320:168–70
11. Bean, B. P. 1985. Two kinds of calcium channels in canine atrial cells. Differences in kinetics, selectivity, and pharmacology. *J. Gen. Physiol.* 86:1–30
12. Bean, B. P., Sturek, M., Puga, A., Hermsmeyer, K. 1986. Calcium channels in muscle cells isolated from rat mesenteric arteries: modulation by dihydropyridine drugs. *Circ. Res.* 59:229–35
13. Beaty, G. N., Cota, G., Nicola Siri, L., Sanchez, J. A., Stefani, E. 1987. Skeletal muscle Ca^{2+} channels. In *Structure and Physiology of the Slow Inward Calcium Channel*, ed. D. J. Triggle, J. C. Venter, 1:123–40. New York: Liss
14. Benham, C. D., Hess, P., Tsien, R. W. 1987. Two types of calcium channels in single smooth muscle cells from rabbit ear artery studied with whole-cell and single-channel recordings. *Circ. Res.* 61(Suppl. I):10–16
15. Benham, C. D., Tsien, R. W. 1987. Noradrenaline increases L-type calcium current in smooth muscle cells of rabbit ear artery independently of α- and β-adrenoreceptors. *J. Physiol.* 390:85P (Abstr.)
16. Bley, K. R., Madison, D. V., Tsien, R. W. 1987. Multiple types of calcium channels in hippocampal neurons: characterization and localization. *Soc. Neurosci. Abstr.* 13:1010 (Abstr.)

17. Boll, W., Lux, H. D. 1985. Action of organic antagonists on neuronal calcium currents. *Neurosci. Lett.* 56:335–39
18. Bonvallet, R. 1987. A low threshold calcium current recorded at physiological Ca concentrations in single frog atrial cells. *Pflügers Arch.* 408:540–42
19. Bossu, J. L., Feltz, A. 1986. Inactivation of the low-threshold transient calcium current in rat sensory neurones: evidence for a dual process. *J. Physiol.* 376:341–57
20. Bossu, J. L., Feltz, A., Thomann, J. M. 1985. Depolarization elicits two distinct calcium currents in vertebrate sensory neurones. *Pflügers Arch.* 403:360–68
21. Carbone, E., Lux, H. D. 1984. A low voltage-activated calcium conductance in embryonic chick sensory neurones. *Biophys. J.* 46:413–18
22. Carbone, E., Lux, H. D. 1984. A low voltage-activated, fully inactivating Ca channel in vertebrate sensory neurones. *Nature* 310:501–2
23. Carbone, E., Lux, H. D. 1987. Kinetics and selectivity of a low-voltage-activated calcium current in chick and rat sensory neurones. *J. Physiol.* 386:547–70
24. Carbone, E., Lux, H. D. 1987. Single low-voltage-activated calcium channels in chick and rat sensory neurones. *J. Physiol.* 386:571–601
25. Carbone, E., Swandulla, D., Lux, H. D. 1988. Block and modulation of neuronal Ca channels by catecholamines, cyclic alcohols and nickel. *Symp. Neurosci.*, ed. G. Biggio, P. F. Spano, G. Toffano, G. L. Gessa. Civieno-Springer-Verlag
26. Chen, C., Corbley, M. J., Roberts, T. M., Hess, P. 1988. Voltage-sensitive calcium channels in normal and transformed 3T3 fibroblasts. *Science* 239:1024–25
27. Chesnoy-Marchais, D., Fritsch, J. 1988. Voltage-gated sodium and calcium currents in rat osteoblasts. *J. Physiol.* 398:291–311
28. Cognard, C., Lazdunski, M., Romey, G. 1986. Different types of Ca^{2+} channels in mammalian skeletal muscle cells in culture. *Proc. Natl. Acad. Sci. USA* 83:517–21
29. Cohen, C. J., McCarthy, R. T. 1987. Nimodipine block of calcium channels in rat anterior pituitary cells. *J. Physiol.* 387:195–225
30. Cohen, C. J., McCarthy, R. T. 1988. Nimodipine block of calcium channels in rat vascular smooth muscle cell lines. *J. Gen. Physiol.* In press
31. Cohen, C. J., McCarthy, R. T., Barrett, P. Q., Rasmussen, H. 1988. Ca channels in adrenal glomerulosa cells: K^+ and angiotensin II increase T-type Ca channel current. *Proc. Natl. Acad. Sci. USA.* 85:2412–16
32. Cota, G. 1986. Calcium channel currents in pars intermedia cells of the rat pituitary gland. Kinetic properties and washout during intracellular dialysis. *J. Gen. Physiol.* 88:83–105
33. Cota, G., Stefani, E. 1986. A fast-activated inward calcium current in twitch muscle fibres of the frog (*Rana montezume*). *J. Physiol.* 370:151–63
34. Cottrell, G. A., Green, K. A. 1987. T, N, and L channels in rat sensory neurons and the actions of baclofen. *J. Physiol.* 392:32P (Abstr.)
35. Deisz, R. A., Lux, H. D. 1985. Gamma-aminobutyric acid-induced depression of calcium currents of chick sensory neurons. *Neurosci. Lett.* 56:205–10
36. DeRiemer, S. A., Sakmann, B. 1986. Two calcium currents in normal rat anterior pituitary cells identified by a plaque assay. *Exp. Brain Res. Suppl.* 14:139–54
37. Docherty, R. J. 1988. Gadolinium selectively blocks a component of calcium current in rodent neuroblastoma x glioma hybrid (NG108-15) cells. *J. Physiol.* 398:33–47
38. Docherty, R. J., Brown, D. A. 1986. Interaction of 1,4-dihydropyridines with somatic Ca currents in hippocampal CA1 neurones of the guinea-pig in vitro. *Neurosci. Lett.* 70:110–15
39. Dolphin, A. C., Scott, R. H. 1987. Calcium channel currents and their inhibition by (−)-baclofen in rat sensory neurones: modulation by guanine nucleotides. *J. Physiol.* 386:1–17
40. Droogmans, G., Callewart, G. 1986. Ca^{2+}-channel current and its modification by the dihydropyridine agonist BAY K 8644 in isolated smooth muscle cells. *Pflügers Arch.* 406:259–65
41. Fedulova, S. A., Kostyuk, P. G., Veselovsky, N. S. 1985. Two types of calcium channels in the somatic membrane of newborn rat dorsal root ganglion neurones. *J. Physiol.* 359:431–46
42. Fenwick, E. M., Marty, A., Neher, E. 1982. Sodium and calcium channels in adrenal chromaffin cells. *J. Physiol.* 331:599–635
43. Flockerzi, V., Oeken, H.-J., Hofmann, F., Pelzer, D., Cavalie, A., Trautwein, W. 1986. Purified dihydropyridine-binding site from skeletal muscle t-tubules is a functional calcium channel. *Nature* 323:66–68
44. Fox, A. P., Nowycky, M. C., Tsien, R.

W. 1987. Kinetic and pharmacological properties distinguishing three types of calcium currents in chick sensory neurones. *J. Physiol.* 394:149–72

45. Fox, A. P., Nowycky, M. C., Tsien, R. W. 1987. Single-channel recordings of three types of calcium channels in chick sensory neurones. *J. Physiol.* 394:173–200

46. Friedman, M. E., Suarez-Kurtz, G., Kaczorowski, G. J., Katz, G. M., Reuben, J. P. 1986. Two calcium currents in a smooth muscle cell line. *Am. J. Physiol.* 250:H699–H703

47. Friel, D. D., Tsien, R. W. 1988. Effects of NGF on Ca channel distribution in PC-12 cells. *Biophys. J.* 53:430a (Abstr.)

48. Fukushima, Y., Hagiwara, S. 1983. Voltage-gated Ca^{2+} channel in mouse myeloma cells. *Proc. Natl. Acad. Sci. USA* 80:2240–42

49. Fukushima, Y., Hagiwara, S. 1985. Currents carried by monovalent cations through calcium channels in mouse neoplastic B lymphocytes. *J. Physiol.* 358:255–84

50. Ganitkevich, V. Ya., Shuba, M. F., Smirnov, S. V. 1987. Calcium-dependent inactivation of potential-dependent calcium inward current in an isolated guinea-pig smooth muscle cell. *J. Physiol.* 392:431–49

51. Garcia, J., Stefani, E. 1987. Appropriate conditions to record activation of fast Ca^{2+} channels in frog skeletal muscle (*Rana pipiens*). *Pflügers Arch.* 408:646–48

52. Gray, R., Johnston, D. 1987. Noradrenaline and β-adrenoceptor agonists increase activity of voltage-dependent calcium channels in hippocampal neurons. *Nature* 327:620–22

53. Gross, R. A., MacDonald, R. L. 1987. Dynorphin A selectively reduces a large transient (N-type) calcium current of mouse dorsal root ganglion neurons in cell culture. *Proc. Natl. Acad. Sci. USA* 84:5469–73

54. Hagiwara, N., Irisawa, H., Kameyama, M. 1988. Contribution of two types of calcium currents to the pacemaker potentials of rabbit sino-atrial node cells. *J. Physiol.* 359:233–53

55. Hagiwara, S. 1983. *Membrane Potential-Dependent Ion Channels in Cell Membrane*, pp. 5–47. New York: Raven. 118 pp.

56. Hagiwara, S., Byerly, L. 1981. Calcium channel. *Annu. Rev. Neurosci.* 4:69–125

57. Hagiwara, S., Ozawa, S., Sand, O. 1975. Voltage-clamp analysis of two inward current mechanisms in the egg cell membrane of a starfish. *J. Gen. Physiol.* 65:617–44

58. Halliwell, J. V. 1983. Caesium-loading reveals two distinct Ca-currents in voltage-clamped guinea-pig hippocampal neurones in vitro. *J. Physiol.* 341:10P–11P

59. Hescheler, J., Rosenthal, W., Hinsch, K. D., Wulfern, M., Trautwein, W., Schultz, G. 1988. Angiotensin II-induced stimulation of voltage-dependent Ca^{2+} currents in an adrenal cortical cell line. *EMBO J.* 7:619–24

60. Hescheler, J., Rosenthal, W., Trautwein, W., Shultz, G. 1987. The GTP-binding protein, G_o, regulates neuronal calcium channels. *Nature* 325:445–47

61. Hille, B. 1984. *Ionic Channels of Excitable Membranes*, pp. 76–98. Sunderland, Mass.: Sinauer. 426 pp.

62. Hirning, L. D., Fox, A. P., McCleskey, E. W., Olivera, B. M., Thayer, S. A., Miller, R. J., Tsien, R. W. 1988. Dominant role of N-type Ca^{2+} channels in evoked release of norepinephrine from sympathetic neurons. *Science* 239:57–61

63. Hirst, G. D. S., Silverberg, G. D., van Helden, D. F. 1986. The action potential and underlying ionic currents in proximal rat middle cerebral arteries. *J. Physiol.* 371:289–304

64. Holz, G. G., Rane, S. G., Dunlap, K. 1986. GTP-binding proteins mediate transmitter inhibition of voltage-dependent calcium channels. *Nature* 319:670–72

65. Hoshi, T., Smith, S. 1987. Large depolarization induces long openings of voltage-dependent calcium channels in adrenal chromaffin cells. *J. Neurosci.* 7:571–80

66. Jahnsen, H., Llinas, R. 1984. Ionic basis for the electroresponsiveness and oscillatory properties of guinea-pig thalamic neurones in vitro. *J. Physiol.* 349:227–47

67. Kameyama, M., Hofmann, F., Trautwein, W. 1985. On the mechanism of β-adrenergic regulation of the Ca channel in the guinea pig heart. *Pflügers Arch.* 405:285–93

68. Kasai, H., Aosaki, T., Fukuda, J. 1987. Presynaptic Ca-agonist ω-conotoxin irreversibly blocks N-type Ca-channels in chick sensory neurons. *Neurosci Res.* 4:228–35

69. Kass, R. S., Sanguinetti, M. C. 1984. Inactivation of calcium channel current in the calf cardiac Purkinje fiber: evidence for voltage- and calcium-mediated mechanisms. *J. Gen. Physiol.* 84:705–26

70. Kay, A. R., Wong, R. K. S. 1987. Cal-

cium current activation kinetics in isolated pyramidal neurones of the CA1 region of the mature guinea-pig hippocampus. *J. Physiol.* 392:603–16

71. Kerr, L. M., Yoshikami, D. 1984. A venom peptide with a novel presynaptic blocking action. *Nature* 308:282–84

72. Kokubun, S., Prod'hom, B., Becker, C., Porzig, H., Reuter, H. 1987. Studies on Ca channels in intact cardiac cells: voltage-dependent effects and cooperative interactions of dihydropyridine enantiomers. *Mol. Pharmacol.* 30:571–84

73. Kostyuk, P. G. 1981. Calcium channels in the neuronal membrane. *Biochim. Biophys. Acta* 650:128–50

74. Kostyuk, P. G., Shuba, M. F., Savchenko, A. N. 1988. Three types of calcium channels in the membrane of mouse sensory neurones. *Pflügers Arch.* 411:661–69

75. Lee, K. S., Noble, D., Lee, E., Spindler, A. J. 1984. A new calcium current underlying the plateau of the cardiac action potential. *Proc. R. Soc. London Ser. B* 223:35–48

76. Leung, A. T., Imagawa, T., Block, B., Franzini-Armstrong, C., Campbell, K. P. 1988. Biochemical and ultrastructural characterization of the 1,4-dihydropyridine receptor from rabbit skeletal muscle. *J. Biol. Chem.* 263:994–1001

77. Lipscombe, D., Madison, D. V., Poenie, M., Reuter, H., Tsien, R. Y., Tsien, R. W. 1988. Spatial distribution of calcium channels and cytosolic calcium transients in growth cones and cell bodies of sympathetic neurons. *Proc. Natl. Acad. Sci. USA* 85:2398–2402

78. Lipscombe, D., Tsien, R. W. 1987. Noradrenaline inhibits N-type Ca channels in frog sympathetic neurones. *J. Physiol.* 377:97P

79. Llinas, R., Yarom, Y. 1981. Properties and distribution of ionic conductances generating electroresponsiveness of mammalian inferior olivary neurones in vitro. *J. Physiol.* 315:569–84

80. Llinas, R., Yarom, Y. 1986. Specific blockage of the low threshold calcium channel by high molecular weight alcohols. *Soc. Neurosci. Abstr.* 12:174

81. Loirand, G., Pacaud, P., Mironneau, C., Mironneau, J. 1986. Evidence for two distinct calcium channels in rat vascular smooth muscle cells in short-term primary culture. *Pflügers Arch.* 407:566–68

82. Ma, J., Coronado, R. 1988. Heterogeneity of conductance states in calcium channels of skeletal muscle. *Biophys. J.* 53:387–95

83. Madison, D. V., Fox, A. P., Tsien, R. W. 1987. Adenosine reduces an inactivating component of calcium current in hippocampal CA3 neurons. *Biophys. J.* 51:30a

84. Marchetti, C., Brown, A. M. 1988. Protein kinase activator 1-oleoyl-2-acetyl-sn-glycerol inhibits two types of calcium currents in GH3 cells. *Am. J. Physiol.* 23:C206–C210

85. Marchetti, C., Carbone, E., Lux, H. D. 1986. Effects of dopamine and noradrenaline on Ca channels of cultured sensory and sympathetic neurons of chick. *Pflügers Arch.* 406:104–11

86. Matteson, D. R., Armstrong, C. M. 1986. Properties of two types of calcium channels in clonal pituitary cells. *J. Gen. Physiol.* 87:161–82

87. McCleskey, E. W. 1985. Calcium channels and intracellular calcium release are pharmacologically different in frog skeletal muscle. *J. Physiol.* 361:231–49

88. McCleskey, E. W., Fox, A. P., Feldman, D. H., Cruz, L. J., Olivera, B. M., et al. 1987. ω-conotoxin: Direct and persistent blockade of specific types of calcium channels in neurons but not muscle. *Proc. Natl. Acad. Sci. USA* 84:4327–31

89. McCobb, D. P., Best, P. M., Beam, K. G. 1988. Developmental changes in Ca^{++} currents from identified chick motoneurones. *Biophys. J.* 53:23a (Abstr.)

90. Miller, R. J. 1987. Calcium channels in neurones. In *Structure and Physiology of the Slow Inward Calcium Channel,* ed. D. J. Triggle, J. C. Venter, 1:161–246 New York: Liss

91. Miller, R. J. 1987. Multiple calcium channels and neuronal function. *Science* 235:46–52

92. Mitra, R., Morad, M. 1986. Two types of calcium channels in guinea-pig ventricular myocytes. *Proc. Natl. Acad. Sci. USA* 83:5340–44

93. Narahashi, T., Tsunoo, A., Yoshii, M. 1987. Characterization of two types of calcium channels in mouse neuroblastoma cells. *J. Physiol.* 383:231–49

94. Nilius, B., Hess, P., Lansman, J. B., Tsien, R. W. 1985. A novel type of cardiac calcium channel in ventricular cells. *Nature* 316:443–46

95. Nowycky, M. C., Fox, A. P., Tsien, R. W. 1985. Three types of neuronal calcium channel with different calcium sensitivity. *Nature* 316:440–43

96. Nowycky, M. C., Fox, A. P., Tsien, R. W. 1985. Long-opening mode of gating

of neuronal calcium channels and its promotion by the dihydropyridine calcium agonist Bay K 8644. *Proc. Natl. Acad. Sci. USA* 82:2178–82

97. Oyama, Y., Tsuda, Y., Sakakibara, S., Akaike, N. 1987. Synthetic ω-conotoxin: a potent calcium channel blocking neurotoxin. *Brain Res.* 424: 58–64

98. Pacaud, P., Loirand, G., Mironneau, C., Mironneau, J. 1987. Opposing effects of noradrenaline on the two classes of voltage-dependent calcium channels of single vascular smooth muscle cells in short-term primary culture. *Pflügers Arch.* 410:557–59

99. Penner, R., Dreyer, F. 1986. Two different presynaptic calcium currents in mouse motor nerve terminals. *Pflügers Arch.* 406:190–97

100. Perney, T. M., Hirning, L. D., Leeman, S. E., Miller, R. J. 1986. Multiple calcium channels mediate neurotransmitter release from peripheral neurons. *Proc. Natl. Acad. Sci. USA* 83:6656–59

101. Plummer, M. R., Logothetis, D. E., Hess, P. 1988. Multiple types of calcium channels in PC12 cells grown in the absence of growth factor. *Biophys. J.* 53:233a (Abstr.)

102. Rane, S. G., Dunlap, K. 1986. Kinase C activator 1,2-oleoylacetylglycerol attenuates voltage-dependent calcium current in sensory neurons. *Proc. Natl. Acad. Sci. USA* 83:184–88

103. Rane, S. G., Holz, G. G., Dunlap, K. 1987. Dihydropyridine inhibition of neuronal calcium current and substance P release. *Pflügers Arch.* 409:361–66

104. Regan, L. J. 1987. Calcium channels in freshly-dissociated rat cerebellar Purkinje cells. *Soc. Neurosci. Abstr.* 13:100 (Abstr.)

105. Reynolds, I. J., Wagner, J. A., Snyder, S. H., Thayer, S. A., Olivera, B. M., Miller, R. J. 1986. Brain voltage-sensitive calcium channel subtypes differentiated by ω-conotoxin fraction GVIA. *Proc. Natl. Acad. Sci. USA* 83:8804–7

106. Rios, E., Brum, G. 1987. Involvement of dihydropyridine receptors in excitation-contraction coupling. *Nature* 325:717–20

107. Rorsman, P. 1988. Two types of calcium currents with different sensitivities to organic Ca^{2+} channel antagonists in guinea-pig pancreatic alpha-2 cells. *J. Gen. Physiol.* 91:243–54

108. Rosenberg, R. L., Hess, P., Reeves, J. P., Smilowitz, H., Tsien, R. W. 1986. Calcium channels in planar lipid bilayers: Insights into mechanisms of ion permeation and gating. *Science* 231:1564–66

109. Sanguinetti, M. C., Kass, R. S. 1984. Voltage-dependent block of calcium channel current by dihydropyridine calcium channel antagonists. *Circ. Res.* 55:336–48

110. Schwarz, T. L., Tempel, B. L., Papazian, D. M., Jan, Y. N., Jan, L. Y. 1988. Multiple potassium-channel components are produced by alternative splicing at the *Shaker* locus in *Drosophila*. *Nature* 331:137–42

111. Sharp, A. H., Imagawa, T., Leung, A. T., Campbell, K. P. 1987. Identification and characterization of the dihydropyridine-binding subunit of the skeletal muscle dihydropyridine receptor. *J. Biol. Chem.* 262:12309–15

112. Streit, J., Lux, H. D. 1987. Voltage dependent calcium currents in PC 12 growth cones and cells during NGF-induced cell growth. *Pflügers Arch.* 408:634–41

113. Sturek, M., Hermsmeyer, K. 1986. Calcium and sodium channels in spontaneously contracting vascular muscle cells. *Science* 233:475–78

114. Suarez-Kurtz, G., Katz, G. W., Reuben, J. P. 1987. Currents carried by sodium ions through transient calcium channels in clonal GH3 pituitary cells. *Pflügers Arch.* 410:345–47

115. Sutor, B., Zieglgansberger, W. 1987. A low-voltage activated, transient calcium current is responsible for the time-dependent depolarizing inward rectification of rat neocortical neurons in vitro. *Pflügers Arch.* 410:102–11

116. Suzuki, N., Yoshioka, T. 1987. Differential blocking action of synthetic ω-conotoxin on components of Ca^{2+} channel current in clonal GH3 cells. *Neurosci. Lett.* 75:235–39

117. Swandulla, D., Armstrong, C. M. 1988. Fast deactivating calcium channels in chick sensory neurons. *J. Gen. Physiol.* 92:197–218

118. Takahashi, M., Catterall, W. A. 1987. Identification of an alpha subunit of dihydropyridine-sensitive brain calcium channels. *Science* 236:88–91

119. Takahashi, M., Catterall, W. A. 1987. Dihydropyridine-sensitive calcium channels in cardiac and skeletal muscle membranes: studies with antibodies against the alpha subunits. *Biochemistry* 26: 5518–26

120. Tanabe, T., Takeshima, H., Mikami, A., Flockerzi, V., Takahashi, H., et al. 1987. Primary structure of the receptor for calcium channel blockers from skeletal muscle. *Nature* 328:313–18

121. Tang, C.-M., Presser, F., Morad, M. 1988. Amiloride selectively blocks the low threshold (T) calcium channel. *Science* 240:213–15

122. Thayer, S. A., Hirning, L. D., Miller, R. J. 1987. The distribution of multiple types of Ca^{2+} channels in rat sympathetic neurons. *Mol. Pharmacol.* 32:579–86

123. Tsien, R. W. 1983. Calcium channels in excitable cell membranes. *Annu. Rev. Physiol.* 45:341–58

124. Tsien, R. W., Hess, P., McCleskey, E. W., Rosenberg, R. L. 1987. Calcium channels: Mechanisms of selectivity, permeation and block. *Annu. Rev. Biophys. Biophys. Chem.* 16:265–90

125. Tsunoo, A., Yoshi, M., Narahashi, T. 1985. Differential block of two calcium channels in neuroblastoma cells. *Biophys. J.* 47:433a (Abstr.)

126. Tsunoo, A., Yoshi, M., Narahashi, T. 1986. Block of calcium channels by enkephalin and somatostatin in neuroblastoma-glioma hybrid NG108-15 cells. *Proc. Natl. Acad. Sci. USA* 83:9832–36

127. Turner, T. J., Goldin, S. M. 1985. Calcium channels in rat brain synaptosomes: Identification and pharmacological characterization. *J. Neurosci.* 5:841–49

128. Twombley, D. A., Narahashi, T. 1986. Phenytoin block of low threshold calcium channels is voltage- and frequency-dependent. *Soc. Neurosci. Abstr.* 12:1193 (Abstr.)

128a. Tytgat, J., Nilius, B., Vereecke, J., Carmeliet, E. 1988. The T-type Ca channel in guinea-pig ventricular myocytes is insensitive to isoproterenol. *Pflügers Arch.* 411:704–6

129. Vivadou, M., Clapp, L. H., Walsh, J. V., Singer, J. J. 1988. Diacylglycerol and acetylcholine regulate one type of Ca^{++} current in smooth muscle cells. *FASEB J.* 2:2497–2504

130. Wanke, E., Ferroni, A., Malgaroli, A., Ambrosini, A., Rozzan, T., Meldolesi, J. 1987. Activation of a muscarinic receptor selectively inhibits a rapidly inactivated Ca^{2+} current in rat sympathetic neurons. *Proc. Natl. Acad. Sci. USA* 84:4313–17

131. Worley, J. F., Deitmer, J. W., Nelson, M. T. 1986. Single nisoldipine-sensitive calcium channels in smooth muscle cells isolated from rabbit intestine mesenteric artery. *Proc. Natl. Acad. Sci. USA* 83:5746–50

132. Yaari, Y., Hamon, B., Lux, H. D. 1987. Development of two types of calcium channels in cultured mammalian hippocampal neurons. *Science* 235:680–82

133. Yatani, A., Seidel, C. L., Allen, J., Brown, A. M. 1987. Whole-cell and single-channel calcium currents of isolated smooth muscle cells from saphenous vein. *Circ. Res.* 60:523–33

134. Yoshino, M., Someya, T., Nishio, A., Yabu, H. 1988. Whole-cell and unitary Ca channel currents in mammalian intestinal smooth muscle cells: evidence for the existence of the types of Ca channels. *Pflügers Arch.* 411:229–31

Annu. Rev. Physiol. 1989. 51:385–99

VARIETIES OF CALCIUM-ACTIVATED POTASSIUM CHANNELS

Ramon Latorre, Andres Oberhauser, Pedro Labarca, and Osvaldo Alvarez

Departamento de Biologia, Facultad de Ciencias, Casilla 653, Universidad de Chile, Santiago, Chile

and

Centro de Estudios Cientificos de Santiago, Casilla 16443, Santiago 9, Chile

INTRODUCTION

The first demonstration that internal calcium is able to regulate potassium flux across membranes was given by Gardos (19) in red blood cells. A more direct approach to this problem was taken by Meech & Strumwasser (51), who observed that a microinjection of calcium was able to hyperpolarize the cell membrane of an *Aplysia* neuron. This response is accompanied by an increase in membrane conductance, and its reversal potential is a function of the external potassium concentration (49). On the basis of these results, a Ca^{2+}-activated K^+ conductance, $G_{K(Ca)}$, was postulated, and Meech (50) suggested that the main role of these channels probably is to link cell metabolism to membrane conductance. Since these seminal observations were made, studies using the patch-clamp (60) and reconstitution techniques (53) have demonstrated that intracellular calcium activates several different K^+ channels (for reviews see 11, 34, 37, 65). Channel conductance, calcium sensitivity, voltage dependence, and pharmacological properties have been used to distinguish between the different channels of this family. Channel conductance ranges from a few to several hundred picosiemens (pS) consequently, attempts have been made to group K(Ca) channels according to their conductance (11, 36). They have been called small potassium (SK; 10, 11) and

385

large potassium (BK or maxi-K; 37, 44) conductance channels. These channels are ubiquitously distributed in cells and tissues that play an important role in secretion in glands, repetitive firing, and afterhyperpolarization in some neurons and myotubes. K(Ca) channels also appear to play an important role in potassium movements in some epithelia. We discuss some of the main conductance, gating, and pharmacological characteristics of K(Ca) channels. A brief glance at the modulation of these channels by cell metabolism is given at the end of this review.

MAXI-K CHANNELS

Conductance, Distribution, and Role

Because of their large conductance, the best studied K(Ca) channels are the maxi-K channels. These channels, 130–300 pS in symmetrical 100–140 mM KCI, Table 1 (34), were the first to be observed both in cell membranes and in planar lipid bilayers (1, 32, 38, 43, 52, 63, 78). They are widely distributed in neurons (1, 46), striated and smooth muscle (6, 12, 38, 63, 76), endocrine and exocrine glands (15, 43, 45, 64), kidney tubules (20, 24, 30) and choroid plexus (14). Although in some cases the role of maxi-K channels is not clear (e.g. in striated muscle membrane), patch-clamp studies have shown that they are involved in the regulation of secretion in endocrine and exocrine glands. Secretagogues such as acetylcholine or cholecystokinin induce a cell membrane hyperpolarization in pancreas acinar cells (64, 71). The messenger-mediated hyperpolarization is due to an increase in the open-state probability of K(Ca) channels with a unit conductance of 200–250 pS. The presence of maxi-K channels in the basolateral plasma membrane of salivary gland acini explains the K^+ loss induced by nerve stimulation or by direct stimulation with secretagogues (65). Cholinergic agonists also induce activation of maxi-K channels in lacrimal glands by increasing the intracellular Ca^{2+} concentration, allowing the extrusion of K^+ during secretion of tears (72).

Prolongation by glucose and quinine of the plateau phase of the action potential in pancreatic β cells was thought to be due to a blockade of the maxi-K channels present in these cells (e.g. 3). However, since the finding that glucose inhibits ATP-sensitive channels, the role of K(Ca) currents in β cells is under reinterpretation (64). Maxi-K channels in β cells probably provide a feedback control of Ca^{2+} uptake (18).

In kidney tubules, large-conductance K(Ca) channels can explain the coupling between K^+ secretion and Na^+ absorption. Maxi-K channels can provide the passive transport pathway from the cell to the lumen in renal collecting ducts (20). Similarly, maxi-K channels have been identified as the electrodiffusive pathway for K^+ ions in the epithelium that secretes cerebrospinal fluid into the ventricles of the brain from the blood (14).

Table 1 Types and distribution of Ca^{2+}-activated K^+ channels

Preparation	Ionic condition[a]	Conductance (pS)	Selectivity	Voltage dependence (a)	Calcium dependence (b)	Ba block (c)	TEA block $Kd(0)_i$, $Kd(0)_o$		Apamin block	ChTx block	References
Maxi-K channels											
Rat myotubes	140 K^+	240	Tl>K>Rb>NH₄>> Na,Li,Cs	11–16mV	40mV/10-fold $V_o(1\mu M)=40mV$	—	60mM	0.3mM	No	—	5, 9, 10
Rabbit T-tubules[b]	100 K^+	260	Tl>K>Rb>NH₄>> Na,Li,Cs	11–13mV	40mV/10-fold $V_o(1\mu M)=40mV$	$Kd(0)_i=36\mu M$ $Kd(0)_o=1.8mM$	45mM	0.29mM	No	Yes	38, 57, 58, 73, 74
Rat axolema[b]	100 K^+	230	K>>Na	yes	yes	—		—	—	—	32
Bovine chromaffin cells	160 K^+	265	K>Rb>Na,Cs	12–15mV	10nM	—	27mM	0.2mM	—	—	43, 44, 79
Rat anterior pituitary cells (AtT-20/D16-16)	140 K^+	200	—	9mV*	60mV/10-fold $V_o(1\mu M)=-30mV$	$K_{0.5o}=2mM$	0.08mM	52.2mM	—	—	77, 78
Rat anterior pituitary cells (GH₃)	150 K^+	250–300	K>>Na	8mV	$V_o(1\mu M)=50mV$	—	$K_{0.5o}(-60)=2mM$		No	—	33
Sympathetic neurons	$5_o/120_iK^+$	100	K>>Na	yes	yes	—		—	—	—	20
Olfactory neurons	140 K^+	130	K>>Na	yes	100nM	—	30mM$_i$, no block		—	—	4
Mouse parotid acini	145 K^+	250	K>>Na	12mV*	1nM	—		—	—	—	45

Tissue	[K]	Value	Selectivity	mV	Ca/Voltage	Kd	Block				Ref
Rat pancreatic β-cells	140 K$^+$	244	K>>Na	15mV*	110mV/10-fold* $V_o(1\mu M)=0mV$	—	—	—	—	—	15, 18
Rabbit smooth muscle[b]	100 K$^+$	230	K>Rb>>Na,Li,Cs	15mV*	30mV/10-fold* $V_o(2\mu M)=60mV$	—	—	—	—	Yes	12
Toad smooth muscle cells	130 K$^+$	250	K>>Na	9mV	80mV/10-fold $V_o(1\mu M)=10mV$	—	—	—	—	—	68
Frog and toad smooth muscle	120 K$^+$	200	K>>Na	yes	10 nM	—	20mM$_o$ for total block	—	—	—	7
Rabbit smooth muscle cells	126 K$^+$	200	K>>Na	yes	10 nM	$K_d(0)_i=70\mu M$ 10mM$_o$ no block	12mM	—	—	—	6
Rabbit cortical collecting tubules	75$_o$/15$_i$K$^+$	90	K>>Na	weak	yes	$K_{0.5i}=10\mu M$	—	—	—	—	30
Medullary thick ascending cells	5$_o$/135$_i$K$^+$	127	K>>Na	10-30mV	10 nM	$K_{0.5i}=2\mu M$* $K_{0.5o}=2mM$	10mM*	200uM*	No	Yes	25, 26
Rabbit collecting duct analgen	140 K$^+$	180	K>>Na	17mV*	100 nM	5mM$_i$ for total block	—	—	—	—	20

SK channels

Rat skeletal muscle	140 K$^+$	12	—	weak	100 nM	—	Not blocked by 5mM$_o$	Yes	—	10
Anterior pituitary cells	150 K$^+$	9–14	K>>Na	indep.	1 uM	—	—	Yes	—	33
Olfactory neurons	140 K$^+$	80	K>>Na	indep.	1 uM	—	—	—	—	46
Human red cells	150 K$^+$	10–40	K>>Na	weak	1 µM	—	—	No	Yes	22, 23, 76a
Aplysia	10$_o$/360$_i$K$^+$	35	K>>Na	44mV	10 nM	—	2–5mM$_o$ for total block	No	Yes	28
Helix pomatia	4$_o$/400$_i$K$^+$	19	—	yes	yes	—	—	—	—	41
Helix aspersa	120 K$^+$	40–60	K>>Na	21mV	30mV/10-fold 10 nM	—	—	—	—	17

---

^{a} = concentrations is in mM. Where no designation of internal concentration is given, symmetrical solutions were used.

^{b} = parameters determined in planar bilayers. For all other channels, patch-clamp technique was used.

(a) = expressed as e-fold change in P$_o$ (fraction of the time in the open state) per x mV.

(b) = expressed as x mV change in V$_o$ (voltage at which P$_o$=0.5) per 10-fold increase in [Ca^{2+}]$_i$; V$_o$(xµM) indicates the voltage at which P$_o$=0.5 at given [Ca^{2+}]. Otherwise the lowest [Ca^{2+}] is given at which channel activity can be seen (at depolarizing voltages).

(c) = K$_{0.5}$ is the concentration of Ba^{2+} at which the P$_o$ is 50% of the control.

* = value calculated from reference.

The repolarizing phase of the action potential and control of the slow wave activity are the roles proposed for maxi-K channels present in some smooth muscle cells (68, 76). In this kind of muscle, maxi-K channels mediate a slow outward current blocked by external tetraethylammonium (TEA). Although maxi-K channels are also present in most nerve and striated muscle cells, their role in these tissues has not yet been completely clarified. Contributions to the repolarizing phase of the action potential, as well as repolarization and stabilization of the transverse tubule membrane, are possible functions of these channels (11).

The Paradox of Large Conductance and High Selectivity

Table 1 shows that most maxi-K channels possess both a large conductance, which is near the limit theoretically expected for a pore (29), and a high cation selectivity. This situation is paradoxical since a high selectivity implies strong interactions of the permeant ion with the selectivity filter (37). These channels have a selectivity sequence, as determined from bi-onic potentials, of $Tl^+ > K^+ > Rb^+ > NH_4 >> Cs^+$, Na^+, Li^+. The permeability ratio between Na^+ and K^+ is less than 0.01 (9, 12, 16, 20, 34, 68, 79; for an exception to this rule see 7). Thus, maxi-K channels are as selective as the delayed rectifier of nerve and muscle, but their conductance is 10- to 50-fold larger. Maxi-K channels can be considered part of the class of multi-ion pores based on the following observations: (a) increasing external K^+ relieves blockade by internal Na^+ by increasing the rate of Na^+ exit from the channel (80); (b) the channel shows "anomalous mole fraction behavior" (16); and (c) voltage-dependent Cs^+ blockade cannot be explained on the basis of a single-ion pore model (13). On the other hand, evidence is mounting that the channel entrances contain a fixed negative charge (31, 35, 41a, 75, A. Villarroel, G. Eisenman, personal communication). These findings [i.e. maxi-K channels are multi-ion channels, and they contain a fixed negative charge in their vestibules (see below)] help explain the mechanisms of ion conduction and account for the large conductance of maxi-K channels. Ion repulsion in the multiply-occupied pore at high permeant ion concentrations increases the rate of K^+ exit, and channel conductance becomes higher than in a single-ion pore (12, 34). At low ion concentration, conductance is high because the negative potential created by the charges concentrates cations at the channel vestibules (35, 75). A direct demonstration that negative charges are located in the channel conduction system of maxi-K channels has been given recently (41a). When channels are modified with trimethyloxonium (TMO), an agent that methylates carboxylic groups, the channel conductance vs KCl concentration curve is dramatically altered. After treatment with TMO, channel conductance is decreased (50% at 5 mM KCl), and the relative decrease is greater at low ionic strength (41a). This result is expected if there is a carboxylic group located at the channel entrance that is altering the local electrostatic potential.

Gross Architecture of Maxi-K Channels

TEA BLOCKADE   Latorre & Miller (37) proposed a structure consisting of two large vestibules connected by a short and narrow tunnel in which the rate limiting steps for ion conduction occur. The evidence for large vestibules comes from the findings that maxi-K channels are blocked by internal and external TEA at different sites (9, 74, 74b, 79). TEA blockade in both cases is weakly voltage dependent. The fact that an ion as large as TEA is able to enter the conduction system of the channel has been taken as evidence that the pore possesses wide entrances (e.g. 2). The internal TEA site or its neighborhood appears to be hydrophobic since potency of blockade is increased as the hydrocarbon chain length of the blocking compound is increased. The external site, on the other hand, is highly selective for TEA (74a). However, TEA blockade does not have the same characteristics in all maxi-K channels. Anterior pituitary cells possess the TEA-selective (low dissociation constant) site in the internal face of the channel (77) and the olfactory neuron maxi-K channel is insensitive to internal TEA (46). For details see Table 1.

STREAMING POTENTIALS   It is assumed that in the narrow tunnel that links the channel vestibules, ions and water cannot pass each other. If this is the case, an osmotic gradient across the channel will promote a streaming potential whose magnitude is related to the number of water molecules and ions constrained in the single filing region (40, 67). The streaming potentials for the skeletal and smooth muscle maxi-K channels incorporated into planar bilayers have been measured (1a). These measurements indicate that the narrow region contains at most four water molecules. Thus, the gross architecture of maxi-K channels as determined from blockade and streaming potential experiments resembles that of a hourglass. Large vestibules containing a fixed negative charge and a short tunnel connecting them are features that would help maxi-K channels to attain their very large conductance.

Gating, Ca^{2+} Sensitivity, and Selectivity of Ca^{2+}-Binding Sites

Gating kinetics of maxi-K channels requires the binding of several Ca^{2+} ions to fully open a channel (5, 42, 48, 52, 58). In the absence of other divalent cations, the Hill coefficients that best describe the probability of the open state vs [Ca^{2+}] curves vary between 2 and 4, which suggests that at least 2–4 calcium ions are required for channel opening (5, 52, 58, 78). However, in the presence of millimolar amounts of Mg^{2+} on the internal side, the Hill coefficients can increase up to 6 and an increase in the apparent affinity of the channel for Ca^{2+} is observed (21). Magnesium does not activate the channel in the absence of Ca^{2+}. In order to fully describe the kinetics in the absence of divalent cations other than Ca^{2+}, McMannus & Magleby (48) reported that six closed and three open states are required, but the results in the presence of Mg^{2+} indicate that the kinetic scheme is probably even more complex.

Maximal sensitivity to change in Ca^{2+} concentration varies widely in maxi-K channels from different types of cells (Table 1). Thus, it has been shown that membrane depolarization can elicit maxi-K channel openings in the virtual absence of Ca^{2+} in mammalian salivary glands (65). In these cells maximal sensitivity to changes in $[Ca^{2+}]$ falls in the range of 10^{-8}–10^{-7} M. By contrast, maximal activation in cultured rat muscle is obtained in the range of 10^{-6}–10^{-4} M $[Ca^{2+}]$ (5). In chromaffin cells and clonal anterior pituitary glands, channel openings at a $[Ca^{2+}]$ of 10^{-8} M can be seen at membrane potentials between -20 and -40 mV (43, 78). The type of lipid surrounding the protein-forming channel may control Ca^{2+} sensitivity. Negatively charged lipids increase the apparent Ca^{2+} sensitivity (57). Interestingly, Ca^{2+} sensitivity is related to cell development in spinal neurons. In young neurons, Ca^{2+} sensitivity is poor or absent, whereas in mature cells raising the $[Ca^{2+}]$ increases the probability of opening (8). This increase in calcium sensitivity is related to the disappearance of the Ca^{2+}-dependent plateau of the action potential in these cells.

Several divalent cations have been studied as agonists of maxi-K channels obtained from rat muscle membrane and incorporated into planar bilayers (61). In the virtual absence of Ca^{2+} in the internal side, the effectiveness of activating the channel is $Cd^{2+} > Sr^{2+} > Mn^{2+} > Fe^{2+} > Co^{2+}$. Cadmium is 100-fold less effective than Ca^{2+} in activating the channel. The ability to activate the channel seems to be based on cation size; only cations with radii greater than 0.072 nm (Co^{2+}) or less than 0.113 nm (Sr^{2+}) are able to activate the channel. Because of the number of divalent cations involved in channel activation and the divalent cation sequence for activation, the Ca^{2+}-binding sites of maxi-K channels resemble calcium-binding proteins such as calmodulin and troponin C. In the presence of Ca^{2+} some divalent cations potentiate Ca^{2+} activation of the skeletal muscle maxi-K channel (21, 61). Cd^{2+}, Mn^{2+}, Co^{2+}, and Ni^{2+} increase the Hill coefficient for the Ca^{2+} activation curve. In particular, Ni^{2+} has the same effect described by Golowash et al (21) for Mg^{2+}. Nickel is not a channel activator by itself, but potentiates the ability of Ca^{2+} to increase the probability of opening. This result suggests the existence of an internal modulatory site that controls channel activation.

A DIGRESSION ON Ca^{2+} AND Ba^{2+} BLOCKADE   Prolonged maxi-K channel closures have been detected in several different preparations (18, 52, 73, 78). Long closures of skeletal muscle maxi-K channels can be explained on the basis of a voltage-dependent binding of Ca^{2+} to the conduction system, which blocks the K$^+$ flux. Membrane depolarization enhances blockade (73). Although long closures can be detected only at [Ca^{2+}] > 10^{-4} M in muscle, the quiescent periods can be seen at [Ca^{2+}] < 10^{-6} M in pancreatic islet and parathyroid cells (18; G. Ehrenstein, personal communication). One important consequence of this behavior is that the probability of maxi-K channel opening can decrease as the [Ca^{2+}] is raised at a fixed potential or at moderate depolarizations at a fixed [Ca^{2+}]. The depolarization that occurs in parathyroid cells in high-calcium solutions can be accounted for by this behavior (G. Ehrenstein, personal communication). A decrease in the probability of opening as the [Ca^{2+}] is raised also substantiates the proposal that maxi-K channels provide a feedback control of Ca^{2+} uptake into islet cells (18). Maxi-K channels are also blocked by Ba^{2+} (6, 20, 26, 30, 73). When added to the intracellular side at a concentration larger than 10^{-7}M, Ba^{2+} induces long channel closures with mean times on the order of several seconds. The long-lived, nonconducting intervals represent the binding of a single Ba^{2+} to the open channel. More recently, evidence has been put forward that Ba^{2+} can be occluded within a closed channel (54, 55). Occluded Ba^{2+} cannot dissociate from the blocking site until after the channel opens. When the channel is in the closed configuration, the site is inaccessible to Ba^{2+} from both the internal and external solutions. These results suggest the existence of "gating regions" located on the internal and external sides of the pore.

Voltage Dependence

Maxi-K channels are voltage dependent. The probability of opening increases an e-fold per 11–15 mV in muscle cells in culture (5, 52), chromaffin cells (44), and skeletal muscle channels incorporated into bilayers (38, 58), per 9 mV in a pituitary cell line (77) and in smooth muscle (68), and per 10–30 mV in medullary thick ascending limb cells in culture (25). Thus, in maxi-K channels the number of apparent gating charges is well conserved. The maxi-K channel voltage dependence appears to be independent of [Ca^{2+}].

SK CHANNELS

SK channels are K(Ca) channels with conductances ≤ 80 pS in symmetrical 140 mM KCl although it appears that channel conductance is distributed continuously from SK to maxi-K channels. In cultured rat skeletal muscle, SK channels with conductances of 4 and 12 pS are found (10). Both channels are more sensitive to Ca^{2+} than the maxi-K channels coexisting in this preparation and thus can be activated by submicromolar concentrations of Ca^{2+}. Actually, by lowering the [Ca^{2+}] to appropriate values, SK channels can be studied in the absence of maxi-K channel activity. The 12-pS channel is essentially voltage independent, very selective for K^+, and not blocked by TEA. This SK channel has the necessary properties to account for afterhyperpolarization in myotubes (4, 70). The afterhyperpolarization in myotubes is blocked by a low molecular weight soluble factor from chick spinal cord. It is possible that this factor regulates the activity of the 12-pS SK channel in vivo (69). A SK channel with a conductance similar (9–14 pS) to that found in rat muscle in culture is found in clonal anterior pituitary cells. As in muscle, this channel is very sensitive to Ca^{2+}, but it is blocked by external TEA (33). *Aplysia* neurons possess a 35-pS channel (Na^+ present in the external solution) (28). The probability of the channel being open is 0.86 at 10^{-6} M Ca^{2+} at 0 mV and increases and e-fold per 44 mV depolarization. Channel activity is completely blocked by 2–5 mM external TEA (cf SK muscle channel). The *Aplysia* SK channel is probably involved in the termination of action potential bursts. SK channels from *Helix* neurons have been incorporated into bilayers made at the tip of patch-clamp pipettes. These channels have a conductance of 40–60 pS in 120 mM symmetrical KCl, which decreases to 20 pS when the external $[K^+]$ is reduced to 1 mM. This last value is similar to the one reported by Lux et al (41) for this channel in cell-attached patches. The probability of opening changes an e-fold per 21 mV change in voltage, and *Helix* SK channels are active when internal $[Ca^{2+}]$ is 10^{-8} M at 0 mV (17). In olfactory neurons, an 80-pS SK channel with voltage-insensitive kinetics is found (46). The probability of opening is 0.5 when the internal $[Ca^{2+}]$ is 10^{-6} M at 40 mV. The 130-pS maxi-K channel found in the same neurons is more sensitive to Ca^{2+} than the SK channel (cf muscle cells, 10). In red cells a SK channel with inward rectifying properties is present (22, 23). The slope conductance of this SK channel at large negative potentials is 40 pS. Furthermore, the channel of the red cell membrane displays single-file behavior, with a flux ratio exponent of about 2.7 (74a). Thus the SK channel in this preparation behaves as a multi-ion channel (see reference 16). The channel is not very voltage dependent and is very sensitive to Ca^{2+}. In summary, SK channels are in general very sensitive to Ca^{2+} and can be divided in two main classes (see Table 1): voltage-dependent (*Aplysia* and *Helix* neurons SK channels) and voltage-independent channels (GH$_3$, muscle, olfactory neurons, and erythrocyte SK channels).

PHARMACOLOGICAL PROFILE

Apamin, a bee venom toxin (27) and charybdotoxin (CTX), a toxin obtained from the venom of the scorpion *Leiurus quinquestriatus* (56), specifically block K(Ca) channels when added to the external medium. The long lasting hyperpolarization in rat muscle cells in culture is blocked by apamin at nanomolar concentrations (66). The 12-pS SK channel present in these cells is also blocked by this venom (10). To our knowledge, this is the only case in which the effect of apamin has been studied at the macroscopic and at the single-channel level. The GH$_3$ cell SK channel is also blocked by nanomolar concentrations of apamin (33). Apamin does not appear to block maxi-K channels. On the other hand, CTX blocks the maxi-K channel from skeletal muscle (56), from smooth muscle (R. Latorre, unpublished observations), and from 1003 EC cell line culture (39) at nanomolar concentrations. Inhibition of K(Ca) channel activity by CTX is not restricted to maxi-K channels. CTX blocks macroscopic K(Ca) currents and the 35-pS SK channel present in *Aplysia* neurons (28). In this preparation CTX has no effect on Na$^+$, Ca^{2+}, delayed rectifier K$^+$, or transient K$^+$ currents. CTX, but not apamin, blocks Ca^{2+}-activated K$^+$ fluxes in red blood cells probably by inhibiting the 40-pS SK channel (76a).

Treatment with *N*-bromoacetamide (NBA) renders the maxi-K channel present in rat skeletal muscle insensitive to internal Ca^{2+} (62), but the remaining channel activity has the same voltage dependence as before treatment with NBA. Distribution of open dwell times shows that NBA abolishes openings of long duration. The most simple explanation of these results is that the modification induced by NBA, a compound that cleaves peptide bonds on the COOH-terminal side of several amino acids, alters the Ca^{2+}-binding sites.

MODULATION OF K(Ca) CHANNELS

Extracellular signals are able to modulate the activity of some K(Ca) channels. Acetylcholine induces a sustained hyperpolarization mediated by a maxi-K channel in lacrimal acinar cells (see above; 72). Recently, Morris et al (59) showed that inositol triphosphate (InsP$_3$) promotes a transient increase in Ca^{2+}-activated K$^+$ current and that a sustained increase in this current is only obtained when InsP$_3$ and tetrakisphosphate (InsP$_4$) are present together in the internal medium of acinar cells of lacrimal glands. These results provide evidence that the messengers regulating Ca^{2+} entry in these cells and, therefore, K(Ca) channel activity are InsP$_3$ and InsP$_4$ acting together; these compounds probably are the messengers regulating K(Ca) currents in other exocrine glands as well. In cultured kidney cells, both forskolin and antidiuretic hormone (ADH) added to external medium increase the mean open time of maxi-K channels (24). Forskolin is an activator of the adenylate cyclase and ADH acts on kidney distal tubules through cAMP-mediated pathways. Therefore, in kidney cells maxi-K channels appear to be modulated via a cAMP-dependent process.

Modulation of the *Helix* SK channel by cAMP-dependent protein phosphorylation has been shown by Ewald et al (17). Application of the catalytic subunit of the protein kinase together with Mg^{2+} and ATP to the inner membrane surface at a fixed [Ca^{2+}] increased the probability of the channel opening both in cell-attached patches and in channels incorporated into bilayers made at the tip of patch-clamp pipettes.

CONCLUSIONS

The patch-clamp and reconstitution techniques have revealed the existence of a family of K$^+$ channels that are activated by intracellular calcium. The maxi-K channels are voltage dependent, highly potassium selective, and blocked by charybdotoxin. However, maxi-K channels have different sensitivities to calcium and TEA in different cells. Small conductance K(Ca) channels, on the other hand, can be divided in several classes: voltage-dependent or voltage-insensitive, apamin-sensitive, or charybdotoxin-sensitive. More studies are necessary to obtain a more detailed characterization of these channels.

ACKNOWLEDGMENTS

The preparation of this manuscript was supported by the Fondo Nacional de Investigacion, Grants 0483–1987 and 0451–1988 NIH Grant GM-35981, and by a Grant from the Tinker Foundation.

Literature Cited

1. Adams, P. R., Constanti, A., Brown, D. A., Clark, R. B. 1982. Intracellular Ca^{2+} activates a fast voltage-sensitive K$^+$ current in vertebrate sympathetic neurones. *Nature* 246:746–49
1a. Alcaya, C., Cecchi, X., Alvarez, O., Latorre, R. 1989. Streaming potential measurements in Ca^{2+}-activated K$^+$ channels from skeletal and smooth muscle: Coupling of ion and water fluxes. *Biophys. J.* In press
2. Armstrong, C. M. 1975. Ionic pores, gates, and gating currents. *Q. Rev. Biophys.* 1:179–210
3. Atwater, I., Dawson, C. M., Ribalet, B., Rojas, E. 1979. Potassium permeability activated by intracellular calcium ion concentration in the pancreatic B-cell. *J. Physiol. London* 288:575–88
4. Barret, J. N., Barret, E. F., Dribin, L. B. 1981. Calcium-dependent slow potassium conductance in rat skeletal myotubes. *Dev. Biol.* 82:258–66
5. Barret, J. N., Magleby, K. L., Pallota, B. S. 1982. Properties of single calcium-activated potassium channels in cultured rat muscle. *J. Physiol. London* 331:211–30
6. Benham, C. D., Bolton, T. B., Lang, K. J., Takewaki, T. 1985. The mechanisms of action of Ba^{2+} and TEA on single Ca^{2+}-activated K$^+$ channels in arterial and intestinal smooth muscle cell membrane. *Pflügers Arch.* 403:120–27
7. Berger, W., Grygorcyk, R., Schwarz, W. 1984. Single K$^+$ channels in membrane evaginations of smooth muscle cells. *Pflügers Arch.* 402:18–23
8. Blair, L. A., Dionne, V. E. 1985. Developmental acquisition of Ca^{2+}-sensitivity by K$^+$ channels in spinal neurons. *Nature* 315:329–31
9. Blatz, A. L., Magleby, K. L. 1984. Ion conductance and selectivity of single calcium-activated potassium channels in cultured rat muscle. *J. Gen. Physiol.* 84:1–23
10. Blatz, A. L., Magleby, K. L. 1986. Single apamin-blocked Ca-activated K$^+$ channels of small conductance in cultured rat skeletal muscle. *Nature* 323:718–20
11. Blatz, A. L., Magleby, K. L. 1987. Calcium-activated potassium channels. *Trends Neurosci.* 10:463–67
12. Cecchi, X., Alvarez, O., Wolff, D. 1986. Characterization of a calcium-activated potassium channel from rabbit

intestinal smooth muscle incorporated into planar bilayers. *J. Membr. Biol.* 91:11–18

13. Cecchi, X., Wolff, D., Alvarez, O., Latorre, R. 1987. Mechanism of Cs$^+$ blockade in a Ca^{2+}-activated K$^+$ channel from smooth muscle. *Biophys. J.* 52:707–16

14. Christensen, C., Zeuthen, T. 1987. Maxi K$^+$ channels in leaky epithelia are regulated by intracellular Ca^{2+}, pH and membrane potential. *Pflügers Arch.* 408:249–59

15. Cook, D. L., Ikeuchi, M., Fuyimoto, D. W. 1984. Lowering of pH inhibits Ca^{2+}-activated K$^+$ channels in pancreatic β-cells. *Nature* 311:269–71

16. Eisenman, G., Latorre, R., Miller, C. 1986. Multi-ion conductance and selectivity in the high conductance Ca^{++}-activated K$^+$ channel from skeletal muscle. *Biophys. J.* 50:1025–34

17. Ewald, D. A., Williams, A., Levitan, I. B. 1985. Modulation of single Ca^{2+}-dependent K$^+$ channel activity by protein phosphorylation. *Nature* 315:503–6

18. Findlay, I. M., Dunne, M. J., Petersen, O. H. 1985. High conductance K$^+$ channel in pancreatic islet cells can be activated and inactivated by internal calcium. *J. Membr. Biol.* 83:169–75

19. Gardos, G. 1958. The function of calcium in the potassium permeability of human erythrocytes. *Biochim Biophys. Acta* 30:653–54

20. Gitter, A. H., Beyenbach, K. W., Chadwick, C. W., Gross, P., Minuth, W. W., Fromter, E. 1987. High-conductance K$^+$ channels in apical membranes of principal cells cultured from rabbit renal cortical collecting duct anlagen. *Pflügers Arch.* 408:282–90

21. Golowash, J., Kirwood, A., Miller, C. 1986. Allosteric effects of Mg^{2+} on the gating of Ca^{2+}-activated K$^+$ channels from mammalian skeletal muscle. *J. Exp. Biol.* 124:5–13

22. Grygorzyk, R., Schwarz, W. 1983. Properties of the Ca^{2+}-activated K$^+$ conductance of human red cells as revealed by the patch-clamp technique. *Cell Calcium* 4:499–510

23. Grygorzyk, R., Schwarz, W., Passow, H. 1984. Ca^{2+}-activated K$^+$ channels in human red cells. *Biophys. J.* 45:693–98

24. Guggino, S. 1986. Channels in kidney epithelial cells. In *Ionic Channels in Cells and Model Systems*, ed. R. Latorre, pp. 207–20. New York: Plenum. 437 pp.

25. Guggino, S. E., Guggino, W. B., Green, N., Sacktor, B. 1987. Ca^{2+}-activated K$^+$ channels in cultured medullary thick ascending limb cells. *Am. J. Physiol.* 252:C121–27

26. Guggino, S. E., Guggino, W. B., Green, N., Sacktor, B. 1987. Blocking agents of Ca^{2+}-activated K$^+$ channels in cultured medullary thick ascending limb cells. *Am. J. Physiol.* 252:C128–37

27. Habermann, E. 1972. Bee and wasp venoms. *Science* 177:314–22

28. Hermann, A., Erxleben, C. 1987. Charybdotoxin selectively blocks small Ca-activated K channels in *Aplysia* Neurons. *J. Gen. Physiol.* 90:27–47

29. Hille, B. 1984. *Ionic Channels of Excitable Membranes.* pp. 184–88. Suderland, Mass: Sinauer. 427 pp.

30. Hunter, M., Lopes, A. G., Boulpaep, E. L., Giebish, G. H. 1984. Single channel recordings of single Ca^{2+}-activated K$^+$ channels in the apical membrane of cortical collecting tubules. *Proc. Natl. Acad. Sci. USA* 81:4237–39

31. Jordan, P. C. 1987. How pore mouth charge distribution alter the permeability of transmembrane ionic channels. *Biophys. J.* 51:297–311

32. Krueger, B. K., French, R. J., Blaustein, M. B., Worley, F. J. 1982. Incorporation of Ca^{2+}-activated K$^+$ channels, from rat brain, into planar bilayers. *Biophys. J.* 37:170a

33. Lang, D. G., Ritchie, A. K. 1988. Pharmacological sensitivities of large and small conductance Ca^{2+}-activated K$^+$ channels. *Biophys. J.* 53:144a

34. Latorre, R. 1986. The large calcium-activated potassium channel. In *Ion Channel Reconstitution*, ed. C. Miller, pp. 431–67. New York: Plenum. 577 pp.

35. Latorre, R., Alvarez, O. 1988. Ion conduction in ion channels: Some inferences about their gross structure. *Commun. Cell Mol. Biophys.* In press

36. Latorre, R., Coronado, C., Vergara, C. 1984. K$^+$ channels gated by voltage and ions. *Annu. Rev. Physiol.* 46:485–95

37. Latorre, R., Miller, C. 1983. Conduction and selectivity in potassium channels. *J. Membr. Biol.* 71:11–30

38. Latorre, R., Vergara, C., Hidalgo, C. 1982. Reconstitution in planar lipid bilayers of a Ca^{2+}-dependent K$^+$ channel from transverse tubule membranes isolated from rabbit skeletal muscle. *Proc. Natl. Acad. Sci. USA* 77:7484–86

39. Leveneu, E., Simonneau, M. 1986. Scorpion venom inhibits selectively Ca^{2+}-activated K$^+$ channels in situ. *FEBS Lett.* 209:165–68

40. Levitt, D. G., Elias, S. R., Hautman, J. M. 1978. Number of water molecules coupled to the transport of sodium,

potassium, and hydrogen ions via grami-cidin, nonactin or valinomycin. *Biochim. Biophys. Acta* 512:436–51

41. Lux, H. D., Neher, E., Marty, A. 1981. Single-channel activity associated with calcium dependent outward current in *Helix pomatia. Pfluegers Arch.* 389: 293–95

41a. MacKinnon, R., Miller, C. 1988. Trimethyloxonium modification of the high conductance Ca^{2+}-activated K^+ channel. *Biophys. J.* 53:260a

42. Magleby, K. L., Pallota, B. 1983. Calcium dependence of open and shut interval distributions from calcium-activated potassium channels in cultured rat muscle. *J. Physiol. London* 344:585–604

43. Marty, A. 1981. Ca-dependent potassium channel with large unitary conductance in chromaffin cell membranes. *Nature* 291:497–500

44. Marty, A. 1983. Ca^{2+}-dependent K channels with large unitary conductance. *Trends Neurosci.* 6:262–65

45. Maruyama, Y., Gallagher, D. V., Peterson, O. H. 1983. Voltage and calcium-activated potassium channels in basolateral acinar cell membranes of mammalian salivary glands. *Nature* 302:827–29

46. Maue, R. A., Dionne, V. E. 1987. Patch-clamp studies of isolated mouse olfactory receptor neurons. *J. Gen. Physiol.* 90:95–125

47. Deleted in proof

48. McMannus, O. B., Magleby, K. L. 1985. The large conductance calcium-activated potassium channel in cultured rat muscle has at least three open states of similar conductance and six shut states. *Biophys. J.* 47:37a

49. Meech, R. W. 1972. Intracellular calcium injection causes increased potassium conductance in *Aplysia* nerve cells. *Comp. Biochem. Physiol.* 42A:493

50. Meech, R. W. 1978. Calcium-dependent potassium activation in nervous tissues. *Annu. Rev. Biophys. Bioeng.* 7:1–18

51. Meech, R. W., Strumwasser, F. 1970. Intracellular calcium injection activates potassium conductance in *Aplysia* nerve cells. *Fed. Proc.* 29:834a

52. Methfessel, C., Boheim, G. 1982. The gating of single calcium-dependent potassium channels is described by an activation/blockade mechanism. *Biophys. Struc. Mech.* 9:35–60

53. Miller, C., ed. 1986. *Ion Channel Reconstitution.* New York: Plenum. 577 pp.

54. Miller, C. 1987. Trapping single ions inside single ion channels. *Biophys. J.* 52:123–26

55. Miller, C., Latorre, R., Reisin, I. 1987. Coupling of voltage-dependent gating and Ba^{++} block in the high conductance Ca^{++}-activated K^+ channel. *J. Gen. Physiol.* 90:427–49

56. Miller, C., Moczydlowski, E., Latorre, R., Phillips, M. 1985. Charibdotoxin, a protein inhibitor of Ca^{2+}-activated K^+ channels from mammalian skeletal muscle. *Nature* 313:316–18

57. Moczydlowski, E., Alvarez, O., Vergara, C., Latorre, R. 1985. Effect of phospholipid surface charge on the conductance and gating of a Ca^{2+}-activated K^+ channel in planar lipid bilayers. *J. Membr. Biol.* 83:273–82

58. Moczydlowski, E., Latorre, R. 1983. Gating kinetics of Ca^{2+}-activated K^+ channels from rat muscle incorporated into planar lipid bilayer: Evidence for two voltage-dependent Ca^{2+} binding reactions. *J. Gen. Physiol.* 82:511–42

59. Morris, A. P., Gallacher, D. V., Irvine, R. F., Petersen, O. H. 1987. Synergism of inositol trisphosphate and tetrakisphosphate in activating Ca^{2+}-dependent K^+ channels. *Nature* 330:653–55

60. Neher, E., Sakmann, B., eds. 1983. *Single-channel Recording.* New York: Plenum. 503 pp.

61. Oberhauser, A., Alvarez, O., Latorre, R. 1988. Activation by divalent cations of a Ca^{2+}-activated K^+ channel from skeletal muscle membrane. *J. Gen. Physiol.* 92:67–86

62. Pallota, B. 1985. *N*-bromoacetamide removes a calcium-dependent component of channel opening from calcium-activated potassium channels in rat skeletal muscle. *J. Gen. Physiol.* 86: 601–11

63. Pallota, B. S., Magleby, K. L., Barret, J. N. 1981. Single channel recordings of Ca^{2+}-activated K^+ currents in rat muscle cell culture. *Nature* 293:471–74

64. Petersen, O. H., Findlay, I. 1987. Electrophysiology of the pancreas. *Physiol. Rev.* 67:1054–1116

65. Petersen, O. H., Maruyama, Y. 1984. Calcium-activated potassium channels and their role in secretion. *Nature* 307:693–96

66. Romey, G., Lazdunski, M. 1984. The coexistence in rat muscle cells of two distinct classes of Ca^{2+}-dependent K^+ channels with different pharmacological properties and different physiological functions. *Biochem. Biophys. Res. Commun.* 118:669–74

67. Rosenberg, P. A., Finkelstein, A. 1978. Interactions of ions and water in grami-

cidin A channels. Streaming potentials across lipid bilayers membranes. *J. Gen. Physiol.* 72:327–40

68. Singer, J. J., Walsh, J. V. 1987. Characterization of calcium-activated potassium channels in single smooth muscle cells using the patch-clamp technique. *Pfluegers Arch.* 408:98–111

69. Suarez-Isla, B. A., Cosgrove, J. A., Thompson, J. M., Rapoport, S. I. 1986. A soluble factor (<4000 Da) from chick spinal cord blocks slow hyperpolarizing afterpotentials in culture rat muscle cells. *Dev. Brain Res.* 30(2):274–77

70. Suarez-Isla, B. A., Rapaport, S. I. 1986. Neurotrophic effects of *in vitro* innervation of cultured muscle cells. Modulation of Ca^{2+}-activated K$^+$ conductances. See Ref. 24, pp. 363–82

71. Susuki, K. C., Petersen, C. H., Petersen, O. H. 1985. Hormonal activation of single K$^+$ channels via internal messenger in isolated pancreatic acinar cells. *FEBS Lett.* 192:307–12

72. Trautman, A., Marty, A. 1984. Activation of Ca-dependent K channels by carbamoylcholine in rat lacrimal glands. *Proc. Natl. Acad. Sci. USA* 81:611–15

73. Vergara, C., Latorre, R. 1983. Kinetics of Ca^{2+}-activated K$^+$ channels from rabbit muscle incorporated into planar bilayers: Evidence for a Ca^{2+} and Ba^{2+} blockade. *J. Gen. Physiol.* 82:543–68

74. Vergara, C., Moczydlowski, E., Latorre, R. 1984. Conduction, blockade, and gating in a Ca^{2+}-activated K$^+$ channel incorporated into planar bilayers. *Biophys. J.* 45:73–76

74a. Vestergaard-Bogind, B., Stampe, P., Christophersen, P. 1985. Single-file dif-

fusion through the Ca^{2+}-activated K$^+$ channel of human red cells. *J. Membr. Biol.* 88:67–75

74b. Villarroel, A., Alvarez, O., Oberhauser, A., Latorre, R. 1988. Probing a Ca^{2+}-activated K$^+$ channel with quaternary ammonium ions. *Pflügers. Arch.* In press

75. Villarroel, A., Eisenman, G. 1987. Surface charge in a barrier model can explain the low concentration I-V behavior of the Ca^{++}-activated K$^+$ channel. *Biophys. J.* 51:546a

76. Walsh, J. V., Singer, J. J. 1983. Ca^{++}-activated K$^+$ channels in vertebrate smooth muscle cells. *Cell Calcium* 4:321–30

76a. Wolff, D., Cecchi, X., Spalvins, A., Canessa, M. 1988. Charybdotoxin blocks with high affinity the Ca ion activated K$^+$ channel of Hb A and Hb S red cells. Individual differences in the number of channels. *J. Membr. Biol.* In press

77. Wong, B. S., Adler, M. 1986. Tetraethylammonium blockade of calcium-activated potassium channels in clonal anterior pituitary cells. *Plügers Arch.* 407:279–84

78. Wong, B. S., Lecar, H., Adler, M. 1982. Single calcium-dependent potassium channels in clonal anterior pituitary cells. *Biophys. J.* 39:313–17

79. Yellen, G. 1984. Ionic permeation and blockade in Ca^{2+}-activated K$^+$ channels of bovine chromaffin cells. *J. Gen. Physiol.* 84:157–86

80. Yellen, G. 1984. Relief of Na$^+$ block of Ca^{2+}-activated K$^+$ channels by external cations. *J. Gen. Physiol.* 84:187–99

Annu. Rev. Physiol. 1989. 51:401–18

MOLECULAR DIVERSITY OF VOLTAGE-SENSITIVE Na CHANNELS

James S. Trimmer and William S. Agnew

Department of Cellular and Molecular Physiology, Yale University School of Medicine, 333 Cedar Street, New Haven, Connecticut 06510

INTRODUCTION

In a wide variety of electrically excitable cells, voltage-sensitive Na channels are responsible for propagation of the action potential. They conduct the inward depolarizing Na^+ currents and are regulated by steeply voltage-dependent gating mechanisms. Their biophysical behavior, pharmacology and, more recently, biochemical properties have been intensively studied. However, it is primarily because of direct structural information derived from molecular cloning studies that our attention has been drawn to an unexpected molecular diversity among Na channels, both between different species and within a single organism.

This brief review emphasizes new findings on variations in Na channel structure derived from molecular biological data. Considered in light of structural models, each variant represents, in effect, a naturally occurring mutation, providing clues about what may be essential and nonessential for channel function. We discuss implications of "divergence" of channels from different species and "diversity" of channels within a species. While some pharmacological and biochemical findings are presented, these topics are more comprehensively reviewed elsewhere (1, 6, 12, 13, 25, 71).

MOLECULAR ORGANIZATION

Na channel proteins have been purified from several tissues, including eel electroplax (3, 4, 53), mammalian skeletal muscle (7, 43), and brain (36, 37,

401

0066-4278/89/0315-0401$02.00

52) and avian heart (47). In each case the proteins comprise a large gly-copeptide-subunit (M_r = 260–295 kilo daltons). The proteins from brain include, in addition to the large (α) subunit, two small glycopeptides (β1 and β2) of 33 and 36 kilo daltons, the peptide portions of which are 20–21,000 daltons. Mammalian muscle proteins also contain one or two small peptides (89). Evidence from the reconstitution of the single peptide electroplax Na channel (18, 74, 75, 91) and expression of mRNAs transcribed in vitro from cDNA templates encoding the brain α-subunits (26, 59, 87) indicate that, in general, the essential channel biophysical and pharmacological properties are attributable to the large peptides.

Our first insights into the possible conformation adopted by the large subunits were provided in 1984 by Noda et al (60), who reported the isolation and sequencing of cDNA clones encoding the electroplax peptide. The pre-dicted amino acid sequence includes 1820 amino acids, corresponding to calculated M_r = 208,321 daltons. The sequence reveals four internally homologous repeats, termed I–IV (or A–D) of about 30,000 daltons (approx-imately 285, 229, 268, and 250 amino acids, respectively). (Domains I, II, III, and IV also contain small nonconserved loops of 189, 20, 43, and 34 amino acids). The first homology domain begins about 120 residues from the amino terminus, with intervening sequences of 159, 206, and 53 amino acids between successive domains, the last followed by a 250-residue carboxyl tail. These extradomain sequences are hydrophilic, and unlikely to span the bilayer. Within each domain, however, a stereotypic pattern of six relatively hydrophobic segments was found, which theoretical models predict may form up to eight membrane-spanning or membrane-penetrating α-helices (28, 32, 33, 42). This is consistent with several models that propose that the protein penetrates the membranes only within the repeats and that the large ex-tradomain sequences are cytoplasmic. In these models about 50% of the protein mass should lie on the cytoplasmic side of the membrane, perhaps 35% within the membrane, while 10–15% should be exposed to the exterior.

There is one especially important deviation in this pattern evident in all of the α-subunits cloned from mammalian brain (41, 58). These peptides contain an additional sequence of ~200 amino acids located between repeats I and II. This segment is hydrophilic and contains six or more consensus sites for phosphorylation by protein kinases A and C (76). This may form a cytoplas-mic lobe involved in neuromodulation. (See also Figure 2).

The large peptides of all characterized Na channels are heavily glycosyl-ated. The electroplax sequence includes ten consensus sequences for N-glycosylation; nine of these are located in the homologous repeats (60). Because theoretical models suggest that the repeats penetrate the membrane, many of these consensus sequences may be exposed to the extracellular surface. The purified electroplax protein contains approximately 85,000 dal-tons of carbohydrate (53). Deglycosylation experiments suggest that much of this is N-linked oligosaccharide, coupled by one or two armed cores to asparagine residues (38). Of these, one set is of simple or hybrid sugars, not containing sialic acid. Another set bears extended polymers of α-2,8-linked polysialic acid. Detected enzymatically and immunochemically (W. M. James & W. S. Agnew, unpublished) these may carry 20 to 40 tandem sialic acids (a total of 110–130 residues), probably extending 100–200 Å from the surface of the protein, well into the extracellular environment. It is apparent that, even within these large oligosaccharide chains, the average number of carbohydrate units per N-linked site is quite high. Thus, it is possible that the contributions of O-linked oligosaccharides to the overall carbohydrate content may be substantial.

The carbohydrate compositions of brain and muscle α-subunits have been reported (30, 51, 72), but the oligosaccharide linkages have not. However, the brain protein does not appear to contain α-2,8-polysialic acid, despite having a large sialic acid component (W. M. James & W. S. Agnew, unpublished). Despite having a somewhat lower degree of glycosylation, the brain and muscle proteins have 16–21 consensus sites for N-glycosylation (41, 58, 92).

Thus, the hypothetical structure of the large subunits is of a continuous peptide folded into four membrane-penetrating pseudo-subunit domains, which may be organized as a tetrameric rosette. The brain proteins exhibit an additional cytoplasmic domain accessible to protein kinases in the cell. Also, in the molecules from brain, the organization of two heavily glycosylated, hydrophobic β-subunits, one of which ($\beta2$) is linked covalently via disulfide bridges to the α-subunit (36, 37, 52), is uncertain.

This organization suggests that the pseudo-subunits should form the ionic pathway, the ion selectivity mechanism, sites for binding of certain (extracellular) neurotoxins and anesthetics, as well as the voltage-sensing elements which must lie in the transmembrane field. Domains involved in weakly voltage-dependent inactivation gating might be exposed to the cell interior.

One intriguing feature of the amino acid sequence is the presence within each pseudo-subunit of segments that may contribute to the voltage sensors. In these segments, designated S-4 by Noda and coworkers (60), every third amino acid is a positively charged lysine or arginine, separated by strongly hydrophobic residues. This pattern of X,X,lys/arg is repeated four times in domain I, five each in II and III, and eight times in IV. Models suggest that these sequences form α-helices with a spiral of charge oriented approximately normal to the membrane (28, 32, 33). In addition to these, a series of negatively charged amino acids, in segments termed S-7, is also present in each repeat. It has been proposed that these negative charges help neutralize the positively charged S-4 domains, and that the two segments move relative to one another during depolarization to produce the net charge displacement associated with gating. Interestingly, just as S-4 of domain IV is quite large, the corresponding S-7 is also large and may adopt a conformation different from those in domains I–III. Conceivably, the differences in the S-4 and S-7 length in different domains may underlie the observation that transitions between different closed resting states involve movement of different amounts of charge (10).

Cloned cDNAs of Homologous Large Peptide Subunits

While cloning of the variable small peptides has not yet been reported, cDNA and genomic sequences encoding several species of large subunit have been described. Following the account of the eel electroplax cDNA, Noda and coworkers identified four distinct Na channel cDNAs from mammalian brain (58). The only difference between two of these (types 1 and 1a) was an extra segment of 33 amino acids in the latter: this small difference could be a cloning artifact. This report gave the coding sequences for brain channels type 1, 1a, and 2, followed subsequently (41) by that for type 3.

Interestingly, Northern blots of skeletal muscle mRNA probed with brain cDNAs yielded minimal hybridization (58). Cooperman et al (17) sub-sequently demonstrated hybridization to a 9.5-kB mRNA species from muscle that was shown to be neither type 1 nor 2. Recently, cDNAs coding for the large peptide have been isolated from a denervated rat skeletal muscle library (92). Sequence analysis of these cDNAs shows that these muscle clones have strong homology with the rat brain species, but represent yet another gene. Partial clones have also been isolated for a rat cardiac Na channel peptide, again representing a distinct gene (84).

In addition to these vertebrate clones, cDNA and genomic sequences, which contain both coding and noncoding regions of portions of two in-vertebrate Na channel genes, have been obtained from the fruit fly *Drosophila melanogaster* (63, 77, 78). Although in neither case has the complete open reading frame been sequenced, the available information provides important comparisons with vertebrate sequences. In situ hybridization studies have localized the two genes on separate chromosomes; surprisingly, the location of these genes does not correspond to known *Drosophila* Na channel mutants, such as *nap, sei,* and *para* (34). It thus appears that Na channel expression, at least in the fly, may be controlled by genes located on a number of different chromosomes.

Homologies and Differences

In general, the amino acid sequences deduced for all of the Na channel peptides so far examined are quite similar. There are variations, however, that provide some constraints on conformational models and the mechanisms of channel function, as well as some insights into possible physiological roles of the Na channel isotypes. Here, we have distinguished between variations that result from divergence and those that reflect diversity. Despite some imprecision in these terms, the distinction may be especially important.

Clearly, differences between Na channels from evolutionarily distant species may arise from accumulation of mutations. These may have no mechanistic consequences, or may be neutralized by compensatory changes elsewhere in the molecule, or may underlie special adaptations unique to a species. Such divergence is an unsurprising consequence of both selection and genetic drift. Other variations, however, may arise because of different functional requirements within particular cell types within a single organism. In mammals, for example, Na channels are evident in central nervous system neurons, glia, peripheral neurons, Schwann cells, skeletal muscle, cardiac myocytes, exocrine cells, and even lymphocytes. The emerging rule is that different tissues and different cell types within a tissue, may express one or more distinct Na channel genes. This represents diversity among members of a Na channel gene family of a single organism, and probably reflects functional specializations not presently understood.

In general, the amino acid sequences of Na channel peptides are highly conserved, most strongly between proteins from the same species, and less strongly between those from different species. Interestingly, the homologies are not uniformly distributed throughout the sequences. Some segments are rigidly conserved, while others have little or no similarity. This raises the question as to what these patterns of homology can tell us about regions of the protein involved in mechanisms of Na channel functions.

To identify strongly and weakly conserved regions, a simple homology density plot can be used (S. Shenkel, H. A. Affolter & W. S. Agnew, unpublished). This plot attempts to avoid errors that may arise when comparing the percent homology of peptide segments of different length. It involves pre-aligning two sequences to be compared, with gaps inserted to maximize similarity. Beginning with a window of 10 amino acids (Figure 1), the fraction of identical and conservatively substituted amino acids within the window is computed. This value is plotted over the first amino acid in the window, the window shifts by one residue, and the process is repeated.

This type of analysis reveals that overall homology between rat brain sequences, such as 1 and 2 in Figure 1, is far closer than between sequences from different species (illustrated by rat brain 2 vs electroplax). With one qualification, the rat muscle sequence is more similar to those from rat brain than to that from electroplax (which is developmentally derived from muscle). The dramatic exception is that both skeletal muscle (92) and electroplax (60) sequences lack the insert between domains I and II that is found in all three (four) brain clones (41, 58). This further suggests that this domain is not mechanistically essential but may be associated with a specialized function, such as neuromodulation or topographical localization.

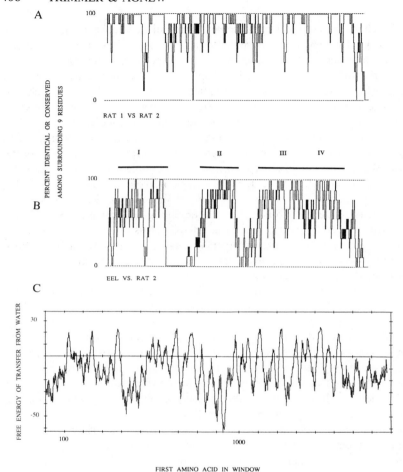

Figure 1 (A) Homology plot comparing amino acid sequences from rat brain 1 and 2. After aligning two sequences, with gaps inserted to allow alignment, the number of identical or conservatively substituted amino acids is computed for a moving window of 10 amino acids. The numerical value for percent homology is plotted above the consensus amino acid number, and the window is moved one amino acid to the right and the process is repeated. The insertion of gaps to produced optimal alignment is indicated by bars above *(r1)* or below *(r2)*. (Analyses by S. Shenkel & H. Affolter). (B) Homology plot for rat brain sequence 2 with that for electroplax. (C) Hydrophobicity plot for eel electroplax sequence, according to Engelman, Steitz, & Goldman (22). Moving window of nine amino acids reveals repeat pattern of hydrophobic sequences within the repeat domains. A larger window of 19 more reliably predicts membrane-spanning domains, but partially obscures the repetitive pattern seen here.

A more careful examination of the homology density plot for brain versus electroplax sequences, reveals a pattern reminiscent of hydrophobicity plots (22, 44) of eel electroplax Na channel (Figure 1). Thus, regions within the pseudo-subunit domains that contain the potentially membrane-spanning hydrophobic segments are highly conserved, often more than 85%. In contrast, the amino and carboxyl tails and segments intervening between domains I–II and II–III are poorly conserved. The short hydrophilic sequence between III–IV is, however, perfectly conserved; this might reflect a close packing of these latter domains in relation to one another. This general pattern of areas of high homology is also evident in comparisons between the closely similar brain proteins and between rat brain and rat muscle proteins, although the deviations are much less pronounced. This is consistent with the notion that the pseudo-subunit domains encompass the mechanistically essential parts of the protein, including those segments involved in ion selective permeation and gating. This is underscored by the observation that the S-4 and S-7 segments are virtually perfectly conserved. Strikingly, these segments are very highly conserved even in the predicted amino acid sequences from partial clones from *Drosophila,* despite separation of invertebrates from vertebrates by about 600,000,000 years of evolution (63, 77, 78).

The homology between corresponding pseudo-subunit domains in different peptides is greater than between pseudo-subunits in a single peptide. This suggests that each pseudo-subunit may play a specialized role in heterotropic cooperative mechanisms for conformational change, and that packing between elements, α-helices within a pseudo-subunit, or at interfaces between domains may not tolerate change. These regions, which likely control conductance, selectivity, and activation gating, may be readily studied by site-directed mutagenesis. For chemical modification studies, the most accessible regions may be on the cytoplasmic surface of the protein. The only function implicated in such studies to date has been inactivation gating (10, 16).

Comparison of consensus sites for glycosylation among electroplax, brain, and skeletal muscle proteins raises an important question for the conformational models that have been advanced (28, 32, 33). Figure 2 illustrates schematically the distribution of these sites for rat brain types 1–3 and electroplax. Interestingly, the small nonconserved loops located in domains I and III appear as though they might serve as pedestals for oligosaccharides extending from the molecule. What stands out clearly, however, is that the hydrophilic segments between I–II and II–III and the carboxyl tail of the protein are abundantly decorated with potential glycosylation sites, despite predictions that these segments will be intracellular (27). Further, one loop, between S4 and S5 in domain II, contains a site conserved in all four peptides, again though theoretical models predict this to be intracellular. Determining

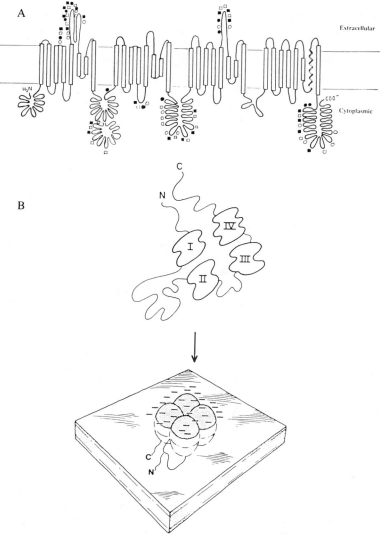

Figure 2 (A) Schematic of alpha-subunit domain structure, adopting the convention of Guy and coworkers (32, 33). Consensus glycosylation sites are indicated by closed circles (eel), open circles (rat 3), closed squares (rat 2) and open squares (rat 1). Note clustering on nonconserved loop in domains I and III, and on interdomains I–II, II–III, and the carboxyl tail. Additional sequence present only in rat brain peptide, between domains I and II contains multiple sites. (B) Schematic of notion of how four domains may form a bracelet structure with tetrameric pseudosymmetry. Note that no evidence is available as to rotational organization of domains.

which of these sites are glycosylated in vivo should provide a test of the conformational models.

THE Na CHANNEL GENE FAMILY

It has long been known that there were variations in the pharmacological and biophysical properties of Na channels from different tissues, from cells in different stages of development, and even in subcellular locations in the same cell. However, it is unclear whether in every case such variations reflect different molecules, or the effects of microenvironment, modulation, or posttranslational modification.

The information afforded by cDNA sequences such as those discussed demonstrates that different Na channel genes are expressed in the same organism. This is proven in the case of the rat and may also be true in *Drosophila*.

The observation that rat brain α-subunits are structurally distinguishable from muscle-type (skeletal muscle and electroplax) channels by the presence of a large additional subunit domain suggests that Na channel isotypes may fall into meaningful structural categories. Furthermore, our first glimpses of the structures of other voltage regulated ion channels, or channel-like proteins, suggest that such proteins may fall into a superfamily. Thus, cDNAs encoding the α_1-dihydropyridine-binding peptide of the four-peptide dihydropyridine receptor complex from rabbit skeletal muscle transverse tubules have been cloned (88). This molecule has been implicated as both an L-type Ca channel and the voltage sensor for excitation-contraction coupling (2, 87a). The predicted 212,000-dalton peptide is organized into four internally similar pseudo-subunits markedly homologous to those in Na channels ($\approx 60\%$ identical or conservatively substituted amino acids), with the same pattern of six hydrophobic segments including pronounced S-4 and S-7 like sequences. This molecule is clearly evolutionarily related to the Na channel large subunits and may represent only one of several Ca channel families (50).

In a markedly different superfamily member, at least 12 cDNAs derived from the *Shaker* locus of *Drosophila*, encoding voltage-activated, inactivating potassium A channels have been cloned and sequenced and found to predict small ($\approx 70,000$-dalton) peptides (8, 39, 64, 80). While the hydrophilic amino and carboxyl termini of these peptides vary, derived by alternative splicing from different sets of three and two exons, respectively, a central membrane-spanning region (from eight exons) is identical in all cases. This domain is closely similar to the Na channel pseudo-subunits, with the stereotypic hydrophobicity profile, complete with S-4 segments having seven repeats of the X,X,lys/arg pattern. It is expected that these peptides may form homo-oligomeric (and possibly hetero-oligomeric) assemblies, perhaps broadly resembling the structure postulated for the Na channels. Homologous cDNAs have been cloned from mouse (90) and rat brain (7a; L. Kaczmarek, in preparation). This distinctive class of potassium A channels clearly represents a variation on a common structural motif.

The extent and physiological significance of Na channel diversity is not yet clear. However, marked variations in pharmacology and unusual tissue distributions may provide clues as to where other distinctive Na channel isotypes may be discovered.

Channels that are TTX and STX Sensitive and Resistant

At least six distinct classes of Na channel neurotoxins have been designated on the basis of competitive binding studies (6, 12, 13). Neurotoxins that exhibit simple competition with one another have been assigned to the same class, although this does not establish that members of a class necessarily bind to the same site: either steric or conformational interference can produce competition. A great deal of evidence has accumulated demonstrating that one such group of mutually competitive neurotoxins, including TTX, STX, and their congeners, can distinguish between Na channels in cells at different stages of development and from different tissues.

TTX and STX are perhaps the most specific of Na channel neurotoxins (25, 40, 71, 79). In most cases binding is rapidly reversible (seconds or minutes) and of high affinity (equilibrium dissociation constant $K_d = 1–10$ nM) to a single, extracellular site on the molecule. The resulting inhibition of Na^+ currents may result from binding at the protein surface to obstruct the conductance pathway or, as seems now more likely (29), from a conformational mechanism. In cardiac Na channels, rates of binding equilibration depend on the gating state (15). In channels incorporated into planar bilayers and treated with the alkaloid neurotoxin batrachotoxin, STX and binding affinities appear to depend on the voltage-sensitive conformation of the protein (24, 29, 31, 54). This voltage dependence may be less exaggerated in channels not treated with batrachotoxin. With one possible exception (55), these toxins are regarded as completely specific for voltage-sensitive Na channels.

Na^+ currents in mammalian cardiac cells are typically resistant to blockade by TTX ($K_{1/2} = 0.6–10$ μM, or greater) and STX ($K_{1/2} = 50–1000$ nM) (5, 11, 14, 15). Direct binding studies have indicated the presence of approximately four times more low affinity STX binding sites than high affinity sites (20, 68, 69): furthermore, studies have suggested that the high affinity sites may be present in sympathetic nerve endings (14). TTX-sensitive components of cardiac Na^+ currents are generally not detected.

In skeletal muscle, the sensitivity to TTX and STX depends on the state of innervation. Channels in neonatal muscle are resistant to TTX and STX (23, 65), but after innervation, high affinity binding is expressed. Following surgical denervation, a population of low affinity channels appears (accounting for 25–50% of the Na^+ current) (35, 65, 67, 73). Reinnervation is followed by expression of only high affinity binding. Myoblasts in culture, unless cocultured with neurons (81), are typically toxin resistant, as are primary muscle cultures (45).

It has also been demonstrated that TTX and STX sensitivities are relatively stable. Both high and low affinity forms can be demonstrated by single channel recording from excised patches (94). They can be demonstrated in isolated membrane fragments (20, 68) and reconstituted into planar bilayers with retention of their characteristic affinities (31). Surprisingly, however, transient expression of Na channels in *Xenopus* oocytes from mRNA isolated from neonatal muscle (M. B. Boyle, unpublished) and cardiac cells (86) has led to detection of only high sensitivity forms. This suggests (86) that sensitivity may result from posttranslational modifications or modulation rather than necessarily from structurally different gene products.

The physiological significance of TTX and STX sensitivity is unclear. Preserving the binding site seems unessential for function. Resistant Na channels from developing or denervated muscle are relatively normal in gating, conductance, and selectivity. Furthermore, treatment of Na channels with the carboxyl-methylating reagent trimethyloxonium tetrafluoroborate completely blocks TTX and STX binding, with minor changes in conductance (83, 85). TTX-insensitive (STX-sensitive) channels are found in puffer fish and salamanders, which accumulate the toxins for their own protection (40). It is thus curious that high sensitivity to these toxins has been preserved in species as distant as insects, mollusks, and vertebrates, and yet varies between muscles (and perhaps neurons) in different states of development or innervation. A possible regulatory role for these binding sites is hinted at by the reported partial purification from brain of a peptide that competitively displaces TTX and STX (46). Further, Barr and coworkers (21), and more recently Moczydlowski et al (55), have discovered a soluble carrier protein with high affinity for STX ($K_d = 0.2$ nM), but not TTX, in frog cardiac and skeletal muscle.

Cone Snail Peptide Toxins

Small basic peptide toxins isolated from the cone snail *Conus geographicus*, called geographutoxin II, or μ-conotoxin, bind competitively with TTX and STX to high affinity Na channels in skeletal muscle and eel electroplax, but not to high affinity neuronal channels nor to low affinity cardiac channels (19, 56, 61, 62). Like TTX and STX, these block Na^+ currents. Planar bilayer studies show that μ-conotoxin binds with a voltage dependence identical to that for TTX and STX derivatives. This indicates that these toxins may bind to overlapping sites and that this molecular region is sharply differentiated between muscle and neurons. This again hints at a physiological significance for this site that may be unrelated to the pure mechanics of channel activity. Interestingly, it has been proposed that a vasoconstrictor peptide from porcine aortic endothelium, which has structural similarities to scorpion and cone snail toxins, may act directly on membrane channels (48). Only further study will reveal whether such findings have any fundamental significance.

Na Channels in Glia and Schwann Cells

Another clue to the diversity of Na channel proteins may be found in their presence in cells not classically considered to be excitable. An example is the discovery of high affinity, STX-binding voltage-sensitive Na channels in Schwann cells of rabbit and cat peripheral nerves in which axons had been lost because of surgically induced Wallerian degeneration (66, 70). They have also been found in Schwann cell bodies in culture (82), in astrocytes from rat and human central nervous systems (9, 57), and even in Schwann cells from squid axon (93). Low affinity sites have also been detected electrophysiologically in astrocytes (93). Schwann cell Na channels exhibit conventional biophysical properties, although activation of peak currents occurs at somewhat more positive potentials than in most neuronal and muscle cells.

The role of such extraneural Na channels is at present unclear. In peripheral neurons, it has been suggested that, to overcome problems of biosynthesis and transport to axonal sites sometimes many centimeters from the cell body, Schwann cells might fabricate Na channels that would then be transferred to the axon for insertion. An alternative speculation, perhaps less justified, is that electrical excitability of extraneural support cells may exist per se, and may play a developmental or regulatory role. In peripheral neurons, myelination markedly affects the rate and safety factor for impulse propagation. If strong Na^+ currents at the nodal site were sufficient to fire closely apposed Schwann cells, a basis for regulating the effects of myelination on impulse propagation would exist.

At present, establishing unique identities for Schwann and glial Na channel proteins awaits cloning studies. Perhaps in conjunction with tissue culture myelination systems, specific cDNA probes and immunological reagents against specific synthetic peptides or fusion proteins will permit the design of decisive experiments to test these and other hypotheses.

Loci of Control of Tissue-Specific Expression

It is not surprising that there should be tissue-specific differences in Na channel gene expression. It is also not surprising that Na channels that mediate the initiation or propagation of action potentials in a Purkinje neuron would be different from those responsible for the spread of an action potential into the transverse tubules of a skeletal muscle fiber. These differences might stem from requirements for neuromodulation. Furthermore, topographical distribution, surface abundance, or interactions with cytoskeletal elements may differ. Channels destined for high density sites in the nodes of Ranvier might be synthesized, targeted for insertion, and activated by mechanisms differing from those defining the spike initiation zone and conductible properties of the axon hillock. Control of some of these properties may be exerted at transcription and at translation.

Evidence for control at the promoter level has been provided by recent studies by Maue et al (49). These investigators fused the 5' untranslated region of brain type 2 Na channels to DNA sequences coding for chloramphenicol acyltransferase (CAT), an enzyme not found in mammalian cells and capable of being detected in autoradiographic assays. When cultured cells derived from various tissues were transfected with this recombinant DNA, selective CAT expression was observed. In human neuroblastoma (NB5), rat chromaffin (PC12), or mouse anterior pituitary (ATT20) cells, CAT was strongly expressed. It was not detected in, among other cell types, mouse fibroblasts (3T3), mouse (C2) or rat (L6) myoblasts, or rat glioma (C6) cells, or a variety of hepatoma lines. By progressively shortening the 5' sequences, they discovered a 200-base segment containing a powerful silencer sequence. Removal of this segment permitted expression in otherwise nonpermissive cells. Further, when this segment was inserted at the 5' side of a promiscuous, heterologous promoter for thymidine kinase (tk), expression was prevented in cells normally receptive to the tk promoter but not to the Na channel–CAT construct. However, expression was enhanced in cells permissive to both sequences (PC12). Thus, tissue-specific expression can be transferred to various promoter sequences.

These initial findings illustrate at least one approach to decoding the controls for Na channel expression, and ultimately to identifying factors that may trigger isotype selection. Fusion of CAT sequences to regulatory sequences for each channel subtype, followed by production of transgenic animals, could allow the anatomical and developmental mapping of different gene types. In addition, it may ultimately prove possible to induce inappropriate channel isotypes by, for example, fusing a muscle-type channel with a brain-type regulatory sequence. Especially if it proves possible to suppress expression of the endogenous forms, this may open the door to resolving developmental or functional phenomena associated with differentiation of the Na channel gene family.

CONCLUSION

In summary, recent biochemical and molecular biological findings confirm earlier indications from pharmacological studies that there is a marked diversity of voltage-sensitive Na channel proteins, even in a single organism. Information from comparisons of primary structure and from recombinant DNA studies should prove helpful in elucidating normal channel function and pharmacology. This, together with new molecular biological, biochemical, and immunological tools, should lead to a more sophisticated view of the role Na channel isotypes play in the function and development of electrically excitable cells.

Literature Cited

1. Agnew, W. S. 1984. Voltage-regulated sodium channel molecules. *Ann. Rev. Physiol.* 46:517–30
2. Agnew, W. S. 1988. Proteins that bridge the gap. *Nature* 334:299–300
3. Agnew, W. S., Levinson, S. R., Brabson, J. S., Raftery, M. A. 1978. Purification of the tetrodotoxin-binding component associated with the voltage-sensitive sodium channel from *Electrophorus electricus* electroplax membranes. *Proc. Natl. Acad. Sci. USA* 75:2606–11
4. Agnew, W. S., Moore, A. C., Levinson, S. R., Raftery, M. A. 1980. Identification of a large peptide associated with the tetrodotoxin binding protein from *Electrophorus electricus. Biochem. Biophys. Res. Commun.* 92:860–66
5. Baer, M., Best, P. M., Reuter, H. 1976. Voltage-dependent action of tetrodotoxin in mammalian cardiac muscle. *Nature* 263:344–45
6. Barchi, R. L. 1988. Probing the molecular structure of the voltage-dependent sodium channel. *Annu. Rev. Neurosci.* 11:455–95
7. Barchi, R. L., Cohen, S. A., Murphy, L. E. 1980. Purification from rat sarcolemma of the saxitoxin binding component of the excitable membrane sodium channel. *Proc. Natl. Acad. Sci. USA* 77:1306–10
7a. Baumann, A., Grupe, A., Ackermann, A., Pongs, O. Structure of the voltage-dependent potassium channel is highly conserved from *Drosophila* to vertebrate central nervous system. *EMBO J.* 7:2457–83
8. Baumann, A., Krah-Jentgens, I., Müller, R., Müller-Holtkamp, F., Kecskemethy, N., et al. 1987. Molecular organization of the maternal effect region of the *Shaker* complex of *Drosophila:* characterization of an I_A channel transcript with homology to vertebrate Na+ channel. *EMBO J.* 6:3419–29
9. Bevan, S., Chiu, S. Y., Gray, P. T., Ritchie, J. M. 1985. The presence of voltage-gated sodium, potassium and chloride channels in rat cultured astrocytes. *Proc. R. Soc. London Ser. B* 225:299–313
10. Bezanilla, F. 1986. Voltage-dependent gating: gating current measurement and interpretation. In *Ionic Channels in Cells and Model Systems,* ed. R. Latorre, pp. 37–52. New York: Plenum
11. Brown, A. M., Lee, K. S., Powell, T. 1981. Sodium current in single rat heart muscle cells. *J. Physiol.* 318:479–500
12. Catterall, W. A. 1980. Neurotoxins that act on voltage-sensitive sodium channels. *Annu. Rev. Pharmacol. Toxicol.* 20:15–43
13. Catterall, W. A. 1986. Molecular properties of voltage-sensitive sodium channels. *Annu. Rev. Biochem.* 55:953–85
14. Catterall, W. A., Coppersmith, J. C. 1981. High affinity saxitoxin receptor sites in vertebrate heart: evidence for sites associated with autonomic nerve endings. *Mol. Pharmacol.* 20:526–32
15. Cohen, C. J., Bean, B. P., Colatsky, T. J., Tsien, R. W. 1981. Tetrodotoxin block of sodium channels in rabbit Purkinje fibers: interaction between toxin binding and channel gating. *J. Gen. Physiol.* 78:383–411
16. Cooper, E. C., Tomiko, S. A., Agnew, W. S. 1987. Reconstituted voltage-sensitive sodium channel from *Electrophorus electricus:* Chemical modifications that alter regulation of ion permeability. *Proc. Natl. Acad. Sci. USA* 84:6282–86
17. Cooperman, S. S., Grubman, S. A., Barchi, R. L., Goodman, R. H., Mandel, G. 1987. Modulation of sodium-channel mRNA levels in rat skeletal muscle. *Proc. Natl. Acad. Sci. USA* 84:8721–25
18. Correa, A. M., Agnew, W. S. 1988. Fusion of native or reconstituted membranes to liposomes, optimized for single channel recording. *Biophys. J.* 54:569–75

19. Cruz, L. J., Gray, W. R., Olivera, B. M., Zeikus, R. D., Kert, L., et al. 1985. *Conus geographicus* toxins that discriminate between neuronal and muscle sodium channels. *J. Biol. Chem.* 260: 9280–88

20. Doyle, D. D., Brill, D. M., Wasserstrom, J. A., Karrison, T., Page, E. 1985. Saxitoxin binding and "fast" Na^+ channel inhibition in sheep heart plasma membrane. *J. Physiol.* 249:H328–36

21. Doyle, D. D., Wong, M., Tanaka, J., Barr, L. 1982. Saxitoxin binding sites in frog myocardial cytosol. *Science* 215: 1117–19

22. Engelman, D. M., Steitz, T. A., Goldman, A. 1986. Identifying nonpolar transbilayer helices in amino acid sequences of membrane proteins. *Annu. Rev. Biophys. Biophys. Chem.* 15:321–23

23. Frelin, C., Vigne, P., Lazdunski, M. 1983. Na^+ channels with high and low affinity tetrodotoxin binding sites in the mammalian skeletal muscle cell. *J. Biol. Chem.* 258:7256–59

24. French, R. J., Worley, J. F. III, Krueger, B. K. 1984. Voltage-dependent block by saxitoxin of sodium channels incorporated into planar lipid bilayers. *Biophys. J.* 45:301–10

25. Fuhrman, F. A. 1986. Tetrodotoxin, tarichatoxin and chiriquitoxin: historical perspectives. *Ann. NY Acad. Sci.* 479:1–14

26. Goldin, A., Snutch, T., Lübbert, H., Dowsett, A., Marshall, J., et al. 1986. Messenger RNA coding for only the α subunit of the rat brain Na channel is sufficient for expression of functional channels in *Xenopus* oocytes. *Proc. Natl. Acad. Sci. USA* 83:7503–7

27. Gordon, R. D., Fieles, W. E., Schotland, D. L., Hogue-Angeletti, R., Barchi, R. L. 1987. Topographical localization of the C-terminal region of the voltage-dependent sodium channel from *Electrophorus electricus* using antibodies raised against a synthetic peptide. *Proc. Natl. Acad. Sci. USA* 84:308–12

28. Greenblatt, R. E., Blatt, Y, Montal, M. 1985. The structure of the voltage-sensitive sodium channel. Inference derived from computer-aided analysis of the *Electrophorus electricus* channel primary structure. *FEBS Lett.* 193:125–34

29. Green, W. N., Weiss, L. B., Andersen, O. S. 1987. Batrachotoxin-modified sodium channels in planar lipid bilayers. Characterization of saxitoxin- and tetrodotoxin-induced closures. *J. Gen. Physiol.* 89:873–903

30. Grishin, E. V., Kovalenko, E. V., Pashkov, V. N., Shamotienko, O. G. 1984. Purification of rat brain sodium channels. *Membr. Biophys. USSR* 1:858–67

31. Gua, X., Uehora, A., Ravindran, A., Bryant, S. H., Hall, S., et al. 1987. Kinetic basis for insensitivity to tetrodotoxin and saxitoxin in Na channels of canine heart and denervated rat skeletal muscle. *Biochemistry* 26:7546–56

32. Guy, H. R. 1988. A model relating sodium channel structure to its function, In *Molecular Biology of Ion Channels. Curr. Top. Membr. Transp.*, ed. W. S. Agnew, T. Claudio, F. J. Sigworth, New York: Academic

33. Guy, H. R., Seetharamulu, P. 1986. Molecular model of the action potential sodium channel. *Proc. Natl. Acad. Sci. USA* 83:508–12

34. Hall, L. M. 1986. Genetic variants of voltage-sensitive sodium channels. *Ann. NY Acad. Sci.* 479:313–24

35. Harris, J. B., Thesleff, S. 1971. Studies on tetrodotoxin dependent action potentials in denervated skeletal muscle. *Acta Physiol. Scand.* 83:382–88

36. Hartshorne, R., Catterall, W. A. 1981. Purification of the saxitoxin receptor from rat brain. *Proc. Natl. Acad. Sci. USA* 78:4620–24

37. Hartshorne, R. P., Messner, D. J., Coppersmith, J. C., Catterall, W. A. 1982. The saxitoxin receptor of the sodium channel from rat brain; evidence for two non-identical β-subunits. *J. Biol. Chem.* 257:13888–91

38. James, W. M., Agnew, W. S. 1987. Multiple oligosaccharide chains in the voltage-sensitive Na channel from *Electrophorus electricus*: Evidence for α-2,8-linked polysialic acid. *Biochem. Biophys. Res. Commun.* 148:817–26

38a. Deleted in proof

39. Kamb, A., Iverson, L. E., Tanouye, M. A. 1987. Molecular characterization of *Shaker*, a *Drosophila* gene that encodes a potassium channel. *Cell* 50:405–13

40. Kao, C. Y. 1966. Tetrodotoxin, saxitoxin and their significance in the study of excitation phenomena. *Pharmacol. Rev.* 18:997–1049

41. Kayano, T., Noda, M., Flockerzi, V., Takahashi, H., Numa, S. 1988. Primary structure of rat brain sodium channel III deduced from the cDNA sequence. *FEBS Lett.* 228:187–94

42. Kosower, E. M. 1985. A structural and dynamic model for the sodium channel of *Electrophorus electricus*. *FEBS Lett.* 182:234–42

43. Kraner, S. D., Tanaka, J. C., Barchi, R. L. 1985. Purification and functional reconstitution of the voltage-sensitive sodium channel from rabbit T-tubular membranes. *J. Biol. Chem.* 260:6341–47

44. Kyte, J., Doolittle, R. F. 1982. A simple method for displaying the hydropathic character of a protein. *J. Mol. Biol.* 157:105–32

45. Lawrence, J. C., Catterall, W. A. 1981. Pharmacological properties of sodium channels in cultured rat heart cells. *Mol. Pharmacol.* 20:533–42

46. Lombet, A., Fosset, M., Romey, G., Jacomet, Y., Lazdunski, M. 1987. Identification in mammalian brain of an endogenous substance with Na^+ channel blocking activities similar to those of tetrodotoxin. *Brain Res.* 417:327–34

47. Lombet, A., Lazdunski, M. 1984. Characterization, solubilization, affinity labeling and purification of the cardiac Na^+ channel using *Tityus* toxin gamma. *Eur. J. Biochem.* 141:651–60

48. Mashashi, Y., Kurimara, H., Kimura, S., Tomobe, Y., Kobayashi, M., et al. 1988. A novel vasoconstrictor peptide produced by vascular endothelial cells. *Nature* 332:411–15

49. Maue, R. A., Cooperman, S., Begley, M., Goodman, R. H., Mandel, G. 1988. Characterization of a region in the rat type II sodium channel gene that confers cell specific expression. *Biophys. J.* 53:17a(Abstr.)

50. McCleskey, E. W., Fox, A. P., Feldman, D., Tsien, R. W. 1986. Different types of calcium channels. *J. Exp. Biol.* 124:177–90

51. Messner, D. J., Catterall, W. A. 1985. The sodium channel from rat brain. Separation and characterization of subunits. *J. Biol. Chem.* 260:10597–604

52. Messner, D. J., Catterall, W. A. 1986. The sodium channel from rat brain. Role of the beta 1 and beta 2 subunits in saxitoxin binding. *J. Biol. Chem.* 261:211–15

53. Miller, J. A., Agnew, W. S., Levinson, S. R. 1983. Principal glycopeptide of the tetrodotoxin/saxitoxin binding protein from *Electrophorus electricus:* Isolation and partial chemical and physical characterization. *Biochemistry* 22:462–69

54. Moczydlowski, E., Garber, S. S., Miller, C. 1984. Batrachotoxin-activated Na^+ channels in planar lipid bilayers. *J. Gen. Physiol.* 84:665–86

55. Moczydlowski, E., Mahar, J., Ravindran, A. 1987. Multiple saxitoxin-binding sites in bullfrog muscle: tetrodotoxin-sensitive sodium channels and tetrodotoxin-insensitive sites of unknown function. *Mol. Pharmacol.* 33:202–11

56. Moczydlowski, E., Olivera, B., Gray, W. R., Strichartz, G. 1986. Discrimination of muscle and neuronal Na-channel subtypes by binding competition between [^{3}H]saxitoxin and μ-conotoxins. *Proc. Natl. Acad. Sci. USA* 83:5321–25

57. Munson, R., Westermark, B., Glaser, L. 1979. Tetrodotoxin-sensitive sodium channels in normal human fibroblasts and normal glial-like cells. *Proc. Natl. Acad. Sci. USA* 76:6425–29

58. Noda, M., Ikeda, T., Kayano, T., Suzuki, H., Takeshima, H., et al. 1986. Existence of distinct sodium channel messenger RNAs in rat brain. *Nature* 320:188–92

59. Noda, M., Ikeda, T., Suzuki, H., Takeshima, H., Takahashi, T., et al. 1986. Expression of functional sodium channels from cloned cDNA. *Nature* 322:826–28

60. Noda, M., Shimizu, S., Tanabe, T., Takai, T., Kayano, T., et al. 1984. Primary structure of *Electrophorus electricus* sodium channel deduced from cDNA sequence. *Nature* 312:121–27

61. Ohizumi, Y., Minoshima, S., Takahashi, M., Nakamura, H., Kobayashi, J. 1986. Geographutoxin II, a novel peptide inhibitor of Na channels of skeletal muscles and autonomic nerves. *J. Pharamacol. Exp. Ther.* 239:243–48

62. Ohizumi, Y., Nakamura, H., Kobayashi, J., Catterall, W. A. 1986. Specific inhibition of [^{3}H]-saxitoxin binding to skeletal muscle sodium channels by geographutoxin II, a polypeptide channel blocker. *J. Biol. Chem.* 261:6149–52

63. Okamoto, H., Sakai, K., Goto, S., Takasu-Ishikawa, E., Hotta, Y. 1987. Isolation of *Drosphila* genomic clones homologous to the eel sodium channel gene. *Proc. Jpn. Acad.* 63:284–88

64. Papazian, D. M., Schwarz, T. L., Tempel, B. L., Jan, Y. N., Jan, L. Y. 1987. Cloning of genomic and complementary DNA from *Shaker*, a putative potassium channel from *Drosophila*. *Science* 237:749–53

65. Pappone, P. 1980. Voltage-clamp experiments in normal and denervated mammalian skeletal muscle. *J. Physiol.* 305:377–410

66. Pellegrino, R. G., Politis, M. J., Ritchie, J. M., Spencer, P. S. 1986. Morphological and biochemical events in Schwann cells accompanying Wallerian degeneration in cat peripheral nerve. *J. Neurocytol.* 15:17–28

67. Redfern, P., Thesleff, S. 1971. Action potential generation in denervated rat skeletal muscle. II. The action of tetrodotoxin. *Acta Physiol. Scand.* 82:70–78

68. Regan, L. J., Rogart, R. B. 1982. Binding of labeled saxitoxin to the TTX-resistant cardiac Na$^+$ channel in rat. *Circulation* 66:11–96

69. Renaud, J. F., Kazazoglou, T., Lombet, A., Chicheportiche, R., Jaimovich, E., et al. 1983. The Na$^+$ channel in mammalian cardiac cells. Two kinds of tetrodotoxin receptors in rat heart membranes. *J. Biol. Chem.* 258:8799–805

70. Ritchie, J. M., Rang, H. P. 1983. Extraneural saxitoxin binding sites in rabbit myelinated nerve. *Proc. Natl. Acad. Sci. USA* 80:2803–7

71. Ritchie, J. M., Rogart, R. B. 1977. The binding of saxitoxin and tetrodotoxin to excitable tissue. *Rev. Physiol. Biochem. Pharamcol.* 79:1–50

72. Roberts, R., Barchi, R. L. 1987. The voltage-sensitive sodium channel from rabbit skeletal muscle: Chemical characterization of subunits. *J. Biol. Chem.* 262:2298–303

73. Rogart, R. B., Regan, L. J. 1985. Two subtypes of sodium channels with tetrodotoxin sensitivity and insensitivity detected in denervated mammalian skeletal muscle. *Brain Res.* 329:314–18

74. Rosenberg, R. L., Tomiko, S. A., Agnew, W. S. 1984. Reconstitution of neurotoxin modulated ion transport by the voltage-regulated sodium channel isolated from the electroplax of *Electrophorus electricus. Proc. Natl. Acad. Sci. USA* 81:1239–43

75. Rosenberg, R. L., Tomiko, S. A., Agnew, W. S. 1984. Single-channel properties of the reconstituted voltage-regulated Na channel isolated from the electroplax of *Electrophorus electricus. Proc. Natl. Acad. Sci. USA* 81:5594–98

76. Rossie, S., Gordon, D., Catterall, W. A. 1987. Identification of an intracellular domain of the sodium channel having multiple cAMP-dependent phosphorylation sites. *J. Biol. Chem.* 262:17530–35

77. Salkoff, L., Butler, A., Scavarda, N., Wei, A. 1987. Nucleotide sequence of the putative sodium channel gene from *Drosophila:* the four homologous domains. *Nucleic Acids Res.* 15:8569–72

78. Salkoff, L., Butler, A., Wei, A., Scavarda, N., Giffen, K., et al. 1987. Genomic organization and deduced amino acid sequence of a putative sodium channel gene in *Drosophila. Science* 237:744–49

79. Schantz, E. J. 1986. Chemistry and biology of saxitoxin and related toxins. *Ann. NY Acad. Sci.* 479:15–23

80. Schwarz, T. L., Tempel, B. L., Papazian, D. M., Jan, Y. N., Jan, L. Y. 1988. Multiple potassium channel components are produced by alternative splicing at the *Shaker* locus in *Drosophila. Nature* 331:137–42

81. Sherman, S. J., Catterall, W. A. 1982. Biphasic regulation of development of the high-affinity saxitoxin receptor by innervation in rat skeletal muscle. *J. Gen. Physiol.* 80:753–68

82. Shrager, P., Chiu, S. Y., Ritchie, J. M. 1985. Voltage-dependent sodium and potassium channels in mammalian cultured Schwann cells. *Proc. Natl. Acad. Sci. USA* 82:948–52

83. Sigworth, F. J., Spalding, B. C. 1980. Chemical modification reduces the conductance of sodium channels in nerve. *Nature* 283:293–95

84. Sills, M. N., Xu, Y. C., Barrachini, E., Goodman, R. H., Cooperman, S. S., et al. 1988. Existence of diverse Na channel mRNAs in rat myocardium: Evidence for a cardiac specific Na channel. *Science.* In press

85. Spalding, B. C. 1980. Properties of toxin resistant sodium channels produced by chemical modification in frog skeletal muscle. *J. Physiol.* 305:485–500

86. Sutton, F., Davidson, N., Lester, H. 1988. Tetrodotoxin-sensitive voltage-dependent Na currents recorded from *Xenopus* oocytes injected with mammalian cardiac muscle RNA. *Mol. Brain Res.* 3:187–92

87. Suzuki, H., Beckh, S., Kubo, H., Yahagi, N., Ishida, H., et al. 1988. Functional expression of cloned cDNA encoding sodium channel III. *FEBS Lett.* 228:195–200

87a. Tanabe, T., Bean, K., Powell, A., Numa, S. 1988. Restoration of excitation-contraction coupling and slow calcium current in dysgenic muscle by dihydropyridine receptor cDNA. *Nature.* In press

88. Tanabe, T., Takeshima, H., Mikami, A., Flockerzi, V., Takahashi, H., et al. 1987. Primary structure of rabbit skeletal muscle dihydropyridine receptor deduced from cDNA sequence. *Nature* 328:313–18

89. Tanaka, J. C., Eccleston, J. F., Barchi, R. L. 1983. Cation selectivity characteristics of the reconstituted voltage-dependent sodium channel purified from rat skeletal muscle sarcolemma. *J. Biol. Chem.* 258:7519–26

90. Tempel, B. L., Jan, Y. N., Jan, L. Y. 1988. Cloning of a probable potassium channel gene from mouse brain. *Nature* 332:837–39

91. Tomiko, S. A., Rosenberg, R. L., Emerick, M. C., Agnew, W. S. 1986. Fluorescence assay for neurotoxin-modulated ion transport by the reconstituted voltage-activated sodium channel isolated from eel electric organ. *Biochemistry* 25:2162–74

92. Trimmer, J. S., Agnew, W. S., Tomiko, S. A., Crean, S. M., Sheng, Z., et al. 1988. Isolation of cDNA clones encoding a full length rat skeletal muscle sodium channel. *J. Neurosci.* (Abstr.). In press

93. Villegas, J., Sevcik, C., Barnola, F. V., Villegas, R. 1975. Grayanotoxin, veratridine and tetrodotoxin-sensitive pathways in the Schwann cell membrane of squid nerve fiber. *J. Gen. Physiol.* 67:369–80

94. Weiss, R. E., Horn, R. 1986. Functional differences between two classes of sodium channels in developing rat skeletal muscle. *Science* 233:361–64

Annu. Rev. Physiol. 1989. 51:419–41

THE RENAL PROXIMAL TUBULE: A Model for Diversity of Anion Exchangers and Stilbene-sensitive Anion Transporters

Peter S. Aronson

Departments of Medicine, and Cellular & Molecular Physiology, Yale University School of Medicine, New Haven, Connecticut 06510

INTRODUCTION

The prototype of plasma membrane anion exchangers is erythrocyte Band 3 (44, 47, 70). Erythrocyte Band 3 mediates the electroneutral 1:1 exchange of monovalent anions such as Cl^- and HCO_3^-. Band 3 can also mediate the electroneutral cotransport of H^+ and $SO_4^=$ in exchange for monovalent anions such as Cl^-. All known transport modes of Band 3 are inhibited with high affinity by disulfonic stilbenes.

In recent years anion transport systems with one or more major properties of Band 3, such as ability to mediate anion exchange and/or sensitivity to inhibition by disulfonic stilbenes, have been demonstrated in the plasma membranes of nonerythroid cells (44). Interestingly, the anion transport systems described in nonerythroid cells have been heterogeneous with respect to substrate and inhibitor affinities, suggesting that there exist several distinct transporters functionally related to Band 3. On the other hand, such apparent heterogeneity may be a function of the varying conditions and methods that have been used to study anion transport in different cells and tissues. Actual diversity of Band 3-related transporters can be most clearly demonstrated when it is confirmed by several methods in a single cell type. In this regard, the mammalian proximal tubule has served as a useful model system for revealing the surprising diversity of anion exchangers and stilbene-sensitive anion transporters found in nonerythroid cells. In this review, the properties

419

0066-4278/89/0315-0419$02.00

of these proximal tubule transport systems will be summarized and related to their likely physiological roles.

URATE-ANION EXCHANGER

A search for a mechanism to account for active urate reabsorption in the dog kidney led to the first identification of a stilbene-sensitive anion exchanger in the proximal tubule. It was found that an inside-alkaline pH gradient drives accumulation of urate against its concentration gradient in dog renal microvillus (luminal, brush border) membrane vesicles (15). The process of pH gradient-stimulated urate uptake is electroneutral (15, 49), saturable (15), sensitive to inhibition by the uricosuric drug probenecid (15, 49), and sensitive to such other anion transport inhibitors as furosemide, 4-acetamido-4'-isothiocyano-2,2'-disulfonic stilbene (SITS), and 4,4'-diisothiocyano-2,2'-disulfonic stilbene (DIDS) (15, 49). These findings indicate that pH-stimulated urate transport reflects a carrier-mediated process of H^+-urate cotransport or OH^--urate exchange rather than nonionic diffusion of uric acid. [It should be emphasized that H^+-anion cotransport and OH^--anion exchange are indistinguishable thermodynamically and probably kinetically (9); for simplicity, this process will be referred to as OH^--anion exchange in the remainder of this review.]

The same transport system has affinity for multiple additional anions including Cl^- (49); p-aminohippurate (PAH) (15, 40) and such other monocarboxylates as n-valerate, lactate, β-hydroxybutyrate, pyruvate, and acetoacetate (40); and dicarboxylates such as maleate, succinate, α-ketoglutarate, and oxaloacetate (40). The pH dependence of interaction with maleate and succinate suggests that it is in the monovalent form that these anions bind to the urate transporter (40). Taken together, the data on substrate specificity imply that the urate exchanger has affinity for any organic anion that has a single anionic group, is at least three carbon atoms in length, and has at least one unsubstituted carbon atom (40).

The directly coupled exchange of two anions is documented when the gradient of one anion induces the oppositely directed, uphill transport of the second anion in the absence of other driving forces. In this way it has been shown that the urate transporter can function in multiple exchange modes involving urate, OH^-, Cl^-, PAH and the additional organic anions listed above. Examples include urate-OH^-, PAH-OH^-, urate-Cl^-, PAH-Cl^-, lactate-OH^-, succinate-OH^-, urate-lactate, urate-succinate, and urate-PAH exchanges, all mediated via the same transport pathway (15, 40, 49).

There are at least three mechanisms by which the urate transporter can account for uphill urate reabsorption across the luminal membrane of the proximal tubule cell, as illustrated in Figure 1. In general, any anion that can

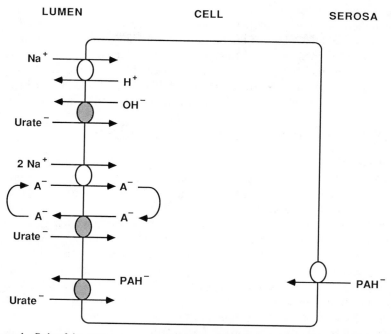

Figure 1   Role of the urate-anion exchanger (denoted by filled symbols) in mediating the uphill absorption of urate across the luminal membrane.

share the urate exchanger and for which there is an outward electrochemical gradient across the luminal membrane potentially may serve to drive urate reabsorption. One such candidate exchange partner is OH^-, as an outward electrochemical OH^- gradient exists across the luminal membrane as a result of active H^+ secretion that takes place largely via Na^+-H^+ exchange (8). Anions that are actively accumulated across the luminal membrane by Na^+-cotransport, such as lactate, and β-hydroxybutyrate (102), can also serve as exchange partners for luminal urate. Indeed, the feasibility of this mechanism was demonstrated by the finding that in the presence of an inward Na^+ gradient, lactate stimulates uphill urate uptake into microvillus membrane vesicles (40). The urate-retaining effects of such monocarboxylic drugs as nicotinate and pyrazinoate likely result from the same process of Na^+-monocarboxylate cotransport in parallel with monocarboxylate-urate exchange (39). The third mechanism for uphill urate transport across the luminal membrane is via exchange for anions, such as PAH, that are accumulated actively across the basolateral membrane of the cell by pathways that will be discussed in detail below.

The presence of the urate exchange pathway has been confirmed in renal microvillus membrane vesicles isolated from rat (50), another animal in which there is net active urate reabsorption in the proximal tubule. Studies in the intact proximal tubule of the rat (99) are consistent with the properties of the luminal membrane urate transporter as determined in isolated vesicle studies. Thus, the absorptive flux of urate is saturable; inhibited by addition of SITS, DIDS, and furosemide to the lumen; inhibited by addition of PAH to the lumen, but stimulated by addition of PAH to the capillary perfusate (99).

MONOCARBOXYLATE-OH⁻ EXCHANGER

In the rabbit proximal tubule there is no evidence for a carrier-mediated absorptive flux of urate. Not surprisingly, urate uptake in rabbit renal microvillus membrane vesicles is stimulated neither by an outward OH^- gradient nor an outward Cl^- gradient (T. C. Massad, J. P. Ach & P. S. Aronson, in preparation), which indicates the absence of the urate exchange pathway described in microvillus membranes from dog and rat kidney. Nevertheless, an inside-alkaline pH gradient stimulates the uphill accumulation of lactate in rabbit renal microvillus membrane vesicles (65). The pH gradient-stimulated uptake of lactate is Na^+-independent, saturable, and sensitive to inhibition by probenecid and furosemide, consistent with a carrier-mediated process of H^+-lactate cotransport or lactate-OH^- exchange (65). Interestingly, pH gradient-stimulated lactate transport is more sensitive to inhibition by α-cyano-4-hydroxycinnamate than by SITS or DIDS (65), as reported for H^+-coupled lactate transport in nonepithelial cells (32, 33, 43, 86). Such other monocarboxylates as pyruvate and acetoacetate share the transport system (65), as in nonepithelial cells (32, 33, 43, 86). The monocarboxylate transporter can function in multiple exchange modes involving these anions. Examples include lactate-OH^-, lactate-lactate, lactate-acetoacetate, and lactate-pyruvate exchanges (T. C. Massad, J. P. Ach & P. S. Aronson, in preparation). There is no direct interaction with Cl^-, PAH, oxalate, or $SO_4^=$ (65), distinguishing this pathway from the other anion exchangers in the proximal tubule. The inhibitor profile of the monocarboxylate-OH^- exchanger also distinguishes it from the pathway mediating Na^+-monocarboxylate cotransport across the luminal membrane of the proximal tubule cell (65). Finally, a monocarboxylate-OH^- exchanger with properties indistinguishable from the luminal membrane system is present in rabbit renal basolateral membrane vesicles (T. C. Massad, J. P. Ach & P. S. Aronson, in preparation).

The possible physiological role of the monocarboxylate-OH^- exchanger in the proximal tubule is illustrated (Figure 2) for the case of lactate. The major route for secondary active lactate absorption is via Na^+ cotransport across the luminal membrane (102). The basolateral membrane lactate-OH^- exchanger then provides a pathway for exit of lactate from the cell, which completes the process of transtubular lactate reabsorption. As pointed out by recent studies

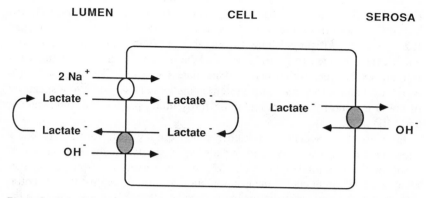

Figure 2   Roles of the monocarboxylate-OH⁻ exchanger in mediating lactate exit across the basolateral membrane, and uptake of base (or secretion of acid) across both cell surfaces.

of the amphibian proximal tubule cell, an important side effect of this process is to drive OH⁻ into the cell (or H⁺ out of the cell) across the basolateral membrane, thereby contributing to intracellular pH regulation (83). A contribution to intracellular pH regulation from lactate-OH⁻ and β-hydroxybutyrate-OH⁻ exchanges sensitive to inhibition by high concentrations of DIDS has been observed in rabbit proximal tubule cells (14).

What then is the function of monocarboxylate-OH⁻ exchange across the luminal membrane? One possibility is that this pathway mediates the backflux of monocarboxylates from cell to lumen. Na⁺-coupled lactate uptake into the cell with recycling of lactate back into the lumen by lactate-OH⁻ exchange (or H⁺-lactate cotransport) would result in net active acid secretion indirectly driven by the luminal membrane Na⁺ gradient. This process may supplement the secondary active H⁺ secretion occurring via luminal membrane Na⁺-H⁺ exchange. Monocarboxylate-dependent acidification might enable the rate of proximal tubule acid secretion to be enhanced in such clinical states as lactic acidosis or ketoacidosis when the filtered load of lactate and/or acetoacetate is increased. Moreover, because Na⁺-lactate cotransport is electrogenic and likely has a stoichiometry of 2 Na⁺ : lactate (10, 68), the scheme for Na⁺-coupled H⁺ secretion occurring via recycling of lactate illustrated in Figure 2 would have a net stoichiometry of 2 Na⁺ : H⁺. In principle, this would allow the generation of a steeper H⁺ gradient than could otherwise be achieved by Na⁺-H⁺ exchange, which has a 1 : 1 stoichiometry (9).

Cl⁻-FORMATE EXCHANGER

An outward formate gradient induces uphill Cl⁻ uptake into rabbit renal microvillus membrane vesicles, and an outward Cl⁻ gradient causes uphill formate uptake. These findings indicate the presence of a transport system mediating Cl^--formate exchange (52). This system is electroneutral (53) and has little or no affinity for HCO_3^-, acetate, lactate, PAH, sulfate, or oxalate (52, 53), thereby distinguishing it from other proximal tubule anion exchangers. Several halides (e.g. Br^-, I^-) and NO_3^- can interact with the Cl^--formate exchanger, which can also mediate Cl^--Cl^-, Cl^--Br^-, and Cl^--NO_3^- exchanges (52, 53). This system is moderately sensitive to a spectrum of anion transport inhibitors including furosemide, probenecid, bumetanide, and DIDS (52, 53).

In contrast to acetate and higher monocarboxylates, formate is not a substrate for the Na^+-monocarboxylate cotransporter in the luminal membrane of the proximal tubule cell (52, 69). However, imposing an inside-alkaline pH gradient causes the accumulation of formate against its concentration gradient in renal microvillus membrane vesicles (52), consistent with the transport of formate via nonionic diffusion of formic acid as previously demonstrated in lipid bilayers (96). Illustrated in Figure 3, entry of formic acid into the cell by nonionic diffusion followed by exchange of intracellular formate for luminal Cl^- results in a net uptake of H^+ and Cl^- inward across the luminal membrane. In essence, formate serves as a coupling factor to allow H^+-coupled Cl^- uptake. In fact, an inside-alkaline pH gradient induces uphill Br^- uptake into renal microvillus vesicles in the presence but not in the absence of formate (52). Moreover, imposing an inward Cl^- gradient causes acidification of the intravesicular space in the presence but not in the absence of formate (46). This confirms the presence of a formate-dependent H^+-coupled Cl^- transport process as predicted by the model in Figure 3. To the extent that active H^+ secretion across the luminal membrane occurs by a Na^+-coupled mechanism such as Na^+-H^+ exchange (Figure 3), the net effect is to accomplish electroneutral Na^+-coupled Cl^- transport. This process is driven by the inward Na^+ gradient that is present across the luminal membrane due to the primary active extrusion of Na^+ across the basolateral membrane via the Na^+,K^+-ATPase.

The physiological relevance of this mechanism is underscored by studies of the intact proximal tubule of rabbit that indicate that addition of physiological concentrations of formate (0.25–0.5 mM) to the luminal and serosal solutions causes 60% stimulation of the rate of NaCl absorption (74). Stimulation of NaCl absorption by formate is not associated with any change in the transepithelial electrical potential difference (74), consistent with the operation of an electroneutral mode of NaCl absorption. Similar concentrations of acetate do not stimulate NaCl absorption (74), consistent with the anion specificity of the Cl^--formate exchanger. The formate-stimulated component of NaCl absorption is inhibited by the addition of DIDS to the lumen or ouabain to the peritubular bath (74), consistent with the model in which stilbene-sensitive

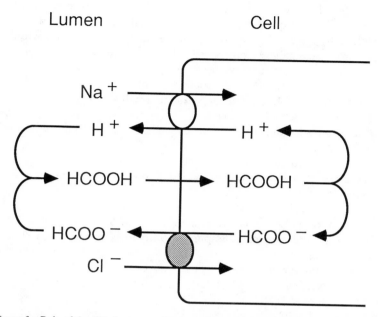

Figure 3 Role of the Cl⁻-formate exchanger in mediating Na⁺-coupled Cl⁻ absorption across the luminal membrane.

Cl⁻-formate exchange is indirectly coupled to the luminal membrane Na⁺ gradient that itself arises from ouabain-sensitive Na⁺ extrusion across the basolateral membrane.

In both the rabbit and rat proximal convoluted tubule, addition of Cl⁻ to an initially Cl⁻-free luminal perfusate causes a much larger acidification of the cell in the presence than in the absence of formate (4, 11). The acidification of the cell induced by Cl⁻ and formate is blocked by luminal DIDS. These findings support the presence of a formate-dependent H⁺-Cl⁻ uptake process across the luminal membrane of the intact proximal tubule cell, as predicted by the model of Cl⁻-formate exchange in parallel with nonionic diffusion of formic acid (Figure 3).

Cl⁻-OXALATE EXCHANGER

Outward gradients of Cl⁻ or formate induce the uphill accumulation of oxalate in rabbit renal microvillus membrane vesicles, which indicates the presence of Cl⁻-oxalate exchange and formate-oxalate exchange (53). Both exchange processes are electrogenic, consistent with the exchange of one oxalate per Cl⁻ or formate (53). One possibility is that Cl⁻-oxalate exchange and formate-oxalate exchange are modes of the same transport pathway that mediates Cl^--formate exchange across the luminal membrane of the proximal tubule cell. However, analysis of the substrate and inhibitor affinities for these processes suggests otherwise (53). More likely, Cl^--oxalate exchange and formate-oxalate exchange occur by a pathway, here termed the Cl^--oxalate exchanger, that is separate from the pathway mediating the majority of Cl^--formate exchange in microvillus membrane vesicles. The Cl^--formate exchanger accepts Cl^- and formate as substrates, has little or no affinity for oxalate, is more sensitive to inhibition by furosemide than by DIDS, and is electroneutral (53). The Cl^--oxalate exchanger also accepts Cl^- and formate as substrates, but has high affinity for oxalate, is much more sensitive to inhibition by DIDS than by furosemide, and is electrogenic (53).

In addition to mediating exchange of oxalate with Cl^- and formate, the Cl^--oxalate exchanger can mediate exchange of oxalate with I^-, NO_3^-, Br^- and OH^- (53, 62). Interestingly, despite its ability to exchange these monovalent anions for oxalate, this system does not seem capable of exchanging monovalent anions for each other. Thus, Cl^--formate, Cl^--I^-, Cl^--NO_3^-, and Cl^--Br^- exchanges take place largely, if not exclusively, via the Cl^--formate exchanger (53).

The rate of Cl^--$SO_4^=$ exchange in rabbit renal microvillus membrane vesicles is much smaller than that of Cl^--oxalate exchange, which suggests that SO_4^- is a poor substrate for the Cl^--oxalate exchanger (53). However, outward gradients of Cl^-, I^- or NO_3^- appreciably stimulate $SO_4^=$ uptake into rat renal microvillus membrane vesicles (71). Whether halide-$SO_4^=$ exchange in rat renal microvillus membrane vesicles is via the Cl^--oxalate exchanger or the $SO_4^=$-HCO_3^- exchanger (see below) has not been evaluated.

The possible physiological role of the Cl^--oxalate exchanger is uncertain. It could participate in transcellular absorption or secretion of oxalate, which undergoes bidirectional transport in the proximal tubule (98). For Cl^--oxalate exchange to contribute significantly to Cl^- absorption, a mechanism enabling oxalate to recycle back across the luminal membrane would be necessary. Oxalate is a poor substrate for Na^+-cotransport in rabbit renal microvillus membrane vesicles (62). Nevertheless, it is possible that oxalate could recycle across the luminal membrane via the Cl^--oxalate exchanger itself. As illustrated in Figure 4, transport of oxalate from lumen to cell could occur by OH^--oxalate exchange or formate-oxalate exchange, driven directly or indirectly by the favorable electrochemical H^+ gradient that results from Na^+-H^+ exchange. The possible recycling of oxalate from lumen to cell via another anion exchanger, the $SO_4^=$-HCO_3^- exchanger, will be discussed below.

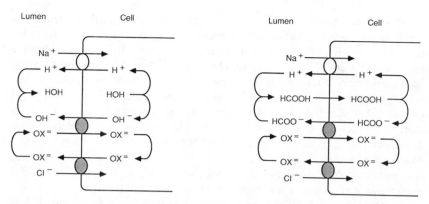

Figure 4 Roles of the Cl⁻-oxalate exchanger (denoted by filled symbols) in mediating Na⁺-coupled Cl⁻ absorption across the luminal membrane.

$SO_4^=$-HCO_3^--EXCHANGER

Outward gradients of HCO_3^- induce the uphill accumulation of $SO_4^=$ in rat (63, 72), rabbit (61), and bovine (87) basolateral membrane vesicles, which indicates the presence of a transporter mediating $SO_4^=$-HCO_3^- exchange. Stimulation of $SO_4^=$ uptake by an inside-alkaline pH gradient in the nominal absence of Cl_2/HCO_3 (42, 61, 63, 72, 87) indicates that the system may be capable of $SO_4^=$ transport via H^+-$SO_4^=$ cotransport or OH^--$SO_4^=$ exchange, but it is also possible that the experimental solutions were not absolutely free of CO_2/HCO_3. The system is shared by oxalate (61) and thiosulfate (61) and is more sensitive to inhibition by DIDS than by furosemide, bumetanide, probenecid, or α-cyano-4-hydroxycinnamate (61). The system is electroneutral, with a stoichiometry of 1 $SO_4^=$ (or oxalate): 2 HCO_3^- or a thermodynamically equivalent process (e.g. 1 $SO_4^=$ (or oxalate): 1 $CO_3^=$) (61).

There is conflicting evidence from membrane vesicle studies about the anion specificity and the possible cotransport of Na^+ via this system. According to one view, the system is Na^+-independent, and there is little or no interaction with such other anions as formate, lactate, PAH, urate, succinate, phosphate, or Cl⁻ (42, 61, 72, 87). Indeed, the absence of interaction with any monovalent anion other than HCO_3^-, and the fact that the system can readily mediate $SO_4^=$-oxalate, $SO_4^=$-$SO_4^=$, oxalate-oxalate, $SO_4^=$-thiosulfate, and oxalate-thiosulfate exchanges (61, 72), together suggest that the system may operate exclusively with divalent anions. Thus, $CO_3^=$ rather than HCO_3^- may be the species that actually exchanges with $SO_4^=$ or oxalate.

Other studies indicate that uphill $SO_4^=$ uptake into renal basolateral membrane vesicles results from inward Na^+ gradients or outward gradients of a spectrum of anions including Cl^-, formate, PAH, succinate, and lactate (26, 63). The basis for this disparity in results is not clear. It is possible that the Na^+ stimulation of $SO_4^=$ uptake observed in these studies results from luminal membrane contamination of basolateral membrane preparations. Another problem is that an outward gradient of one anion can generate a pH gradient that can indirectly affect the transport of a second anion, which thereby mimics direct anion exchange. For example, in one study the ability of an outward lactate gradient to induce the uphill transport of sulfate and oxalate was abolished when the generation of a transmembrane pH gradient was prevented with nigericin (61). In any event, studies examining basolateral membrane transport systems in the intact proximal tubule strongly favor the concept that the $SO_4^=$-HCO_3^- exchanger has narrow specificity, with affinity for oxalate and thiosulfate but little or no interaction with PAH, lactate, succinate, or Na^+ (93).

$SO_4^=$-HCO_3^- exchange is also demonstrable in luminal membrane vesicles isolated from rat (71), bovine (87), and rabbit (S.-M. Kuo & P. S. Aronson, in preparation) kidney cortex. Studies using membrane vesicles isolated from rabbit kidney indicate that the properties of the luminal membrane $SO_4^=$-HCO_3^- exchanger (e.g. electroneutral anion exchange, little or no interaction with Cl^-, ability to transport oxalate) are virtually identical to those of the basolateral membrane $SO_4^=$-HCO_3^- exchanger (S.-M. Kuo & P. S. Aronson, in preparation). The properties of the $SO_4^=$-HCO_3^- exchanger are also similar in luminal and basolateral membranes of bovine kidney (87). In both types of bovine membrane preparations, the rate of $SO_4^=$-Cl^- exchange is quite modest compared to the rate of $SO_4^=$-HCO_3^- exchange. In contrast, more appreciable $SO_4^=$-Cl^- exchange has been observed in rat microvillus membrane vesicles (71). This difference from results in rabbit and bovine membranes may indicate that in the rat either the luminal membrane Cl^--oxalate exchanger has appreciable affinity for $SO_4^=$, or the luminal membrane $SO_4^=$-HCO_3^- exchanger has appreciable affinity for Cl^-.

The possible physiological roles of the $SO_4^=$-HCO_3^- exchanger are illustrated in Figure 5. Three of its modes of operation ($SO_4^=$-HCO_3^- exchange, oxalate-HCO_3^- exchange, and $SO_4^=$-oxalate exchange) are shown across the luminal and basolateral membranes. Let us first consider the role of the $SO_4^=$-HCO_3^- exchanger in proximal tubular $SO_4^=$ reabsorption. The principal pathway for secondary active $SO_4^=$ uptake across the luminal membrane is via Na^+-$SO_4^=$ cotransport driven by the luminal membrane Na^+ gradient (64, 75). This in turn generates outward $SO_4^=$ gradients across both cell membranes. Exit of $SO_4^=$ via basolateral membrane $SO_4^=$-HCO_3^- exchange would complete the process of transcellular $SO_4^=$ absorption. Analogous with the case of lactate transport discussed above, a predicted side effect of

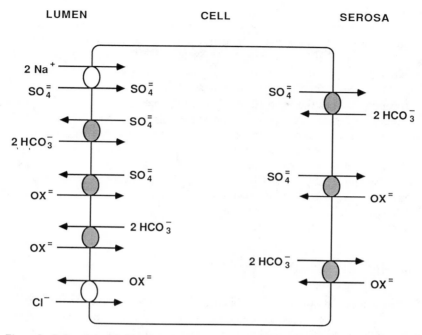

Figure 5   Roles of the $SO_4^=$(oxalate)-HCO_3^- exchanger (denoted by filled symbols) in mediating $SO_4^=$ exit across the basolateral membrane, uptake of HCO_3^- across both cell surfaces, and uptake of oxalate across both cell surfaces.

this process is to drive HCO_3^- uptake into the cell across the basolateral membrane, thereby contributing to intracellular pH regulation. Backflux of $SO_4^=$ from cell to lumen in exchange for HCO_3^- would also drive HCO_3^- into the cell. Na^+-coupled $SO_4^=$ uptake into the cell with recycling of $SO_4^=$ back into the lumen by $SO_4^=$-HCO_3^- exchange would result in net active HCO_3^- absorption indirectly coupled to the luminal membrane Na^+ gradient. Because Na^+-$SO_4^=$ cotransport is electroneutral with a 2 Na^+:$SO_4^=$ stoichiometry (64, 91), Na^+-coupled HCO_3^- absorption occurring via recycling of $SO_4^=$ would have a net stoichiometry of Na^+: SO_4 per acid-base equivalent, which is the same as that of the Na^+-H^+ exchanger.

Oxalate-HCO_3^- and oxalate-$SO_4^=$ exchanges across the luminal and basolateral membranes may participate in the bidirectional transport of oxalate that occurs in the proximal tubule (98). With particular regard to Cl^- transport, recall the need for a mechanism to recycle oxalate back into the cell across the luminal membrane if significant Cl^- absorption is to occur via the Cl^--oxalate exchanger. Outward gradients of $SO_4^=$ and $HCO_3^=$ are present across the luminal membrane owing to the secondary active absorption of $SO_4^=$ and secretion of acid, respectively. Uphill transport of oxalate into the cell across the luminal membrane could therefore take place by oxalate-$SO_4^=$ exchange and oxalate-HCO_3^- exchange, which are modes of the $SO_4^=$-HCO_3^- exchanger. To the extent that direct $SO_4^=$-Cl^- exchange could take place across the luminal membrane (not illustrated in Figure 5), Na^+-$SO_4^=$ cotransport with recycling of $SO_4^=$ in exchange for luminal Cl^- could contribute to active Cl^- absorption without the need for oxalate as an intermediary.

Studies using isolated perfused proximal tubules of the rabbit strongly support the participation of basolateral membrane anion exchange an transtubular $SO_4^=$ transport (18). As mentioned above, studies in the in situ microperfused rat proximal tubule generally support the presence of a basolateral membrane $SO_4^=$-HCO_3^- exchanger shared by oxalate but separate from the pathways mediating transport of larger dicarboxylates and PAH (93). The possible roles of the $SO_4^=$(oxalate)-HCO_3^- exchanger in proximal tubule acid-base and Cl^- transport remain to be evaluated.

Na^+-INDEPENDENT Cl^--HCO_3^- EXCHANGER

Outward gradients of HCO_3^- induce the uphill accumulation of Cl^- in rat (37) and rabbit (38) renal basolateral membrane vesicles, consistent with the presence of Cl^--HCO_3^- exchange. Stimulation of Cl^- uptake by an inside-alkaline pH gradient in the nominal absence of CO_2/HCO_3 (37, 38) indicates that the system may be capable of Cl^- transport via H^+-Cl^- cotransport or Cl^--OH^- exchange, but it is also possible that the experimental solutions were not absolutely free of CO_2/HCO_3. Cl^--HCO_3^- exchange is electroneutral, sensitive to inhibition by DIDS, and is observed in the complete absence of Na^+ (37, 38).

As already discussed, the weight of evidence suggests that Cl^- interacts poorly if at all with the basolateral membrane $SO_4^=$-HCO_3^- exchanger. Similarly, $SO_4^=$, at concentrations that saturate the $SO_4^=$-HCO_3^- exchanger, has little inhibitory effect on the rate of Cl^--HCO_3^- exchange in rabbit renal basolateral membrane vesicles (S. M. Grassl & P. S. Aronson, unpublished observations). Thus, unlike red cell Band 3 which mediates transport of both Cl^- and $SO_4^=$, renal basolateral membranes appear to contain separate Cl^--HCO_3^- and $SO_4^=$-HCO_3^- exchangers.

There is conflicting evidence concerning the activity of Cl^--OH^- or Cl^--HCO_3^- exchange in luminal membrane vesicles. Whereas some studies have found that the apparent coupling between fluxes of Cl^- and OH^- can be almost entirely eliminated by maneuvers designed to prevent the generation of anion diffusion potentials that would otherwise influence anion fluxes (23, 46, 79), other studies have supported the existence of an appreciable rate of direct electroneutral Cl^--OH^- exchange (25, 82, 97). Probably a more relevant issue is whether appreciable $Cl^--HCO_3^-$ exchange takes place in luminal membrane vesicles, since in preparations where $Cl^--HCO_3^-$ exchange has been clearly documented—such as amphibian renal microvillus membrane vesicles (78), mammalian renal basolateral membrane vesicles (37, 38), and ileal microvillus membrane vesicles (59)—the stimulation of Cl^- flux by an imposed pH gradient is much larger in the presence than in the absence of a CO_2/HCO_3 buffer system. In fact, the results of studies that have measured the effect of HCO_3^- gradients on Cl^- flux in renal microvillus membrane vesicles do not rule out the presence of a small component of $Cl^--HCO_3^-$ exchange on the luminal membrane of the proximal tubule cell (37, 53).

The possible physiological role of the basolateral membrane $Cl^--HCO_3^-$ exchanger is illustrated in Figure 6. The outward electrochemical gradient for HCO_3^- is greater than that for Cl^- across the basolateral membrane (21, 24, 104). Thus, the net process mediated would be the exchange of intracellular HCO_3^- for peritubular Cl^-. By facilitating the exit of HCO_3^- accumulated in the cell as the result of H^+ secretion across the luminal membrane, the basolateral membrane $Cl^--HCO_3^-$ exchanger would participate in the process of transtubular HCO_3^- absorption. Indeed, studies of HCO_3^- transport in the intact proximal tubule of the rat support a role for basolateral $Cl^--HCO_3^-$ exchange in mediating transtubular HCO_3^- absorption (19, 92), although this probably represents a minor pathway for basolateral exit of HCO_3^- compared to $Na^+-HCO_3^-$ cotransport (3, 6, 20, 73).

Luminal membrane $Cl^--HCO_3^-$ exchange could play a role in the absorption of Cl^-, as the uptake of Cl^- into the cell would be driven by the outward HCO_3^- gradient across the luminal membrane. However, as discussed, stud-

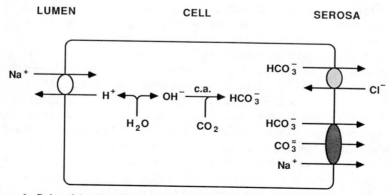

Figure 6   Roles of the $Cl^--HCO_3^-$ exchanger and the $Na^+-HCO_3^-$ cotransporter in mediating exit of HCO_3^- across the basolateral membrane.

ies using microvillus membrane vesicles suggest that the rate of $Cl^- - OH^-$ or $Cl^- - HCO_3^-$ exchange, if it occurs at all, is modest compared to the rate of Cl^--formate exchange (25, 46, 52). Furthermore, as mentioned above, studies on intact proximal tubules of rat and rabbit find that addition of Cl^- to an initially Cl^--free luminal perfusate causes a much larger acidification of the cell in the presence of than in the absence of formate (4, 11), which indicates that Cl^--formate exchange is the dominant mechanism for luminal membrane Cl^--base exchange. Indeed, the rate of luminal membrane Cl^--base exchange measured even in the absence of added formate may represent Cl^--formate exchange to the extent that formate is produced in proximal tubule cells. On the other hand, the formate-independent rate of luminal membrane Cl^--base exchange may reflect true $Cl^- - HCO_3^-$ exchange. Thus, although present evidence argues against an appreciable rate of luminal membrane $Cl^- - HCO_3^-$ exchange in the mammalian proximal tubule, a low rate of luminal membrane $Cl^- - HCO_3^-$ exchange cannot be excluded.

Na^+-COUPLED $Cl^- - HCO_3^-$ EXCHANGER

Intracellular pH regulation in invertebrate cells occurs predominantly via the operation of a Na^+-dependent $Cl^- - HCO_3^-$ exchanger (17, 88). This transport system couples the electroneutral, HCO_3^--dependent movement of 1 Na^+ and two equivalents of base in one direction, to the movement of 1 Cl^- in the opposite direction. Through the operation of this system the inwardly directed electrochemical gradient for Na^+ can drive the uphill entry of HCO_3^- into the cell, coupled to the efflux of Cl^- from the cell.

Studies on the amphibian proximal tubule suggest that basolateral membrane Na^+-coupled $Cl^- - HCO_3^-$ exchange plays a major role in mediating the exit of Cl^- from the cell (41). Given that the mechanism of Cl^- exit across the basolateral membrane of the mammalian proximal tubule cell has not been defined with certainty, attention has recently been focused on the possible presence of the Na^+-coupled $Cl^- - HCO_3^-$ exchanger at this site.

Studies using basolateral membrane vesicles have yielded conflicting evidence on this issue. Whereas there was no effect of Na^+ on HCO_3^- gradient-stimulated fluxes of Cl^- in rat basolateral membrane vesicles (37), an outward Na^+ gradient augmented the rate of HCO_3^- gradient-stimulated uptake of Cl^- into rabbit basolateral membrane vesicles (27). It should be recognized that observing *trans*-stimulation of Cl^- flux by Na^+ does not prove that Cl^- flux is actually coupled to a flux of Na^+. *Trans*-stimulation by Na^+ could result from a direct or indirect modifier effect of internal Na^+ on the rate of Cl^- transport. Proof of coupled transport of two solutes requires either that a gradient of one solute can drive the uphill transport of the second solute in the absence of other driving forces, or that mutual stoichiometric coupling of fluxes of the two solutes can be demonstrated (7, 90). Neither of these criteria has been met for the case of Na^+-coupled Cl^--HCO_3^- exchange in renal basolateral membrane vesicles.

Studies of the rat proximal tubule cell indicate that the effects of peritubular Cl^- on intracellular pH are largely Na^+-dependent, consistent with the presence of Na^+-coupled Cl^--HCO_3^- exchange across the basolateral membrane (6). However, as just discussed, such an observation does not by itself prove the presence of a Na^+-coupled Cl^--HCO_3^- exchanger. Thus although there is suggestive evidence for a Na^+-coupled Cl^--HCO_3^- exchanger that may play an important role in mediating exit of Cl^- across the basolateral membrane of the proximal tubule cell, further studies are needed to clarify this issue.

Na^+-HCO_3^- COTRANSPORTER

A process of basolateral membrane Na^+-HCO_3^- cotransport was first described in studies of intracellular pH regulation in the amphibian proximal tubule (16). Studies using membrane vesicles (1, 36) and microperfusion of renal tubules (3, 13, 73, 103) have confirmed the presence of this transport system in the basolateral membrane of the rabbit and rat proximal tubule.

Na^+-HCO_3^- cotransport is sensitive to inhibition by disulfonic stilbenes, is Cl^--independent, and is electrogenic and associated with a net flux of negative charge, consistent with the cotransport of more than one equivalent of base per Na^+ (1, 3, 13, 16, 36, 73, 103). In fact, the stoichiometry of cotransport is 3 HCO_3^-:Na^+, or a thermodynamically equivalent process (85, 103).

The ionic mechanism of the Na^+-HCO_3^- cotransporter has been evaluated in rabbit renal basolateral membrane vesicles (84). Na^+ uptake is stimulated when [$CO_3^=$] is increased at constant [HCO_3^-], which indicates the existence of a transport site for $CO_3^=$. In the presence of HCO_3^-, Na^+ influx is stimulated by an inward sulfite gradient. Sulfite-stimulated Na^+ influx is DIDS-sensitive, consistent with the idea that it occurs via the Na^+-HCO_3^- cotransport system. Increasing [$CO_3^=$] at constant [HCO_3^-] reduces the stimulation of Na^+ influx by sulfite and suggests competition between sulfite and $CO_3^=$ at a common divalent anion site. Additional divalent anions that were tested, such as $SO_4^=$, oxalate and $HPO_4^=$, do not interact at this site. Sulfite stimulation of Na^+ influx is absolutely HCO_3^--dependent and increases as a function of [HCO_3^-], which indicates the presence of a separate HCO_3^- site. These findings suggest that the actual stoichiometry of cotransport is 1 HCO_3^- : 1 $CO_3^=$: 1 Na^+.

The possibility that Na^+ interacts via ion pair formation with $CO_3^=$ was also evaluated (84). Li^+, which has higher affinity than Na^+ for ion pair formation with $CO_3^=$, has >5-fold lower affinity than Na^+ for the Na^+-

HCO_3^- cotransport system; an argument against ion pair formation. Moreover, the organic cation harmaline acts as a competitive inhibitor of Na^+ influx and suggests the existence of a distinct cation site. Thus, the process of Na^+-HCO_3^- cotransport likely takes place via $1:1:1$ cotransport of $CO_3^=$, HCO_3^-, and Na^+ on distinct sites.

The physiological role of the Na^+-HCO_3^- cotransporter, as illustrated in Figure 6, is to mediate the exit of HCO_3^- across the basolateral membrane of the proximal tubule cell. Indeed, studies of rat and rabbit proximal tubules indicate that this pathway is not only the predominant mechanism for exit of HCO_3^- across the basolateral membrane (3, 73, 103), but is the predominant acid-base transporter influencing intracellular pH in these cells (5, 60). It should be emphasized that because of the stoichiometry of the transporter (3 equivalents of base, one Na^+, and two negative charges per transport cycle), the inside-negative membrane potential is sufficient to drive HCO_3^- exit against the inward concentration gradients of HCO_3^- and Na^+ that are present across the basolateral membrane of the proximal tubule cell under physiological conditions (73, 103, 104).

p-AMINOHIPPURATE-DICARBOXYLATE EXCHANGER

PAH is secreted in the proximal tubule against a large concentration gradient and the uphill step is located at the basolateral membrane (89). However, studies using renal cortical basolateral membrane vesicles have yielded conflicting data on the mechanism for uphill PAH transport. In several studies (12, 34, 51, 54, 56, 80) an inward Na^+ gradient was found to stimulate the rate of PAH uptake, consistent with a process of Na^+-PAH cotransport; yet in another study (81), PAH uptake was unchanged when extravesicular Na^+ was replaced by K^+, an argument against Na^+-PAH cotransport. More consistent has been the observation of PAH-PAH exchange (12, 34, 45, 54, 56, 81) that suggests the presence of an anion exchange process for PAH transport across the basolateral membrane.

Results of a recent study using rat renal basolateral membrane vesicles may explain these discrepancies (81). Outward gradients of dicarboxylates greater than 4 carbon atoms in length (e.g. glutarate, suberate) stimulate PAH uptake, consistent with the presence of a PAH-dicarboxylate exchanger. This process is Na^+-independent. The basolateral membrane contains a separate transport system that mediates the Na^+ cotransport of dicarboxylates of 4–6 carbon atoms in length (22, 94). An inward Na^+ gradient drives uphill PAH uptake into basolateral membrane vesicles in the presence of a dicarboxylate such as glutarate (5 carbons in length) that can share the PAH-exchanger and the Na^+-dicarboxylate cotransporter (81). In essence, the recycling of the dicarboxylate couples PAH transport to the Na^+ gradient across the basolateral membrane (81), as shown in Figure 7. It has been suggested (81) that contamination of mannitol- and gluconate-containing media with dicarboxylates accounts for the apparently direct stimulation of PAH uptake by Na^+ in earlier studies.

As shown in Figure 7, the physiological role of the dicarboxylate-PAH exchanger is to mediate uphill PAH uptake into the cell across the basolateral membrane, driven by the outward gradients of dicarboxylates that are accumulated in the cell by Na^+ cotransport across both cell surfaces (22, 102). This model is supported by studies on the intact proximal tubule of the rat that indicate that the process of PAH uptake across the basolateral membrane involves an interaction with dicarboxylates via a pathway separate from that mediating Na^+-dicarboxylate cotransport (93, 94). As mentioned above, studies on the microperfused rat tubule also support the notion that the PAH transporter (i.e. PAH-dicarboxylate exchanger) is separate from the basolateral $SO_4^=$ transporter (i.e. $SO_4^=$-HCO_3^- exchanger) (93, 94).

RELATIONSHIP TO ANION TRANSPORTERS IN OTHER CELLS AND TISSUES

The anion exchangers and stilbene-sensitive transporters unequivocally shown to be present in the proximal tubule are listed in Table 1, along with their membrane localization. A complete review of similar transport processes in other tissues is beyond the scope of the present chapter. Nevertheless, it should be emphasized that systems with similar if not identical properties to those listed in Table 1 are indeed present outside the proximal tubule. Examples include cinnamate-sensitive lactate-OH^- exchange (or H^+-lactate cotransport) in red cells (32, 33, 43) and Ehrlich ascites cells (86); formate-

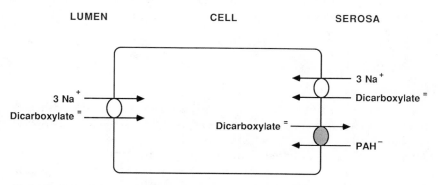

Figure 7   Role of the PAH-dicarboxylate exchanger in mediating active uptake of PAH across the basolateral membrane.

Table 1   Anion exchange and stilbene-sensitive transport processes in the mammalian proximal tubule

Transporter	Membrane localization
Urate/anion exchanger	Luminal
Monocarboxylate/OH^- exchanger	Luminal and basolateral
Cl^-/formate exchanger	Luminal
Cl^-/oxalate exchanger	Luminal
$SO_4^=$(oxalate)/HCO_3^- exchanger	Luminal and basolateral
Cl^-/HCO_3^- exchanger	Basolateral
Na^+/HCO_3^- cotransporter	Basolateral
PAH/dicarboxylate exchanger	Basolateral

Cl^- exchange and Cl^--oxalate exchange in ileal brush border membrane vesicles (57, 58); SO_4^- (oxalate)-HCO_3^- exchange by a pathway not shared by Cl^- in liver canalicular membrane vesicles (67); Cl^--HCO_3^- exchange by a pathway not shared by $SO_4^=$ in ileal brush border membrane vesicles (58, 59) and liver canalicular membrane vesicles (66); and Cl^--independent, electrogenic Na^+-HCO_3^- cotransport in corneal endothelial cells (48) and gastric oxyntic cells (30).

None of the proximal tubule anion transporters listed in Table 1 has properties identical to red cell Band 3, which can mediate Cl^--HCO_3^- exchange but also has appreciable affinity for $SO_4^=$; and which can mediate transport of Na^+-$CO_3^=$ but only in electroneutral exchange for Cl^- (35). There is evidence for yet additional anion exchangers and/or stilbene-sensitive transporters that are distinct from Band 3 and from the pathways listed in Table 1. One example is a transport system mediating Cl^--$SO_4^=$ exchange that is distinct from the Cl^--HCO_3^- exchanger in a glioma cell line (100). The independence of pathways mediating Cl^--$SO_4^=$ exchange and Cl^--HCO_3^- exchange is also well-documented in the ileum, where the two processes are segregated to the basolateral membrane and the luminal membrane, respectively (59, 76).

CONCLUSION

The proximal tubule and other tissues contain multiple anion exchangers and/or stilbene-sensitive transporters that are distinct from each other and from erythrocyte Band 3. The differences in properties among these transporters subserve their varied physiological roles. Yet each of these transporters is similar to Band 3 in one or more important properties. It is therefore tempting to speculate that these transporters are structurally related to Band 3. Indeed, the existence of proteins structurally related to Band 3 has been recently documented in nonerythroid cells by use of immunologic and molecular biologic techniques (2, 28, 29, 31, 55, 77, 95, 101). During the next few years, comparing the structural and functional properties of Band 3-related transporters with each other and with Band 3 itself should provide important insight into the molecular mechanisms underlying anion transport.

ACKNOWLEDGMENT

The author's work in this area has been supported by National Institutes of Health grants DK-17433 and DK-33793, and an Established Investigatorship from the American Heart Association.

Literature Cited

1. Akiba, T., Alpern, R. J., Eveloff, J., Calamina, J., Warnock, D. G. 1986. Electrogenic sodium/bicarbonate co-transport in rabbit renal cortical basolateral membrane vesicles. *J. Clin. Invest.* 78:1472–78

2. Alper, S. L., Kopito, R. R., Lodish, H. F. 1987. A molecular biological approach to the study of anion transport. *Kidney Int.* 32(Suppl. 23):S117–28

3. Alpern, R. J. 1985. Mechanism of basolateral membrane H$^+$/OH$^-$/HCO$_3^-$ transport in the rat proximal tubule convoluted tubule. A sodium-coupled electrogenic process. *J. Gen. Physiol.* 86:613–36

4. Alpern, R. J. 1987. Apical membrane chloride/base exchange in the rat proximal convoluted tubule. *J. Clin. Invest.* 79:1026–30

5. Alpern, R. J., Chambers, M. 1986. Cell pH in the rat proximal convoluted tubule. Regulation by luminal and peritubular pH and sodium concentration. *J. Clin. Invest.* 78:502–10

6. Alpern, R. J., Chambers, M. 1987. Basolateral membrane Cl/HCO$_3$ exchange in the rat proximal convoluted tubule. *J. Gen. Physiol.* 89:581–98

7. Aronson, P. S. 1981. Identifying secondary active transport in epithelia. *Am. J. Physiol.* 240:F1–11

8. Aronson, P. S. 1983. Mechanisms of active H$^+$ secretion in the proximal tubule. *Am. J. Physiol.* 245:F647–59

9. Aronson, P. S. 1985. Kinetic properties of the plasma membrane Na$^+$-H$^+$ exchanger. *Annu. Rev. Physiol.* 47:545–60

10. Barac-Nieto, M., Murer, H., Kinne, R. 1980. Lactate-sodium cotransport in rat renal brush border membranes. *Am. J. Physiol.* 239:F496–506

11. Baum, M. 1988. Effect of luminal chloride on cell pH in rabbit proximal tubule. *Am. J. Physiol.* 254:F677–83

12. Berner, W., Kinne, R. 1976. Transport of p-aminohippuric acid by plasma membrane vesicles isolated from rat kidney cortex. *Pflügers Arch.* 361:269–77

13. Biagi, B. A. 1985. Effects of the anion transport inhibitor, SITS, on the proximal straight tubule of the rabbit perfused *in vitro*. *J. Membr. Biol.* 88:25–31

14. Bidet, M., Merot, J., Tauc, M., Poujeol, P. 1988. Role of monocarboxylic acid transport in intracellular pH regulation of isolated proximal cells. *Biochim. Biophys. Acta* 938:247–69

15. Blomstedt, J. W., Aronson, P. S. 1980. pH gradient-stimulated transport of urate and para-aminohippurate in dog renal microvillus membrane vesicles. *J. Clin. Invest.* 65:931–34

16. Boron, W. F., Boulpaep, E. L. 1983. Intracellular pH regulation in the renal proximal tubule of the salamander. Basolateral HCO$_3^-$ transport. *J. Gen. Physiol.* 81:53–94

17. Boron, W. F., McCormick, W. C., Roos, A. 1981. pH regulation in barnacle muscle fibers: dependence on extracellular sodium and bicarbonate. *Am. J. Physiol.* 240:C80–89

18. Brazy, P. C., Dennis, V. W. 1981. Sulfate transport in rabbit proximal convoluted tubule: presence of anion exchange. *Am. J. Physiol.* 241:F300–307

19. Brisolla-Diuana, A., Amorena, C., Malnic, G. 1985. Transfer of base across the basolateral membrane of cortical tubules of rat kidney. *Pflügers Arch.* 405:209–15

20. Burckhardt, B.-Ch., Cassola, A. C., Frömter, E. 1984. Electrophysiological analysis of bicarbonate permeation across the peritubular cell membrane of rat kidney proximal tubule. II. Exclusion of HCO$_3^-$-effects on other ion permeabilities and of coupled electroneutral

HCO$_3^-$ transport. *Pflügers Arch.* 401: 43–51

21. Burckhardt, B.-Ch., Sato, K., Frömter, E. 1984. Electrophysiological analysis of bicarbonate permeation across the peritubular cell membrane of rat kidney proximal tubule. I. Basic observations. *Pflügers Arch.* 401:34–42

22. Burckhardt, G. 1984. Sodium-dependent dicarboxylate transport in rat renal basolateral membrane vesicles. *Pflügers Arch.* 401:254–61

23. Cassano, G., Stieger, B., Murer, H. 1984. Na/H- and Cl/OH- exchange in rat jejunal and rat proximal tubular brush border membrane vesicles. *Pflügers Arch.* 400:309–17

24. Cassola, A. C., Mollenhauer, M., Frömter, E. 1983. The intracellular chloride activity of rat kidney proximal tubular cells. *Pflügers Arch.* 399:259–65

25. Chen, P.-Y., Illsley, N. P., Verkman, A. S. 1988. Renal brush-border chloride transport mechanisms characterized using a fluorescent indicator. *Am. J. Physiol.* 254:F114–20

26. Chen, P.-Y., Verkman, A. S. 1987. Renal basolateral membrane anion transporter characterized by a fluorescent disulfonic stilbene. *J. Membr. Biol.* 100:1–12

27. Chen, P.-Y., Verkman, A. S. 1988. Sodium-dependent chloride transport in basolateral membrane vesicles isolated from rabbit proximal tubule. *Biochemistry* 27:655–60

28. Cox, J. V., Lazarides, E. L. 1988. Alternative primary structures in the transmembrane domain of the chicken erythroid anion transporter. *Mol. Cell. Biol.* 8:1327–35

29. Cox, J. V., Moon, R. T., Lazarides, E. 1985. Anion transporter: highly cell-type-specific expression of distinct polypeptides and transcripts in erythroid and nonerythroid cells. *J. Cell Biol.* 100:1548–57

30. Curci, S., Debellis, L., Frömter, E. 1987. Evidence for rheogenic sodium bicarbonate cotransport in the basolateral membrane of oxyntic cells of frog gastric fundus. *Pflügers Arch.* 408:497–504

31. Demuth, D. R., Showe, L. C., Ballantine, M., Palumbo, A., Fraser, P. J., et al. 1986. Cloning and structural characterization of a human nonerythroid band 3-like protein. *EMBO J.* 5:1205–14

32. Deuticke, B., Beyer, E., Forst, B. 1982. Discrimination of three parallel pathways of lactate transport in the human erythrocyte membrane by inhibitors and kinetic properties. *Biochim. Biophys. Acta.* 684:96–110

33. Dubinsky, W. P., Racker, E. 1978. The mechanism of lactate transport in human erythrocytes. *J. Membr. Biol.* 44:25–36

34. Eveloff, J. 1987. *p*-Aminohippurate transport in basal-lateral membrane vesicles from rabbit renal cortex: stimulation by pH and sodium gradients. *Biochim. Biophys. Acta* 897:474–80

35. Funder, J. 1980. Alkali metal cation transport through the human erythrocyte membrane by the anion exchange mechanism. *Acta Physiol. Scand.* 108:31–37

36. Grassl, S. M., Aronson, P. S. 1986. Na$^+$/HCO$_3$ cotransport in basolateral membrane vesicles isolated from rabbit renal cortex. *J. Biol. Chem.* 261:8778–83

37. Grassl, S. M., Holohan, P. D., Ross, C. R. 1987. Cl$^-$-HCO$_3^-$ exchange in rat renal basolateral membrane vesicles. *Biochim. Biophys. Acta* 905:475–84

38. Grassl, S. M., Karniski, L. P., Aronson, P. S. 1985. Cl-HCO$_3$ exchange in rabbit renal cortical basolateral membrane vesicles. *Kidney Int.* 27:282 (Abstr.)

39. Guggino, S. E., Aronson, P. S. 1985. Paradoxical effects of pyrazinoate and nicotinate on urate transport in dog renal microvillus membranes. *J. Clin. Invest.* 76:543–47

40. Guggino, S. E., Martin, G. J., Aronson, P. S. 1983. Specificity and modes of the anion exchanger in dog renal microvillus membrane vesicles. *Am. J. Physiol.* 244:F612–21

41. Guggino, W. B., London, R., Boulpaep, E. L., Giebisch, G. 1983. Chloride transport across the basolateral cell membrane of the *Necturus* proximal tubule: dependence on bicarbonate and sodium. *J. Membr. Biol.* 71:227–40

42. Hagenbuch, B., Stange, G., Murer, H. 1985. Transport of sulphate in rat jejunal and rat proximal tubular basolateral membrane vesicles. *Pflügers Arch.* 405:202–8

43. Halestrap, A. P. 1976. Transport of pyruvate and lactate into human erythrocytes. *Biochem. J.* 156:193–207

44. Hoffmann, E. K. 1986. Anion transport systems in the plasma membrane of vertebrate cells. *Biochim. Biophys. Acta* 864:1–31

45. Hori, R., Takano, M., Okano, T., Kitazawa, S., Inui, K.-I. 1982. Mechanisms of *p*-aminohippurate transport by brush-border and basolateral membrane vesicles isolated from rat kidney cortex. *Biochim. Biophys. Acta* 692:97–100

46. Ives, H. E., Chen, P.-Y., Verkman, A. S. 1986. Mechanism of coupling between Cl⁻ and OH⁻ transport in renal brush-border membranes. *Biochim. Biophys. Acta* 863:91–100

47. Jennings, M. L. 1985. Kinetics and mechanism of anion transport in red blood cells. *Annu. Rev. Physiol.* 47:519–33

48. Jentch, T. J., Keller, S. K., Koch, M., Wiederholt, M. 1984. Evidence for coupled transport of bicarbonate and sodium in cultured bovine corneal endothelial cells. *J. Membr. Biol.* 81:189–204

49. Kahn, A. M., Aronson, P. S. 1983. Urate transport via anion exchange in dog renal microvillus membrane vesicles. *Am. J. Physiol.* 244:F56–63

50. Kahn, A. M., Branham, S., Weinman, E. J. 1983. Mechanism of urate and *p*-aminohippurate transport in rat renal microvillus membrane vesicles. *Am. J. Physiol.* 245:F151–58

51. Kahn, A. M., Shelat, H., Weinman, E. J. 1985. Urate and *p*-aminohippurate transport in rat renal basolateral vesicles. *Am. J. Physiol.* 249:F654–61

52. Karniski, L. P., Aronson, P. S. 1985. Chloride/formate exchange with formic acid recycling: a mechanism of active chloride transport across epithelial membranes. *Proc. Natl. Acad. Sci. USA* 82:6362–65

53. Karniski, L. P., Aronson, P. S. 1987. Anion exchange pathways for Cl⁻ transport in rabbit renal microvillus membranes. *Am. J. Physiol.* 253:F513–21

54. Kasher, J. S., Holohan, P. D., Ross, C. R. 1983. Na⁺ gradient-dependent *p*-aminohippurate (PAH) transport in rat basolateral membrane vesicles. *J. Pharmacol. Exp. Ther.* 227:122–29

55. Kay, M. M. B., Tracey, C. M., Goodman, J. R., Cone, J. C., Bassel, P. S. 1983. Polypeptides immunologically related to band 3 are present in nucleated somatic cells. *Proc. Natl. Acad. Sci. USA* 80:6882–86

56. Kinsella, J. L., Holohan, P. D., Pessah, N. I., Ross, C. R. 1979. Transport of organic ions in renal cortical luminal and antiluminal membrane vesicles. *J. Pharmacol. Exp. Ther.* 209:443–50

57. Knickelbein, R. G., Aronson, P. S., Dobbins, J. W. 1986. Oxalate transport by anion exchange across rabbit ileal brush border. *J. Clin. Invest.* 77:170–75

58. Knickelbein, R. G., Aronson, P. S., Schron, C. M., Dobbins, J. W. 1985. Substrate and inhibitor specificity of anion exchangers on the brush border membrane of rabbit ileum. *J. Membr. Biol.* 88:199–204

59. Knickelbein, R., Aronson, P. S., Schron, C. M., Seifter, J., Dobbins, J. W. 1985. Na and Cl transport across rabbit ileal brush border. II. Evidence for Cl : HCO₃ exchange and mechanism of coupling. *Am. J. Physiol.* 249:G236–45

60. Krapf, R., Berry, C. A., Alpern, R. J., Rector, F. C., Jr. 1988. Regulation of cell pH by ambient bicarbonate, carbon dioxide tension, and pH in the rabbit proximal convoluted tubule. *J. Clin. Invest.* 81:381–89

61. Kuo, S.-M., Aronson, P. S. 1988. Oxalate transport via the sulfate-HCO₃ exchanger in rabbit renal basolateral membrane vesicles. *J. Biol. Chem.* 263:9710–17

62. Kuo, S.-M., Aronson, P. S. 1988. Oxalate-OH exchange in rabbit renal microvillus membrane vesicles. *FASEB J.* 2:A753 (Abstr.)

63. Löw, I., Friedrich, T., Burckhardt, G. 1984. Properties of an anion exchanger in rat renal basolateral membrane vesicles. *Am. J. Physiol.* 246:F334–42

64. Lücke, H., Stange, G., Murer, H. 1979. Sulfate-ion/sodium-ion co-transport by brush-border membrane vesicles from rat kidney cortex. *Biochem. J.* 182:223–29

65. Massad, T. C., Ach, J. P., Aronson, P. S. 1987. pH-coupled lactate transport in renal microvillus membrane vesicles. *Kidney Int.* 31:412 (Abstr.)

66. Meier, P. J., Knickelbein, R., Moseley, R. H., Dobbins, J. W., Boyer, J. L. 1985. Evidence for carrier-mediated chloride/bicarbonate exchange in canalicular rat liver plasma membrane vesicles. *J. Clin. Invest.* 75:1256–63

67. Meier, P. J., Valantinas, J., Hugentobler, G., Rahm, I. 1987. Bicarbonate sulfate exchange in canalicular rat liver plasma membrane vesicles. *Am. J. Physiol.* 253:G461–68

68. Mengual, R., Leblanc, G., Sudaka, P. 1983. The mechanism of Na⁺-L-lactate cotransport by brush-border membrane vesicles from horse kidney. *J. Biol. Chem.* 256:15071–78

69. Nord, E. P., Wright, S. H., Kippen, I., Wright, E. M. 1983. Specificity of the Na⁺-dependent monocarboxylic acid transport pathway in rabbit renal brush border membranes. *J. Membr. Biol.* 72:213–21

70. Passow, H. 1986. Molecular aspects of band 3 protein-mediated anion transport across the red blood cell membrane. *Rev. Biochem. Pharmacol.* 103:61–223

71. Pritchard, J. B. 1987. Sulfate-bicar-

bonate exchange in brush-border membranes from rat renal cortex. *Am. J. Physiol.* 252:F346–56

72. Pritchard, J. B., Renfro, J. L. 1983. Renal sulfate transport at the basolateral membrane is mediated by anion exchange. *Proc. Natl. Acad. Sci. USA* 80:2603–7

73. Sasaki, S., Shiigai, T., Yoshiyama, N., Takeuchi, J. 1987. Mechanism of bicarbonate exit across the basolateral membrane of rabbit proximal straight tubule. *Am. J. Physiol.* 252:F11–18

74. Schild, L., Giebisch, G., Karniski, L. P., Aronson, P. S. 1987. Effect of formate on volume reabsorption in the rabbit proximal tubule. *J. Clin. Invest.* 79:32–38

75. Schneider, E. G., Durham, J. C., Sacktor, B. 1984. Sodium-dependent transport of inorganic sulfate by rabbit renal brush-border membrane vesicles. *J. Biol. Chem.* 259:14591–99

76. Schron, C. M., Knickelbein, R. G., Aronson, P. S., Dobbins, J. W. 1987. Evidence for carrier-mediated Cl-SO$_4$ exchange in rabbit ileal basolateral membrane vesicles. *Am. J. Physiol.* 253:G404–10

77. Schuster, V. L., Bonsib, S. M., Jennings, M. L. 1986. Two types of collecting duct mitochondria-rich (intercalated) cells: lectin and band 3 cytochemistry. *Am. J. Physiol.* 251:C347–55

78. Seifter, J. L., Aronson, P. S. 1984. Cl$^-$ transport via anion exchange in *Necturus* renal microvillus membranes. *Am. J. Physiol.* 247:F888–95

79. Seifter, J. L., Knickelbein, R., Aronson, P. S. 1984. Absence of Cl-OH exchange and Na-Cl cotransport in rabbit renal microvillus membrane vesicles. *Am. J. Physiol.* 247:F753–59

80. Sheikh, M. I., Møller, J. V. 1982. Na$^+$-gradient-dependent stimulation of renal transport of *p*-aminohippurate. *Biochem. J.* 208:243–46

81. Shimada, H., Moewes, B., Burckhardt, G. 1987. Indirect coupling to Na$^+$ of *p*-aminohippuric acid uptake into rat renal basolateral membrane vesicles. *Am. J. Physiol.* 253:F795–801

82. Shiuan, D., Weinstein, S. W. 1984. Evidence for electroneutral chloride transport in rabbit cortical brush border membrane vesicles. *Am. J. Physiol.* 247:F837–47

83. Siebens, A. W., Boron, W. F. 1987. Effect of electroneutral luminal and basolateral lactate transport on intracellular pH in salamander proximal tubules. *J. Gen. Physiol.* 90:799–831

84. Soleimani, M., Aronson, P. S. 1988. Ionic mechanism of Na$^+$:HCO$_3^-$ cotransport in renal basolateral membrane vesicles (BLMV). *Kidney Int.* 33:407 (Abstr.)

85. Soleimani, M., Grassl, S. M., Aronson, P. S. 1987. Stoichiometry of Na$^+$-HCO$_3^-$ cotransport in basolateral membrane vesicles isolated from rabbit renal cortex. *J. Clin. Invest.* 79:1276–80

86. Spencer, T. L., Lehninger, A. L. 1976. L-lactate transport in Ehrlich ascites-tumour cells. *Biochem. J.* 154:405–14

87. Talor, Z., Gold, R. M., Yang, W.-C., Arruda, J. A. L. 1987. Anion exchanger is present in both luminal and basolateral renal membranes. *Eur. J. Biochem.* 164:695–702

88. Thomas, R. C. 1977. The role of bicarbonate, chloride and sodium ions in the regulation on intracellular pH in snail neurons. *J. Physiol. (London)* 273:317–38

89. Tune, B. M., Burg, M. B., Patlak, C. S. 1969. Characteristics of *p*-aminohippurate transport in proximal renal tubules. *Am. J. Physiol.* 217:1057–63

90. Turner, R. J. 1983. Quantitative studies of cotransport systems: models and vesicles. *J. Membr. Biol.* 76:1–15

91. Turner, R. J. 1984. Sodium-dependent sulfate transport in renal outer cortical brush border membrane vesicles. *Am. J. Physiol.* 247:F793–98

92. Ullrich, K. J., Papavassilou, F. 1987. Contraluminal bicarbonate transport in the proximal tubule of the rat kidney. *Pflügers Arch.* 410:501–4

93. Ullrich, K. J., Rumrich, G. 1988. Contraluminal transport systems in the proximal renal tubule involved in the secretion of organic anions. *Am. J. Physiol.* 254:F453–62

94. Ullrich, K. J., Rumrich, G., Fritzch, G., Klöss, S. 1987. Contraluminal *para*-aminohippurate (PAH) transport in the proximal tubule of the rat kidney. II. Specificity: aliphatic dicarboxylic acids. *Pflügers Arch.* 408:38–45

95. Wagner, S., Vogel, R., Lietzke, R., Koob, R., Drenckhahn, D. 1987. Immunochemical characterization of a band 3-like anion exchanger in collecting duct of human kidney. *Am. J. Physiol.* 253:F213–21

96. Walter, A., Gutknecht, J. 1984. Monocarboxylic acid permeation through lipid bilayer membranes. *J. Membr. Biol.* 77:255–64

97. Warnock, D. G., Yee, V. J. 1981. Chloride uptake by brush border membrane vesicles isolated from rabbit renal cortex. *J. Clin. Invest.* 67:103–15

98. Weinman, E. J., Frankfurt, S. J., Ince,

A., Sansom, S. 1978. Renal tubular transport of organic acids. *J. Clin. Invest.* 61:801–6

99. Weinman, E. J., Sansom, S. C., Bennett, S., Kahn, A. M. 1983. Effect of anion exchange inhibitors and *para*-aminohippurate on the transport of urate in the rat proximal tubule. *Kidney Int.* 23:832–37

100. Wolpaw, E. W., Martin, D. L. 1986. Sulfate-chloride exchange transport in a glioma cell line. *Biochim. Biophys. Acta* 855:302–11

101. Wolpaw, E. W., Martin, D. L. 1986. A membrane protein in LRM55 glial cells cross-reacts with antibody to the anion exchange carrier of human erythrocytes. *Neurosci. Lett.* 67:42–47

102. Wright, E. M. 1985. Transport of carboxylic acids by renal membrane vesicles. *Annu. Rev. Physiol.* 47:127–41

103. Yoshitomi, K., Burckhardt, B.-C., Frömter, E. 1985. Rheogenic sodium-bicarbonate cotransport in the peritubular cell membrane of rat renal proximal tubule. *Pflügers Arch.* 405:360–66

104. Yoshitomi, K., Frömter, E. 1985. How big is the electrochemical difference of Na^+ across rat renal proximal tubular cell membranes in vivo? *Pflügers Arch.* 405(Suppl. 1):S121–26

Annu. Rev. Physiol. 1989. 51:443–57

PROPERTIES AND DIVERSITY OF (Na-K-Cl) COTRANSPORTERS

Mark Haas

Departments of Pathology and Cellular and Molecular Physiology, Yale University School of Medicine, New Haven, Connecticut 06510

INTRODUCTION

A specific pathway that mediates the coupled, electrically neutral transport of Na, K, and Cl ions across cell membranes is present in a wide variety of animal tissues, and appears to serve a number of different physiological functions. (Na-K-Cl) cotransport is involved in transport of salt and water across both reabsorptive and secretory epithelia, including the thick ascending limb of Henle's loop (TALH) of mammalian kidney (33), distal tubule of amphibian kidney (67), Necturus gallbladder (12), shark rectal gland (46), rabbit parotid (91), and flounder intestine (72, 73). In other cells, including Ehrlich ascites tumor cells (30, 31) and human red blood cells (17), (Na-K-Cl) cotransport may play a role in the maintenance and regulation of cell volume. In excitable cells, such as squid axon (4, 85) and cardiac myocytes (57), this cotransporter may regulate the ion gradients that determine the resting membrane potential, and recent evidence suggests that the cotransport system of chick cardiac myocytes is stimulated by catecholamines, which enhance cardiac contractility (57). In avian red cells, (Na-K-Cl) cotransport is also stimulated by β-adrenergic catecholamines (44, 89, 92), and the high rate of cotransport in these cells may contribute to extrarenal potassium regulation in birds (43). Reduced levels of (Na-K-Cl) cotransport in vascular smooth muscle cells may reflect or even contribute to the pathogenesis of essential hypertension (71). As we continue to find (Na-K-Cl) cotransport in an increasing number of tissues, this pathway will likely be found to serve still other physiological functions, and abnormalities in its operation or regulation may prove to be important in the pathophysiology of specific disease states.

In this review, we compare properties of (Na-K-Cl) cotransport systems

443

from a wide variety of cells and tissues; these properties include stoichiometry, inhibition by loop diuretics, density of cotransporters in the cell membrane and turnover number, modes of regulation, and protein(s) that appear to comprise the cotransport system. We also review recent studies examining the relationship of (Na-K-Cl) cotransport to other cation-chloride cotransport systems [i.e. (Na-Cl) and (K-Cl) systems] in a number of cell types.

STOICHIOMETRY OF (Na-K-Cl) COTRANSPORT

In all tissues examined to date, (Na-K-Cl) cotransport is an electrically neutral process. Geck et al (31) demonstrated a stoichiometry of 1Na:1K:2Cl for the cotransport process in Ehrlich ascites cells, and this stoichiometry has since been found in nearly all tissues examined, ranging from intact epithelia and cultured epithelial cells to red blood cells from mammalian and avian species (9, 16, 44, 63, 73). The one clear exception to the 1Na:1K:2Cl stoichiometry is in the squid axon, where a cotransport of (2Na:1K:3Cl) has been shown in influx and efflux directions (4, 85).

An important consideration in interpreting stoichiometries of (Na-K-Cl) cotransport is the presence of one-for-one, chloride-dependent K/K and Na/Na exchanges. In at least some tissues, these exchanges occur in parallel with (Na-K-Cl) cotransport, and appear to represent partial reactions of the (Na-K-Cl) cotransporter (16, 56, 59, 60). The result of such exchanges can be discrepancies between cotransport stoichiometries obtained in net flux and unidirectional (tracer) flux studies in the same cells. For example, in duck red cells (43, 44) the stoichiometry of (Na-K-Cl) cotransport is found to be 1Na:1K:2Cl both in net flux studies and in "zero-trans" experiments in which unidirectional ion effluxes are studied in media free of Na, K, and Cl. However, when tracer Na and K effluxes are measured from fresh cells into media high in potassium, the chloride-dependent (or bumetanide-sensitive, see below) K efflux exceeds that of Na, because of the presence of K/K exchange (44, 59). Likewise, when unidirectional effluxes are measured using cells with an elevated Na content and high-Na media, Na efflux exceeds K efflux, as a result of Na/Na exchange (59). Thus, the apparent stoichiometry of (Na-K-Cl) cotransport, based on tracer fluxes, can vary depending on which exchange (K/K or Na/Na) is the predominant partial reaction of the cotransporter under the conditions used (59, 60). Similar chloride-dependent cation exchanges are found in human (11, 16, 19, 94) and ferret (C. Lytle & T. J. McManus, personal communication) red cells. The stoichiometry of 2Na:1K:3Cl reported for bumetanide-sensitive tracer influxes in ferret red cells (45) may thus reflect the presence of Na/Na exchange, since these cells lack Na,K-ATPase activity and are thus high in Na content (22).

INHIBITION BY AND BINDING OF LOOP DIURETICS

A property of all (Na-K-Cl) cotransport systems is inhibition by loop diuretics, including furosemide and bumetanide (79, 81, 87). Bumetanide, which in most tissues half-maximally (IC_{50}) inhibits cotransport at 0.05–0.5 μM under physiological ionic conditions (see below), has become the inhibitor of choice for most in vitro studies of (Na-K-Cl) cotransport. The cotransporter in the apical membrane of rabbit renal papillary surface epithelium is especially sensitive to bumetanide, with an IC_{50} of 5×10^{-11} M and full inhibition at 10^{-9} M (86). By contrast, the cotransport system in the basolateral membrane of shark rectal gland epithelium requires 5-μM bumetanide for 50% inhibition, and $\sim$100 μM for complete inhibition (81). At a concentration of 5 μM, bumetanide is still a rather specific inhibitor of (Na-K-Cl) cotransport in most tissues, though at 100 μM it partially inhibits other transport pathways including anion exchange (37) and (K-Cl) cotransport (50) in red cells.

Studies of the binding of radiolabelled loop diuretics have proven to be a valuable tool for understanding the mechanism by which these agents inhibit (Na-K-Cl) cotransport. Forbush & Palfrey (26) synthesized [^{3}H]bumetanide and studied its binding to membranes isolated from dog kidney outer medulla. Since then, many studies of the binding of [^{3}H]bumetanide and other diuretics to intact cells and membrane preparations from tissues exhibiting (Na-K-Cl) cotransport have been performed (24, 25, 32, 36, 38, 46, 47, 65, 74, 84). Those studies using [^{3}H]bumetanide are summarized in Table 1, which indicates the variability of different tissues with respect to affinity for [^{3}H]bumetanide and density of binding sites. Despite this variability, loop diuretic binding to different tissues is characterized by common properties, which appear to indicate a common mechanism of inhibition of (Na + K + Cl) cotransport by these diuretics in all tissues: (*a*) Loop diuretic binding requires the simultaneous presence of Na, K, and Cl in the binding medium. Removal of any one of these ions markedly reduces diuretic binding. Furthermore, the stimulatory effects of Na and K on diuretic binding appear to reflect binding of these ions to their respective sites on the cotransporter. For example, half-maximal stimulation of [^{3}H]bumetanide binding to dog kidney membranes occurs at 2-mM Na and 1-mM K, respectively (26); these are the respective levels of $[Na]_o$ and $[K]_o$ saturable required to half-maximally ($K\frac{1}{2}$) proimite (Na-K-Cl) cotransport in mammalian kidney TALH (33). Likewise, in duck red cells $\sim$4-mM [K] and $\sim$10mM$[Na]_o$ are required for both half-maximal [^{3}H]bumetanide binding and (Na-K-Cl) cotransport influx (38, 89). (*b*) While low concentrations of Cl are required for diuretic binding, high levels of Cl inhibit this binding, consistent with ion flux studies that suggest competition between loop diuretics and Cl for a common site (42, 58). Together, these findings suggest that loop diuretics bind preferably to a form

Table 1 Binding of [³H]bumetanide to tissues exhibiting (Na–K–Cl) cotransport

Tissue	Preparation	Affinity ($K^{1/2}$) (μM)	Maximal binding	Reference
Dog kidney outer medulla	Crude membranes	0.05	2–5 pmol/mg prot	26
Dog kidney outer medulla	Sucrose gradient purified membranes	0.05	10–30 pmol/mg prot	26
Dog kidney cortex	Crude membranes	0.06	0.5–1.5 pmol/mg prot	26, 39
Bovine kidney outer medulla	Crude microsomal membranes	0.16	10.5 pmol/mg prot	74
Rabbit kidney cortex	Basolateral membrane fraction	1.3–1.8	78 pmol/mg prot	36
Winter flounder intestine	Crude microsomal membranes	0.12	7.3 pmol/mg prot	74
Winter flounder intestine	Brush border membranes	0.53	20.4 pmol/mg prot	74
Shark rectal gland	Crude membranes	5–10	20–100 pmol/mg prot	24, 25
MDCK cells	Intact cells	0.33	7.0×10^5 sites/cell	84
Duck red cells	Intact cells	0.06–0.15	750–1500 sites/cell (2.5–5.0 pmol/mg prot.)[a]	38
Ferret red cells	Intact cells	0.022	12000 sites/cell (120 pmol/mg prot.)[a]	65
Ehrlich ascites cells[b]	Intact cells	8.7	$1.5–2.0 \times 10^6$ sites/cell (48–64 pmol/mg prot.)	47

[a]Based on a volume of 160 μm² and 56 μm² for duck and ferret red cells, respectively, and 3×10^{-12} mg membrane protein per μm² (human red cell ghosts; Ref. 15).

[b]The Ehrlich cells used in this study are reported to exhibit (Na–Cl), rather than (Na–K–Cl) cotransport (47).

of the cotransporter to which Na, K, and one Cl are already bound; the diuretic would then compete for the second Cl site.

The simultaneous determination of saturable [³H]bumetanide binding and (Na-K-Cl) cotransport activity in intact cells provides a direct correlation between binding and inhibition of cotransport (38), and allows the estimation of the turnover number of the cotransporter in several cell types. In duck red cells at 41°C, this number is ~4000/sec (38), which is considerably greater than that of Na,K-ATPase (~150/sec at 37°C; Ref. 48), but still much lower than that of the red cell anion exchange pathway (~50,000/sec at 38°C; Ref. 7). The very high rate of (Na-K-Cl) cotransport across the apical membrane of mammalian TALH epithelium (~2 nmol Na/cm² · sec; Ref. 35) suggests the turnover of the cotransporter in this tissue also exceeds 1000/sec (56). By contrast, turnover numbers for the (Na-K-Cl) cotransporter of Madin-Darby canine kidney (MDCK) cells were found to range from 120 to 850/sec at 37°C (84). Even lower is the turnover of 50/sec reported for bumetanide-sensitive Na transport in Ehrlich ascites cells, though the strain of Ehrlich cells studied appears to exhibit (Na-Cl), rather than (Na-K-Cl) cotransport (47).

REGULATION OF (Na-K-Cl) COTRANSPORT

Table 2 summarizes the wide variety of factors that have been found to stimulate or inhibit (Na-K-Cl) cotransport in different cells and tissues. It indicates that the regulation of this cotransport system is complex and varies considerably between different tissues. At the molecular level, however, little is known about the mechanisms involved in regulation of this cotransport pathway. (Na-K-Cl) cotransport activity in many cell types requires intracellular *ATP* (e.g. 31, 45, 85), though it is not obligatorily coupled to ATP hydrolysis (31). This suggests that cotransport may be regulated, at least in some tissues, by phosphorylation of regulatory proteins or even the cotransporter itself. This idea is supported by the recent findings in internally dialyzed squid axons that the onset of inhibition of cotransport after the start of dialysis with ATP-free solutions is delayed when the axons are treated with the phosphatase inhibitors fluoride or vanadate (3). Alper et al (2) identified a 230,000-dalton (230-kDa) integral membrane protein of turkey red cells, termed goblin, which is phosphorylated in response to catecholamines or cyclic *AMP*. Phosphorylation of a 37-kDa proteolytic fragment of goblin occurs with a dose-response for isoproterenol and a time course after iso-proterenol exposure that are identical to those for activation of (Na-K-Cl) cotransport in turkey red cells. However, it is not clear if goblin phosphoryla-tion is necessary for activation of avian red cell cotransport by catecho-lamines. If it is, other means for activation of cotransport must also exist, since cell shrinkage and hypoxia both activate this pathway without increasing

Table 2 Physiological regulators of (Na−K−Cl) cotransport

Factors that stimulate (Na−K−Cl) cotransport

Factor	Tissue (References)
Cell shrinkage	Duck red cells (43, 52, 88), turkey red cells (80, 92), rat red cells (18), ferret red cells (65), frog skin (93), Ehrlich ascites cells (30), rabbit medullary TALH (20)
β-Adrenergic catecholamines, cAMP	Duck red cells (44, 53, 54, 89), turkey red cells (2, 79, 92), cultured chick heart cells (57)
Atrial natriuretic factor, cGMP	Vascular smooth muscle cells (69, 70)
Growth factors[a]	Fibroblasts (5, 78, 82, 83), vascular smooth muscle cells (76, 77)
Vasopressin	Fibroblasts (5), vascular endothelial cells (8), rabbit renal papillary surface epithelium (86)
Insulin	3T3 fibroblasts (5)
Angiotensin II	Vascular smooth muscle cells (90)
Bradykinin	Vascular endothelial cells (8)
Phorbol ester (TPA)	Hamster lung fibroblasts (83)
Hypoxia	Duck red cells (62), turkey red cells (80)
Increased $[Ca^{2+}]_c$	Vascular endothelial cells (8), vascular smooth muscle cells (90)
Increased $[Mg^{2+}]_c$	Ferret red cells (56)

Factors that inhibit (Na−K−Cl) Cotransport

Factor	Tissue (References)
Cell swelling	Duck red cells (43), human red cells (1)
Cyclic AMP	Vascular smooth mucle cells[b] (69, 76, 90), vascular endothelial cells[b] (8), fibroblasts[b] (78), human red cells (28), ferret red cells (65)
Atrial natriuretic factor, cGMP	Winter flounder intestine (72)
Phorbol esters	3T3 preadipocytes (68), vascular smooth muscle cells (77)
Increased $[Ca^{2+}]_c$	Human red cells (28), ferret red cells (23)

[a]Includes α-thrombin, epidermal and fibroblast growth factors, and serum (Ref. 5 only).
[b]Inhibitory effect is also produced by β-adrenergic catecholamines, which increase cellular cAMP levels.

phosphorylation of goblin or its 37-kDa fragment (2). In winter flounder intestine, inhibition of (Na-K-Cl) cotransport by cyclic GMP may be associated with phosphorylation of a 50-kDa protein (13).

The cellular and molecular mechanisms involved in activation of (Na-K-Cl) cotransport by cell shrinkage remain an even greater mystery, though evidence from related, volume-sensitive transport pathways suggests the possible involvement of divalent cations and the membrane skeleton. In *amphiuma* red cells, inhibitors of calcium-calmodulin-mediated processes (e.g. phenothiazines) augment stimulation of Na/H exchange by cell shrinkage (10). In ferret red cells, both shrinkage and increasing intracellular ionized Mg ($[Mg^{2+}]_c$) within the physiological range increase cotransport activity (56, 65). It is not known how or if shrinkage of ferret red cells (or other tissues with volume-sensitive cotransport systems) affects $[Mg^{2+}]_c$ or $[Ca^{2+}]_c$. However, an increase in either of these could explain the stimulation of cotransport in avian red cells by hypoxia (62, 80). Conversion of oxy- to deoxyhemoglobin in red cells increases $[Mg^{2+}]_c$ and $[Ca^{2+}]_c$ since deoxyhemoglobin binds organic phosphates; upon oxygenation hemoglobin releases these compounds, which are then free to bind divalent cations. The membrane skeleton, because of its dynamic nature and association with integral membrane proteins (61), appears to be an ideal means for sensing cell volume and transmitting this information to ion transport systems. A role for the membrane skeleton in regulation of (Na-K-Cl) cotransport has not yet been established; however, in Necturus gallbladder stimulation of (K-Cl) cotransport by cell swelling is prevented if the epithelium is first treated with cytochalasin, which disrupts actin microfilaments (27).

Another fundamental question yet unanswered is whether factors that stimulate (Na-K-Cl) cotransport do so by increasing the number of transporters in the cell membrane, the turnover of these transporters, or both. In duck red cells, shrinkage and catecholamines, which stimulate cotransport, also promote an equivalent increase in saturable [³H]bumetanide binding (38). This suggests that these stimuli may act by promoting insertion of cotransporters into the cell membrane. However, it is also possible that these stimuli cause a change in the conformation of cotransporters already in the membrane and that only these activated transporters bind [³H]bumetanide with high affinity. Additional studies, perhaps involving development of specific antibodies to the cotransporter, are clearly needed to resolve this question.

STRUCTURE OF THE (Na-K-Cl) COTRANSPORTER

Several studies in different tissues have attempted to identify proteins comprising the (Na-K-Cl) cotransport system by photoaffinity labelling using radiolabelled loop diuretics. We have used [³H]4-benzoyl-5-sulfamoyl-3-(3-thenyloxy) benzoic acid ([³H]BSTBA) to photolabel membranes from dog kidney, duck red cells, and shark rectal gland (24, 39–41). BSTBA is a bumetanide analog, which is a potent loop diuretic (66), and contains a photoreactive benzophenone group. BSTBA inhibits (Na-K-Cl) cotransport in duck red cells and competes with [³H]bumetanide for binding sites on dog kidney membranes and duck red cells with an affinity similar to that of bumetanide itself (39, 41). Furthermore, [³H]BSTBA binds to each of the tissues we have studied with an affinity similar to that of [³H]bumetanide (see Table 1). Figure 1 illustrates an experiment in which [³H]BSTBA-photolabelled membranes from dog kidney, duck red cells, and shark rectal gland are run in parallel lanes on the same SDS-polyacrylamide gel. We find a single, broad peak of specific [³H]BSTBA photoincorporation for each membrane type; this peak is centered at ~150 kDa for dog kidney and duck red cell membranes, and at ~200 kDa for shark rectal gland membranes. The amount of [³H]BSTBA incorporation into each peak is noted in the legend to Figure 1; the rectal gland membranes incorporate far more [³H]BSTBA than do the red cell and kidney membranes (less rectal gland protein was loaded onto the gel), corresponding to the higher [³H]bumetanide binding capacity of the rectal gland membranes (Table 1). The criteria by which we identify these peaks as representing specific photolabelling are as follows (24, 39–41): (a) Labelling is not observed when the medium containing [³H]BSTBA also contains a concentration of unlabelled bumetanide 25–50 times the [³H]BSTBA concentration. (b) The photoincorporation of [³H]BSTBA into these proteins shows a saturable dependence on [³H]BSTBA concentration, with K½ values equal to those for reversible binding of [³H]BSTBA to each tissue. (c) [³H]BSTBA incorporation into these proteins requires the simultaneous presence of Na, K, and Cl in the medium containing [³H]BSTBA. (d) If duck red cells are shrunken or exposed to norepinephrine during incubation with [³H]BSTBA, the amount of [³H]BSTBA incorporation into the ~150-kDa protein is markedly increased (41), just as saturable [³H]bumetanide binding (38) and (Na-K-Cl) cotransport activity (89) are markedly stimulated under these conditions.

Jørgensen et al (49) found that a 34-kDa protein was photolabelled when pig kidney membranes were exposed to ultraviolet (UV) light in the presence of 12-μM [³H]bumetanide. However, these experiments were done using Cl-free media, in which high-affinity [³H]bumetanide binding to kidney membranes does not occur (26). We repeated this experiment using dog kidney membranes and media containing Na, K, Cl, and 0.2-μM [³H]bumetanide and also found incorporation of label in the ~40-kDa region (but not at 150 kDa). However, this labelling was less than 50% inhibited when 10-μM unlabelled bumetanide was added to the medium containing [³H]bumetanide (40). This suggests that the labelled protein(s) do not represent part of the (Na-K-Cl) cotransporter, but instead represent low-affinity bumetanide binding sites such as the basolateral (K-Cl) cotransport system of the TALH (34) or protein(s) related to the red cell anion exchange protein, band 3 (37). We also identify proteins in dog kidney membranes that incorporate [³H]BSTBA with low affinity, one of 50–60 kDa and other(s) that run with the tracking dye on 6.5 or 7.5% SDS-polyacrylamide gels (39; also see Figure 1).

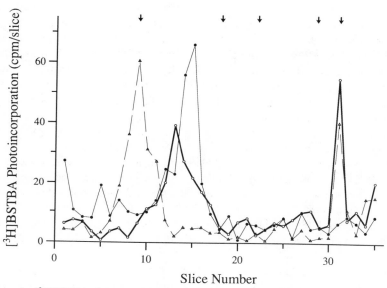

Figure 1 [³H]BSTBA photoincorporation into membranes from dog kidney cortex (*open circles, thick lines*), duck red cells (*closed circles, thin lines*), and shark rectal gland (*open triangles, dashed lines*). Membranes or intact red cells were incubated with 0.2-μM (kidney, red cell) or 0.5-μM (rectal gland) [³H]BSTBA (0.5 Ci/mmol; Ref. 39) for 15 minutes to allow for equilibrium binding as previously described (24, 39, 41). The membranes were then washed (red cells were lysed and the ghosts washed) and photolyzed at 0°C, solubilized in buffer containing 2% sodium dodecyl sulfate (SDS), and run in parallel lanes on a 6.5% acrylamide SDS gel. The gel was stained with Coomassie blue and cut into 4-mm slices, which were digested with 30% H_2O_2 and counted to determine the distribution of [³H]BSTBA in the membrane proteins. Data given are counts per minute (cpm) in each slice, after subtracting a background of 40 cpm/slice. The location of molecular weight standards on the gel are noted by the arrows (from left to right: 200, 116, 92, and 66 kDa, and the tracking dye). The amount of protein loaded onto the gel was 1.15 mg for duck red cell membranes, 0.80 mg for dog kidney membranes, and 0.20 mg for shark rectal gland membranes. [³H]BSTBA incorporation into the 150-kDa region (slices 12–16) is 0.44 pmol/mg protein for duck red cell membranes and 0.41 pmol/mg for dog kidney membranes; incorporation into the 200-kDa region (slices 7–11) is 1.98 pmol/mg for shark rectal gland membranes. We find the efficiency of [³H]BSTBA photolabelling for each membrane type is ~10% (24, 39, 41).

O'Grady et al (75) identified a ~6-kDa peptide from both bovine kidney and winter flounder intestine that is directly photolabelled with [³H]bumetanide (0.5 μM). This labelling is inhibited by addition of 5-μM unlabelled bumetanide to the photolysis medium, or by removal of Cl from this medium, which suggests this small peptide could represent a component of the (Na-K-Cl) cotransporter. DiStefano et al (14) reported photolabelling of a 24-kDa protein when intact segments of rabbit cortical TALH were exposed to UV light in the presence of [³H]azidopiretanide. This incorporation was found to be associated with a 20% irreversible inhibition of (Na-K-Cl) cotransport activity. Amsler & Kinne (6) likewise observed irreversible inhibition of bumetanide-sensitive ^{86}Rb fluxes in cultured renal epithelial cells (LLC-PK$_1$) after exposure of cells to UV light in the presence of bumetanide, though no attempt to identify a photolabelled protein was made in this study. Kinne et al (51) reported an apparent molecular weight of 80–90 kDa for the (Na-K-Cl) cotransporter of rabbit kidney TALH membrane vesicles, based on radiation inactivation studies.

Feit and coworkers (21) recently constructed a bumetanide affinity column using 4'-azidobumetanide coupled to Sepharose by photolysis. Membranes from a strain of Ehrlich ascites cells reported to have (Na-Cl), rather than (Na-K-Cl) cotransport were solubilized in n-octylglucoside and passed over this column. Two major proteins were retained by this column and eluted with 200-μM bumetanide. On reducing gels, these proteins had molecular weights of 76 kDa and 38–39 kDa, though on nonreducing, nondenaturing gels the eluted material ran as a single, broad peak centered in the 180–200-kDa region (21).

The diversity of molecular weights reported in the above studies raises the question of whether all of the proteins identified could represent components of the (Na-K-Cl) cotransporter. This cotransporter could be comprised of multiple subunits and the studies of Feit and coworkers (21) suggest this for the (Na-Cl) cotransport system of Ehrlich cells. Low-molecular-weight proteins identified in photoaffinity labelling studies could also represent proteolytic fragments of larger component(s) of the (Na-K-Cl) cotransport system. Structural differences (including subunit structure) between cotransporters of different species must also be considered. For example, noting the comparatively low affinity of the shark rectal gland cotransporter for [3H]bumetanide (Table 1), it is not altogether surprising that the protein identified in rectal gland membranes by [3H]BSTBA photolabelling has a different molecular weight than [3H]BSTBA-labelled proteins from dog kidney and duck red cells (Figure 1).

RELATIONSHIP OF (Na-K-Cl) COTRANSPORT TO OTHER CATION-CHLORIDE COTRANSPORT SYSTEMS

A number of cells and tissues have been found to exhibit Na-independent (K-Cl) cotransport or K-independent (Na-Cl) cotransport, in addition to (Na-K-Cl) cotransport. At present, it is not clear if these kinetically different cotransport processes represent distinct pathways or alternate modes of the same complex pathway that are expressed under different physiological conditions. In a number of different cell types, indirect evidence exists that is at least consistent with the latter concept. In duck red cells, cell swelling in the absence of catecholamines activates a Na-independent (K-Cl) cotransport

(43). However, when catecholamines are present, the swelling-induced (K-Cl) cotransport is abolished and replaced or overridden by (Na-K-Cl) cotransport (43). Exposure of human red cells to the sulfhydryl reagent N-ethylmaleimide has the opposite effect, stimulating (K-Cl) cotransport and inhibiting (Na-K-Cl) cotransport (16, 55). Under isotonic conditions, furosemide-sensitive Na influx in isolated cells from rabbit medullary TALH is unaffected by the K gradient, and furosemide-sensitive K influx is minimal. However, when the cells are shrunken both furosemide-sensitive Na and K fluxes are stimulated, and the flux of each ion is dependent on the presence of the other (20). The findings suggest that these cells exhibit either (Na-Cl) or (Na-K-Cl) cotransport, depending on cell volume.

Unfortunately, ion flux data such as those discussed above are not definitive evidence that the (Na-K-Cl) cotransport system can mediate other modes of ion transport such as (Na-Cl) and (K-Cl) cotransport. Proof of this will require study of the function of the (Na-K-Cl) cotransporter in the known absence of other cation-chloride cotransport activity; this can be accomplished by purification of the (Na-K-Cl) cotransporter and reconstitution of it in phospholipid vesicles, or by cloning the gene for the cotransporter and expressing the gene product in cells known to lack cation-chloride cotransport activity (e.g. a cotransport-deficient mutant cell line; Refs. 29, 64). The identification of proteins that appear to represent at least part of the (Na-K-Cl) cotransport system of different tissues (see above) is an important first step toward this goal, and several laboratories are currently working to purify these proteins.

ACKNOWLEDGMENTS

Biff Forbush has collaborated with me on all of our diuretic binding and photoaffinity labelling studies, including those presented here (Figure 1), and has provided insightful comments on this manuscript. We are grateful to the National Institutes of Health (grant AM-17433) and the American Heart Association, Connecticut Affiliate (grant G-12-867) for research support and to Dr. Peter Feit for his generous gift of BSTBA. The author is a John A. and George L. Hartford Fellow.

Literature Cited

1. Adragna, N. C., Tosteson, D. C. 1984. Effect of volume changes in ouabain-insensitive net outward cation movement in human red cells. *J. Membr. Biol.* 78:43–52

2. Alper, S.L., Beam, K. G., Greengard, P. 1980. Hormonal control of Na-K cotransport in turkey erythrocytes. Multiple site phosphorylation of goblin, a high molecular weight protein of the plasma membrane. *J. Biol. Chem.* 255:4864–71

3. Altamirano, A. A., Breitwieser, G. E.,

Russell, J. M. 1988. Vanadate and fluoride effects on Na-K-Cl cotransport in squid giant axon. *Am. J. Physiol.* 254:C582–86

4. Altamirano, A. A., Russell, J. M. 1987. Coupled Na/K/Cl efflux. "Reverse" unidirectional fluxes in squid giant axons. *J. Gen. Physiol.* 89:669–86

5. Amsler, K., Donahue, J. J., Slayman, C. W., Adelberg, E. A. 1985. Stimulation of bumetanide sensitive K transport in Swiss 3T3 fibroblasts by serum and

454   HAAS

mitogenic hormones. *J. Cell. Physiol.* 123:257–63

6. Amsler, K., Kinne, R. 1986. Photoinactivation of sodium-potassium-chloride cotransport in LLC-PK_1/Cl 4 cells by bumetanide. *Am. J. Physiol.* 250:C799–806

7. Brahm, J. 1977. Temperature-dependent changes of chloride transport kinetics in human red cells. *J. Gen. Physiol.* 70:283–306

8. Brock, T. A., Brugnara, C., Canessa, M., Gimbrone, M. A. Jr. 1986. Bradykinin and vasopressin stimulate Na-K-Cl cotransport in cultured endothelial cells. *Am. J. Physiol.* 250:C888–95

9. Brown, C. D. A., Murer, H. 1985. Characterization of a Na:K:2Cl cotransport system in the apical membrane of a renal epithelial cell line (LLC-PK_1). *J. Membr. Biol.* 87:131–39

10. Cala, P. M., Mandel, L. J., Murphy, E. 1986. Volume regulation by Amphiuma red blood cells: cytosolic free Ca and alkali metal-H exchange. *Am. J. Physiol.* 250:C423–29

11. Canessa, M., Brugnara, C., Cusi, D., Tosteson, D. C. 1986. Modes of operation and variable stoichiometry of the furosemide-sensitive Na and K fluxes in human red cells. *J. Gen. Physiol.* 87:113–42

12. Davis, C. W., Finn, A. L. 1985. Effect of mucosal sodium removal on cell volume in Necturus gallbladder epithelium. *Am. J. Physiol.* 249:C304–12

13. DeJonge, H. R., Vaandrager, A. B., O'Grady, S. M., Field, M. 1985. A 50-kDa protein in flounder intestine brush borders (BB) is phosphorylated by cGMP and Ca-CaM kinases and is specifically dephosphorylated by a cAMP-activated phosphatase. *Fed. Proc.* 45:4281

14. DiStefano, A., Wangemann, P., Friedrich, T., Burckhardt, G., Okonomopoulos, R. R., Englert, H. C., Lang, H. J., Greger, R. 1986. Photoaffinity labelling of the Na-2Cl-K carrier. *Pflügers Arch.* 406:R59

15. Dodge, J. T., Mitchell, C., Hanahan, D. J. 1963. The preparation and some characteristics of hemoglobin-free ghosts of human erythrocytes. *Arch. Biochem. Biophys.* 100:119–28

16. Duhm, J. 1987. Furosemide-sensitive K (Rb) transport in human erythrocytes: modes of operation, dependence on extracellular and intracellular Na, kinetics, pH dependency and the effect of cell volume and N-ethylmaleimide. *J. Membr. Biol.* 98:15–32

17. Duhm, J., Göbel, B. O. 1984. Role of the furosemide-sensitive Na/K transport system in determining the steady-state Na and K content and volume of human erythrocytes in vitro and in vivo. *J. Membr. Biol.* 77:243–54

18. Duhm, J., Göbel, B. O. 1984. Na-K transport and volume of rat erythrocytes under dietary K deficiency. *Am. J. Physiol.* 246:C20–29

19. Dunham, P. B., Stewart, G. W., Ellory, J. C. 1980. Chloride-activated passive potassium transport in human erythrocytes. *Proc. Natl. Acad. Sci. USA* 77:1711–15

20. Eveloff, J. L., Calamia, J. 1986. Effect of osmolality on cation fluxes in medullary thick ascending limb cells. *Am. J. Physiol.* 250:F176–180

21. Feit, P. W., Hoffmann, E. K., Schiødt, M., Kristensen, P., Jessen, F., et al. 1988. Purification of proteins of the Na/Cl cotransporter from membranes of Ehrlich ascites cells using a bumetanide-sepharose affinity column. *J. Membr. Biol.* 103:135–47

22. Flatman, P. W. 1983. Sodium and potassium transport in ferret red cells. *J. Physiol.* 341:545–57

23. Flatman, P. W. 1987. The effects of calcium on potassium transport in ferret red cells. *J. Physiol.* 386:407–23

24. Forbush, B. III, Haas, M. 1988. Identification of a 200K dalton component of the Na,K,Cl-cotransport system in membranes from dogfish shark rectal gland. *Biophys. J.* 53:222a

25. Forbush, B. III, Palfrey, H. C. 1982. Bumetanide and benzmetanide binding to membranes from shark rectal gland and canine kidney. *Biophys. J.* 37:161a

26. Forbush, B. III, Palfrey, H. C. 1983. [^{3}H]Bumetanide binding to membranes isolated from dog kidney outer medulla. Relationship to the Na,K,Cl cotransport system. *J. Biol. Chem.* 258:11787–92

27. Foskett, J. K., Spring, K. R. 1985. Involvement of calcium and cytoskeleton in gallbladder epithelial cell volume regulation. *Am. J Physiol.* 248:C27–36

28. Garay, R. P. 1982. Inhibition of the Na/K cotransport system by cyclic AMP and intracellular Ca^{2+} in human red cells. *Biochim. Biophys. Acta* 688:786–92

29. Gargus, J. J. 1987. Selectable mutations altering two mechanisms of mammalian K transport are dominant. *Am. J. Physiol.* 252:C515–22

30. Geck, P., Pfeiffer, B. 1985. Na + K + 2Cl cotransport in animal cells and its role in volume regulation. *Ann. NY Acad. Sci.* 456:166–82

31. Geck, P., Pietrzyk, C., Burckhardt, B.-C., Pfeiffer, B., Heinz, E. 1980. Elec-

trically silent cotransport of Na,K, and Cl in Ehrlich cells. *Biochim. Biophys. Acta* 600:432–47

32. Giesen-Crouse, E. M., Welsch, C., Imbs, J. L., Schmidt, M., Schwartz, J. 1985. Characterisation of a high-affinity piretanide receptor on kidney membranes. *Eur. J. Pharmacol.* 114:23–31

33. Greger, R. 1985. Ion transport mechanisms in thick ascending limb of Henle's loop mammalian nephrons. *Physiol. Rev.* 65:760–97

34. Greger, R., Schlatter, E. 1983. Properties of the basolateral membrane of cortical thick ascending of Henle's loop of rabbit kidney. *Pflügers Arch.* 396:325–34

35. Greger, R., Schlatter, E., Lang, F. 1983. Evidence for electroneutral sodium chloride cotransport in the cortical thick ascending limb of Henle's loop of rabbit kidney. *Pflügers Arch.* 396:308–14

36. Griffiths, N. M., Simmons, N. L. 1987. Attribution of [³H]bumetanide binding to the Na + K + Cl "cotransporter" in rabbit renal cortical plasma membranes: a caveat. *Q. J. Exp. Physiol.* 72:313–29

37. Gunn, R. B. 1985. Bumetanide inhibition of anion exchange in human red blood cells. *Biophys. J.* 47:326a

38. Haas, M., Forbush, B. III. 1986. [³H]bumetanide binding to duck red cells. Correlation with inhibition of (Na + K + 2Cl) co-transport. *J. Biol. Chem.* 261:8434–41

39. Haas, M., Forbush, B. III. 1987. Photolabeling of a 150-kDa (Na + K + Cl) cotransport protein from dog kidney with a bumetanide analogue. *Am. J. Physiol.* 253:C243–52

40. Haas, M., Forbush, B. III. 1987. Na,K,Cl-cotransport system: Characterization by bumetanide binding and photolabelling. *Kidney Intl.* 32:S134–40

41. Haas, M., Forbush, B. III. 1988. Photoaffinity labelling of a 150 kDa (Na + K + Cl)-cotransport protein from duck red cells with an analog of bumetanide. *Biochim. Biophys. Acta* 939:131–44

42. Haas, M., McManus, T. J. 1983. Bumetanide inhibits (Na + K + 2Cl) co-transport at a chloride site. *Am. J. Physiol.* 245:C235–40

43. Haas, M., McManus, T. J. 1985. Effect of norepinephrine on swelling-induced potassium transport in duck red cells. Evidence against a volume-regulatory decrease under physiological conditions. *J. Gen. Physiol.* 85:649–67

44. Haas, M., Schmidt, W. F. III, McManus, T. J. 1982. Catecholamine-stimulated ion transport in duck red cells. Gradient effects in electrically neutral (Na + K + 2Cl) co-transport. *J. Gen. Physiol.* 80:125–47

45. Hall, A. C., Ellory, J. C. 1985. Measurement and stoichiometry of bumetanide-sensitive (2Na:1K:3Cl) cotransport in ferret red cells. *J. Membr. Biol.* 85:205–13

46. Hannafin, J., Kinne-Saffran, E., Friedman, D., Kinne, R. 1983. Presence of a sodium-potassium-chloride cotransport system in the rectal gland of Squalus acanthias. *J. Membr. Biol.* 75:73–83

47. Hoffmann, E. K., Schiodt, M., Dunham, P. 1986. The number of chloride-cation cotransport sites on Ehrlich ascites cells measured with [³H]bumetanide. *Am. J. Physiol.* 250:C688–93

48. Jørgensen, P. L. 1975. Isolation and characterization of the components of the sodium pump. *Q. Rev. Biophys.* 7:239–74

49. Jørgensen, P. L., Peterson, J., Rees, W. D. 1984. Identification of a Na,K,Cl-cotransport protein of M_r 34,000 from kidney by photolabelling with [³H]bumetanide. *Biochim. Biophys. Acta* 775:105–10

50. Kaji, D. 1986. Volume sensitive K transport in human erythrocytes. *J. Gen. Physiol.* 88:719–38

51. Kinne, R. K. H., Kinne-Saffran, E., Schoelermann, B., Schuetz, H., Doell, G. 1987. Functional molecular size of rabbit kidney Na,K,Cl cotransporter. *Kidney Intl.* 31:171

52. Kregenow, F. M. 1971. The response of duck erythrocytes to hypertonic media: further evidence for a volume-controlling mechanism. *J. Gen. Physiol.* 58:396–412

53. Kregenow, F. M. 1973. The response of duck erythrocytes to norepinephrine and an elevated extracellular potassium: volume regulation in isotonic media. *J. Gen. Physiol.* 61:509–27

54. Kregenow, F. M., Robbie, E. D., Orloff, J. 1976. Effect of norepinephrine and hypertonicity on K influx and cyclic AMP in duck erythrocytes. *Am. J. Physiol.* 231:306–12

55. Lauf, P. K., Adragna, N. C., Garay, R. P. 1984. Activation by N-ethyl-maleimide of a latent K-Cl flux in human red blood cells. *Am. J. Physiol.* 246:C385–90

56. Lauf, P. K., McManus, T. J., Haas, M., Forbush, B. III, Duhm, J., et al. 1987. Physiology and biophysics of chloride

and cation cotransport across cell membranes. *Fed. Proc.* 46:2377–94

57. Liu, S., Jacob, R., Piwnica-Worms, D., Lieberman, M. 1987. (Na + K + 2Cl) co-transport in cultured embryonic chick heart cells. *Am. J. Physiol.* 253:C721–30

58. Ludens, J. H. 1982. Nature of the inhibition of Cl transport by furosemide: Evidence for competitive inhibition of active transport of toad cornea. *J. Pharmacol. Exp. Ther.* 223:25–29

59. Lytle, C., Haas, M., McManus, T. J. 1986. Chloride-dependent obligate cation exchange: a partial reaction of (Na + K + 2Cl) co-transport. *Fed. Proc.* 45:548

60. Lytle, C., McManus, T. J. 1986. A minimal kinetic model of (Na + K + 2Cl) cotransport with ordered binding and glide symmetry. *J. Gen. Physiol.* 88:36a

61. Marchesi, V. T. 1983. The red cell membrane skeleton: recent progress. *Blood* 61:1–11

62. McManus, T. J., Allen, D. W. 1968. Some factors which alter passive cation movements in duck red cells. In *Metabolism and Membrane Permeability of Erythrocytes and Thrombocytes*, ed. E. Deutsch, E. Gerlach, K. Moser, pp. 428–30. Stuttgart: Thieme Verlag

63. McRoberts, J. A., Erlinger, S., Rindler, M. J., Saier, M. H. Jr. 1982. Furosemide-sensitive salt transport in the Madin-Darby canine kidney cell line: Evidence for the cotransport of Na, K, and Cl. *J. Biol. Chem.* 257:2260–66

64. McRoberts, J. A., Tran, C. T., Saier, M. H. Jr. 1983. Characterization of low potassium-resistant mutants of the Madin-Darby canine kidney cell line with defects in NaCl/KCl symport. *J. Biol. Chem.* 258:12320–26

65. Mercer, R. W., Hoffman, J. F. 1985. Bumetanide-sensitive Na/K cotransport in ferret red blood cells. *Biophys. J.* 47:157a

66. Neilsen, O. B. T., Bruun, H., Bretting, C., Feit, P. W. 1975. Aminobenzoic acid diuretics. 7. 3-Substituted 4-phenyl-, 4-arylcarbonyl-, and 4-arylmethyl-5-sulfamoylbenzoic acids and related compounds. *J. Med. Chem.* 18:41–50

67. Oberleithner, H., Guggino, W., Giebisch, G. 1983. Effect of furosemide on luminal sodium, chloride, and potassium transport in the early distal tubule of Amphiuma kidney. *Pflügers Arch.* 396:27–33

68. O'Brien, T. G., Krzeminski, K. 1983. Phorbol ester inhibits furosemide-sensitive potassium transport in BALB/c

3T3 preadipose cells. *Proc. Natl. Acad. Sci. USA* 80:4334–38

69. O'Donnell, M. E., Owen, N. E. 1986. Atrial natiuretic factor stimulates Na/K/Cl cotransport in vascular smooth muscle cells. *Proc. Natl. Acad. Sci. USA* 83:6132–36

70. O'Donnell, M. E., Owen, N. E. 1986. Role of cyclic GMP in atrial natiuretic factor stimulation of Na,K,Cl cotransport in vascular smooth muscle cells. *J. Biol. Chem.* 261:15461–66

71. O'Donnell, M. E., Owen, N. E. 1988. Reduced Na-K-Cl cotransport in vascular smooth muscle cells from spontaneously hypertensive rats. *Am. J. Physiol.* 255:C169–80

72. O'Grady, S. M., Field, M., Nash, N. T., Rao, M. C. 1985. Atrial natiuretic factor inhibits Na-K-Cl cotransport in teleost intestine. *Am. J. Physiol.* 249:C531–34

73. O'Grady, S. M., Musch, M. W., Field, M. 1986. Stoichiometry and ion affinities of the Na-K-Cl cotransport system in the intestine of the winter flounder (Pseudopleuronectes americanus) *J. Membr. Biol.* 91:33–41

74. O'Grady, S. M., Palfrey, H. C., Field, M. 1987. Na-K-Cl cotransport in winter flounder intestine and bovine kidney outer medulla: [^{3}H]bumetanide binding and effects of furosemide analogues. *J. Membr. Biol.* 96:11–18

75. O'Grady, S. M., Palfrey, H. C., Field, M. 1987. Characteristics and functions of Na-K-Cl cotransport in epithelial tissues. *Am. J. Physiol.* 253:C177–92

76. Owen, N. E. 1984. Regulation of Na/K/Cl cotransport in vascular smooth muscle cells. *Biochem. Biophys. Res. Commun.* 125:500–8

77. Owen, N. E. 1985. Effect of TPA on ion fluxes and DNA synthesis in vascular smooth muscle cells. *J. Cell. Biol.* 101:454–59

78. Owen, N. E., Prastein, M. L. 1985. Na/K/Cl cotransport in cultured human fibroblasts. *J. Biol. Chem.* 260:1445–51

79. Palfrey, H. C., Feit, P. W., Greengard, P. 1980. cAMP-stimulated cation cotransport in avian erythrocytes: inhibition by "loop" diuretics. *Am. J. Physiol.* 238:C139–48

80. Palfrey, H. C., Greengard, P. 1981. Hormone-sensitive ion transport systems in erythrocytes as models for epithelial ion pathways. *Ann. NY Acad. Sci.* 372:291–308

81. Palfrey, H. C., Silva, P., Epstein, F. H. 1984. Sensitivity of cAMP-stimulated salt secretion in shark rectal gland to

"loop" diuretics. *Am. J. Physiol.* 246: C242–46

82. Panet, R., Fromer, I., Atlan, H. 1982. Differentiation between serum stimulation of ouabain-resistant and sensitive Rb influx in quiescent NIH 3T3 cells. *J. Membr. Biol.* 70:165–69

83. Paris, S., Pouyssegur, J. 1986. Growth factors activate the bumetanide-sensitive Na/K/Cl cotransport in hamster fibroblasts. *J. Biol. Chem.* 261:6177–83

84. Rugg, E. L., Simmons, N. L., Tivey, D. R. 1986. An investigation of [^{3}H]bumetanide uptake in a cultured renal cell line (MDCK) *Q. J. Exp. Physiol.* 71:165–82

85. Russell, J. M. 1983. Cation coupled chloride influx in squid axon: role of potassium and stoichiometry of the process. *J. Gen. Physiol.* 81:909–25

86. Sands, J. M., Knepper, M. A., Spring, K. R. 1986. Na-K-Cl cotransport in apical membrane of rabbit renal papillary surface epithelium. *Am. J. Physiol.* 251:F475–84

87. Schlatter, E., Greger, R., Weidtke, C. 1983. Effect of "high ceiling" diuretics on active salt transport in the cortical thick ascending limb of Henle's loop of rabbit kidney. Correlation of chemical structure and inhibitory potency. *Pflügers Arch.* 396:210–17

88. Schmidt, W. F. III, McManus, T. J. 1977. Ouabain-insensitive salt and water movements in duck red cells. I. Kinetics of cation transport under hypertonic conditions. *J. Gen. Physiol.* 70:59–79

89. Schmidt, W. F. III, McManus, T. J. 1977. Ouabain-insensitive salt and water movements in duck red cells. II. Norepinephrine stimulation of sodium plus potassium cotransport. *J. Gen. Physiol.* 70:81–97

90. Smith, J. B., Smith, L. 1987. Na/K/Cl cotransport in cultured vascular smooth muscle cells: Stimulation by angiotensin II and calcium ionophores, inhibition by cyclic AMP and calmodulin antagonists. *J. Membr. Biol.* 99:51–63

91. Turner, R. J., George, J. N., Baum, B. J. 1986. Evidence for a Na/K/Cl cotransport system in basolateral membrane vesicles from rabbit parotid. *J. Membr. Biol.* 94:143–52

92. Ueberschär, S., Bakker-Grunwald, T. 1985. Effects of ATP and cAMP on the (Na + K + 2Cl) cotransport system in turkey erythrocytes. *Biochim. Biophys. Acta* 818:260–66

93. Ussing, H. H. 1985. Volume regulation and basolateral co-transport of sodium, potassium, and chloride ions in frog skin epithelium. *Pflügers Arch.* 405:R57

94. Wiley, J. S., Cooper, R. A. 1974. A furosemide-sensitive co-transport of sodium plus potassium in the human red cell. *J. Clin. Invest.* 53:745–55

Annu. Rev. Physiol. 1989. 51:459–71

HOMOLOGIES BETWEEN SUGAR TRANSPORTERS FROM EUKARYOTES AND PROKARYOTES

Stephen A. Baldwin

Departments of Biochemistry & Chemistry, and Protein & Molecular Biology, Royal Free Hospital School of Medicine (University of London), Rowland Hill Street, London NW3 2PF, United Kingdom

Peter J. F. Henderson

Department of Biochemistry, University of Cambridge, Tennis Court Road, Cambridge CB2 1QW, United Kingdom

INTRODUCTION

The mechanisms used by cells to take up sugars reflect the sugar concentrations in their normal environments. In mammals, blood glucose concentration is regulated between about 5–10 mM, and most cells take up sugar by passive facilitated diffusion. Active, sodium-dependent glucose transport occurs in only a few tissues, in particular the kidney and small intestine (34, 70). In contrast, bacterial cells encounter widely varying concentrations of different sugars (12, 20); thus, a variety of active sugar transport systems are necessary (36, 61). Their energy source may be phosphoenol pyruvate [the phosphotransferase systems (61, 62)], ATP [the binding protein–dependent systems (3)], or transmembrane electrochemical gradients of ions [H^+-sugar and Na^+-sugar symport systems (36, 61)].

Several mammalian and bacterial sugar transport proteins and one yeast sugar transport protein have recently been sequenced. The active, sodium-dependent transporter from rabbit small intestine shows no apparent sequence similarities to either the mammalian or yeast passive glucose transporters or any of the bacterial transporters (15a, 34). However, extensive sequence homologies have recently been discovered between the mammalian and yeast

459

0066-4278/89/0315-0459$02.00

passive glucose transporters and some bacterial H^+-sugar symporters (15a, 56). In this review we compare these phyletically distant transporters to derive a unified model for their structure, and we discuss its implications for their molecular mechanism.

MAMMALIAN PASSIVE SUGAR TRANSPORT SYSTEMS

Glucose Transport in the Human Erythrocyte

The best characterized mammalian passive glucose transporter is that of the human erythrocyte (68). It is not hormonally regulated, but its kinetic features mirror those seen in most other mammalian tissues, including fat and muscle, where transport is stimulated by insulin (65). A notable exception is the hepatocyte (18, see below). The erythrocyte system has a broad substrate specificity, with the following order of apparent affinities: 2-deoxy-D-glucose > D-glucose ≈ 6-deoxy-D-glucose > D-mannose > D-galactose ≈ 2-deoxy-D-galactose > D-xylose > L-arabinose > D-fucose >> L-fucose > L-rhamnose >> L-glucose (6, 51).

The transporter constitutes about 5% of the total protein in the human erythrocyte membrane (1) and has been purified to near homogeneity (5, 48). It migrates as a very broad band of M_r 55,000 on SDS/polyacrylamide gels because of heterogeneous glycosylation (31), but after deglycosylation it migrates as a sharp band of apparent M_r 46,000 or 38,000 for unheated or boiled gel samples, respectively (33, 52). This single polypeptide appears to constitute the entire transporter since after reconstitution into lipid vesicles, its kinetic parameters resemble those in the intact erythrocyte (19, 67). It also binds the inhibitor of transport, cytochalasin B, with an unaltered K_d of 10^{-7} M and a stoichiometry of about 1 molecule per polypeptide chain (5). The binding is competitively inhibited by D-glucose and is reversible (5, 43), but irreversible, covalent labeling by cytochalasin B is effected by ultra violet irradiation (15, 64).

The complete sequences of two transporters that are recognized by antibodies against the erythrocyte protein, those from the human hepatoma cell line HepG2 and from rat brain, were recently deduced via the sequences of cDNA clones (7, 58). Their sequences (492 residues) are 97.6% identical, corresponding to proteins of M_r 54,117 and 56,133, respectively. Mass spectrometry and sequencing studies on the erythrocyte protein showed that its sequence is probably identical to that predicted for the hepatoma protein and that neither the N-terminal nor C-terminal sequences were proteolytically processed after synthesis (58). The anomalously low apparent M_r of the deglycosylated protein discussed above must, therefore, reflect abnormal electrophoretic migration of this hydrophobic molecule.

Glucose Transport in Other Eukaryotic Cells

Putative glucose transport proteins have been identified in a wide range of mammalian tissues by Western blotting using antibodies against the human erythrocyte transporter. Recently, it was found that the reactivity of such antibodies towards rat brain transporters and the transporters of adipocytes or skeletal muscle differed, which suggests that the transporters of insulin-responsive and nonresponsive tissues may be distinct (66). Whether this difference is one of amino acid sequence or of posttranslational modification remains unknown. However, the transporter of the hepatocyte is clearly distinct from those of other cells: its kinetics are quantitatively different from those of the erythrocyte; it binds cytochalasin B about tenfold less tightly (18); it is not recognized by antibodies against the erythrocyte protein (7), and the sequence of the rat liver glucose transporter, though homologous, is quite distinct from the virtually identical rat brain and human hepatoma sequences (H. F. Lodish, personal communication). The liver-type transporter gene is also expressed in kidney, pancreatic islets, and intestine.

BACTERIAL PROTON-LINKED SUGAR TRANSPORT SYSTEMS

There are at least six different proton-linked sugar transport proteins in *Escherichia coli* (36, 45). The most intensively investigated, the H^+-lactose symporter (45, 46), exhibits little or no sequence homology either to the mammalian passive sugar transporters or to other bacterial H^+-sugar symporters (11, 56). The other known symporters in *E. coli* are for D-xylose, L-arabinose, D-galactose, L-fucose, and L-rhamnose (9, 36, 38). Most is known about the first three, which constitute only 0.1–0.5% of the membrane protein even in fully induced, wild-type strains (38, 54, 55). However, the cloning, sequencing, and amplified expression of the appropriate genes is facilitating their investigation. Their properties are now considered in detail.

The H^+-Xylose Transporter, XylE, in E. coli

An uncoupler-sensitive, H^+-linked transport system for D-xylose has been characterised in *E. coli* (25, 50). Neither L-arabinose, D-glucose, nor D-galactose are very effective alternative substrates (23, 50). The activity of the system is inhibited by *N*-ethylmaleimide, and D-xylose or 6-deoxy-D-glucose protect against this inactivation (23). This phenomenon enabled identification of the transporter as a protein of apparent M_r 37,000–41,000 on SDS/polyacrylamide gels (23, 38). Cytochalasin B does not inhibit the activity of XylE, nor does it react covalently with the protein upon photoactivation (own unpublished results).

After locating the gene *xylE,* which encodes the transport activity, its DNA was cloned and sequenced (24, 25). The deduced reading frame predicted a 491-residue, hydrophobic protein of M_r 53,603. The somewhat lower apparent M_r for the protein may derive from abnormal electrophoretic mobility, as was the case for the mammalian passive glucose transporter, rather than from proteolytic cleavage. The sequence of the XylE protein can be readily aligned with the human or yeast passive glucose transporters; XylE and the human transporter have 136 identical residues and at least 126 conservative substitutions (Figure 1; 15a, 56).

The H^+-Arabinose Transporter, AraE, in E. coli

An uncoupler-sensitive transport system for L-arabinose in *E. coli* was reported some time ago (10) and was subsequently characterized as an H^+-arabinose symporter (21) encoded by the *araE* gene. Its sugar binding specificity is in the approximate rank order: 6-deoxy-D-galactose ≈ L-arabinose > 6-deoxy-D-glucose > D-xylose >> D-galactose ≈ D-glucose (21, 38, own unpublished results). The absence of the 6-OH and the configuration of the 4-OH are critical features for optimal binding.

Transport activity is inhibited by *N*-ethylmaleimide, and substrates protect against this inhibition (38, 54). This phenomenon, together with dual isotope labeling of *araE*[+]/*araE*[−] strains, enabled identification of a protein of apparent M_r ~36,000 on SDS/polyacrylamide gels (54). Its identity was confirmed by amplifying the expression of the *araE* gene so that its product is clearly visible on gels (57). We recently showed that the activity of AraE is inhibited by cytochalasin B (concentration required for 50% inhibition = 1–3 μM), that the inhibitor binds with a dissociation constant of approximately 1 μM, and that [^{3}H]-cytochalasin B can be used to photolabel the transporter. Substrates protect against this labeling in the order of effectiveness given above (own unpublished results).

The *araE* gene has now been cloned and sequenced (57). It encodes a 472-residue, hydrophobic protein of M_r 51,683. The discrepancy between the protein's apparent M_r (36,000) and the predicted value parallels the situation for the xylose and glucose transport proteins. The sequence can be readily aligned with both XylE and the human or yeast passive glucose transporter: XylE and AraE have 140 identical residues and at least 124 conservative substitutions; AraE and the human glucose transporter have 137 identical residues and at least 129 conservative substitutions (Figure 1).

The H^+-Galactose Transporter, GalP, in E. coli

The existence of at least two separate transport systems for D-galactose in *E. coli* was established some time ago (60). One of these, Mgl, is a binding protein type and the other, GalP, is proton linked (37, 41). Many sugar

Figure 1 Aligned sequences of the *E. coli* H⁺-xylose (Xyl) and H⁺-arabinose (Ara), and the *S. cerevisiae* glucose (Gl1), and the human glucose (Gl2) transport proteins (15a, 56, 58). Residues that are identical in two or more sequences are boxed. The locations of the predicted membrane-spanning α-helices are indicated by the dotted outlines.

analogues are substrates for GalP, with an approximate rank order: D-glucose > 2-deoxy-D-glucose > D-galactose > 6-deoxy-D-glucose > D-talose > 2-deoxy-D-galactose > D-mannose > D-fucose > D-xylose >> L-glucose ≈ L-arabinose (37, 38, 41, 60, own unpublished results). In contrast to AraE, the presence of a 6-OH and the glucose configuration of the 4-OH favor sugar binding. Interestingly, although D-glucose is actually the best substrate, GalP is not a route of D-glucose entry during growth because this sugar does not induce expression of the gene *galP*.

Transport activity is inhibited by *N*-ethylmaleimide, and substrates protect the protein against reaction (38, 55). This property was exploited to identify a protein of apparent M_r approximately 37,000 on SDS/polyacrylamide gels (38, 55), substantiated by comparing the protein complement of *galP*$^+$ with *galP*$^-$ strains using dual-isotope-labeled amino acids and one- or two-dimensional gel electrophoresis (38, 55). Like AraE, the activity of GalP is inhibited by cytochalasin B (concentration required for 50% inhibition = 3–10 μM). Direct measurements have shown that the inhibitor binds with a dissociation constant of approximately 1 μM. The protein can also be photolabeled by [^{3}H]-cytochalasin B (own unpublished results).

The *galP* gene is currently being sequenced. Thus far, the predicted N-terminal sequence of 96 amino acids shows strong similarity to AraE, XylE, and the glucose transporters.

A UNIFIED MODEL FOR MAMMALIAN AND BACTERIAL SUGAR TRANSPORTERS

Polypeptide Arrangement in the Membrane

Most models of membrane proteins are based upon predictions derived from hydropathic analyses of their sequences (49); only the structures of bacterial photosynthetic reaction center proteins have actually been determined at high resolution (29). Hydropathy plots of AraE, XylE, and the glucose transporters are very similar to one another, with a central, very hydrophilic segment (about 60 residues) and 6 hydrophobic segments on either side (56). Analysis of each sequence by the algorithm of Eisenberg et al (30) independently predicts the presence of 12 membrane-spanning α-helices at very similar positions (24, 57, 58). This and other information led to the proposal of a model for the arrangement in the membrane of the glucose transporter polypeptide and, by extension, of AraE and XylE (Figure 2; 24, 58). The N- and C-terminal regions and the central hydrophilic region of the sequence are predicted to be on the cytoplasmic side of the membrane. In addition to the membrane-spanning α-helices, both the central and C-terminal hydrophilic, extramembranous regions of the sequences are predicted to contain α-helical segments (13, 24, 57).

Several lines of investigation on the glucose transporter now support this model. Circular dichroism (16, 59) and infrared spectroscopic studies (2, 13, 17) indicate that both the intramembranous and extramembranous regions of the protein are largely α-helical. Antibodies raised against a synthetic C-

OUTSIDE

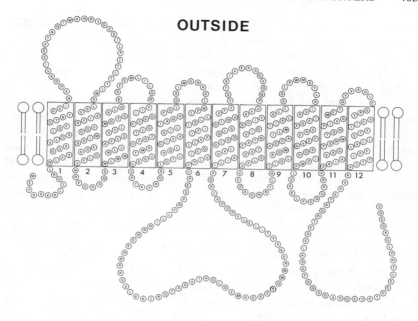

Figure 2 A model for the arrangement of the human hepatoma glucose transporter in the membrane. Numbered rectangles indicate putative membrane-spanning α-helices.

terminal peptide of the transporter bound solely to the cytoplasmic surface of the erythrocyte membrane, confirming the location of the C terminus (22). Also, water-soluble peptides were isolated after digestion of the membrane-bound transporter with trypsin, which cleaves the protein only at the cytoplasmic surface of the membrane (52); these peptides originated from the regions comprising residues 213–269 in the central, hydrophilic segment of the sequence, and residues 457–492 at the C terminus, demonstrating their cytoplasmic location (13). The extracellular glycosylation site was located using antibodies directed against a synthetic, N-terminal peptide of the transporter. These antibodies identified the large (apparent $M_r = 30,000$), membrane-bound tryptic fragment of the transporter, which contains the glycosylation site(s), as comprising the N-terminal half of the protein (14, 22). Within this region the only potential site of N-linked glycosylation is Asn_{45}, which is consistent with its predicted location in an extracellular loop connecting putative transmembrane helices 1 and 2 (58).

The three-dimensional arrangement of the 12 membrane-spanning helices is still unknown. However, several helices are predicted to be amphipathic and might therefore together form a polar pore across the membrane (58). Deuterium and tritium exchange experiments on the glucose transporter revealed that a substantial proportion of the intramembranous peptide backbone is readily accessible to solvent, which supports the presence of such an aqueous channel (2, 44). The possible arrangements of the 12 helices are constrained by the apparent shortness of many of the loops that connect them, presumably, at the membrane surfaces (Figure 2): The helices adjacent in the sequence are likely to be adjacent in the tertiary structure. A further constraint applies if the transport proteins arose as a result of an internal gene duplication event (56). Several regions of the sequences are repeated in the N- and C-terminal halves, including the RXGRR motif (discussed below) between helices 2 and 3 and helices 8 and 9. If the ancestral transporter contained only 6 membrane-spanning helices, the modern protein could comprise 2 bundles of 6 helices disposed about a pseudo twofold symmetry axis near the channel.

Conserved Features of the Sequences

The human glucose transporter, AraE, and XylE contain identical residues at 75 positions, with conservative substitutions at a further 121 positions (Figure 1). These residues are likely to be important for the structure and mechanism of these proteins. Glycine, the most frequently conserved amino acid, particularly in the proposed transmembrane helices, constitutes more than 20% of the identical residues in the three proteins. The conservation of these and a number of proline residues probably reflects the unique structural properties of their side chains. Basic and acidic residues are also frequently conserved. A particularly striking example of conservation of basic residues occurs in the motif RXGRR (above), where R can be replaced by K, and X is usually a large, hydrophobic residue. The motif is predicted to form a β-turn, linking the adjacent helices. The positively charged side chains probably interact with the head groups of membrane lipids.

Since all three transporters are inhibited by sulfhydryl reagents (8, 23, 38, 54, 55), it is surprising that no cysteine residues are conserved (56). Of course, such inhibition may stem from steric hindrance of substrate binding or translocation rather than from an essential mechanistic role of -SH groups. The bacterial transporters, unlike the eukaryote transporters, catalyze the cotransport of a proton with the sugar. The proton-translocating residue(s) might be expected to be conserved only in the bacterial proteins. Likely candidates for such residues are histidine, glutamate, and aspartate. Despite the proposed involvement of histidine in proton translocation by the functionally similar H^+-lactose transporter of *E. coli* (45, 46), no such residues are conserved in the bacterial proteins. Four acidic residues are conserved in the bacterial but not the mammalian transporters, but only one, Asp_{39} (in AraE), is located in a putative membrane-spanning helix.

The Sugar-Binding Site

The regions of the transporters involved in sugar binding remain unclear. However, some recent advances in our understanding have come from the use of cytochalasin B, an inhibitor that seems to bind to the substrate site (32, 68). Tryptic digestion of the glucose transporter, which removes the large, hydrophilic regions exposed on the cytoplasmic side of the membrane, destroys its transport activity (4). However, it does not prevent the binding of cytochalasin B albeit with reduced affinity (14). Furthermore, the binding is still attenuated by D-glucose (13, 47), which indicates that the substrate-binding site is (partly) retained in the membrane-spanning regions of the protein. Further evidence for the location of the substrate binding site(s) comes from tryptic digestion of the [^{3}H]-cytochalasin B-labeled glucose transporter; the label appeared in a membrane-bound fragment of apparent M_r 18,000, comprising residues 270–456 (13, 14, 28). Thus, at least part of the binding site lies within the C-terminal half of the protein. Experiments using 2-nitro-5-thiocyanobenzoic acid to cleave the labeled protein at cysteine residues and N-bromosuccinimide to cleave at tryptophan residues yielded fragmentation patterns consistent with a labeling site somewhere between Phe_{389} (at the cytoplasmic end of helix 10) and Trp_{412} (in the middle of helix 11) (14, 40). Photolabeling of the transporter with cytochalasin B probably results from photoactivation of an aromatic amino acid residue in the protein rather than from activation of the inhibitor (27). Interestingly, the only aromatic residue conserved in both the bacterial and mammalian transporters in this region of the sequence is Trp_{412}, which may, therefore, be the site of labeling.

[^{3}H]-cytochalasin B binds to, and thus photolabels exclusively, a cytoplasmically exposed substrate site in the glucose transporter (26). In contrast, an outward-facing substrate-binding site (or the substrate-binding site in its outward-facing conformation) has been photolabeled using a membrane-impermeant bis-mannose derivative (40). Cleavage of the transporter after labeling with this agent yields fragment patterns consistent with a labeling site between Cys_{347} (in helix 9) and Trp_{363} (in the extracellular loop connecting helices 9 and 10). Therefore, it is likely that the region containing helices 9, 10, and 11 forms a part of the substrate-binding site.

CONCLUSIONS

The homologies between the sugar transporters from E. coli and mammals clearly indicate their common ancestry. We anticipate the discovery of other, related sugar transporters, perhaps in algae, yeasts, and plants where H^+-linked sugar transport does occur. Indeed, during the preparation of this manuscript, the sequence of an homologous glucose transporter from the yeast *Saccharomyces cerevisiae* was published (15a). Out of the 884 residues of this protein, those from 86 to 581 are 28–31% identical to those of the bacterial and mammalian transporters (15a, Figure 1); the C-terminal 87 residues are not necessary for the transport function (15a). Interestingly, the H^+-glucose transporter of the protozoan parasite *Leishmania donovani* is already known to be inhibited and photolabeled by cytochalasin B, which implies that is has a structure similar to the transporters discussed here (71). Searches of the protein sequence data bases have not yet detected other closely related proteins. However, two other bacterial transport proteins do show limited sequence homology with the sugar transporters. The plasmid-encoded citrate transporter of *E. coli* (42, 63) has 12 predicted membrane-spanning regions that can be aligned with those of the sugar transporters to reveal a pattern of 55 conserved residues, which may, therefore, be important for the common function of substrate transport (56); in particular, the RXGRR motif is found at the same two locations as in the sugar transporters. Also, the transposon-encoded or plasmid-encoded tetracycline-cation antiporters have 12 predicted membrane-spanning α-helices, and some patterns of conserved residues that have been identified in the sugar transporters, including an RXGRR motif between helices 2 and 3 in the N-terminal region (39).

The mechanism of transport remains unclear although substrate translocation via a polar cleft surrounded by amphipathic α-helices seems possible. Most available kinetic evidence for the passive mammalian transporter is consistent with a single substrate site that is alternately exposed to the extracellular or cytoplasmic side of the membrane through a conformational change (68). Several workers have rejected this model on the basis of kinetic anomalies and favor more complex models in which the simultaneous binding of two sugar molecules can occur (35). However, recent redeterminations of a number of kinetic parameters have supported the adequacy of the single site model (53, 69). Much less is known about the H^+-sugar symporter mechanisms although it is interesting that energization increases the apparent affinity for sugar by over 100-fold, at least for AraE. The sequence similarities discussed above suggest that they share a common mechanism with the passive sugar transporters. Therefore, future studies comparing the bacterial and mammalian transporters should greatly enhance the understanding of the molecular mechanisms of both active and passive sugar transport.

ACKNOWLEDGMENTS

Research in the authors' laboratories is supported by the Medical Research Council, Science and Engineering Research Council, British Diabetic Association, Wellcome Trust, and SmithKline Foundation. We are indebted to Dr. M. T. Cairns, Professor H. F. Lodish, Dr. M. C. J. Maiden, Mr. T. MacDonald, Dr. D. C. M. Moore, Ms. K. Petro, Dr. G. Smith, and Dr. T. J. Wheeler for access to unpublished data and for stimulating discussions.

Literature Cited

1. Allard, W. J., Lienhard, G. E. 1985. Monoclonal antibodies to the glucose transporter from human erythrocytes. Identification of the transporter as an M_r = 55,000 protein. *J. Biol. Chem.* 260:8668–75

2. Alvarez, J., Lee, D. C., Baldwin, S. A., Chapman, D. 1987. Fourier transform infrared spectroscopic study of the structure and conformational changes of the human erythrocyte glucose transporter. *J. Biol. Chem.* 262:3502–9

3. Ames, G. F.-L. 1986. Bacterial periplasmic transport systems: structure, mechanism, and evolution. *Ann. Rev. Biochem.* 55:397–425

4. Baldwin, J. M., Lienhard, G. E., Baldwin, S. A. 1980. The monosaccharide transport system of the human erythrocyte. Orientation upon reconstitution. *Biochim. Biophys. Acta* 599:699–714

5. Baldwin, S. A., Baldwin, J. M., Lienhard, G. E. 1982. Monosaccharide transporter of the human erythrocyte. Characterization of an improved preparation. *Biochemistry* 21:3836–42

6. Barnett, J. E. G., Holman, G. D., Munday, K. A. 1973. Structural requirements for binding to the sugar-transport system of the human erythrocyte. *Biochem. J.* 131:211–21

7. Birnbaum, M. J., Haspel, H. C., Rosen, O. M. 1986. Cloning and characterisation of a cDNA encoding the rat brain glucose-transporter protein. *Proc. Natl. Acad. Sci. USA* 83:5784–88

8. Bloch, R. 1974. Human erythrocyte sugar transport. Identification of the essential residues of the sugar carrier by specific modification. *J. Biol. Chem.* 249:1814–22

9. Bradley, S. A., Tinsley, C. R., Muiry, J. A., Henderson, P. J. F. 1987. Proton-linked L-fucose transport in *Escherichia coli*. *Biochem. J.* 248:495–500

10. Brown, C. E., Hogg, R. W. 1972. A second transport system for L-arabinose in *Escherichia coli* B/r. *J. Bacteriol.* 111:606–13

11. Büchel, D. E., Gronenborn, B., Müller-Hill, B. 1980. Sequence of the lactose permease gene. *Nature* 283:541–45

12. Button, D. K. 1985. Kinetics of nutrient-limited transport and microbial growth. *Microbiol. Rev.* 49:270–97

13. Cairns, M. T., Alvarez, J., Panico, M., Gibbs, A. F., Morris, H. R., et al. 1987. Investigation of the structure and function of the human erythrocyte glucose transporter by proteolytic dissection. *Biochim. Biophys. Acta* 905: 295–310

14. Cairns, M. T., Elliot, D. A., Scudder, P. R., Baldwin, S. A. 1984. Proteolytic and chemical dissection of the human erythrocyte glucose transporter. *Biochem. J.* 221:179–88

15. Carter-Su, C., Pessin, J. E., Mora, R., Gitomer, W., Czech, M. P. 1982. Photoaffinity labelling of the human erythrocyte glucose transporter. *J. Biol. Chem.* 257:5419–25

15a. Celenza, J. L., Marshall-Carlson, L., Carlson, M. 1988. The yeast SNF3-gene encodes a glucose transporter homologous to the mammalian protein. *Proc. Natl. Acad. Sci. USA* 85:2130–34

16. Chin, J. J., Jung, E. K. Y., Chen, V., Jung, C. Y. 1987. Structural basis of human erythrocyte glucose transporter function in proteoliposome vesicles: circular dichroism measurements. *Proc. Natl. Acad. Sci. USA* 84:4113–16

17. Chin, J. J., Jung, E. K. Y., Jung, C. Y. 1986. Structural basis of human erythrocyte glucose transporter function in reconstituted vesicles. α-helix orientation. *J. Biol. Chem.* 261:7101–4

18. Ciaraldi, T. P., Horuk, R., Matthaei, S. 1986. Biochemical and functional characterization of the rat liver glucose-transport system. *Biochem. J.* 240:115–23

19. Connolly, T. J., Carruthers, A., Melchior, D. L. 1985. Effects of bilayer cholesterol on human erythrocyte hexose transport protein activity in synthetic lecithin bilayers. *Biochemistry* 24:2865–73

20. Cooper, R. A. 1986. Convergent pathways of sugar catabolism in bacteria. In *Carbohydrate Metabolism in Cultured Cells*, ed. M. J. Morgan, pp. 461–91. London: Plenum

21. Daruwalla, K. R., Paxton, A. T., Henderson, P. J. F. 1981. Energisation of the transport systems for arabinose and comparison with galactose transport in *Escherichia coli*. *Biochem. J.* 200:611–27

22. Davies, A., Meeran, K., Cairns, M. T., Baldwin, S. A. 1987. Peptide-specific antibodies as probes of the orientation of the glucose transporter in the human erythrocyte membrane. *J. Biol. Chem.* 262:9347–52

23. Davis, E. O. 1985. Xylose transport in *Escherichia coli*. PhD thesis, Univ. Cambridge

24. Davis, E. O., Henderson, P. J. F. 1987. The cloning and DNA sequence of the gene *xylE* for xylose-proton symport in *E. coli* K12. *J. Biol. Chem.* 262:13928–32

25. Davis, E. O., Jones-Mortimer, M. C., Henderson, P. J. F. 1984. Location of a

structural gene for xylose-H$^+$ symport at 91 min on the linkage map of *Escherichia coli* K12. *J. Biol. Chem.* 259:1520–25

26. Devés, R., Krupka, R. M. 1978. Cytochalasin B and the kinetics of inhibition of biological transport. A case of asymmetric binding to the glucose carrier. *Biochim. Biophys. Acta* 510:339–48

27. Deziel, M., Pegg, W., Mack, E., Rothstein, A., Klip, A. 1984. Labelling of the human erythrocyte glucose transporter with 3H-labelled cytochalasin B occurs via protein photoactivation. *Biochim. Biophys. Acta* 772:403–6

28. Deziel, M. R., Rothstein, A. 1984. Proteolytic cleavages of cytochalasin B binding components of band 4.5 proteins of the human red blood cell membrane. *Biochim. Biophys. Acta* 776:10–20

29. Diesenhofer, J., Epp, O., Miki, K., Huber, R., Michel, H. 1985. Structure of the protein subunits in the photosynthetic reaction centre of *Rhodopseudomonas viridis* at 3A resolution. *Nature* 318:618–24

30. Eisenberg, D., Schwarz, E., Komaromy, M., Wall, R. 1984. Analysis of membrane and surface protein sequences with the hydrophobic moment plot. *J. Mol. Biol.* 179:125–42

31. Gorga, F. R., Baldwin, S. A., Lienhard, G. E. 1979. The monosaccharide transporter from human erythrocytes is heterogeneously glycosylated. *Biochem. Biophys. Res. Commun.* 91:955–61

32. Griffin, J. F., Rampal, A. L., Jung, C. Y. 1982. Inhibition of glucose transport in human erythrocytes by cytochalasins: a model based on diffraction studies. *Proc. Natl. Acad. Sci. USA* 79:3759–63

33. Haspel, H. C., Birnbaum, M. J., Wilk, E. W., Rosen, O. M. 1985. Biosynthetic precursors and *in vitro* translation products of the glucose transporter of human hepatocarcinoma cells, human fibroblasts, and murine preadipocytes. *J. Biol. Chem.* 260:7219–25

34. Hediger, M. A., Coady, M. J., Ikeda, T. S., Wright, E. M. 1987. Expression, cloning and cDNA sequencing of the Na$^+$/glucose co-transporter. *Nature* 330:379–81

35. Helgerson, A. L., Carruthers, A. 1987. Equilibrium ligand binding to the human erythrocyte glucose transporter. *J. Biol. Chem.* 262:5464–75

36. Henderson, P. J. F. 1986. Active transport of sugars into *Escherichia coli*. See Ref. 20, pp. 409–60

37. Henderson, P. J. F., Giddens, R. A., Jones-Mortimer, M. C. 1977. Transport of galactose, glucose and their molecular analogues by *Escherichia coli* K12. *Biochem. J.* 162:309–20

38. Henderson, P. J. F., Macpherson, A. J. S. 1986. Assay, genetics, proteins, and reconstitution of proton-linked galactose, arabinose and xylose transport systems of *Escherichia coli*. *Methods Enzymol.* 125:387–429

39. Hillen, W., Schollmeier, K. 1983. Nucleotide sequence of the Tn10 encoded tetracycline resistance gene. *Nucleic Acids Res.* 11:525–39

40. Holman, G. D., Rees, W. D. 1987. Photolabelling of the hexose transporter at external and internal sites: fragmentation patterns and evidence for a conformational change. *Biochim. Biophys. Acta* 897:395–405

41. Horne, P., Henderson, P. J. F. 1983. The association of proton movement with galactose transport into subcellular membrane vesicles of *Escherichia coli*. *Biochem. J.* 210:699–705

42. Ishiguro, N., Sato, G. 1985. Nucleotide sequence of the gene determining plasmid-mediated citrate utilisation. *J. Bacteriol.* 164:977–82

43. Jung, C. Y., Rampal, A. L. 1977. Cytochalasin B binding sites and glucose transport carrier in human erythrocyte ghosts. *J. Biol. Chem.* 252:5456–63

44. Jung, E. K. Y., Chin, J. J., Jung, C. Y. 1986. Structural basis of human erythrocyte glucose transporter function in reconstituted system. Hydrogen exchange. *J. Biol. Chem.* 261:9155–60

45. Kaback, H. R. 1986. Proton electrochemical gradients and active transport: the saga of *lac* permease. *Ann. NY Acad. Sci.* 456:291–304

46. Kaback, H. R. 1987. Use of site-directed mutagenesis to study the mechanism of a membrane transport protein. *Biochemistry* 26:2071–76

47. Karim, A. R., Rees, W. D., Holman, G. D. 1987. Binding of cytochalasin B to trypsin and thermolysin fragments of the human erythrocyte hexose transporter. *Biochim. Biophys. Acta* 902:402–5

48. Kasahara, M., Hinkle, P. C. 1977. Reconstitution and purification of the D-glucose transporter from human erythrocytes. *J. Biol. Chem.* 252:7384–90

49. Kyte, J., Doolittle, R. F. 1982. A simple method for displaying the hydropathic character of a protein. *J. Mol. Biol.* 157:105–32

50. Lam, V. M. S., Daruwalla, K. R., Henderson, P. J. F., Jones-Mortimer, M. C. 1980. Proton-linked D-xylose transport in *Escherichia coli*. *J. Bacteriol.* 143:396–402

51. LeFevre, P. G. 1961. Sugar transport in the red blood cell: structure-activity relationships in substrates and antagonists. *Pharmacol. Rev.* 13:39–70

52. Lienhard, G. E., Crabb, J. H., Ransome, K. J. 1984. Endoglycosidase F cleaves and oligosaccharides from the glucose transporter of the human erythrocyte. *Biochim. Biophys. Acta* 769:404–10

53. Lowe, A. G., Walmsley, A. R. 1986. The kinetics of glucose transport in human red blood cells. *Biochim. Biophys. Acta* 857:146–54

54. Macpherson, A. J. S., Jones-Mortimer, M. C., Henderson, P. J. F. 1981. Identification of the AraE transport protein of *Escherichia coli*. *Biochem. J.* 196:269–83

55. Macpherson, A. J. S., Jones-Mortimer, M. C., Horne, P., Henderson, P. J. F. 1983. Identification of the GalP galactose transport protein of *Escherichia coli*. *J. Biol. Chem.* 258:4390–96

56. Maiden, M. C. J., Davis, E. O., Baldwin, S. A., Moore, D. C. M., Henderson, P. J. F. 1987. Mammalian and bacterial sugar transport systems are homologous. *Nature* 325:641–43

57. Maiden, M. C. J., Jones-Mortimer, M. C., Henderson, P. J. F. 1988. Cloning, DNA sequence and amplified expression of the *araE* gene coding H^+-arabinose symport in *Escherichia coli*. *J. Biol. Chem.* 263:8003–10

58. Mueckler, M., Caruso, C., Baldwin, S. A., Panico, M., Blench, I., et al. 1985. Sequence and structure of a human glucose transporter. *Science* 229:941–45

59. Pawagi, A. B., Deber, C. M. 1987. D-Glucose binding increases secondary structure of human erythrocyte monosaccharide transport protein. *Biochem. Biophys. Res. Commun.* 145:1087–91

60. Rotman, B., Ganesan, A. K., Guzman, R. 1968. Transport systems for galactose and galactosides in *Escherichia coli*: substrate and inducer specificities. *J. Mol. Biol.* 36:247–60

61. Saier, M. H. 1985. *Mechanisms and Regulation of Carbohydrate Transport in Bacteria.* New York: Academic

62. Saier, M. H. Jr., Yamada, M., Erni, B., Suda, K., Lengeler, J. W., et al. 1988. Sugar permeases of the bacterial PEP-dependent phosphotransferase system: sequence comparisons. *FASEB J.* 2:199–208

63. Sasatsu, M., Misra, T. K., Chu, L., Ladagga, R., Silver, S. 1985. Cloning and DNA sequence of a plasmid-determined citrate utilisation system in *Escherichia coli*. *J. Bacteriol.* 164:983–93

64. Shanahan, M. F. 1982. Cytochalasin B. A natural photoaffinity ligand for labeling the human erythrocyte glucose transporter. *J. Biol. Chem.* 257:7290–93

65. Simpson, I. A., Cushman, S. W. 1986. Hormonal regulation of mammalian glucose transport. *Annu. Rev. Biochem.* 55:1059–89

66. Wang, C. 1987. The D-glucose transporter is tissue-specific. Skeletal muscle and adipose tissue have a unique form of glucose transporter. *J. Biol. Chem.* 262:15689–95

67. Wheeler, T. J., Hinkle, P. C. 1981. Kinetic properties of the reconstituted glucose transporter from human erythrocytes. *J. Biol. Chem.* 256:8907–14

68. Wheeler, T. J., Hinkle, P. C. 1985. The glucose transporter of mammalian cells. *Annu. Rev. Physiol.* 47:503–17

69. Wheeler, T. J., Whelan, J. D. 1988. Infinite-*cis* kinetics support the carrier model for erythrocyte glucose transport. *Biochemistry* 27:1441–50

70. Wright, J. K., Seckler, R., Overath, P. 1986. Molecular aspects of sugar ion cotransport. *Annu. Rev. Biochem.* 55:225–48

71. Zilberstein, D., Dwyer, D. M., Matthaei, S., Horuk, R. 1986. Identification and biochemical characterisation of the plasma membrane glucose transporter of *Leishmania donovani*. *J. Biol. Chem.* 261:15053–57

Annu. Rev. Physiol. 1989. 51:473–85

THE CALCIUM PUMP OF THE SURFACE MEMBRANE AND OF THE SARCOPLASMIC RETICULUM

H. J. Schatzmann

Department of Veterinary Pharmacology, University of Bern, Switzerland

INTRODUCTION

This chapter is not a review of the surface membrane Ca^{2+} pump (SMP) (97, 106) and the sarcoplasmic reticulum Ca^{2+} pump (SRP) (23–25, 35, 36, 113), but a comparison of the two main ATP-driven uphill Ca^{2+} transport systems. References are merely illustrative, and the reader is referred to two excellent monographs (20, 81) for comprehensive information.

There is considerable evidence that the SMP is similar in all vertebrate and invertebrate cells (100), with perhaps the exception of the hepatocyte (56, 76). As the human red cell SMP is the best known example, this review primarily discusses human red cells and rabbit fast striated muscle sarcoplasmic reticulum (SR).

Since Ca^{2+} transport is outward at the surface membrane (SM) and inward into SR vesicles, *cis* designates the side from which and *trans* the side to which Ca^{2+} moves.

SIMILIARITIES

Structure

The SMP is a protein with a molecular mass of 140 kDa; SRP has a molecular mass of 110 kDa (3, 59). There is only one type of peptide chain in either system, but within the membrane the homodimer seems to be the dominant and possibly the only functional form (10, 11). In the red cell, this view derives from target size analysis by radiation inactivation (11, 38); in the SR it

473

0066–4278/89/0315-0473$02.00

was beautifully demonstrated by the generation of two-dimensional crystal within the membrane (4, 9, 109, 110). However, it is unknown whether there is any cooperativity between the two monomers.

Handling of Ca^{2+}

Both SMP and SRP physiologically operate against a gradient of Ca^{2+}_{cis} / Ca^{2+}_{trans} of $\sim$ 1 : 10,000 at 0.1–1 μM $[Ca^{2+}]_{cis}$ and the turnover rate is on the order of 10^3 min^{-1}. The apparent affinity for Ca^{2+} is high on the cis-side (K^{cis}_{Ca} = 0.1–1 μM) and low on the $trans$side (K^{trans}_{Ca} = 2 mM for SR and $\sim$ 10 mM for SM) (39, 40, 54, 72). The true K_{Ca} values are probably not far from the apparent ones in SRP (108). In both systems, Ca^{2+} transport or ATPase function, on one hand, or binding of Ca^{2+} at the high affinity site on the other (SR), yield Hill coefficients for Ca^{2+} between 1 and 2, which means that at least 2 Ca^{2+} ions are involved (43, 52, 92, 93, 104). However, direct measurement of the number of Ca^{2+} ions transported per ATP hydrolyzed yields 2 ions for SR (118)[for exceptions see (15, 67)] and 1 for SM (81, 90).

A fixed Ca / ATP stoichiometry at variable $[Ca^{2+}]$ must not be mistaken for perfect coupling which thermodynamically means that the free energy gained by the Ca^{2+} gradient is equal to the free energy expenditure of ATP hydrolysis (maximal efficiency η_{max} = 100%, coupling factor q = 1). For any real system η_{max} is < 100% (49). By varying the Ca^{2+} gradient and the ratio ATP / (ADP · P$_i$) and excluding the effect of leaks in parallel, in inside-out vesicles from human red cells, a $q \sim$ 0.93 (corresponding to $\eta_{max} \sim$ 46%) was found for SMP (Wüthrich, unpublished data). For SRP, a rough estimate from maximal Ca^{2+} accumulation suggests a η_{max} well below 100% (51).

H^+ ions compete with Ca^{2+} at the cis and $trans$ binding site in either system (31, 37, 102). This necessarily leads to the postulate of $Ca^{2+} - H^+$ exchange, and it was indeed shown that the system creates a H^+ gradient (74, 107). The accepted 1 Ca^{2+}: 2 H^+ stoichiometry has been challenged by the finding that SR vesicles attached to a black lipid film give rise to a current across the film in the direction of the Ca^{2+} movement (33). A 1 : 1 stoichiometry, as may be the case for red blood cells (31) and cardiac sarcolemma (54a), would allow for both H^+ transport and net charge transfer.

Mg^{2+} Requirement

In both systems, the presence of free Mg^{2+} ions on the cis-side is a nearly absolute requirement (see below). The claim that Mg^{2+} serves as a counter ion in SR is rather improbable (14), and in red cells, Mg^{2+} was shown not to be translocated during Ca^{2+} transport (98). High Mg^{2+} concentration is inhibitory (50); the true K^{Mg}_i is $\sim$ 200 μM in SMP (7). The inhibition seems to be due to competition with Ca^{2+} at the transport site.

Dual Role of ATP

Both systems present two ATP binding sites of vastly different affinity (68, 83, 119). The high affinity site (1 μM range) is the hydrolytic site proper, the low affinity site (100–300 μM range) accelerates the reaction by a factor of about 10 in SMP and more in SRP. It is not clear if the two sites are separate or whether one site changes affinity in a cyclic fashion. At any rate, the two sites cannot exist simultaneously on the same molecule (71). For the high affinity site, MgATP is believed to be the true substrate in SRP, but for the SMP, free ATP (and perhaps even CaATP) (70, 77, 79) probably can serve as a substrate as well; MgATP has been proposed as the required species at the low affinity site in either system (1, 70).

The Reaction Cycle

Both systems undergo a reaction cycle (Figure 1) in which the protein is phosphorylated and dephosphorylated, and alternates between two conformations with the Ca^{2+} transport site in *cis* or *trans* position (E_1, E_2) (20, 81). The phosphorylated intermediates are acid-stable acylphosphates (aspartylphosphates) (17) that can be decomposed by hydroxylamine. The elementary steps of the cycle are most probably similar in both systems (Figure 1).

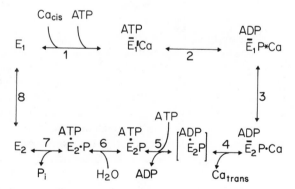

Figure 1   Proposal for reaction cycle in surface membrane and sarcoplasmic reticulum Ca pump (SMP, SRP). E_1, E_2: conformations of pump protein; translocation occurence step 3; EP covalent bond; ($\cdot$) low and (|) high affinity non-covalent ATP, ADP or Ca^{2+} bond; (*) "occluded" Ca^{2+}; [ ] "ADP-insensitive" E (no evidence in SMP). In forward mode (clockwise): invading arrows: preceding E has increased affinity, emerging arrows: preceding E has decreased affinity. Mg^{2+} not shown: it probably enters at step 1 and is liberated at step 7; step 3 (4) decisive for acceleration by Mg^{2+}; it is unclear what happens between ATP·E_2 and ATP/E_1 (step 8). Step 6 (7, 8?) decisive for acceleration by ATP at low affinity site.

E · P signifies that after cleavage of the covalent bond, phosphate (P_i) remains attached by a noncovalent bond within the active site. In the SRP this Michaelis complex has been intimated by various experiments (28, 65).

The ATP sites are clearly situated on the *cis*-side in SRP and SMP, and for the SMP it was demonstrated that P_i is released on the *cis* side (104). In both systems ATP and Ca^{2+}-binding at the start of the reaction cycle are random (48, 66, 81, 99); the second step (Figure 1, 2) requires Ca^{2+} and is accelerated by Mg^{2+} (7, 48, 100) [high $[Ca^{2+}]$ can replace Mg^{2+} (7)]. This action of Mg^{2+} does not account for its very large positive effect on the overall rate. Dephosphorylation is accelerated by Mg^{2+} (117) and high concentrations of ATP (> 100 013M) (7, 21, 29), and for the SMP it was shown that the main acceleration by Mg^{2+} occurs at step 3 (Figure 1, 3) and that ATP (or MgATP) is required beyond step 3. Thus, if it is correct that ATP at the low affinity site is necessary for steps 6 and 7, ATP enters the phosphorylated site (E_2P), most probably after the departure of ADP (1, 65). The release of Ca^{2+}_{trans} precedes dephosphorylation in SRP (60), and it is highly probable that this is equally true for the SMP.

Originally, the Mg^{2+} site on the phosphorylated enzyme appeared occluded (i.e. not in equilibrium with the medium) in SRP (30) but not in SMP (80). Recently, however, it was shown for SMP that 50 μM Ca^{2+} renders E_1P unreactive to Mg^{2+}, whereas even 5 mM Ca^{2+} are unable to displace Mg^{2+} after it had access to E_1 (7), indicating occlusion of Mg^{2+}. Some E forms seem to be free of Mg^{2+} in SRP, a conclusion reached because certain inhibitors are competitively antagonized by Mg^{2+} (62). This implies that Mg^{2+} affinity is high in the E_1 form and low in the E_2 form, i.e. that the system indeed undergoes a Mg^{2+} cycle.

Both systems are stimulated some 30–100% by K^+ or Na^+ (20, 81, 105) (in the SMP also by Rb^+, Cs^+, and NH^{+4}) but not Li^+. Under certain conditions, however, inhibition of SRP was seen (18). For the SMP it was shown that K^+ cannot be claimed as counter ion (88). In spite of some controversy (85), it is concluded that monovalent cations exert their influence on the *cis* side only (53). In both systems the overall rate increases together with steady state concentration of phosphorylated enzyme (20, 55, 81).

In view of the suggestion that the dimer is a predominant state of the pump protein within the natural membrane, it is tempting to assume that the enzyme is governed by half-of-the-sites kinetics, with the two monomers out of phase by 180° (one in the E_2 form when the other is in the E_1 form). The fact that the high affinity ATP-site attributed to E_1 and the low affinity site attributed to E_2, cannot coexist (71) supports this assumption. However, direct proof is missing.

Lipid and Protein Chemistry

Activity in both systems is destroyed by removal of the surrounding phospholipids (20, 63, 81, 84); however, these phospholipids can be replaced by detergents. For the SR it was shown that 29 of the 30 closely associated lipid molecules may be replaced by detergent without impairing function (16).

Proteolytic degradation patterns of the membrane-bound or the purified protein, and the recent sequencing of the complete SRP (3, 59) and of a central 90-kDa part of SMP (111) have led to proposals for a tertiary structure. The ATP binding site (NH$_2$· Lys-Gly-Ala-Ser-Glu in SMP; NH$_2$· Lys-Gly-Ala-Pro-Glu in SRP) (112), the phosphorylation site (45) (identical over 10 amino acids), and the ionophoric site (near the core of the membrane) are not equally far apart on the peptide chain of both systems. The high number of glutamates in the helices S$_1$, S$_2$, and S$_3$ bordering on the membrane are candidates for Ca^{2+} binding.

DIFFERENCES

Protein Chemistry

The molecular mass of SRP is 30 kDa less than that of SMP. In addition to the 10-kDa calmodulin (CAM)-binding stretch at the COOH terminal (see below), a 50-kDa peptide can be trimmed from the NH$_2$ end of SMP without detrimental effects on function. The central domain of 80-kDa remains associated with the membrane, transports Ca^{2+}, splits ATP, and forms a phosphorylated intermediate (91). Comparison of a 90-kDa sequence of the SMP (111) with the complete SRP (3, 59) clearly shows that the SMP protein must have an extension of unknown function at the NH$_2$ end and a shorter one at the COOH end containing the $\sim$ 30 amino acids of the CAM-binding domain (44).

Interestingly, the overall similarity between the two Ca pumps is not any closer than that between either the Na pump or proton pump (111).

Calmodulin Requirement

SMP is stimulated by calmodulin (32, 47), whereas SRP is not. If three of its four metal binding sites are occupied by Ca^{2+} ($K_{Ca} \sim 1$ μM), CAM binds with a K_d in the nanomolar range to the SMP (46). Consequently, the affinity of the transport site for Ca^{2+} increases 30-fold (93–95), that of the low affinity site for ATP 100-fold (87), K$^+$ becomes more effective (92), the maximal rate of the pump increases somewhat (93–95), and the Ca^{2+}-dependent ADP - ATP exchange rate increases 8-fold (12); however, the steady state phosphorylated enzyme level remains the same (69, 70). The

CAM association proceeds slowly (taking seconds to reach equilibrium). Sharff & Foder (95) calculated that at physiological [Ca] $_{cis}$, [Mg] $_{cis}$, and [CAM] in human red cells, the pump-CAM complex is dissociated. Owing to this low association rate the pump activity increases slowly when the Ca^{2+} leak increases abruptly, so that [Ca] $_{cis}$ overshoots before attaining the new steady state. Thus the CAM mechanism imparts hysteretic behavior to the Ca^{2+} homeostasis system (96).

It was demonstrated by controlled proteolysis of the purified enzyme and of inside-out vesicles that the CAM-binding part lies near the carboxyl end of the pump molecule within a 10-kDa fragment (91, 120). This terminal fragment exerts an inhibitory action in the absence of CAM. The finding that the CAM-like effect of proteolysis requires the presence of Ca^{2+} (89) was not confirmed (91). Interestingly, acidic phospholipids and fatty acids also mimic the action of CAM (73) on the intact protein although minor kinetic differences between activation by CAM and acidic lipids exist (26).

Reversibility

It stands to reason that the cycle must be composed of reversible single steps (double arrows in Figure 1). Thus, the system as a whole must be reversible and a *trans - cis* Ca^{2+} gradient should be to run the system backwards (counterclockwise in Figure 1), with osmotic energy driving ATP synthesis from P_i and ADP. This is thermodynamically sound and has indeed been demonstrated experimentally for both systems (2, 20, 27, 34, 61, 86, 114). However, a quantitative difference between the two systems might signal a fundamental divergence. In the SRP, the rate of ATP synthesis at a Ca^{2+} concentration ratio of $\sim 10^5$ approaches the rate of the forward reaction if [P_i] is made 10 mM and [ADP] 2 mM (20, 61). In the SMP, under a Ca^{2+}-ratio of $\sim 10^6$ (i.e. approximately equal force as in the SR experiments if 1 Ca^{2+}: 1 ATP holds) the backward rate at pH 7.4 was found to be a very small fraction of the maximal forward rate at a comparable [P_i] x [ADP] product (101, 114). For the SRP, it was shown that at pH 7.4 the backward rate is slower than at pH 6 (19), but this does not explain the very low rate observed in SMP at pH 7.4. The backward reaction P_i + ADP $\rightarrow$ ATP is accompanied by an ADP-induced *trans*-to-*cis* movement of Ca^{2+}, which was also very much smaller in SMP than in SRP (101, 114). The backward rate is only .05 –1% of the forward rate in SMP (101). Cavieres (12, 13) recently measured ADP-ATP exchange in SMP of red cells as was done in the early SR experiments (25, 36). The method uses [^{3}H]ADP to find the rate of [^{3}H]ATP formation in the steady state. The appearance of labeled ATP was rapid and strongly dependent on Mg^{2+}. This is in accord with a rapid, Mg^{2+}-dependent reaction of E_2P with ADP [80]. Since step 3 (Figure 1) is exquisitely Mg^{2+}-

dependent and since there is no evidence in SMP for an ADP-insensitive EP in the presence of Mg^{2+} (80), ADP must stay attached after the transport step, and all reverse reactions must be rapid between E$_2$P and the release of ATP, which leaves us with E$_2$ + P$_i$ → E$_2$P as the only slow backward reaction. This indicates that steps 6–7 are strongly poised in the clockwise direction in the SMP of red cells, while this obviously is not true in the SRP (42, 51). This agrees with the finding that phosphorylation of the protein from P$_i$ is easy in the SR (64) but difficult in the SMP of red cells (57). ATP at the low affinity site accelerates E$_2$P ⇌ E$_2$ + P$_i$ in both systems (65, 80). If it did so in the SMP more strongly than in SRP, the difference between the two systems would be accentuated in the backward reaction whose demonstration requires low ATP cencentration.

In the steady state most of the enzyme is phosphorylated in SRP (51), unlike in SMP where phosphorylation is not faster than dephosphorylation (see 108). La^{3+} is thought to block the system at step 3 (or 4) leading to accumulation of E$_1$P (or E$_1$P + E$_2$P) (58). In SMP 0.1–0.2-mM La^{3+} increases EP fourfold or more compared to the steady state total EP (58). In SR this effect is less marked (116, 117), possibly because E$_2$P is a sink for E at equilibrium with La^{3+} (and in the steady state) due to the reaction E$_2$ + P$_i$ ⇌ E$_2$P not being poised to the left.

The apparent affinity for vanadate (HVO$_4^{2-}$) seems to be higher in SMP than SRP (1, 22, 75, 78, 103). Since E$_2$ very probably is the form that binds vanadate, the observed difference in apparent affinity is compatible with the different behaviors of steps 6–7 in the two systems.

Substrate Specificity

In both systems the affinity for other nucleotides is much lower than for ATP (34, 90). However, the SR can sustain slow transport also on acetylphosphate, paranitrophenylphosphate (pNPP) (41) and others (20). pNPP inhibits Ca^{2+} pumping in red cell SMP (6), yet it is hydrolyzed. The hydrolysis rate is dependent on Ca^{2+} and low ATP concentration, and is accelerated by K$^+$ (5, 82). Therefore, the low affinity ATP site accepts pNPP and the high affinity site must be occupied by ATP for rapid pNPP cleavage (5). Accordingly, pNPP is a competitive inhibitor for the ATP hydrolysis ($K_i \approx 5.7$ mM), but in addition it interferes, with much higher affinity, with phosphorylation from ATP (103).

Immunological Difference

Several studies (8, 112, 115) show that inhibitory antibodies distinguish between the two systems.

Table 1 Behavior of surface membrane Ca^{2+} pump (SMP) and sarcoplasmic reticulum Ca^{2+} pump (SRP) in the dephosphorylating limb of the cycle

Behavior	SMP	SRP
E_2 binds ATP (low affinity)	yes	yes
Evidence for E_2Ps with different ADP-affinities	no	yes (?)
$E_2P \rightleftharpoons E_2 + P_i$	$\rightleftharpoons$	$\rightleftharpoons$
accelerated by ATP	yes (in the presence of CAM[a])	yes (?)
$E_2 \rightleftharpoons E_1$ accelerated by ATP	no (?)	yes
E_2 accepts pNPP[b]	yes	yes
pNPP sustains	phosphatase activity	Ca-pump activity

[a]CAM = calmodulin.
[b]pNPP = paranitrophenyl phosphate.

SUMMARY

The molecular architectures of SMP and SRP differ, yet the functional analogies between CAM-associated SMP and SRP are numerous. Most of the divergences observed may have their root in different behavior during dephosphorylation (see Table 1).

Literature Cited

1. Andersen, J. P., Møller, J. V. 1985. The role of Mg^{2+} and Ca^{2+} in the simultaneous binding of vanadate and ATP at the phosphorylation site of sarcoplasmic reticulum Ca^{2+}-ATPase. *Biochim. Biophys. Acta* 815:9–15
2. Barlogie, B., Hasselbach, W., Makinose, M. 1971. Activation of calcium efflux by ADP and inorganic phosphate. *FEBS Lett.* 12:267–68
3. Brandl, C. J., Green, M., Korczak, B., MacLennan, D. H. 1986. Two Ca^{2+}-ATPase genes: Homologies and mechanistic implication of deduced amino acid sequence. *Cell* 44:597–607
4. Buhle, E. Jr., Knox, B. E., Serpersu, E., Aebi, U. 1983. The structure of the Ca^{2+}-ATPase as revealed by electron microscopy and image processing of ordered arrays. *J. Ultrastruct. Res.* 85:186–203
5. Caride, A. J., Rega, A. F., Garrahan, P. J. 1982. The role of the sites for ATP of the CA^{2+}-ATPase from human red cell membranes during Ca^{2+} phosphatase activity. *Biochim. Biophys. Acta* 689:421–28

6. Caride, A. J., Rega, A. F., Garrahan, P. J. 1983. Effects of *p*-nitrophenylphosphate on Ca^{2+} transport in inside-out vesicles from human red cell membranes. *Biochim. Biophys. Acta* 734:363–67
7. Caride, A. J., Rega, A. F., Garrahan, P. J. 1986. The reaction of Mg^{2+} with the Ca^{2+}-ATPase from human red cell membranes and its modification by Ca^{2+}. *Biochim. Biophys. Acta* 863:165–77
8. Caroni, P., Zurini, M., Clark, A. 1982. The calcium pumping ATPase of heart sarcolemmal vesicles. *Proc. Natl. Acad. Sci. USA* 77:6354–58
9. Castellani, L., Hardwick, P. M. D., Vibert, P. 1985. Dimer ribbons in the three dimensional structure of sarcoplasmic reticulum. *J. Mol. Biol.* 185:579–94
10. Cavieres, J. D. 1983. The molecular size of the red cell calcium pump with and without calmodulin. *J. Physiol.* 343:96P
11. Cavieres, J. D. 1984. Calmodulin and the target size of the $(Ca^{2+} + Mg^{2+})$

-ATPase of human red cell ghosts. *Biochim. Biophys. Acta* 771:241–44

12. Cavieres, J. D. 1987. Fast reversal of the initial reaction step of the plasma membrane (Ca^{2+} + Mg^{2+}) -ATPase. *Biochim. Biophys. Acta* 899:83–92

13. Cavieres, J. D., Reynolds, C. J. 1987. Biphasic Ca^{2+} effect on ATP-ADP exchange catalyzed by the Ca^{2+}-pump of human red cells. *J. Physiol.* 391:19P

14. Chiesi, M., Inesi, G. 1980. Adenosine-5' -triphosphate dependent fluxes of manganese and hydrogen ions in sarcoplasmic reticulum vesicles. *Biochemistry* 19:2912–18

15. Deamer, D. W. 1973. Isolation and characterization of a lysolecithin-adenosine triphosphatase complex from lobster muscle microsomes. *J. Biol. Chem.* 248:5477–85

16. Dean, W. L., Tanford, C. 1978. Properties of a delipidated, detergent-activated Ca^{2+} -ATPase. *Biochemistry* 17:1683–90

17. Degani, C., Boyer, P. D. 1973. A borohydride reduction method for the characterization of acylphosphate linkage in proteins and its application to sarcoplasmic reticulum adenosine triphosphatase. *J. Biol. Chem.* 248:8222–25

18. DeMeis, L. 1972. Phosphorylation of membranous protein of sarcoplasmic reticulum. Inhibition by Na$^+$ and K$^+$. *Biochemistry* 11:2460–65

19. DeMeis, L. 1976. Regulation of steady state level of phosphoenzyme and ATP synthesis in sarcoplasmic reticulum vesicles during reversal of the Ca^{2+} -pump. *J. Biol. Chem.* 251:2055–62

20. DeMeis, L. 1981. *The Sarcoplasmic Reticulum.* New York: Wiley. 163 pp.

21. DeMeis, L., Boyer, P. D. 1978. Induction by nucleoside triphosphate hydrolysis of a form of sarcoplasmic reticulum ATPase capable of medium phosphate-oxygen exchange in the presence of calcium. *J. Biol. Chem.* 253:1556–59

22. Dupont, Y., Bennett, N. 1982. Vanadate inhibition of the Ca^{2+}-dependent conformational change of the sarcoplasmic reticulum Ca^{2+} -ATPase. *FEBS Lett.* 139:237–40

23. Ebashi, S. 1960. Calcium binding and relaxation in the actomyosin system. *J. Biochem.* 48:150–51

24. Ebashi, S. 1961. Calcium binding activity of vesicular relaxing factor. *J. Biochem.* 50:236–44

25. Ebashi, S., Lipmann, F. 1962. Adenosinetriphosphate-linked concentration of calcium ions in a particulate fraction of rabbit muscle. *J. Cell Biol.* 14:389–400

26. Enyedi, A., Flura, M., Sarkadi, B., Gardos, G., Carafoli, E. 1987. The maximal velocity and the calcium affinity of the red cell calcium pump may be regulated independently. *J. Biol. Chem.* 262:6425–30

27. Ferreira, H. G., Lew, V. L. 1975. Catransport and Ca-pump reversal in human red blood cells. *J. Physiol.* 252:86P

28. Fröhlich, J. P., Taylor, E. W. 1976. Transient state kinetic effects of calcium ion on sarcoplasmic reticulum adenosine triphosphatase. *J. Biol. Chem.* 251:2307–15

29. Garrahan, P. J., Rega, A. F. 1978. Activation of partial reaction of the Ca^{2+} -ATPase from human red cells by Mg^{2+} and ATP. *Biochim. Biophys. Acta* 513:59–65

30. Garrahan, P. J., Rega, A. F., Alonso, G. L. 1976. The interaction of magensium ions with the calcium pump of sarcoplasmic reticulum. *Biochim. Biophys. Acta* 448:121–32

31. Gassner, B., Luterbacher, S., Schatzmann, H. J., Wüthrich, A. 1988. Dependence of the red blood cell calcium pump on the membrane potential. *Cell Calcium* 9:95–103

32. Gopinath, R. M., Vincenzi, F. F. 1977. Phosphodiesterase protein activator mimics red blood cell cytoplasmic activator of (Ca^{2+} + Mg^{2+}) -ATPase. *Biochem. Biophys. Res. Commun.* 77:1203–9

33. Hartung, K., Grell, E., Hasselbach, W., Bamberg, E. 1987. Electrical pump currents generated by Ca^{2+} -ATPase of sarcoplasmic reticulum vesicles adsorbed on black lipid films. *Biochim. Biophys. Acta* 900:209–20

34. Hasselbach, W. 1978. The reversibility of the sarcoplasmic calcium pump. *Biochim. Biophys. Acta* 515:23–53

35. Hasselbach, W., Makinose, M. 1961. Die Calciumpumpe der "Erschlaffungsgrana" des Muskels und ihre Abhängigkeit von der ATP Spaltung. *Biochem. Z.* 333:518–28

36. Hasselbach, W., Makinose, M. 1963. Ueber den Mechanismus des Calciumtransports durch die Membran des sarkoplasmatischen Retikulums. *Biochem. Z.* 339:94–111

37. Hill, T. L., Inesi, G. 1982. Equilibrium cooperative binding of calcium and protons by sarcoplasmic reticulum ATPase. *Proc. Natl. Acad. Sci. USA* 79:3978–82

38. Hymel, L., Maurer, A., Berenski, C. Y., Jung, S., Fleischer, S. 1984. Target size of calcium pump protein from skeletal muscle. *J. Biol. Chem.* 259:4890–95

39. Ikemoto, N. 1974. The calcium binding sites involved in the regulation of the purified adenosinetriphosphatase of sarcoplasmic reticulum. *J. Biol. Chem.* 249:649–51

40. Ikemoto, N. 1975. Transport and inhibitory Ca^{2+} binding sites on the ATPase enzyme isolated from sarcoplasmic reticulum. *J. Biol. Chem.* 250:7219–24

41. Inesi, G. 1971. *p*-Nitrophenyl phosphate hydrolysis and Ca^{2+} ions transport in fragmented sarcoplasmic reticulum. *Science* 171:901–4

42. Inesi, G. 1985. Mechanism of calcium transport. *Annu. Rev. Physiol.* 47:573–601

43. Inesi, G., Kurtzmack, M., Coan, C., Lewis, D. E. 1980. Cooperative calcium binding and ATPase activation in sarcoplasmic reticulum vesicles. *J. Biol. Chem.* 255:3025–31

44. James, P., Maeda, M., Fischer, R., Verma, A. K., Krebs, J., et al. 1988. Identification and primary structure of a calmodulin binding domain of the Ca^{2+} pump of human erythrocytes. *J. Biol. Chem.* 263:2905–10

45. James, P., Zvaritch, E. I., Shakhparonow, M. I., Penniston, J. T., Carafoli, E. 1987. The amino-acid sequence of the phosphorylation domain of the erythrocyte Ca^{2+} ATPase. *Biochem. Biophys. Res. Commun.* 149:7–12

46. Jarrett, H. W., Kyte, J. 1979. Human erythrocyte calmodulin. *J. Biol. Chem.* 254:8237–44

47. Jarrett, H. W., Penniston, J. T. 1977. Partial purification of the $Ca^{2+} + Mg^{2+}$ -ATPase activator from human erythrocytes. Its similarity to the activator of $3':5'$ -cyclic nucleotide phosphodiesterase. *Biochem. Biophys. Res. Commun.* 77:1210–16

48. Kanazawa, T., Yamada, S., Yamamoto, T., Tonomura, Y. 1971. Reaction mechanism of the Ca^{2+} -dependent ATPase of sarcoplasmic reticulum from skeletal muscle. *J. Biochem.* 70:95–123

49. Kedem, O., Caplan, S. R. 1965. Degree of coupling and its relation to efficiency of energy conversion. *Trans. Faraday Soc.* 61:1897–1911

50. Klinger, R., Wetzker, R., Fleischer, I., Frunder, H. 1980. Effect of calmodulin, Ca^{2+} and Mg^{2+} on the $(Ca^{2+} + Mg^{2+})$-ATPase of erythrocyte membranes. *Cell Calcium* 1:229–40

51. Kodama, T. 1985. Thermodynamic analysis of muscle ATPase mechanisms. *Physiol. Rev.* 65:467–551

52. Kosk-Kosicka, D., Inesi, G. 1985.

53. Kratje, R. B., Garrahan, P. J., Rega, A. F. 1983. The effects of alkali metal ions on active Ca^{2+} transport in reconstituted ghosts from human red cells. *Biochim. Biophys. Acta* 731:40–46

54. Kratje, R. B., Garrahan, P. J., Rega, A. F. 1985. Two modes of inhibition of the Ca^{2+} pump in red cells by Ca^{2+}. *Biochim. Biophys. Acta* 816:365–78

54a. Kuwayama, H. 1988. The membrane potential modulates the ATP-dependent Ca^{2+} pump of cardiac sarcolemma. *Biochim. Biophys. Acta* 940:295–99

55. Larocca, J. N., Rega, A. F., Garrahan, P. J. 1981. Phosphorylation and dephosphorylation of the Ca^{2+} -pump of human red cells in the presence of monovalent cations. *Biochim. Biophys. Acta* 645:10–16

56. Lotersztajn, S., Hanoune, J., Pecker, F. 1981. A high affinity calcium-stimulated, magnesium-dependent ATPase in rat liver plasma membrane. *J. Biol. Chem.* 256:11209–15

57. Luterbacher, S. 1982. *Die Teilreaktionen der ATP-Spaltung durch das isolierte Protein der Ca^{2+} -Pumpe und der Erythrocytenmembran.* PhD thesis. Univ. Bern. 112 pp.

58. Luterbacher, S., Schatzmann, H. J. 1983. The site of action of La^{3+} in the reaction of the human red cell membrane Ca^{2+}-pump ATPase. *Experientia* 39:311–12

59. MacLennan, D. H., Brandl, C. J., Bozena, K., Green, M. 1985. Amino-acid sequence of $Ca^{2+} + Mg^{2+}$ -dependent ATPase from rabbit muscle sarcoplasmic reticulum, deduced from its complementary DNA sequence. *Nature* 316:696–700

60. Makinose, M. 1973. Possible function states of the enzyme of the sarcoplasmic calcium pump. *FEBS Lett.* 37:140–43

61. Makinose, M., Hasselbach, W. 1971. ATP synthesis by the sarcoplasmic calcium pump. *FEBS Lett.* 12:271–72

62. Makinose, M., Loer, G., Boll, W. 1987. Screening of useful drugs for the sequence analysis of the partial reaction steps involved in the reaction cycle of the sarcoplasmic Ca^{2+} -transport enzyme. *Top. Mol. Pharmacol.* 4:129–46

63. Martonosi, A., Donley, J., Halpin, R. A. 1968. Sarcoplasmic reticulum. III. The role of phospholipids in the adeno-

Cooperative calcium binding and calmodulin regulation in the calcium dependent adenosinetriphosphatase purified from the erythrocyte membrane. *FEBS Lett.* 189:67–71

sine triphosphatase activity and Ca^{2+} transport *J. Biol. Chem.* 243:61–70

64. Masuda, H., DeMeis, L. 1973. Phosphorylation of the sarcoplasmic reticulum membrane by orthophosphate. Inhibition by calcium ions. *Biochemistry* 12:4581–85

65. McIntosh, D. B., Boyer, P. D. 1983. Adenosine-5' -triphosphate modulation of catalytic intermediates of calcium ion activated adenosinetriphosphatase of sarcoplasmic reticulum subsequent to enzyme phosphorylation. *Biochemistry* 22:2867–75

66. Meissner, G. 1973. ATP and Ca^{2+} binding by the Ca^{2+} pump protein of sarcoplasmic reticulum. *Biochim. Biophys. Acta* 298:906–26

67. Meltzer, S., Berman, M. C. 1984. Effects of pH, temperature and calcium concentration on the stoichiometry of the calcium pump of sarcoplasmic reticulum. *J. Biol. Chem.* 259:4244–53

68. Muallem, S., Karlish, S. J. D. 1979. Is the red cell calcium pump regulated by ATP? *Nature* 277:238–40

69. Muallem, S., Karlish, S. J. D. 1980. Regulatory interaction between calmodulin and ATP on the red blood cell Ca^{2+} pump. *Biochim. Biophys. Acta* 597:631–36

70. Muallem, S., Karlish, S. J. D. 1981. Studies on the mechanism of regulation of the red cell Ca^{2+} pump by calmodulin and ATP. *Biochim. Biophys. Acta* 647:73–86

71. Muallem, S., Karlish, S. J. D. 1983. Catalytic and regulatory ATP binding sites of the red cell Ca^{2+} pump studied by irreversible modification with fluorescin isothiocyanate. *J. Biol. Chem.* 258:169–75

72. Nakamura, Y., Tonomura, Y. 1982. Changes in affinity for calcium ions with the formation of two kinds of phosphoenzyme in the Ca^{2+}, Mg^{2+} dependent ATPase of sarcoplasmic reticulum. *J. Biochem.* 91:449–61

73. Niggli, V., Adunyah, E. S., Carafoli, E. 1981. Acid phospholipids in saturated fatty acids and limited proteolysis mimic the effect of calmodulin on the purified erythrocyte Ca^{2+}-ATPase. *J. Biol. Chem.* 256:8588–92

74. Niggli, V., Sigel, E., Carafoli, E. 1982. The purified Ca^{2+} -pump of human erythrocyte membranes catalyzes an electroneutral Ca^{2+}-H$^+$ exchange in reconstituted liposomal systems. *J. Biol. Chem.* 257:2350–56

75. Ortiz, A., Garcia-Carmona, F., Garcia-Canovas, T., Gomez-Fernandez, J. C. 1984. A kinetic study of the interaction of vanadate with the Ca^{2+} + Mg^{2+} -dependent ATPase from sarcoplasmic reticulum. *Biochem. J.* 221:213–22

76. Pecker, F., Lotersztajn, S. 1985. Fe^{2+} and other divalent metal ions uncouple Ca^{2+} transport from (Ca^{2+} + Mg^{2+}) -ATPase in rat liver plasma membranes. *J. Biol. Chem.* 260:731–35

77. Penniston, J. T. 1982. Substrate specificity of the erythrocyte Ca^{2+} -ATPase. *Biochim. Biophys. Acta* 688:735–39

78. Pick, U. 1982. The interaction of vanadate ions with the Ca-ATPase from sarcoplasmic reticulum. *J. Biol. Chem.* 257:6111–19

79. Rega, A. F., Garrahan, P. J. 1975. Calcium dependent phosphorylation of human erythrocyte membranes. *J. Membr. Biol.* 22:313–27

80. Rega, A. F., Garrahan, P. J. 1978. Calcium-ion dependent dephosphorylation of the Ca^{2+} -ATPase of human red cells by ADP. *Biochim. Biophys. Acta* 507:182–84

81. Rega, A. F., Garrahan, P. J. 1986. *The Ca^{2+} -Pump of Plasma Membranes.* Boca Raton, Fl.:CRC. 173 pp.

82. Rega, A. F., Richards, D. E., Garrahan, P. J. 1973. Calcium ion dependent *p*-nitrophenyl phosphate phosphatase activity and calcium ion dependent adenosine triphosphatase activity from human erythrocyte membranes. *Biochem. J.* 136:185–94

83. Richards, D. E., Rega, A. F., Garrahan, P. J. 1978. Two classes of site for ATP in the Ca^{2+} -ATPase from human red cell membranes. *Biochim. Biophys. Acta* 511:194–201

84. Roelofsen, B., Schatzmann, H. J. 1977. The lipid requirement of the (Ca^{2+} + Mg^{2+}) -ATPase in the human erythrocyte membrane, as studied by various highly purified phospholipases. *Biochim. Biophys. Acta* 464:17–36

85. Romero, P. J. 1981. Active calcium transport in red cell ghosts resealed in dextran solutions. *Biochim. Biophys. Acta* 649:404–18

86. Rossi, J. P. F. C., Garrahan, P. J., Rega, A. F. 1978. Reversal of the calcium pump in human red cells. *J. Membr. Biol.* 44:37–46

87. Rossi, J. P. F. C., Rega, A. F., Garrahan, P. J. 1985. Compound 48/80 and calmodulin modify the interaction of ATP with the (Ca^{2+} + Mg^{2+}) -ATPase of red cell membranes. *Biochim. Biophys. Acta* 816:379–86

88. Rossi, J. P. F. C., Schatzmann, H. J.

1982. Is the red cell calcium pump electrogenic? *J. Physiol* 327:1–15

89. Rossi, J. P. F. C., Schatzmann, H. J. 1982. Trypsin activation of the red cell Ca^{2+} -pump ATPase is calcium-sensitive. *Cell Calcium* 3:583–90

90. Sarkadi, B. 1980. Active calcium transport in human red cells. *Biochim. Biophys. Acta* 604:159–90

91. Sarkadi, B., Enyedi, A., Földes-Papp, Z., Gardos, G. 1986. Molecular characterization of the *in situ* red cell membrane calcium pump by limited proteolysis. *J. Biol. Chem.* 261:9552–57

92. Scharff, O. 1978. Stimulating effect of monovalent cations on activator-dissociated and activator-associated states of Ca^{2+} -ATPase in human erythrocytes. *Biochim. Biophys. Acta* 512:309–17

93. Scharff, O. 1980. Kinetics of calcium-dependent membrane ATPase in human erythrocytes. In *Membrane Transport in Erythrocytes*, ed. U. V. Larsen, H. H. Ussing, J. O. W. Wieth, pp. 236–54. Copenhagen: Munksgaard

94. Scharff, O., Foder, B. 1978. Reversible shift between two states of Ca^{2+} -ATPase in human erythrocytes mediated by Ca^{2+} and a membrane bound activator. *Biochim. Biophys. Acta* 509:67–77

95. Scharff, O., Foder, B. 1982. Rate constants for calmodulin binding to Ca^{2+} -ATPase in erythrocyte membranes. *Biochim. Biophys. Acta* 691:133–43

96. Scharff, O., Foder, B., Skibsted, U. 1983. Hysteretic activation of the Ca^{2+} -pump revealed by calcium transients in human red cells. *Biochim. Biophys. Acta* 730:295–305

97. Schatzmann, H. J. 1966. ATP dependent Ca^{2+} extrusion from human red cells. *Experientia* 22:364–68

98. Schatzmann, H. J. 1975. Active calcium transport and Ca^{2+} -activated ATPase in human red cells. *Curr. Top. Membr. Transp.* 6:125–68

99. Schatzmann, H. J. 1977. Role of magnesium in the $(Ca^{2+} + Mg^{2+})$-stimulated membrane ATPase of human red blood cells. *J. Membr. Biol.* 35:149–58

100. Schatzmann, H. J. 1985. Calcium extrusion across the plasma membrane by the calcium-pump and the Ca^{2+} - Na^+ exchange system. In *Calcium and Cell Physiology*, ed. D. Marmé, pp. 18–52. Berlin: Springer-Verlag

101. Schatzmann, H. J. 1986. The plasma membrane calcium pump. In *Intracellular Calcium Regulation*, ed. H. Bader, K. Gietzen, J. Rosenthal, R. Rüdel, H. U. Wolf, pp. 47–56. UK: Manchester Univ. Press

102. Schatzmann, H. J. 1986. The human red cell calcium pump. *Fortsch. Zool.* 33:435–42. Membrane Control, Lüttgau (Hrsg.). Stuttgart: Fischer-Verlag

103. Schatzmann, H. J., Luterbacher, S., Stieger, J., Wüthrich, A. 1987. Some inhibitors of the calcium pump of red blood cells. *Top. Mol. Pharmacol.*, ed. A. S. V. Burgen, G. C. K. Roberts, B. M. 4:147–68. Anner. Amsterdam: Elsevier

104. Schatzmann, H. J., Roelofsen, B. 1977. Some aspects of the Ca-pump in human red blood cells. In *Biochemistry of Membrane Transport*, ed. G. Semenza, E. Carafoli, pp. 389–400. Berlin: Springer-Verlag

105. Schatzmann, H. J., Rossi, G. L. 1971. $(Ca^{2+} + Mg^{2+})$-activated membrane ATPases in human red cells and their possible relations to cation transport. *Biochim. Biophys. Acta* 241:379–92

106. Schatzmann, H. J., Vincenzi, F. F. 1969. Calcium movements across the membrane of human red cells. *J. Physiol.* 201:369–95

107. Smallwood, J. I., Waisman, D. M., Lafrenière, D., Rasmussen, H. 1983. Evidence that the erythrocyte Ca-pump catalyzes a Ca^{2+}: n H^+ exchange. *J. Biol. Chem.* 258:11092–97

108. Tanford, Ch. 1982. Steady state of an ATP-driven calcium pump: Limitations and thermodynamic parameters. *Proc. Natl. Acad. Sci. USA* 79:6161–65

109. Taylor, K., Dux, L. 1984. Structure of the vanadate induced crystals of sarcoplasmic reticulum Ca-ATPase. *J. Mol. Biol.* 174:193–204

110. Taylor, K., Dux, L. 1986. Three-dimensional reconstruction of negatively stained crystals of the Ca^{2+}-ATPase from muscle sarcoplasmic reticulum. *J. Mol. Biol.* 187:417–27

111. Verma, A. K., Filoteo, A., Stanford, D. R., Wieben, E. D., Penniston, J. T., et al. 1988. Complete primary structure of a human plasma membrane Ca^{2+} pump. *J. Biol. Chem.* 263:14152–59

112. Verma, A. K., Gorski, J. P., Penniston, J. T. 1982. Antibodies directed toward human erythrocyte Ca^{2+}-ATPase: Effect of enzyme function and immunoreactivity of Ca^{2+} -ATPases from other sources. *Arch. Biochem. Biophys.* 215:345–54

113. Weber, A., Herz, R., Reiss, I. 1966.

Study of the kinetics of Ca^{2+} -transport by isolated fragmented sarcoplasmic reticulum. *Biochem. Z.* 345:329–69

114. Wüthrich, A., Schatzmann, H. J., Romero, P. 1979. Net ATP synthesis by running the red cell calcium pump backwards. *Experientia* 35:1589–90

115. Wuytack, F., de Schutter, G., Verbist, J., Casteels, R. 1983. Antibodies to the calmodulin-binding   Ca^{2+}-transport ATPase from smooth muscle. *FEBS Lett.* 154:191–95

116. Wuytack, F., Raeymakers, L., de Schutter, G., Casteels, R. 1982. Demonstration of the phosphorylated intermediates of the Ca^{2+} transport ATPase in a microsomal fraction and in a (Ca^{2+}Mg^{2+})-ATPase purified from smooth muscle by means of calmodulin affinity chromatography. *Biochim. Biophys. Acta* 693:45–52

117. Yamada, S., Tonomura, Y. 1972. Reaction mechanism of the Ca^{2+} -dependent ATPase of sarcoplasmic reticulum from skeletal muscles. VII. Recognition and release of Ca^{2+} ion. *J. Biochem.* 72: 417–25

118. Yamada, S., Yamamoto, T., Tonomura, Y. 1970. Reaction mechanism of the Ca^{2+} dependent ATPase of sarcoplasmic reticulum from skeletal muscle. III. Ca^{2+} uptake and splitting of ATP. *J. Biochem.* 67:789–94

119. Yamamoto, T., Tonomura, Y. 1967. Reaction mechanism of the Ca^{2+} dependent ATPase of sarcoplasmic reticulum from skeletal muscle. *J. Biochem.* 62:558–75

120. Zurini, M., Krebs, J., Penniston, J. T., Carafoli, E. 1984. Controlled proteolysis of the purified Ca^{2+} -ATPase of the erythrocyte membrane. A correlation between structure and function of the enzyme. *J. Biol. Chem.* 259:618–27

SPECIAL TOPIC: OPTICAL APPROACHES TO NEURON FUNCTION

Larry Cohen, Section Editor

Department of Physiology, Yale University School of Medicine, New Haven, Connecticut 06510

INTRODUCTION

The following five reviews present an account of the results that have been obtained using optical methods for monitoring physiological events in the nervous system. This is not to imply that optical methods have not been useful in other areas of physiology; these measurements have been reviewed elsewhere (3, 5, 9, 17, 22).

There are several factors that make optical methods interesting to physiologists and neuroscientists. First is the possibility of making simultaneous measurements from multiple sites. Because many different neurons in a nervous system are active during each behavior, it is obviously important to be able to monitor activity at many sites simultaneously. Similarly, different parts of a neuron may perform different functions and again it would be essential to make simultaneous observations over the whole structure of the neuron. Second, optical measurement can be made with very high time resolution. Some optical indicators of activity are known to respond to

487

changes in neuron physiology with time constants of less than 1.5 μsec. Other indicators of activity, such as light scattering, can be much slower, with latencies and durations in the range of seconds, but the optical recordings still reflect real-time measurements of events in the nervous system. Third, optical measurements are in some sense noninvasive. The degree of noninvasiveness varies from measurements of intrinsic signals, which appear to be completely innocuous, to measurements using dyes where the possibility of pharmacology and photodynamic damage must be considered. The relative noninvasiveness of optical recordings has allowed measurements from membrane processes (e.g. T-tubules and presynaptic terminals) that are far too small to be studied with microelectrodes. The reviews that follow will give some indication as to how well it has been possible to exploit these advantages of optical measurements.

While there will be only brief comparisons with other kinds of measurements of activity, in mammalian brains, e.g. 2-deoxyglucose, positron emission tomography, nuclear magnetic resonance, or magnetic field measurements, optical measurements do provide a much larger spatial-temporal bandwidth. However, at present optical methods cannot be used to record from deep in a tissue, an important capability that these other methods do provide. Four kinds of optical signals will be discussed; light scattering, NADH fluorescence, dye indicators of membrane potential, and dye indicators of intracellular calcium concentration.

Light scattering changes that accompany trains of stimuli to nerves were first described by Hill and Keynes in 1949 (11, 12). Somewhat later Aubert et al (2) described changes in NADH fluorescence that accompanied trains of action potentials in slices of electric organ. With the advent of signal averagers it was possible to measure the changes in light scattering and birefringence that accompany individual action potentials in nerves and single axons (6), but many trials (1,000–10,000) had to be averaged to detect these intrinsic signals. Even before those results were published, the late David Gilbert (personal communication) suggested that optical signals might be used to follow activity in the nervous system. Soon thereafter Tasaki and collaborators (21) found changes in the fluorescence of axons that were stained with several dyes; several years later changes in dye absorption (15) and birefringence (16) were also found. Almost all of these dye signals were shown to depend on changes in membrane potential (7, 8, 18) although there was some early disagreement (5). The first attempt to use optical indicators of intracellular ion concentration was measurement of calcium with the dye murexide (13); although subsequent investigation (14) suggested that those results may have been an artifact. Later Ashley and Ridgeway introduced the use of the photoprotein aequorin (1). Following the suggestion of John Cooper (personal communication), the Arsenazo class of dye indicators of calcium was first used (4). More recently, Roger Tsien and collaborators have developed a new class of calcium dyes based on the chemical structure of the chelator EGTA. The individual reviews that follow will emphasize both the importance and the difficulty in finding dyes that maximize the signal-to-noise ratio and at the same time minimize effects on the physiology.

The first multi-site measurements of brain activity were made by Schuette et al (20) who used an image intensifier and camera tube to monitor changes in NADH fluorescence from cortex during epileptic seizures. This was followed by methods using several individual silicon photodiodes (19) and later by the use of arrays of photodiodes (10).

Even though optical recording methods were only recently introduced, a variety of the reviews that follow indicate that they have been applied to neurobiological problems that range from dendritic diversity in single neurons to activity maps that cover large areas of mammalian cortex.

Literature Cited

1. Ashley, C. C., Ridgway, E. B. 1970. On the relationship between membrane potential, calcium transient and tension in single barnacle muscle fibres. *J. Physiol.* 209:105–30
2. Aubert, X., Chance, B., Keynes, R. D. 1964. Optical studies of the biochemical events in the electric organ of *Electrophorus. Proc. R. Soc. London, Ser. B* 160:211–45
3. Bashford, C. L., Smith, J. C. 1979. The use of optical probes to monitor membrane potential. *Methods Enzymo.* 55:569–86
4. Brown, J. E., Cohen, L. B., De Weer, P., Pinto, L. H., Ross, W. N., Salzberg, B. M. et al 1975. Rapid changes in intracellular free calcium concentration. Detection by metallochromic indicator dyes in squid giant axon. *Biophys. J.* 15:1155–60
5. Cohen, L. B., Salzberg, B. M. 1978. Optical measurement of membrane potential. *Rev. Physiol. Biochem. Pharmacol.* 83:35–88
6. Cohen, L. B., Keynes, R. D., Hille, B. 1968. Light scattering and birefringence changes during nerve activity. *Nature* 218:438–41
7. Cohen, L. B., Landowne, D., Shrivastav, B. B., Ritchie, J. M. 1970. Changes in fluorescence of squid axons during activity. *Biol. Bull.* 139:418–19
8. Cohen, L. B., Salzberg, B. M., Davila, H. V., Ross, W. N., Landowne, D., et al. 1974. Changes in axon fluorescence during activity: molecular probes of membrane potential. *J. Membr. Biol.* 19:1–36

9. Freedman, J. C., Laris, P. C. 1981. Electrophysiology of cells and organelles: Studies with optical potentiometric indicators. *Int. Rev. Cytol. Suppl.* 12:177–246
10. Grinvald, A., Cohen, L. B., Lesher, S., Boyle, M. B. 1981. Simultaneous optical monitoring of activity of many neurons in invertebrate ganglia using a 124-element photodiode array. *J. Neurophysiol.* 45:829–40
11. Hill, D. K. 1950. The effect of stimulation on the opacity of a crustacean nerve trunk and its relation to fibre diameter. *J. Physiol.* 111:283–303
12. Hill, D. K., Keynes, R. D. 1949. Opacity changes in stimulated nerve. *J. Physiol.* 108:278–81
13. Jobsis, F. F., O'Connor, M. J. 1966. Calcium release and reabsorption in the sartorius muscle of the toad. *Biochem. Biophys. Res. Comm.* 25:246–52
14. Maylie, J., Irving, M., Sizto, N. L., Boyarsky, G., Chandler, W. K. 1987. Calcium signals recorded from cut frog twitch fibers containing tetramethylmurexide. *J. Gen. Physiol.* 89:145–76
15. Ross, W. N., Salzberg, B. M., Cohen, L. B., Davila, H. V. 1974. A large change in dye absorption during the action potential. *Biophys. J.* 14:983–86
16. Ross, W. N., Salzberg, B. M., Cohen, L. B., Grinvald, A., Davila, H. V. 1977. Changes in absorption, fluorescence, dichroism, and birefringence in stained giant axons: optical measurement of membrane potential. *J. Membr. Biol.* 33:141–83

17. Salzberg, B. M. 1983. Optical recording of electrical activity in neurons using molecular probes. In *Current Methods in Cellular Neurobiology,* ed. J. L. Barker, J. F. McKelvy, 139–87 pp. New York: Wiley

18. Salzberg, B. M., Bezanilla, F. 1983. An optical determination of the series resistance in *Loligo. J. Gen. Physiol.* 82:807–17

19. Salzberg, B. M., Grinvald, A., Cohen, L. B., Davila, H. V., Ross, W. N. 1977. Optical recording of neuronal activity in an invertebrate central nervous system: simultaneous monitoring of several neurons. *J. Neurophysiol.* 40:1281–91

20. Schuette, W. H., Willard, B. E. E., Whitehouse, C., Lewis, D. V., O'Connor, M. 1974. A television fluorimeter for monitoring oxidative metabolism in intact tissue. *Med. Instrum.* 8:331–33

21. Tasaki, I., Watanabe, A., Sandlin, R., Carnay, L. 1968. Changes in fluorescence, turbidity, and birefringence associated with nerve excitation. *Proc. Natl. Acad. Sci. USA* 61:883–88

22. Waggoner, A. S. 1979. Dye indicators of membrane potential. *Annu. Rev. Biophys. Bioeng.* 8:47–68

Annu. Rev. Physiol. 1989. 51:491–506

CHANGES IN INTRACELLULAR CALCIUM DURING NEURON ACTIVITY

W. N. Ross

Department of Physiology, New York Medical College, Valhalla, New York 10595

INTRODUCTION

Calcium levels in neurons change in response to chemical and electrical events. These changes may trigger secretion or other processes, or may only be incidental consequences of neuronal activity. Knowledge of the time course, amplitude, and spatial distribution of these changes can reveal information both about the events which caused the changes and the processes they initiate or modulate. In principle, optical techniques, using the appropriate indicators, are the best way to follow these changes since they are fast enough to track most physiological events and they can be extended easily to record from many locations. There has been a great increase in these kinds of measurements in recent years. This is largely due to progress in three areas: (*a*) a new generation of calcium sensitive dyes, (*b*) improved techniques for measuring these changes, especially computer-based imaging techniques, and (*c*) an expanded appreciation of the kinds of questions which might be answered by these measurements. Progress in these three areas has not proceeded independently. As is often the case, new techniques have suggested new problems to investigate, and these problems have, in turn, driven the demand for new indicators and technologies. In this review we will concentrate on these newer developments. The restriction of the discussion to calcium changes in neurons is somewhat procrustean since there is extensive overlap in both the techniques used and the problems investigated across many cell types. In fact, methods of measuring calcium transients include many contributions by muscle physiologists, and the use of the newer fluorescent imaging techniques has been largely the province of cell biologists.

491

0066-4278-/89/0315-0491$02.00

Discussion of intracellular calcium measurements can be organized around two basic kinds of questions: (*a*) What are the spatial and temporal distributions of free calcium concentration in a cell at rest or when activated by agonists or events with a time scale of seconds to minutes?; (*b*) What is the distribution, amplitude, and time course of calcium transients evoked by electrical activity on the millisecond time scale. This division suggests itself because at the current state of development the techniques and many of the scientific questions are different in the two time ranges. Many aspects of this discussion have been summarized before. Some of these reviews are listed in the references (5, 14, 74, 78, 84, 85).

CALCIUM LEVELS

Until recently free calcium concentrations in neurons or other cells could only be measured with ion selective electrodes or with null point comparisons in internally dialyzed neurons. Ion selective electrodes are difficult to make, often cause injury to the impaled cell (and consequently alter the calcium level), and calibrations may be inaccurate in the submicromolar range. They can only measure values at one location at a time and their slow response time makes them suitable for only a few applications (43, 60). Nevertheless, this technique still has important uses, especially in examining cells in vivo, where optical methods may not be applicable (53).

Aequorin

Aequorin luminescence has been used to measure resting and activated calcium concentrations in squid axons. The luminescence of this photoprotein in axoplasm (detected by photomultipliers) was compared to the luminescence of a similar amount of aequorin injected into buffers of varying calcium concentrations. Two groups obtained matches with buffers containing 100–300 nM (8) or 20–60 nM (28, 59) free calcium. Considering the difficulty of this technique the difference in values is not significant. Relative calcium levels are easier to measure with this indicator and a number of basic facts about calcium regulation in neurons were first established with aequorin. In particular, it was shown that most intracellular calcium is bound to cytoplasmic buffers and that mitochondrial regulation is only significant when high calcium loads are impressed on the cells (7, 17, 18, 59).

Arsenazo III

Arsenazo III has also been used to measure calcium levels in squid axons and other neurons (28). This dye, one of a series of metallochromic indicators, binds calcium with an effective dissociation constant of about 40 μM (2), although recent experiments have shown that the stoichiometry is not purely

1 : 1 (56, 62, 78). The absorption spectrum of the dye differs in the bound and unbound form and calcium changes can be monitored by detecting absorption changes at a suitable wavelength, usually 660 nm (19, 28). The dye also binds magnesium and hydrogen ions that affects the dye : calcium reaction as well as directly causing absorption changes. Consequently, several wavelengths must be monitored to control for changes in the concentration of these other ions. There has also been considerable controversy about the validity of in vitro calibrations for measurements in cytoplasm (10, 12, 13, 61). However, when used in null point experiments in squid axons, similar values of free calcium were obtained as with aequorin (28). In most experiments absorption changes in the physiological range of intracellular calcium are very small and considerable care must be used in measuring them. A typical procedure has been to use a rotating wheel to alternate between two different wavelengths and a sensitive photodiode or photomultiplier to detect the light levels (18, 33). A more sensitive method is to use broadband illumination and to separate the transmitted light into two bands with a dichroic mirror. The two wavelengths can then be followed continuously without loss of intensity (6, 37). Antipyralazo III, another metallochromic dye, has been used extensively by muscle physiologists (e.g 10, 12). Because of its higher dissociation constant and faster kinetics, it is more suitable than arsenazo III for measuring the calcium changes associated with excitation-contraction coupling. Since calcium concentrations in neurons usually do not appear to reach such high concentrations and the transients are considerably slower than in muscle, these properties may not be advantageous for measurements on these cells. This dye has not yet been used by neurobiologists.

Tetracarboxylate Indicators

PROPERTIES   Recently a series of tetracarboxylate dyes has been synthesized that overcome many of the problems with aequorin and the metallochromic dyes and additionally have several other properties that have made them important (36, 82). These strongly fluorescent compounds bind calcium with high affinity (dissociation constants for most of them are in the submicromolar range) and selectivity. Interference from hydrogen and magnesium ions is much less than with aequorin and arsenazo III. In addition, two attractive aspects are that the calcium levels they report can be calibrated and analogues of the dyes can be nondisruptively loaded into cells (83). These properties mean that the dyes can be used to determine calcium levels in suspensions of cells in a cuvette, in many isolated cells in a culture dish, and in cells that are too small to be safely penetrated with a microelectrode. The first popular dye of this class to be synthesized was quin2 (82). Although it was used to estimate calcium levels in a variety of preparations (86), it had a number of acknowledged limitations. It was not highly fluorescent, it required

UV excitation, its effective affinity constant for binding calcium was too low to use for reporting calcium levels in stimulated cells, and it was not easy to calibrate. Consequently, Tsien and his colleagues synthesized several new dyes which overcome most of these difficulties (36). Fura-2 is the most widely used of this series. A membrane permeant analogue, fura-2-AM, has also been created. It has acetoxymethyl groups linked with ester bonds to the carboxylates. After penetrating the cell, cytoplasmic esterases cleave these groups leaving the impermeant, free-acid form trapped in the cell. Cells therefore can be loaded by microinjection of fura-2 or populations of cells can be loaded by incubating them with fura-2-AM. The fluorescence quantum yield of fura-2 is high enough that only low intracellular concentrations are needed in order to make measurements with a good signal-to-noise ratio, even from isolated cells, as long as the calcium levels are changing slowly. However, the high affinity of this dye for calcium also makes it a good buffer and normal cells processes may be affected. This is especially true of events which induce transient changes in intracellular calcium. In practice it is necessary to evaluate this problem for each preparation (see below).

Imaging techniques can be used with fura-2 to estimate calcium levels simultaneously in many cells or many positions within a single cell (26, 57, 87). Because path length and dye concentration are not needed in calculating the ratio which quantitates calcium, each point in the image can be treated independently. This ratio imaging works particularly well in culture conditions where the cells are relatively flat with most parts in focus and there is little background fluorescence.

APPLICATIONS   Measurements using these dyes are just beginning and are being made at an increasing rate. Rather than comprehensively review those measurements which have been made so far, a few representative experiments on neurons are described that illustrate the range of questions which have been examined.

Connor (25) measured calcium levels in dispersed cells from embryonic rat diencephalon that extend processes with filopodia. Using ratio imaging of cells loaded with fura-2-AM, he estimated resting somatic calcium levels as 60–80 nM with significantly higher levels in growing neurites [a result also found in sympathetic neurons (45)]. Nonextended and extended cells that had stopped growing had uniform calcium levels in the 30–70 nM range. A similar elevation of growth cone calcium was found by Cohan et al (23) in identified isolated *Helisoma* neurons. They also found that electrical activity and serotonin elevated calcium beyond this level and inhibited further growth. Kudo & Ogura (40) showed that L-glutamate induced a dose-dependent elevation of intracellular calcium in isolated hippocampal neurons from the rat. Nitrendipine blocked a similar calcium increase induced by high extracellular potassium without significantly affecting the L-glutamate induced increase. This suggests that in these cells L-glutamate can elevate intracellular calcium due to an influx of calcium through both L-glutamate receptor-coupled and voltage-sensitive ionic channels. Connor et al (27) did similar experiments on rat cerebellar granule cells in explant cultures using GABA, glutamate, and kainate as agonists. Both groups reported considerable heterogeneity in the calcium response to the agonists among populations of cells that were thought to be more homogeneous. Lipscombe et al (45) showed that ratio imaging could also follow the time course of calcium changes in different parts of a neuron if the temporal transitions were not too rapid. They showed that caffeine in the presence of high external potassium causes oscillations in cytoplasmic calcium levels in sympathetic neurons, which are larger in the soma than in growth cones. These kinds of experiments, where the effects of various neurotransmitters and pharmacological agents are assayed for their effects on regional calcium levels in neurons, are important applications of this technique.

PROBLEMS   With so many advantages over previous methods of measuring calcium, fura-2 and its analogues have become the indicators of choice where steady-state levels or slowly varying levels of calcium are desired. However, there are a few problems with this technique that suggest caution in interpreting the calculated values as accurately representing free cytoplasmic calcium concentration (85). First, fura-2 was shown to be concentrated in some organelles and not always distributed uniformly in the cytoplasm. In some preparations the dye was associated with mitochondria (72), in others with lysosomes (49) or secretory granules (4, 32). Interestingly, the degree of localization varies in different cell types from highly punctate in endothelial cells (72) to uniform in cerebellar granule cells (27). This problem may be unique to fura-2 since other dyes of the same class (like indo-1) are found to be uniformly distributed in the same kinds of cells which show punctate loading with fura-2 (72). To a first approximation this compartmentalization may not matter since the calculated calcium concentration should be independent of dye concentration. However, any optical technique yields a calcium concentration by integrating intensities over some intracellular volume. If the dye concentration is not uniform then the result is biased towards the value in that part of the volume which contains the highest dye concentration, in this case towards organelles which may have different calcium concentrations than the cytoplasm (88). A second kind of problem is the validity of in vitro calibrations for reporting in vivo calcium concentrations. Measurements of dye diffusion in muscle cytoplasm indicate that a significant fraction of the dye is bound to cytoplasmic components (11). It is not known if and how much this binding affects the dye:calcium reaction.

Also, the dissociation constant of this reaction is sensitive to viscosity and cytoplasmic viscosity is not well known. However, in one experiment the calcium levels were calibrated in vivo by making the cell membranes permeable with ionomycin. This calibration did not differ significantly from that determined in vitro (87). Additional problems are found when fura-2-AM is used. In some cases the cell does not completely hydrolize the ester bonds and the intermediates have fluorescence properties that interfere with the calcium quantitation (68). Also, this membrane permeant dye will get into most intracellular compartments and, if calcium is nonuniformly distributed in the cell, it may be difficult to interpret the measured levels if the compartments are not spatially resolved.

CALCIUM TRANSIENTS

Measurements of rapid changes in intracellular calcium initiated by an electrical event require different approaches than the ones used to measure slow changes. Most of the problems that are examined by measuring fast calcium transients seek different kinds of information than questions approached with measurements of slow changes. In this time range it is often more interesting to know when, where, and how much calcium has entered a cell rather than what calcium concentration has been reached.

Magnitude of Calcium Entry

The first measurements of calcium transients in neurons were of the magnitude of calcium entry during electrical stimulation and the time course of removal of this calcium. These kinds of experiments were designed to characterize the voltage-dependent conductances responsible for the calcium changes and to describe the properties of the pumps or buffers that were involved in calcium regulation. Brown et al (19) detected voltage-dependent calcium entry into squid axons. Using absorbance changes of arsenazo III as an indicator of calcium changes they confirmed the earlier experiments of Baker et al (8) showing that calcium entered through both "early" and "late" channels. TTX blockage and double pulse inactivation of the absorbance transients showed that the early channel was the sodium channel. These experiments also showed that the kinetics of the dye:calcium reaction were fast enough to follow the influx of calcium into the axon with a delay of less than a millisecond.

Several groups measured the amount of calcium entry into neuronal cell bodies when stimulated with pairs of identical short pulses. Stinnakre (73), Eckert et al (30) and Lux & Heyer (47), all using aequorin, found larger amplitude calcium signals from the second pulse and suggested that calcium entry could be facilitated. However, Smith & Zucker (71) and Ahmed &

Connor (1) both showed that this result was an artifact of using aequorin with its nonlinear luminescence versus calcium response, in combination with the spatial inhomogeneity of the calcium in the cell cytoplasm. Using arsenazo III, which has a linear absorbance change at 660 nm in response to added calcium in the physiological range (6, 50, 51), they found equal amplitude responses to the double pulse protocol, a result which has since been confirmed by several other groups (22, 63).

Optical evidence for calcium entry inactivation is stronger in some preparations. Both Tillotson (79) and Bruner et al (20), using absorbance changes of arsenazo III, showed that a prepulse causing calcium entry, but not the membrane potential change itself, reduced calcium entry to a test pulse.

The magnitude of calcium entry during voltage clamp pulses to the cell bodies of invertebrate neurons (1, 20, 34) and the presynaptic terminal of the squid giant synapse (6) has also been examined. In each case the calcium changes were blocked by external Cd^{2+}, Co^{2+} or 0 mM external Ca^{2+}, showing that there is no direct potential dependent release of calcium from internal stores during the stimulus. However, secondary release of calcium as a consequence of calcium entry or receptor activation may still occur (45). Calcium entry versus potential was bell-shaped as suggested by direct measurements of clamp currents when other conductances were blocked (3, 6). This kind of experimental protocol has also been used to examine the modulation of calcium accumulation. Boyle et al (16) showed that serotonin increased the calcium signal following cell stimulation in voltage-clamped *Aplysia* neurons, and Lewis et al (44) showed that dopamine reduced calcium entry. By moving the position of the detector over the cell the latter group also showed that the dopamine effect was maximal in the neuropil and not the cell body.

Time Course

The time course of the return of a calcium transient to baseline is indicative of the speed of buffering, sequestration, or pumping out of free calcium from the cytoplasm. Since calcium diffuses slowly in cytoplasm compared to the time course of most electrically induced transients, different regions of a neuron respond independently to the changes in calcium. There is no a priori reason for assuming that all parts of the cell will respond in the same way. Therefore it is important to try to measure the time course from the relevant location before relating it to other cellular events like secretion or calcium-regulated conductances. Several experiments have shown that the recovery time course is faster at the edge of the neuron compared with the center (65, 69). This is likely to be related to the stronger buffering power of the cytoplasm at the edge of the cell (54, 80) and/or the effect of membrane pumps. Also, in barnacle neurons the recovery time was shown to be faster in the neuropil than in the soma or axon (65). But most experiments have not had both the spatial and temporal resolution to measure the time course in a compartment directly under the membrane that might be compared with the membrane events. Nevertheless, Gorman & Thomas (33) and Ahmed & Connor (1), using only a single detector, found that the recovery time in cell bodies of *Aplysia* or *Archidoris monterysis* was approximately the same as the time course of the calcium-activated potassium conductance. Stockbridge & Ross (76), using a photodiode array, found the same result comparing calcium transients in the presynaptic terminal of the barnacle photoreceptor with membrane potential measured in the photoreceptor axon. This result was more compelling since the small dimensions of the terminal processes ensured that diffusion equilibrium was reached faster than the recovery time of the transient. Therefore, the optically measured time course, which averaged over the volume of the processes, probably was close to the time course directly under the membrane. At the squid giant synapse the recovery time course of an action potential induced calcium transient (measured with a single detector) is much longer than the time course of the calcium current or the postsynaptic potential (6, 22). But the volume of the presynaptic terminal in this preparation is too large for diffusion equilibrium to be reached during the time course of the transient, so it should not be expected that the optically measured time course would reflect changes just under the membrane. Smith et al (70) have recently made some progress on this problem using time-lapse imaging of fura-2 fluorescence after stimulation of the synapse. These measurements have much better spatial resolution, but the frame rate is still too slow to follow the critical events related to secretion. Ultimately, the time resolution of this kind of measurement will be limited by the kinetics of the dye : calcium reaction and the lack of knowledge of the microenvironment just under the membrane.

Postsynaptic Signals

Calcium transients in neurons also occur as a consequence of synaptic activation. The calcium entry is either part of the postsynaptic current or a consequence of a voltage-dependent calcium conductance increase activated by the synaptic potential, or both. These kinds of transients have been demonstrated at the squid giant synapse (41) and at the neuromuscular junction (50) using aequorin and arsenazo III as the indicators. In both preparations it was demonstrated that there was a significant receptor-activated calcium current by detecting optical signals while the postsynaptic element was voltage-clamped to a steady potential. In these preparations postsynaptic calcium entry was also demonstrated following direct ionophoretic application of the agonists glutamate (31) and acetylcholine (50). The same approach has been used to demonstrate calcium entry through NMDA receptors in sympathetic neurons (48). Measurements on postsynaptic cells can be extended with imaging techniques to map sites of synaptic contact between neurons and to characterize the synaptic properties at each location. In cerebellar slices a photodiode array measured the spatial distribution of calcium transients associated with the climbing fiber Purkinje-cell synapse (66).

Location of Calcium Entry

Since calcium diffuses slowly in the cytoplasm, the site of a calcium increase immediately after a stimulus must be close to the channel location. Several groups have used this approach to localize calcium channels at the presynaptic terminals of selected neurons. Stockbridge & Ross (76) injected arsenazo III into the axon and presynaptic terminal of the barnacle photoreceptor and found that calcium entry was detected only in the last 50 μm of the terminal endings when the cell was uniformly depolarized. This region corresponds exactly to the location of synaptic contacts with second order cells in the barnacle supraesophageal ganglion. Llinás et al (46) injected aequorin into the giant presynaptic terminal of the squid. This region was viewed with an image intensifier and television camera and the presynaptic terminal was intensely stimulated. The locations of induced luminescence were observed to be in just that area which makes contact with the postsynaptic elements. Smith et al (70) repeated this experiment using fura-2 as the calcium sensor. They found that calcium entry occurred first from the membrane facing the postsynaptic sites, and then diffused into the center of the presynaptic digit. This result is consistent with the observations of Pumplin et al (58) who detected characteristic bumps on the presynaptic face in freeze-fractures that they interpreted as calcium channels.

Cells with calcium channels localized only at the presynaptic terminal may be unusual. Using the same optical techniques, calcium entry has been detected in many locations in neurons, some of which could not possibly be sites of synaptic contact. Voltage-dependent calcium transients have been recorded from isolated neurons in culture (15, 63), from the dendrites or processes of many cells (26, 35, 66), and the axons of some invertebrate neurons (65). It is still an open and interesting question whether the calcium channels at these locations are the same as at synapses (52). The distribution of these calcium channels may vary during development or in different growth conditions. For example, Ross et al (63) found that Retzius cells from the leech send out processes with a low calcium channel density when plated on Concanavalin A, but the same cells have a higher density of channels in their processes when plated on a lamininlike molecule extracted from the ganglionic capsule (64).

This kind of experiment, where the magnitudes of calcium transients are interpreted in terms of calcium channel density, has several difficulties. The proportionality constant between channel density and transient amplitude depends on the membrane area observed by the detector, the membrane potential, and the buffering power of the cytoplasm in the region of the detector. All of these may be different in different parts of the cell. In some cases the isopotentiality of the cell can be demonstrated and estimates of the membrane area reasonably made. But the buffering power of neural cytoplasm in different regions is a relatively unexplored parameter (54, 80) and conclusions based on this assumption must be viewed with caution. The examples of high densities of calcium channels at presynaptic terminals are most convincing because almost no calcium entry was detected in the axons close to the synapses.

Indicators of Electrical Events

Since the rising phase of a calcium transient is almost coincident in time with the electrical event which caused it, the detection of a transient can also be used as an indicator of an action potential or synaptic potential. In this case the calcium signal is serving much the same function as the detection of an event using voltage-sensitive dyes. Stinnakre & Tauc (75) using aequorin, and Gorman & Thomas (33) using arsenazo III showed that optical signals could be detected in response to individual action potentials in the soma of neuron R15 of *Aplysia* if the firing rate was not too high. They also found slow calcium changes that matched the potential change in the interburst interval in this cell. Although these experiments demonstrated that calcium transients could be used in this way their value was limited because only a single location was observed and this site was at the same point as the recording electrode. When multiple detectors or imaging devices are used, comparative measurements from many locations in a cell or from many cells can be made. In this case much more information is available than can be obtained from a few electrodes. An example of this technique is the recording of the complex spatial and temporal distribution of multiple calcium spikes in the dendrites of Purkinje cells in brain slices from the guinea pig cerebellum (67). Similar experiments have followed the calcium fluxes resulting from action potentials in neurons from barnacle (65) and crab ganglia (35). In each of these cases regional variations of the calcium signals were found which could be interpreted in terms of different distributions of membrane potential from moment to moment.

Fura-2 or other fluorescent calcium indicators can also be used to detect rapid calcium changes although as yet there are only a few examples of this approach. Lev-Ram & Grinvald (42) detected calcium changes in myelinated nerves following electrical stimulation and suggested that this transient calcium increase activated a potassium conductance in the axons. Transient calcium increases were also detected from isolated hippocampal neurons. Using the jumps in fluorescence as an indicator of electrical activity, Ogura et al (55) demonstrated synchronized and nonsynchronized firing among the cells that could be blocked by TTX and several neurotransmitter antagonists.

Comparison of Indicators

The same criteria do not always apply when comparing the usefulness of techniques for measuring fast calcium transients with those applied to evaluate methods for measuring slow changes in calcium concentration. For transients important considerations are sensitivity, linearity of response, and the ability to follow changes without problems due to the buffering of the calcium by the indicator or slow kinetics of the dye:calcium reaction. Good sensitivity means being able to detect small calcium changes with a good signal-to-noise ratio. Many of the same considerations apply as when evaluating ways of detecting signals with voltage-sensitive dyes (24). The fluorescent dyes, especially those with a low K_d, show a large fractional change in emission intensity on binding calcium. However the intensity is usually low so the various sources of noise in the detection system may make it difficult to record the transient accurately, especially if good time resolution is required. Increasing the emission intensity by increasing the incident light intensity or raising the dye concentration may cause photodynamic damage or excessive calcium buffering. Absorbance changes of calcium-sensitive dyes in neurons produce a much smaller fractional change in transmitted intensity. But this intensity can be measured with great accuracy. The choice between the two methods will depend upon the preparation and some of the other factors discussed below.

Linearity of response is important where there are significant variations in calcium concentration within the volume from which the detector records. Nonlinear indicators in the physiological range will exaggerate contributions from high or low concentration regions within the volume (88). This problem is most severe in the moments immediately after the transient is initiated. Arsenazo III and other dyes with high dissociation constants are better in this respect.

The dissociation constant also affects the extent to which the dye buffers or blunts the calcium change during a transient. For a given concentration of dye an indicator with a lower K_d will be a stronger buffer. While normal cellular homeostatic mechanisms may be able to restore calcium levels to their original values when a strong buffer is introduced, it is less likely that they can compensate during a fast transient. For example, Timmerman & Ashley (81) and Baylor & Hollingworth (11) found significant slowing of calcium transients in striated muscle injected with more than 25–50 μM fura-2. The amount of slowing is likely to differ from preparation to preparation, but their results suggest that the loading of 100–200 μM fura-2 in many reported experiments will be too high to accurately follow calcium transients. Metallochromic indicators have a higher K_d and are therefore weaker buffers. But higher concentrations of these dyes must be used to get good recordings and several papers have reported the slowing of physiological events when these dyes were used to measure calcium changes (22, 65). This suggests that for each indicator a balance must be found between the need to have good sensitivity and the need to have low buffering. For arsenazo III a concentration of 0.3 mM has been used in neuronal preparations without deleterious effects. Arsenazo III also has more complicated stoichiometry than fura-2 or antipyralazo III (12, 29, 38, 39). This has made it difficult to use this dye to interpret the fast transients in muscle. However, the time course of transients in neurons appears to be significantly slower. If this is generally true then any of these indicators can be used.

Measurement Techniques

Several experiments have shown that photomultipliers can be used to record fast calcium transients in a single trial from fura-2 loaded cells (9, 21, 42). Presumably this technique can be extended to a multidetector system. Currently used low light level imaging systems do not have sufficient time resolution to follow fast transients in neurons or other cell types. Most of the groups that have reported experiments using this technique have used very sensitive SIT cameras or image intensifiers as a front end to digital image processors, although a cooled solid-state CCD camera has also been used (25). The video-based systems are capable of frame rates of 30 Hz. However, the small size of the pixel elements and the low light level of the emitted fluorescence, both of which result in excessive shot noise, forced these groups to average many frames (or to integrate for 200 msec or more on the CCD camera) in order to obtain a signal-to-noise ratio adequate to determine calcium levels. It is likely that technical improvements and more sophisticated averaging procedures will increase the effective time resolution of these imaging systems. Photodiode arrays have been used to record the spatial pattern of calcium changes in cells loaded with absorbance sensitive dyes (35, 63, 65, 66). These arrays, used in conjunction with appropriate amplifiers and computers can resolve intensity changes on the order of 0.001% with a time resolution better than 1 msec (24). So far their spatial resolution is much worse than video systems or CCD arrays, but newer devices with many more elements are expected to be available. Although they have yet to be tested with the fluorescent calcium indicators, it is likely that they will work for these dyes as well.

FUTURE DIRECTIONS

Since changes in cytosolic calcium levels are essential parts of so many signalling processes, it is likely that interest in measuring these changes will continue to grow. With many of these measurements neurons can be treated like other cells and progress in understanding neuronal mechanisms will interrelate with other aspects of cell biology. For other events, especially those connected with membrane excitability and synaptic interactions, neurons, and measurements on them, will remain a separate category. It is likely that progress in dye synthesis and imaging technology will continue to make these measurements easier. Useful new dyes would include indicators that (*a*) do not bind to cell components or enter intracellular organelles (or which enter selective organelles), (*b*) have a range of dissociation constants, (*c*) have greater fluorescence or absorbance changes on binding calcium, and (*d*) are resistant to bleaching and cause little photodynamic damage. New imaging devices would have both high temporal and high spatial resolution (including depth resolution). Clearly needed, but not yet defined, are new procedures for dealing with the tremendous amount of data produced with this technique in a way that usefully reveals physiological information.

ACKNOWLEDGMENTS

Research in the author's laboratory has been supported by the USPHS, the Irma T. Hirschl Foundation, and the Whitaker Foundation.

Literature Cited

1. Ahmed, Z., Connor, J. A. 1979. Measurement of calcium influx under voltage clamp in molluscan neurones using the metallochromic dye arsenazo III. *J. Physiol.* 286:61–82
2. Ahmed, Z., Kragie, L., Connor, J. A. 1980. Stoichiometry and apparent dissociation constant of the calcium-arsenazo III reaction under physiological conditions. *Biophys. J.* 32:907–20
3. Akaike, N., Lee, K. S., Brown, A. M. 1978. The calcium current of *Helix* neuron. *J. Gen. Physiol.* 71:509–31
4. Almers, W., Neher, E. 1985. The calcium signal from fura-2 loaded mast cells depends strongly on the method of dye loading. *FEBS Lett.* 192:13–18
5. Ashley, C. C., Campbell, A. K. 1979. *Detection and Measurement of Free Ca²⁺ in Cells.* New York: Elsevier. 461 pp.
6. Augustine, G. J., Charlton, M. P., Smith, S. J. 1985. Calcium entry into voltage-clamped presynaptic terminals of squid. *J. Physiol.* 367:143–62
7. Baker, P. F., DiPolo, R. 1984. Axonal calcium and magnesium homeostasis. In *Curr. Top. in Membr. and Transp.* ed. P. F. Baker, pp. 195–247. New York: Academic
8. Baker, P. F., Hodgkin, A. L., Ridgway, E. B. 1971. Depolarization and calcium entry in squid giant axons. *J. Physiol.* 218:709–55
9. Barcenas-Ruis, L., Wier, G. 1987.

Voltage dependence of intracellular [Ca] transients in guinea pig ventricular myocytes. *Circ. Res.* 61:148–54
10. Baylor, S. M., Chandler, W. K., Marshall, M. W. 1982. Use of metallochromic dyes to measure changes in myoplasmic calcium during activity in frog skeletal muscle fibres. *J. Physiol.* 331:139–77
11. Baylor, S. M., Hollingworth, S. 1988. Fura2 Ca²⁺ transients in frog skeletal muscle fibers. *J. Physiol.* 403:151–92
12. Baylor, S. M., Hollingworth, S., Hui, C. S., Quinta-Ferreira, M. E. 1986. Properties of the metallochromic dyes arsenazo III, antipyralazo III and azo I in frog skeletal muscle fibres at rest. *J. Physiol.* 377:89–141
13. Beeler, T. J., Schibeci, A., Martonosi, A. 1980. The binding of arsenazo III to cell components. *Biochim. Biophys. Acta* 629:317–27
14. Blinks, J. R., Wier, W. G., Hess, P., Prendergast, G. 1982. Measurement of Ca²⁺ concentrations in living cells. *Prog. Biophys. Mol. Biol.* 40:1–114
15. Bolsover, S. R., Spector, I. 1986. Measurements of calcium transients in the soma, neurite, and growth cone of single cultured neurons. *J. Neurosci.* 6:1934–40
16. Boyle, M. B., Klein, M., Smith, S. J., Kandel, E. 1984. Serotonin increases intracellular Ca²⁺ transients in voltage clamped sensory neurons of *Aplysia*

504   ROSS

californica Proc. Natl. Acad. Sci. USA 81:7642–46

17. Brinley, F. J., Tiffert, T., Scarpa, A. 1978. Mitochondria and other calcium buffers of squid axon studied *in situ*. *J. Gen. Physiol.* 72:101–27

18. Brinley, F. J., Tiffert, T., Scarpa, A., Mullins, L. J. 1977. Intracellular calcium buffering capacity in isolated squid axons. *J. Gen. Physiol.* 70:355–84

19. Brown, J. E., Cohen, L. B., De Weer, P., Pinto, L. H., Ross, W. N., et al. 1975. Rapid changes of intracellular free calcium concentration. *Biophys. J.* 15:1155–60

20. Bruner, J., Czternasty, G., Shimahara, T., Stinnakre, J. 1986. Arsenazo III transients and calcium current in normally non-spiking neuronal soma of crayfish. *J. Physiol.* 374:571–83

21. Cannell, M. B., Berlin, J. R., Lederer, W. J. 1987. Effect of membrane potential changes on the calcium transient in single rat cardiac muscle cells. *Science* 238:1419–24

22. Charlton, M. P., Smith, S. J., Zucker, R. S. 1982. Role of presynaptic calcium ions and channels in synaptic facilitation and depression at the squid giant synapse. *J. Physiol.* 323:173–93

23. Cohan, C. S., Connor, J. A., Kater, S. B. 1987. Electrically and chemically mediated increases in intracellular calcium in neuronal growth cones. *J. Neurosci.* 7:3588–99

24. Cohen, L. B., Lesher, S. 1986. Optical monitoring of membrane potential: methods of multisite measurement. In *Optical Methods in Cell Physiology*, ed. P. De Weer, B. M. Salzberg, pp. 71–99. New York: Wiley

25. Connor, J. A. 1986. Digital imaging of free calcium changes and of spatial gradients in growing processes in single, mammalian central nervous system cells. *Proc. Natl. Acad. Sci. USA* 83:6179–83

26. Connor, J. A., Kretz, R., Shapiro, E. 1986. Calcium levels measured in a presynaptic neurone of *Aplysia* under conditions that modulate transmitter release. *J. Physiol.* 375:625–42

27. Connor, J. A., Tseng, H., Hockberger, E. 1987. Depolarization- and transmitter-induced changes in intracellular Ca^{2+} of rat cerebellar granule cells in explant cultures. *J. Neurosci.* 7:1384–1400

28. DiPolo, R., Requena, J., Brinley, F. J., Mullins, L. J., Scarpa, A., Tiffert, T. 1976. Ionized calcium concentrations in squid axons. *J. Gen. Physiol.* 67:433–67

29. Dorogi, P. L. 1984. Kinetics and mechanism of Ca^{2+} binding to arsenazo III and antipyralazo III. *Biochim. Biophys. Acta* 799:9–19

30. Eckert, R., Tillotson, D., Ridgway, E. B. 1977. Voltage dependent facilitation of Ca^{2+} entry in voltage-clamped aequorin-injected molluscan neurons. *Proc. Natl. Acad. Sci. USA* 74:1748–52

31. Eusebi, F., Miledi, R., Parker, I., Stinnakre, J. 1985. Post-synaptic calcium influx at the giant synapse of the squid during activation by glutamate. *J. Physiol.* 369:183–97

32. Goligorsky, M. S., Hruska, K. A., Loftus, D. J., Elson, E. L. 1986. Alpha₁-adrenergic stimulation and cytoplasmic free calcium concentration in cultured renal proximal tubular cells: evidence for compartmentalization of quin-2 and fura-2. *J. Cell. Physiol.* 128:466–74

33. Gorman, A. L. F., Thomas, M. V. 1978. Changes in the intracellular concentration of free calcium ions in a pacemaker neurone measured with the metallochromic indicator dye arsenazo III. *J. Physiol.* 275:357–76

34. Gorman, A. L. F., Thomas, M. V. 1980. Intracellular calcium accumulation during depolarization in a molluscan neurone. *J. Physiol.* 308:259–85

35. Graubard, K., Ross, W. N. 1985. Regional distribution of calcium influx into bursting neurons detected with arsenazo III. *Proc. Natl. Acad. Sci. USA* 82:5565–69

36. Grynkiewicz, G., Poenie, M., Tsien, R. Y. 1985. A new generation of calcium indicators with greatly improved fluorescence properties. *J. Biol. Chem.* 260:3440–50

37. Irving, M., Maylie, J., Sizto, N. L., Chandler, W. K. 1987. Intrinsic optical and passive electrical properties of cut frog twitch fibers. *J. Gen. Physiol.* 89:1–40

38. Jackson, A. P., Timmerman, M. P., Bagshaw, C. R., Ashley, C. C. 1987. The kinetics of calcium binding to fura-2 and indo-1. *FEBS Lett.* 216:35–39

39. Kao, J., Tsien, R. Y. 1988. Ca^{2+} binding kinetics of fura-2 and azo-1 from temperature jump relaxation measurements. *Biophys. J.* 53:635–39

40. Kudo, Y., Ogura, A. 1986. Glutamate-induced increase in intracellular Ca^{2+} concentration in isolated hippocampal neurones. *Br. J. Pharmacol.* 89:191–98

41. Kusano, K., Miledi, R., Stinnakre, J. 1975. Post-synaptic entry of calcium induced by transmitter action. *Proc. R. Soc. London Ser. B* 189:49–56

42. Lev-Ram, V., Grinvald, A. 1987. Activity-dependent calcium transients in

central nervous system myelinated axons revealed by the calcium indicator fura-2. *Biophys. J.* 52:571–76

43. Levy, S., Tillotson, D. 1987. Ability of calcium selective microelectrodes to measure fast and local Ca^{2+} transients in nerve cells. *Can. J. Physiol. Pharmacol.* 65:904–14

44. Lewis, D. V., Evans, G. B., Wilson, W. A. 1984. Dopamine reduces slow outward current and calcium influx in burst-firing neuron R15. *J. Neurosci.* 4:3014–20

45. Lipscombe, D., Madison, D. V., Poenie, M., Reuter, H., Tsien, R. Y., Tsien, R. W. 1988. Spatial distribution of calcium channels and cytosolic calcium transients in growth cones and cell bodies of sympathetic neurons. *Proc. Natl. Acad. Sci. USA* 85:2398–2402

46. Llinás, R. R. 1984. The Squid Giant Synapse. In *Curr. Top. Membr. Transp.* 22:519–46

47. Lux, H. D., Heyer, C. B. 1977. An aequorin study of a facilitating calcium current in bursting pacemaker neurons of *Helix pomatia* neurons. *Pflügers Arch.* 394:61–69

48. MacDermott, A. B., Mayer, M. L., Westbrook, G. L., Smith, S. J., Barker, J. L. 1986. NMDA-receptor activation increases cytoplasmic calcium concentration in cultured spinal cord neurones. *Nature* 321:519–22

49. Malgaroli, A., Milani, D., Meldolesi, J., Pozzan, T. 1987. Fura-2 measurements of cytosolic free Ca^{2+} in monolayers and suspensions of various types of animal cells. *J. Cell. Biol.* 105:2145–55

50. Miledi, R., Parker, I., Schalow, G. 1980. Transmitter induced calcium entry across post-synaptic membrane at frog endplates measured using arsenazo III. *J. Physiol.* 300:197–212

51. Miledi, R., Parker, I., Zhu, P. H. 1982. Calcium transients evoked by action potentials in frog twitch muscle fibres. *J. Physiol.* 333:655–79

52. Miller, R. J. 1987. Multiple calcium channels and neuronal function. *Science* 235:46–52

53. Morris, M. E., Krnjevic, K., MacDonald, J. F. 1985. Changes in intracellular free Ca ion concentration evoked by electrical activity in cat spinal neurons *in situ*. *Neuroscience* 14:563–80

54. Mullins, L. J., Requena, J. 1979. Calcium measurement in the periphery of an axon. *J. Gen. Physiol.* 74:393–413

55. Ogura, A., Iijima, T., Amano, T., Kudo, Y. 1987. Optical monitoring of excitatory synaptic activity between cul-

tured hippocampal neurons by multi-site Ca fluorimetry. *Neurosci. Lett.* 78:69–74

56. Palade, P., Vergara, J. 1983. Stoichiometries of arsenazo III-Ca complexes. *Biophys. J.* 43:355–69

57. Poenie, M., Alderton, J., Steinhardt, R. A., Tsien, R. Y. 1986. Calcium rises abruptly and briefly throughout the cell at the outset of anaphase. *Science* 233:886–89

58. Pumplin, D. W., Reese, T. S., Llinas, R. 1981. Are the presynaptic membrane particles the calcium channels? *Proc. Natl. Acad. Sci. USA* 78:7210–13

59. Requena, J., DiPolo, R., Brinley, F. J., Mullins, L. J. 1977. The control of ionized calcium in squid axons. *J. Gen. Physiol.* 70:329–53

60. Requena, J., Whittembury, J., Tiffert, J., Eisner, D. A., Mullins, L. J. 1984. A comparison of measurements of intracellular Ca by electrode and optical indicators. *Biochim. Biophys. Acta* 805:393–404

61. Riollet, S., Champeil, P. 1987. The calcium sensitive dye arsenazo III inhibits calcium transport and ATP hydrolysis by the sarcoplasmic reticulum calcium pump. *Anal. Biochem.* 162:160–62

62. Rios, E., Schneider, M. F. 1981. Stoichiometry of the reactions of calcium with the metallochromic dyes antipyralazo III and arsenazo III. *Biophys. J.* 36:607–621

63. Ross, W. N., Arechiga, H., Nicholls, J. G. 1987. Optical recording of calcium and voltage transients following impulses in the cell bodies and processes of identified leech neurones in culture. *J. Neurosci.* 7:3877–87

64. Ross, W. N., Arechiga, H., Nicholls, J. G. 1988. Influence of substrate on the distribution of calcium channels in identified leech neurons in culture. *Proc. Natl. Acad. Sci. USA* 85:4075–78

65. Ross, W. N., Stockbridge, L. L., Stockbridge, N. L. 1986. Regional properties of calcium entry in barnacle neurons determined with arsenazo III and a photodiode array. *J. Neurosci.* 6:1148–59

66. Ross, W. N., Werman, R. 1987. Mapping calcium transients in the dendrites of Purkinje cells from the guinea-pig cerebellum *in vitro*. *J. Physiol.* 389:319–36

67. Ross, W. N., Werman, R. 1988. Spatial and temporal patterns of spontaneous and evoked calcium dependent events in the dendrites of guinea pig cerebellar Purkinje cells *in vitro*. *Soc. Neurosci.* 14:758 (Abstr.)

68. Scanlon, M., Williams, D., Fay, F. S.

1987. A Ca-insensitive form of fura-2 associated with polymorphonuclear leukocytes. *J. Biol. Chem.* 262:6308–12

69. Smith, S. J. 1980. Ca^{++} regulation in gastropod nerve cell bodies. In *Molluscan Nerve Cells: From Biophysics to Behavior*, ed. J. Koester, J. H. Byrne, pp. 81–91. New York: Cold Spring Harbor Lab.

70. Smith, S. J., Osses, L. R., Augustine, G. J. 1987. Fura-2 imaging of localized calcium accumulation within squid 'giant' presynaptic terminals. In *Calcium and Ion Channel Modulation*, ed. A. D. Grinnell, D. Armstrong, M. B. Jackson, pp. 147–55. New York: Plenum

71. Smith, S. J., Zucker, R. S. 1980. Aequorin response facilitation and intracellular calcium accumulation in molluscan neurones. *J. Physiol.* 300:167–96

72. Steinberg, S., Bilezikian, J., Al-Awqati, Q. 1987. Fura-2 fluorescence is localized to mitochondria in endothelial cells. *Am. J. Physiol.* 253:C744–C747

73. Stinnakre, J. 1977. Calcium movements across synaptic membranes and the release of transmitter. In *Synapses*, ed. G. A. Cottrell, P. N. R. Usherwood, pp. 117–36. New York: Academic

74. Stinnakre, J. 1981. Detection and measurement of intracellular calcium. *Trends Neurosci.* 4:46–50

75. Stinnakre, J., Tauc, L. 1973. Calcium influx in active *Aplysia* neurones detected by injected aequorin. *Nature* 242:113–15

76. Stockbridge, N. L., Ross, W. N. 1984. Localized Ca^{2+} and calcium activated potassium conductance in terminals of a barnacle photoreceptor. *Nature* 309:266–68

77. Thomas, M. V. 1979. Arsenazo III forms 2:1 complexes with Ca and 1:1 complexes with Mg under physiological conditions. *Biophys. J.* 25:541–48

78. Thomas, M. V. 1982. *Techniques in Calcium Research*. New York: Academic. 214 pp.

79. Tillotson, D. 1980. Ca^{2+} dependent inactivation of Ca^{2+} channels. See Ref. 69, pp. 41–48

80. Tillotson, D., Gorman, A. L. F. 1980. Non-uniform Ca^{2+} buffer distribution in a nerve cell body. *Nature* 286:816–17

81. Timmerman, M. P., Ashley, C. C. 1986. Fura-2 diffusion and its use as an indicator of transient free calcium changes in single striated muscle cells. *FEBS Lett.* 209:1–8

82. Tsien, R. Y. 1980. New calcium indicators and buffers with high selectivity against magnesium and protons: Design synthesis and properties of prototype structures. *Biochemistry* 19:2396–2404

83. Tsien, R. Y. 1981. A non-disruptive technique for loading calcium buffers and indicators into cells. *Nature* 290:527–28

84. Tsien, R. Y. 1983. Intracellular measurements of ion activities. *Annu. Rev. Biophys. Bioeng.* 12:91–116

85. Tsien, R. Y., Poenie, M. 1986. Fluorescence ratio imaging; a new window into intracellular ionic signaling. *Trends Biochem. Sci.* 11:450–55

86. Tsien, R. Y., Pozzan, T., Rink, T. J. 1984. Measuring and manipulating cytosolic Ca^{2+} with trapped indicators. *Trends Biochem. Sci.* 9:263–66

87. Williams, D. A., Fogarty, K. E., Tsien, R. Y., Fay, F. S. 1985. Calcium gradients in single smooth muscle cells revealed by the digital imaging microscope using fura-2. *Nature* 318:558–61

88. Yue, D. T., Wier, G. W. 1985. Estimation of intracellular [Ca^{2+}] by nonlinear indicators: a quantitative analysis. *Biophys. J.* 48:533–37

Annu. Rev. Physiol. 1989. 51:507–26

OPTICAL RECORDING OF VOLTAGE CHANGES IN NERVE TERMINALS AND IN FINE NEURONAL PROCESSES

B. M. Salzberg

Department of Physiology, School of Medicine, University of Pennsylvania, Philadelphia, Pennsylvania 19104-6085

INTRODUCTION

Optical techniques for the measurement and analysis of transmembrane electrical events have found a wide range of applications over the past decade and a half because, while they usually provide less detailed information than the voltage clamp, they offer certain advantages over the voltage clamp and other conventional measurement techniques. Because the membranes of interest are not mechanically violated, optical methods are comparatively noninvasive. Spatial resolution is limited only by microscope optics and noise considerations. Already changes in membrane potential from regions of an isolated cell with linear dimensions of approximately one micron can be measured. Also, optical sectioning, with near elimination of scattering by means of confocal imaging, may soon permit optical recording from comparably small regions of cells in intact ganglia or brains. Temporal resolution is limited by the physical response of the probes ($< 2 \mu$s; B. M. Salzberg, A. L. Obaid, & F. Bezanilla, unpublished observations) and by the bandwidth imposed upon the measurement, again usually by noise considerations; response times faster than typical membrane time constants are readily achieved. Because mechanical access is not required, unusual latitude is possible in the choice of preparation, and voltage changes may be monitored in membranes that are otherwise inaccessible. Also, since no recording electrodes are employed and the measurements are made at a distance from

507

0066-4278-/89/0315-0507$02.00

the preparation—that is, in the image plane of an optical apparatus—changes in potential can be recorded simultaneously from numerous sites. Several recent reviews on optical measurement of membrane potential (7, 14, 17, 58, 73) should be consulted by the reader interested in technical details.

The evidence that optical methods using voltage-sensitive dyes produce measurements that are equivalent, at least in a limited sense, to electrode measurements, is detailed elsewhere (7, 8, 11, 12, 27, 54, 55, 60, 61). Indeed, under certain conditions (59), an optical measurement of membrane potential is superior to an electrode measurement. My purpose here is to review the application of optical techniques to some of the less-accessible elements of the nervous system, e.g. to vertebrate nerve terminals and fine neuronal processes in intact ganglia and in slices, sites for which electrode methods are particularly ill-suited. Since the initial demonstration, in 1973 (60), of optical recording of the action potential in a single invertebrate neuron, improvements in probe sensitivity (21, 27, 55), photostability, and freedom from toxicity, together with technical advances that permit multiple-site optical recording of transmembrane voltage (MSORTV) (18, 61, 69), have resulted in the gradual extension of optical techniques to these relatively hidden realms of the nervous system. This review begins with a description of the earliest optical measurements of electrical activity in fine processes and growth cones of tumor cells in vitro and then describes more recent efforts to monitor electrical activity in neuritic extensions of identified neurons in cell culture. Next, the discussion turns, to optical studies of some of the fine processes of cells within intact invertebrate ganglia and to recent experiments on the nature of the action potential in the nerve terminals that comprise an intact region of the vertebrate brain. Finally, I review the application of potentiometric probes to small-caliber nerve fibers, dendritic processes, and glial cells, all in brain slices obtained from mammals and fishes.

OPTICAL RECORDING FROM FINE PROCESSES OF CELLS IN CULTURE

In 1981 Grinvald et al (25) first used a 10×10 array of photodiodes to monitor changes in light transmission from different regions of N1E-115 neuroblastoma cells maintained in culture and stained with the merocyanine-rhodanine dye WW 401 (55). In these optical recordings, the soma was stimulated with a microelectrode and 50 sweeps were averaged. The action potential could be detected along all of the processes, and regional differences in the shape of the spike were reported. In other experiments, a HeNe laser "microbeam" was used to record fluorescence changes, in a single sweep, from processes and growth cones of N1E-115 cells stained with the pyrazo-oxonol dye WW 802 ([1,3-dipentylbarbituric acid-(5)]-[1-p-sulfophenyl-3-

methyl-5-pyrazolone-(4)]-pentamethinoxonol) (23). Dye bleaching and phototoxicity severely limited the duration of these experiments, but crude estimates of space constants were reported based upon regional variations in $\Delta F/F$. As the authors were careful to note, however, this method makes several untestable assumptions, including that of spatially uniform dye binding. Careful comparison of the time course of the optical signals from different sites, with cable theory (28), provides a method that is better matched to optical measurement, in which fidelity to the time course of the voltage change is generally reliable, whereas the amplitude of the signal depends upon many factors that are impossible to assess. With more sensitive fluorescence probes (21) and improvements in the apparatus (20), a single-sweep optical recording of the action potential in the 2-μm wide process of a neuroblastoma cell was obtained using a mercury arc and a reference photodiode for subtraction of lamp noise.

In one of the most interesting early applications of these methods, simultaneous recordings of calcium action potentials were obtained (19) from growth cones and somata of N1E-115 cells. This recording was accomplished using a microelectrode to record from the soma and a 5-mW HeNe laser to monitor electrical changes in the 40–60 μm growth cone, which had been stained with WW 802. Figure 1 shows results of an experiment in which the neurite of an N1E-115 cell was stimulated close to its growth cone; the resulting responses were recorded optically from the growth cone and electrically from the soma. The long delay (30 ms) between the peak of the action potential in the growth cone and the peak of the somatic response, together with the very slow rate of rise of the somatic response, suggests (19) that the regenerative response was confined to the growth cone and not propagated through the neurite. The results of these experiments confirmed the presence of the calcium action potentials reported by Moolenaar & Spector (39) in these cells and provided indirect evidence for the generation of these responses in neurites at or near the growth cone.

While numerous technical improvements were reported in the period 1981–1983, including extraordinary gains in the magnitude of $\Delta F/F/mV$ (20, 21, 25), multiple-site optical recording from cultured neurons and their processes using fluorescence probes and photodetector arrays, was not. Probe limitations, particularly relatively low quantum yields and problems with photodynamic damage, together with detector arrays and amplifier circuit designs that were not ideally matched to the properties of the existing probes, resulted in few attempts to exploit the potential power of MSORTV to study cells in culture.

Around this time, several groups (4, 10, 15, 52, 67, 69a) established the techniques necessary for the growth of isolated invertebrate neurons in culture and demonstrated the formation and maintenance of synaptic interactions

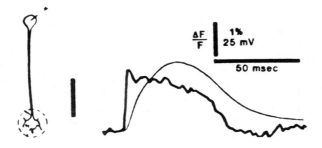

Figure 1 Evidence for Ca^{2+} action potentials at or near the growth cone in a N1E-115 neuroblastoma cell. The saline contained 15 mM TEA and 1 μM TTX. The thick trace is the fluorescence recording from the growth cone. The thin trace is the microelectrode recording from the soma. (Adapted from reference 19.)

between identified pairs of cells. These advances suggested the possibility of using optical techniques to monitor the patterning of electrical activity in truly simple nervous systems, neuronal ensembles that are literally constructed cell-by-cell, using identified invertebrate central neurons. Optical methods are particularly well suited to the study of such simple two-dimensional nervous systems. Recently, Parsons et al (49) used a system for MSORTV based on a 12 × 12 photodiode array to monitor voltage changes in somata, initial segments, and fine processes of identified *Aplysia californica* neurons maintained in cell culture (4, 10, 67). Cultured neurons (3–7 days) were stained with the pyrazo-oxonol dye RH 155 (22) 0.05–0.2 mg/ml; 10 min), and changes in extrinsic absorption (700 ± 20 nm) could be recorded from the initial segments of identified neurons with signal-to-noise ratios in the range of 20–50:1 in a single sweep. The invasion of fine neuritic processes could also be monitored without signal averaging. Chemical and electrical synapses were established between known pairs of cells isolated from the abdominal ganglion (4), and optical recordings were obtained from presynaptic and postsynaptic elements. In several experiments, a volley of action potentials in the presynaptic neuron markedly inhibited firing in the postsynaptic cell, and the pattern of electrical activity was monitored optically for 8 sec (49).

OPTICAL RECORDING OF ELECTRICAL ACTIVITY FROM FINE PROCESSES OF INVERTEBRATE NEURONS IN SITU

The prospect of using optical techniques to record postsynaptic potentials or other electrical activity from fine processes of single cells in a central nervous system preparation in situ intrigued early workers (9). In general, the central nervous systems of both vertebrates and invertebrates are so densely packed and heterogeneous that the optical isolation of specific neuronal processes within, for example, the neuropile tangle of many invertebrates is feasible only in limited situations. Two distinctly different approaches are possible, and both were eventually employed. Either technique does, in principle, allow one to monitor electrical activity by optical means selectively from individual cells or regions of cells within a highly complex neuronal matrix.

In the first method (53), an entire ganglion is stained with an impermeant potentiometric probe in the conventional fashion, i.e. bath application, and the cell body is then driven repetitively with a microelectrode. When the optical signal from the neuropile is averaged extensively (200–400 trials), only signals (absorption changes) related to potential changes in the processes of the driven cell sum coherently, and electrical events in the fine processes may be distinguished from unrelated electrical activity occurring throughout the ganglion. Spatially resolved optical signals are then related to neuronal structure after injection with an anatomical marker such as Lucifer yellow. Using this approach, Ross & Krauthamer (33, 53) found that some of the fine processes of neurons in the barnacle supraesophageal ganglion are excitable while others are not. They also detected the spike initiation zone along a large axon and estimated space constants for various neuronal processes in this system. This approach has certain obvious advantages, including relative ease of application, but it is unlikely to be of much use for recording postsynaptic events from fine processes in the neuropile or studying the electrical behavior of these processes if more than one neuron is active.

In the second technique (1, 26, 46), application of the molecular probe is confined to the cell of interest by intracellular staining with an impermeant but diffusible dye. The optical behavior of potentiometric probes applied intracellularly had already been investigated in voltage-clamped squid giant axons; impermeant, charged dyes were microinjected (8, 11) and internally perfused (27, 35a, 57), and absorbance or fluorescence changes in response to step changes in transmembrane voltage were studied. For studies on leech (*Hirudo medicinalis*) central neurons, 11 new styryl dyes were synthesized and evaluated for use as iontophoretically injected potentiometric probes (26). Desiderata for intracellular probes are more demanding (26) than for extracellular probes. The styryl dye RH 461 exhibited many of the requisite properties; using it intracellularly allowed researchers (1, 26, 46) to monitor action potentials from a 3-μm axon and record small synaptic potentials from the processes of single cells near the site of initiation in leech segmental ganglia. Selective application of a fluorescent probe confers important advantages over indiscriminate extracellular staining. First, regions of the neurons of interest, away from the soma, may be immediately visualized and their electrical behavior monitored optically against the background (anatomical and electrical) of the tangled neuropile. Second, this technique permits optical recording of synaptic potentials at or near the site of initiation, with relatively little signal averaging, even when the synaptic locus lies within a complex neuropile.

With this second technique, a variety of inherently difficult experiments in synaptic physiology become feasible. For example, the sites of synaptic inputs from different presynaptic cells may be determined, and the integration and processing of these inputs and their transmission to the spike initiation zone(s) may be studied. Similarly, the invasion of signals, both input and output, into different regions of the neuronal arborization, may be investigated, and the effects of neurotransmitters, neuromodulators, and drugs, as well as the patterning of activity may be examined. Of course, many similar experiments may soon become practical in the central nervous systems of higher animals, especially if additional dye synthesis and screening results in probes that are more sensitive and less phototoxic when applied intracellularly.

OPTICAL STUDIES OF EXCITATION AT VERTEBRATE NERVE TERMINALS

Smaller and still less accessible than the fine axonal and dendritic processes of neurons are the presynaptic, and more generally, the neurosecretory terminals of vertebrate neurons, which have largely eluded the electrodes of electrophysiologists. Although a complete understanding of the physiology of synaptic transmission in higher animals depends upon a detailed knowledge of electrical events in axon terminals, their small size (0.5–5 μm) has made direct recording of electrical activity difficult or impossible. The demonstration, in 1983 (66), that potentiometric probes could be used to record membrane potential changes in the very small nerve terminals that comprise nearly all of the excitable membrane in the neurohypophyses of amphibia suggested that, for the first time, the action potential in the intact nerve terminals of a vertebrate could be monitored, a capability that would contribute significantly to our understanding of excitation-secretion coupling and synaptic transmission in higher animals. The nerve terminal action potential in the neurohypophysis of *Xenopus* could be recorded optically, in a single sweep, with an excellent signal-to-noise ratio (66); the nerve terminal action potential illustrated in Figure 2*b* exhibits a rapid upstroke that is primarily the result of a fast, inward Na^+ current, a rapid repolarizing phase resulting from K^+ efflux, and an after-hyperpolarization that depends upon a calcium-mediated increase in K^+ conductance ($g_{K(Ca)}$). Following the block of voltage-sensitive Na^+ channels by tetrodotoxin (TTX), direct electric field stimulation revealed a small Ca^{2+} component of the action potential upstroke (66). When the

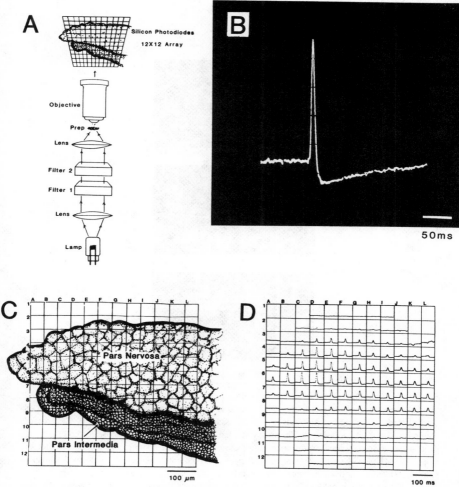

Figure 2 Multiple-site optical recording of transmembrane voltage (MSORTV) in the neurohy-pophysis of *Xenopus*. (*a*) Schematic diagram of the optical portion of the MSORTV system. Collimated light from an incandescent source is rendered quasimonochromatic with interference and heat filters and focused on the preparation using a brightfield condenser. A water immersion objective projects a real image of the preparation onto the central 124 elements of a 144-element photodiode array whose photocurrent outputs are converted to voltages, a.c.-coupled and ampli-fied, multiplexed, digitized, and stored in a PDP 11/34A computer under direct memory access. A full frame is recorded every 0.8 ms. (*b*) A photograph of an oscilloscope recording of the change in transmitted light intensity monitored by one element (E5) of the MSORTV system after a single, brief shock to the hypothalamus. This element monitored intensity changes from a region of the pituitary entirely within the pars nervosa. The fractional change in intensity during the action potential was approximately 0.25%; single sweep, 722 ± 21 nm; response time of 1.1 ms (10–90%); a.c.-coupling time constant 1 s. (*c*) Drawing of the region of the posterior pituitary imaged on the photodiode array, showing the positions of the individual detector elements with respect to the tissue. Objective × 20; 0.33 numerical aperture (*d*) Extrinsic absorption changes recorded in a single sweep after stimulation of the hypothalamus, superimposed on corresponding elements of the photodiode array. The five elements in each corner of the array were not connected. (Adapted from reference 66.)

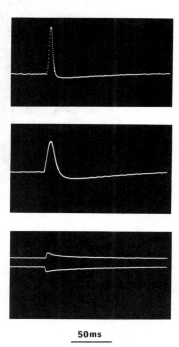

50 ms

Figure 3 Cadmium-sensitive active calcium responses in the presence of TEA and TTX. Optical recording of action potentials in intact nerve terminals of the *Xenopus* neurohypophysis stained with 0.1 mg/ml of the merocyanine-rhodanine dye NK 2761 for 25 min. Records of changes in light transmission at 700 nm by stained nerve terminals in response to direct electric field stimulation. Here and in the following figure the output of a single representative detector from the MSORTV system is shown. (*Top*) Action potential recorded in normal Ringer's solution. (*Center*) Active response of the nerve terminals after 20-min exposure to 5-mM TEA plus 2-μM TTX in normal Ringer's solution. (*Bottom*) Passive response during remaining 15 min after addition of 0.5-mM Cd^{2+} to the TEA-TTX Ringer's solution bathing the preparation, upon stimulation with normal and reversed polarity; 700 nm; rise time of the light measuring system (10–90%) was 1.1 ms. Temperature 18–22°C. (Adapted from reference 44.)

terminal depolarization was prolonged by blocking voltage-dependent K^+ channels with tetraethylammonium (TEA) (30), large active responses were observed (Figure 3). These responses were blocked reversibly by 0.5 mM $CdCl_2$ and were sensitive to $[Ca^{2+}]_o$ (0.1–10 mM). In normal $[Ca^{2+}]_o$, these local responses apparently arise from an inward Ca^{2+} current associated with hormone (oxytocin and arginine vasopressin) release from these nerve terminals. (At low $[Ca^{2+}]_o$ (0.2 mM), Na^+ appears to contribute to the TTX-insensitive current, presumably through Ca^{2+} channels (44).)

The after-hyperpolarization that is such a prominent feature of both the normal action potential and the calcium response in the terminals of the frog neurohypophysis proved to be a sensitive assay for putative blockers of $g_{K(Ca)}$. Charybdotoxin (CTX), a protein toxin derived from scorpion venom, blocks calcium-sensitive potassium channels derived from rat skeletal muscle (37). At 50 nM, CTX selectively blocks the component of the action potential that reflects the increase in $g_{K(Ca)}$ in the terminals during the normal action potential (Figure 4) and during the calcium spike (45). The fact that the height of the calcium spike is increased in the presence of CTX was taken to indicate that the target of the venom is $g_{K(Ca)}$ rather than g_{Ca} itself (41, 45).

Because the $g_{K(Ca)}$-dependent afterpotential of the spike is a sensitive indicator of calcium entry into the terminals of the neurohypophysis (66), the authors used this component of the optical signal to study properties of the calcium channels in a population of vertebrate nerve terminals. Inorganic blockers of calcium channels such as Ni^{2+}, Co^{2+}, Mn^{2+}, Gd^{3+}, and La^{3+} blocked calcium currents in the neurohypophysis of *Xenopus,* although with a potency less than that of cadmium ion (66). Aminoglycoside antibiotics such as neomycin, gentamicin, and streptomycin also blocked calcium currents in these terminals (50), and this block was relieved by elevated Ca^{2+}.

Other organic modifiers of calcium channel behavior have been used by several authors to distinguish different calcium channel types in a variety of preparations (38). Previously, however, these pharmacological tools could not be used to study calcium channels in the intact nerve terminals of a vertebrate, as opposed to dissociated preparations such as synaptosomes (2a, 39a) or secretosomes (4a). Using the extrinsic absorption changes exhibited by the terminals of the frog neurohypophysis stained with the merocyanine-rhodanine dye NK 2761, researchers conducted experiments (41, 62) that helped define the pharmacological profile of the calcium channels present in intact neurosecretory terminals of vertebrates. The dihydropyridine compounds nifedipine and Bay-K 8644 were without effect at concentrations ranging from 2–5 μM; the spikes remained absolutely unchanged for up to 1 h in the presence of either compound, while the peptide toxin ω-conotoxin GVIA (47) (1 μM) rapidly abolished the after-hyperpolarization of the normal action potential by blocking calcium entry (and not by reducing $g_{K(Ca)}$). These results demonstrated directly the effect of ω-conotoxin on the calcium channels involved in the release of neuropeptides (41, 62) from the intact nerve terminals of vertebrates. Although these results provided the first direct evidence from measurements on intact nerve terminals, they are consistent with the findings of others who used patch clamp of neuronal preparations (13, 36). The insensitivity to dihydropyridines is apparently at variance with some reports of dihydropyridine block of neuronal calcium channels [for review, see (72)]. Rane, Holz, & Dunlap (51) concluded, however, that chronic depolarization is required to achieve nifedipine block of calcium channels in chick dorsal root ganglion (DRG) neurons but is not required for

50 ms

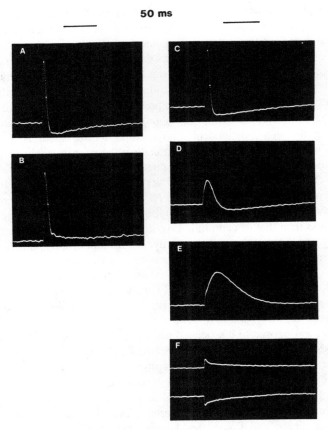

Figure 4   The effect of charybdotoxin (CTX) on the action potential in the nerve terminals of the neurohypophysis of *Xenopus*. (*A*) The action potential recorded optically in normal Ringer's solution after the neurohypophysis was stained with 0.1 mg/ml NK 2761. (*B*) An 8-min exposure to 50-mM CTX abolishes the after-hyperpolarization that results from a calcium-dependent potassium conductance. (*C*) Control action potential in a different preparation. (*D*) Active calcium response recorded optically in a different preparation that was bathed (8 min) in a Ringer's solution containing 5-mM TEA and 1-μM TTX. (*E*) The calcium action potential recorded 23 min after the addition of 50-nM CTX to the Ringer's solution already containing 5-mM TEA and 1-μM TTX. The after-hyperpolarization of the pure calcium spike is eliminated without blocking calcium entry (the upstroke is, in fact, larger). (*F*) The purely passive responses (both polarities) remaining after the addition of 500-μM Cd^{2+} to the Ringer's solution containing CTX, TTX, and TEA. All traces are the analog outputs of a single representative element of the photodiode array; single sweep; direct electric field stimulation; 700 ± 35 nm; a.c.-coupling time constant 400 ms; response time constant (10–90%) 1.1 ms. (Adapted from reference 45.)

Bay-K 8644 action (29). The optical results with nifedipine are consistent with this interpretation, although the failure to observe any enhancement of calcium channel activity in the presence of Bay-K 8644 clearly is not.

Optical recording methods were also used to study the action potential in intact mammalian nerve terminals in the neurohypophysis of the CD-1 mouse (42, 63). Many of the observations were similar to those found in the frog. In one important respect, however, optical measurements on mammalian nerve terminals produced a profound surprise. That is, in some mammals, but not in amphibia, excitation of the magnocellular neuron terminals in the neurohypophysis is accompanied by large, rapid changes in light scattering, measured as transparency (64) and these intrinsic optical signals are closely correlated with the secretion of arginine vasopressin and oxytocin as measured by radioimmunoassay (16). These experiments are described in detail elsewhere (16, 64).

OPTICAL STUDIES OF SMALL CALIBER NERVE FIBERS IN BRAIN SLICES

The introduction of brain slices for the study of neuronal interactions within the central nervous systems of higher animals (34, 35, 68, 74) marked a significant advance in central nervous system neurophysiology in that exceptional control of the cellular environment was possible during prolonged microelectrode penetrations. Because electrode recordings are generally limited to single sites on relatively large neuronal elements, however, investigators thought that multiple-site optical recording techniques might facilitate the study of the electrical properties of the finer axons and dendrites in the brain as well as the study of neuronal circuitry. Three regions of the brain, the hippocampus, the cerebellum, and the olfactory bulb, seemed particularly amenable to the use of optical methods because of their highly organized and relatively well understood structures.

Mammalian Hippocampus

Rat hippocampal slices were the first preparation in which MSORTV was used (24) to monitor the spread of electrical activity; indeed, this report was the first demonstration that potentiometric dyes bind to neuronal membranes in the mammalian brain and change their optical properties in response to electrical activity. Averaged (10–30 times) changes in the light intensity transmitted by slices of hippocampus stained with the merocyanine-rhodanine dye WW 401 were recorded by a photodiode array. In these experiments, stimulation of the Schaffer collateral-commissural pathway in the stratum radiatum gave rise to short latency (2–4 ms), fast optical signals, which were followed by longer latency slow signals with durations of 20–50 ms. The fast signals were insensitive to Mg^{2+} block of synaptic transmission but were abolished in TTX. The authors (24) identified these signals as reflecting action potentials propagating in Schaffer collateral axons, while the slow signals, which were eliminated in low-Ca^{2+} Ringer's solution, were thought to represent excitatory postsynaptic potentials generated in the apical dendrites of the pyramidal cells. These signals arose in the stratum radiatum, where the presynaptic signals were also seen, and they spread into somata (stratum pyramidale) and dendrites (stratum oriens), as shown by recordings from 10 loci along the axis of CA1 pyramidal cells (Figure 5). Several novel procedures were introduced, some of which have become standard in the use of optical methods to study slices of vertebrate brain. Extracellular recordings of field potentials were used to verify the significance of the optical signals, and pharmacological interventions, together with measurement of conduction velocity, refractory period, and facilitation, helped the researchers identify

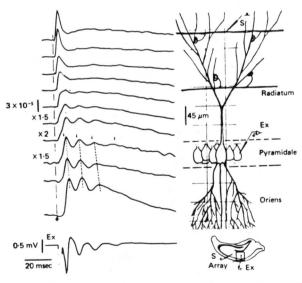

Figure 5 Optical recordings from 10 loci along the axis of CA1 pyramidal cells. The thin arrows show the times of the peaks of the electrically recorded field potential shown at the bottom. The dotted line shows the latency of the optically detected field potential at the stratum radiatum. The stimulating electrode was placed 100 μM away from the recording area. The time of the stimulus is marked by a thick arrow. Ten averaged optical signals along the cell's long axis are shown. (*Right*) Drawing of the various regions along the cell axis, showing the position of the stimulating (*S*) and recording (*Ex*) electrodes and the relative positions of the 10 individual photodetectors (out of 124). (*Bottom right*) A drawing of the slice shows the area monitored optically (*square*) and the approximate position of stimulating and recording electrodes. (Adapted from reference 24.)

the sources of the optical signals. Studies were reported of the properties of small unmyelinated fibers in, for example, the Schaffer collateral system, and the authors also noted that, at least "in principle, some of the slow optical signals may come from glia . . .." The authors also clearly discussed the advantages and disadvantages of optical recording from brain slices. The disadvantages included difficulties in interpreting complex optical signals arising from heterogeneous populations of cells within the field of view of a single detector. Thus, activity detected at the stratum radiatum reflected the action potentials of presynaptic elements, the postsynaptic responses of apical dendrites, the passive spread from pyramidal cell somata, the activity of other interneurons, and possibly, the responses of glial elements.

Saggau, Galvan, & ten Bruggencate (56) also took advantage of the hippocampal slice preparation's favorable properties for optical recording; they used guinea pig hippocampus to study the long-term potentiation (LTP) (2, 3) of synaptic transmission, which has been proposed as a component of memory (70, 71). In these experiments, reported in 1986 (56), Saggau and collaborators demonstrated that long-term changes in the efficacy of synaptic transmission in the in vitro hippocampus could be monitored using the potentiometric styryl dye RH 414 and a single photodiode detector to follow changes in epifluorescence from a $250 \times 250 \ \mu m^2$ region that included the stratum pyramidale (56). They could record voltage-dependent fluorescence signals for several hours from a single brain slice preparation and showed that these optical signals originated in stimulus-induced changes in postsynaptic membrane potential and exhibited LTP of synaptic transmission. The signals were always accompanied by the usual LTP phenomena (2) monitored by extracellular electrodes: namely, enhanced field excitatory post synaptic potentials (EPSP) and increased amplitude and decreased latency of the population spike.

Skate Cerebellum

The cerebellum has a less complex cellular architecture than the hippocampus; in particular, the cerebelli of some elasmobranch fishes are smooth and have a molecular layer that is even simpler than its mammalian counterpart (40). During 1985–1986, a novel fish brain slice preparation was developed from the cerebellum of the skate (31, 32, 65) that proved to be extremely robust and reliable, and an MSORTV system was used to demonstrate its properties by recording electrical activity from 124 sites simultaneously. In this system, the extraordinarily high signal-to-noise ratio facilitated the study of the ionic basis of the action potential and other electrical properties of the parallel fibers, a system of nonmyelinated axons in the molecular layer that are too small for microelectrode penetration. Using the pyrazo-oxonol dye RH 482 (22), the authors found that the upstroke of the parallel fiber action potential depends upon sodium entry, the repolarization depends upon potassium efflux, and a prominent after-hyperpolarization results from a calcium-mediated potassium conductance. A completely unexpected finding was the observation that a closely related dye, RH 155, which differed only in the substitution of two methyl groups for two propyls, exhibited a high affinity for glial cells as well as neurons and could be used to monitor changes in $[K^+]_o$ because it detected changes in glial membrane potential (32). After staining the preparation for 1 h in a 0.2 mg/ml solution of RH 155, the authors found that the extrinsic absorption changes in the molecular layer in response to a single stimulus exhibited a fast component that represents the parallel fiber action potential and a large, long-lasting signal that reflects the changes in glial membrane potential (Figure 6). This latter signal effectively monitors the glial membranes' response to the accumulation of potassium in the extracellular space. Interventions that modified the extracellular volume fraction (32), and thereby affected the accumulation of potassium, produced large changes in the optical signals that monitored glial depolarization. For example, the use of hypertonic and hypotonic bathing solutions resulted in decreases and increases, respectively, in the magnitude of the extrinsic absorption changes that tracked $[K^+]_o$. Blocking the activity of the Na^+/K^+ pump by means of ouabain prolonged the time course of the optical signal that monitored elevated potassium in the extracellular space. In addition, changes in temperature (8°C–19°C) altered the kinetics of the slow component in a manner consistent with effects on the rate of turnover of the Na^+/K^+ pump (43). Finally, it was possible to demonstrate that calcium channel blockers such as cadmium ion decreased the optical signal that reflected the extracellular accumulation of potassium.

Thus, interesting observations followed serendipitously from the initial decision to try to take advantage of the expected favorable properties of an elasmobranch cerebellar slice preparation. Most notable was the finding that closely related dyes have different relative affinities for different membranes in the same preparation. (I expect this finding to prove extremely useful for the study of brain structures containing different cell types.) In addition, the extraordinary sensitivity of the slow component of the optical signal to calcium and calcium channel blockers (32) suggests that much of the potassium that accumulates in the cerebellum of the skate passes through Ca^{2+}-dependent K^+ channels, and that, at least in this preparation, intracellular calcium is critically involved in potassium homeostasis.

Multiple-Site Optical Recording from Slices of Olfactory Structures

Multiple-site optical recording together with conventional electrophysiological techniques have also been used to study electrical activity in various layers

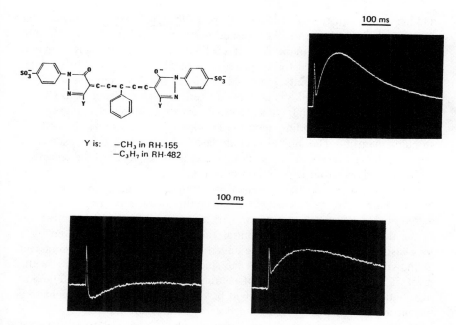

Figure 6 The RH 155 absorption signal in skate cerebellar slices reveals a slow component in addition to the spike that represents the parallel fiber action potential. (*Top left*) Structural formulae of two closely related pyrazo-oxonol dyes. RH 482 has symmetrically placed propyl groups, which are shortened to methyl groups in RH 155. (*Top right*) Extrinsic absorption change obtained from a coronal slice that had been stained for 1 h with 0.2 mg/ml RH 155 in elasmobranch Ringer's solution, upon stimulation of the molecular layer with a bipolar electrode. This signal exhibits a large, slow wave following the parallel fiber action potential. (*Bottom*) A double-staining experiment. The panel on the left shows the usual parallel fiber action potential obtained after staining the preparation with 0.2 mg/ml RH 482. The panel on the right shows the signal recorded from the same locus after restaining with 0.2 mg/ml RH 155. All records are single sweeps, recorded by single representative photodetectors from the photodiode array; a.c.-coupling time constant 3 s; temperature 23–25°C. (Adapted from reference 32.)

of the olfactory bulb of the Atlantic skate *Raja erinacea* (5). In the living animal, orthodromic stimulation evoked field potentials whose current generators were studied by laminar and current source density analyses (5). Components were identified that corresponded to excitation of the glomerulus, depolarization of granule cells, and probably, reexcitation of mitral cells.

Optical recordings of electrical activity from 500-μm slices of skate olfactory bulb in vitro were obtained after staining with RH 155. Following orthodromic stimulation, two depolarizing responses were evoked. A fast signal, observed in the upper region of the glomerular layer, seemed to reflect the compound action potential in the olfactory nerve (cf reference 48). A signal of longer duration was observed in the zone between the glomerulus and the mitral somata and in deeper layers. Both signals exhibited the correct wavelength dependence for the dye and were abolished by 2 μM TTX. In contrast with the results in the skate cerebellum (see above), the slow signal in this preparation appeared to be synaptically mediated. Barium (5–10 mM), which depolarizes glial cells, increased the size of the slow component, which suggests that this optical signal does not reflect a glial response to $[K^+]_o$. Different condition/test intervals produced partial or complete suppression of the test response, depending upon the location of the recording site and the stimulus intensity. The inhibition could last more than 5 s; at brief intervals (50 ms), the test responses were shortened as a consequence of the enhanced inhibition arising from reexcitation of mitral cells.

From the optical and field potential recordings, the authors concluded (5) that extremely prolonged changes in excitability occur following a volley of activity in the olfactory nerve. First, there appears to be a period of facilitation in the dendritic arborization of mitral cells. This period is followed by a long-lasting one of inhibition. The underlying neural mechanisms are as yet unknown, but it seems likely that the study of electrical phenomena at the level of the dendritic processes of neurons, particularly the spatiotemporal distribution of graded potentials, will be extremely important in elucidating the mechanism of plasticity in this system, as in many others.

Multiple-site optical recordings have also been obtained from slices of mammalian olfactory structures (6). Electrical activity was monitored from 124 sites in the olfactory bulb and pyriform and sulcal cortices of the CD-1 mouse, but these experiments require further analysis before definite conclusions can be drawn. However, the ability since 1982 to measure membrane potential changes in a wide variety of brain slice preparations has been most welcome, and I expect that improvements in dye sensitivity and technique will lead to interesting results in other cerebelli and hippocampi and in sensory cortices. One particularly exciting prospect is that intracellular injection of potentiometric dyes (26) into identified cell types in brain slices (or injection of calcium indicators, see chapter by Ross, this volume) will permit the study of the physiology of fine dendritic arborizations in concert with their very beautiful anatomy.

ACKNOWLEDGMENT

Nearly all of the work described here from my own laboratory was carried out together with Dr. A. L. Obaid and I am deeply grateful to her, as well as to our other collaborators, T. D. Parsons, H. Gainer, R. Flores, A. Konnerth, A. Cinelli, R. K. Orkand, and D. M. Senseman. I am also grateful to L. B. Cohen and his colleagues for providing us with their software for data acquisition and display. Supported by United States Public Health Service grant NS 16824.

Literature Cited

1. Agmon, A., Hildesheim, R., Anglister, L., Grinvald, A. 1982. Optical recordings from processes of individual leech CNS neurons iontophoretically injected with a new fluorescent voltage-sensitive dye. *Neurosci. Lett.* 10:S35 (Abstr.)

2. Anderson, P., Sundberg, S. H., Sveen, O., Swann, J. W., Wigstrom, H. 1980. Possible mechanisms for long-lasting potentiation of synaptic transmission in hippocampal slices from guinea-pigs. *J. Physiol.* 302:463–82

2a. Blaustein, M. P., Goldring, J. M. 1975. Membrane potentials in pinched-off presynaptic nerve terminals monitored with a fluorescent probe: Evidence that synaptosomes have potassium diffusion potentials. *J. Physiol.* 247:589–615

3. Bliss, T. V. P., Lomo, T. 1973. Long-lasting potentiation of synaptic transmission in the dentate area of the anesthetized rabbit following stimulation of the perforant path. *J. Physiol.* 232:331–56

4. Camardo, J., Proshansky, E., Schacher, S. 1983. Identified *Aplysia* neurons form specific chemical synapses in culture. *J. Neurosci.* 3:2614–20

4a. Cazalis, M., Dayanithi, G., Nordmann, J. J. 1987. Hormone release from isolated nerve endings of the rat neurohypophysis. *J. Physiol.* 390:55–70

5. Cinelli, A. R., Salzberg, B. M. 1987. Extrinsic optical signals, evoked field potentials, and single unit recordings from the olfactory bulb of the skate (*Raja erinacea*). *Biol. Bull.* 173:435–36 (Abstr.)

6. Cinelli, A. R., Salzberg, B. M. 1987. Optical recording of electrical activity from slices of olfactory structures: Extrinsic signals from olfactory bulb and pyriform and sulcal cortices. *Neurosci. Abstr.* 13:1411 (Abstr.)

7. Cohen, L. B., Salzberg, B. M. 1978. Optical measurement of membrane potential. *Rev. Physiol., Biochem. Pharmacol.* 83:33–88

8. Cohen, L. B., Salzberg, B. M., Davila, H. V., Ross, W. N., Landowne, D., et al. 1974. Changes in axon fluorescence during activity: Molecular probes of membrane potential. *J. Membr. Biol.* 19:1–36

9. Cohen, L. B., Salzberg, B. M., Grinvald, A. 1978. Optical methods for monitoring neuron activity. *Annu. Rev. Neurosci.* 1:171–82

10. Dagan, D., Levitan, I. B. 1981. Isolated identified *Aplysia* neurons in cell culture. *J. Neurosci.* 1:736–40

11. Davila, H. V., Cohen, L. B., Salzberg, B. M., Shrivastav, B. B. 1974. Changes in ANS and TNS fluorescence in giant axons from *Loligo*. *J. Membr. Biol.* 15:29–46

12. Davila, H. V., Salzberg, B. M., Cohen, L. B., Waggoner, A. S. 1973. A large change in axon fluorescence that provides a promising method for measuring membrane potential. *Nature New Biol.* 241:159–60

13. Fox, A. P., Nowycky, M. C., Tsien, R. W. 1987. Kinetic and pharmacological properties distinguishing three types of calcium currents in chick sensory neurons. *J. Physiol.* 394:149–72

14. Freedman, J. C., Laris, P. C. 1981. Electrophysiology of cells and organelles: Studies with optical potentiometric indicators. *Int. Rev. Cytol.* 12:177–246 (Suppl.)

15. Fuchs, P. A., Nicholls, J. G., Ready, D. F. 1981. Membrane properties and selective connections of identified leech neurones in culture. *J. Physiol.* 316:203–23

16. Gainer, H., Wolfe, S. A. Jr., Obaid, A. L., Salzberg, B. M. 1986. Action potentials and frequency-dependent secretion in the mouse neurohypophysis. *Neuroendocrinology* 43:557–63

17. Grinvald, A. 1985. Real time optical mapping of neuronal activity: from single growth cones to the intact mammalian brain. *Annu. Rev. Neurosci.* 8:263–305

18. Grinvald, A., Cohen, L. B., Lesher, S., Boyle, M. B. 1981. Simultaneous optical monitoring of activity of many neurons in invertebrate ganglia using a 124-element photodiode array. *J. Neurophysiol.* 45:829–40

19. Grinvald, A., Farber, I. C. 1981. Optical recording of calcium action potentials from growth cones of cultured neurons with a laser microbeam. *Science* 212:1164–67

20. Grinvald, A., Fine, A., Farber, I. C., Hildesheim, R. 1983. Fluorescence monitoring of electrical responses from small neurons and their processes. *Biophys. J.* 42:195–98

21. Grinvald, A., Hildesheim, R., Farber, I. C., Anglister, L. 1982. Improved fluorescent probes for the measurement of rapid changes in membrane potential. *Biophys. J.* 39:301–8

22. Grinvald, A., Hildesheim, R., Gupta, R., Cohen, L. B. 1980. Better fluorescent probes for optical measurement of changes in membrane potential. *Biol. Bull.* 159:484 (Abstr.)

23. Grinvald, A., Kamino, K., Lesher, S., Cohen, L. B., Wang, C.-H., Waggoner, A. S. 1978. *Biophys. J.* 21:82a (Abstr.)

24. Grinvald, A., Manker, A., Segal, M. 1982. Visualization of the spread of electrical activity in rat hippocampal slices by voltage-sensitive optical probes. *J. Physiol.* 333:269–91

25. Grinvald, A., Ross, W. N., Farber, I. 1981. Simultaneous optical measurement of electrical activity from multiple sites on processes of cultured neurons. 1981. *Proc. Natl. Acad. Sci. USA* 78: 3245–49

26. Grinvald, A., Salzberg, B. M., Lev-Ram, V., Hildesheim, R. 1987. Optical recording of synaptic potentials from processes of single neurons using intracellular potentiometric dyes. *Biophys. J.* 51:643–51

27. Gupta, R. K., Salzberg, B. M., Grinvald, A., Cohen, L. B., Kamino, K., et al. 1981. Improvements in optical methods for measuring rapid changes in membrane potential. *J. Membr. Biol.* 58:123–37

28. Hodgkin, A. L., Rushton, W. A. H. 1946. The electrical constants of a crustacean nerve fibre. *Proc. R. Soc. London Ser. B.* 133:444–79

29. Holz, G. G. IV, Kream, R. W., Dunlap, K. 1988. Characterization of the electrically evoked release of Substance P from dorsal root ganglion neurons. *J. Neurosci.* 8:463–71

30. Katz, B., Miledi, R. 1969. Tetrodotoxin-resistant electrical activity in presynaptic terminals. *J. Physiol.* 203:459–87

31. Konnerth, A., Obaid, A. L., Salzberg, B. M. 1985. Elasmobranch cerebellar slices in vitro: selective binding of potentiometric probes allows optical recording of electrical activity from different cell types. *Biol. Bull.* 169:553 (Abstr.)

32. Konnerth, A., Obaid, A. L., Salzberg, B. M. 1987. Optical recording of electrical activity from parallel fibres and other cell types in skate cerebellar slices in vitro. *J. Physiol.* 393:681–702

33. Krauthamer, V., Ross, W. N. 1984. Regional variations in excitability of barnacle neurons. *J. Neurosci.* 4:673–82

34. Llinas, R., Sujimori, M. 1980. Electrophysiological properties of in vitro Purkinje cell somata in mammalian cerebellar slices. *J. Physiol.* 305:171–95

35. Llinas, R., Sujimori, M. 1980. Electrophysiological properties of in vitro Purkinje cell dendrites in mammalian cerebellar slices. *J. Physiol.* 305:197–213

35a. Loew, L. M., Cohen, L. B., Salzberg, B. M., Obaid, A. L., Bezanilla, F. 1985. Charge-shift probes of membrane potential. Characterization of aminostyrylpyridinium dyes on the squid giant axon. *Biophys. J.* 47:71–77

36. McCleskey, E. W., Fox, A. P., Feldman, D. H., Cruz, L. J., Olivera, B. M., et al. 1988. ω-Conotoxin: Direct and persistent block of specific types of calcium channels in neurons but not muscle. *Proc. Natl. Acad. Sci. USA.* 84:4327–31

37. Miller, C., Moczydlowski, E., Latorre, R., Phillips, M. 1985. Charybdotoxin, a protein inhibitor of single Ca^{2+}-activated K^+ channels from mammalian skeletal muscle. *Nature* 313:316–18

38. Miller, R. J. 1987. Multiple calcium channels and neuronal function. *Science* 235:46–52

39. Moolenaar, W. H., Spector, I. 1978. Ionic currents in cultured mouse neuroblastoma cells under voltage clamp conditions. *J. Physiol.* 278:265–86

39a. Nachsen, D. A., Blaustein, M. P. 1980. Some properties of potassium-stimulated calcium uptake in presynaptic nerve endings isolated from rat brain. *J. Gen. Physiol.* 76:709–28

40. Nicholson, C., Llinas, R., Precht, W. 1969. Neural elements of the cerebellum in elasmobranch fishes: structural and functional characteristics. In *Neurobiology of Cerebellar Evolution and Development*, ed. R. Llinas, pp. 215–43. Chicago: American Medical Association-ERF

41. Obaid, A. L., Flores, R., Salzberg, B. M. 1987. Omega-Conotoxin blocks dihydropyridine-insensitive calcium channels in the intact nerve terminals of the frog neurohypophysis. *Neurosci. Abstr.* 13:99

42. Obaid, A. L., Gainer, H., Salzberg, B. M. 1983. Optical recording of action potentials from mammalian nerve terminals *in situ*. *Biol. Bull.* 165:530 (Abstr.)

43. Obaid, A. L., Konnerth, A., Salzberg, B. M. 1986. Optical monitoring of potassium accumulation in slices of skate (*Raja erinacea*) cerebellum in vitro. *Biol. Bull.* 171:496–97 (Abstr.)

44. Obaid, A. L., Orkand, R. K., Gainer, H., Salzberg, B. M. 1985. Active calcium responses recorded optically from nerve terminals of the frog neurohypophysis. *J. Gen. Physiol.* 85:481–89

45. Obaid, A. L., Salzberg, B. M. 1985. Selective block of the calcium-mediated potassium conductance ($g_{k(Ca)}$) in vertebrate nerve terminals by Charybdotox-

in (CTX): An optical demonstration using the neurohypophysis of *Xenopus*. *J. Gen. Physiol.* 86:19a–20a (Abstr.)

46. Obaid, A. L., Shimizu, H., Salzberg, B. M. 1982. Intracellular staining with potentiometric dyes: optical signals from identified leech neurons and their processes. *Biol. Bull.* 163:388 (Abstr.)

47. Olivera, B. M., Gray, W. R., Zeikus, R., McIntosh, J. M., Varga, J., et al. 1985. Peptide neurotoxins from fish-hunting cone snails. *Science* 230:1338–43

48. Orbach, H. S., Cohen, L. B. 1983. Optical monitoring of activity from many areas of the in vitro and in vivo salamander olfactory bulb: A new method for studying functional organization in the vertebrate central nervous system. *J. Neurosci.* 3:2251–62

49. Parsons, T. D., Kleinfeld, D., Raccuia, G. F., Obaid, A. L., Salzberg, B. M. 1988. Multiple site optical recording of electrical activity in identified *Aplysia* neurons maintained in culture: Coupled pairs see the light. *J. Gen. Physiol.* In press (Abstr.)

50. Parsons, T. D., Obaid, A. L., Salzberg, B. M. 1986. Aminoglycoside antibiotics block calcium currents in nerve terminals of the frog neurohypophysis: An optical demonstration using potentiometric probes. *Biol. Bull.* 171:497 (Abstr.)

51. Rane, S. G., Holz, G. G. IV, Dunlap, K. 1987. Dihydropyridine inhibition of neuronal calcium current and substance P release. *Pflügers Arch.* 409:361–66

52. Ready, D. F., Nicholls, J. G. 1979. Identified neurons isolated from leech CNS make selective connections in culture. *Nature* 282:67–69

53. Ross, W. N., Krauthamer, V. 1984. Optical measurements of potential changes in axons and processes of neurons of a barnacle ganglion. *J. Neurosci.* 4:659–72

54. Ross, W. N., Salzberg, B. M., Cohen, L. B., Davila, H. V. 1974. A large change in dye absorption during the action potential. *Biophys. J.* 14:983–86

55. Ross, W. N., Salzberg, B. M., Cohen, L. B., Grinvald, A., Davila, H. V., et al. 1977. Changes in absorption, fluorescence, dichroism, and birefringence in stained giant axons: Optical measurement of membrane potential. *J. Membr. Biol.* 33:141–83

56. Saggau, P., Galvan, M., ten Bruggencate, G. 1986. Longterm potentiation of guinea pig hippocampal slices monitored by optical recording of neuronal activity. *Neurosci. Lett.* 69:53–58

57. Salzberg, B. M. 1978. Optical signals from squid giant axons following perfusion or superfusion with potentiometric probes. *Biol. Bull.* 155:463–64 (Abstr.)

58. Salzberg, B. M. 1983. Optical recording of electrical activity in neurons using molecular probes. In *Current Methods in Cellular Neurobiology*, ed. J. Barker, J. McKelvy, pp. 139–87 New York: Wiley

59. Salzberg, B. M., Bezanilla, F. 1983. An optical determination of the series resistance in *Loligo*. *J. Gen. Physiol.* 82:807–18

60. Salzberg, B. M., Davila, H. V., Cohen, L. B. 1973. Optical recording of impulses in individual neurons of an invertebrate central nervous system. *Nature* 246:508–9

61. Salzberg, B. M., Grinvald, A., Cohen, L. B., Davila, H. V., Ross, W. N. 1977. Optical recording of neuronal activity in an invertebrate central nervous system: Simultaneous monitoring of several neurons. *J. Neurophysiol.* 40:1281–91

62. Salzberg, B. M., Obaid, A. L., Flores, R. 1987. Calcium channels required for neuropeptide release in the intact nerve terminals of vertebrate neurohypophyses are sensitive to Omega-conotoxin and insensitive to dihydropyridines: Optical studies with and without voltage-sensitive dyes. *Biol. Bull.* 173:435–36 (Abstr.)

63. Salzberg, B. M., Obaid, A. L., Gainer, H. 1984. Optical methods monitor action potentials and secretory activity at the nerve terminals of vertebrate neurohypophyses. *J. Gen. Physiol.* 84:3a–4a (Abstr.)

64. Salzberg, B. M., Obaid, A. L., Gainer, H. 1985. Large and rapid changes in light scattering accompany secretion by nerve terminals in the mammalian neurohypophysis. *J. Gen. Physiol.* 86:395–411

65. Salzberg, B. M., Obaid, A. L., Konnerth, A. 1986. Selective binding of potentiometric probes allows optical recording of electrical activity from different cell types in elasmobranch cerebellar slices *in vitro*. *Biophys. J.* 49:365a (Abstr.)

66. Salzberg, B. M., Obaid, A. L., Senseman, D. M., Gainer, H. 1983. Optical recording of action potentials from vertebrate nerve terminals using potentiometric probes provides evidence for sodium and calcium components. *Nature* 306:36–40

67. Schacher, S., Proshansky, E. 1983. Neurite regeneration by *Aplysia* neurons in dissociated cell culture: Modulation

by *Aplysia* hemolymph and the presence of initial axonal segment. *J. Neurosci.* 3:2403–13

68. Schwartzkroin, P. A. 1975. Characteristics of CA1 neurons recorded intracellularly in the hippocampus *in vitro* slice preparation. *Brain Res.* 85:423–36

69. Senseman, D. M., Horwitz, I. S., Salzberg, B. M. 1987. MSORTV imaging of electrotonic conduction in a syncitium: Optical recording of polarization spread in a simple salivary gland. *J. Exp. Zool.* 244:79–88

69a. Kaczmarek, L., Finbow, M., Revel, J. P., Strumwasser, F. 1977. The morphology and coupling of *Aplysia* bag cells within the abdominal ganglion and in cell cultures. *J. Neurobiol.* 10:535–50

70. Swanson, L. W., Teyler, T. J., Thompson, R. F. 1982. Hippocampal long-term potentiation: mechanisms and implications for memory. *Neurosci. Res. Prog. Bull.* 20:611–769

71. Teyler, T. J., Dicenna, P. 1985. The role of hippocampus in memory: a hypothesis. *Neurosci. Biobehav. Rev.* 9:377–89

72. Tsien, R. W. 1986. Modulation of calcium current in heart cells and neurons. In *Neuromodulation*, ed. I. B. Levitan, L. K. Kaczmarek, New York: Oxford Univ. Press

73. Waggoner, A. S. 1979. Dye indicators of membrane potential. *Annu. Rev. Biophys. Bioeng.* 8:47–63

74. Yamamoto, C. 1972. Intracellular study of seizure-like afterdischarges elicited in thin hippocampal section *in vitro. Exp. Neurol.* 35:154–64

Annu. Rev. of Physiol. 1989. 51:527–41

OPTICAL MEASUREMENT OF ACTION POTENTIAL ACTIVITY IN INVERTEBRATE GANGLIA

Larry Cohen, Hans-Peter Höpp, Jian-Young Wu, and Chun Xiao

Department of Physiology, Yale University School of Medicine, New Haven, Connecticut 06510

Jill London

Department of BioStructure and Function, University of Connecticut Health Science Center, Farmington, Connecticut 06032

Dejan Zečević

Institute of Biological Research, Belgrade Yugoslavia

INTRODUCTION

The original motivation for developing optical methods for monitoring neuron activity was the hope that such methods could be used to record all of the action potential activity of all the neurons in simpler invertebrate ganglia during behaviors (7). There was a further expectation that this kind of information would be useful for working out the neuron interactions that generated these behaviors.

Neurobiologists study the activity of individual neurons with the long range goal of describing the neuron activity that underlies behavior, and understanding how changes in this activity and the interactions of neurons can account for behavioral plasticity. Techniques which use microelectrodes to monitor activity are limited in that they can observe single cell activity in only as many cells as one can simultaneously place electrodes. In the first attempt to use voltage-sensitive dyes in ganglia (17), we were fortunate to be able to monitor

527

066-4278/89/0315-0527$02.00

activity in a single neuron because the photodynamic damage with dyes available at that time was severe. Now, however, with better dyes and methods, the spike activity of hundreds of individual neurons may be recorded simultaneously (13, 23). Nevertheless, despite considerable effort and progress since 1971, obtaining larger signal-to-noise ratios remains an important experimental goal.

The ability to measure the activity of many neurons simultaneously has raised new problems (see below). It seems to us that these recordings will force a more pessimistic view of the present understanding of the neuronal basis of apparently simple behaviors. In this review, we attempt to provide a critical summary of the present capabilities of optical recordings of membrane potential in invertebrate central nervous systems and an evaluation of the results that have been obtained. Several earlier reviews have appeared (6, 10, 16).

METHODS

Opisthobranch molluscs have been the preparation of choice because their central nervous systems have relatively few, relatively large neurons (1–4) and it is thought that every cell body is fully invaded by the action potential. This last characteristic is important for optical recordings because the signal-to-noise ratio for action potential measurements in ganglia is not large and this ratio would be reduced if the cell bodies did not have a full sized action potential.

In general, the optical monitoring technique is based on a system for monitoring changes in the absorption or fluorescence of a voltage-sensitive dye that has stained a piece of nervous tissue. In optical recordings from intact invertebrate ganglia, the signal-to-noise ratio in absorption has been larger than in fluorescence for *Aplysia californica* (22) and for the leech, *Hirudo medicinalis*, where absorption signals with the oxonol dye RGA509 were larger (E. Elliott, A. H. Cohen, C. Xiao, et al, unpublished results) than fluorescence signals with the styryl, RH237 (9). Figure 1 compares absorption signals and microelectrode recordings from a single neuron in a barnacle ganglion. The changes in absorption mirrored both sub-and suprathreshold events recorded with the microelectrode. A small subthreshold membrane potential change (*left*) as a result of injection of depolarizing current is recorded electrically (*bottom trace*). A small change in the light absorption (*top traces*) by the cell is recorded simultaneously. When the cell is stimulated to give an action potential (*right*) the optical trace also reflects this activity. Similar optical signals from individual neurons in ganglia have been obtained in several other species and by several laboratories (1, 9, 15, 21; S. Shiono, unpublished results using *Aplysia* ganglia). Although Yagodin et al (21) were unable to detect optical signals from action potentials in insect connectives, this appears to be a problem of dye penetration through the connective tissue sheath. None of the 12 dyes we tested penetrated through the sheath of the cockroach abdominal cord, but in desheathed preparations, action potentials were detected with two analogues of the oxonol, RH155 (J.-Y. Wu, H.-P. Höpp, C. Xiao, & L. B. Cohen, unpublished results).

For multiple site recording the ganglion is placed in the object plane of a microscope objective which then forms a magnified real image of the gangli-on at its image plane. A 12 × 12 array of silicon photodiodes is positioned at this plane to record the light transmitted by the ganglion. A detailed discus-sion of the apparatus and methods has appeared (5).

Pharmacological and Photodynamic Effects of the Dyes

Pharmacological effects, photodynamic damage, and bleaching have been examined in ganglia from five species. The amounts of these effects were species dependent. In the isolated ocellus-supraesophageal ganglion prepara-

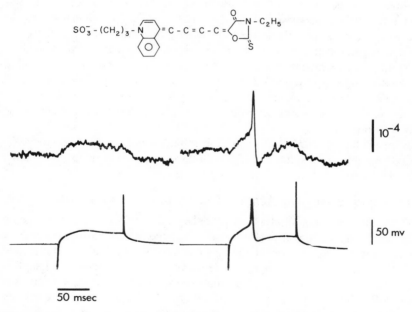

Figure 1   Comparison of changes in light absorption with membrane potential changes in a stained barnacle neuron. These signals were recorded in single trials. For both subthreshold and action potential activity, the optical signals (top traces) have a shape that is essentially identical to the electrode signals (bottom traces). The electrode artifacts that appear at the beginning and end of the current step do not occur on the optical recording. The structure of the merocyanine dye used in this experiment is shown at the top. [Modified from (18)].

tion from the barnacle, several dyes at several concentrations had to be screened to find staining conditions that did not affect the electrical response to a light stimulus to the ocellus, but did give relatively large optical signals (8). The off-response of the preparation did decline after several optical recordings indicating that there was some photodynamic damage. In addition, bleaching of the dye would occur after several minutes of constant illumination.

In experiments on a semi-intact *Navanax* preparation (see below) stained with 0.5 mg/ml of the oxonol dye, RH155 [NK3041], for 30 minutes, photodynamic damage and bleaching was insignificant (13). Constant illumination of a preparation for 20 minutes resulted in little if any change in the pattern of neuronal activity or in signal size. The pharmacological effects of dyes were examined in behavioral experiments in *Navanax*. Response to food and subsequent feeding were compared with animals whose buccal ganglia either had or had not been stained. Few, if any, changes in behavior were observed as a result of staining.

In contrast, when the staining procedure for *Navanax* was used in experiments on the *Aplysia* gill-withdrawal reflex, there were apparent pharmacological effects in some preparations (23). Also, the number of active neurons detected optically seemed to decrease by about 5–10% from trial to trial suggesting that there was either photodynamic damage or dye bleaching. The *Aplysia* experiments might have benefited from additional dye screening to look for dyes with reduced toxic effects. While more than 1000 dyes have been tested on squid axons, only 20–30 dyes were tested in *Aplysia*.

In preliminary experiments on two other species, *Helix aspersa* and *Hirudo*, photodynamic damage was undetectable in one (*Helix*) and relatively severe in the other (*Hirudo*) using the same oxonol dyes (D. Zecevic, C. Xiao, unpublished results). Clearly, pharmacologic effects and photodynamic damage must be evaluated for each preparation.

Determining Neuron Activity from Photodiode Outputs

When individual photodiodes were placed over the in-focus images of specific cell bodies, a large signal was recorded only in the detector positioned directly over the stimulated cell body indicating that the optical signal was confined to the expected area of the image (18). However, when the image of a ganglion is formed on a 12 × 12 diode array, the correspondence of cells and detectors is lost. The light from larger cells will fall on several detectors and the activity of such a cell will be recorded as simultaneous events on neighboring detectors. In addition, one detector may receive light from and record the activity of several cells. Finally, the images of some neurons will cover the entire area of a diode and the signal recorded on that detector will be relatively large while other detectors will receive only a small part of the cells' image and those signals will be small.

These concepts are illustrated in Figure 2, which shows a small portion of an array measurement from an *Aplysia* abdominal ganglion. In the top section, original recordings from seven of the photodiodes from the array are shown. At the number 1 there are synchronously occurring action potentials on all seven detectors. This synchronous event occurs frequently (>20) and we presume that each synchronous event represents an action potential in one relatively large neuron. The activity of this cell is represented by the vertical lines on trace 1 of the analyzed results shown in the bottom section. The activity of a second cell (number 2) is indicated by the spike on 119 and a small signal on its neighbor, 120. The activity of two additional neurons was similarly identified. Several of the problems associated with multicellular recordings are also illustrated by this figure. One problem arises from the signal-to-noise ratio. There may be an additional spike on detectors 114 and 121 between the number 3 and the stimulus (*arrow*), but the signal-to-noise ratio was not large enough to be certain. A second problem results from the fact that, following the stimulus, there is a great deal of activity and it would be easy for this activity to obscure small signals and lead to an underestimation in the number of active neurons. A third problem is that the analysis is very tedious and time consuming. The kind of analysis illustrated in this figure has been used to generate the raster data shown in Figures 5 and 6.

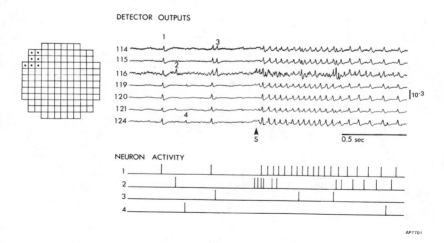

Figure 2   Optical recordings from a portion of a 12 × 12 array from an *Aplysia* abdominal ganglion. The drawing to the left represents the relative position of the detectors whose activity is displayed. In the top section, the original data from seven detectors is illustrated. The numbers to the right of each trace identifies the detector from which the trace was taken. In the bottom section the results of our analysis of this data into the spike activity of our neurons is indicated. [Modified from (23)].

Spatial Resolution

RESOLUTION IN THE Z AXIS   An attempt was made to determine how well a
single detector would discriminate between cells that were in the same x-y
position but were not in the same focal plane. To determine the resolution in
the z axis, the size of the optical signal was measured as a function of focal
position (Figure 3) (18). The signal size was reduced by 50% when the neuron
was moved +/−300 μm out of focus using optics with a nominal numerical
aperture of 0.4. [The actual numerical aperture in Salzberg et al (13) was less
than 0.4, since the condenser iris was partially closed, following the procedure for Kohler illumination.] Thus with ganglia that are less than 600 μm
thick, one can focus in the middle of the ganglion and record signals from the
activity of neurons at the top and at the bottom. This strategy was followed in
the attempts to obtain relatively complete recordings from *Navanax* and
Aplysia ganglia discussed below.

LIGHT SCATTERING   Light scattering by the ganglion will blur the images of
neurons and spread the light from a neuron over a larger area of the image
plane. The estimates of neuron size were made from the number of detectors
on which the activity of the cell was seen and scattering (and out of focus
signals) will cause these estimates to be too large. To determine the magnitude of the scattering effect, a small spot of light was focused on the object

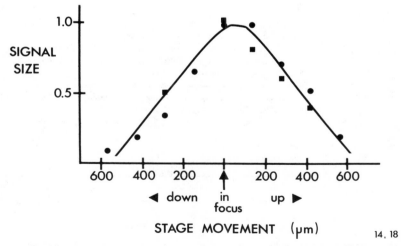

Figure 3   Size of the optical signal depends on the position of the cell body relative to the plane
of focus. A 50% decrease in signal size is seen when the soma is moved either 300 μm up or
down from the plane of focus. [Modified from (18)].

plane. In the absence of a ganglion, the light from the spot fell on a single photo-detector (Figure 4, *top*). A *Navanax* buccal ganglion was then placed in the light path and the intensities again recorded (Figure 4, *bottom*). While the largest intensity was recorded on the detector which originally had almost all of the light, some surrounding detectors now received much more light. But, because the intensity on the surrounding detectors was less than 1/3 the intensity on the central detector, scattering in *Navanax* ganglia does not greatly distort estimates of cell sizes. Light scattering will also reduce the amount of light that reaches a cell and reduce the amount that is collected by the objective to form its image. In the experiment shown in Figure 4, the presence of the ganglion reduced the intensity reaching the central detector by a factor of ten. While some of the light that is lost from the central detector can be seen on the adjacent detectors, there must be additional light loss due

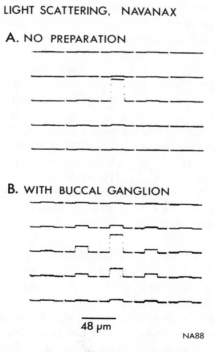

LIGHT SCATTERING, NAVANAX

A. NO PREPARATION

B. WITH BUCCAL GANGLION

48 µm

NA88

Figure 4   Measurement of light scattering by a *Navanax* buccal ganglia. The top section is a measurement of the response of 25 adjacent detectors when a small spot of light was focused in the object plane on a single detector and a shutter was opened during the recording. Almost all of the light reached a single photodiode. The bottom section is the response of the same 25 detectors, but now a buccal ganglion has been placed between the object plane and the objective. The presence of the ganglion increased the amount of light detected on detectors surrounding the central detector. [Modified from (13)].

to scattering at relatively large angles. A tenfold light loss will cause a reduction in the signal-to-noise ratio by a factor of three in a shot noise limited measurement.

In *Aplysia,* the scattering by abdominal ganglia from small animals (1–2 g) was similar to the scattering in *Navanax* while the scattering of ganglia from 100 g animals was markedly worse (M. Rioult, J.-Y. Wu, L. B. Cohen, unpublished results). The *Aplysia* experiments discussed below were carried out on animals weighing 2–30 g.

Recording from Navanax Buccal Ganglia During Feeding

The diode array was used to monitor activity from the buccal ganglion of a minimally dissected preparation during feeding. The feeding movements consist of the protraction of the mouth, prey contact and grasping with the lips, followed by an explosive expansion of the pharynx. This expansion creates a negative pressure so that the prey is sucked into the pharynx where it is subsequently digested. Neurons controlling the expansion have been described and reside in the buccal ganglion (19, 20).

The action potential data from one experiment are displayed in raster diagrams in Figure 5. The column of small numbers on the far left represents the number of detectors on which this particular neuron's activity was recorded. Individual frames from a videotape made during the feeding are displayed at the bottom. Action potential activity was detected in 22 neurons. Several large cells, on detectors 121 and 18, were active during the expansion. We think that cell 121 is the G-motorneuron previously identified by Levitan et al (12) and Spira et al (19). The firing of the individual buccal neurons occurs at characteristic times during the feeding and thus an initial clue about neuron function can be obtained from the timing of its activity. This kind of inference was more difficult to make from the *Aplysia* results discussed below.

It was important to determine the completeness of this optical recording in *Navanax.* Was activity detected in only 22 neurons because the appartus lacked the sensitivity to detect activity in most neurons or because only 22 were active? To determine the completeness, the number of neurons that could be identified by their action potential signals after maximal stimulation was compared with the number of cell bodies present in the ganglion. To obtain the first number, neurons were activated by stimulating each of the peripheral nerves and connectives with suction electrodes. To determine the number of cell bodies, ganglia were stained with methylene blue and the number of neurons counted using a computer-interfaced microscope (1, 14). The results of this comparison for three preparations are shown in Table 1. On average the optical recordings were about 70% complete. A number of

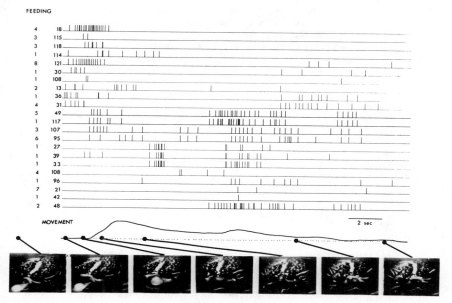

Figure 5 Raster diagram from an optical recording of the *Navanax* buccal ganglion during feeding. The bottom trace is a recording from the movement transducer which had been positioned on the pharynx; an upward deflection indicates expansion. The timing of the videotape frames at the bottom are indicated by the dots. There is a small piece of food that can be seen in the lower left corner of the first three frames which is completely engulfed by the fifth frame. The numbers to the far left indicate the number of neurons on which the signal was seen; the numbers adjacent to the traces are identification numbers indicating the detector output used for entering the spike times into the computer. [Modified from (13)].

possible errors in this estimate have been discussed (13). Most, but not all, of these errors would lead to an underestimation of the completeness. If we use the value of 70% then the actual number of active neurons during *Navanax* feeding would be about 30.

Recording from the Aplysia abdominal ganglion during the gill withdrawal reflex

The same dye and similar appartus were used to make recordings from the *Aplysia* abdominal ganglion during the gill withdrawal reflex (23). In this case, a more reduced preparation consisting of siphon, siphon nerve, ganglion, genital and brachial nerves, and gill (11) was used. The siphon skin was given a light mechanical touch, and the gill movements were recorded on videotape. An eight second raster diagram of the spike activity measured

Table 1. Completeness of the optical recordings from *Navanax*

Preparation	Number of neurons whose activity was detected optically	Cell bodies in the ganglion	% Complete
89	140	183	77
93	128	162	79
95	112	203	55

during a withdrawal in a preparation that had been acutely sensitized is illustrated in Figure 6. Included in this figure are 105 neurons whose activity was detected optically and an additional 45 neurons whose activity was detected via extracellular electrode measurements from nerves. The mechanical stimulus occurred at the time indicated by the bar at the bottom.

One important difference between the *Aplysia* and *Navanax* experiments is the larger number of cell bodies in the *Aplysia* ganglion, either 700 (3) or 1100 (4). With a photodiode array of only 124 elements, the number of neurons per detector in the *Aplysia* experiment is relatively large and it is often difficult to distinguish activity in neighboring small neurons. The *Aplysia* recordings are likely to be less complete than those from *Navanax*. Zecevic et al (23) estimated that the actual number of activated neurons during the gill-withdrawal reflex in the acutely sensitized ganglion was between 250 and 400. Thus, the recording illustrated in Figure 6 was approximately 50% complete.

We were surprised at the large number of neurons that were activated by the light mechanical stimulation of the siphon skin. Certainly it is possible, or even likely, that not all of these neurons are in the pathway between siphon

⟶

Figure 6 Raster diagram of the action potential activity recorded optically from an *Aplysia* abdominal ganglion during a gill-withdrawal reflex. The touch to the siphon occurred at the time of the bar labeled STIM. In this recording, from an acutely sensitized preparation, activity in 150 neurons was measured. We think this recording is incomplete and that the actual number of active neurons was between 250 and 400. The neurons were arbitrarily divided into three groups. At the top are neurons that were spontaneously active in the two seconds prior to the stimulus; in the middle are neurons that were silent before the stimulus. Included in this figure are 105 neurons whose activity was detected optically and an additional 45 neurons whose activity was detected via extracellular electrode measurements from nerves (indicated by the vertical bars on the left). Neuron activity that was detected on both optical and electrode recordings was omitted from the electrode section. The numbers adjacent to the traces are identification numbers indicating the detector output used for entering the spike times into the computer. [Modified from (23)].

A. SENSITIZED

STIM

1 SEC

A10407

sensory neurons and gill motor neurons. But, providing the evidence that they are not would seem to be impractical with presently available neurobiological tools. In fact, it is not easy to think of a practical experiment that will allow one to determine the contribution of any particular synaptic connection or group of synaptic connections in generating the gill withdrawal or in accounting for its plasticity. It will be a challenge to neurobiologists to develop methods for understanding circuits of this complexity.

DIFFICULTIES

SIGNAL-TO-NOISE RATIO   It is clear that signal-to-noise ratios adequate for recording action potentials in cell bodies in invertebrate ganglia have been obtained. And, with the presently available dyes, pharmacological effects and photodynamic damage are not overwhelming problems. But, it is also clear that the signal-to-noise ratios for smaller potential changes or cells with smaller membrane areas would not be adequate for single trial measurements. This means that similar methods would be difficult to apply to ganglia where only small electrotonicaly spread action potentials reached the cell body. Similarly, synaptic potentials are difficult to detect in single trials (8, 18). It would seem that the only hope for understanding behaviors that involve more than a few cells is to develop the means for recording most of the synaptic activity. Improvements in the signal-to-noise ratio will be necessary if optical measurements are to achieve this sensitivity.

PROBLEMS CAUSED BY THE DIFFICULT ANALYSIS   The analysis of the data to generate the raster displays like that shown in Figure 6 was difficult and time consuming even though considerable effort has gone into the computer programs designed to facilitate the process. It took about 30 hours to do the analysis for Figure 6 and perhaps 100 hours to analyze the results of a maximal electrical stimulation. The fact that the analysis is so time consuming severely hampers progress. One would prefer to screen new dyes on ganglia by determining the completeness of the recording for each dye. But, because it takes too long to analyze this kind of result, only the size of the largest signals was used to judge the dyes. This simpler procedure is adequate only if one can assume that the cell body staining is uniform and that the signal per unit membrane area is independent of cell size.

Similarly, the time required for analysis means that many analyses that could be done have not yet been done. For example, we routinely record two gill-withdrawal responses in each behavioral state and we could ask whether the same neurons are participating in both responses. But this analysis has not yet been done. Since the amount of data generated is large and its analysis slow and difficult there is considerable motivation for developing more automatic analysis programs.

TOO MANY CELLS ACTIVE AT ONCE   The large number of active neurons has caused unanticipated difficulties. In the *Aplysia* experiments, almost all of the detected cells are active during the first second after the mechanical stimulus (Figure 6). At this time there are many action potential signals on every detector, and some detectors have so many signals from so many cells that the optical recording has a noisy baseline. This excess noise caused two kinds of problems in the analysis. First, small signals will be obscured causing an underestimation of the number of cells. Second, this excess noise, and for that matter all action potential signals, will add noise to the results of spike-triggered averaging and reduce the sensitivity for detecting synaptic potentials. Spike-triggered averaging would be more successful on the kind of data obtained from *Navanax* where the activity of the individual neurons is more spread out in time (Figure 5) as opposed to the data from *Aplysia* where the spike activity is more clustered (Figure 6).

SUMMARY

Optical monitoring methods have reached the level of development where activity from a network of cells can be recorded in a minimally-dissected behaving animal. The spike activity in the buccal ganglion of *Navanax* was monitored during feeding (13) and activity in the *Aplysia* abdominal ganglion was monitored during the gill-withdrawal reflex (23). Approximately 30 neurons in the *Navanax* buccal ganglion were active during feeding and between 250 and 400 neurons in the *Aplysia* abdominal ganglion were active during the gill-withdrawal reflex. A reasonably complete understanding of the neuronal basis of the gill withdrawal may not be possible with presently available scientific methods. Substantial improvements in signal-to-noise ratio in optical measurements will be necessary before the majority of synaptic potentials can be detected optically. Understanding circuits that involve more than a few neurons will be a challenge to neurobiologists.

FUTURE DIRECTIONS

One obvious objective is to improve the sensitivity of optical measurements. We hope that better dyes will become available, ones that will produce larger signals in response to voltage changes in the membrane. We also hope to increase the spatial resolution of the apparatus by incorporating the array with more elements. This should be especially helpful in experiments on ganglia like that from *Aplysia* with relatively large numbers of neurons. The use of preparations with less scattering (1) would also improve the signal-to-noise ratio.

Additional information is needed to characterize the cells participating in the behavior. One possibility is to monitor the direction of spike propagation in peripheral nerves and match their timing with soma recordings. Activity of cells with peripheral nerve spikes propagating outward are of possible motor neuron origin; activity of axons spikes propagating toward the ganglion may be from sensory neurons. But, thus far only 20% of the activity recorded optically and electrically was matched (23), so this procedure may be useful for only a fraction of the active neurons.

ACKNOWLEDGMENTS

We are grateful to W. N. Ross and B. M. Salzberg for comments on the manuscript. The research described was supported in part by Public Health Service Grant NS08437.

Literature Cited

1. Boyle, M. B., Cohen, L. B., Macagno, E. R., Orbach, H. S. 1983. The number and size of neurons in the CNS of gastropod molluscs and their suitability for optical recording of activity. *Brain Res.* 266:305–17
2. Bullock, T. H., Horridge, G. A., eds. 1965. *Structure and Function In the Nervous Systems of Invertebrates.* San Francisco: Freeman
3. Cash, D., Carew, T. J. 1989. A quantitative analysis of the development of the central nervous system in juvenile *Aplysia californica. Neurobiology* In press
4. Coggeshall, R. E. 1967. A light and electron microscope study of the abdominal ganglion of *Aplysia californica. J. Neurophysiol.* 30:1263–87
5. Cohen, L. B., Lesher, S. 1986. Optical monitoring of membrane potential: methods of multisite optical measurement. *Soc. Gen. Physiol. Ser.* 40:71–99
6. Cohen, L. B., Salzberg, B. M. 1978. Optical measurement of membrane potential. *Rev. Physiol. Biochem. Pharmacol.* 83:35–88
7. Davila, H. V., Salzberg, B. M., Cohen, L. B., Waggoner, A. S. 1973. A large change in axon fluorescence that provides a promising method for measuring membrane potential. *Nature New Biol.* 241:159–160
8. Grinvald, A., Cohen, L. B., Lesher, S., Boyle, M. B. 1981. Simultaneous optical monitoring of activity of many neurons in invertebrate ganglia using a 124-element photodiode array. *J. Neurophysiol.* 45:829–40
9. Grinvald, A., Hildesheim, R., Farber, I. C., Anglister, L. 1982. Improved fluorescent probes for the measurement of rapid changes in membrane potential. *Biophys. J.* 39:301–8
10. Grinvald, A., Frostig, R. D., Lieke, E., Hildesheim, R. 1988. Optical imaging of neuronal activity. *Physiol. Rev.* 68:1285–1366
11. Kupfermann, I., Pinsker, H., Castellucci, V., Kandel, E. R. 1971. Central and peripheral control of gill movements in *Aplysia. Science* 174:1252–56
12. Levitan, H., Tauc, L., Segundo, J. P. 1970. Electrical transmission among neurons in the buccal ganglion of a mollusc, *Navanax* inermis. *J. Gen. Physiol.* 55:484–96
13. London, J. A., Zečević, D., Cohen, L. B. 1987. Simultaneous optical recording of activity from many neurons during

feeding in *Navanax. J. Neurosci.* 7:649–61

14. Macagno, E. 1980. Number and distribution of neurons in leech segmental ganglia. *J. Comp. Neurol.* 190:283–302

15. Ross, W. N., Reichardt, L. F. 1979. Species-specific effects on the optical signals of voltage-sensitive dyes. *J. Membr. Biol.* 48:343–56

16. Salzberg, B. M. 1983. Optical recording of electrical activity in neurons using molecular probes. In *Current Methods in Cellular Neurobiology*, ed. J. L. Barker, J. F. McKelvy, pp. 139–87 New York: Wiley

17. Salzberg, B. M., Davila, H. V., Cohen, L. B. 1973. Optical recording of impulses in individual neurons of an invertebrate central nervous system. *Nature* 246:508–9

18. Salzberg, B. M., Grinvald, A., Cohen, L. B., Davila, H. V., Ross, W. N. 1977. Optical recording of neuronal activity in an invertebrate central nervous system: simultaneous monitoring of several neurons. *J. Neurophysiol.* 40:1281–91

19. Spira, M. E., Spray, D. C., Bennett, M. V. L. 1980. Synaptic organization of expansion motoneurons of *Navanax* inermis. *Brain Res.* 195:241–69

20. Woolacott, M. 1974. Patterned neural activity associated with prey capture in *Navanax. J. Comp. Physiol.* 94:69–84

21. Yagodin, S., Puskdarev, Y. P., Slutsky, V. M. 1989. Species specific effects of voltage-sensitive dyes on the optical signals of some invertebrates. *J. Membr. Biol.* In press

22. Zečević, D., London, J. A., Cohen, L. B. 1985. Simultaneous optical recording from many cells from *Aplysia* abdominal ganglia using fluorescence. *Neurosci. Lett.* 22:370

23. Zečević, D., Wu, J.-Y., Cohen, L. B., London, J. A., Höpp, H.-P., Xiao, C. 1988. Many cells in the *Aplysia* abdominal ganglion are active during the gill-withdrawal reflex. Submitted for publication

Annu. Rev. Physiol. 1989. 51:543–59
Copyright © 1989 by Annual Reviews Inc. All rights reserved

OPTICAL IMAGING OF CORTICAL ACTIVITY: Real-time imaging using extrinsic dye-signals and high resolution imaging based on slow intrinsic-signals

Edmund E. Lieke, Ron D. Frostig, Amos Arieli, Daniel Y. Ts'o, Rina Hildesheim, and Amiram Grinvald

IBM Research Division at Thomas J. Watson Research Center; Laboratory of Neurobiology, The Rockefeller University; and Department of Neurobiology, The Weizmann Institute of Science, New York

THE ADVANTAGES OF OPTICAL IMAGING OF CORTICAL ACTIVITY

The processing of sensory information, coordination of movement and other higher brain functions are carried out by millions of neurons that form elaborate networks. Individual neurons are synaptically connected to hundreds or thousands of other neurons that shape their response properties. How these neurons and their intricate connections endow the brain with its remarkable performance is one of the central questions in neurobiology.

In the mammalian brain, cells that perform a given function or share common functional properties are often grouped together (e.g., the orientation and ocular dominance columns of the visual cortex). Attaining an understanding of the three dimensional functional organization of such groups of cells is a key step towards revealing the mechanisms of information processing in a given cortical region. Thus, especially promising are experimental methods that allow the visualization of the functional organization of a cortical region, particularly methods that provide high spatial and temporal resolution. Currently there is a surge of interest in several imaging techniques that yield information about the spatial distribution of active neurons in the brain. These methods include the 2-deoxyglucose method (2-DG), radioactive imaging of changes in blood flow, electroencephalography, magnetoencephalography, positron emmision tomography (PET), nuclear magnetic resonance imaging (MRI), and thermal imaging. Each technique has advantages as well

543

as significant limitations, and most techniques still suffer from either limited spatial resolution, temporal resolution, or both.

Optical imaging of cortical activity is an attractive technique for providing new insights to both the organization and function of the mammalian brain. Among its advantages over other methodologies are (a) the direct recording of the summed intracellular activity of neuronal populations, including the detection of subthreshold synaptic potentials in fine neuronal processes and terminals, (b) the imaging of spatio-temporal patterns of activity of neuronal populations with submillisecond time resolution in vitro and in the living brain, and (c) the possibility of repeated measurements from the same cortical region with different experimental or stimulus conditions over an extended time. However, unlike some of the other imaging techniques, optical imaging is limited to exposed surfaces of the brain up to a depth of 0.5–~2 mm.

Optical Imaging of Neuronal Activity With Dyes

The discovery and development of suitable voltage-sensitive-dyes (7, 9, 17) has been the key to the successful application of optical recording because different preparations often require dyes with different properties (43). The preparation under study is first stained by bath application of the dye. The dye molecules bind to the external surface of excitable membranes and act as molecular transducers that transform changes in membrane potential into optical signals (7, 17). The resulting changes in the absorption or the emitted fluorescence occur in microseconds and linearly correlate with the electrical activity of the stained neurons. These changes are then monitored with light measuring instrumentation. By using an array of photodetectors (128 detectors), positioned in the microscope image plane, the activity of many individual targets can be detected simultaneously (16). Optical imaging with voltage-sensitive dyes permits the visualization of cortical activity with a submillisecond time resolution and a spatial resolution of 50–100 microns. It is important to note that optical signals recorded from the cortex are different than those recorded from single cells or their individual processes and thus should be interpreted with care. In optical recordings from cortex single cell activity is not resolved and the optical signal represents the sum of intracellular membrane potential changes, in both pre- and postsynaptic neuronal elements, as well as a possible contribution from the depolarization of neighboring glial cells (31–33). Since the optical signals measure the integral of the membrane potential changes (integrating membrane area as well as time), slow subthreshold synaptic potentials in the extensive dendritic arborization are easily detected by optical recording. Thus optical signals, when properly dissected (see 17), can provide information about elements of neuronal processing that are usually unavailable from single unit recording.

However, the instrumentation required to record these fast optical signals with a high spatial resolution over a large area requires fast detectors with many more pixels and is currently expensive. Other limitations of the use of dyes are briefly discussed below.

Optical Imaging Based on Intrinsic Signals

Another imaging strategy based on the slower intrinsic changes in the optical properties of active brain tissue permits visualization of active cortical regions at high spatial resolution and without some of the problems associated with voltage-sensitive dyes. Possible sources for these activity-dependent intrinsic signals include either changes in physical properties of the tissue itself or changes in the absorption, fluorescence, or other optical properties of intrinsic molecules having significant absorption or fluorescence. The existence of small intrinsic optical changes associated with metabolic activity in many tissues, has been known since the pioneering experiments of Kelin in 1925 (29) or Millikan in 1937 (38) on the absorption of cytochromes and hemoglobin. The first optical recording of activity-related optical signals in neuronal preparation was made almost forty years ago by Hill & Keynes (23) who detected light scattering changes in active nerves. Changes in absorption or fluorescence of intrinsic chromophores were extensively investigated by Chance and his colleagues (5), and Jobsis and his colleagues (26). However, the intrinsic optical signals were usually small and slow. Until recently the optical measurement of intrinsic signals was not applied to the imaging of spatial patterns of sensory evoked neuronal activity (for reviews see 5, 6, 37).

The remainder of this review will provide examples of work that illustrate the types of experimental strategies and results that have been obtained from optical imaging of cortical activity with and without voltage-sensitive-dyes. It will then discuss the relative merits of each approach. Since most of the publications in this area have been already reviewed, we will emphasize recent work that was published in abstracts. The important experiments of Gross et al (21, 22), Blasdel & Salama (3), and Kauer (27) who utilized voltage-sensitive dyes and slower video-imaging techniques are discussed in another chapter of this volume. The technical details of optical imaging techniques cannot be presented here but are nevertheless crucial for optimizing these techniques and evaluating the feasibility of new types of experiments. For earlier reviews see (7, 8, 13, 14, 17, 20, 35, 39, 44–46, 48, 49).

STUDIES OF THE ORGANIZATION AND INTERACTIONS OF NEURONAL POPULATIONS IN VIVO UTILIZING VOLTAGE-SENSITIVE DYES

The detection of spatio-temporal patterns of activity in mammalian brain slices (19) suggested that optical imaging techniques could prove to be a

useful tool for the study of the mammalian brain in vivo. However preliminary experiments in rat visual cortex revealed several complications for in
vivo optical imaging that included large noise due to respiratory and heartbeat
motion. In addition, the relative opacity and the packing density of the cortex
limited the penetration of the excitation light and the ability of available dyes
to stain deep layers of the cortex. Orbach & Cohen (40) first demonstrated
that optical signals could be obtained in vivo, by observing responses in the
salamander olfactory bulb after electrical stimulation of the whole olfactory
nerve. These responses were small even with the use of a strong stimulus, and
thus prompted a search for more appropriate dyes for in vivo imaging. Such
dyes (e.g. RH-414, RH-704, RH-795) were developed at the Weizmann
Institute and proved useful in extensive dye screening experiments on rat, cat,
and monkey cortices. In addition, an effective remedy for the large heartbeat
noise was found by synchronizing the data acquisition with the EKG and
subtracting a no-stimulus trial (15, 41).

Topographical Mapping of Sensory-Evoked Responses

Among the first applications of in vivo real-time optical imaging using the
voltage-sensitive dyes were experiments that visualized the topographic distribution of sensory responses. The frog retinotectal connections is one such
topographically organized system. The optical signals obtained from the
tectum in response to discrete visual stimuli corresponded well to the known
retinotopic map of the tectum. However, in addition to a focus of excitation,
the spatial distribution of the signals showed smaller, delayed activity (3–20
msec) covering a much larger area than expected from classical single unit
mapping (15).

Similar mapping experiments were performed in the rat somatosensory
cortex, where the simple organization of the whisker barrels offered a convenient preparation for testing new strategies. When the tip of a whisker was
gently moved, optical signals were observed in the corresponding cortical
barrel field (Figure 1). However a discrepancy was noted between the size of
an individual barrel recorded optically (1300 μm) and the histologically
defined barrel (300–600 μm in layer IV of the cortex). This difference is
reasonable considering that most of the optical signal originates from the
superficial cortical layers (I–III) and that barrel neurons extend long processes
to neighboring barrels (41).

Retinotopic imaging experiments in monkey striate cortex (34) also showed
activity over a cortical area much larger than predicted from standard receptive field analysis, but consistent with the anatomical finding of long-range
horizontal connections in visual cortex (12).

These optical imaging experiments on the topographic distribution of sensory processing all demonstrated a central focus of excitation corresponding
to the applied stimulus, and a surrounding area of delayed cortical activity

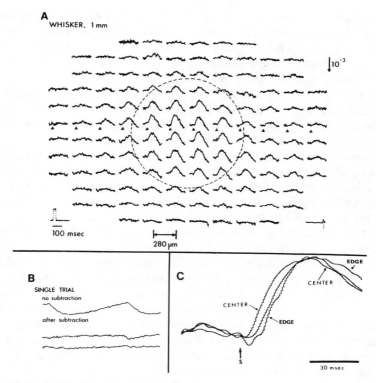

Figure 1 Optical imaging of a whisker barrel in rat somatosensory cortex. (*a*) The spatial distribution of the optical signals that resulted from a 1 mm whisker deflection, in a 3.4 × by 3.4 mm cortical area (32 trials were averaged). (*b*) Removal of the heart beat noise by subtraction. (*c*) Comparison of the time course of the optical signals in the center of the barrel and its periphery (modified from Reference 41).

(e.g. Figure 1c) larger than predicted by single unit recording. Possible explanations for the expanded area of optically detected activity include (*a*) the optical pickup of axonal activity in long-range horizontal connections that spread far beyond the directly activated area, (*b*) a large contribution from subthreshold excitation of postsynaptic neurons at the regions where neurons are not actually firing in response to the given stimulus, (*c*) a smearing of neuronal signals by slower glial signals (31–33) that spread across the electrically coupled glial syncitium, (*d*) a large contribution from layer 1, whose functional organization is not well characterized, and (*e*) spread due to light scattering (40, 41).

Surround Inhibition Revealed by Optical Imaging

Although the amplitude of optical signals is linearly related to the membrane potential change, the detection of positive optical signals in a given cortical region does not necessarily imply that inhibition is not present. For example, a strong inhibition may not be accompanied by marked hyperpolarization and, furthermore, it may be masked by a larger depolarization at other neuronal sites. In addition, action potentials in inhibitory axons may also mask the small hyperpolarization in the postsynaptic cells. Thus, it was important to determine whether the surround activity in the topographic mapping experiments discussed above had any inhibitory component. The surround signals were tested with more revealing stimulus paradigms and with the use of pharmacological agents that block inhibitory synapses.

Upon presenting a second spot of light that was delayed and displaced (26°) from a preceding spot of light, optical imaging of the frog tectum showed that the activity evoked by a second flash was inhibited by the first flash (by 60%). When a single light spot was used, application of the GABA blocker bicuculline led to a tenfold increase in the region of excitation, consistent with the notion that inhibitory interactions shape the excitation area (15). (For similar experiments in rat cortex see 36.)

In the studies of the rat somatosensory cortex, stimulation of two whiskers that were relatively far apart evoked responses in two circumscribed areas. A large overlap in the response area was obtained when neighboring whiskers were stimulated, but the individual responses could be resolved only if they were activated with some delay (>20 msec). Activity evoked by one whisker often inhibited the activity evoked by another whisker when the interstimulus interval was 20–120 msec and indicated a surround inhibition extending 2–4mm in the rat somatosensory cortex (41).

In preliminary experiments, strong inhibitory center-surround interactions were also revealed by optical imaging of a 6 × 6 mm region of monkey striate cortex. Four interlaced visual patterns of moving gratings were presented, stimulating either a small center field or the surround alone, or both together, with center and surround gratings having either matching or orthogonal orientations. The results indicate that the interactions between center and surround stimuli have a strong inhibitory component (34), even if the retinotopically activated surround is more than 6 mm away from the cortical activity evoked by the center stimulus. At least part of this surround inhibition was of cortical origin.

Patterns and Foci of Epileptiform Discharges Revealed by Real-Time Optical Imaging in Rat and Cat Cortex

The analyses of spatio-temporal patterns of epileptic discharges as well as the investigation of their underlying mechanisms have been of great interest to investigators of epilepsy, but detailed analysis could not be performed easily with conventional electrical recordings. Epileptiform activity can be induced in the cortex by topical application of bicuculline. The resulting spontaneous interictal events occur at a frequency of 0.1–5Hz and are produced by a synchronous activation of a large number of neighboring neurons. This massive activity produces very large optical signals that can be detected without averaging (41). In rat somatosensory cortex, initial studies showed the spatial patterns of epileptiform activity, but did not reveal any detailed time structure to its propagation (41). Although the amplitudes of the signals were relatively uniform, a more recent analysis of the millisecond time structure of the signals revealed the actual epileptic focus of the activity (20). A recent set of experiments by London and her colleagues (36) on rat somatosensory cortex has confirmed this conclusion and, in addition, found that in the presence of bicuculline stimulation of one whisker evoked much larger activity with longer time delay and covered a larger cortical area.

One intriguing issue is whether the epileptic focus is stationary and whether repeated episodes have similar patterns of propagation. These questions were explored with multiple segments of optical recording, each lasting 20 seconds, over a period of several minutes. It was found through detailed temporal analysis that the foci were not stationary in a 2×2 mm cortical area, and the discharge patterns and their propagation velocity varied during the occurrence of multiple interictal events (Figure 2). These studies clearly show the importance of the ability to analyze cortical activity at the millisecond level; without this ability critical information may not be discovered. A comparison of the optical signals with a surface recording of the EEG indicated that often major components of the EEG detected electrically were missing from the optical recordings. These findings indicate that these missing events did not originate from the superficial layers of the optically monitored region of cortex but from a more distant source (1, 33). Thus optical recording has an improved spatial selectivity over surface recording of the EEG.

Visualization of Spatio-Temporal Organization of Neuronal Assemblies

A neuronal assembly may be defined as a group of neurons that cooperate to perform a specific computation required for a specific task. The activity of cells in an assembly is timelocked (coherent). However, the cells that comprise an assembly may be spatially intermixed with cells in other neuronal assemblies that are performing different computational tasks. Therefore, techniques that can visualize only the average population activity in a given cortical region, as described above, may not be adequate to study neuronal assemblies. What is needed, then, is a method to discriminate between the operations of several colocalized assemblies. A promising solution to this problem is to use the timelocked activity of the assembly neurons to visualize selectively only that assembly. The firing of a cell that is part of the assembly can serve as a source of synchronization for this selective visualization. We, therefore, combined single unit recordings and subsequent spike-triggered

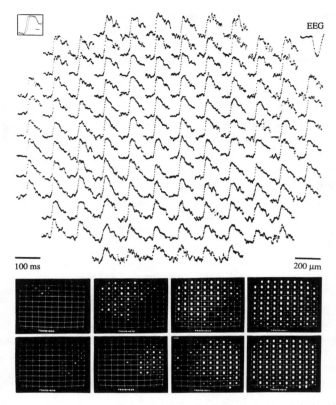

Figure 2 Spatio-temporal pattern of an epileptiform discharge (evoked by topical application of bicuculline) in cat cortex. Top: the raw optical data for one interictal event. The bottom eight frames from a display processor illustrate the temporal sequences of activity of two different interictal events. For each pixel in a frame, the amplitude of the optical signal at that site is represented by the size of the symbol. The top four frames show an epileptiform wave that propagated from the top left to the bottom right of the imaged cortex, whereas the second event (corresponding to the raw data shown at the top) propagated from right to left. The propagation velocity was 0.2 m/sec for the first wave and 0.4 m/sec for the second. The inset in the top left compares traces from the anterior and posterior portions of the imaged cortical field (2 × 2 mm).

averaging of the optical recordings (from 124 sites) to study the spatio-temporal organization of ongoing (spontaneous) activity of neuronal assemblies. Of particular interest was the finding that whereas the averaged optical signal at the electrode site had a peak that coincided with the occurrence of the single unit discharges, in other cortical sites the spatio-temporal pattern of spontaneous activity of neuronal assemblies was nonuniform over even a small region of cortex; in as short a distance as 200 μm, the activity exhibited a different time course and amplitude. No such nonuniformity was detected in multi-electrode local EEG recordings, which indicates that optical imaging has better spatial resolution for studying neuronal assemblies (2).

Visualization of Connectivity Between Neuronal Populations in the Living Brain

Extracellular injections of anatomical tracers (e.g. HRP; horse radish peroxidase) in a given cortical site can map patterns of connectivity from neural populations that have projections in the injected site, but the results are available only after postmortem histological processing. Techniques using optical imaging, in contrast, have the potential to directly visualize site to site connectivity in the living brain. Orbach & Van Essen (42) have demonstrated that such measurements may provide a powerful tool for pathway tracing in vivo. By applying short trains of focal extracellular stimulation to a site in rat striate cortex, optical signals were observed immediately in the stimulation site, and, after a 5 msec delay, in the corresponding locations in extrastriate cortical areas. Similar experiments regarding visual areas in the squirrel monkey were reported recently (42a). It would be important to know whether this approach reveals a patchy distribution of cortical connections comparable to that shown by previous studies using anatomical tracers. Preliminary results by other groups have also reported the optical mapping of projection areas with either extracellular stimulation of nerve bundles innervating the piriform cortex (4), the olfactory bulb (27, 28), or focal surface stimulation in the cerebellum (30).

In addition to tracing connections, such techniques may also provide information about the functional properties of the revealed connections by manipulating stimulus conditions. The local application of specific drugs may also help to elucidate the nature of synaptic transmission involved.

OPTICAL IMAGING OF ACTIVITY USING INTRINSIC SIGNALS

The use of intrinsic signals has several distinct advantages. Since no dye is required, the measurement of intrinsic signals is less invasive, can be made for an indefinite period of time, and is free of several technical complications associated with the use of dyes (e.g. photodynamic damage, bleaching, and pharmacological side effects; see 7, 17).

Blasdel & Salama (3) stated that intrinsic signals were not useful for mapping the functional organization of monkey striate cortex. In contrast we have found that the intrinsic signals have proved to be useful for mapping in the monkey striate cortex, as well as in other preparations. For example, in rat somatosensory cortex, the map of a whisker barrel was observed using a photodetector array to monitor the decreases in reflected light intensity that correspond to cortical activation from whisker stimulation. A similar map was later obtained with the voltage-sensitive dye signals, thus confirming the map produced by the slow intrinsic signals. Thus, although the intrinsic signal was at least two orders of magnitude slower than dye signals, nevertheless it was useful for mapping known functional components of the cortex (18).

Determining the Source and Nature of the Intrinsic Signals

Experiments on the nature of the intrinsic signals useful for functional imaging have revealed a mixture of at least two major components. One component of the intrinsic signal originates from changes in blood volume that are probably a result of local capillary recruitment in an activated area. These changes appear as an increase in hemoglobin absorption. A detailed characterization of the time course and saturation of this optical signal may help to improve the performance of PET imaging, which is based on a similar mechanism (10). The second component to the intrinsic signal originates from the light scattering that accompanies changes in the cortical tissue after activation [e.g. ion and water movement, expansion and contraction of extracellular spaces, capillary expansion, neurotransmitter release; see review by Cohen (6)]. The blood volume component of the intrinsic signal dominates between 500–700 nm while the light scattering component dominates in the near infrared region above 800 nm. These two components have different time courses. Nevertheless, maps of functional organization obtained in both regions of the spectrum were identical either in area 17 of the macaque monkey or area 18 of the cat. Thus each component can be used for functional mapping (11).

Mapping of Functional Organization in Visual Cortex

A prominent feature of the visual cortex is the arrangement of cells with like orientation preference in columns or bands (25). The optical imaging of the orientation columns with the aid of intrinsic signals required the separate collection of signals for each of two presented moving gratings of orthogonal orientation and subsequent analytical comparison. A moving grating stimulus evoked intrinsic signals over a large region of cortex. However, at each cortical site the signals evoked by the optimal stimulus orientation were somewhat larger than the signals evoked by the orthogonal orientation (Figure 3A). The spatial distribution of the regions preferring the horizontal stimulus is shown as a two-state coded map in Figure 3B and the raw data is shown in Figure 3C. To obtain a more precise map of the orientation columns the results from vertical and horizontal stimuli presentations were combined with results from presentations at orientations of 45° and 135°. The resulting map is shown in the bottom left of Figure 3. The orientation map was confirmed, using a double-blind procedure, by making a series of 42 electrode penetra-

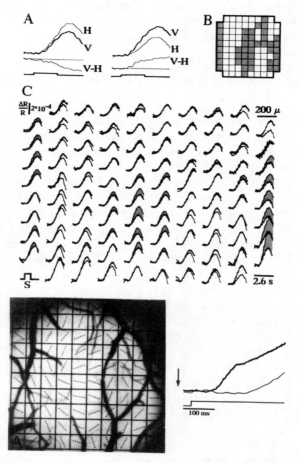

Figure 3   Imaging of the orientation columns in cat visual cortex with intrinsic optical signals. (*A*) In one cortical site (left traces), single units preferentially responded to gratings with horizontal orientation. The corresponding intrinsic signal (thin trace) was larger than that obtained in response to the vertical stimuli (thick trace). In a second cortical site (right), single units had preferential responses to the gratings with vertical orientation and the opposite result was obtained. (*B*) The spatial distribution of cortical regions preferring the horizontal stimulus (shaded area). (*C*) The raw data showing the distribution of the signals in 96 cortical sites for horizontal (thin traces) and vertical stimuli. Bottom left: Superimposed on the picture of the exposed cortex are dashed bars showing the optimal stimulus orientation for each cortical site as determined by combining results using four different stimulus orientations. Bottom right: A comparison between the time course of voltage-sensitive-dye signal (bold trace) and an intrinsic signal (thin trace). Note the expanded time course relative to A. (Compare the time course shown here with that shown in Figure 1 of Reference 3).

tions (18). In cat visual cortex, when we used a similar strategy to visualize the orientation columns with the fast voltage-sensitive-dye signals, the resulting orientation maps were identical to those obtained with the aid of the slow intrinsic signals.

Increasing the Spatial Resolution of Intrinsic Signal Imaging with a CCD Camera

Gross et al (21, 22), Blasdel & Salama (3) and Kauer (27) have demonstrated in imaging experiments with dyes that standard and economical video techniques may be used to permit higher spatial resolution optical imaging at the expense of time resolution. However, in addition to the poorer time resolution relative to photodiode arrays, a standard video camera also has a poor signal-to-noise ratio, usually no better than 100:1. A slow-scan CCD (charge-coupled device) camera offers improved signal-to-noise ratios (e.g. 1400:1), while retaining the advantages of higher spatial resolution and moderate cost and complexity. We have employed such a CCD camera for the optical imaging at high spatial resolution of the intrinsic signals, where the millisecond time resolution of photodiode arrays is not required (11, 47).

CCD imaging of the intrinsic signals has enabled us to image directly in vivo several of the features of the functional organization of cat and monkey visual areas 17 and 18 (47). In each type of experiment, a separate set of frames from the CCD camera is collected for each of several opponent visual stimulus conditions (e.g. vertical vs. horizontal orientation, left eye vs. right eye, or one eye vs. closed eyes etc.) and the resulting sets of frames are compared. This procedure has revealed the orientation columns in the cat areas 17 and 18 to a higher spatial resolution than possible with the photodiode arrays. Similar success has been obtained in the monkey visual cortex, where the CCD optical imaging has revealed the orientation and ocular dominance columns (Figure 4), the blobs, and the thick and thin stripes (24) of area 18 usually only seen with postmortem cytochrome oxidase histology.

Infrared Imaging of Functional Organization through the Intact Dura

A particularly promising result of studies of the nature and wavelength-dependence of the intrinsic signals, as discussed above, is the ability to optically image cortical activity through the normally opaque dura covering the brain. Because of its penetrating power and reduced absorption by hemoglobin, near infrared light has allowed us to image, using the CCD camera, the orientation columns of the cat and the ocular dominance columns of the monkey through the intact dura. The obtained maps proved to be identical to maps obtained after the dura was removed. This ability to image the function-

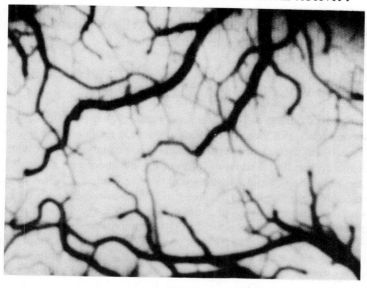

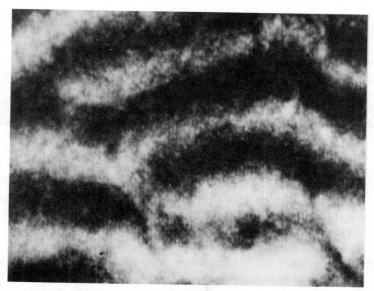

Figure 4   Ocular dominance columns in monkey striate cortex. The frames show an area of 4 × 3 mm. Top: CCD picture of the exposed cortex showing the vasculature of the imaged brain area. The area 17/18 border was 2 mm beyond the left edge of the image. Bottom: The ocular dominance columns, obtained by presenting moving gratings of various orientations to the right and left eye individually, averaging the optically recorded pictures of the exposed cortex for each eye, and subtracting the two sets of frames. This map was confirmed by comparison with cytochrome oxidase histology.

al organization of cortex through the dura (11) will be advantageous for research on awake behaving animal preparations.

COMPARISON OF OPTICAL IMAGING WITH AND WITHOUT VOLTAGE-SENSITIVE DYES

The principal advantage of cortical mapping using voltage-sensitive dyes is its millisecond time resolution, in contrast to the time resolution of the intrinsic signals that is in the order of seconds. This time resolution is important for a detailed understanding of flow of information and its processing at different cortical sites. The trade-off for the good time resolution is a loss in spatial resolution. It is much easier to obtain a good signal-to-noise ratio if signals are slow—a measurement of small slow-signals with a rise-time of a second rather than a millisecond may yield a 33-fold improvement in the signal-to-noise ratio, due to the square root relationship between the number of samples and signal-to-noise ratio (when the measurement is shot noise limited). The spatial resolution of optical imaging of cortex with the current voltage-sensitive dyes is not ultimately limited by the number of pixels of the photodetector or the available computer and instrumentation capabilities, but instead is limited by obtainable signal size and concomitant photodynamic damage. Without a significant improvement in the quality of the present dyes, we estimated that a 64×64 pixel array is close to the usable limit. In addition to the photodynamic damage associated with the dyes upon prolonged or intense illumination, the use of dyes has other difficulties such as bleaching, limited depth of penetration into the cortex, and possible pharmacological side effects. The extent of pharmacological side effects on cortical function has not been carefully evaluated.

Since the imaging of the intrinsic optical signals makes no use of dyes, the technique does not suffer from the possibility of photodynamic damage and extensive averaging can be used to yield much higher spatial resolution. The slow time course of the intrinsic signals further facilitates the use of more economical cameras (e.g. video, CCDs) to achieve higher spatial resolution. Optical imaging with intrinsic signals is less invasive and therefore can be repeated over a long period of time. As we have shown, the imaging of the intrinsic signals may also be performed through the intact dura, a very promising prospect that would probably be quite difficult to implement with dyes. These advantages suggest that optical imaging with intrinsic signals may also have clinical applications.

CONCLUSIONS

Until recently most of the research effort was focused on improvements of the technology and its exploitation in new directions. Nevertheless, the results discussed in the chapters of this section indicate that optical recording has already provided new and previously unobtainable information about the function of the nervous system at various levels from single growth cones or nerve terminals to the living mammalian brain. Furthermore, the technology suitable for visualization of brain activity is immediately applicable to the visualization of other physiological parameters that can be investigated with suitable probes (e.g. Ca^{2+}, pH, neurotransmitters, hormones).

There is a growing perception (or perhaps a naive hope) in brain research that understanding of the complex function of the brain will require simultaneous recordings from many sites. This idea has led to a considerable effort in the design of arrays of extracellular electrodes. We feel that optical imaging and multi-electrode techniques are very complementary and that a combination of the two techniques will form the basis of particularly promising studies in the investigation of brain function.

Several technical difficulties still complicate the use of optical imaging for the study of neuronal activity, but possible solutions have been outlined in previous reviews. Looking beyond these remaining technical issues however, it is clear that new methods to handle and analyze the large amount of data need to be developed, as well as new conceptual frameworks that will aid in the design of experimental paradigms and the interpretation of the resultant data. These needs call for additional multidisciplinary efforts to advance our understanding of the development and organization of the central nervous system and the fascinating strategies it uses for higher brain functions.

ACKNOWLEDGMENTS

We thank Drs. L. Katz, C. D. Gilbert, L. B. Cohen, and T. N. Wiesel for their critical and useful comments. Our work was supported by IBM and grants from the National Institutes of Health (NS 14716), the U.S.-Israel Binational Science Foundation, The U.S. Air Force, Klingenstein Foundation, and Dupont.

Literature Cited

1. Arieli, A., Frostig, R. D., Lieke, E., Hildesheim, R., Grinvald, A. 1987. Cortical correlates of the EEG revealed by real-time optical imaging of neuronal activity in cat cortex. *Soc. Neurosci. Abstr.* 13:52
2. Arieli, A., Grinvald, A. 1988. Dynamic patterns of on-going coherent activity in neuronal assemblies revealed by real-time optical imaging in cat cortex. *Soc. Neurosci. Abstr.* 14:1122
3. Blasdel, G. G., Salama, G. 1986. Voltage-sensitive dyes reveal a modular organization in monkey striate cortex. *Nature* 321:579–85
4. Cattarelli, M., Cohen, L. B. 1986. Optical recording of the piriform cortex electrical activity induced by lateral olfactory tract stimulations in the rat. *Soc. Neurosci. Abstr.* 12:1357
5. Chance, B., Cohen, P., Jobsis, F., Schoener, B. 1962. Intracellular oxidation-reduction states in vivo. *Science* 137:499–508
6. Cohen, L. B. 1973. Changes in neuron structure during action potential propagation and synaptic transmission. *Physiol. Rev.* 53:373–418
7. Cohen, L. B., Lesher, S. 1986. Optical monitoring of membrane potential:

methods of multisite optical measurement. *Opt. Methods Cell Physiol.* 40:71–99

8. Cohen, L. B., Salzberg, B. M., Grinvald, A. 1978. Optical methods for monitoring neuron activity. *Annu. Rev. Neurosci.* 1:171–82

9. Davila, H. V., Salzberg, B. M., Cohen, L. B. 1973. A large change in axon fluorescence that provided a promising method for measuring membrane potential. *Nature New Biol.* 24:159–60

10. Fox, P. T., Mintun, M. A., Raichle, M. E., Miezin, F. M., Allman, J. M., Van Essen, D. C. 1986. Mapping human visual cortex with positron emission tomography. *Nature* 323:806–9

11. Frostig, R. D., Lieke, E. E., Ts'o, D. Y., Grinvald, A. 1988. Infra-red imaging of functional organization of visual cortex through the intact dura using a CCD camera. *Soc. Neurosci. Abstr.* 14:897

12. Gilbert, C. D., Wiesel, T. N. 1983. Clustered intrinsic connections in cat visual cortex. *J. Neurosci.* 3:1116–33

13. Grinvald, A. 1984. Real time optical imaging of neuronal activity: from single growth cones to the intact brain. *Trends Neurosci.* 7:143–50

14. Grinvald, A. 1985. Real-time optical mapping of neuronal activity: from single growth cones to the intact mammalian brain. *Annu. Rev. Neurosci.* 8:263–305

15. Grinvald, A., Anglister, L., Freeman, J. A., Hildesheim, R., Manker, A. 1984. Real time optical imaging of naturally evoked electrical activity in the intact frog brain. *Nature* 308:848–50

16. Grinvald, A., Cohen, L. B., Lesher, S., Boyle, M. B. 1981. Simultaneous optical monitoring of activity of many neurons in invertebrate ganglia, using a 124 element 'Photodiode' array. *J. Neurophysiol.* 45:829–40

17. Grinvald, A., Frostig, R. D., Lieke, E., Hildesheim, R. 1988. Optical imaging of neuronal activity. *Physiol. Rev.* 68:1285–365

18. Grinvald, A., Lieke, E., Frostig, R. D., Gilbert, C. D., Wiesel, T. N. 1986. Functional architecture of cortex revealed by optical imaging of intrinsic signals. *Nature* 324:361–64

19. Grinvald, A., Manker, A., Segal, M. 1982. Visualization of the spread of electrical activity in rat hippocampal slices by voltage sensitive optical probes. *J. Physiol.* 333:269–91

20. Grinvald, A., Segal, M., Kuhnt, U., Hildesheim, R., Manker, A., et al.

1986. Real-time optical mapping of neuronal activity in vertebrate CNS in-vitro and in vivo. *Opt. Methods Cell Physiol.* 40:165–97

21. Gross, D., Loew, L. M., Webb, W. W. 1985. Spatially resolved optical measurement of membrane potential distribution in single cells. *Biophys. J.* 47:270a

22. Gross, D., Loew, L. M., Webb, W. W. 1986. Optical imaging of cell membrane potential changes induced by applied electric fields. *Biophys. J.* 50:339–48

23. Hill, D. K., Keynes, R. D. 1949. Opacity changes in stimulated nerve. *J. Physiol.* 108:278–81

24. Hubel, D. H., Livingstone, M. S. 1987. Segregation of form, color and stereopsis in primate area 18. *J. Neurosci.* 7:3378–415

25. Hubel, D. H., Wiesel, T. N. 1962. Receptive fields, binocular interactions and functional architecture in the cat's visual cortex. *J. Physiol.* 160:106–54

26. Jobsis, F. F., Keizer, J. H., LaManna, J. C., Rosental, M. J. 1977. Reflectance spectrophotometry of cytochrome aa₃ in vivo. *J. Appl. Physiol.: Respirat. Environ. Exercise Physiol.* 43:858–72

27. Kauer, J. S. 1988. Real-time imaging of evoked activity in local circuits of the salamander olfactory bulb. *Nature* 331:166–68

28. Kauer, J. S., Senseman, D. M., Cohen, L. B. 1987. Order-elicited activity monitored simultaneously from 124 regions of the salamander olfactory bulb using voltage-sensitive dye. *Brain Res.* 418:255–61

29. Kelin, D. 1925. On cytochrome, a respiratory pigment, common to animals, yeast, and higher plants. *Proc. R. Soc. London Ser. B* 98:312–39

30. Kim, J. H., Dunn, M. B., Ebner, T. J. 1987. Use of voltage sensitive dyes to image spatial patterns of cerebellar neuronal activity. *Soc. Neurosci. Abstr.* 13:228

31. Konnerth, A., Orkand, R. K. 1986. Voltage sensitive dyes measure potential changes in axons and glia of frog optic nerve. *Neurosci. Lett.* 66:49–54

32. Konnerth, A., Obaid, A. L., Salzberg, B. M. 1987. Optical recording of electrical activity from parallel fibers and other cell types in skate cerebellar slices in vitro. *J. Physiol.* 393:681–702

33. Lev-Ram, V., Grinvald, A. 1986. Ca²⁺ and K⁺-dependent communication between central nervous system myelinated axons and oligodendrocytes revealed by voltage-sensitive dyes. *Proc. Natl. Acad. Sci. USA* 83:6651–55

34. Lieke, E. E., Frostig, R. D., Ratzlaff, E. H., Grinvald, A. 1988. Center/surround inhibitory interaction in macaque V1 revealed by real time imaging *Soc. Neurosci. Abstr.* 14:1122

35. Loew, L. M. 1988. How to choose a potentiometric membrane probe. In *Spectroscopic Membrane Probes,* ed. L. M. Loew, 2:139–52. Boca Raton, Fla.: CRC

36. London, J. A., Wu, J.-Y., Rioult, M., Cattarelli, M., Cohen, L. B. 1987. The spread of epileptiform discharges in rat somatosensory cortex measured with a voltage sensitive dye. *Soc. Neurosci. Abstr.* 13:365

37. Mayevsky, A., Chance, B. 1982. Intracellular oxidation-reduction state measured in situ by a multichannel fiberoptic surface fluorometer. *Science* 217:537–40

38. Millikan, G. A. 1937. Experiments on muscle hemoglobin in vivo; the instantaneous measurement of muscle metabolism. *Proc. R. Soc. London Ser. B* 123:218–41

39. Orbach, H. S. 1987. Monitoring electrical activity in rat cerebral cortex. See Ref. 35, 3:115–35

40. Orbach, H. S., Cohen, L. B. 1983. Simultaneous optical monitoring of activity from many areas of the salamander olfactory bulb. A new method for studying functional organization in the vertebrate CNS. *J. Neurosci.* 3:2251–62

41. Orbach, H. S., Cohen, L. B., Grinvald, A. 1985. Optical mapping of electrical activity in rat somatosensory and visual cortex. *J. Neurosci.* 5:1886–95

42. Orbach, H. S., Van Essen, D. C. 1987. Pathway tracing in vivo: projection foci in rat extrastriate cortex using voltage sensitive dyes. *ARVO Abstr.* 28:197

42a. Orbach, H. S., Fellman, D. J., Van Essen, D. C. 1988. Pathway tracing in primate visual cortex using voltage sensitive dyes. *Soc. Neurosci. Abstr.* 14:898

43. Ross, W. N., Reichardt, L. F. 1979. Species-specific effects on the optical signals of voltage sensitive dyes. *J. Membr. Biol.* 48:343–56

44. Salzberg, B. M. 1983. Optical recording of electrical activity in neurons using molecular probes. In *Current Methods in Cellular Neurobiology,* ed. J. Barker, J. McKelvy, pp. 139–87. New York: Wiley

45. Salzberg, B. M., Obaid, A. L., Gainer, H. 1985. Large and rapid changes in light scattering accompany secretion by nerve terminals in the mammalian neurohypophysis. *J. Gen. Physiol.* 86:395–411

46. Tasaki, I., Warashina, A. 1976. Dye membrane interaction and its changes during nerve excitation. *Photochem. Photobiol.* 24:191–207

47. Ts'o, D. Y., Frostig, R. D., Lieke, E. E., Grinvald, A. 1988. Functional organization of visual area 18 of macaque as revealed by optical imaging of activity-dependent intrinsic signals. *Soc. Neurosci. Abstr.* 14:898

48. Waggoner, A. S. 1979. Dye indicators of membrane potential. *Annu. Rev. Biophys. Bioeng.* 8:47–63

49. Waggoner, A. S., Grinvald, A. 1977. Mechanisms of rapid optical changes of potential sensitive dyes. *Ann. NY Acad. Sci.* 303:217–42

Annu. Rev. Physiol. 1989. 51:561–81

VISUALIZATION OF NEURONAL ACTIVITY IN MONKEY STRIATE CORTEX

Gary G. Blasdel

Department of Neurobiology, Harvard Medical School, 220 Longwood Avenue, Boston, Massachusetts 02115

INTRODUCTION

The greatest recent success at describing the functional anatomy of one neocortical area was achieved by Hubel & Wiesel (11) whose work on primary visual (striate) cortex has provided tantalizing information about the topographical organization of two response properties, ocular dominance and orientation selectivity. The first of these is associated with depth perception and refers to the response preference that a neuron shows for one eye or the other. The second property, orientation selectivity, relates to contour detection and refers to the preference that a neuron shows for edges at particular orientations. Hubel & Wiesel's work has established that both properties remain constant with depth, yet vary systematically with lateral displacement. For ocular dominance this variation arises from the interdigitation of two sets of slabs, each about 0.5 mm wide, and each containing neurons dominated by one eye or the other. For orientational preference this variation occurs continuously; lateral movements through cortex produce regular and predictable shifts (or rotations) in preferred orientation. At intervals however, that correspond roughly (and curiously) to the widths of ocular dominance slabs, there are sudden jumps in preferred orientation or reversals in the direction of change that disrupt the continuity.

Given the obvious importance that lateral arrangements play in the ordering of cortical information, one naturally wonders whether or not there might be a convenient way of studying them—a technique that possibly would allow the direct visualization of responses in cortex to different visual stimuli. The

561

0066-4278/89/0315-0561$02.00

mapping of multi-unit activity, with microelectrodes, offered an early solution. However this approach proved far too time consuming and traumatic to sample more than a few points in one piece of tissue, and consequently hasn't found much use in studies of large cortical areas. Metabolic mapping, using radioactive sugars like 2-deoxyglucose (18, 25), offers better spatial resolution but has no temporal resolution and, worse, can only be used once—a limitation that makes it impossible, for example, to compare responses in one piece of tissue to different stimuli or even to do a control.

In an abstract sense then, it might be said that all of these approaches (such as multi-unit recording, metabolic mapping) have as their logical and common intent the conversion of cortical response patterns to visual images. They differ only in their strategies for accomplishing this, as well, perhaps, as in the number of steps involved. A method that achieves this conversion directly, one where the activity over a wide area of cortex can be visualized directly as it occurs (with film or a TV, for example), would be an obvious improvement.

The first suggestion that such an approach might indeed work came from Cohen et al (6, 7) who showed that some aspects of neuronal activity are accompanied by changes in birefringence and light scattering. Later it became clear that larger optical signals could be obtained from certain impermeant, membrane bound, optical probes of membrane potential (voltage sensitive dyes)—the first highly successful example being merocyanin 540 (8)—if these dyes were first used to stain the tissue. Although the dyes used initially suffered from low signal noise ratios and high toxicity, their technology has improved steadily (8, 9) and current, state-of-the-art probes offer spatial and temporal resolutions as good as the imaging devices used to monitor them.

The technologies and histories of various strategies for mapping optical activity are already covered in other chapters in this section. Accordingly I will concentrate on video imaging strategies that I developed in conjunction with Guy Salama three years ago at the University of Pittsburgh and that we used successfully (and for the first time) to map activity patterns generated by specific visual stimuli in monkey striate cortex (4).

METHODS

Macaque monkeys are virtually unique among experimental animals in that their exquisitely well organized striate cortex lies conveniently (for optical studies at least) at the back of the head. Hence, in order to view a large area, one has only to remove the overlying bone and dura. This is accomplished with a one-inch diameter trephine, applied to the cranium just behind the lunate sulcus and just lateral to the midline, after the animal has been anesthetized and prepared according to established procedures (2). A stainless steel chamber, equipped with a glass window to stabilize cortical pulsations, and inlet and outlet tubes to allow the introduction and elimination of dye solution is then cemented to the skull (see Figure 1).

All experiments begin with conventional electrophysiological recordings, (*a*) to ensure that cortical cells are healthy (that is, expressing normal response properties), and (*b*) to document some instances of these properties (e.g.

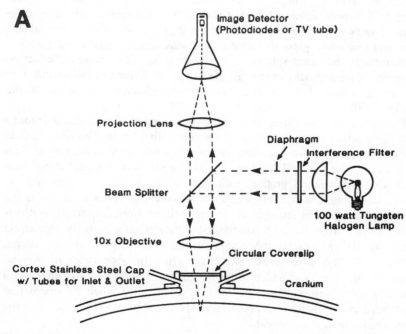

Figure 1 Experimental arrangement for monitoring voltage-sensitive dyes in monkey striate cortex. A hole (25 mm in diameter) was cut in the cranium, a stainless steel ring cemented to the skull, and the dura removed. The ring had stainless steel inlet and outlet tubes to bathe the cortical surface with dye solution (0.1% in balanced salt solution). A second ring containing a round glass coverslip was screwed into the first ring to form a watertight compartment. The position of the glass could be adjusted to dampen cortical pulsations and provide an optically smooth window for viewing the cortex. A condenser lens collimated light from a 100 Watt tungsten halogen lamp and directed it through an interference filter (720 nm +/− 20 nm, Omega Optical, Brattleboro, Vermont), an aperture, and then to the reflective surface of a beam splitter. Reflected light passed through an objective lens and glass coverslip onto the cortical surface. Reflected and scattered light from the cortex passed back through the coverslip, to the objective lens and through a projection lens, to the image detector (photodiodes or the TV camera). The averaged response of one photodiode appears in Figure 2. (4).

orientation selectivity and ocular dominance) for comparison with the optical images of neuronal activity that are obtained subsequently. During these recordings the eyes are aligned with the center of the video monitor used to provide visual stimulation, and after their completion an optical microscope is positioned over the animal's head. A schematic diagram of this apparatus appears in Figure 1. Light from a tungsten halogen lamp passes through a collimator, interference filter, and beam splitter (in some cases a small off-set mirror that blocks only a small portion of the optical path), which deflects light through a protective window onto the cortical surface. The light penetrates cortex, which is surprisingly transparent at longer wavelengths, for some distance before it is absorbed or dispersed. Some of it returns, however, over an indeterminant depth, back through the cortical surface and protective glass to the objective lens which collects and passes it back through the beam splitter to a projection lens that images it either on an array of photodiodes or (for all the images described in this chapter) on the image sensing element of a Newvicon-based television camera (Cohu model 5300).

Figure 2 shows the temporal dynamics of an optical signal obtained from a 100 μm patch of cortex as it responds to visual stimulation. The wavy trace at the top depicts the averaged response to ten trials, each consisting of 1) a two-second blank period followed by 2) two seconds of visual stimulation with a drifting vertical grating, followed by 3) two seconds of stimulation with a horizontal grating, followed by 4) two seconds of blank screen. In the middle trace one can see optical signals deriving from respiratory and cardiovascular activity that also contributed to the optical signal. By subtracting these signals one obtains the bottom trace, which depicts visually driven activity. A short while (150–200 msec) after the appearance of vertical contours one sees 1) a sudden inflection followed by 2) a steady increase in absorbance as these contours move, 3) a small glitch when the orientation switches from vertical to horizontal, and 4) a decay back to baseline when the horizontal contours disappear.

Since the signals persist for several seconds, they are likely to derive, at least in part, from sources intrinsic to cortex, ones most likely developing from the dilation of capillary beds. But these intrinsic signals are slow, usually on the order of several seconds (10), and therefore, the short latency onset in Figure 2, along with the sharp inflections (reflecting high frequency signal components) suggest that parts at least derive from the faster responding optical probe (merocyanine oxazalone of NK2367) that has been added. The situation is complicated and open to endless argument (10). The important thing to recognize, though, is that regardless of mechanism these signals correlate overwhelmingly (as shown below) with every electrophysiological and anatomical analysis used to verify them. And accordingly, they

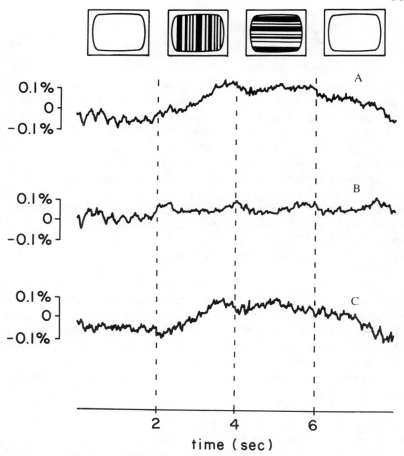

Figure 2 (*a*) Averaged response to ten successive presentations of vertical and horizontal gratings, as seen by one photodiode that surveyed a 100 μm patch of cortex. Because visual stimuli were presented in synchrony with cardiovascular and respiratory events, the latter contribute a prominent signal to this trace, one that can be isolated rather easily by averaging while the animal views a blank screen (*b*) and subtracted from the original signal in (*a*) to reveal those components developing specifically in response to visual stimulation (*c*). By using this approach (23), one sees that there is sudden increase in the absorption for this part of cortex that corresponds temporally to the onset of a drifting vertical grating. A small glitch appears where the grating changes from vertical to horizontal, and the trace returns to baseline again when the horizontal grating fades back into a blank screen. The increase in absorption, though separated by a notch that occurs both in response to vertical and to horizontal, suggests separate responses by separate regions of cortex (monitored by the same photodiode), as opposed to a general response by one region, since in the latter case there is no reason why the signal should falter between the presentation of vertical and horizontal. The relatively large signal size, as well as the long duration for which it could be maintained, suggested the possibility of using a TV camera to achieve greater spatial resolution.

provide a direct means of visualizing cortical activity patterns, one with obvious usefulness.

Video Imaging Technology

Up until a few years ago television cameras had been considered several times, as a means of monitoring optical signals, and each time dismissed. Their most obvious limitation is that they are slow, taking approximately 30 msec per frame, which falls well outside the time span of most neuronal events (action potentials) that typically occur within a msec or less. Worse, most TV's have a limited dynamic range, usually 200 or less, which means they are incapable of detecting even a relatively large 0.1% change in radiance. And even if the camera could be improved, the A/D convertors on most commercially available digitizers have only 8 bits (256 grey levels) that certainly are incapable, in their simplest implementation, of detecting signals smaller than 0.25%.

In retrospect it should be pointed out that most TV cameras are still too slow to monitor action potentials. But one has an advantage in studies of striate cortex since many of the current, burning issues—the organization of iso-orientation bands, their relationship to ocular dominance—can be re-solved with static imaging. In other words, the 30 msecs or more that it takes a TV camera to scan an image is not a problem. In fact, since cortical activity patterns can be sustained for many seconds, one can degrade the temporal resolution even further (by averaging frames) to improve the signal-noise ratio. And because the spatial resolution of most TV cameras is frankly much greater than necessary, the signal-noise ratio can be enhanced even further through lateral averaging.

The camera that we used initially (Cohu model 5300) boasted an un-characteristically high dynamic range of 60dB (signal/noise of 1000). By collecting 900 frames (at a 60Hz frame rate and horizontal vertical resolution of 512/240), and averaging laterally the 8 pixels in each 4 by 2 square (approximately square due to the 4:3 aspect ratio for horizontal and vertical), we obtained 7200 effective samples for each point on a 128 by 120 grid. Since the contribution from normally distributed noise decreases as the square root of the sample size there is a theoretical 80-fold improvement in dynamic range that can be achieved in this fashion. In actual practice however the improve-ment (as determined with the calibrated emissions of a red light emitting diode [LED]) was less, usually not more than tenfold. Still, a dynamic range of 10,000 is more than enough to detect the 0.1% signals that we know can be obtained from monkey striate cortex. (see Figure 7).

It might be added, in passing, that the digitization problem, alluded to above, resolves itself when averaging is employed to remove noise. In the absence of noise, signals smaller than the digitization steps do not register, no matter how many samples are averaged. But if there is enough noise to jostle the least significant bit, the probability of this happening is modulated by the subthreshold signals which, if consistent from trial to trial, are retained in the average, even as the noise that enabled their capture is removed—a process referred to as dithering in the jargon of electrical engineers.

One major difficulty with this system, which should not be underestimated, concerns calibration. Due to the number of concatenated, nonlinear steps in the digitization of each image, and the often unpredictable ways in which they interact, gain is difficult to judge. In practice, therefore, when it is important to document signal size accurately, it usually makes more sense to measure it directly with a photodiode inserted into one image plane of the microscope.

Cortical Staining

As noted earlier, the mechanisms responsible for the optical signals monitored from cortex are far from clear and probably derive from many factors. Dyes that give good signals in simple neuronal preparations appear not to work well in cortex (L. B. Cohen, personal communication). In some cases, dyes that perform poorly in simple preparations work much better. At least one reason for this appears to be the correlation between dye performance and the tightness of membrane binding. Dyes giving the best optical signals also bind membranes tightly and this makes it hard for them to penetrate the pia, a watertight and largely unremovable barrier that protects the cortex. Less remarkable dyes, on the other hand, which have a lower affinity for cell membranes, pass through more easily.

Merocyanine oxazalone, the dye used in these studies, was applied in a saline solution at a concentration of approximately 0.1% for one hour before being rinsed away. From the top pair of images in Figure 3, both of which were obtained at 540 nm, one sees little difference before and after staining. The blood vessels are darker than cortex in either case. But at 680 nm the staining is obvious; cortex looks darker after staining than before, to such an extent that the contrast with the vasculature reverses, an event that suggests dye penetration beyond the most superficial laminae.

At longer wavelengths (700 and 720 nm) the contrast between cortex and vasculature becomes less pronounced, weakening to the point where it virtually disappears at 720 nm (the wavelength used to monitor optical signals). Accordingly, even if the staining with this dye made no voltage dependent contribution to the optical signals, it still makes a cosmetic one by decreasing the contrast between cortex and the overlying vasculature, an effect that greatly diminishes the magnitude of the artifacts produced when vessels constrict and dilate in a manner that cannot be controlled or predicted.

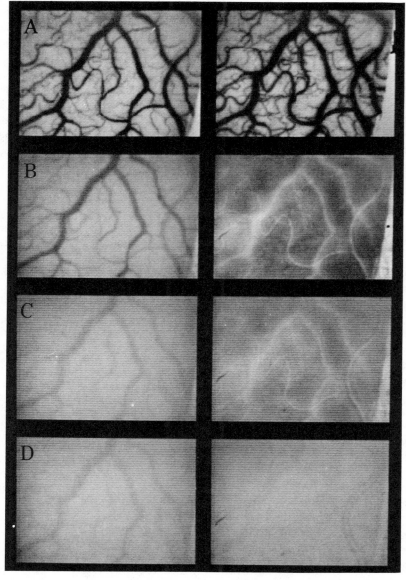

Figure 3 In A, B, C, and D image pairs of cortex as it appears *(left)* before and *(right)* after staining, under monochromatic illumination at wavelengths of 540, 680, 700, and 720 nm, respectively. From D, it is apparent that one incidental consequence of cortical staining with NK2367 is the near elimination of contrast between the vasculature and the underlying cortex, a cosmetic effect that greatly diminishes the severity of vascularly induced artifacts.

Noise Sources

In Figure 4A one sees an image of striate cortex as it appeared to the optical system under white (broad band) illumination. Since the optical system has a relatively high numerical aperture (0.2) and is focused 200–300 μm beneath

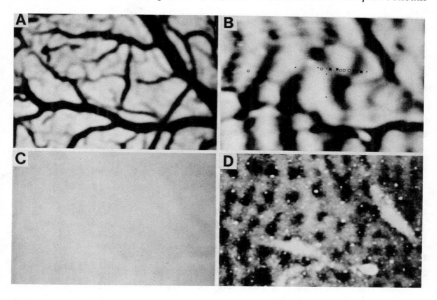

Figure 4 (*a*) Cortical blood vessels viewed under white light. They appear out of focus because the optical system was focused 300 μm below the pial surface. This patch of cortex was located just behind the lunate sulcus in the right hemisphere. Posterior, anterior, medial, and lateral correspond to the top, bottom, right and left of the image frame respectively. The border between areas 17 and 18 lies parallel to and just below the lower border of this frame. The height and width of this image corresponds to a 4 × 5 mm patch of cortex. (*b*) The familiar pattern of ocular dominance bands is produced by subtracting images accumulated during visual stimulation of the contralateral eye from images accumulated during stimulation of the ipsilateral eye (all orientations). This produces an intensity difference of 0.2% between the dark and light bands. The bands have an average width of 0.5 mm, run vertically into the border between areas 17 and 18, and correspond to the rows of cytochrome oxidase blobs, which appear in (*d*). The spots in (*b*) illustrate the location of 16 electrode penetrations conducted in this region of cortex before and after studies were conducted with voltage sensitive dyes. The small black dots indicate sites that yielded binocular responses, open squares indicate sites dominated by the contralateral eye, and closed squares indicate sites dominated by the ipsilateral eye. In agreement with the photodiode results, the correspondence between the dark bands and the closed squares indicates that stained cortical tissue darkens with increased electrical activity (see text). (*c*) The result of subtracting two time averaged images while the monkey viewed a blank grey screen. The same algorithm was used as in (*b*). (*d*) At the end of the experiment, the same piece of cortex was sectioned tangentially and stained for cytochrome oxidase. The section shown here was aligned and expanded (necessary on account of tissue shrinkage) according to the positions of blood vessels so that they laid in register with the images in (*a*)–(*c*). Note that during examination of the histological preparations, no evidence was found of tissue damage attributable to repeated applications of the dye over more than 8 weeks. (4).

the cortical surface, blood vessels lying above the surface appear fuzzy. In Figure 4C, after the cortex has been stained, one sees the result of subtracting two images, each derived from the average of 900 frames obtained separately while the monkey looked at a blank grey screen. This is a control image that indicates the amount of noise inherent to this system while the cortex is presumed to be inactive.

Three of the most important noise sources are (a) the camera system, computer and associated electronics, (b) background discharges from cortical cells, and (c) the vasculature, which, in its homeostatic efforts to service the cortex, adjusts its perfusion in a manner that isn't always predictable. Of the three, the electronic noise is dealt with most easily. It can be minimized from the start through the careful selection of optimal components and residual elements can generally be removed through averaging. Neuronal noise, deriving from the background discharges known to characterize cortical cells, presents less of a problem in stimulated, as opposed to idle, cortex, and its contribution also yields to averaging.

Vascular noise, however, presents a more difficult problem. While the regular components (e.g. those deriving from heartbeat and respiratory activity) can be measured independently (23) while the cortex is inactive (or, better, performing some unrelated or complimentary task) and subtracted, there are many irregular and unpredictable components that cannot. And if too long a time intervenes between the visual presentation of two stimuli whose cortical effects are to be compared, the artifacts become difficult to remove. The only recourse one has therefore is to narrow the time between successive stimulus presentations while minimizing less predictable elements, for example, by ensuring that the animal remains stably anesthetized. While interstimulus intervals are limited at the short end by intrinsic, optical correlates of neuronal activity (10) (which can persist for as long as 10–15 sec) one can optimize other parameters to the point where vascular noise only presents a problem in those regions covered by the largest vessels, ones larger than 0.5–1.0 mm in diameter.

Ocular Dominance

Figure 4B shows the pattern of cortical activity that develops when the two eyes are stimulated alternately with high contrast, multi-frequency, square wave gratings, at all orientations. This image was produced by subtracting one cortical image, obtained during stimulation of the left eye, from one obtained during stimulation of the right. The dark and light bands correspond to cortical regions dominated by the right and left eyes. The correspondence between these bands and those described initially by Hubel & Wiesel (15, 16, 21) can be verified in many ways. They are about the same width (0.2–0.5 mm) and shape, and they also run perpendicularly into the border of

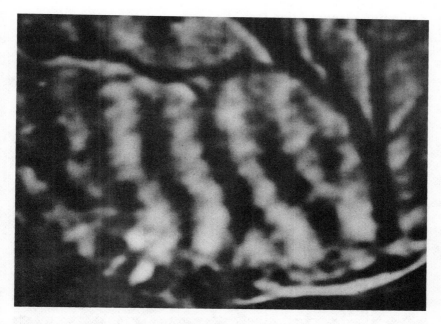

Figure 5   As noted in the legend to Figure 4B, as well as in the text, one indication that the bands in Figure 4B derive from alterations in ocular dominance, like those observed initially by Hubel & Wiesel (15), is the observation that they run perpendicularly into the border between areas 17 and 18 (21). Under the lower power magnification of this image, where the horizontal frame width corresponds to 8 mm, one can see this directly.

striate cortex [located parallel to and below the bottom of the frame in Figure 4 (see Figure 5)]—something that ocular dominance bands are known to do (21).

But the identity of these bands may also be checked directly, with electrodes. The results of 16 electrode penetrations, made in the same patch of cortex, are indicated in Figure 4B. Filled and open squares indicate dominance by the right and left eyes respectively, and correspond to the dark and light bands in the image. On the other hand, the dots, which indicate balanced binocular responses, aggregate at the boundaries between them.

As a final test one can check the correspondence between bands in 4B and the cytochrome oxidase blobs that are known to populate the centers of ocular dominance bands (11, 19, 22, 25). By retrieving the patch of cortex imaged in Figure 4, sectioning it tangentially, and reacting the most superficial sections to reveal the presence of cytochrome oxidase, a mitochondrial enzyme, one can identify blobs in the same piece of tissue. Comparing Figures 4B and 4D one can see that they correspond to the centers of both the light and the dark bands in Figure 4B.

Retinoptic Organization

While it is clear from the visualization of ocular dominance bands in living cortex that this approach works (especially to vision neurobiologists who have fantasized about these structures for years), the point can be made less abstractly by exploiting the fuzzy retinotopic organization that has been known to characterize striate cortex since the early 1900s, and showing how images that the animal sees appear on the cortical surface.

Figures 6A and B show the activity dependent patterns that were generated in a 13 × 9 mm patch of cortex by the movement of three slits oriented either

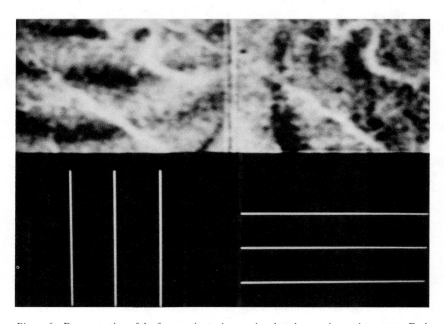

Figure 6   Demonstration of the fuzzy retinotopic mapping that characterizes striate cortex. Each of these images was obtained from a low power image of cortex where the horizontal frame width corresponded to 13 mm. After single units recorded from the central region had been used to align receptive fields for the two eyes with the center of a video monitor used to present visual stimuli, three jiggling lines were presented at either a vertical *(left)* or a horizontal *(right)* orientation. Video images of cortex were then averaged while the animal viewed these stimuli, and control images that were obtained while the animal viewed a blank grey screen, were subtracted to yield the two images in this figure. On the left three clear horizontal bands of active cortex lie parallel to the 17–18 border (which corresponds to the vertical meridian in visual space) while vertically projecting traces generated by the presentation of horizontal lines are clearly evident on the right. The visual stimuli used to generate these images appear below. The fuzziness of the bands in these images results in part from the fact that each point in visual space subtends a lateral distance of approximately 2 mm in cortex; but also from the fact that the thin lines moved back and forth over a distance corresponding to 20% of the interline separation.

horizontally or vertically in the visual field. Since the boundary of striate cortex (which represents the vertical meridian) lies parallel to, and just below, the bottom of each frame, the three dark stripes that develop in response to vertical stimulation are horizontal while the bands that develop in response to horizontal lines are vertical.

Orientation and Its Organization

While the demonstrations in Figures 4, 5 and 6 promote confidence in this approach, they reveal little new information. Ocular dominance bands have been known for years and the generally retinotopic layout of striate cortex has been appreciated even longer. And since the value of any new approach lies more in its ability to reveal something new, it seems worthwhile mentioning at least one of the new insights that the optical monitoring of cortical activity has made possible.

Returning to the patch of cortex shown in Figure 4, one can see the activity patterns generated by oriented contours presented to both eyes at four different orientations in Figure 7. For each of the four frames in this figure positive and negative images were accumulated during the presentation of contours at one orientation and its orthogonal (vertical and horizontal, for example), and subtracted. Accordingly, positive (dark) values in this image indicate a preference for the primary orientation while negative (light) values indicate a preference for the orthogonal orientation. Intermediate values indicate less or no preference. The white squares correspond to the 16 electrode recording sites discussed earlier. Where the preferred orientation lay within 22 degrees of the primary orientation, the square is outlined in black. The tendency for all such squares to lie within (or near) the centers of the darkest zones reveals a correspondence that is about as good as one can expect, given the range (usually on the order of 30–60 degrees) over which most cortical cells respond, as well as the fact that there are only four alternatives for comparison.

The images in Figure 7, though, provide little insight into the distribution of orientation preferences across the cortical surface, and the sampling of more activity patterns for orientations at closer intervals, (Figure 8) only makes the situation worse. Even though these patterns collectively contain all the information that one might need to define orientation selectivity at every location, it still isn't obvious how they interrelate. Each image tells a lot about the responses of different regions to one orientation (or its orthogonal) but nothing about the responses of any one region to different orientations. This information would be inadequate even in the case of microelectrode recordings if, for example, one knew only the activity of a single unit responding to one orientation. In order to judge orientation selectivity, the responses of one

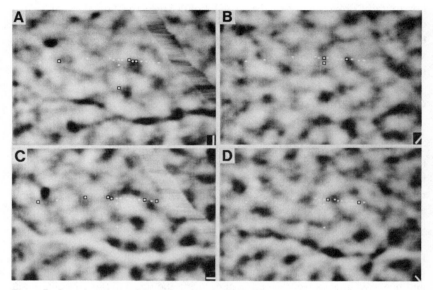

Figure 7 Iso-orientation activity patterns produced by four separate orientations, vertical, right oblique, horizontal, and left oblique. Each image was compiled separately and related to a reference image generated by the orthogonal orientation. This subtraction was necessary to minimize the effects of activity-dependent hyperemia. For example, images of cortex taken during presentations of horizontal were subtracted from images taken during presentations of vertical to produce the pattern in A. The observation that vertical and horizontal patterns shown in A and C are complementary underscores the consistency of the result. White dots indicate the positions of electrode recording sites. Those outlined in black denote locations where sampled cells preferred orientations within 22.5 degrees of the one presented. These correlate with the darker parts of each image and never overlap with the lighter ones. Major blood vessels, which sometimes produce shadows caused by uncontrollable dilation during image acquisition, have been blocked out to prevent unwanted influences on adjacent regions of the same image during subsequent normalization and image processing.

cell, or cortical region must be compared for different orientations, and the separate images in Figure 7 do not facilitate such a comparison.

While there are, in principle, many ways to approach this problem, we (4) chose one that entailed conversion of the response patterns to vector fields, which then could be added. Each vector field was created by normalizing one activity pattern (so that maximal and minimal responses were equivalent), and transforming scaler values at every location into vectors, with magnitude (r) given by intensity and angle (θ) given by twice the angle of the oriented contours used to generate the pattern. Since each image consists of positive and negative values (signifying responses to one orientation and its orthogonal) the resulting vector field consists of positive and negative vectors as well, all with the same angle. It is possible, though, to think of negative

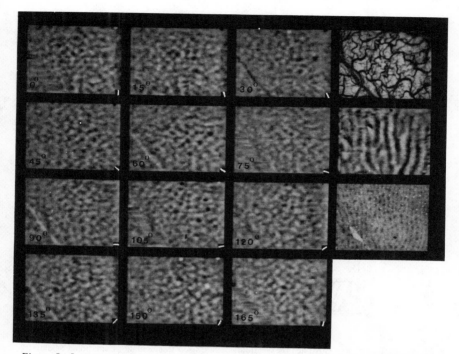

Figure 8 Low power activity patterns in striate cortex. The horizontal width of each frame corresponds to 8 mm on the cortical surface, and the lower border lies parallel to the boundary between cortical areas 17 and 18. At the top of the right hand column one sees the vascular pattern that lies over this part of cortex, as it appeared under white light. Suggestions (10) that this vasculature is somehow responsible for the optical patterns seen by Blasdel & Salama (4) are easily countered by comparing this image with that appearing below, where the ocular dominance bands have been visualized in the same part of cortex. As one can deduce from these two images, vascular events (at least in the case of the smaller vessels) play little or no role; light at 720 nm actually allows one to see through the smaller vessels. And from the image at the bottom of this column, which depicts the pattern of cytochrome oxidase blobs in the same tissue, one knows that the ocular dominance bands are genuine. The twelve images in the three columns on the left depict activity patterns generated by contours moving bidirectionally at 12 different orientations (indicated on the lower left and right of each image, respectively, in degrees and by the tilt of a short bar—that is, in increments of 15 degrees). Note the difficulty one has in making comparisons among these images.

vectors as positive ones rotated through 180 degrees. The general scheme is illustrated in Figure 9.

One should note that the orientation of the bidirectionally moving contours (used as visual stimuli) undergoes a complete cycle when rotated through 180 degrees, which means that this angle (of stimulus presentation) must be doubled so that it corresponds to standard polar vectors, which undergo a

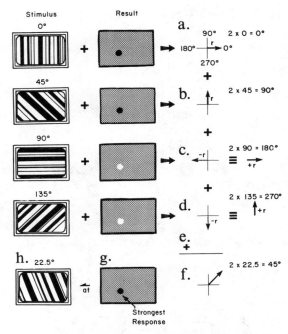

Figure 9 This figure illustrates the vectoral method used to calculate orientational selectivity and preference for each part of the video field. These operations are illustrated, for simplicity, with a single point; however, the operation is easily extended to all the points in any given image. The inputs for this operation consist of multiple, separate, iso-orientation patterns (see Figure 8), each resulting from the difference in activity generated by the presentation of contours at one orientation and its orthogonal. For each image the cortical regions preferring the primary orientation appear darker than average, while those preferring the orthogonal orientation appear lighter than average. The darker or lighter the region, the stronger the preference. Intermediate levels, on the other hand, indicate no preference, meaning that the region either didn't respond, or else that it responded equally to both orientations. The angle of the primary orientation is doubled and combined with the response intensity at the indicated point to yield a vector (a, b, c, d). This means that for one input image, even though vector magnitudes may vary, the vectors all have the same orientation. As indicated for the bottom two conversions (c, d), a negative magnitude corresponds formally to a rotation through 180 degrees. Note that this conversion has the desirable feature of producing a 180 degree phase shift for vectors deriving from othogonal orientations, which, if their magnitudes are equal, should cancel. After the intensity values for all the images have been converted into this format, the vectors are added (e) to yield a new vector (f) whose orientation corresponds to twice the orientation preference (h) for one bit of cortex, and whose magnitude (g) indicates selectivity.

complete cycle when rotated through 360 degrees. In addition, pixel input values (where each pixel can have positive or negative values, to encode respectively the responses to one orientation or its orthogonal) equate positive and negative responses with a rotation through 90 degrees, and when this angle is doubled the format becomes equivalent to the vectoral one (where negative values correspond to positive ones rotated through 180 degrees).

Once the vector conversion has been accomplished, the resulting fields are summed to produce an output field with many different sized vectors at different orientations. Since the input field contained equal contributions from several (usually 8 or 12) opposing orientations, an equivalent sized input vector for each orientation at one location in the field—an event that denotes equivalent responses—produces an output sum of zero, in which case there is no selectivity for orientation. A large positive value for one input vector, on the other hand, coupled with a large negative value for its opposite, and minimal values for all the others—a situation that corresponds to maximal selectivity for one orientation—sums to produce an output vector of maximal magnitude whose orientation now corresponds to twice the angle of orientation preference. In short, the magnitude of each vector in the output field reflects orientational selectivity (or tuning) while the angle corresponds to twice the preferred orientation.

Once the vector fields have been summed the result can be displayed in several ways, either in polar coordinates where images of magnitude and angle components, (Figures 10A and B) reveal distributions of orientation selectivity (tuning) and preference, or in Cartesian coordinates (Figure 10A, B), where the X and Y components of each vector correspond to components correlated with contours at $0°(0°/2)$ and $45°$ $(90°/2)$ respectively. Positive (dark) and negative (light) values in 10A, indicate preferences for vertical and horizontal. Since this is the format of the original input data (the only difference being that the values in Figures 11A and B derive from 12 times as many samples, at different orientations) it should be possible to compare the images in Figures 11A and 11B with the initial input values that were actually achieved with paired contours at vertical and horizontal as well as at left and right oblique (Figures 11C and 11D, which also appear in Figure 8). From Figures 11E and F, where the transition points in Figures 11A and B are indicated by white lines to facilitate comparison, one can see that the patterns do indeed correspond to one another, the major difference being a substantially greater and less noisy signal in Figures 11A and B—a logical consequence of the greater number of samples.

In conclusion then, one can say (with some confidence at this point) that optical approaches to the monitoring of neuronal activity are feasible, and that one can use currently available (and relatively inexpensive) video imaging technology to visualize activity patterns in the cortex of living animals. The approach is still young, with many variations and improvements still to be tried. But it has already made it possible to visualize patterns in animals that remain alive and healthy, and consequently has also made it possible to obtain many different activity patterns from the same piece of tissue and thereby

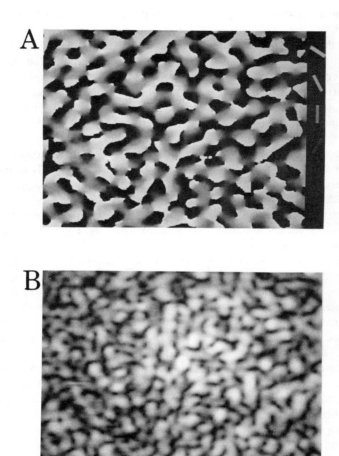

Figure 10 These images depict orientation and magnitude components of the vector field resulting from the operation in Figure 9, after it has been applied to the 12 images in Figure 8. The grey scale in (*a*) indicates the preferred orientation, while the grey scale in (*b*) corresponds to the absolute selectivity for any particular orientation.

permit comparisons across stimuli. A simple and still preliminary analysis of results achieved in this fashion has resolved the riddle of how orientation preferences are distributed across the cortical surface and, furthermore, has shown that this distribution is characterized by two dimensional patches (where orientation shifts evenly) and one dimensional borders (where it does

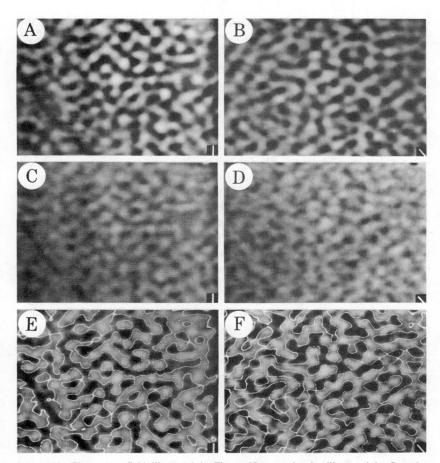

Figure 11 The vector field illustrated in Figure 10 may also be illustrated in Cartesian coordinates. The images in A and B depict the X and Y components of this vector field. Since these values represent idealized cortical responses to contours at 0 and 45 degrees, as inferred from the responses to all twelve orientations, one can compare these images to those input images that actually were generated by stimuli with primary orientations of 0 and 45 degrees. These appear below, in C and D. They reappear in E and F where thin white lines, corresponding to the positions of intermediate grey values in A and B, have been added to facilitate comparison. As one can see from this comparison, the silhouettes of activity in A and B indicated by these lines are virtually identical to those in E(C) and F(D), the major difference being the much better signal/noise ratio for the images in A and B.

not) that serve to segregate the patches (see 1 and 4 for further discussion). The one dimensional borders, moreover, show a striking tendency to propagate down the centers of ocular dominance columns, overlapping in many cases with the extensive system of cytochrome oxidase blobs. (3, 9, 20). This correlation would have been difficult to make before the advent of this approach.

There are still a number of technical limitations, however. Temporal resolution continues to be poor, mostly on account of the large number of averages required to reduce noise, but also because of lag (an inescapable limitation of most conventional TV imaging tubes), which for small signals can persist for several seconds. This problem presumably will yield to the introduction of newly available CCD cameras, which don't have any lag.

Another problem concerns the lack of control that one has over the depth from which signals arise. Although the mechanisms are not yet understood, the signals responsible for images in this chapter probably develop from events in the upper half mm of cortex. In its present form, therefore, this approach is limited to the study of cortical phenomena (e.g. ocular dominance, orientation, retinotopic position) that are known to be constant with depth. Greater control over the depth from which signals arise, to an extent that might permit optical sectioning with a resolution of 100 μm or less, would be a welcome addition that may follow from the implementation of confocal optics if these ever prove feasible.

The ability to look repeatedly at the same piece of tissue, in some cases over a period of weeks makes this approach ideal for studies of cortical development (20, 23) and there are any number of new parameters, like color, spatial frequency, direction selectivity, (5) whose lateral distributions can now be investigated and compared with those of ocular dominance and orientation visualized in the same tissue.

ACKNOWLEDGMENT

This work was supported by grants from the National Eye Institute (EY05403, EY06586-01). My thanks to Jenny Lund for helpful comments on the manuscript as well as to Suzanne Holback and Jacqueline Mack, who provided excellent technical assistance during various phases of this work.

Literature Cited

1. Blasdel, G. G. 1988. Topography of visual function as shown with voltage sensitive dyes. In *Sensory Systems.* ed. J. S. Lund
2. Blasdel, G. G., Fitzpatrick, D. 1983. Physiological organization of layer 4 in macaque striate cortex. *J. Neurosci.* 4:880–95
3. Blasdel, G. G., Fitzpatrick, D. 1984. Physiological organization of layer 4 in macaque striate cortex. *J. Neurosci.* 4, 880–95.
4. Blasdel, G. G., Salama, G. 1986.

Voltage-sensitive dyes reveal a modular organization in the monkey striate cortex. *Nature* 218:579–85
5. Blasdel, G. G., Tootell, R. B. H. 1987. Studies of orientation and motion selectivity in monkey striate cortex using optical techniques. *Neurosci.* 13:2 (Abstr.)
6. Cohen, L. B., Keynes, R. D., Hille, B. 1968. Light scattering and birefringence changes during nerve activity. *Nature* 218:579–85
7. Cohen, L. B., Keynes, R. D., Lan

downe, D. 1972. Changes in axon light-scattering that accompany the action potential: current dependent components. *J. Physiol.* 224:727–52

8. Cohen, L. B., Salzberg, B. M., Davila, H. V., Ross, W. N., Landowne, D., et al. 1974. Changes in axon fluorescence during activity: molecular probes of membrane potential. *J. Membr. Biol.* 19:1–36

9. Grinvald, A., Anglister, L., Hildesheim, R., Freeman, J. A. 1983. Optical monitoring of naturally evoked dynamic patterns of neural activity from the intact frog optic tectum using a photodiode array. *Soc. Neurosci.* 9(1): 540 (Abstr.)

10. Grinvald, A., Lieke, E., Frostig, R. P., Gilbert, C., Wiesel, T. M. 1986. Functional architecture of cortex revealed by optical imaging of intrinsic signals. *Nature* 324:361–64

11. Horton, J. C., Hubel, D. H. 1980. Regular patchy distribution of cytochrome oxidase staining in primary visual cortex of macaque monkey. *Nature* 292:762–64

12. Hubel, D. H., Wiesel, T. N. 1962. Receptive fields, binocular interaction and functional architecture of monkey striate cortex. *J. Physiol.* 160:106–54

13. Hubel, D. H., Wiesel, T. N. 1965. Binocular interaction in striate cortex of kittens reared with artificial squint. *J. Neurophysiol.* 28:1029–40

14. Hubel, D. H., Wiesel, T. N. 1968. Receptive fields and functional architecture of monkey striate cortex. *J. Physiol.* 195:215–43

15. Hubel, D. H., Wiesel, T. N. 1972. Laminar and columnar distribution of geniculo-cortical fibers in the macaque monkey. *J. Comp. Neurol.* 146:421–50

16. Hubel, D. H., Wiesel, T. N. 1974. Uniformity of monkey striate cortex: A par-allel relationship between field size, scatter, and magnification factor. *J. Comp. Neurol.* 158:295–06

17. Hubel, D. H., Wiesel, T. N., LeVay, S. 1974. Visual field of representation in layer IV C of monkey striate cortex. *Soc. Neurosci.* 19:264 (Abstr.)

18. Hubel, D. H., Wiesel, T. N., Stryker, M. P. 1978. Anatomical demonstration of orientation columns in macaque monkey. *J. Comp. Neurol.* 177:361–80

19. Humphrey, A. L., Hendrickson, A. E. 1983. Background and stimulus-induced patterns of high metabolic activity in the visual cortex (area 17) of the squirrel and macaque monkey. *J. Neurosci.* 3:345–58

20. Kiorpes, L., Blasdel, G. G. 1987. Optical studies of macaque striate cortex during development. *Neurosci.* 13:1243 (Abstr.)

21. LeVay, S., Hubel, D. H., Wiesel, T. H. 1975. The pattern of ocular dominance columns in macaque striate cortex revealed by a reduced silver stain. *J. Comp. Neurol.* 159:559–76

22. Livingstone, M. S., Hubel, D. H. 1984. Anatomy and physiology of a color system in the primate visual cortex. *J. Neurosci.* 4:309–56

23. Orbach, H. S., Cohen, L. B., Grinvald, A. 1985. Optical mapping of electrical activity in rat somatosensory and visual cortex. *J. Neurosci.* 5:1886–95

24. Tootell, R. H., Hamilton, S. L., Silverman, M. S., Switkes, E. 1988. Functional anatomy of macaque striate cortex. I. ocular dominance, binocular interactions, and baseline conditions. *J. Neurosci.* 5:

25. Wong-Riley, M. T. T. 1976b. Changes in the visual system of monocularly sutured or enucleated cats demonstrable with cytochrome oxidase histochemistry. *Brain Res.* 14:271–91

COMPARATIVE PHYSIOLOGY

NUTRIENT TRANSPORT

Introduction, Fred N. White, *Section Editor*

The mechanisms underlying transport of nutrients from the environment to organisms, as well as within organisms following ingestion, form the core of the two reviews that follow.

The review by Stephen Wright and Donal Manahan focuses on the uptake of nutrients across the integument by aquatic animals. Natural waters may contain considerable dissolved organic matter (glucose, amino acids) in addition to particulate materials of nutritional value. Dissolved organic matter (DOM) has been estimated at about 1 mg per liter of sea water with a probable total mass of 10^{15} kg, the equivalent of a century of primary productivity. Interest in DOM as a nutrient source for marine organisms was initially stimulated by Putter at the beginning of the present century. However, convincing evidence that DOM was, in fact, a potentially important source of nutrient for marine organisms had to wait for the appropriate methods to study transport of DOM across the integumentary-environmental interface. Wright and Manahan treat us with a discourse on DOM uptake, focusing on marine invertebrates, with a goal of suggesting a general description of integumental transport of DOM among soft-bodied marine organisms. They also call attention to the importance of studying these processes in larval forms and during and following their transformation into adults.

The ontogeny of intestinal nutrient transport among vertebrates is the focus of the review by Randal Buddington and Jared Diamond. Their review reveals new insights into the developmental transition from prenatal to postnatal patterns for transporters of amino acids, sugars, peptides, vitamins, and bile salts. Species represented in the review represent forms that are altricial, precocial, ectotherms, endotherms, herbivores, and carnivores. These authors give us a view of transport along the length of the intestine as well as along the crypt-villus axis of the mucosa of the intestine. Readers will learn, as they are conducted along the length axis, that transitions in transporter function may not be only spatially abrupt but temporarily dynamic as the prenatal-postnatal transition occurs. For example, in adult mammals the colon most usually engages in absorption of NaCl and water, nutrient uptake being negligible. However, fetal and neonatal rats possess colonic Na-dependent glucose and alanine transporters as well as Na-independent alanine transporters, which resemble those of the small intestine. By postnatal day 5 these colonic transporters disappear. Likewise, the small intestine-like Na-dependent transport of aldohexoses and some 14 amino acids that reside in neonatal piglet colon are lost by day 10 of postnatal life. Further developmental dynamics are revealed during the time of weaning when cellular restructuring of enterocytes and transport potentialities rapidly occur. These processes are not only described but the authors probe a difficult problem of developmental biology: what is the nature of the signals that "instruct" the intestine to switch on the appropriate transporters at the right time? This is exciting stuff and the authors clearly demonstrate that the gut is not a dull place to invest intellectual interest.

These two reviews, under the banner of Comparative Physiology, represent the tone of a renaissance in the field of nutrient uptake. Both reviews seek, through the study of diverse organisms, to discover unifying rules of similarity among specific animal groups as well as those features of nutrient uptake that transcend narrow taxonomic groupings. These reviews also offer investigators interested in nutrient uptake a host of intriguing avenues to pursue in the field and laboratory.

Annu. Rev. Physiol. 1989. 51:585–600

INTEGUMENTAL NUTRIENT UPTAKE BY AQUATIC ORGANISMS

Stephen H. Wright

Department of Physiology, University of Arizona, Tucson, Arizona 85724

Donal T. Manahan

Department of Biology, University of Southern California, Los Angeles, California 90089

INTRODUCTION

Seawater contains about ten times more reduced carbon in solution than in particulate form (65). This observation has led to the compelling suggestion that aquatic animals acquire nutrients through direct absorption of dissolved organic material (DOM) into the integument. Though discussed in the early 1860s in the reports of the RV *Challenger* expedition (62), Putter (48) was the first to champion this idea, and the interest of environmental physiologists has waxed and waned for 75 years. Renewed interest in this area has followed on the heels of recent technical innovations that have permitted the careful study of several aspects of "Putter's hypothesis." This paper provides a brief review of the general features of integumental nutrient transport and a more detailed discussion of the current understanding of (*a*) the adaptational strategies of this process and (*b*) the role of DOM uptake in the nutrition of aquatic animals.

GENERAL FEATURES OF INTEGUMENTAL TRANSPORT

The literature documenting the points described below has been extensively reviewed (24, 60). Therefore, we emphasize recent, representative studies. The results of work previous to 1980 can be summarized as follows: (*a*)

585

0066–4278/89/0315–0585$02.00

Species from 18 classes representing 13 phyla were shown to accumulate DOM from seawater. (*b*) This uptake occurs directly across the general body surface though specialized integumental structures (e.g. gills and parapodia) may play a primary role in some species. (*c*) Transport is generally described by Michaelis-Menten kinetics, with separate pathways showing a clear specificity for distinct structural classes of substrate. These carrier-mediated processes result in a net accumulation into the organism of nutrient molecules from dilute solution in seawater. (*d*) Marine arthropods do not appear to be capable of accumulating DOM. Likewise, freshwater invertebrates have a limited capability to accumulate DOM though there may be important exceptions to this general rule. Finally, neither freshwater nor marine vertebrates accumulate DOM with the same facility as the soft-bodied marine invertebrate phyla.

MECHANISM OF INTEGUMENTAL DOM TRANSPORT

It is increasingly apparent that the integument of marine invertebrates has a dual role. First, it serves as a barrier to the passive loss of the endogenous, low molecular weight organic molecules that play a pivotal role in cellular metabolism and volume regulation (19). The magnitude of this task is evident when one considers that the concentration of, for example, free amino acids (FAA) in integumental tissues is greater than 0.1 M (19), while the concentration of FAA in seawater is typically less than 1 μM (65). Thus, the integument must sustain chemical concentration gradients that exceed 10^5–10^6 to 1.

Second, the integument is actively involved in the accumulation of nutrient molecules from surrounding seawater. In effect, the integument must serve simultaneously as a skin and as an extension of the intestinal mucosa, without the aid of the fine environmental control enjoyed by the latter organ. Studies on the mechanisms of integumental transport have focused on the cellular adaptations leading to these opposing characteristics.

The discussion of DOM uptake in this review is based, for the most part, on studies with comparatively few species of marine bivalve, polychaete, coelenterate, and echinoderm. Nevertheless, similarities between the characteristics of transport in these organisms suggest that a general description of integumental transport in soft-bodied marine invertebrates is warranted though details of the process(es) as expressed in different species are likely to vary.

Organization of the Integument

It is worth emphasizing that the integument has the basic structure of an epithelial cell layer. The cells are polarized, with the apical aspect facing seawater while the basolateral aspect is exposed to the blood or hemolymph of the organism. The apical membrane typically has a microvillous brush border, which increases the area exposed to seawater. For example, microvilli of cells from the gill of the marine mussel *Mytilus edulis* increase the apical membrane area by 10- to 18-fold (73). In some cases, the apical membrane may be overlaid by a cuticle; the resulting diffusional barrier to the movement of small molecules can have an important impact on the kinetics of nutrient exchange (20) (discussed below).

The permeability of the apical brush border to the passive flux of nutrient molecules appears to be very low. Estimates of amino acid permeability coefficients for the integument of *Mytilus* gill range from 0.6 to 14×10^{-9} cm s^{-1} (73). Thus, effectively, the only avenue for such molecules to cross the integument is via carrier-mediated pathways.

Specialized regions of the integument often represent primary sites of DOM uptake. For example, the gill of marine bivalves is the principal site of glucose and amino acid uptake (44) although this may merely reflect the large surface area of integument represented by this organ (25). On the other hand, a study employing frozen section/freeze-dry autoradiography clearly showed that cycloleucine uptake by the marine polychaete *Glycera dibranchiata* occurs primarily at the parapodial gill surfaces (9). Likewise, the velum and the developing gill buds are the primary sites of glycine uptake in larval bivalves (32).

Whereas a great deal is known about transport across the brush border membrane into integumental cells, there is virtually no information on the flux of nutrients across the basolateral aspect of these cells.

Kinetic Adaptations of Integumental Transport

The concentration dependency of DOM uptake is generally described by Michaelis-Menten kinetics. Rates of transport of individual substrates per unit of absorptive tissue are defined by the kinetic constants, J_{max} (maximal rate of transport) and K_t (apparent Michaelis constant; the substrate concentration resulting in half-maximal transport). J_{max} indicates the transport capacity for a given substrate. Because there are several ways to express J_{max} (e.g. per unit mass or unit area), it is often difficult to compare the available values between different species (47). Nevertheless, when expressed per unit of apparent absorptive surface, the transport capacity for glycine of such different systems as the gill of the mussel *Mytilus californianus* (68) and the general integument of the sand dollar *Dendraster excentricus* (57) are similar (1.2 and 3.6 nmol cm^{-2} min^{-1}, respectively). These rates represent the high end of integumental transport capacity. For other systems and substrates, rates can be much lower; in *Nereis diversicolor*, for example, the J_{max} for integumental glucose uptake is 0.03 nmol cm^{-2} min^{-1} (20). Yet, the transport capacity of integumental tissues is generally low when compared to those of vertebrate or invertebrate intestine, where rates are often 100–600 nmol cm^{-2} min^{-1} (1, 27).

The total transport capacity of the integument is a function of both the kinetics of uptake and the area of tissue involved in DOM accumulation. Karazov et al (28) emphasized the importance of total transport capacity when considering the impact of nutrient absorption by an organ. The integument, with its surface specializations for gas exchange or filter feeding, can present a large surface area for nutrient absorption. Unfortunately, comparatively little is known about either the surface area or the specific transport characteristics of invertebrate gastrointestinal systems (1). Such information is necessary in order to compare accurately the absorptive capacity of the integument to that of the more widely recognized traditional organs for nutrient absorption.

The extent of transport capacity under physiologically relevant conditions is dictated by the apparent affinity of transporters for substrate. Compared to their intestinal counterparts, integumental transporters have a high affinity for substrate. The apparent K_t is usually <100 μM and in many cases is <10 μM (47). In fact, it is useful to consider two groups of integumental systems, those with apparent K_ts less than 10 μM, and those with values greater than 10 μM. Significantly, the former group tends to be populated by species or developmental stages that live within, or are effectively exposed to, the water column, where DOM concentrations are very low; FAA levels in near shore water are typically <1 μM. For example, the K_t of integumental amino acid transporters in mussels from the genus *Mytilus* ranges from 1 to $\approx$10 μM (25, 68, 69), and FAA transporters of larval sea urchins of the genera *Paracentrotus* and *Strongylocentrotus* have K_ts of 1–7 μM (3, 12). Animals with $K_t >10$ μM are often found on or in the sediment and therefore may be exposed to the higher concentrations of DOM characteristic of interstitial waters; FAA levels in pore water expressed from sediment cores or in water collected under rocks sitting on the surface of the sediment range from 10 to 100 μM (21). For example, the apparent K_t of amino acid transporters in the body wall of sediment-dwelling polychaetes typically ranges from 20 to 90 μM (47).

It is likely that the apparent range of K_t values described above is due, at least in part, to the complicating influence of unstirred layers. The presence of an unstirred layer above a transporting epithelium causes an overestimate of experimentally determined Michaelis constants because transport activity reduces substrate concentration near the membrane. Consequently, the effective substrate concentration is always less than the concentration in the bulk medium (67). Convective movements of water produced by filter feeding or larval swimming activity disrupts unstirred layers. Therefore, it may be no coincidence that a low K_t is often associated with these latter habits. Likewise, the inevitable presence of unstirred layers above the integument of many sediment dwelling organisms may explain the higher K_t often associated with such organisms.

There is recent evidence that changes in the apparent affinity of integumental transporters may also be the result of developmental processes that coincide with changes in habitat of the developing larva. After two days of development, larvae of *Strongylocentrotus purpuratus* appear to have a single, high affinity transport process ($K_t \simeq 1$ μM). At day four, however, the kinetics of alanine uptake become biphasic with the appearance of a second, low affinity ($K_t \simeq 100$ μM) process (D. T. Manahan, unpublished observations). Addition of this second pathway may be a preparatory response to the higher concentration of substrate associated with the benthic environment of the settled larva. Alternatively, it may reflect the exposure of the larva to "microzones" within the water column that contain higher nutrient concentrations than those associated with bulk seawater (see below).

The adaptive significance of the comparatively high affinities of integumental transporters for nutrient is clearly evident. For the extreme case of filter-feeding animals exposed to substrate levels of 0.5–1.0 μM, a K_t of 5 μM means that 10–15% of the transport capacity of the integument is realized, with a near first-order response to any transient increases in substrate concentration that may occur.

The presence of an unstirred layer, or of other means of effectively confining a substrate-containing solution relatively near to the integument, may play an important role in limiting losses of organic substrates from integumental cells. Gomme (20) suggested that the unstirred layer within and above the cuticle of *N. diversicolor* traps solutes lost from surface cells and thereby increases the probability that these solutes will be reaccumulated by integumental transporters. This "recycling" role was subsequently shown to be a characteristic of integumental transport in *Mytilus* gill as well (72). Although unstirred layers are minimal in the gill, solutes lost from upstream sites become substrates for downstream transporters. By recycling endogenous materials, such as amino acids, integumental transporters may play an important role in the normal maintenance of cell volume.

Parallel Pathways for DOM Uptake

The integument has a number of separate, parallel transport pathways with varying degrees of specificity for different structural classes of nutrients. For example, the gills of marine bivalves have separate pathways for anionic, cationic, and zwitterionic (i.e. neutral) amino acids (59, 68). Indeed, in *Mytilus* gill, neutral amino acids appear to be transported by at least two processes, one with a high degree of specificity for cationic amino acids and the other specific for imino acids (43, 68). Similarly, uptake of alanine into the body wall of *G. dibranchiata* involves two separate pathways (58).

Transport of taurine, a β-amino acid and the major constituent of the cellular FAA pool of a number of marine invertebrates, occurs by a separate pathway in *Mytilus* gill tissue (68, 71) although in mantle tissue from *M. edulis,* taurine uptake appears to involve a pathway that is inhibited by α-zwitterionic amino acids (49). Stereospecificity of amino acid transporters appears to be limited; for example, *d*- and *l*-isomers of neutral amino acids compete for a common pathway in bivalves (59). Recently, however, a unique *d*-alanine transporter was described for coelomocytes of *G. dibranchiata* (46), which raises the issue of whether separate integumental transport pathways exist for these compounds in at least some species.

The structural specificity of integumental sugar transporters has not received the same degree of attention as transporters for amino acids. D-glucose transport has been reported to occur in bivalves, coelenterates, and polychaetes (reviewed in 70). In the only detailed study of structural specificity of integumental glucose transport, Albrechtsen & Gomme (2) found strong similarities between transport in the integument of *N. diversicolor* and transport reported in apical membranes of vertebrate intestinal and renal epithelia, with the exception that *l*-glucose was a potent inhibitor of *d*-glucose transport in *Nereis*. It is not clear if pathways specific for other structural classes of low molecular weight carbohydrate exist within the integument although recent reports that compounds such as fructose (39), mannitol (18), and other low molecular weight carbohydrates (50) can be found in relatively large concentrations in natural waters indicate that a survey of transport of such compounds is warranted.

Uptake of constituents of the DOM other than amino acids and glucose has received little attention, but there is evidence for uptake of such diverse compounds as dipeptides, long and short chain fatty acids, creatine, and prostaglandins into the integument of different invertebrates (reviewed in 70). In light of the fact that amino acids and carbohydrates constitute <10% of the DOM pool, the failure to survey more completely the presence of transporters for other classes of organic compounds has restricted our understanding of nutritional potential of integumental transport.

Energetics of Integumental DOM Uptake

Net accumulation of DOM represents transport against extreme chemical concentrations gradients. For example, taurine can be accumulated into gills of intact *Mytilus* from concentrations <20 nM in the face of cellular taurine concentrations that exceed 0.1 mol kg wet wt^{-1} (72). A similar ability to concentrate FAA has been reported for representative echinoderms (15) and polychaetes (42).

Transmembranous ion gradients, particularly the Na$^+$ electrochemical gradient, provide the driving force for uphill transport of organic solutes in many animal cells through coupling the fluxes of nutrient and activator ion (10). Indeed, transport of amino acids and sugars into several bivalves, polychaetes, and echinoderms has been shown to require Na^+ in seawater (reviewed in 70). Furthermore, concentrative uptake of amino acids and sugars into apical membrane vesicles isolated from *M. edulis* gill (43) and from tentacles of the sea anemone *Anemonia sulcata* (8) is driven by a Na^+ gradient directed into the lumen of the vesicles. Thus, integumental transport probably involves the basic mechanism responsible for nutrient uptake in a wide variety of epithelial systems.

Examination of the thermodynamics and kinetics of the coupling of DOM and Na^+ fluxes has revealed the strategy used by integumental systems to move nutrients against such extreme chemical gradients. For example, based upon the equations describing the maximum amino acid gradients in *Mytilus* gill that can be supported by the electrochemical gradient for Na^+, it has been suggested that at least 3 Na^+ ions must be coupled to the transport of taurine or alanine (34). The observation that Na^+ activation of integumental amino acid transport is a sigmoid, rather than hyperbolic, function of external Na^+ (69) indicates that more than one Na^+ ion (perhaps as many as seven) are involved in the transport process. In the polychaete *G. dibranchiata*, kinetic analyses suggest that alanine uptake into the body wall involves at least 3 Na^+ ions (58). Significantly, activation of transport in these systems requires relatively large concentrations of Na^+. Half-maximal activation of alanine uptake by the predominant system in *G. dibranchiata* requires 440 mM Na^+ (58), while the K_{50} (the sodium concentration resulting from half-maximal transport) for alanine and taurine transport in *M. californianus* requires 335 and 325 mM Na^+, respectively (69).

These kinetic characteristics may explain, at least in part, the ability of the integument to serve both as a barrier to the passive loss of organic molecules from high cellular concentrations and as an organ for net nutrient uptake. Despite the low affinity of integumental transporters for Na^+, the very large concentration of this ion in seawater (425–450 mM) assures the catalytic activation of a large fraction of transport capacity. However, the very low cytoplasmic Na^+ concentration (e.g. $\simeq 11$ mM in *M. californianus* gill; S. H. Wright, unpublished observations) effectively prevents transporters from operating as an efflux pathway. For example, abolition of the inwardly directed Na^+ gradient by removal of Na^+ from seawater has a small (less than 3-fold) stimulatory effect on amino acid efflux from *Mytilus* gill tissue, whereas collapsing the gradient by increasing cytoplasmic Na^+ from approximately 11 to 130 mmol l cell water^{-1} (by incubation in seawater containing the ionophore nigericin) increases amino acid efflux by more than 20-fold (S. H. Wright, unpublished observations). Thus, the maintenance of a low cytoplasmic Na^+ activity, presumably through action of a ouabain-inhibitable

Na$^+$ pump, serves to establish a transmembranous steady state condition that effectively limits integumental transporters to an influx mode of action.

Regulation of Integumental Uptake

Acute decreases in external salinity inhibit the rate of FAA uptake into euryhaline marine polychaetes (55) and bivalves (73); however, the comparatively high rates of FAA uptake into intact *M. edulis* acclimated to 50% seawater reported by Jørgensen (25) suggest that there may be an upregulation of transport associated with long-term adaptation to changes in salinity. Increases in amino acid efflux are also noted when *Mytilus* is exposed to reduced salinity although this also appears to be a transient response to an acute exposure (73).

The mechanism by which changes in salinity influence integumental permeability are not known. The divalent cations Ca^{2+} and Mg^{2+} have been shown to regulate membrane permeability to amino acids in bivalve cardiac tissue (45). Decreases in external Mg^{2+} or Ca^{2+} increase efflux of FAA from isolated *M. californianus* gills though inhibition of amino acid uptake occurs only with decreases in external Mg^{2+} (61). These effects were only noted, however, after extreme reductions in external divalent cation concentrations (e.g. <20 mM Mg^{2+}). On the other hand, amino acid uptake by larval *S. purpuratus* is insensitive to changes in external Mg^{2+} concentration (7).

Exposure to elevated concentrations of substrate also effect integumental nutrient transport. When intact *M. edulis* were exposed for 24 hr to 2 mM glycine, subsequent rates of net glycine accumulation were depressed compared to rates measured in animals acclimated to seawater without amino acids (25). Though exposure to a 2-mM concentration of substrate represents a nonphysiological condition, this observation does suggest that the integument may possess a regulatory response to elevations in substrate that prevents alteration of intracellular FAA concentrations during episodes of prolonged exposure to comparatively high substrate levels. Similarly, exposure of larval *S. purpuratus* to external serine concentration of 50 μM for as little as 4 hr results in an increase in intracellular serine, which is associated with an increase in serine efflux (13). Significantly, prolonged exposure to serine does not change the unidirectional influx of this compound; uptake of labeled serine, when corrected for changes in the external serine-specific activity during the course of the experiment, appears unchanged. The physiological relevance of these observations, which include exposures to substrate levels unlikely to be encountered in the natural habitat, is not clear. Nevertheless, the regulation of integumental transport by environmental factors is an area that has received little attention and warrants further study.

Changes in nutrient uptake that occur during development have also received too little attention. Rates of amino acid and nucleoside uptake into sea urchin eggs increase by up to 40-fold over the first 60 min following fertilization (3, 16, 40). A similar activation of amino acid uptake occurs upon fertilization of bivalve eggs (31). This stimulation of uptake represents a progressive increase, initiated by fertilization, of Na-dependent transport processes (3, 16). Unfertilized eggs are characterized by a rapid net loss of amino acids (D. T. Manahan, unpublished observations), which is consistent with the fact that FAA transport is limited to Na-independent (i.e. nonconcentrative) pathways (3). A transition from net amino acid efflux to net influx follows fertilization and the activation of Na-dependent transporters (D. T. Manahan, unpublished observations), which suggests a recycling of endogenous substrate similar to that seen in the adult integument (20, 72).

Preliminary studies with larval *S. purpuratus* suggested that over the course of the first few days of development, the kinetic characteristics of amino acid uptake change in a manner consistent with the expression of a new class of transporter(s) with a decreased affinity but larger capacity for substrate (D. T. Manahan, unpublished observations). The developmental and regulatory processes associated with these changes, and their adaptive significance, are not understood and represent new research fronts in the study of integumental transport.

NUTRITIONAL ROLE OF INTEGUMENTAL TRANSPORT

Indirect Estimates of the Contribution of DOM to Energy Metabolism

Most available estimates of the energetic significance of DOM uptake have come from studies with adult organisms where the kinetics of transport have been best characterized. The general approach, first used in this context by Stephens (54), has been to compare (*a*) the caloric input from transport, as determined from measured rates of uptake with (*b*) the caloric needs of the organism, as determined by measured rates of oxygen consumption. Ferguson (17) used this approach in a comprehensive study of 21 species, representing 7 phyla, for which he measured the uptake of amino acids from submicromolar concentrations. He concluded that the rate of amino acid uptake could support from 2–42% of oxidative metabolism, depending on the species. This range is representative of the nutritional potential of the integumental input for different adult (reviewed in 70) and larval invertebrates (14, 33).

There are, however, several critical assumptions that underly such estimates of the role of DOM in invertebrate energetics. First, even though the kinetics of specific integumental transport processes may be well defined, the data are very scant for the actual substrate concentrations in the immediate microenvironments of all species investigated. Hence, even though K_t and

J_{max} may be carefully measured, the value of [S] inserted into the Michaelis-Menten equation is usually a matter of conjecture. In addition, there is limited information on the metabolic fate of transported substrates; the actual contribution of the substrate to catabolic and anabolic processes is almost never measured. Finally, estimates of metabolic rates are based on oxygen consumption; if there is an anaerobic component to metabolism, this method will underestimate metabolic needs.

The importance of these assumptions has been discussed in detail (see 56, 70) and it is increasingly apparent that the comparatively small data base on DOM concentrations in seawater is a critical element to understanding the quantitative role of integumental transport in animal nutrition. Knowledge of amino acid concentrations in various microhabitats is rapidly increasing through studies employing sensitive high-performance liquid chromatography (HPLC) techniques (30, 38). Manahan et al (35) used HPLC to measure FAA in the immediate habitat of *M. edulis* (Newport Bay, California) and found that the total amino acid concentration ($\approx$300 nM) could account for 34% of the animal's aerobic respiration. O'Dell & Stephens (42) made HPLC measurements of FAA in the benthic microhabitat of the worm *Pareurythoe californica*. Values ranged from 3 to 18 μM, which could account for 10–50% of the carbon required for oxidative metabolism. Thus, the recent data for both adult and larval invertebrates suggest that the nutritional potential of the integumental uptake of amino acids, which comprise only about 1% of the total DOM pool (65), is quite large and could make a significant contribution to the metabolic needs of a variety of animals.

Even with advances in the understanding of the quantitative and qualitative profile of DOM in marine waters, the above approach to studying the nutritional role of integumental transport is limited to statements on the potential of the process to provide metabolic substrates. Direct tests of the ability of DOM to sustain metabolism and growth, clearly the most conclusive approach to this issue, have in the past been complicated by the presence of microbial contaminants. Recent advances in the use of larval systems have, however, renewed interest in the direct approach.

Direct Estimates of the Nutritional Role of DOM: Growth

Almost all studies on the nutritional role of DOM uptake have, in fact, been limited to discussions of only two components of the total DOM pool, namely amino acids and sugars. This has been, in part, due to the relative ease of measurement of these classes of compounds (particularly the former). Very few organic compounds comprising the DOM of marine waters have been characterized (64). Thus, quantifying the uptake rates of individual compounds, though clearly of value for understanding transport mechanisms and nutritional potential of integumental nutrient pathways, yields only an indirect, incomplete estimate of the importance of DOM to invertebrate energy metabolism. A more direct answer would be obtained if it could be demonstrated that animals can grow or sustain themselves in particle-free natural seawater. Unfortunately, a quantitative assessment of the contribution that the naturally occurring pool of DOM makes to the total energy and nutritional needs of marine invertebrates has remained elusive.

Recent studies with embryos and larvae suggest that these stages of the life cycle may be good models for assaying the direct role of DOM in metazoan growth. Many larvae of most higher taxa lack a gut and mechanisms for collecting particulate food (63). Instead, they are provisioned by the parent with an abundant supply of yolk, which provides energy and metabolites for growth and development. Nonfeeding larvae are provisioned with a much greater amount of yolk than are feeding larvae (11). W. B. Jaeckle & D. T. Manahan (unpublished observations) developed an energy budget for larvae of the gastropod *Haliotis rufescens*, whose larva is nonfeeding (lecithotrophic) throughout its life span. During development, the organic biomass increased by 18% from the egg to the larva (2 days), with most of the increase in the form of lipid. Calculations based on changes in the biochemical composition of larvae at various stages throughout the life span revealed that energy from endogenous reserves could only supply 15% of the energetic needs (oxygen consumption) of the embryonic and larval stages. Because the rates of utilization of biochemical reserves did not meet the metabolic needs, it would seem that these nonfeeding larvae require an exogenous source of organic carbon. Under the experimental conditions, the only organic material available to the developing larvae is dissolved and at concentrations found in natural sea water. Therefore, approximately 85% of the total energetic cost for development of these nonfeeding larvae must be supplied by DOM. These findings support previous suggestions (29, 36) that much of the energy used during the development of nonfeeding larvae may not be derived from the yolk.

Similar conclusions with regard to the role of DOM in larval development have been reached for feeding larvae (planktotrophic). Embryos and larvae of *S. purpuratus*, cultured in particulate-free seawater, showed a net gain for each of the major biochemical components (protein, lipid, and carbohydrate) during the first two days of development (F. M. Shilling, D. T. Manahan, unpublished observations). In contrast, the crustacean *Artemia salina* balanced its energy budget by use of its biochemical reserves. This was as expected because *A. salina*, as other crustaceans, lacks integumental transport processes and therefore cannot utilize DOM directly (4). These studies of the comparative energetics of development suggest that it is the use of DOM that accounts for the missing energy input during development of soft-bodied marine invertebrates.

Heterogeneity of DOM Distribution

The rates of production of DOM, and its standing-stock concentrations, are linked to the rates of primary production and heterotrophic uptake processes, especially by bacteria (6). During growth, phytoplankton release low molecular weight DOM into seawater although the percent of fixed carbon released in this form is not well established (18, 52). Given the natural variability in oceanic primary production rates, it is not surprising that there is a large variation in the amounts of DOM in different environments.

However, it is now evident that this variation can be very large even over relatively small spatial scales. For example, Smith (53) found that the concentrations of DOM, measured as organic nitrogen, differed by a factor of 1000 in samples taken just 2 m apart. Implying differences on even smaller scales, multiphasic transport kinetics have been observed in isolated strains of marine bacteria where K_t values for dissolved glucose range from 3 nM to 4 mM (41). These authors concluded that "microzones" of very high nutrient concentration exist in small volumes that are relevant to bacteria, but are beyond the technical limits of direct chemical determination. The appearance during development of biphasic kinetics for amino acid transport in sea urchin larvae (mentioned earlier) also supports this idea. However, the concept that microzones contain enhanced nutrient concentrations is highly controversial (66). Clearly, the data on the organic chemical composition of seawater are still too sparse (22) to permit generalizations concerning ambient concentrations that are relevant to most marine invertebrates.

FUTURE DIRECTIONS

The study of integumental transport in aquatic organisms is at a particularly exciting point. We see the following four general subject areas as central to the study of integumental transport during the next several years. All are capable of being resolved.

1. The physiology of integumental transporters. What are the molecular mechanisms of integumental transport and to what extent are such processes homologous, to emphasize the extremes, to bacterial and mammalian nutrient transporters? What molecular adaptations of these processes result in their very high affinities for substrate? How are they regulated both during development and in response to changes in DOM encountered by the adult organism? These and other questions can now be addressed using the tools of molecular biology and the insights acquired from the studies described above.

2. The contribution of accumulated DOM to specific metabolic pathways. What is the fate of accumulated substrates and how is it influenced by the

developmental and nutritional status of the organism? A better balance between the understanding of the physiology of the transport process itself and of the nutrient metabolism of organisms is necessary. Such studies should proceed hand-in-hand with more comprehensive studies of the biochemistry of invertebrate nutrition.

3. Concentrations of DOM in natural waters. What are the spatial and temporal distributions of DOM in different marine habitats? Comprehensive surveys must be made, emphasizing diel, seasonal, and habitat variability in DOM concentrations in relevant environments. In addition, as transport systems for an increasingly wide range of organic substrates become better characterized, new analytical techniques for measurement of these compounds in natural waters must be developed and applied to environmental surveys. Finally, rates of production and turnover of DOM need to be understood better if the ecological relevance of DOM as a metazoan nutrient pool is to be fully appreciated.

4. Importance of DOM relative to other sources of nutrition. What is the relative contribution of particulate organic matter (POM) vs DOM in animal nutrition? Larval systems offer valuable models for the study of this question. However, this issue needs to addressed through measurements of the various fractions composing the POM and DOM in specific environments, including those of all developmental stages of an organism, integrated with studies of DOM accumulation and POM assimilation. The tools for such measurements are either in hand or (in the case of analysis of DOM in natural waters) in development. This crucial issue can be effectively addressed at this time.

SUMMARY

Integumental nutrient transport is a widespread characteristic of soft-bodied marine invertebrates. These processes, which are qualitatively similar to the Na-dependent transporters of intestinal epithelia, have kinetic and energetic characteristics that make them particularly well suited for accumulating materials from the extremely low substrate concentrations found in seawater. Despite the low concentrations of DOM in natural waters, rates of DOM uptake are large and clearly capable of supporting a significant fraction of the metabolic needs of some species. Indeed, recent studies with larval invertebrates suggest that integumental uptake of DOM may play a pivotal role in animal nutrition. Current and future studies on the mechanism and regulation of these processes, on the metabolic fate of accumulated DOM, and on the distribution of DOM in natural waters, promise to resolve the remaining issues on the role of integumental transport in the nutrition of aquatic organisms.

ACKNOWLEDGMENTS

Portions of this work were supported by NSF grants PCM82–16745, DCB85–17769 to SHW and NSF grant OCE86–08869 and Department of Commerce Sea Grants (USC R/RD #27 and #35) to DTM.

Literature Cited

1. Ahearn, G. A. 1988. Nutrient absorption by the invertebrate gut. In *Advances in Environmental and Comparative Physiology*, ed. R. Gilles. Berlin: Springer-Verlag. 2:91–129

2. Albrechtsen, S., Gomme, J. 1984. Specificity of D-glucose transport by the apical membrane of *Nereis diversicolor* epidermis. *Biochim. Biophys. Acta* 770: 47–54

3. Allemand, D., De Renzis, G., Ciapa, B., Girard, J.-P., Payan, P. 1984. Characterization of valine transport in sea urchin eggs. *Biochim. Biophys. Acta* 722:337–46

4. Anderson, J. W., Stephens, G. C. 1969. Uptake of organic material by aquatic invertebrates, VI. Role of epiflora in apparent uptake of glycine by marine crustaceans. *Mar. Biol.* 4:243–49

5. Deleted in proof

6. Azam, F. T., Fenchel, J. G., Field, J. S., Gray, J. S., Meyer-Rell, L. A., Thingstad, F. 1983. The ecological role of water-column microbes in the sea. *Mar. Ecol. Prog. Ser.* 10:257–63

7. Bellis, S., Davis, J. P., Stephens, G. C. 1987. The lack of effect of magnesium on the uptake of amino acids by the sea urchin *Strongylocentrotus purpuratus*. *J. Exp. Zool.* 244:383–88

8. Buck, M., Schlichter, D. 1987. Driving forces for the uphill transport of amino acids into epidermal brush border membrane vesicles of the sea anemone, *Anemonia sulcata* (Cnidaria, Anthozoa). *Comp. Biochem. Physiol.* 88A:273–79

9. Chien, P. K., Rice, M. A. 1985. Autoradiographic localization of exogenously supplied amino acids after uptake by the polychaete *Glycera dibranchiata* Ehlers. *Wasmann J. Biol.* 43:60–71

10. Crane, R. K. 1977. The gradient hypothesis and other models of carrier mediated active transport. *Rev. Physiol. Biochem. Pharmacol.* 78:101–63

11. Crisp, D. J. 1974. Energy relations of marine invertebrate larvae. *Thalassia, Jugosl.* 10:103–20

12. Davis, J. P., Keenan, C. L., Stephens, G. C. 1985. Na⁺-dependent amino acid transport in bacteria-free sea urchin larvae. *J. Comp. Physiol.* 156:121–27

13. Davis, J. P., Stephens, G. C. 1984. Regulation of net amino acid exchange in sea urchin larvae. *Am. J. Physiol.* 247:R1029–R1037

14. Davis, J. P., Stephens, G. C. 1984. Uptake of free amino acids by bacteria-free larvae of the sand dollar *Dendraster excentricus*. *Am. J. Physiol.* 247:R733–R739

15. Davis, J. P., Stephens, G. C., Rice, M. A. 1985. Net entry of amino acids into the brittle star *Ophionereis annulata*. *Comp. Biochem. Physiol.* 81A:899–903

16. Epel, D. 1972. Activation of an Na⁺-dependent amino acid transport system upon fertilization of sea urchin eggs. *Exp. Cell. Res.* 72:74–89

17. Ferguson, J. C. 1982. A comparative study of the net metabolic benefits derived from the uptake and release of free amino acids by marine invertebrates. *Biol. Bull.* 162:1–17

18. Fogg, G. E. 1983. The ecological significance of extracellular products of phytoplankton photosynthesis. *Bot. Mar.* 26:3–14

19. Gilles, R. 1979. Intracellular organic osmotic effectors. In *Mechanisms of Osmoregulation in Animals*, ed. R. Gilles, 1:111–54. New York: Wiley

20. Gomme, J. 1981. Recycling of D-glucose in collagenous cuticle: a means of nutrient conservation? *J. Membr. Biol.* 62:47–52

21. Henrichs, S. M., Farrington, J. W. 1979. Amino acids in interstitial waters of marine sediments. *Nature* 297:955–59

22. Henrichs, S. M., Williams, P. M. 1985. Dissolved and particulate amino acids and carbohydrates in the sea surface microlayer. *Mar. Chem.* 17:141–63

23. Deleted in proof

24. Jørgensen, C. B. 1976. August Putter, August Krogh, and modern ideas on the use of dissolved organic matter in aquatic environments. *Biol. Rev.* 51:291–328

25. Jørgensen, C. B. 1983. Patterns of uptake of dissolved amino acids in mussels (*Mytilus edulis*). *Mar. Biol.* 73:177–82

26. Deleted in proof

27. Karazov, W. H. 1988. Intestinal nutrient

transport in vertebrates. See Ref. 1, pp. 131–72

28. Karasov, W. H., Solberg, D. H., Diamond, J. M. 1985. What transport adaptations enable mammals to absorb sugars and amino acids faster than reptiles? *Am. J. Physiol.* 249:G271–G283

29. Lawrence, J. M., McClintock, J. B., Guille, A. 1984. Organic level and caloric content of eggs of brooding asteroids and an echinoid (Echinodermata) from Kerguelen (South Indian Ocean). *Int. J. Invert. Reprod. Dev.* 7:249–57

30. Lindroth, P., Mopper, K. 1979. High performance liquid chromatographic determination of subpicomole amounts of amino acids by precolumn derivatization with *o*-phthaldialdehyde. *Anal. Chem.* 51:1667–74

31. Manahan, D. T. 1983. The uptake of dissolved glycine following fertilization of oyster eggs, *Crassostrea gigas* (Thunberg). *J. Exp. Mar. Biol. Ecol.* 68:53–58

32. Manahan, D. T., Crisp, D. J. 1983. Autoradiographic studies on the uptake of dissolved amino acids from sea water by bivalve larvae. *J. Mar. Biol. Assoc. UK* 63:673–82

33. Manahan, D. T., Davis, J. P., Stephens, G. C. 1983. Bacteria-free sea urchin larvae: selective uptake of neutral amino acids from sea water. *Science* 220:204–6

34. Manahan, D. T., Wright, S. H., Stephens, G. C. 1983. Simultaneous determination of net uptake of 16 amino acids by a marine bivalve. *Am. J. Physiol.* 244:R832–R838

35. Manahan, D. T., Wright, S. H., Stephens, G. C., Rice, M. A. 1982. Transport of dissolved amino acids by the mussel, *Mytilus edulis:* demonstration of net uptake from natural sea water. *Science* 215:1253–55

36. McClintock, J. B., Pearse, J. S. 1986. Organic and energetic content of eggs and juveniles of antarctic echinoids and asteroids. *Comp. Biochem. Physiol.* 85A:341–45

37. Deleted in proof

38. Mopper, K., Dawson, R. 1986. Determination of amino acids in sea water—recent chromatographic developments and future directions. *Sci. Total Environ.* 49:115–31

39. Mopper, K., Dawson, R., Liebezeit, G., Ittekkot, V. 1980. The monosaccharide spectra of natural waters. *Mar. Chem.* 10:55–66

40. Nishioka, D., Killian, C. E., McGwin-Scully, N. F. 1985. Increased uptake of nucleosides in the activation of sea urchin eggs. In *Transport Processes*

Iono- and Osmoregulation, ed. R. Gilles, M. Gilles-Baillien, 1:303–25. Berlin: Springer-Verlag. 483 pp.

41. Nissen, H., Nissen, P., Azam, F. 1984. Multiphasic uptake of D-glucose by an oligotrophic marine bacterium. *Mar. Ecol. Prog. Ser.* 16:155–60

42. O'Dell, S. J., Stephens, G. C. 1986. Uptake of amino acids by *Pareurythoe californica:* substrate interaction modifies net flux from the environment. *Biol. Bull.* 171:682–93

43. Pajor, A. M., Wright, S. H. 1987. Characteristics of L-alanine uptake in apical membrane vesicles isolated from marine bivalve gill epithelium. *J. Membr. Biol.* 96:209–23

44. Péquignat, E. 1973. A kinetic and autoradiographic study of the direct assimilation of amino acids and glucose by organs of the mussel *Mytilus edulis*. *Mar. Biol.* 19:227–44

45. Pierce, S. K. Jr., Greenberg, M. J. 1973. The initiation and control of free amino acid regulation of cell volume in salinity stressed marine bivalves. *J. Exp. Biol.* 59:435–46

46. Preston, R. L. 1987. D-alanine transport and metabolism by the coelomocytes of the bloodworm, *Glycera dibranchiata* (polychaeta). *Comp. Biochem. Physiol.* In press

47. Preston, R. L., Stevens, B. R. 1982. Kinetic and thermodynamic aspects of sodium-coupled amino acid transport by marine invertebrates. *Am. Zool.* 22:709–21

48. Putter, A. 1909. *Die Ernahrung der Wassertiere und der Stoffhaushalt der Gewasser.* Jena: Fischer

49. Rice, M. A., Stephens, G. C. 1988. Influx and transepithelial flux of amino acids in the mussel, *Mytilus edulis. J. Exp. Biol.* 135:275–87

50. Sakugawa, H., Handa, N., Ohta, K. 1985. Isolation and characterization of low molecular weight carbohydrates dissolved in seawater. *Mar. Chem.* 17:341–62

51. Deleted in proof

52. Sharp, J. H. 1973. Excretion of organic matter by marine phytoplankton: Do healthy cells do it? *Limnol. Oceanogr.* 22:381–99

53. Smith, D. F. 1986. Small-scale spatial heterogeneity in dissolved nutrient concentrations. *Limnol. Oceanogr.* 31:167–71

54. Stephens, G. C. 1963. Uptake of organic material by aquatic invertebrates. II. Accumulation of amino acids by the bamboo worm, *Clymenella torquata*. *Comp. Biochem. Physiol.* 10:191–202

55. Stephens, G. C. 1964. Uptake of organic material by aquatic invertebrates. III. Uptake of glycine by brackish-water annelids. *Biol. Bull.* 126:150–62
56. Stephens, G. C. 1988. Epidermal amino acid transport in marine invertebrates. *Biochim. Biophys. Acta* 947:113–38
57. Stephens, G. C., Volk, M. J., Wright, S. H., Backlund, P. S. 1978. Transepidermal transport of naturally occurring amino acids in the sand dollar, *Dendraster excentricus. Biol. Bull.* 154:335–47
58. Stevens, B. R., Preston, R. L. 1980. The effect of sodium on the kinetics of L-alanine influx by the integument of the marine polychaete *Glycera dibranchiata. J. Exp. Zool.* 211:129–38
59. Stewart, M. G. 1978. Kinetics of neutral amino-acid transport by isolated gill tissue of the bivalve *Mya arenaria* (L.). *J. Exp. Mar. Biol. Ecol.* 32:39–52
60. Stewart, M. G. 1979. Absorption of dissolved organic nutrients by marine invertebrates. *Oceanogr. Mar. Biol. Ann. Rev.* 17:163–92
61. Swinehart, J. H., Crowe, J. H., Giannini, A. P., Rosenbaum, D. A. 1980. Effects of divalent cations on amino acid and divalent cation fluxes in gills of the bivalve mollusc, *Mytilus californianus. J. Exp. Zool.* 212:389–96
62. Thomson, C. W. 1874. *The Depths of the Sea.* London: Macmillan
63. Thorson, G. 1950. Reproductive and larval ecology of marine invertebrates. *Biol Rev.* 25:1–45
64. Wangersky, P. J. 1978. Production of dissolved organic matter. In *Marine Ecology,* ed. O. Kinne, 4:115–220. New York: Wiley
65. Williams, P. J. le B. 1975. Biological and chemical aspects of dissolved organic material in sea water. In *Chemical Oceanogr.,* ed. J. P. Riley, G. Skirrow, 2:301–63. New York: Academic
66. Williams, P. J. le B., Muir, L. R. 1981. Diffusion as a constraint on the the biological importance of microzones in the sea. In *Ecohydrodynamics,* ed. J. C. J. Nihoul. Amsterdam: Elsevier
67. Winne, D. 1973. Unstirred layer, source of biased Michaelis constant in membrane transport. *Biochim. Biophys. Acta* 298:27–31
68. Wright, S. H. 1985. Multiple pathways for amino acid transport in *Mytilus* gill. *J. Comp. Physiol. B* 156:259–67
69. Wright, S. H. 1987. Alanine and taurine transport by the gill epithelium from a marine bivalve: effect of sodium on influx. *J. Membr. Biol.* 95:37–45
70. Wright, S. H. 1988. Integumental nutrient transport in marine invertebrates. In *Advances in Environmental and Comparative Physiology,* ed. R. Gilles, 2: 173–218. Heidelberg: Springer-Verlag
71. Wright, S. H., Secomb, T. W. 1984. Epidermal taurine transport in marine mussels. *Am. J. Physiol.* 247:R346–R355
72. Wright, S. H., Secomb, T. W. 1986. Epithelial amino acid transport in marine mussels: role in net exchange of taurine between gills and sea water. *J. Exp. Biol.* 121:251–70
73. Wright, S. H., Secomb, T. W., Bradley, T. J. 1987. Apical membrane permeability of *Mytilus* gill: influence of ultrastructure, salinity, and competitive inhibitors on amino acid fluxes. *J. Exp. Biol.* 129:205–30

Annu. Rev. Physiol. 1989. 51:601–19

ONTOGENETIC DEVELOPMENT OF INTESTINAL NUTRIENT TRANSPORTERS

Randal K. Buddington[1] and Jared M. Diamond

Physiology Department, University of California Medical School, Los Angeles, California 90024-1751

INTRODUCTION

The central problem of developmental biology is to understand why different cells of a multicellular organism, despite sharing the same DNA, express different subsets of those genes at a given time, and why each cell expresses different genes at different times. This problem is conspicuous for the vertebrate gastrointestinal tract, which undergoes two dramatic developmental transitions associated with changing functional demands. At the first and more abrupt transition, coinciding with birth in mammals and hatching in birds, the gut assumes from the yolk sac or placenta the responsibility for extracting nutrients. At the second transition, coinciding with weaning in mammals and metamorphosis in amphibia, many species experience a marked change in diet.

Ontogenetic development has been intensively studied for many gut functions, such as secretion of enzymes and gastric acid (30–32, 41, 42). Less information has been available for intestinal nutrient transporters, but studies of their development are now proliferating. Our review begins by summarizing patterns of prenatal and postnatal development for transporters of sugars, amino acids, peptides, bile salts, and vitamins. We then consider developmental changes in regionalization of transport along two axes: the length of the intestine, and the crypt/villus axis of the intestinal mucosa. After

---

[1]Address at time of publication: Department of Biological Sciences, Mississippi State University, Mississippi State, Mississippi 39762-5759

601

0066-4278/89/0315-0601$02.00

discussing the mechanisms and signals underlying these developmental changes, we conclude by asking whether nutrient transporters ever impose a bottleneck on growth. A companion review in this volume (Ferraris & Diamond) discusses the related problem of reversible regulation of transporter expression by dietary solutes.

Most of our information is derived from eleven species: rat, rabbit, human, chicken, sheep, pig, guinea pig, dog, cat, catfish, and monkey-face prickleback (in descending order of approximate numbers of publications). These species cover a broad spectrum from altricial (rat, rabbit, dog, and cat) to precocial (chicken and guinea pig), from ectotherm to endotherm, and from herbivores (rabbit, sheep, and guinea pig), to omnivores (rat, human, chicken, pig, and dog) to carnivore (cat) as adults. This comparative approach makes it possible to address questions of ultimate cause that single-species studies are unable to illuminate.

Available studies are divided nearly equally between those measuring brush-border uptake (by membrane vesicles, the everted sleeve technique, or electrophysiological methods) and transepithelial transfer (by everted sacs or in vivo methods). Ontogenetic changes in basolateral membrane transport have not yet been studied. We focus on studies in which transport was measured in several life-history stages of the same species by the same authors, using the same method. Most studies express the results as transport rates per quantity of tissue (i.e. per weight, length, surface area, or protein content of intestine). In addition, four recent studies of rat, rabbit, cat, and chicken (14, 15, 53, 77) determined brush-border uptake rates as a function of position along the entire length of the small intestine, thus making it possible to calculate by integration the uptake capacity of the whole intestine normalized to the animal's body weight. Uptake capacities are the quantities of most physiological interest and reflect developmental changes in mass of absorptive tissue as well as in tissue-specific uptake rates.

PRENATAL DEVELOPMENT

At the moment a mammal is born, placental nutrition is abruptly cut off, and the gut suddenly assumes the whole burden of nutrient extraction. Intestinal nutrient transporters must already be present at birth so that the gut can "take off running." How long before birth do the transporters appear?

The answer varies with species and also with solute, as depicted in Figure 1. In each species, transporters do not appear until the intestinal epithelium itself differentiates and forms crypts, villi, and microvilli. However, the time of transporter appearance and morphological differentiation differs widely between species and is correlated in part with the precocity of the neonate in

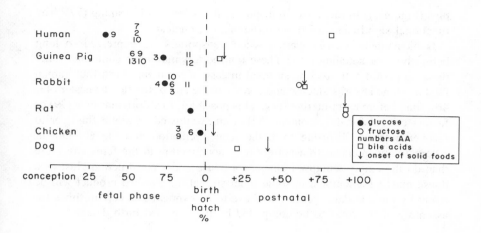

Figure 1 Initial appearances of intestinal nutrient transporters. Times are expressed as percentages of the normal gestation period. "glucose" = aldohexose transporter. ↓ = start of weaning (mammals) or feeding (chicken). 2 = leucine, 3 = lysine, 4 = methionine, 5 = phenylalanine, 6 = valine, 7 = alanine, 9 = glycine, 10 = proline, 11 = betaine, 12 = dimethyl-glycine, 13 = sarcosine. From various sources.

other respects at birth or hatching. Thus, guinea pigs, which can run and ingest solid food on the day of birth, express transporters at the beginning of the second half of gestation, while rats and rabbits, which are born with their eyes closed and unable to regulate food intake or body temperature, express transporters only towards the end of gestation. A minor discrepancy is that humans, which are less helpless than rats or rabbits at birth but more helpless than guinea pigs, express transporters relatively much earlier than guinea pigs. Seemingly even more puzzling is that chickens, the species otherwise most precocial at birth, are relatively the latest to express transporters. However, prenatal development may differ too much between birds and mammals to warrant this comparison; transporter development in chickens should instead be compared with development in an altricial bird species.

Differentiation of the intestinal mucosa does not trigger expression of all transporters; there are differences among transporters in the time of first expression within the same species (Figure 1). Glucose and amino acid (AA) transporters appear prenatally, while bile acid and fructose transporters and ileal receptors for cobalamin appear only postnatally. There are even differences among AAs: Basic AA transport in cats declines more steeply postnatally than does neutral AA transport; in human fetuses, transport of lysine and phenylalanine appears later than transport of alanine, leucine, taurine, and valine (49); and lysine transport is also prenatally late in guinea pigs (Figure 1). In rats lysine transport remains low until weaning (77)! The functional significance of these differences is unclear.

Is biosynthetic energy wasted when transporters are expressed so long before birth or hatching (40)? These transporters may have additional functions: to permit extra-uterine survival in case of premature birth [but human fetal intestine absorbs glucose and glycine at the end of the first trimester (43, 46), long before extra-uterine survival is possible], to absorb nutrients (79) or factors critical for development (52) from swallowed amniotic fluid, or to recover nutrients diffusing from the fetal circulation into the gut lumen. Alternatively, prenatal transporters may not function in the fetus any more than do the empty window frames of a house under construction. Just as a house must be assembled in some order so that the finished product will be ready by the due date, genes may have to be expressed at certain times for assembly of the fetus to be completed by the expected birth date.

POSTNATAL DEVELOPMENT

Aldohexose Transporters

Glucose transport varies reversibly with momentary dietary carbohydrate levels in omnivorous species (see Ferraris & Diamond, this volume), and is programmed genetically to be higher in herbivores (whose natural diet is carbohydrate rich) than in carnivores (whose natural diet is carbohydrate poor) (12). One might expect developmental differences in glucose transport since carbohydrate levels of the natural diet vary with developmental stage in most species. For example, carbohydrate levels in milk are higher than those in the adult diet for most mammalian carnivores but lower than adult levels for herbivores. The left half of Figure 2 depicts the developmental changes in brush-border glucose uptake per mg of tissue for four species, as measured by everted sleeves, while the right half of the figure depicts the corresponding uptake capacities (of the whole intestine, normalized to body weight).

Four features of Figure 2 are striking: First, rate and capacity of glucose uptake reach a brief peak in the chick around 2 weeks after hatching. At that time, yolk reserves become exhausted and the gut becomes the sole supply route for nutrients (53).

Second, among the four species, cats exhibit the steepest age-related decline in dietary carbohydrate (which is much lower in meat than in milk). Glucose transport also declines markedly with age in sheep (5, 62), which consume much carbohydrate both as adults and as suckling lambs but as adults ferment most carbohydrate to volatile fatty acids in the rumen so that little glucose reaches the intestine.

Third, the ratio of galactose to glucose uptake declines with age in cats, paralleling the decline in dietary galactose when suckling mammals are

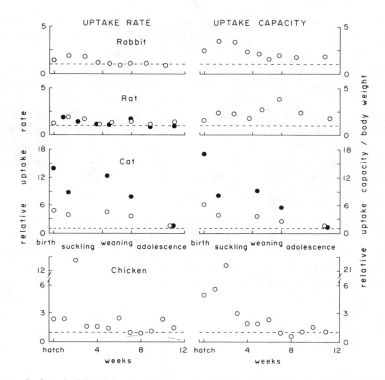

Figure 2 Intestinal brush-border aldohexose uptake in rabbit (14), rat (77), cat (15), and chicken (53) as a function of postpartum developmental stage. Values are relative to adult values (mammals) or 12-week values (chickens). *(left)* Uptake rates, measured at 50 mM by the everted-sleeve method, averaged over the length of the small intestine. *(right)* Corresponding uptake capacity of the whole length of the small intestine, divided by body weight. ○ = glucose, ● = galactose.

weaned off the milk diet. In adults, galactose and glucose compete for the same aldohexose transporter(s), but adult mice appear to have two or more aldohexose transporters, which differ in their ratio of galactose to glucose affinity (74). Thus, Figure 2 suggests developmental shifts in ratios of different aldohexose transporters; a transporter with high galactose affinity is preferentially expressed first. Kinetic analyses also suggest developmental shifts in aldohexose transporters that differ in V_{max} and K_m (23).

Finally, glucose uptake rates remain fairly constant or decline moderately with age in rats, rabbits, and chickens (except for the spike at 2 weeks in chicks), while uptake capacity per body weight declines with age in rabbits and chickens, and peaks in rats during weaning (Figure 2). A postweaning decline in uptake has been confirmed for these three species by other methods (e.g. 7, 68, 76), including brush-border membrane vesicles (21, 23, 24), and has also been observed for guinea pig (17). At first, this age-related decline in glucose transport in omnivorous or herbivorous species may appear disconcerting since the dietary carbohydrate levels encountered as adults are as high as or higher than those in milk. However, recall that the quantity of physiological significance to an animal is the summed uptake capacity of its whole intestine. Metabolic rates (and hence caloric needs) normalized to body weight decline with body size and age in virtually all species. Thus, while caloric needs, and hence glucose uptake capacity, increase with size or age, they do so more slowly than body weight, with the result that uptake capacity per body weight declines. This decline, in turn, arises from the age-related decline of glucose transport rate per mg of intestine (left side of Figure 2).

Fructose Transporter

Like glucose transporters, fructose transporter activity of omnivorous species varies reversibly with momentary dietary fructose levels (see Ferraris & Diamond, this volume) and is programmed genetically to match the usual fructose level of a species' natural diet (14, 15). Figure 3 extends these relations by demonstrating that fructose transporter activity is also matched developmentally to dietary fructose. Milk contains little fructose in all mammal species. Upon weaning, fructose transport rises steeply in rats and rabbits, whose usual adult diet contains fructose, but not in cats, whose usual adult diet contains little fructose.

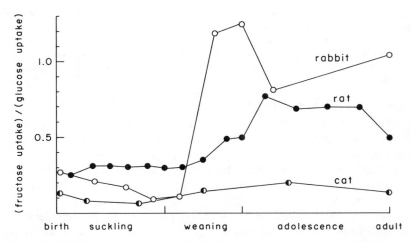

Figure 3 Brush-border fructose uptake divided by glucose uptake (measured at 50 mM by the everted-sleeve method) as a function of postpartum developmental stage. Uptake rates are for jejunum (rat), ileum (rabbit), or averaged over the whole small intestine (cat). Sources as in Figure 2.

Amino Acid and Peptide Transporters

Like sugars, AAs and peptides can be used for calories. Unlike sugars, which are nonessential, AAs and peptides are collectively essential to supply nitrogen, and many AAs are individually essential because the body does not synthesize them. Young animals have the highest growth rates and protein needs: Omnivores and herbivores tend to select foods with higher protein levels when young than when old, many herbivorous fish species are carnivorous when young, and birds that are frugivorous as adults feed insects to their nestlings. Certain AAs that are nonessential in adults are conditionally essential in young animals, which cannot synthesize them fast enough to meet requirements. For instance, suckling but not adult rats require dietary taurine (50). Thus, developmental changes in AA and peptide transporters are to be expected.

Figure 4, similar to the left half of Figure 2, plots the developmental changes in brush-border uptake per mg tissue for AA, as measured by everted intestinal sleeves of rats, rabbits, cats, and chickens. Four conclusions follow from Figure 4:

First, while uptake rates generally decline with age, lysine uptake in rats rises steeply after weaning. We already noted that expression of the lysine transporter is also delayed (albeit prenatal) compared to that of other AA

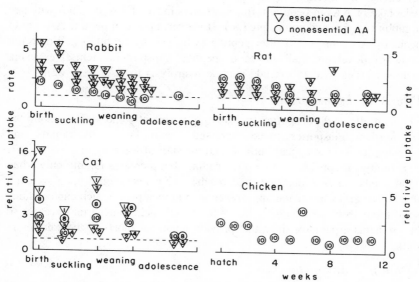

Figure 4 As Figure 2, except for amino acid uptake. 1 = arginine, 2 = leucine, 3 = lysine, 4 = methionine, 8 = aspartate, 10 = proline.

transporters in humans and guinea pigs, but we do not understand the functional reason for the delay.

Second, in chickens the uptake capacity (not shown in Figure 4) for proline, as that for glucose, exhibits a spike when yolk reserves are exhausted 2 weeks after hatching. Both the rate and capacity for proline exhibit a further spike at 6 weeks, when feather molt reaches its peak.

Third, there is a greater postnatal decline in uptake for essential AAs than nonessential AAs. Averaging results for all available AAs from several sources reveal uptake rates for essential AAs are 3.3, 3.0, and 2.0 times adult values during the first half of the suckling period, second half of the suckling period, and weaning/adolescent stages, respectively. Corresponding factors for nonessential AAs are only 2.4, 1.6, and 1.3, respectively. This difference reflects the fact that young, growing animals have a disproportionate need of essential AAs to synthesize new proteins.

Finally, even among transporters for essential AAs there are differing developmental patterns, in pigs as well as in the four species of Figure 4 (14, 15, 53, 66, 77, 80). An extreme example is the rat transporter for taurine, which is essential only in suckling animals and declines to low levels after weaning (50). The postweaning rise in lysine transport and the fall in leucine transport in rats provide another example. Similarly, the various AA transporters are regulated independently and sometimes oppositely by dietary protein or AA levels in adults (see Ferraris & Diamond, this volume).

Uptake of AAs in peptide form, as of AAs in free form, declines with age in rabbit (27, 58) and guinea pig (36). However, uptake of peptide AAs could occur by AA transporters after peptide hydrolysis by peptidases. We do not know of developmental studies of peptide transporters themselves using techniques designed to exclude peptide hydrolysis to AAs (e.g. 22).

Bile Acid Transporter

The ileal bile acid transporter appears only postnatally and is thus among the last nutrient transporters to be expressed (Figure 1). In rats, rabbits, and humans, it does not appear until around the start of weaning (e.g. 2, 34, 47, 51). In dogs it appears well before weaning, but increases rapidly only when solid foods are first ingested, and reaches adult levels only upon weaning (45). The earliest postnatal appearance is in guinea pigs, which can consume solid foods from the first day (35). Why the bile acid transporter develops so late remains a paradox since fats provide much (or most) of the calories in milk.

Vitamin Transporters

Development of vitamin transport has been studied by transepithelial methods only for a few vitamins in a few species. Suckling rats already transport folate, riboflavin, and biotin at about 5 times, 3 times, and one-seventh of adult rates (59–61). Studies of choline uptake in chickens (69) and rats (67) revealed no age-related changes. Cobalamin is interesting because its uptake in adults is absolutely dependent on intrinsic factor (IF) produced in the stomach, but rats are born with an undifferentiated stomach that does not produce IF. Instead, fetal and neonatal rats absorb cobalamin even faster than adults, but by an IF-independent mechanism that declines as the IF-dependent process takes over (6). Guinea pigs, in keeping with their generalized precocity, are born with a differentiated stomach and IF-dependent cobalamin uptake.

REGIONALIZATION OF TRANSPORT

Regionalization Along the Length of the Intestine

The most striking developmental change in regionalization of transporters along the mammalian gut involves the colon, which in adults of many species absorbs NaCl and water but not nutrients. However, fetal and neonatal rat colon possess Na^+-dependent glucose and alanine transporters and Na^+-independent alanine transporters similar to those of the small intestine until postnatal day 5, when the colonic transporters disappear (55–57). Neonatal piglet colon resembles the small intestine in structure and in Na^+-dependent transport of aldohexoses and at least 14 different AAs (29, 37, 38, 66, 72). Within the first day after birth Na^+ uptake doubles, and by day 10 these colonic nutrient transporters are lost. Age-related declines in nutrient transport are also observed in rabbit colon (14) and chicken cecum (54) but not in cat colon (15).

As for regionalization within the small intestine itself, this possibility is ignored in most developmental studies, which instead focus on jejunum, the region of adult intestine with the highest nutrient uptake. However, Figure 5 depicts developmental changes in regionalization of nutrient transport from studies of rat (77), rabbit (14), and cat (15). The upper panel of Figure 5 illustrates three cases of regionalization that are relatively independent of age, with the ratio of proximal to distal uptake remaining either well above 1.0 (riboflavin in rat), near 1.0 (AAs in rat), or well below 1.0 (AAs in rabbit). Glucose and AA uptake by cat intestine (middle panel of Figure 5) shows a constrasting pattern: The proximal-to-distal uptake ratio starts out very high (4.0–7.4) and declines steeply with age. Finally, the bottom panel of Figure 5 illustrates patterns opposite to those of the middle panel: The proximal-to-distal uptake ratio increases with age for biotin and folate uptake in rat intestine.

Thus, studies that assume the jejunum to be the main site of nutrient uptake and that ignore other regions may actually be missing the principal site.

Furthermore, the region that furnishes the main site for one solute at one age may not do so for another solute or another age.

Regionalization Along the Crypt/Villus Axis

Differentiation along the crypt/villus axis is among the most distinctive features of the adult intestine. As is well known, enterocytes of adults are produced by mitosis confined to the crypts, then migrate up the villus, where they differentiate and begin to express transporters and hydrolases, only to reach the villus tip and be shed a few days after leaving the crypts. The life cycle of enterocytes in fetal and neonatal intestine differs in four major respects: Migration rates along the crypt/villus axis are much slower (44); the enterocyte life span is correspondingly much longer (weeks instead of days; 1, 38, 73); nutrient uptake can occur along the whole crypt/villus axis, not just near the villus tips (71); and at least in mice, mitosis occurs along the whole axis, not just in the crypts (4).

These developmental changes in the enterocyte life cycle have at least four major consequences for nutrient absorption:

1. Since the mitotic rate of the neonatal intestine is high (26) but the cell sloughing rate is low, the mucosal cell mass grows rapidly: in some mammals, by up to 100% in the first day after birth (75)! This growth is the main factor behind the increase in intestinal uptake capacity with age (Figure 6).

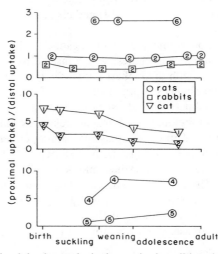

Figure 5 Ratio of brush-border uptake in the proximal small intestine to uptake in the distal small intestine, measured by 50 mM by the everted-sleeve method. 1 = glucose, 2 = amino acids (averaged for all AAs measured in that species), 4 = folate, 5 = biotin, 6 = riboflavin. From Refs. 14, 15, 59–61, 77.

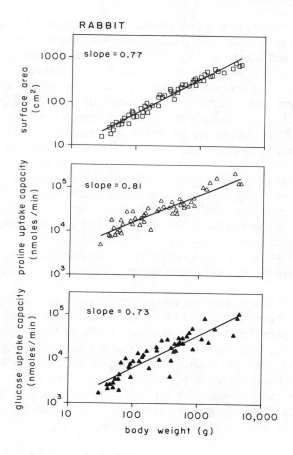

Figure 6 Surface area, proline uptake capacity, and glucose uptake capacity of the whole length of the small intestine, plotted as a function of body weight in rabbits from birth to adulthood, on a double-logarithmic graph. Uptake capacities were measured at 50 mM. From Ref. 14.

2. Since uptake occurs in all neonatal enterocytes, not just in villus tip cells, uptake rates per mg of mucosa should tend to be high. This must be a major factor underlying the observed tendency for uptakes per mg to decline with age (Figures 2 and 4): Crypt enterocytes in adult intestine do not contribute to uptake.

3. As discussed by Ferraris & Diamond (this volume), reversible regulation of transporter activities of adult intestine by dietary solutes involves two distinct mechanisms: reversible reprogramming of mature enterocytes and irreversible programming of crypt cells by dietary conditions prevailing as the cells differentiate. Because neonatal enterocytes have such a long life

span, rapid reprogramming of mucosal absorptive capabilities by shedding older cell generations and replacing them with younger generations would be inefficient in neonates. We are not aware of any evidence that dietary solutes can specifically regulate activities of their intestinal transporters or hydrolases in a neonatal mammal, as occurs for almost all intestinal transporters and hydrolases in the adult (Ferraris & Diamond, this volume). Instead, cases of precocious maturation that seem to be induced in neonatal intestine by diet are due to stress and hormone release associated with diet changes, not to the dietary solutes acting as regulatory signals (25).

On reflection, this resistance of neonatal mammalian intestine to reprogramming by dietary solutes makes functional sense. During the suckling phase the diet's composition is relatively constant, and the neonatal intestine is not called upon to adapt to a changing diet. Analogously, dietary carbohydrate levels do not regulate glucose uptake by intestines of strictly carnivorous species because such species are not called upon in nature to adapt to changing dietary carbohydrate levels (11, 13, 16).

4. Around the time of weaning, enterocyte migration rates accelerate, enterocyte life spans shorten, and as a result the enterocyte population of the suckling animal is shed. Its replacement by the adult-type epithelium and adult-type enterocyte life cycle is associated with major changes in hydrolases and transporters, such as the weaning-related decline in lactase and in galactose transport, rise in sucrase and in fructose and bile acid transport, and appearance of reversible regulation of transporters by their dietary substrates. These changes may constitute a suite of functions expressible only in the adult-type intestinal epithelium.

MECHANISTIC BASES FOR THE DEVELOPMENTAL CHANGES

At least three mechanisms contribute to the developmental changes in intestinal nutrient transporters discussed above. These mechanisms consist of changes in transporter number, in type of transporter, and in membrane fluidity.

While developmental changes in intestinal nutrient transporter number have yet to be measured directly, they have been inferred from kinetic analyses that revealed declines in V_{max} without changes in the K_m of glucose uptake in brush-border membrane vesicles from chick (68) and rat (21, 23) intestines.

A familiar example of developmental sequences of related proteins performing the same function is provided by various human hemoglobins that differ in AA sequence. Hemoglobins Gower and Portland are expressed until about 10 weeks of embryonic life, followed by fetal hemoglobin, which disappears around 5 months postnatally, yielding at last to adult hemoglobins A and A_2. Such sequences will probably be identified for some intestinal transporters. Promising candidates include the age-related replacement of IF-independent by IF-dependent cobalamin uptake in rat ileum (6), the age-related replacement of galactose-preferring aldohexose transporters by glucose-preferring aldohexose transporters in cats and possibly other mammals (Figure 2), and the shifts from Na^+-independent to Na^+-dependent AA transporters in pig (38), rat (3, 50), and rabbit (18).

Membrane fluidity decreases with age in rats because of declines in the ratios of protein per lipid and cholesterol per phospholipid and a rise in the ratio of unsaturated per saturated fatty acid (10, 39, 63, 64). Several authors (9, 28, 65) suggested that these fluidity changes are related to intestinal transporter function, as demonstrated for the function of the erythrocyte glucose transporter (70). Decrease of membrane fluidity from intestinal crypt to villus (8) and from jejunal to ileal brush-border (64) may be relevant to transport differences in those situations as well.

SIGNALS

What "tells" the intestine to turn on the right transporters at the right time? This question exemplifies the broader question of developmental signals, whose identification is the central problem of developmental biology. Two classes of signals suggest themselves for the gastrointestinal tract (19): external signals, such as the changes in dietary solute inputs associated with weaning or hormones present in milk (e.g. epidermal growth factor), and internal signals, which are hard-wired genetically to occur at a certain time, independent of external circumstances. The internal signals in turn may either be centrally released hormones (e.g. glucocorticoid and thyroid hormones) that control many aspects of gastrointestinal development (30, 32, 33, 41, 42); or they may instead be local timers within the responding cells (e.g. enterocytes) themselves. While signalling in the control of lactase and sucrase expression has received much attention, there are only a few clues about signals controlling expression of intestinal transporters.

Recall that the fructose transporter turns on in rats around the time of weaning, when dietary fructose is normally first encountered. Does dietary fructose itself serve as an external signal controlling the transporter? Toloza & Diamond (77) proved that this is not the case by maintaining rat pups on a fructose-free artificial milk ration beyond the normal time of weaning and by showing that the fructose transporter still turned on at the usual time (around 3 weeks postnatally). Hence the signal must be internal.

Similarly, the monkey-fish prickleback normally switches from carnivory to herbivory as it grows, and its ratio of proline to glucose transport normally declines in step with the decline in dietary protein per carbohydrate ratio. But the transporter shift still occurs in fish maintained in the laboratory on a constant ration (12) so that an internal signal rather than the external one of dietary solute input must be responsible. The same conclusion applies to an omnivorous fish, the catfish, whose proline per glucose transport ratio normally declines during development in step with (but not triggered by) a decline in dietary protein per carbohydrate ratio (12).

Glucose transport normally declines in lambs around the time of weaning, when ingestion of complex carbohydrates, ruminal fermentation of carbohydrate to fatty acids, and hence a decline in sugar input to the intestine would normally begin. In lambs prevented from weaning and constrained to continue to drink milk, the onset of intestinal glucose transport is delayed and reduced in magnitude but not prevented (62). Hence, in this case both external and internal factors operate.

INTESTINAL AREA, CAPACITY, AND DIGESTIVE BOTTLENECKS

As an animal grows, its intestine also grows. Therefore, absolute values of intestinal uptake capacities (not capacities divided by body weight) increase with age although increases in uptake per mg of tissue also contribute for some solutes (e.g. fructose in mammals). Figure 6 shows the regularity of the increases in intestinal surface area and uptake capacity for sugars and AAs with body weight in a growing rabbit, and hence how finely tuned is the intestine's growth to the growing animal's nutrient requirements.

Table 1 summarizes, for five species, the slopes of double-logarithmic plots like Figure 6. A slope of 1.0 means that intestinal surface area or proline or glucose uptake capacity increases in direct proportion to body weight, while a slope below 1.0 means that the increase is less than proportional to body weight. (Recall that basal metabolic rate increases as the 0.75 power of body weight in growing animals.) Table 1 shows that all slopes are below 1.0 or close to 1.0 so that uptake capacity divided by body weight either declines or remains constant. Comparing the slopes of Table 1 with the capacities per body weight in Figure 2, one sees that the slopes are lowest and the declines in capacity per body weight steepest in cats, less so in rabbits, while in rats the slopes are close to 1.0 and capacity per body weight is fairly constant with age. Table 1 also shows that the ratio of the slope for glucose to that for proline exceeds 1.0 in rabbits, rats, and catfish, which take in more carbohydrate and less protein as they grow. Hence, glucose uptake capacity must increase faster with body weight than does proline uptake capacity. The highest slope (1.9) is for monkey-face prickleback, which switches from carnivory to herbivory as it grows. For cats, the ratio of slopes is much less

Table 1 Log/log slopes against body weight[a].

Species	Slope			Glucose slope/ proline slope
	surface area	glucose capacity	proline capacity	
Rat	1.08	1.08	0.93	1.16
Rabbit	0.77	0.78	0.67	1.16
Cat	0.70	0.47	0.71	0.66
Catfish	0.81	1.12	1.00	1.12
Prickleback	0.68	0.81	0.43	1.88
Trout	0.89	—	0.78	—

[a]Values correspond to Figure 6. Refs. 12, 14, 15, 77.

than 1.0 because suckling, but not adult, cats consume much carbohydrate; hence, glucose transport relative to proline transport decreases from suckling to adult cats.

We have calculated the daily uptake capacities for proline and glucose and compared them against estimated actual daily dietary inputs of these solutes in rats, rabbits, and cats at various stages from birth to weaning. While both calculations are only approximate, the most striking feature of our calculations is that the ratios of capacity to input are of the order of 1 for both solutes in all three species at all ages. Hence, the intestine never possesses an enormous excess absorptive capacity. Instead, just enough intestine and transporters are synthesized to absorb the expected nutrient loads so that biosynthetic energy is not wasted on unneeded tissue and molecules but ingested nutrients are not wasted either. The intestine exemplifies the motto, "Enough but not too much." Ferraris & Diamond (this volume) show that the same motto applies to regulation of transporter activities by dietary substrate levels in the adult.

Our calculations also suggests that these ratios of uptake capacity to dietary input are somewhat higher in growing rabbits than in growing rats. That is, rabbits may have slightly more excess absorptive capacity than rats, whose intestine may operate closer to the level where transporters would impose a digestive bottleneck on growth. If this difference is real, it might explain why suckling rabbits nursed with twice the usual amount of milk exhibit increased growth rates (48), while similarly overfed infant rats cannot respond with increased growth until after 10 days postpartem (78).

SUMMARY AND OUTLOOK

New information about intestinal transporter development is accumulating rapidly. Most transporters are first expressed prenatally, but the time varies with species and transporter. Striking postnatal changes in expression include the declines of galactose and taurine transport, the postweaning turn-on of mammalian fructose, bile acid, and (in rats) lysine transporters, surges in chicken transporters when yolk reserves are exhausted and when feather molt peaks, and the steeper postnatal decline in transport for essential AAs than nonessential AAs. There are major shifts in transporter distribution along the axes from duodenum to colon and from crypt to villus. Mechanisms of these developmental changes may include changes in transporter number and membrane fluidity, plus sequential replacement of related transporters by each other. In the few well-studied cases to date, genetically hard-wired signals prove more important than external dietary signals in controlling transporter development. Growth of intestinal absorptive capacity is closely matched to the growing animal's needs.

We are just acquiring the background facts needed to address the most interesting questions in this area. Obvious unsolved problems include to resolve developmental patterns for discrete hexose and amino acid transporters, to understand the functional significance of why transporters appear either prenatally and postnatally, to identify the underlying molecular mechanisms and signals, and to test whether species differ in excess absorptive capacity in ecologically meaningful ways.

ACKNOWLEDGMENTS

It is a pleasure to record our debt to many colleagues who generously provided manuscripts, data, and suggestions. Supported by NIH grants GM 14772 and AM 17328 (UCLA Center for Ulcer Research and Education).

Literature Cited

1. Altmann, G. G., Enesco, M. 1967. Cell number as a measure of distribution and renewal of epithelial cells in the small intestine of growing and adult rats. *Am. J. Anat.* 121:319–36
2. Barnard, J. A., Ghishan, F. K., Wilson, F. A. 1985. Ontogenesis of taurocholate transport by rat ileal brush border membrane vesicles. *J. Clin. Invest.* 75:869–73
3. Bartsocas, C. S. 1977. Developmental aspects of amino acid transport. *Biol. Neonate* 31:60–64
4. Beaulieu, J.-F., Calvert, R. 1987. Hormonal regulation of epithelial cell proliferation in the fetal mouse duodenum in vitro. *Anat. Rec.* 217:250–55
5. Beechey, R. B., Kemp, R. B., Shirazi-Beechey, S. P. 1987. Changes in the intestinal transport activities during the maturation of sheep. *J. Physiol.* 396:27P
6. Boass, A., Wilson, T. H. 1963. Development of mechanisms for intestinal absorption of vitamin B_{12} in growing rats. *Am. J. Physiol.* 204:101–4
7. Bogner, P. H., Haines, I. A. 1964. Functional development of active sugar transport in the chick intestine. *Am. J. Physiol.* 207:37–41
8. Brasitus, T. A., Dudeja, P. K. 1985. Alterations in the physical state and composition of brush border membrane lipids of rat enterocytes during differentiation. *Arch. Biochem. Biophys.* 240:483–88
9. Brasitus, T. A., Schachter, D., Mamouneas, T. G. 1979. Functional interactions of lipids and proteins in rat intestinal microvillus membranes. *Biochemistry* 18:4136–44
10. Brasitus, T. A., Yeh, K.-Y., Holt, P. R., Schachter, D. 1984. Lipid fluidity and composition of intestinal microvillus membranes isolated from rats of different ages. *Biochim. Biophys. Acta* 778:341–48

11. Buddington, R. K. 1987. Does the natural diet influence the intestine's ability to regulate glucose absorption? *J. Comp. Physiol.* 157:677–88
12. Buddington, R. K., Chen, J. W., Diamond, J. M. 1987. Genetic and phenotypic adaptation of intestinal nutrient transport to diet in fish. *J. Physiol.* 393:261–81
13. Buddington, R. K., Chen, J. W., Diamond, J. M. 1989. Adaptive flexibility of the intestinal nutrient transporters is dependent on the evolutionary diet. *Am. J. Physiol.* In press
14. Buddington, R. K., Diamond, J. M. 1989. Ontogenetic development of nutrient transporters in rabbit intestine. *Am. J. Physiol.* In press
15. Buddington, R. K., Diamond, J. M. 1989. Ontogenetic development of nutrient transporters in cat intestine. *Am. J. Physiol.* In press
16. Buddington, R. K., Hilton, J. W. 1987. Intestinal adaptations of rainbow trout to changes in dietary carbohydrate. *Am. J. Physiol.* 253:G489–96
17. Butt, J. H. II, Wilson, T. H. 1968. Development of sugar and amino acid transport by intestine and yolk sac of the guinea pig. *Am. J. Physiol.* 215:1468–77
18. Cooke, H. J., Pfankuche, L., Cooke, A. R. 1980. Tryptophan transport by isolated newborn rat jejunum. *Am. J. Physiol.* 239:G306–10
19. Diamond, J. M. 1986. Hard-wired local triggering of intestinal enzyme expression. *Nature* 324:408
20. Diamond, J. M., Karasov, W. H. 1984. Effect of dietary carbohydrate on monosaccharide uptake by mouse small intestine *in vitro. J. Physiol.* 349:419–40
21. Doubek, W. G., Armbrecht, H. J. 1987. Changes in intestinal glucose transport over the lifespan of the rat. *Mech. Ageing Dev.* 39:91–102
22. Ferraris, R. F., Kwan, W. W., Diamond, J. M. 1988. Regulatory signals for intestinal amino acid transporters and peptidases. *Am. J. Physiol.* 255:G151–57
23. Freeman, H. J., Quamme, G. A. 1986. Age-related changes in sodium-dependent glucose transport in rat small intestine. *Am. J. Physiol.* 251:G208–17
24. Ghishan, F. K., Wilson, F. A. 1985. Developmental maturation of D-glucose transport by rat jejunal brush-border membrane vesicles. *Am. J. Physiol.* 248:G87–92
25. Goda, T., Yamada, K., Bustamante, S., Edmond, J., Grimes, J., Koldovsky, O. 1985. Precocious increase of sucrase activity by carbohydrates in the small intestine of suckling rats. I. Significance of the stress effect of sugar-induced diarrhea. *J. Pediatr. Gastroenterol. Nutr.* 4:468–75
26. Goldspink, D. F., Lewis, S. E. M., Kelly, F. J. 1984. Protein synthesis during the developmental growth of the small and large intestine of the rat. *Biochem. J.* 217:527–34
27. Guandalini, S., Rubino, A. 1982. Development of dipeptide transport in the intestinal mucosa of rabbits. *Pediatr. Res.* 16:99–103
28. Hayashi, K., Kawasaki, T. 1982. The characteristic changes of amino acid transport during development in brush border membrane vesicles of the guinea pig ileum. *Biochim. Biophys. Acta* 691:83–90
29. Henin, S., Smith, M. W. 1976. Electrical properties of pig colonic mucosa measured during early post-natal development. *J. Physiol.* 262:169–87
30. Henning, S. J. 1981. Postnatal development: coordination of feeding, digestion, and metabolism. *Am. J. Physiol.* 241:G199–214
31. Henning, S. J. 1984. Hormonal and dietary regulation of intestinal enzyme development. In *Intestinal Toxicology*, ed. C. M. Schiller, pp. 17–32. New York: Raven. 252 pp.
32. Henning, S. J. 1985. Ontogeny of enzymes in the small intestine. *Annu. Rev. Physiol.* 47:231–45
33. Henning, S. J. 1987. Functional development of the gastrointestinal tract. In *Physiology of the Gastrointestinal Tract*, ed. L. R. Johnson, pp. 286–300. New York: Raven. 1780 pp. 2nd ed.
34. Heubi, J. E., Fellows, J. L. 1985. Postnatal development of intestinal bile salt transport. Relationship to membrane physicochemical changes. *J. Lipid Res.* 26:797–805
35. Heubi, J. E., Fondacaro, J. D. 1982. Postnatal development of intestinal bile salt transport in the guinea pig. *Am. J. Physiol.* 243:G189–94
36. Himukai, M., Konno, T., Hoshi, T. 1980. Age-dependent changes in intestinal absorption of dipeptides and their constituent amino acids in the guinea pig. *Pediatr. Res.* 14:1272–75
37. James, P. S., Smith, M. W. 1976. Methionine transport by pig colonic mucosa measured during early post-natal development. *Am. J. Physiol.* 262:151–68
38. Jarvis, L. G., Morgan, G., Smith, M. W., Wooding, F. B. P. 1977. Cell replacement and changing transport

function in the neonatal pig colon. *J. Physiol.* 273:717–29

39. Keelan, M., Walker, K., Thomson, A. B. R. 1985. Intestinal morphology, marker enzymes and lipid content of brush border membranes from rabbit jejunum and ileum: effect of aging. *Mech. Ageing Dev.* 31:49–68

40. Koldovsky, O. 1972. Hormonal and dietary factors in the development of digestion and absorption. In *Nutrition and Development*, ed. M. Winick, pp. 135–200. New York: Wiley. 245 pp.

41. Koldovsky, O. 1981. Developmental, dietary, and hormonal control of intestinal disaccharidases in mammals (including man). In *Carbohydrate Metabolism and Its Disorders*, ed. P. J. Randle, D. F. Steiner, W. J. Whelan, 3:481–522. London: Academic

42. Koldovsky, O. 1984. Development of human gastrointestinal functions: interaction of changes in diet composition, hormonal maturation, and fetal genetic programming. *J. Am. Coll. Nutr.* 3:131–38

43. Koldovsky, O., Heringova, A., Jirsova, V., Jirasek, J. E., Uher, J. 1965. Transport of glucose against a concentration gradient in everted sacs of jejunum and ileum of human fetuses. *Gastroenterology* 48:185–87

44. Koldovsky, O., Sunshine, P., Kretchmer, N. 1966. Cellular migration of intestinal epithelia in suckling and weaned rats. *Nature* 212:1389–90

45. Lester, R., Smallwood, R. A., Little, J. M., Brown, A. S., Piasecki, G. J., Jackson, B. T. 1977. Fetal bile salt metabolism. *J. Clin. Invest.* 59:1009–16

46. Levin, R. J., Koldovsky, O., Hoskova, J., Jirsova, V., Uher, J. 1968. Electrical activity across human foetal small intestine associated with absorption processes. *Gut* 9:206–13

47. Little, J. M., Lester, R. 1980. Ontogenesis of intestinal bile salt absorption in the neonatal rat. *Am. J. Physiol.* 239:G319–23

48. McNitt, J. I., Moody, G. L. Jr. 1988. Milk intake and growth rates of suckling rabbits. *Proc. N. Am. Rabbit Congress.* In press

49. Moriyama, I. S. 1986. Development of fetal organs and adaptation to extrauterine life. *Acta Obstet. Gynaecol. Jpn. Engl. Ed.* 38:1227–37

50. Moyer, M. S., Goodrich, A. L., Rolfes, M. M., Suchy, F. J. 1988. Ontogenesis of intestinal taurine transport: evidence for a β carrier in developing rat jejunum. *Am. J. Physiol.* 254:6870–77

51. Moyer, M. S., Heubi, J. E., Goodrich, A. L., Balistreri, W. F., Suchy, F. J. 1986. Ontogeny of bile acid transport in brush border membrane vesicles from rat ileum. *Gastroenterology* 90: 1188–96

52. Mulvihill, S. J., Stone, M. M., Debas, H. T., Fonkalsrud, E. W. 1985. The role of amniotic fluid in fetal nutrition. *J. Pediatr. Surg.* 20:668–72

53. Obst, B. S., Diamond, J. M. 1989. Ontogenetic development of nutrient transporters in chicken intestine. *Auk.* In press

54. Planas, J. M., Villa, M. C., Ferrer, R., Moreto, M. 1986. Hexose transport by chicken cecum during development. *Pflüegers Arch.* 407:216–20

55. Potter, G. D., Burlingame, S. M. 1986. Glucose-coupled sodium absorption in the developing rat colon. *Am. J. Physiol.* 250:G221–26

56. Potter, G. D., Lester, R. 1984. The developing colon and nutrition. *J. Pediatr. Gastroenterol. Nutr.* 3:485–81

57. Potter, G. D., Schmidt, K. L., Lester, R. 1983. Glucose absorption by in vitro perfused colon of the fetal rat. *Am. J. Physiol.* 245:G424–30

58. Rubino, A. 1975. Absorption of amino acids and peptides during development. *Mod. Probl. Paediatr.* 15:201–12

59. Said, H. M., Ghishan, F. K., Greene, H. L., Hollander, D. 1985. Developmental maturation of riboflavin intestinal transport in the rat. *Pediatr. Res.* 19:1175–78

60. Said, H. M., Ghishan, F. K., Murrell, J. E. 1985. Ontogenesis of intestinal transport of 5-methyltetrahydrofolate in the rat. *Am. J. Physiol.* 249:G567–71

61. Said, H. M., Redha, R. 1988. Ontogenesis of the intestinal transport of biotin in the rat. *Gastroenterology* 94:68–72

62. Scharrer, R., Liebich, H.-G., Raab, W., Promberger, N. 1979. Influence of age and rumen development on intestinal absorption of galactose and glucose in lambs. *Zentralbl. Veterinaermed. Reihe A* 26:95–105

63. Schwarz, S. M., Hostetler, B., Ling, S., Mone, M., Watkins, J. B. 1985. Intestinal membrane lipid composition and fluidity during development in the rat. *Am. J. Physiol.* 248:G200–7

64. Schwarz, S. M., Ling, S., Hostetler, B., Draper, J. P., Watkins, J. B. 1984. Lipid composition and membrane fluidity in the small intestine of the developing rabbit. *Gastroenterology* 86:1544–51

65. Schwarz, S. M., Ling, S., Hostetler, B.,

Watkins, J. B. 1982. Taurocholate transport in the developing ileum: structural functional relationships. *Gastroenterology* 82:1174

66. Sepulveda, F. V., Smith, M. W. 1979. Different mechanisms for neutral amino acid uptake by new-born pig colon. *J. Physiol.* 286:479–90

67. Sheard, N. F., Zeisel, S. H. 1986. An *in vitro* study of choline uptake by intestine from neonatal and adult rats. *Pediatr. Res.* 20:768–72

68. Shehata, A. T., Lerner, J., Miller, D. S. 1981. Development of brush-border membrane hexose transport system in chick jejunum. *Am. J. Physiol.* G102–8

69. Shehata, A. T., Lerner, J., Miller, D. S. 1984. Development of nutrient transport systems in chick jejunum. *Am. J. Physiol.* 246:G101–7

70. Shinitzky, M., Borochov, H., Wilbrandt, W. 1980. Lipid fluidity as a physiological regulator of membrane transport and enzyme activities. In *Membrane Transport in Erythrocytes,* ed. U. V. Lassen, H. H. Ussing, J. O. Wieth, pp. 91–107. Copenhagen: Munksgaard. 557 pp.

71. Smith, M. W. 1981. Autoradiographic analysis of alanine uptake by newborn pig intestine. *Experientia* 37:868–70

72. Smith, M. W., James, P. S. 1976. Amino acid transport by the helicoidal colon of the new-born pig. *Biochim. Biophys. Acta* 419:391–94

73. Smith, M. W., Jarvis, L. G. 1978. Growth and cell replacement in the new-born pig intestine. *Proc. R. Soc. London Ser. B* 203:69–89

74. Solberg, D. H., Diamond, J. M. 1987. Comparison of different dietary sugars as inducers of intestinal sugar transporters. *Am. J. Physiol.* 252:G574–84

75. Thompson, J. F., Singh, M., Wang, Y., Zucker, C., Heird, W. C. 1986. Developmental differences in the effect of natural feeding on early enteric mucosal growth of guinea pigs. *J. Pediatr. Gastroenterol. Nutr.* 5:643–47

76. Thomson, A. B. R. 1979. Unstirred water layer and age-dependent changes in rabbit jejunal D-glucose transport. *Am. J. Physiol.* 236:E685–91

77. Toloza, E. M., Diamond, J. M. 1989. Ontogenetic development of nutrient transporters in rat intestine. *Am. J. Physiol.* In press

78. West, D. B., Diaz, J., Woods, S. C. 1982. Infant gastronomy and chronic formula infusion as a technique to overfeed and accelerate weight gain of neonatal rats. *J. Nutr.* 112:1339–43

79. Wright, G. H., Nixon, D. A. 1961. Absorption of amniotic fluid in the gut of foetal sheep. *Nature* 190:816

80. Younoszai, M. K., Smith, C., Finch, M. H. 1985. Comparison of in vitro jejunal uptake of L-valine and L-lysine in the rat during maturation. *J. Pediatr. Gastroenterol. Nutr.* 4:992–97

ENDOCRINOLOGY

ENDOCRINE REGULATION OF GENE EXPRESSION

Introduction, Jack L. Kostyo, *Section Editor*

Much of the early history of the field of endocrinology was dominated by the discovery of new hormones and investigations of their actions on complex physiological processes, such as growth, reproduction, and intermediary metabolism, at the whole organism level. As the details of physiological processes at the cellular and molecular level began to unfold, endocrinologists focused their attention on the interactions of hormones with cells and how these interactions are translated into changes in cell function that ultimately result in physiological regulation at the organ and organism level. It soon became apparent that many of the actions of hormones resulting in changes in structure or function of the organism were caused by hormone-mediated changes in the amounts of key proteins produced by cells, such as enzymes, receptors, or other hormones. It is now widely recognized that many hormones exert such effects by altering the expression of the genes for these key proteins.

Today, the field of endocrinology is dominated by efforts to uncover the molecular mechanisms that translate the interaction of a hormone with its target cell into a change in gene expression. Remarkable progress has been

621

made to date, and given the advances being made in the understanding of gene regulation throughout the discipline of biology, endocrine research in this area should be most fruitful for some time to come. The Endocrinology section of this volume contains six chapters describing work on the regulation of gene expression by a variety of hormones. Given the burgeoning nature of this research, these six chapters provide the reader with a sampler, rather than a comprehensive coverage, of the exciting work in progress in this area of endocrinology.

Annu. Rev. Physiol. 1989. 51:623–39

REGULATION OF GENE EXPRESSION BY THYROID HORMONE

Herbert H. Samuels[1,2], *Barry Marc Forman*[2], *Zebulun D. Horowitz*[1], *and Zheng-Sheng Ye*[2]

[1]The Division of Molecular Endocrinology, Department of Medicine, and [2]the Department of Pharmacology, New York University Medical Center, New York, NY, 10016

INTRODUCTION

Research over the past decade using intact animals and cultured cells has provided compelling evidence that the thyroid hormones (3, 5, 3', 5'-tetraiodo-L-thyronine L-T4, and 3, 5, 3'triiodo-L-thyronine L-T3) exert their effects in various cells and tissues by stimulating the accumulation of mRNAs that code for specific proteins. Thyroid-hormone–dependent effects that have been studied in detail include regulation of growth hormone gene expression in cultured rat pituitary cell lines (16, 18, 41, 51, 65, 70, 76, 78, 83, 94) stimulation of malic enzyme mRNA in the liver (1, 49, 50, 80, 87) as well as several other genes that encode hepatic proteins of unknown function (S_{11} and S_{14}) (5, 46, 58, 85) and stimulation of the α-myosin heavy chain gene in the myocardium (15, 19, 32, 47, 81). In addition to stimulating gene expression, the thyroid hormones also inhibit the expression of certain genes, most notably thyrotropin (6, 39, 79) and the β-myosin heavy chain gene (15, 19, 32, 47, 81). Concerning the genes indicated, the effects of the thyroid hormones (both positive and negative regulation) occur fully or primarily at the transcriptional level.

Abundant evidence indicates that most if not all of the significant cellular responses regulated by the thyroid hormones are mediated by a cellular receptor localized to the cell nucleus (56, 64). This evidence has been derived from studies in intact animals (56, 58) and cultured cells (64, 68, 71, 94). Several related strains of growth-hormone–producing rat pituitary cell lines

0066-4278/89/0315-0623$02.00

(GH$_1$, GH$_3$, GH$_4$, and GC) provide excellent cell culture models for studying thyroid hormone action. In these cells physiological concentrations of L-T3 and L-T4 stimulate growth hormone synthesis and growth hormone mRNA accumulation (16, 18, 41, 51, 65, 70, 76, 78, 83, 94), and the kinetics of stimulation are similar to that of the anterior pituitary after thyroid hormone injection (28). These cell lines contain thyroid hormone nuclear receptors that have affinity and hydrodynamic properties similar to those of receptors in various tissues in vivo. A review of the effects of the thyroid hormones on hepatic gene expression has been published (58). In this chapter we review recent developments in the study of thyroid hormone action involving cloning of thyroid-hormone-receptor–related mRNAs and use of the rat growth hormone gene as a model to identify *cis*-acting DNA sequences and *trans*-acting regulatory proteins required for transcriptional stimulation of the gene by thyroid hormone.

GENERAL PROPERTIES OF THYROID HORMONE RECEPTORS

The affinity of thyroid hormone receptors for L-T3, L-T4, and other iodothyronines parallels the iodothyronine biologic potency in cultured cells (68) and in intact animals (75). If the affinity for receptor and the biologic potency of L-T3 is assigned the value of 1, the values for three other well-studied iodothyronines are: triiodothyroacetic acid (TRIAC), 3.0; L-T4, 0.10; and 3, 3'5'-triiodo-L-thyronine (reverse-L-T3), 0.01. These relative affinities have been found for receptor in rat brain, liver, and kidney and for receptor in a variety of cultured cell lines derived from the rat and other species (64, 68, 74, 75). Scatchard analysis of hormone binding to receptor demonstrates linear plots with no evidence for positive or negative cooperativity (38, 69, 71a, 72). GH$_1$ and GC cell nuclei contain approximately 15,000–20,000 receptor molecules per cell nucleus (62, 69, 71a, 72, 94). The anterior pituitary and rat liver have approximately 8,000–10,000 receptors per cell nucleus, whereas other tissues have lower levels of receptor abundance (57, 59, 77). Unlike steroid hormone receptors, no cytoplasmic counterpart of the nuclear receptor has been identified when cells are lysed (8, 72), and these receptors can associate with nuclear components in the absence of ligand (38, 72, 82). Thyroid hormone receptor in nuclear extracts can associate with DNA in vitro (48, 61), and the receptor appears to be predominantly located to linker DNA regions in chromatin (26, 35, 61).

GH$_1$ cell receptor, extracted from nuclei with buffer containing 0.4 M KC1, has a sedimentation coefficient of 3.8 S, a Stokes radius of 3.3 nm, and a particle density of 1.36 g/cm^3 (61). Micrococcal nuclease digestion studies of chromatin suggest the GH$_1$ receptor protects a DNA fragment of approximately 35 base pairs (bp) (61). Based on the sedimentation coefficient, the Stokes radius, and the particle density, the molecular weight (M_r) of the salt-extracted receptor was estimated to be 54,000 (61). Similar results have also been reported for receptor extracted from rat liver nuclei by high salt concentrations (M_r = 50,000, Stokes radius = 3.5 nm) (44). The DNA binding properties of the receptor are retained when the salt concentration is lowered to 0.1 M KCl (48, 61), and the affinity of salt-extracted receptor for iodothyronines (72) is identical to that of receptor in isolated nuclei (71b), which suggests that the interaction of receptor with DNA does not alter its affinity for ligand. The structure of the GH_1 cell receptor was also examined using a photoaffinity-label derivative of $L-[^{125}I]T3$, which, on exposure to ultraviolet light (254 nm), covalently modifies residues that are sterically favored in the hormone-binding domain (8, 31, 60). These studies identified two photoaffinity-labeled receptor forms in GH_1 cells: an abundant 47,000 M_r component and a less abundant 57,000 M_r doublet species (8, 31, 60). Results of studies combining the techniques of photoaffinity labeling (60) and dense amino acid labeling (62) indicated that the two M_r receptor forms have similar receptor synthetic rates but different half-lives (the half-life of the 57,000 M_r form is approximately 2 hr, whereas the half-life of the 47, 000 M_r form is approximately 6 hr) (8). Results of recent studies in which several thyroid-hormone-receptor–related cDNAs have been cloned support the view that cells may express more than one thyroid hormone receptor protein.

THE THYROID HORMONE RECEPTOR IS RELATED TO THE AVIAN ERYTHROBLASTOSIS VIRUS v-erbA GENE

The avian erythroblastosis virus (AEV) induces sarcomas and erythroblastosis in vivo and induces transformation of fibroblasts and erythroblasts to neoplastic phenotypes in vitro (89). Two domains of the AEV genome were functionally identified: the v-erbA region and the v-erbB region (89). The v-erbB gene encodes a truncated, constitutively active epidermal growth factor receptor (17, 23, 27, 33, 55). Although v-erbB is responsible for the transforming potential of the AEV, v-erbA is required for the full effect of v-erbB (13, 21, 24). A human homolog of the v-erbA gene was identified on human chromosome 17 near the breakpoint found typically in human promyelocytic leukemia, while v-erbB was localized to chromosome 7 (14, 63, 84). Using v-erbA sequences as a probe, Vennstrom & Bishop (88) first identified that chick cells expressed a cellular homolog (c-erbA) of the v-erbA gene.

Following the cloning of the human glucocorticoid receptor cDNA (30), Weinberger et al (90) noted that a cysteine-rich region of the glucocorticoid receptor showed a high degree of amino acid homology (approximately 50%) with a region of the v-erbA gene. With the cloning of other steroid hormone receptor cDNAs (e.g. progesterone and estrogen receptor) (10, 25, 34, 40), the cysteine-rich region of each receptor was also found to show high homology with a cysteine-rich region of the *v-erbA* gene. Based on a comparison of the regions of amino acid homology of the human and chick estrogen receptor, Krust et al (40) divided the domains of the proteins into regions labeled A, B, C, D, E, and F. Between the chick and human estrogen receptors, the cysteine-rich C regions showed 100% homology, and the long E region at the carboxy-terminal end of the protein showed 94% homology. Other regions showed much lower levels of homology. The C region of the various steroid receptors has been mapped to the DNA-binding region (29, 52), and the sequence of the cysteine-rich region is similar but not identical to other regulatory proteins (e.g. TFIIIA) that contain zinc-associated "DNA-binding fingers." Other regions of the molecule, however, may also be important in influencing the transcriptional response that might mediate protein-protein contact of receptor with other regulatory proteins. The E region of the various steroid receptors appears to contain the ligand-binding domain and shows lower degrees of homology between the different steroid receptors (40).

Using a *v-erbA* probe to the E region of the viral gene, cellular homologs of *v-erbA* have recently been isolated from a chick embryo cDNA library (73, 88) and a human placenta cDNA library (91). The in vitro translation products of RNA transcripts of these clones were found to bind L-T3, L-T4, and other iodothyronine analogs with the same relative affinity (73, 91) as found for thyroid hormone nuclear receptor in GH_1 cells and other rat tissues (68, 74). The chick *c-erbA* encodes a 408–amino-acid protein, while the human *c-erbA* isolated from the placental library encodes a 456-amino-acid protein. The gene that encodes the human *c-erbA* was localized to chromosome 3 (91), whereas previous studies localized a *v-erbA*–related sequence to chromosome 17 (14, 84), which suggests that the human genome has at least two *erbA*-related genes. Unlike chick *c-erbA,* the *v-erbA* gene product (75,000 M_r containing viral gag sequences at the N-terminus) does not bind to thyroid hormone (73). It is, however, a DNA binding protein, which suggests it might act to block or constitutively activate gene expression (73). Both the human and chick *c-erbA*s show high homology within the putative DNA-binding C region (68 amino acids) and by analogy to steroid hormone receptors, the putative ligand-binding E region (206 amino acids) (73, 91). Other regions of these *c-erbA*s are less conserved, however, and Weinberger et al have suggested that the cloned chick *c-erbA* is more related to the *erbA* gene on human chromosome 17 than to the one on chromosome 3 (91).

As of early 1988, two other *c-erbA* cDNAs had been cloned and sequenced (2, 86). Thompson et al (86) isolated a *c-erbA* cDNA from a whole rat brain cDNA library; it codes for a protein of 410 amino acids. In contrast to the *c-erbA* isolated from the human placental library, the rat brain *c-erbA* cDNA showed preferential hybridization to human chromosome 17. The rat brain *c-erbA* showed greater homology with the chick *c-erbA* in the putative DNA-binding C region (97%) and the putative ligand-binding E region (94%) than with the comparable regions of the human placental *c-erbA* (90% in the C region and 85% in the E region). Results from hybridization studies with the rat brain *c-erbA* cDNA using total RNA from a variety of tissues and cells identified an abundant 2.6 kb mRNA and less abundant mRNA species of approximately 5.0 and 6.0 kb in the brain, kidney, gut and heart, and to a lesser degree in the lung, testes, and spleen but not in liver. These results suggest this *c-erbA*–related mRNA might be expressed in a tissue-specific manner. In addition to the apparent low expression of an mRNA related to the brain *c-erbA* in liver, the relative affinity of the translated *c-erbA* protein for TRIAC, L-T3, and L-T4 was reported to be different from the affinity of the endogenous receptor studied in liver and in GH_1 cells. The affinity for TRIAC and L-T3 were identical, and the affinity for L-T4 was approximately 50-fold lower than for the other two compounds (86). These relative affinities, however, differ from that reported for receptor in rat brain nuclei (74), which suggests that the cloned rat brain *c-erbA* protein is not significantly expressed in brain or is expressed in a small subset of brain cells and would not be detected in analysis of whole brain nuclei.

Benbrook & Pfahl (2) recently isolated a *c-erbA* clone from an adult human testes cDNA library; the clone encodes a protein of 490 amino acids and shows greater homology with the chick *c-erbA* in the putative DNA-binding C region (96%) and the putative ligand-binding E region (94%) than with the comparable regions of the human placental *c-erbA* (87% in the C region and 84% in the E region). The high homology with the chick *c-erbA* protein suggests that this human *c-erbA* may be a product of the previously identified *v-erbA*–related gene on human chromosome 17. The affinity was only reported for L-T3, however, so whether the ligand-binding properties of the human testes *c-erbA* are similar to or different from those reported for the other *c-erbA* proteins remains unknown.

The identification of several *c-erbA* thyroid-hormone-receptor–related cDNA clones has been interpreted to suggest tissue-specific or functional heterogeneity of thyroid hormone receptors (86). In our view, the information available is too premature to draw these conclusions. First, we have found that the chick *c-erbA* and human placental *c-erbA* similarly regulate thyroid hormone response genes in transfected cells (20a). Therefore, additional information is required to determine whether these *c-erbA* proteins regulate gene expression in a functionally different fashion or influence the expression of different genes. Second, the fact that a specific-size *c-erbA* mRNA is more abundant than other *c-erbA*–related species does not necessarily indicate that it codes for the nuclear-associated receptor detected in a particular cell or tissue. Such evidence would require the cloning of the different-size *c-erbA*–

related mRNAs in various tissues, followed by the development of specific antibody probes to assess the level of expression of the protein encoded by each *c-erbA* mRNA. Nevertheless, cloning of these *c-erbA*s is a major advance in the study of thyroid hormone action and should facilitate our understanding of how the receptor transcriptionally regulates gene expression.

DNA SEQUENCES OF THE RAT GROWTH HORMONE GENE THAT MEDIATE BASAL AND REGULATED EXPRESSION BY THYROID HORMONE

Studies of several thyroid-hormone–responsive genes indicate that regulation occurs fully or partly at the transcriptional level. This level of regulation is true for genes in which L-T3 stimulates (e.g. rat growth hormone) (18, 83, 94) or inhibits (e.g. thyrotropin) (6, 39, 79) expression. The transcription rate of the growth hormone and thyrotropin genes is modulated within minutes of thyroid hormone exposure (79, 94), which supports the notion that the thyroid-hormone–receptor complex binds to *cis*-acting DNA sequences (referred to as a thyroid hormone response element) and that this element modulates gene transcription rates. Virtually all thyroid-hormone–responsive genes (e.g. rat growth hormone, thyrotropin, S_{14}, malic enzyme, and the α-myosin and β-myosin heavy chain genes) are regulated in a cell-specific or tissue-specific fashion. Therefore, in addition to defining the location of a thyroid hormone response element(s), researchers must identify the *trans*-acting factors and *cis*-acting elements involved in mediating cell-specific expression to fully understand how thyroid hormone modulates the expression of these genes.

Because the sequence of the rat growth hormone gene is known and cultured rat-growth-hormone–producing cells are available for transfection, current information on the *cis*-acting elements and *trans*-acting factors involved in thyroid-hormone–regulated expression has come from studies of the rat growth hormone gene (7, 12, 20, 22, 37, 42, 43, 54, 93, 95, 96). As discussed below, however, some disagreement exists concerning the location of the *cis*-acting sequences of the rat growth hormone gene that mediate cell-specific and thyroid-hormone–regulated expression. Figure 1 shows the location and sequence of the regulatory elements identified in various studies. Functional identification of these DNA elements has been derived from studies of stable and transient transfection using chimeric plasmids in which 5'-flanking gene sequences have been linked to reporter genes. The xanthine-guanine phosphoribosyl transferase gene *(XGPT)* (7) and the neomycin resistance gene (neo) (12, 93) have been used as reporter genes for stable transfection studies, and the chloramphenicol acetyl transferase gene *(CAT)* has been used for analysis by transient transfection (20, 22, 37, 42, 43, 54, 95, 96).

The chimeric plasmids that contain varying lengths of rat-growth-hormone–5'-flanking DNA linked to these reporter genes have been respectively referred to as pGH-xgpt, pGH-neo, and pGH-cat.

Stable Transformation Studies

Using GC cells stably transformed with a pGH-xgpt plasmid containing 1800 bp of 5'-flanking DNA of the rat growth hormone gene, Casanova et al (7) showed that sequences between -1800 and $+7$ contain elements that are sufficient to account for the extent of thyroid hormone stimulation of the gene. S_1 nuclease mapping documented accurate transcriptional initiation of the gene for both basal and thyroid-hormone–regulated expression (7). In contrast, when the rat growth hormone gene was used to transfect heterologous cells, correct transcriptional initiation and L-T3 regulation did not occur (36). These results suggest that rat growth hormone producing cells contain *trans*-acting factors that dictate cell-specific expression of the gene. Using a series of pGH-neo deletion mutants to stably transform GC cells, Crew & Spindler (12) concluded that the elements that mediated thyroid-hormone–regulated expression were contained within the first 235 bp of

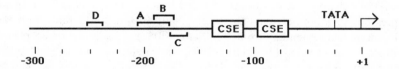

A.   -208   -178
       CTGGCAAAGGCGGCGGTGGAAAGGTAAGATC

B.   -190   -170
       GAAAGGTAAGATCAGGGACGT

C.   -178   -163
       CAGGGACGTGACCGCA

D.   -254   -241
       GGGTGGTCTCTGTA

Figure 1 *Cis*-acting elements in the 5'-flanking region of the rat growth hormone gene. The sequences thought to be involved in mediating cell-specific basal expression ($-137/-107$ and $-95/-65$) are indicated by the two boxed regions designated CSE. Also shown are sequences (*A, B, C,* and *D*) that have been reported to contain elements (fully or partly) that behave functionally as thyroid hormone response elements. References for these sequences are as follows: 96, sequence *A*; 37, sequence *B*; 22, sequence *C*; 93, sequence *D*.

5'-flanking DNA. More recent stable transformation studies by the same investigators indicated, however, that the DNA sequence that mediated thyroid hormone stimulation of the gene was located between −254 and −241 (Figure 1, sequence *D*) (93). This result differs from those obtained using transient gene expression, which are described below.

Transient Gene Expression Studies

Larsen et al (42) initially reported thyroid hormone regulation studies in which GC cells were transiently transfected with various pGH-cat plasmids. When GC cells were transfected with a pGH-cat plasmid extending to −1753 bp, L-T3 stimulated *CAT* gene expression 2.8-fold. The extent of *CAT* stimulation by L-T3 increased to 4-fold to 5-fold with deletions to −237 and −211; it then fell to approximately 2-fold with a deletion to −202. No stimulation was found with deletions extending to −183 and −137, which suggests that sequences between −211 and −183 were important in mediating thyroid hormone stimulation. Flug et al (20) studied a series of pGH-cat vectors with 5'-flanking deletions extending to −1800, −530, −312, −236, −208, −181, −145, and −104. Basal *CAT* expression was similar for all the deletion mutants extending from −1800 to −145, while basal expression with the −104 deletion mutant was about 3-fold lower. L-T3 stimulated *CAT* gene expression to a similar maximal level (about 10-fold to 15-fold) with the deletion mutants extending from −1800 to −208. L-T3 stimulation decreased with a deletion to −181 (2-fold to 3-fold), while deletions to −145 and −104 eliminated thyroid hormone stimulation. These results generally agree with those of Larsen et al (42) except that some L-T3 stimulation was found with the −181 deletion. These results suggest that a strong thyroid hormone response element is located between −208 and −181 and a second, weaker functional element is located 3' of −181 bp.

The study by Flug et al (20) also suggested that sequences within the first 145 bp of 5'-flanking DNA are important in mediating cell-specific basal expression. None of the pGH-cat deletion mutants was found to express *CAT* in heterologous cells, which included Rat2 fibroblasts, H4 rat hepatoma cells, AtT-20 mouse pituitary cells that express proopiomelanocortin, or monkey kidney epithelial cells (CV-1 and Cos 7) (20, 96). The 3-fold to 4-fold higher level of basal expression of the −145 compared with the −104 deletion mutant in GC cells indicates that sequences between −145 to −104, which are highly conserved among the rat, human, and bovine growth hormone genes, play important roles in enhancing the extent of basal expression of the gene (20). This conclusion is further supported by studies that indicate that a cell-specific nuclear protein, found only in rat-growth-hormone–producing cells, generates a DNase I footprint between −95 and −65 (9, 95, 96) and between −137 and −107 (92, 96). The location of these cell-specific DNA elements (indicated as CSE) is shown in Figure 1. Similar results were reported for the human growth hormone gene (45), and this protein was found to enhance transcription of the human gene in an in vitro HeLa cell transcription system (3).

Evidence indicates the protein-DNA complexes that form in the two regions may be generated by the same protein or by proteins that recognize a similar sequence motif (TAAAT) found at the center of the two footprinted regions (45, 96). Results of functional studies indicate that the enchanced level of cell-specific expression of the -145 vs the -104 deletion mutant is due to a cooperative interaction of the protein(s) that bind to the $-95/-65$ and $-137/-107$ regions (96). Therefore, results of studies with both the rat and human growth hormone genes strongly support the notion that the $-137/-107$ and $-95/-65$ regions (Figure 1) function as elements that mediate cell-specific basal expression of these genes. These results and those of studies by Nelson et al (54) using other heterologous cells and a pGH-cat plasmid extending to -235, differ with results of recent studies by Larsen et al (43), who reported that a "silencer" element located between -554 and -237 is responsible for the suppression of rat growth hormone gene expression in heterologous but not homologous cells. The reason for this discrepancy is unclear and requires additional investigation.

Cell-Specific and Thyroid Hormone Response Elements in Thyroid Hormone Stimulation of Rat Growth Hormone Gene Expression

Flug et al (20) examined whether the highly conserved region between -145 and -104 was essential for thyroid-hormone–regulated expression. They studied L-T3 regulation of internal deletion mutants in which upstream sequences (e.g. $-530/-237$ and $-236/-146$) were ligated to the -104 promoter region. Only the $-236/-146$ region conferred L-T3–regulated expression to the -104 promoter, which indicates that sequences upstream of -236 and between -146 and -104 are not essential for regulated expression by thyroid hormone. More recently, Ye et al (96) reported that DNA from $-236/-178$ conferred full L-T3 regulation to the -104 rat growth hormone gene promoter and the sequence ($-236/-178$) functioned in either normal or inverted orientations. No significant L-T3 stimulation resulted when DNA from -181 to -146 was ligated in either orientation to the promoter, while full L-T3 stimulation occurred when only a 31-nucleotide fragment extending from -208 to -178 (Figure 1, sequence A) was ligated to the promoter (96). In contrast with the homologous rat growth hormone promoter, sequences between -236 and -146 did not confer L-T3 regulation to an enhancerless SV40 viral promoter, which indicates that the upstream region necessary for thyroid-hormone–regulated expression functions most efficiently with its homologous promoter (20). Similar results were also found using an enhancerless Rous Sarcoma viral promoter (96). Regulated expression of these heterologous promoters occurred, however, if sequences containing the cell-specific basal elements were ligated to the foreign promoters along with the upstream thyroid hormone response element, and this regulation occurred independent of the orientation of these elements (96).

These results suggest that the thyroid hormone and cell-specific elements of the rat growth hormone gene function as an enhancer like unit and are both required to confer efficient thyroid-hormone–regulated expression to heterologous promoters. Ye et al (96) proposed that thyroid hormone stimulates gene expression by acting via its receptor to enhance the function of the cell-specific basal element(s). This model proposed that the receptor binds to the −208/-178 region (96) and that the L-T3–receptor complex acts to stabilize or enhance the protein-DNA interactions of the cell-specific basal element to form a more active transcription complex that stimulates the level of gene expression.

Protein-DNA Interactions of Sequences That Function as Thyroid Hormone Response Elements

To clarify the above or other models of thyroid hormone regulation of gene expression, evidence is needed that the receptor binds to sequences that function as a thyroid hormone response element. A direct interaction of receptor with these sequences would strengthen the notion that the L-T3– receptor complex directly activates the gene and that stimulation is not mediated by another gene product stimulated by L-T3. In a recent study, Koenig et al (37) ligated DNA from −210 to −126 and from −237 to −139 to the rat growth hormone promoter extending to −137; both recombinants showed stimulation by L-T3. No stimulation was found, however, when DNA between −190 and −172 was deleted from these fragments, which suggests that a thyroid hormone response element was fully or partly localized to this region (Figure 1, sequence B). Using a partially purified thyroid hormone receptor preparation from rat liver (0.2%) and a −237/−56 fragment of the rat growth hormone gene, methylation interference was used to attempt to footprint the receptor binding region (37). Although methylation of two sites (−185 and −186) decreased protein binding, the major region where methylation interference prevented protein binding was at −176 to −174 and at −172 and −171. These results are in keeping with the −190 to −172 internal deletion mutants reported by Koenig et al (37), but the major sites of methylation interference (−176 to −174, and −172 and −171) are outside of the sequence (−208/−178) (Figure 1, sequence A) that Ye et al (96) found to contain a functional thyroid hormone response element. Since the liver receptor preparation used in the methylation interference study was only 0.2%

pure, verification that the protein-DNA complex identified was formed by receptor was not possible. Identification of the thyroid hormone response elements in the internal deletion mutant studies of Koenig et al (37) (-190 to -172) and Ye et al (96) (-208 to -178) suggests, however, that a functionally important region (fully or partly) resides between -190 and -178).

In contrast with these studies, Glass et al (22) recently suggested that the thyroid hormone response element of the rat growth hormone gene resides between -177 and -166 (Figure 1, sequence C). This suggestion is based on the observation that a $-235/-45$ fragment of the gene could confer L-T3 stimulation to a -107 Herpes viral thymidine kinase (TK) promoter, while no stimulation was found when sequences from -177 to -166 were internally deleted. When DNA from -186 to -158 was linked to the TK promoter, moderate L-T3 stimulation occurred (2.7-fold). In support of their functional results, Glass et al (22) identified a DNase I footprint extending from -178 to -163 (Figure 1, sequence C), using 8 fmol of a DNA fragment and a salt extract of GC cell nuclei (containing 12 fmol of receptor) that was not further purified. In these extract preparations, which contain an abundance of DNA binding proteins, the receptor represents approximately 0.002% of the total protein. The impurity of the receptor preparation and the lack of a control (such as extracts from cells with very low receptor levels) raises the possibility that the $-178/-163$ footprint is formed by a protein other than receptor.

FUTURE DIRECTIONS

Taken together, results of the transient expression studies (20, 22, 37, 42, 96) indicate that DNA between -209 and -166 functions as a thyroid hormone response element involved in regulated expression of the rat growth hormone gene. The difference in the location of this element(s) identified by transient expression and the element identified ($-254/-241$) by Wight et al using stable transformation (Figure 1) (93) raises the possibility that several regions may be able to function as thyroid hormone response elements, depending on the location of these sequences relative to other regulatory elements of the promoter and the nature of the promoter used for functional analysis. More definitive studies are required to document the precise location of the sequence that functions as the dominant thyroid hormone response element of the gene. This localization will require constructing a series of point or multiple mutations across the $-254/-166$ region of the gene using the 5'-flanking region containing sequences from -254 to $+7$. Analysis of the function of these recombinants coupled with footprinting studies of these constructions using purified receptor in vitro are required to precisely identify the DNA sequences required for thyroid-hormone–regulated expression of the rat growth hormone gene.

Precise identification of the region(s) required for thyroid-hormone–regulated expression of the rat growth hormone, however, will not provide a complete picture of how the thyroid-hormone–receptor complex activates or inhibits gene expression. As indicated, the results of Ye et al (96) suggested that both an upstream thyroid hormone response element and a cell-specific basal element are necessary for L-T3 regulation of the rat growth hormone gene. To account for these observations, Ye et al (96) proposed a model in which the L-T3–receptor complex binds to its cognate sequence and acts to stabilize or enhance the protein-DNA interactions of the cell-specific basal element to form a more active transcription complex that increases the level of gene expression. This model can be tested by in vivo footprinting of the cell-specific elements of the endogenous rat growth hormone gene after L-T3 incubation.

Recent studies on the mouse mammary tumor virus (MMTV) promoter support an analogous two-element model for glucocorticoid hormone stimulation of gene expression. Inactivation of the binding site for the NF-I transcription factor (or a protein with a similar recognition sequence e.g. TGGCA-binding protein) markedly lowers stimulation by glucocorticoid hormones without significantly altering the basal activity of the gene (4, 53). Furthermore, in vivo footprinting indicates that glucocorticoid hormone incubation increases the association of NF-I with its cognate sequence (11), which suggests that the glucocorticoid receptor enhances NF-I binding or interacts with NF-I to from a transcription complex that activates expression of the MMTV promoter. Since the control elements of thyroid-hormone–responsive genes other than rat growth hormone have not yet been reported, determining whether two or more elements are necessary for efficient L-T3–regulated expression in other systems is not possible. However, a two-element model provides a mechanism to explain how thyroid hormone, presumably acting via the same receptor, can positively (e.g. rat growth hormone) or negatively (e.g. thyrotropin) regulate gene expression. Whether positive or negative regulation occurs would depend on the hormone-receptor complex acting in *cis* to enhance or suppress the effect of a second *trans*-acting regulatory protein(s) that plays a central role in determining the rate of expression of the gene.

Additional studies are required to support this hypothesis, since positive and negative regulation may be mediated by structurally similar but different thyroid hormone receptors. The observation that the human genome contains at least two *erbA*-related genes on different chromosomes raises this possibility (14, 63, 84, 91). Significant progress has been made in the study of thyroid hormone action since the initial identification of thyroid hormone nuclear receptors in liver and kidney (57) and in cultured cells (71a). Future advances in this field require the cloning of thyroid hormone receptor mRNAs from various tissues and cells to identify their structure and function. In addition, other thyroid hormone response genes are being isolated and sequenced. Identification of the thyroid hormone response elements of other genes and the regulatory proteins that mediate their expression should ultimately provide a comprehensive view of the detailed mechanisms involved in positive and negative regulation of thyroid-hormone–responsive genes in various cells and tissues.

ACKNOWLEDGMENTS

The authors' research described here was supported by grants DK16636 (H.H.S.) and DK01372 (Z.D. H.), by an M.D.-Ph.D. Training Grant from the National Institute of Health (B.M.F.), and by the Sackler Institute of Graduate Biomedical Sciences at New York University (Z.-S.Y.). We thank Mary McCarthy for expert secretarial assistance. We also acknowledge those who have contributed (both past and present) to studies described here from one author's laboratory (H.H.S.): Ana Aranda, Juan Casanova, Richard P. Copp, Frances Flug, Laura Jacocko, Hae-Young Park, Angel Pascual, Andrew J. Perlman, Hadjira Sahnoun, Lawrence E. Shapiro, Frederick Stanley, Jir S. Tsai, Barry M. Yaffe, and Chang-Ren Yang.

Literature Cited

1. Back, D. W., Wilson, S. B., Morris, S. M., Goodridge, A. G. 1986. Hormonal regulation of lipogenic enzymes in chick embryo hepatocytes in culture. *J. Biol. Chem.* 261:12555–61
2. Benbrook, D. Pfahl, M. 1987. A novel thyroid hormone receptor encoded by a cDNA clone from a human testis library. *Science* 238:788–91
3. Bodner, M., Karin, M. 1987. A pituitary-specific *trans*-acting factor can stimulate transcription from the growth hormone promoter in extracts of nonexpressing cells. *Cell* 50:267–75
4. Buetti, E., Kuhnel, B. 1986. Distinct sequence elements involved in the glucocorticoid regulation of the mouse mammary tumor virus promoter identified by linker scanning mutagenesis. *J. Mol. Biol.* 190:379–89
5. Carr, F. E., Jump, D. B., Oppenheimer, J. H. 1984. Distribution of thyroid hormone-responsive translation products in rat liver polysome and postribosomal ribonucleoprotein populations. *Endocrinology* 115:1737–45
6. Carr, F. E., Need, L. R., Chin, W. W. 1987. Isolation and characterization of the rat thyrotropin beta-subunit gene. *J. Biol. Chem.* 262:981–87

7. Casanova, J., Copp, R. P., Janocko, L., Samuels, H. H. 1985. 5'-Flanking DNA of the rat growth hormone gene mediates regulated expression by thyroid hormone. *J. Biol. Chem.* 260:11744–48
8. Casanova, J., Horowitz, Z. D., Copp, R. P., McIntyre, W. R., Pascual, A., Samuels, H. H. 1984. Photoaffinity labeling of thyroid hormone nuclear receptors: influence of n-butyrate and analysis of the half-lives of the 57,000 and 47,000 molecular weight receptor forms. *J. Biol. Chem.* 259:12084–91
9. Catanzaro, D. F., West, B. L., Baxter, J. D., Reudelhuber, T. L. 1987. A pituitary-specific factor interacts with an upstream promoter element in the rat growth hormone gene. *Mol. Endocrinol.* 1:90–96
10. Connelly, D. M., Sullivan, W. P., Toft, D. O., Birnbaumer, M., Cook, R. G., et al. 1986. Molecular cloning of the chicken progesterone receptor. *Science* 233:767–70
11. Cordingley, M. G., Riegel, A. T., Hager, G. L. 1987. Steroid-dependent interaction of transcription factors with the inducible promoter of mouse mammary tumor virus *in vivo*. *Cell* 48:261–70
12. Crew, M. D., Spindler, S. R. 1986.

Thyroid hormone regulation of the transfected rat growth hormone promoter. *J. Biol. Chem.* 261:5018–22

13. Damm, K., Beug, H., Graf, T., Vennstrom, B., 1987. A single point mutation in erbA restores the erythroid transforming potential of a mutant avian erythroblastosis virus (AEV) defective in both erbA and erbB oncogenes. *EMBO J.* 6:375–82

14. Dayton, A. I., Selden, J. R., Laws, G., Dorney, D. J., Finan, J., et al. 1984. A human c-erb-A oncogene homologue is closely proximal to the chromosome 17 breakpoint in acute promyelocytic leukemia. *Proc. Natl. Acad. Sci. USA* 81: 4495–99

15. Dillmann, W. H., Barrieux, A., Reese, G. S. 1984. Effect of diabetes and hypothyroidism on the predominance of cardiac myosin heavy chains synthesized *in vivo* or in a cell free system. *J. Biol. Chem.* 259:2035–38

16. Dobner, P. R., Kawasaki, E. W., Yu, L.-Y., Bancroft, F. C. 1981. Thyroid or glucocorticoid hormone induces pregrowth-hormone mRNA and its probable nuclear precursor in rat pituitary cells. *Proc. Natl. Acad. Sci. USA* 78: 2230–34

17. Downward, J., Yarden, Y., Mayes, E., Scarce, G., Totty, N., et al. 1984. Close similiarity of epidermal growth factor receptor and v-erb-B oncogene protein sequences. *Nature* 307:521–26

18. Evans, R. M., Birnberg, N. C., Rosenfeld, M. G. 1982. Glucocorticoid and thyroid hormones transcriptionally regulate growth hormone gene expression. *Proc. Natl. Acad. Sci. USA* 79:7659–63

19. Everett, A. W., Clark, W. A., Chizzonite, R. A., Zak, R. 1983. Change in the synthesis rates of alpha- and beta-myosin heavy chains in rabbit heart after treatment with thyroid hormone. *J. Biol. Chem.* 258:2421–25

20. Flug, F., Copp, R. P., Horowitz, Z. D., Janocko, L., Plotnick, M., Samuels, H. H. 1987. *Cis*-acting elements of the rat growth hormone gene which mediate basal and regulated expression by thyroid hormone. *J. Biol. Chem.* 262:6373–82

20a. Forman, B. M., Yang, C.-R., Stanley, F., Casanova, J., Samuels, H. H. 1988. c-erba proto-oncogenes mediate thyroid hormone-dependent and independent regulation of the rat growth hormone and prolactin genes. *Mol. Endocrinol.* 2: 902–11

21. Frykberg, L., Palmieri, S., Beug, H., Graf, T., Hayman, M. J., Vennstrom, B. 1983. Transforming capacities of

avian erythroblastosis virus mutants deleted in the erb A or erb B oncogenes. *Cell* 32:227–38

22. Glass, C. K., Franco, R., Weinberger, C., Albert, V. R., Evans, R. M., Rosenfeld, M. G. 1987. A c-erb-A binding site in rat growth hormone gene mediates *trans*-activation by thyroid hormone. *Nature* 329:738–41

23. Goodwin, R. G., Rottman, F. M., Calloghan, T., Kung, H. J., Maroney, P. A., Nilsen, T. W. 1986. C-erb B activation in avian leukosis virus-induced erythroblastosis: multiple epidermal growth factor receptor mRNA's are generated by alternative mRNA processing. *Mol. Cell. Biol.* 6:3128–33

24. Graf, T., Beug, H. 1983. Role of v-erb-A and V-erb-B oncogenes of avain erythroblastosis virus in erythroid cell transformation. *Cell* 34:7–9

25. Green, S., Walter, P., Kumar, V., Krust, A., Nornert, J. M., et al. 1986. Human oestrogen receptor cDNA: sequence, expression, and homology to v-erb-A. *Nature* 320:134–39

26. Groul, D. J. 1980. 3,5,3'-Triiodo-L-thyronine receptor-containing chromatin fragments: production by nuclease digestion. *Endocrinology* 107:994–99

27. Hayman, M. J., Ramsay, G. M., Savin, K., Kitchner, G. 1983. Identification and characterization of the avian erythroblastosis virus erb B gene product as a membrane glycoprotein. *Cell* 32: 579–88

28. Hervas, F., Morreale de Escobar, G., Escobar Del Ray, F. 1975. Rapid effects of single small doses of L-thyroxine and triiodo-L-thyronine on growth hormone as studied in the rat by radioimmunoassay. *Endocrinology* 97:91–101

29. Hollenberg, S. M., Giguere, V., Segui, P., Evans, R. M. 1987. Colocalization of DNA-binding and transcriptional activation functions in the human glucocorticoid receptor. *Cell* 49:39–46

30. Hollenberg, S. M., Weinberger, C., Ong, E. S., Cerelli, G., Oro, A., et al. 1985. Primary structure and expression of a functional glucocorticoid receptor cDNA. *Nature* 318:635–41

31. Horowitz, Z. D., Sahnoun, H., Pascual, A., Casanova, J., Samuels, H. H. 1988. Analysis of photoaffinity label derivatives to probe thyroid hormone receptor in human fibroblasts, GH_1 cells, soluble receptor preparations. *J. Biol. Chem.* 263:6636–42

32. Izumo, S., Nadal-Ginard, B., Mahdavi, V. 1986. All members of the myosin heavy chain multigene family respond to thyroid hormone in a highly tissue

specific manner. *Science* 231:597–600
33. Jansson, M., Philipson, L., Vennstrom, B. 1983. Isolation and characterization of multiple human genes homologous to the oncogenes of avian erythroblastosis virus. *EMBO J.* 2:561–65
34. Jeltsch, J. M., Krozowski, Z., Quirin-Stricker, C., Gronemyer, H., Simpson, R. J., et al. 1986. Cloning of the chicken progesterone receptor. *Proc. Natl. Acad. Sci. USA* 83:5424–28
35. Jump, D. B., Seelig, S., Schwartz, H. L., Oppenheimer, J. H. 1981. Association of thyroid hormone receptor with rat liver chromatin. *Biochemistry* 20:6781–89
36. Karin, M., Eberhardt, N. L., Mellon, S. H., Malich, N., Richards, R. I., et al. 1984. Expression and hormonal regulation of the rat growth hormone gene in transfected mouse cells. *DNA* 3:147–55
37. Koenig, R. J., Brent, G. A., Warne, R. L., Larsen, P. R., Moore, D. D. 1987. Thyroid hormone receptor binds to a site in the rat growth hormone promoter required for induction by thyroid hormone. *Proc. Natl. Acad. Sci. USA* 84:5670–74
38. Koerner, D., Schwartz, H. L., Surks, M. I., Oppenheimer, J. H., Jorgensen, E. C. 1975. Binding of selected iodothyronine analogues to receptor sites of isolated rat hepatic nuclei: high correlation between structural requirements for nuclear binding and biological activity. *J. Biol. Chem.* 250:6417–23
39. Kourides, I. A., Gurr, J. A., Wolf, O. 1984. The regulation and organizaton of thyroid stimulating hormone genes. *Recent Prog. Horm. Res.* 40:79–120
40. Krust, A., Green, S., Argos, P., Kumar, V., Walter, P., et al. 1986. The chicken oestrogen receptor sequence: homology with v-erb-A and the human oestrogen and glucocorticoid receptors. *EMBO J.* 5:891–97
41. Kumara-Siri, M. H., Surks, M. I. 1985. Regulation of growth hormone mRNA synthesis by 3,5,3'-Triiodo-L-thyronine in cultured growth hormone-producing rat pituitary tumor cells GC Cells.: dissociation between nuclear iodothyronine receptor concentration and growth hormone mRNA synthesis during the deoxyribonucleic acid synthesis phase of the cell cycle. *J. Biol. Chem.* 260:14529–37
42. Larsen, P. R., Harney, J. W., Moore, D. D. 1986. Sequences required for cell-type specific thyroid hormone regulation of rat growth hormone promoter activity. *J. Biol. Chem.* 261:14373–76
43. Larsen, P. R., Harney, J. W., Moore,

D. D. 1986. Repression mediates cell-type-specific expression of the rat growth hormone gene. *Proc. Natl. Acad. Sci. USA* 83:8283–87
44. Latham, K. R., Ring, J. C., Baxter, J. D. 1976. Solubilized nuclear "receptors" for thyroid hormones: physical characteristics and binding properties, evidence for multiple forms. *J. Biol. Chem.* 251:7388–97
45. Lefevre, C., Imagawa, M., Dana, S., Grindlay, J., Bodner, M., Karin, M. 1987. Tissue-specific expression of the human growth hormone gene is conferred in part by the binding of a specific *trans*-acting factor. *EMBO J.* 6:971–81
46. Liaw, C. W., Towle, H. C. 1984. Characterization of a thyroid hormone-responsive gene from rat. *J. Biol. Chem.* 259:7253–60
47. Lompre, A.-M. Nadal-Ginard, B., Mahdavi, V. 1984. Expression of the cardiac ventricular alpha-and beta-myosin heavy chain genes is developmentally and hormonally regulated. *J. Biol. Chem.* 259:6437–46
48. MacLeod, K. M., Baxter, J. D. 1976. Chromatin receptors for thyroid hormones: interactions of the solubilized proteins with DNA. *J. Biol. Chem.* 251:7380–87
49. Magnuson, M. A., Dozin, B., Nikodem, V. M. 1985. Regulation of specific rat liver messenger ribonucleic acids by triiodothyronine. *J. Biol. Chem.* 260:5906–12
50. Magnuson, M. A., Nikodem, V. M. 1983. Molecular cloning of a cDNA sequence for rat malic enzyme: direct evidence for induction *in vivo* of rat liver malic enzyme mRNA by thyroid hormone. *J. Biol. Chem.* 258:12712–17
51. Martial, J. A., Baxter, J. D., Goodman, H. M., Seeburg, P. H. 1977. Regulation of growth hormone messenger RNA by thyroid and glucocorticoid hormones. *Proc. Natl. Acad. Sci. USA* 74:1816–20
52. Miesfeld, R., Godowski, P. J., Maler, B. A., Yamamoto, K. R. 1987. Glucocorticoid receptor mutants that define a small region sufficient for enhancer activation. *Science* 236:423–27
53. Miksicek, R., Borgmeyer, U., Nowock, J. 1987. Interaction of the TGGCA-binding protein with upstream sequences is required for efficient transcription of mouse mammary tumor virus. *EMBO J.* 6:1355–60
54. Nelson, C., Crenshaw, E. B. III, Franco, R., Lira, S. A., Albert, V. R., et al. 1986. Discrete *cis*-active genomic sequences dictate the pituitary cell type-specific expression of rat prolactin and

growth hormone genes. *Nature* 322: 557–62

55. Nilsen, T. W., Maroney, P. A., Goodwin, R. G., Rottman, F. M., Crittenden, L. B., et al. 1985. C-erb B activation in ALV-induced erythroblastosis: novel mRNA processing and promoter insertion result in expression of an aminotruncated EGF receptor. *Cell* 41:719–28

56. Oppenheimer, J. H. 1983. The nuclear receptor-triiodothyronine complex: relationship to thyroid hormone distribution, metabolism, biological action. In *Molecular Basis of Thyroid Hormone Action,* ed. J. H. Oppenheimer, H. H. Samuels, pp. 1–35. New York: Academic

57. Oppenheimer, J. H., Koerner, D., Schwartz, H. L., Surks, M. I. 1972. Specific nuclear triiodothyronine binding sites in rat liver and kidney. *J. Clin. Endocrinol. Metab.* 35:330–33

58. Oppenheimer, J. H., Schwartz, H. L., Mariash, C. N., Kinlaw, W. B., Wong, N.C.W., Freake, H. C. 1987. Advances in our understanding of thyroid hormone action at the cellular level. *Endocr. Rev.* 8:288–308

59. Oppenheimer, J. H., Schwartz, H. L., Surks, M. I. 1974. Tissue differences in the concentration of triiodothyronine nuclear binding sites in the rat: liver, kidney, pituitary, heart, brain, spleen, testis. *Endocrinology* 95:897–903

60. Pascual, A., Casanova, J., Samuels, H. H. 1982. Photoaffinity labeling of thyroid hormone nuclear receptors in intact cells. *J. Biol. Chem.* 257:9640–47

61. Perlman, A. J., Stanley, F., Samuels, H. H. 1982. Thyroid hormone nuclear receptor: evidence for multimeric organization in chromatin. *J. Biol. Chem.* 257:930–38

62. Raaka, B. M., Samuels, H. H. 1981. Regulation of thyroid hormone nuclear receptor levels in GH₁ Cells by 3,5,3'-triiodo-L-thyronine: use of dense amino acid labeling to determine the influence of hormone on the receptor half-life and the rate of appearance of newly synthesized receptor. *J. Biol. Chem.* 256: 6883–89

63. Raines, M. A., Lewis, W. G., Crittenden, L. B., King, H. J. 1985. C-erb B activation in avian leukosis virus-induced erythroblastosis: clustered integration sites and the arrangement of provirus in the c-erb-B alleles. *Proc. Natl. Acad. Sci. USA* 82:2287–91

64. Samuels, H. H. 1983. Identification and characterization of thyroid hormone receptors and action using cell culture techniques. See Ref. 56, pp. 35–64

65. Samuels, H. H., Shapiro, L. E. 1976.

Thyroid hormone stimulates *de novo* growth hormone synthesis in cultured GH₁ cells: evidence for the accumulation of a rate limiting RNA species in the induction process. *Proc. Natl. Acad. Sci. USA* 73:3369–73

66. Deleted in proof

67. Deleted in proof

68. Samuels, H. H., Stanley, F., Casanova, J. 1979. Relationship of receptor affinity to the modulation of thyroid hormone nuclear receptor levels and growth hormone synthesis by L-triiodothyronine and iodothyronine analogs in cultured GH₁ cells. *J. Clin. Invest.* 63:1229–40

69. Samuels, H. H., Stanley, F., Shapiro, L. E. 1976. Dose-dependent depletion of nuclear receptors by L-triiodothyronine: evidence for a role in the induction of growth hormone synthesis in cultured GH₁ cells. *Proc. Natl. Acad. Sci. USA* 73:3877–81

70. Samuels, H. H., Stanley, F., Shapiro, L. E. 1977. Modulation of thyroid hormone nuclear receptor levels by 3,5,3'-triiodothyronine in GH₁ cells: evidence for two functional components of nuclear receptor and relationship to the induction of growth hormone synthesis. *J. Biol. Chem.* 252:6052–60

71. Samuels, H. H., Stanley, F., Shapiro, L. E. 1979. Control of growth hormone synthesis in cultured GH₁ cells by 3,5,3'-triiodo-L-thyronine and glucocorticoid agonists and antagonists: studies on the independent and synergistic regulation of the growth hormone response. *Biochemistry* 18:715–21

71a. Samuels, H. H., Tsai, J. S. 1973. Thyroid hormone action in cell culture: demonstration of nuclear receptors in intact cells and isolated nuclei. *Proc. Natl. Acad. Sci. USA* 70:3488–92

71b. Samuels, H. H., Tsai, J. S. 1974. Thyroid hormone action: demonstration of similar receptors in isolated nuclei of rat liver and cultured GH₁ cells. *J. Clin. Invest.* 53:656–59

72. Samuels, H. H., Tsai, . S., Casanova, J., Stanley, F. 1974. Thyroid hormone action: *in vitro* characterization of solubilized nuclear receptors from rat liver and cultured GH₁ cells. *J. Clin. Invest.* 54:853–56

73. Sap, J., Munoz, A., Damm, K., Goldberg, Y., Ghysdael, J., et al. 1986. The c-erb-A protein is a high-affinity receptor for thyroid hormone. *Nature* 324: 635–40

74. Schwartz, H. L., Oppenheimer, J. H. 1978. Nuclear triiodothyronine receptor sites in brain: probable identity with hepatic receptors and regional distribution. *Endocrinology* 103:267–73

75. Schwartz, H. L., Trence, D., Oppenheimer, J. H., Jiang, N. S., Jump, D. B. 1983. Distribution and metabolism of L- and D-triiodothryonine (T3) in the rat: preferential accumulation of L-T3 by hepatic and cardiac nuclei as a probable explanation of the differential biologic potency of T3 enantiomers. *Endocrinology* 113:1236–43

76. Seo, H., Vassart, G., Brocas, H., Refetoff, S. 1977. Triiodothyronine stimulates specifically growth hormone mRNA in rat pitutitary tumor cells. *Proc. Natl. Acad. Sci. USA* 74:2054–58

77. Shadlow, A. R., Surks, M. I., Schwartz, H. L., Oppenheimer, J. H. 1972. Specific triiodothyronine binding sites in the anterior pituitary of the rat. *Science* 176:1252–54

78. Shapiro, L. E., Samuels, H. H., Yaffe, B. M. 1978. Thyroid and glucocorticoid hormones synergistically control growth hormone mRNA in cultured GH₁ cells. *Proc. Natl. Acad. Sci. USA* 75:45–49

79. Shupnik, M. A., Chin, W. W., Habener, J. F., Ridgway, E. C. 1985. Transcriptional regulation of the thyrotropin subunit genes by thyroid hormone. *J. Biol. Chem.* 260:2900–3

80. Siddiqui, U. A., Goldflam, T., Goodridge, A. G. 1981. Nutritional and hormonal regulation of the translational levels of malic enzyme and albumin mRNA's in avian liver cells *in vivo* and in culture. *J. Biol. Chem.* 256:4544–50

81. Sinha, A. M., Umeda, P. K., Kavinsky, C. J., Rajamanickam, C., Hsu, J.-J., et al. 1982. Molecular cloning of mRNA sequences for cardiac alpha- and beta-form myosin heavy chains: expression in ventricles of normal, hypothyroid, thyrotoxic rabbits. *Proc. Natl. Acad. Sci. USA* 79:5847–51

82. Spindler, S. R., MacLeod, K. M., Ring, J., Baxter, J. D. 1975. Thyroid hormone receptors: binding characteristics and lack of hormonal dependency for nuclear localization. *J. Biol. Chem.* 250:4113–19

83. Spindler, S. R., Mellon, S. H., Baxter, J. D. 1982. Growth hormone gene transcription is regulated by thyroid and glucocorticoid hormones in cultured rat pituitary tumor cells. *J. Biol. Chem.* 257:11627–32

84. Spurr, N. K., Solomon, S., Jansson, M., Sheer, D., Goodfellow, P. N., et al. 1984. Chromosomal localization of the human homologues to the oncogenes erb A and erb B. *EMBO J.* 3:159–63

85. Tao, T. Y., Towle, H. C. 1986. Coordinate regulation of rat liver genes by thyroid hormone and dietary carbohydrates. *Ann. NY Acad. Sci.* 478:20–30

86. Thompson, C. C., Weinberger, C., Lebo, R., Evans, R. M. 1987. Identification of a novel thyroid hormone receptor expressed in the mammalian central nervous system. *Science* 237:1610–14

87. Towle, H. C., Mariash, C. N., Schwartz, H. L., Oppenheimer, J. H. 1981. Quantitation of rat liver messenger ribonucleic acid for malic enzyme induction by thyroid hormone. *Biochemistry* 20:3486–92

88. Vennstrom, B., Bishop, J. M. 1982. Isolation and characterization chicken DNA homologues to the putative oncogenes of avian erythroblastosis virus. *Cell* 28:135–43

89. Vennstrom, B., Fanshier, L., Moscovici, C., Bishop, J. M. 1980. Molecular cloning of the avian erythroblastosis virus genome and recovery of oncogenic virus by transfection of chicken cells. *J. Virol.* 36:575–85

90. Weinberger, C., Hollenberg, S. M., Rosenfeld, M. G., Evans, R. M. 1985. Domain structure of human glucocorticoid receptor and its relationship to the v-erb-A oncogene product. *Nature* 318:670–72

91. Weinberger, C., Thompson, C. C., Ong, E. S., Lebo, R., Gruol, D. J., Evans, R. M. 1986. The c-erb-A gene encodes a thyroid hormone receptor. *Nature* 324:641–46

92. West, B. L., Catanzaro, D. F., Mellon, S. H., Cattini, P. A., Baxter, J. D., Reudelhuber, T. L. 1987. *Mol. Cell. Biol.* 7:1193–97

93. Wight, P. A., Crew, M. D., Spindler, S. R. 1987. Discrete positive and negative thyroid hormone-responsive transcription regulatory elements of the rat growth hormone gene. *J. Biol. Chem.* 262:5659–63

94. Yaffe, B. M., Samuels, H. H. 1984. Hormonal regulation of the growth hormone gene: relationship of the rate of transcription to the level of nuclear thyroid hormone-receptor complexes. *J. Biol. Chem.* 259:6284–91

95. Ye, Z.-S., Samuels, H. H. 1987. Cell and sequence-specific binding of nuclear proteins to 5'-flanking DNA of the rat growth hormone gene. *J. Biol. Chem.* 262:6313–17

96. Ye, Z.-S., Forman, B. M., Aranda, A., Pascual, A., Park, H.Y., et al. 1988. Rat growth hormone gene expression: both cell-specific and thyroid hormone response elements are required for thyroid hormone regulation. *J. Biol. Chem.* 263:821–29

Annu. Rev. Physiol. 1989. 51:641–52

HORMONAL REGULATION OF MILK PROTEIN GENE EXPRESSION

Barbara K. Vonderhaar and Suzanne E. Ziska

Laboratory of Tumor Immunology and Biology, National Cancer Institute, National Institutes of Health, Bethesda, Maryland 20892

INTRODUCTION

Throughout the life of the mammal development of the mammary gland is dependent on the interaction of multiple hormones and growth factors with several different cell types. During lactation these hormones and growth factors interact with the epithelial cells of the mammary gland to produce milk with a very high, and unique, protein content. This chapter focuses on hormones that regulate milk protein gene expression during lactation.

Physiology of the Gland During Pregnancy and Lactation

The lactating mammary gland has a highly developed structure distinct from that seen at any other developmental stage. The rate of development is maximal during pregnancy and occurs in several stages (61). The first stage, occurring during early pregnancy, is characterized by cellular proliferation of the distal portion of the ductal tree into alveoli in response to elevated levels of estrogen and progesterone. Development at this stage includes proliferation of epithelial cells as well as enlargement of individual cells. As pregnancy proceeds the alveolar lobules increase in size and number as new lobules develop from the terminal ends and lateral walls of the ductules. Mammary fat pads regress and vascularization of the gland increases (61).

In the later stages of pregnancy, the alveoli are lined with irregular layers of columnar cells containing large vacuoles that quickly become secretory under the influence of lactogenic and adrenal steroid hormones. Acinar luminae become filled with colostrum in preparation for birth and lactation (61).

The beginning of lactation is signaled by a sudden decrease in the circulating high levels of estrogen and progesterone and the end of prolactin inhibi-

0066-4278/89/0315-0641$02.00

tion (61). During lactation the histologic appearance of the mammary gland undergoes very few significant changes. Vascularization continues to increase to support continued milk production. The alveolar cells are no longer vacuolated, and the glandular epithelium continues to predominate over the fat cells (61).

Hormone and Growth Factors in Differentiation

Over the years an increasing number of hormones and growth factors known to be involved in the differentiation of the mammary gland have been discovered. Undoubtedly other factors will also prove to be involved. Possibly lactation has been the differentiated state most widely studied; in particular, the production of milk proteins by the mammary gland has been the focus of many investigations. The mechanisms of hormonal and growth factor regulation of milk protein gene expression have been studied most successfully using a biochemical approach. Presently, cDNA clones have been obtained for most milk proteins (see specific protein, this review). Genomic clones for many are also available. The isolation of these DNA clones, the specific mRNAs, and the corresponding proteins now allows for the examination of the roles of various hormones and growth factors in the regulation of milk protein gene expression.

MILK PROTEINS: EFFECTS OF HORMONES ON TRANSCRIPTION AND TRANSLATION

Caseins

PROTEIN STRUCTURE AND FUNCTION   Caseins are perhaps the most abundant protein produced by the lactating mammary gland. Their biological function is to provide supersaturating concentrations of calcium, phosphates, and essential amino acids. Casein nomenclature is based on the species of origin. Bovine caseins are classified as α_{s1}, α_{s2}, β and κ; rabbit, rodent, ovine, and human caseins are designated α, β, κ, and γ. Classification is based on specific physiochemical properties. Alpha$_{s1}$, α_{s2}, and β caseins (rat and bovine) are calcium sensitive since they can be precipitated in the presence of low calcium levels (63), while the κ caseins are not. The calcium-sensitive caseins are maintained in stable suspension via their interaction with κ casein (63). Kappa caseins are phosphoglycoproteins (35).

GENE STRUCTURE   The casein proteins derive from a multigene family that has arisen by intra- and intergenic duplication of a primordial gene (64). cDNA sequences for caseins from many mammalian species are now available. For an extensive review, see Yu-Lee et al (64). DNA sequence analysis of caseins from rat, mouse, guinea pig, and cow reveals much divergence in the nucleotide sequences. Despite this great divergence, three regions of the casein gene family are highly conserved. These include the 5' flanking region, a casein kinase phosphorylation site (site of calcium binding), and a signal peptide sequence. The rat casein genes, as well as those from other species, vary tremendously in size. The rat α casein gene covers 10–15 kilobases (kb), th β casein gene 7.5 kb, and the γ casein gene 15 kb. The casein gene family occurs as a gene cluster (17) and has been localized to chromosome 5 (17) in mouse and chromosome 2 in sheep (36). Sequence analysis reveals the rat α, β, and γ caseins are analogous to the bovine α_{s1}, β, and α_{s2} caseins, respectively (47).

The 5' noncoding region and the signal peptide coding region are formed from separate exons of similar size in all three rat and the bovine α_{s1} caseins (48, 65). Indeed, the 5' flanking region appears to be more highly conserved than the entire mature coding and intron regions (64). The exon encoding the signal peptide of all the calcium-sensitive caseins has a uniform size of 63 base pairs (bp) and is the most highly conserved (64). The signal peptides from all three calcium-sensitive caseins are 15 amino acids long, with a Lys in position 2 and a Cys in position 8 (27). The amino acid in these particular positions are thought to be important in the translocation, recognition, and removal (30) of signal peptides, events that are directly related to the efficiency of casein secretion into milk. This secretion is known to be hormonally regulated (2, 54).

Comparison of the first 200 bp of the 5' flanking regions of the β and γ casein DNA sequences reveals three regions of 70% or greater homology (64, 65). Conservation of the 5' noncoding region may be related to the formation of potential secondary structures (Z-DNA) that may have a role in transcription and posttranscriptional regulation of casein synthesis (64). Regulation of the three rat casein genes (α, β, γ) during mammary gland development and hormone induction during explant culture occurs in a coordinated manner (26). This coordinated expression may be a reflection of well-conserved regions of sequence homology residing within the 5' flanking region (64) and/or the presence of specific sequences shown in other systems to play a regulatory role in gene expression.

Rat and mouse κ casein cDNA clones have been isolated (37, 52) and the amino acid sequence has been deduced for comparison with other isolated κ caseins (52). Comparison of the deduced protein sequence for rat and mouse peptides shows a protein chain of 160 amino acids for mouse and 157 for rat. Kappa casein from rat and mouse shows a 73% sequence homology but only 43–46% when either is compared to ovine κ casein. The signal peptide sequence is identical in rat and mouse and the rat/mouse precursor shows a 62% homology with the ovine precursor. The exact length of the signal peptide is conserved in all three species.

Rat and mouse 5' noncoding regions show 83% homology, while the homology varied from 82 to 87% between 3' coding and noncoding regions (52). Genomic clones have not yet been isolated. Mouse lactating mammary gland contains two different κ casein messages (and two different polyadenylation sites), while rat contains only one (52).

Potential regulatory sequences   Stretches of polypurine/pyrimidine nucleotides have been implicated in DNA structure-function relationships (21, 40). These sequences may allow DNA to attain a specific structure (Z-DNA) that could be involved in enhancing gene transcription (22). The presence of (CA 39) and (TG38) repeats in the 5' noncoding exon and fourth intron of rat α casein, but not β or γ, may be responsible for the higher basal levels of α casein, compared to β or κ, seen in virgin rats and in explants cultured in the absence of hormones (26). Further examination of the nucleotide sequence, particularly in the 5' flanking region, reveals novel sequence features that may also prove to be involved in regulation of gene expression. Such features include (*a*) the presence of S1 nuclease-sensitive sites, (*b*) nonuniform TATA box sequences, and (*c*) the presence of AT-rich promoter regions rather than the more common GC-rich regions (15, 34).

Coordinate induction of sets of genes in other systems has been linked to the presence of conserved, short (9–24 bp), repetitive sequences (18). Such sequences like the TGTT sequence found in the bovine α_{s1} gene (64) may be analogous. These sequences do not resemble hormone binding sites and their function is unknown (18).

One of the most interesting features of the casein DNA sequences is that of the hormone receptor binding sites. Since casein gene expression is known to be differentially regulated by hormones, it was of interest to study the hormone receptor binding sites. Most known or potential hormone receptor binding sites, at least in casein DNA, occur in the 5' flanking region. The sequence TGT(T/C)CT, which is part of the glucocorticoid receptor binding site (55), is found at multiple sites in the 5' flanking region (64). Bovine α_{s1} casein DNA has three such sites, occurring at -120, -210, and -270, while rat γ casein has only two sites, at -230 and -480 (64). Rat α casein DNA has only one such site, at -360. The complement of the rat γ casein -230 site shows sequence homology with the estrogen receptor in the chicken vitellogin II gene, while the hexanucleotide at -480 immediately follows a sequence having good homology with two sequences in the chicken lysozyme gene (26) that bind the heterologous rabbit progesterone receptor. Both rat and bovine β caseins also have this hexanucleotide in the 5' noncoding region (6, 9). The bovine α_{s1} gene sits in close proximity to several sequences homologous with the progesterone receptor (26, 39). There is also one site located in an intron (64). The functional significance of two different potential hormone binding sites overlapping is unknown.

HORMONAL REGULATION   Although a number of hormones have direct DNA binding sites, not all hormonal regulation of milk protein gene expression occurs at the DNA level. Both polypeptide and steroid hormones influence transcription and translation of milk protein genes. Once mRNA synthesis is induced, protein synthesis ultimately depends on a number of transcriptional conditions, such as the rate of transcription and the transcript half-life. Insulin (I), glucocorticoids [usually hydrocortisone (H)], and prolactin (Prl) are necessary for synthesis (18, 43) and accumulation (18) of casein mRNA by rat and mouse mammary gland explants.

The role of I, H, and Prl in the induction and accumulation of the rat 25-kd casein mRNA (12, 56) has been examined. In the presence of I and H, Prl exerts a stabilizing influence on the mRNA by extending the transcript half-life approximately 4-fold compared with that of transcript from explants cultured in I and H alone (12, 56). Prolactin enhances casein mRNA transcription and stabilizes the transcript once it is made (18, 48). Rosen et al (48) have shown that within 1 hr after Prl addition casein mRNA accumulates, and this results in a 9.5-fold induction for α caseins and 250-fold induction for γ casein after 24 hr. Placental lactogen can substitute for Prl (33). In most mammalian systems casein induction is modulated by Prl in the presence of I and H. In marsupials (32) Prl alone can induce casein synthesis. In other systems Prl alone can induce casein synthesis [human (16)] and mRNA accumulation [rabbit (14)] in explants.

Chomczynski et al (12) have examined the effect of glucocorticoids on transcript half-life and report that the presence of H in culture with I and Prl also dramatically increases the half-life (20 hr versus 1 hr) compared with transcripts from explants cultured in I and Prl alone. Thus induction of transcription requires IHPrl, whereas transcript stabilization is due to H and Prl alone. Others also report (18) that H is necessary for maximal accumulation of message and that there is a 3.3-fold increase in casein transcripts from explants cultured in I and H over those cultured in I alone. Hydrocortisone is postulated to act by decreasing nuclear degradation of the transcript (12) and can be replaced by other corticoids, such as aldosterone and corticosterone (59).

Induction of transcription of the rat 25-kd casein gene has been shown (11) to require I and Prl in the presence of H, while stabilization is not dependent upon I. However, in the mouse (3), I is essential for casein mRNA accumulation (14-fold increase over original levels) in mammary epithelial cells from midpregnant mice and is important to translation, since no immune-precipitable casein was detected in explants cultured in H and Prl alone. In experiments where epidermal growth factor (EGF) and somatomedin C replaced I, neither could promote nor increase mRNA accumulation, whereas both support RNA accumulation in the rough endoplasmic reticulum (3).

Insulin-like growth factor-I (IGF-I) is able to substitute for I, although at substantially higher concentrations (43).

Progesterone inhibits accumulation of casein mRNA during pregnancy (49) and when administered with Prl in vivo or in explant cultures (48). It may act by competing for the glucocorticoid receptor, but ultimately it promotes interaction of the progesterone receptor complex with the DNA.

Kappa caseins are under the control of Prl, since the κ casein mRNA level increased in organ culture (62) and rat and mouse mammary glands 4.5-fold as gestation progressed to lactation (37).

Alpha-Lactalbumin

PROTEIN STRUCTURE   Alpha-lactalbumin is the major whey protein derived from lactating mammary tissue in most mammalian species, except mice and rats (7). Molecular weight varies among species (mouse 14,000, rat 21,800 and 22,500, cow 14,200). Recently α-lactalbumin was isolated from the marsupial (32). Its current known function in the mammary gland is to act as a specifier protein for galactosyl transferase (GT). Alpha-lactalbumin lowers the K_m of glucose so that GT can utilize glucose as an acceptor of the galactose moiety of UDP-galactose in the formation of lactose (8).

GENE STRUCTURE   cDNA clones for a α-lactalbumin are currently available from a number of species [rabbit (28), guinea pig (13), and human (19)], and the DNA sequence for the rat α-lactalbumin gene has been determined (44). The rat gene occupies 3.5 kb and consists of four exons. Comparison of nucleotide sequences shows that there is greater nucleotide divergence within the rodents than within primates (19). The 5' flanking region is highly conserved in that region where the progesterone and glucocorticoid receptors occur. Comparison of the whey 5' flanking sequences (-110 to -140) of human and rat α-lactalbumin and the five casein genes (bovine α_{s1} and α_{s2}, rat α, β, and γ) shows well-conserved sequence homology (20). Human and guinea pig pre-α-lactalbumin show 80% nucleotide sequence homology; high degrees of homology also exist in the coding and 3' noncoding regions as well (19). The expression of α-lactalbumin, like that of other milk proteins, is hormonally regulated (54). However, α-lactalbumin does not increase in a coordinate manner with casein or galactosyl transferase (4).

HORMONAL REGULATION   Both H and Prl in the presence of I are required for maximal mRNA induction in the mouse (4, 43, 54, 55). In the marsupial, however, prolactin alone ($-$IH) can cause maximal induction of mRNA synthesis and accumulation (39) and no increase is seen when explants are cultured in the presence of I and H alone. In the absence of Prl, IH and EGF can induce α-lactalbumin synthesis in the rat mammary gland. However, Prl is required in the mouse and rabbit (56). In recent studies mouse placental lactogen has been shown to increase α-lactalbumin secretion in the absence of Prl (53).

Glucocorticoids are known to exhibit a biphasic effect on α-lactalbumin production (45) in both rats and mice. Although H is necessary for induction of mRNA synthesis and accumulation, high concentrations of this hormone inhibit α-lactalbumin accumulation (42) and secretion (2). Dexamethasone shows a similar biphasic profile (45). Quirk et al (46) postulate that the enhanced response seen at low steroid levels is due to occupancy of type II glucocorticoid receptors, since type II–specific ligands alone can increase α-lactalbumin production.

Induction of α-lactalbumin mRNA synthesis and accumulation is more sensitive to I than to IGF-I, but IGF-I can substitute for I (43). The effects of I and IGF-I are not additive (43).

In most mammalian systems progesterone inhibits α-lactalbumin synthesis (60). In marsupials progesterone is unable to inhibit induction of α-lactalbumin mRNA accumulation (39).

Thyroid hormone [triiodothyronine (T3)] selectively enhances α-lactalbumin but not casein synthesis in the mouse (2). This enhanced expression is due to increases in both mRNA accumulation (66) and protein synthesis (60). T3 is able to overcome the inhibition of α-lactalbumin secretion caused by high levels of H (2). Addition of T3 to the culture medium of midpregnant mouse mammary glands induces the synthesis of two forms of α-lactalbumin (2), whereas only one form is synthesized in the absence of T3. Only one form of α-lactalbumin is secreted, regardless of the presence or absence of T3 in the culture medium (2).

Whey Acidic Protein

PROTEIN STRUCTURE   Another protein from the milk whey fraction, whey acidic protein (WAP), is the major whey protein in rodent and rabbit milks (23). WAP is an acid, cysteine-rich protein comprised of 137 amino acids (rat) or 134 (mouse) (10), with an approximate M_r of 14,000. WAP is a member of a family of functionally related proteins, the four disulfide core proteins (23), and its gene is known to reside on a different chromosome than the casein genes (17). The function is unknown (10).

GENE STRUCTURE   The rat WAP gene covers approximately 2.8 kb (10, 48), and the mouse gene 3.3 kb (10); both genes consist of four exons and three introns (10). Genes from both species have been sequenced and comparison (10) of the cDNA sequences reveals, as with the casein genes, the 3' noncoding region is more highly conserved than the coding region (24). WAP from both mouse and rat has an altered promoter sequence (TTTAAAT), which is similar to that found in both the α and γ caseins (50). Comparison of the remainder of the 5' flanking sequences of the caseins and α-lactalbumin with that of WAP reveals no similarities. Multiple glucocorticoid binding sites in the 5' flanking region have been reported [rat (48)].

HORMONAL REGULATION   As with the casein genes, maximal induction of WAP mRNA synthesis requires the presence of I, glucocorticoids, and Prl (26), although induction of the WAP protein is regulated in a developmentally analogous but not identical fashion (10).

Recently, the promoter region of the mouse WAP gene (1) was linked to the activated human Ha-*ras* oncogene and the construct was introduced into the mouse germline. Tissue-directed and hormone-dependent WAP expression was conferred on the Ha-*ras* oncogene. The regulatory sequences controlling WAP expression are located within the 5' flanking sequence (1).

Transferrin/Lactoferrin

PROTEIN STRUCTURE   Transferrin and casein are the major milk proteins synthesized by the lactating mammary gland from rabbit (5); in addition, transferrin recently was identified as a major mouse milk protein (31). Transferrin and lactoferrin bind iron and have bacteriocidal properties. The M_r of bovine transferrin is 86,100.

HORMONAL REGULATION   Rabbit mammary gland explants require the presence of the hormones I, H, and Prl to synthesize both casein and transferrin (5). However, the rabbit system is unique in that transferrin synthesis is independent of both H and Prl while casein synthesis is not (5, 54). Transferrin synthesis is dependent upon I, since explants cultured in the presence of Prl alone show reduced levels of this protein. In the mouse, regulation of transferrin synthesis and secretion is distinctly different from that of other milk proteins (31). Transferrin synthesis in explant cultures is insensitive to lactogenic hormones; however, this synthesis in vivo is regulated by pregnancy, since production greatly increases during pregnancy and lactation. Thus the regulation and regulatory factors involved in transferrin synthesis remain to be determined.

Galactosyl Transferase

PROTEIN STRUCTURE   Galactosyl transferase (GT) is a membrane-bound and soluble enzyme found in intracellular and extracellular (milk) locations. In the mammary gland GT functions in concert with α-lactalbumin to synthesize lactose. Bovine GT has three forms with differing M_r; 54,000, 48,000, and 42,000 (for review see 25). GT from human milk has an approximate M_r of 43,000.

GENE STRUCTURE   Recently partial bovine cDNA clones were obtained from lactating mammary gland (38) and from kidney epithelial cells (51). A full-length cDNA clone was obtained from human liver (29). The bovine cDNA clones primarily carry sequences from the 3' coding and noncoding regions, while the full-length human cDNA clone is used to localize the gene to chromosome 4 by Southern analysis.

HORMONAL REGULATION   Bolander & Topper (4) report that GT and α-lactalbumin synthesis are asynchronous. Lactose synthetase activity is shown to follow GT synthesis but not α-lactalbumin synthesis, and GT synthesis more closely parallels that of the caseins (4). As with the other milk proteins discussed, I, H, and Prl are necessary for maximal protein expression. In particular, Prl is shown to be essential for GT synthesis, since explants grown in IH alone have low levels of GT activity compared with those seen in explants grown in IHPrl (57). Prl can be replaced by placental lactogen and H can be replaced by spermidine (41). Progesterone does not inhibit the synthesis of GT by IHPrl (58).

CONCLUSION

Considerable work on the hormonal regulation of milk protein gene expression has been done. Advances in molecular biology over the past ten years have permitted the identification and sequencing of genomic and cDNA clones for the majority of currently known milk proteins. From this work, the actual nucleotide sequences of the proteins have been determined or verified. More importantly, features that are both 5' and 3', as well as internal (intron) sites, have been identified as having potential regulatory functions. Similarity of nucleotide sequence features in different milk protein genes may reveal the mechanism by which coordinate expression occurs. Tissue- or cell-specific factors will undoubtedly play a role in differential expression, possibly by influencing transcription, transcript stabilization, or translation. Hormones are already known to affect transcription, stabilization, and translation, and further clarification of their collective and individual contributions to expression can be expected.

Literature Cited

1. Andres, A. C., Schonenberger, C. A., Groner, B., Henninghausen, L., Le Meur, M., et al. 1987. Ha-*ras* oncogene expression directed by a milk protein gene promoter: tissue specificity, hormonal regulation, and tumor induction in transgenic mice. *Proc. Natl. Acad. Sci. USA* 84:1299–1303

2. Bhattacharjee, M., Vonderhaar, B. K. 1984. Thyroid hormones enhance the synthesis and secretion of α-lactalbumin by mouse mammary tissue in vitro. *Endocrinology* 115:1070–77
3. Bolander, F. F. Jr., Nicholas, K. R., Van Wyk, J. J., Topper, Y. J. 1981. Insulin is essential for accumulation of

casein mRNA in mouse mammary epithelial cells. *Proc. Natl. Acad. Sci. USA* 78:5682–84

4. Bolander, F. F. Jr., Topper, Y. J. 1981. Asynchronous hormonal induction of lactose synthetase components, α-lactalbumin and galactosyl transferase, in relation to lactose secretion by mouse mammary explants. *Endocrinology* 108:1594–96

5. Bradshaw, J. B., Hatton, J., White, D. A. 1985. The hormonal control of protein N-glycosylation in the developing rabbit mammary gland and its effect upon transferrin synthesis and secretion. *Biochim. Biophys. Acta* 847:344–51

6. Breathnach, R., Chambon, P. 1981. Organization and expression of eucaryotic split genes coding for proteins. *Annu. Rev. Biochem.* 50:349–83

7. Brew, K., Hill, R. L. 1975. Lactose biosynthesis. *Rev. Physiol. Biochem. Pharmacol.* 72:105–57

8. Brodbeck, U., Ebner, K. E. 1966. Resolution of a soluble lactose synthetase into two protein components and solubilization of microsomal lactose synthetase. *J. Biol. Chem.* 241:762–64

9. Calos, M. P., Miller, J. H. 1980. Transposable elements. *Cell* 20:579–95

10. Campbell, S. M., Rosen, J. M., Henninghausen, L. C., Streck-Jurk, U., Sippel, A. E. 1984. Comparison of the whey acidic protein genes of the rat and mouse. *Nucleic Acids Res.* 12:8685–97

11. Chomczynski, P., Qasba, P., Topper, Y. J. 1984. Essential role of insulin in transcription of the rat 25,000 molecular weight casein gene. *Science* 226:1326–28

12. Chomczynski, P., Qasba, P., Topper, Y. J. 1986. Transcriptional and post-transcriptional roles of glucocorticoids in the expression of the rat 25,000 molecular weight casein gene. *Biochem. Biophys. Res. Commun.* 134:812–18

13. Craig, R. K., Hall, L., Parker, D., Campbell, P. N. 1981. The construction, identification and partial characterization of plasmids containing guinea pig milk protein complementary DNA sequences. *Biochem. J.* 194:989–98

14. Devinoy, E., Houdebine, L. M., DeLouis, C. 1978. Role of prolactin and glucocorticoids in the expression of casein genes in rabbit mammary gland organ culture: quantification of casein mRNA. *Biochim. Biophys. Acta* 517:360–66

15. Dynan, W. S., Tjian, R. 1983. The promoter-specific transcription factor Spl

binds the upstream sequences in the SV40 early promoter. *Cell* 35:79–87

16. Gaffney, E. V., Polanowski, F. P., Blackburn, S. E., Lambiase, J. T., Burke, R. E. 1976. Cultures of normal human mammary cells. *Cell Differ.* 5:69–81

17. Gupta, P., Rosen, J. M., D'Eustachio, P., Ruddle, F. H. 1982. Localization of the casein gene family to a single mouse chromosome. *J. Cell Biol.* 93:199–204

18. Guyette, W. A., Matusik, R. J., Rosen, J. M. 1979. Prolactin-mediated transcriptional and post-transcriptional control of casein gene expression. *Cell* 7:1013–23

19. Hall, L., Davies, M. S., Craig, R. K. 1981. The construction, identification and characterization of plasmids containing human α-lactalbumin cDNA. *Nucleic Acids Res.* 9:65–84

20. Hall, L., Emery, D. C., Davis, M. S., Parker, D., Craig, R. K. 1987. Organisation and sequence of the human α-lactalbumin gene. *Biochem. J.* 242:735–42

21. Hamada, H., Pretrino, M. G., Kakunaga, T., Seidman, M., Stollar, B. D. 1984. Characterization of genomic poly(dT-dG)·poly(dC-dA) sequences: structure, organization and conformation. *Mol. Cell. Biol.* 4:2610–21

22. Hamada, H., Seldman, M., Howard, B. H., Gordon, C. M. 1984. Enhanced gene expression by the poly(dT-dG·poly(dC-dA) sequence. *Mol. Cell. Biol.* 4:2622–30

23. Henninghausen, L. G., Sippel, A. E. 1982. Mouse whey acidic protein is a novel member of the family of 'four-disulfide core' proteins. *Nucleic Acids Res.* 10:2677–84

24. Henninghausen, L. G., Sippel, A. E., Hobbs, A. A., Rosen, J. M. 1982. Comparative sequence analysis of the mRNAs coding for mouse and rat whey protein. *Nucleic Acids Res.* 10:3733–44

25. Hill, R. L., Brew, K. 1975. Lactose synthetase. *Adv. Enzymol.* 43:411–90

26. Hobbs, A. A., Richards, D. A., Kessler, D. J., Rosen, J. M. 1982. Complex hormonal regulation of rat casein gene expression. *J. Biol. Chem.* 257:3598–3605

27. Hobbs, A. A., Rosen, J. M. 1982. Sequence of rat α- and γ-casein mRNAs: evolutionary comparison of the calcium-dependent rat casein multigene family. *Nucleic Acids Res.* 10:8079–98

28. Hopp, T. P., Woods, K. R. 1979. Primary structure of rabbit α-lactalbumin. *Biochemistry* 18:5182–90

29. Humphreys-Beher, M. G., Bunnell, B., van Tuinen, P., Ledbetter, D. H., Kidd, V. J. 1986. Molecular cloning and chromosomal localization of human 4-β-galactosyl transferase. *Proc. Natl. Acad. Sci. USA* 83:8918–22

30. Inouye, S., Soberan, X., Franceschini, T., Nakamura, K., Itakura, K., et al. 1982. Role of positive charge on the amino-terminal region of the signal peptide in protein secretion across the membrane. *Proc. Natl. Acad. Sci. USA* 79:3438–41

31. Lee, E. Y., Barcellos-Hoff, M. H, Chen, L. H., Parry, G., Bissel, M. J. 1987. Transferrin is a major mouse milk protein and is synthesized by mammary epithelial cells. *In Vitro Cell. Dev. Biol.* 23:221–26

32. Maher, F., Nicholas, K. R. 1987. Pituitary-induced lactation in mammary gland explants from the pregnant tammar *(Macropus eugenii)*: a negative role for cyclic AMP. *Comp. Biochem. Physiol.* 87:1107–17

33. Markoff, E., Talamantes, F. 1980. The lactogenic response of mouse mammary explants to mouse prolactin and growth hormone. *Endocr. Res. Commun.* 7:269–78

34. McKnight, S. L., Kingsbury, R. C., Spence, A., Smith, M. 1984. The distal transcription signals of the herpes virus tK gene share a common hexanucleotide control sequence. *Cell* 37:253–62

35. Mercier, J. C., Brignon, G., Ribadeau-Dumas, B. 1973. Structure primaire de la caséine κB bovine. Séquence complète. *Eur. J. Biochem.* 35:222–35

36. Mercier, J. C., Gaye, P., Soulier, S., Hue-Delahue, D., Vilotte, J. L. 1985. Construction and identification of recombinant plasmids carrying cDNAs coding for ovine α_{s_1}-, α_{s_2}-, β-, κ casein, and β-lactoglobulin. Nucleotide sequence of α_{s1}-casein cDNA. *Biochimie* 67:959–71

37. Nakhasi, H. L., Grantham, F. H., Gullino, P. M. 1984. Expression of κ-casein in normal and neoplastic rat mammary gland is under the control of prolactin. *J. Biol. Chem.* 259:14894–98

38. Narimatsu, H., Sinha, S., Brew, K., Okayama, H., Qasba, P. K. 1986. Cloning and sequencing of cDNA of bovine N-acetylglucosamine (β1→4) galactosyl transferase. *Proc. Natl. Acad. Sci. USA* 83:4720–24

39. Nicholas, K. R., Tyndale-Biscoe, C. H. 1985. Prolactin-dependent accumulation of α-lactalbumin in mammary gland explants from the pregnant wallaby *(Macropus eugenii). J. Endocrinol.* 106:337–42

40. Nordheim, A., Rich, A. 1983. Negatively supercoiled simian virus 40 DNA contains Z-DNA segments within transcriptional enhancer sequences. *Nature* 303:674–79

41. Oka, T. 1974. Spermidine in hormone-dependent differentiation of mammary gland in vitro. *Science* 184:78–80

42. Ono, M., Oka, T. 1980. α-lactalbumin-casein induction in virgin mouse mammary explants: dose-dependent differential action of cortisol. *Science* 207:1367–69

43. Prosser, C. G., Sankaran, L., Henning-hausen, L., Topper, Y. J. 1987. Comparison of roles of insulin and insulin-like growth factor I in casein gene expression and in the development of α-lactalbumin and glucose transport activities in the mouse mammary epithelial cells. *Endocrinology* 120:1411–16

44. Qasba, P. K., Safaya, S. K. 1984. Similarities of the nucleotide sequences of rat α-lactalbumin and chicken lysozyme genes. *Nature* 308:377–80

45. Quirk, S. J., Gannell, J. E., Fullerton, M. J., Funder, J. W. 1986. Mechanisms of biphasic action of glucocorticoids on alpha lactalbumin production by rat mammary gland explants. *J. Steroid Biochem.* 24:413–16

46. Quirk, S. J., Gannell, J. E., Fullerton, M. J., Funder, J. W. 1986. Specificity and mechanism of biphasic action of glucocorticoids on α-lactalbumin production by rat mammary gland explants. *Endocrinology* 118:909–14

47. Rosen, J. M. 1987. Milk protein gene structure and expression. In *The Mammary Gland: Development, Regulation and Function*, ed. M. C. Neville, C. W. Daniel, pp. 301–22. New York: Plenum

48. Rosen, J. M., Jones, W. K., Rodgers, J. R., Compton, J. R., Bisbee, C. A., et al. 1985. Regulatory sequences involved in the hormonal control of casein gene expression. *Ann. NY Acad. Sci.* 464:87–99

49. Rosen, J. M., O'Neal, D. L., McHugh, J. E., Comstock, J. P. 1978. Progesterone-mediated inhibition of casein mRNA and polysomal casein synthesis in the rat mammary gland during pregnancy. *Biochemistry* 17:290–97

50. Rosen, J. M., Rodgers, J. R., Couch, C. H., Bisbee, C. A., David-Inouye, Y., et al. 1986. Multihormonal regulation of milk protein gene expression. *Ann. NY Acad. Sci.* 478:63–76

51. Shaper, N. L., Shaper, J. H., Meuth, J.

L., Fox, J. L., Chang, H., et al. 1986. Bovine galactosyl transferase: identification of a clone by direct immunological screening of a cDNA expression library. *Proc. Natl. Acad. Sci. USA* 83:1573–77

52. Thompson, M. D., Dave, J. R., Nakhasi, H. L. 1985. Molecular cloning of mouse mammary gland κ- casein: comparison with rat κ-casein and rat and human γ-fibrinogen. *DNA* 4:263–71

53. Thordarson, G., Villalobos, R., Colosi, P., Southard, J., Ogren, L., et al. 1986. Lactogenic response of cultured mouse mammary epithelial cells to mouse placental lactogen. *J. Endocrinol.* 109:263–74

54. Topper, Y. J., Freeman, C. S. 1980. Multiple hormone interactions in the developmental biology of the mammary gland. *Physiol. Rev.* 60:1049–1106

55. Topper, Y. J., Nicholas, K. R., Sankaran, L., Kulski, J. K. 1984. Insulin biology from the perspective of studies on mammary gland development. In *Biochemical Actions of Hormones*, ed. G. Litwack, 11:163–86. New York/London: Academic

56. Topper, Y. J., Sankaran, L., Chomczynski, P., Prosser, C., Qasba, P. 1986. Three stages of responsiveness to hormones in the mammary cell. *Ann. NY Acad. Sci.* 464:1–10

57. Turkington, R. W., Brew, K., Vanaman, T. C., Hill, R. L. 1968. The hormonal control of lactose synthetase in the developing mouse mammary gland. *J. Biol. Chem.* 243:3382–87

58. Turkington, R. W., Hill, R. L. 1969. Lactose synthetase: progesterone inhibition of the induction of alphalactalbumin. *Science* 163:1458–60

59. Turkington, R. W., Juergens, W. G.,

Topper, Y. J. 1967. Steroid structural requirements for mammary gland differentiation in vitro. *Endocrinology* 80:1139–42

60. Vonderhaar, B. K. 1977. Studies on the mechanism by which thyroid hormones enhance α-lactalbumin activity in explants from mouse mammary glands. *Endocrinology* 100:1423–31

61. Vonderhaar, B. K. 1984. Hormones and growth factors in mammary gland development. In *Control of Cell Growth and Proliferation*, ed. C. M. Venziale, pp. 11–33. New York: Van Vostrand Reinhold

62. Vonderhaar, B. K., Nakhasi, H. L. 1985. Bifunctional activity of EGF on the expression of α- and κ-caseins in rodent mammary glands in vitro. *Endocrinology* 119:1178–84

63. Waugh, D. F. 1971. Formation and structure of casein micelles. In *Milk Proteins*, ed. H. A. McKenzie, 2:3–85. New York: Academic

64. Yu-Lee, L.-Y., Richter-Mann, L., Couch, C. H., Stewart, A. F., Mackinlay, A. G., et al. 1986. Evolution of the casein multigene family: conserved sequences in the 5' flanking and exon regions. *Nucleic Acids Res.* 14:1883–1902

65. Yu-Lee, L.-Y., Rosen, J. M. 1983. The rat casein multigene family. I. Fine structure of the γ-casein gene. *J. Biol. Chem.* 258:10794–10804

66. Ziska, S. E., Bhattacharjee, M., Herber, R. L., Qasba, P. K., Vonderhaar, B. K. 1988. Thyroid hormone regulation of α-lactalbumin: Differential glycosylation and messenger ribonucleic acid synthesis in mouse mammary glands. *Endocrinology* 123:2242–48

Annu. Rev. Physiol. 1989. 51:653–81

OVARIAN STEROID ACTION ON GENE EXPRESSION: Mechanisms and Models

C. Rories and T. C. Spelsberg

Department of Biochemistry and Molecular Biology, Mayo Clinic and Mayo Graduate School of Medicine, Rochester, Minnesota 55905

INTRODUCTION

The chapter deals with the mechanism of action of ovarian steroids, estrogen (E) and progesterone (P), on gene expression and was written for the general scientific community. Brief reviews of various aspects of the field, utilizing information from more recent publications, are presented. Because of space limitations, the authors emphasize certain aspects of this field and cite only example references, including reviews. Models outlining the known and the speculated steps of steroid action are graphically depicted. For more comprehensive reviews of the general area of steroid action on gene expression, the readers are referred to the following references: (4, 64, 88, 114, 117, 118a, 141, 156, 171, 179a).

Basic Mechanism of Action of Steroid Hormones on Gene Expression

Figure 1 outlines the general model of steroid action on gene expression. Ovarian steroid hormones circulate in the blood, both free and as complexes with blood binding proteins (BP). The free steroids diffuse in and out of all cells (Step 1, Figure 1), but are retained only in target cells via complexes with intranuclear binding proteins termed receptors (R) (Step 2, Figure 1). These receptors are steroid and tissue specific (61, 118a). Each receptor binds its respective steroid with high affinity, displaying equilibrium dissociation constant (K_d) in the range of 10^{-9} to 10^{-10}M. Once bound by the steroid hormones, the receptor molecules undergo a conformational change termed

653

0066-4278/89/0315-0653$02.00

activation (Step 3) that allows them to bind with high affinity to nuclear acceptor sites on the chromatin (Step 4, Figure 1) (179a). These events occur as early as five minutes after steroid injection into an animal. It is estimated that there are 4,000 to 10,000 nuclear acceptor sites per cell available for binding steroid receptors, with an even larger number of acceptor sites that appear to be masked (i.e. not available for binding receptors) in the intact chromatin (107, 172, 179a). The binding of steroid-receptor complexes to nuclear acceptor sites results in the alteration of gene transcription (Step 5, Figure 1) and/or, in some cases, alteration of posttranscriptional steps causing a change in levels of steady-state specific RNAs (Steps 6 & 7, Figure 1) and proteins (Steps 8 and 9, Figure 1) (75, 88, 114, 117, 179a). The subsequent physiological effects of steroids in cells are observed 12 to 24 hours after steroid treatment. Specific aspects of this steroid action pathway are described in more detail later in this review.

Steroids regulate the physiology of target cells by controlling the levels of both messenger RNA (mRNA) and protein species in cells. The chronology of the steps in this process with regard to the time of injection of radiolabeled steroids is as follows: Steroid-receptor complex formation ($\sim$1–3 min), binding to nuclear acceptor sites ($\sim$2–5 min), effects on RNA synthesis (minutes to several hours when considering both early and late genes), and finally, changing protein profiles due to changes in protein synthesis and protein turnover (4 hours and longer) (64, 88, 162). Therefore, steroid receptors represent one of the first intracellular gene regulatory proteins to be identified. The activity of receptor molecules is triggered by the steroids, which represent the external signals. Since the receptor species for any given steroid

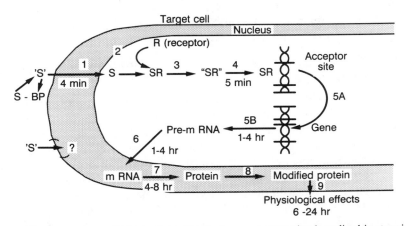

Figure 1   The basic mechanisms of steroid action on gene expression is outlined in stepwise (numbered) fashion. S represents the steroid; BP represents serum binding protein; R represents the receptor.

are thought to be the same in different tissues of an organism, it is the difference between nuclear binding sites (acceptor sites) that probably plays a role in the tissue-specific responses to the steroids. Further, the binding of the receptor to these acceptor sites appears to be the nuclear event immediately preceding the steroid-induced alterations in gene transcription. Thus, characterizing these initial nuclear binding sites (acceptor sites) is extremely important and has been an area of intense investigation as described in this review.

Steroid Regulation of Gene Expression: Transcription vs Posttranscriptional Regulation

For purposes of brevity, we discuss only a few examples of steroid action on gene expression. For further information, the readers are referred to recent reviews of this particular area of steroid action (5, 88, 114, 141, 155, 178). Although glucocorticoids have been reported to alter the levels of only a few protein species in certain target cells in culture (80), the action of the sex steroids (E and androgens) induce cell differentiation and tissue growth and, therefore, must ultimately affect the expression of a multitude of genes in target cells (64, 88, 118b, 119, 179a).

Steroids appear to regulate gene expression at the level of transcription and/or posttranscriptional events, the latter including effects on mRNA processing, mRNA stabilization, protein synthesis, and processing/secretion. Some genes whose rates of transcription are regulated by estrogens are the mammary gland casein gene (139) and the pS2 gene of MCF-7 human breast cancer cells (23). Progesterone regulates the rate of transcription of the avian ovalbumin gene (109) and the rabbit endometrial uteroglobin gene (104). Changes in the rate of transcription of most structural genes are detected between one and four hours after the steroid enters the cell (4, 64, 88, 114, 117, 118a, 141, 171, 179a). These steroids may regulate gene transcription by regulating the activity of transcription factors (40, 86) or via alterations in chromatin structure (5, 25, 53). The enhanced transcription of genes by estrogens is not due to steroid-induced gene amplification (51, 71, 142) or to gene sequence rearrangements (20, 188).

Posttranscriptional regulation of gene expression by ovarian steroids includes (a) estrogen regulation of mRNA processing in the rabbit uterus (i.e. selecting which mRNA species leaves the nucleus) (31); (b) estrogen regulation of albumin mRNA stabilization in the avian liver (195), and of Apo VLDL III mRNAs in the avian liver (i.e. determining the half-life of mRNA) (195); and finally (c) estrogen regulation of both transcription and mRNA stabilization, e.g. the ovalbumin mRNA in the avian oviduct (78, 109, 177) and the vitellogenin gene in the frog and avian livers (21, 22, 154, 155, 178). Studies demonstrating the regulation of gene expression at the level of protein synthesis and processing by steroids have also been reported (88, 179a). Since protein synthesis inhibitors have a multitude of effects on the physiology of the cell, and because it is difficult to interpret their effects on gene expression, studies on the utilization of these inhibitors are not described in this review.

STRUCTURES OF RECEPTORS AND CLUES TO THEIR BIOLOGICAL ACTION

Our knowledge of the structure and function of ovarian steroid receptors has grown significantly with the cloning, sequencing, and functional analysis of cDNAs encoding the progesterone receptors (PR) from chicken (38, 83) and rabbit (103), as well as the cDNAs encoding the estrogen receptors (ER) from human (66, 67), chicken (99), mouse (194a), and frog (191). Alignment of the amino acid sequences of the ER from different animal species shows that three separate blocks of residues (domains) of the ER are highly conserved among warm-blooded species, with three other domains showing relative variability (66). Two of these highly conserved domains, the central (DNA-binding) domain, and the C-terminal (steroid-binding) domain, show very high homology to corresponding regions of the frog ER (191). In addition to the marked evolutionary conservation within a single family (species) of receptor, the DNA-binding and steroid-binding domains are highly conserved between different classes of steroid receptors (66). The amino acid residues of the DNA-binding domain are thought to fold into two adjacent protruding DNA-binding domains. These structural elements are called DNA-binding fingers in recognition of their similarity to the zinc-stabilized DNA-binding fingers of *Xenopus laevis* transcription factor IIIA (50, 95, 111).

The DNA-binding domains of receptor molecules display an enhanced binding to DNA sequences that function as enhancers of transcription of steroid-regulated genes (65). The DNA-binding domain appears to be the only portion of a receptor protein absolutely required to mediate transcription of a steroid-responsive gene (74, 100, 110), with the possible exception of a short piece of the flanking hinge region on the C-terminal side of the DNA-binding domain (1). Functional analysis of receptor deletion mutants has localized the steroid-binding domain to the C-terminal half of the receptor protein (58, 100). This experimental approach reveals that the highly conserved protein domains serve analogous functions in progesterone (68), estrogen (1, 100), and glucocorticoid receptors (58, 74, 110). Moreover, homology of the steroid receptor DNA-binding domain to similar domains in thyroid hormone receptor (192), retinoic acid receptor (127), yeast, and *Drosophila* DNA-binding proteins (50, 95) indicates that steroid receptors belong to a larger family of DNA-binding proteins that regulate gene expression in eukaryotes.

Recent studies provide strong evidence that unoccupied ovarian steroid receptors are localized predominantly in the cell nucleus (84, 193). The binding by steroids activates receptors in a way that appears to involve a change in the structure of the receptor molecule, possibly as a result of the phosphorylation of the receptor molecule (179b). The activation results in tight binding of receptor to specific nuclear acceptor sites (169, 172, 179a). Little is known about the mechanism by which steroids activate their receptor. Studies with glucocorticoid receptor indicate that, in the absence of bound steroid, the steroid-binding domain masks the DNA-binding domain, and that binding of steroid causes a change that somehow exposes the DNA-binding fingers, allowing them to bind DNA and activate transcription (59). Similar studies with the human estrogen receptor are contradictory. One group reports that deletion of the steroid-binding domain of the estrogen receptor gives constitutively high activation of transcription (in absence of hormone), supporting the above proposal (1), while another group shows that a nearly identical deletion results in loss of transcriptional activity (66). The steroid-binding portion of the glucocorticoid receptor also appears to play an active role in nuclear localization of the receptor (129). It is not known whether the C-terminal portions of ovarian steroid receptors have similar nuclear localization capacities. We also have little understanding of how the interaction of active steroid receptors with their specific DNA-binding sites leads to induction or repression of transcription of genes. The receptor presumably makes contact with other proteins during this process, but there are no data that clearly identify a portion of a steroid receptor that participates in protein to protein contacts in the course of tissue-specific regulation of gene expression.

Several interesting observations have been made regarding the steroid receptor hinge region, which consists of amino acid residues between the DNA-binding and steroid-binding domains. One portion of the ER hinge region has similarity to sturgeon protamine, a DNA-binding protein (8b), and the corresponding protein of the GR has the capacity to promote nuclear localization (8c, 129). A second portion of the ER hinge region is structurally similar to the DNA-binding domain of the tetracycline repressor, a prokaryotic gene regulatory protein (8c). Such observations suggest that steroid receptors may have a second chromatin or DNA-binding domain in addition to the known DNA-binding finger domain. Other aspects of steroid receptor structure and function not yet explained include the association of receptors with 90- and 72-kd heat shock proteins (48, 132, 151) and the molecular basis for the regulation of the biological activities (activation) of receptors (19b, 75, 167) including the role of receptor phosphorylation in receptor activity (56, 77, 175).

STEROID REGULATORY ELEMENTS

The ovarian steroids (as well as the androgens and glucocorticoids) control the timing and magnitude of expression of a multitude of genes in tissue-specific patterns. The expression of these genes changes with time and the development of the target tissue. The chromatin proteins and higher order chromatin structures responsible for determining whether a steroid-sensitive gene will respond to steroids in a given tissue at a given time are just beginning to be identified. Major chromatin/DNA structures are established during tissue cytodifferentiation. Interestingly, specific DNA sequence elements have been found that play a role in steroid action on gene expression. These short (15–35-bp) DNA elements endow a heterologous promoter with the capacity to respond to steroids when positioned somewhere in the vicinity of the promoter, and thus are referred to as steroid-responsive elements (SRE). For instance, a DNA plasmid was constructed with the 35-bp estrogen-responsive element (ERE) from the *Xenopus laevis* vitellogenin A2 gene positioned upstream from the promoter/origin of the thymidine kinase (TK) gene of *Herpes simplex* virus (93). When transfected into MCF-7 cells, a human breast cancer cell line containing estrogen receptors, expression of the gene adjacent to the TK promoter was regulated by estrogen. Without the ERE, the TK promoter/gene combination was unresponsive to estrogen (93). This experimental approach demonstrates that a short DNA sequence can mediate steroid regulation of gene expression. It also reveals the evolutionary conservation of these DNA domains, since the SRE in the frog is recognized by proteins mediating estrogen control of gene expression in human cells.

Both progesterone responsive elements (PREs) and EREs have been identified and characterized using cell culture assays such as the one described above (26, 137, 153, 173, 189). Variation in the sequences of the PREs that have been described makes it difficult to define a consensus sequence recognized by the progesterone receptor. However, more than twenty putative glucocorticoid responsive elements (GREs) and EREs have been compared and a consensus GRE sequence (15) and a consensus ERE sequence (186) have been deduced. A common feature of these SREs is a conserved 13–15-bp core sequence consisting of a palindrome of two 5- or 6-bp sequences flanking three central base pairs of variable sequence (15, 173, 186, 189). It is somewhat disconcerting that the SREs responding to different steroids, have very similar sequences; in fact, an estrogen responsive element can be converted to a GRE by changing only two base pairs (108). This is especially remarkable since the nuclear acceptor sites are specific for a particular steroid receptor species (69, 73, 98, 166). In any case, the SREs act as hormone inducible enhancer elements, conferring steroid inducibility on a gene when present in either orientation, as well as when located from 150- to 2500-bp either upstream (on the 5' side) from the gene, or downstream (on the 3' side) of the gene (27, 82, 108). SRE-type sequences are often present upstream of a number of genes in multiple copies (15, 112, 124, 186). It may be that many of the SRE-type sequences are nonfunctional in vivo; however, in at least two cases, multiple copies of SREs act cooperatively in vivo in the induction of gene expression in response to steroids (82, 108).

Many questions arise regarding the biological and molecular functions of these sequences in mediating steroid regulation of transcription. For instance, are genes that respond to several steroids, such as the oviduct egg white protein genes (113) and the rat liver α_{2u}-globulin gene (28), regulated by multiple, steroid-specific SREs or by a common, nonspecific SRE? Would a common SRE be involved in the coordinate regulation of a variety of genes in the same tissue by the same steroid, e.g. the common response of the egg white protein genes to estrogen or progesterone in the avian oviduct? Comparing the various SREs, one notes that some have strong dyadic sequence symmetry, while others lack this palindromic symmetry (15, 108). Do such variations in SRE sequences play a role in defining the tissue specificity of steroid response shown by genes such as the oviduct lysozyme (136) and ovalbumin (97) genes? The recent development of in vitro systems that display steroid regulation of gene transcription (41, 85, 122) could provide an excellent opportunity for discerning the role of the DNA sequences and the specific protein factors involved in the complex steroid regulation of gene expression. In any case, the SREs play an essential role in steroid regulation of gene expression. The exact function of these SREs is unknown but possible models are proposed at the end of this review.

THE SEARCH FOR THE NUCLEAR ACCEPTOR SITES

Introduction

The nuclear acceptor sites (binding sites) for steroid receptors are important because they are involved in the nuclear event immediately preceding the steroid-induced alteration of gene transcription (88, 163, 172, 179a). It appears that an interaction between steroid hormone receptors with nuclear acceptor sites is required for steroid regulation of gene expression. Thus, what constitutes the acceptor sites is extremely important and has been an area of intense investigation.

To date, there are two main approaches and philosophies to studying the nuclear acceptor sites for steroid receptors. One approach used by Yamamoto and coworkers (27, 124, 125) and others (6, 7, 15, 37, 39, 40, 43, 112, 115, 124, 137, 149, 173, 184, 185, 189) involves the analysis of the binding of steroid receptors directly to various clones of specific DNA sequences, which reside in or near steroid-regulated structural genes. These binding sequences are often referred to as SREs since the binding sites are often the same as the SREs describe above. Another approach, taken by this laboratory (60–62, 76, 107, 130, 161–172, 179a, 180, 190), Ruh and coworkers (140, 143–147, 158–160), Barrack and coworkers (3, 9–14), and others (29, 30, 35, 42, 45, 55, 70, 89, 92, 94, 96, 105, 120, 123, 126, 176, 187), involves the investigation of the specific binding of steroids or steroid receptors with native structures of whole nuclei, the nuclear chromatin (interphase chromosomes), as well as nuclear and chromatin substructures. We classify the whole latter group under the general term of chromatin/matrix acceptor sites, especially since our recent studies suggest that the acceptor sites in the nuclear matrix (3, 12, 89, 92) and the chromatin acceptor sites may be one and the same (76). The general properties of these three classes of acceptor sites are outlined in Table 1.

Specific DNA Sequences (Steroid Regulatory Elements) as Acceptor Sites

There have been many papers reporting the enhanced cell-free binding of steroid receptors to specific DNA sequences, i.e. the SREs, which either reside within or neighbor steroid regulated genes (6, 27, 37, 43, 112, 115, 124, 125, 184). These sites are often referred to as SREs since the binding sites and the SREs described above are the same. Since many of these studies have utilized glucocorticoid receptors (GR), some discussion of this steroid system is included. The avian oviduct lysozyme and ovalbumin genes have been analyzed for progesterone receptor binding. In the latter system, SREs

Table 1 Comparisons of properties of three reported classes of nuclear acceptor sites for steroid receptors

Variable	Nuclear matrix acceptor sites	Chromatin acceptor sites	DNA regulatory sequence (SRE)
Composition	Protein and DNA complexes	Protein and DNA complexes	DNA
Steroid ligand	Required	Required	Required for in vivo activity, but not for binding[a]
Native receptor structure	Required	Required	Not required
Saturable binding	Yes	Yes	No
High-affinity binding	Yes	Yes	Unclear[b]
Competes with unlabelled steroid receptor complex	Yes	Yes	No data available
Receptor specificity ER vs PR vs AR vs GR	Yes	Yes	Unclear[c]
DNase resistant in nuclei or chromatin	Yes	Yes	No data available
In vitro binding correlates with in vivo binding	Yes	Yes[d]	Yes
Estimated sites/cells	(500–9,000/cell)	(6,000–10,000/cell)	(?)

[a]GR binds MMTV LTR in absence of steroid (194b).
[b]Estimates of preferred binding of PR over DNA vary from 20-fold (112) to 3500-fold (128). No saturation observed, so no affinities can be absolutely calculated.
[c]PR and GR bind some sites upstream of 2 genes (184). More data is needed comparing binding of other steroid receptors as well.
[d]See Spelsberg & Halberg (167), Boyd & Spelsberg (19b).

located about 220 bases upstream from the transcription start site were shown to bind receptor preferentially over nonspecific DNA in cell-free binding assays (37, 115, 137, 185), and to be required for hormone-induced transcription in vivo by gene transfer and deletion analyses (43, 137). A similar SRE for progesterone was found farther upstream from the uteroglobin gene in rabbit uteri (6).

More extensive studies were performed using the glucocorticoid receptor and the mouse mammary tumor virus (MMTV). These studies identified similar SRE domains in the long terminal repeat region about 200 bases upstream from the transcription start site of the MMTV genes. These domains display an enhanced binding of the glucocorticoid receptors (124, 149, 184) as well as a role in the regulation of transcription in vivo (24, 27, 79, 131). Interestingly, sequences that function as PREs also appear to respond to glucocorticoids (173, 184). It is not clear whether all PREs also function as GREs in vivo. These two classes of steroid receptors (GR and PR) also bind the same PRE but recognize different structural features of the PRE sequences. The GR and PR display some differences in DNA footprinting and bind the specific sequences with different relative affinities (185).

Many experimental approaches have demonstrated a preference for steroid receptor binding to SREs over other DNA sequences (15, 112, 149, 189). The fact that SREs are the only DNA elements identified to date as necessary and sufficient for conferring steroid inducibility on a gene promoter in transfection assays suggests that these DNA sequences may be sites of interaction with active steroid receptors. The discovery of SREs as essential components of the system by which steroids regulate transcription of at least some genes is an exciting contribution to our understanding of the molecular mechanisms of steroid action.

Although the SREs are required for steroid regulation of transfected genes, there remain major concerns as to their serving as acceptor sites for steroid receptors. First, although DNA footprinting analyses have indicated a preference for receptor binding to these DNA domains, detailed analyses of the glucocorticoid receptor MMTV system have shown a disagreement among laboratories concerning the actual nucleotides involved (112). Second, no studies to date have reported adequate data that the receptor binding to these DNA-binding sites is saturable. Thus, binding kinetics or the affinity of binding cannot be ascertained since these binding sites are nonsaturable (6, 7, 27, 37, 43, 112, 115, 124, 125, 184). Third, excesses of purified receptors apparently are required to generate the DNase protection footprints. Such large excesses certainly reduce the specificity and indicate a lower affinity of binding. Cordingley et al (39, 40) reported that the GR binds with much lower affinity to the glucocorticoid responsive element (GRE) of MMTV genomic sequences than does the transcription factor nuclear factor 1 (NF-1), which shows a K_d of 10^{-11} M. As reviewed by Edwards et al (48), it has been estimated that at least three orders of magnitude difference in binding affinities are required for a DNA-binding protein to distinguish effectively between specific and nonspecific binding sites on the eukaryote genome (49, 102, 182). However, only a 2–20-fold enhancement of steroid receptor binding to SRE sequences over that to bacterial or calf thymus genomic DNA has been reported (27, 48, 111, 124, 125). Therefore, the identification of a specific binding to the SREs is probably not possible based on results from studies published to date. Fourth, if the steroid receptors do indeed interact with SREs in vivo, several observations suggest that this interaction is only transient, or displays a much less stable binding compared to that of other DNA-binding proteins and their respective DNA-binding sites. For example, glucocorticoids induce the binding of the transcription factor NF-1 to the steroid-inducible MMTV LTR promoter to create a clearly defined exonuclease III footprint at a specific nuclease-protected DNA domain (40). In contrast, the GRE of the same gene shows a barely discernable change in sensitivity to exonuclease III when bound by the GR. Similarly, DNA footprint analysis of the binding of estrogen receptor to the ERE of the rat prolactin gene has not been successful (189). Finally, receptor binding to SRE sites does not show a steroid receptor specificity (115), a property characteristic of a variety of steroid receptor acceptor sites when assessed under in vivo intact cells, or cell-free binding assay conditions (69, 73, 98, 166).

Some investigators studying the direct binding of steroid receptors to these SREs conclude that these particular DNA sequences, while necessary for the process of steroid regulation of gene expression, may not represent the primary binding sites for steroid receptors (87, 112). These investigators further conclude that other factors such as chromosomal acceptor proteins must be required to generate specific acceptor sites (87, 112).

Among the challenges in molecular endocrinology research are finding answers to the following questions: (a) Are the interactions of steroid receptors with the SREs specific, i.e. saturable and with high affinity and dependent on the native receptor? (b) Are there specific chromatin acceptor proteins that help direct steroid receptors to these SREs by binding to these DNA sequences to generate sites with the required specificity of receptor binding? (c) Do these SREs play a role in the structure of chromatin that determines the tissue and developmental specificity of steroid response? (d) How are SREs related, positionally and functionally, to the chromatin acceptor sites that have been shown to bind receptors with high affinity and specificity?

The Chromatin Acceptor Sites

This class of sites was identified by a different approach than that taken with the SREs wherein analyses of steroid receptor bindings were initially performed in vivo in and then cell-free binding assays with intact nuclei and nuclear components. Two general classes of nuclear acceptor sites have been described using modifications of the same approach with isolated nuclei: these are the chromatin acceptor sites and the nuclear matrix acceptor sites. Many properties of these two classes of sites appear to be similar, as discussed below (3, 12, 35, 42, 76, 89, 92, 146, 147, 172) and may even represent the same class of acceptor sites (76).

The authors' laboratory has studied the chromatin acceptor sites for the avian oviduct PR for years. These sites appear to consist of specific chromatin acceptor proteins bound to DNA, possibly to specific DNA sequences (60–62, 76, 88, 130, 163–170, 172, 179a, 180, 190). The binding of [^{3}H]progesterone in vivo in the avian oviduct was first characterized and a cell-free binding assay was then developed. This cell-free binding of [^{3}H]PR to avian oviduct chromatin and dehistonized chromatin, termed nucleoacidic protein (NAP), displayed a saturable, high-affinity ($K_d \sim 10^{-9}$–10^{-10} M), receptor-dependent binding (130, 163, 172, 190) with similar levels of receptor molecules bound per cell as determined in vivo (161, 162, 166, 167). The receptor must be activated and bound with the steroid ligand to display specific binding to these chromatin acceptor sites (75, 130, 166, 172, 179a, 190). Many of the PR acceptor sites were found to be masked in intact oviduct chromatin, and could be unmasked (or expressed) by removal of the chromatin masking proteins using moderate levels of chaotropic salts (e.g. 4-M guanidine hydrochloride) to obtain nucleoacidic protein fraction (NAP) consisting of the DNA and tightly bound acceptor protein (107, 172). The masked and unmasked PR acceptor sites in the avian oviduct chromatin display the same binding affinities and steroid receptor specificities and thus appear to be the same sites (107, 164, 172, 179a). The binding of [^{3}H]PR was diminished by the addition of nonradiolabeled PR complexes but not by the addition of nonradiolabeled ER complexes (98, 166). Therefore, these acceptor sites display a steroid receptor specificity in cell-free binding assays as found in vivo in the avian oviduct (98) and in other steroid target tissue systems (69, 73). Using these cell-free assay conditions in two separate steroid target tissue systems, Roth and coworkers (29) and Spelsberg and coworkers (169) were able to display at least a partial competition between the in vivo binding to nuclear acceptor sites with those measured in the cell-free binding assays.

When the tightly bound nonhistone chromatin protein fraction that contains the acceptor proteins is removed from the residual chromatin to generate pure genomic DNA, specific binding in the cell-free binding assays is lost (163, 165, 167, 168, 170, 172, 179a, 181, 190). The chromatin acceptor sites can then be reconstituted by reannealing this same fraction of chromatin proteins to this genomic hen DNA (60–62, 163, 165, 172, 180). These reconstituted sites display the same specific PR-binding properties as the native (unreconstituted) acceptor sites. The reconstitution method was used to analyze for PR acceptor activity (i.e. acceptor protein) in the same fraction of avian oviduct chromatin proteins during its purification with a variety of chromatographic procedures. The acceptor activity has recently been purified over 100,000-fold to apparent homogeneity as a 10-kd protein (62). This 10-kd acceptor protein has a unique N-terminal sequence of H_2N-Met-Ile-Pro-Pro-Val-Gln-Val-Ser-Pro-Leu-Ile-Lys-Phe- and an amino acid composition with a slightly acidic pI and marked hydrophobicity (A. Goldberger & T. C. Spelsberg, unpublished data). Using antibodies against this protein, a 10- and a 6-kd species were detected by Western immunoblots (62).

Additional studies have supported biological relevance of these particular PR acceptor proteins. The 10-kd acceptor protein was reannealed to hen DNA, the acceptor protein DNA complex partially digested with DNase and used as an immunogen to prepare monoclonal antibodies against the complex (61). Antibodies against the reconstituted 10-kd acceptor protein DNA complexes were capable of inhibiting the specific PR, but not the ER binding, to undissociated native acceptor sites in oviduct chromatin (60). These same antibodies were used by ELISA to show that similar antigens existed in the chromatin extracts of different animal species (60). In summary, these studies indicate that (a) the isolated acceptor proteins are structural components of the chromatin acceptor sites for PR, (b) the reconstituted sites closely resemble the native (undissociated) sites, and (c) the PR acceptor sites appear to be conserved during evolution.

The reconstitution of specific PR acceptor sites can be achieved with other mammalian genomic DNAs but not prokaryote, plant, insect, or viral DNAs (180). These results suggest that specific DNA sequences are involved in these chromatin acceptor sites and that these sequences are also conserved during evolution (163, 168, 170). Additional studies are in progress to further characterize the avian oviduct PR acceptor proteins and to identify the analogous PR acceptor proteins in human endometrial chromatin. Interestingly, when the cloned genomic ovalbumin gene containing 2-kilobase flanking domains was used, no specific PR acceptor sites were generated. This indicates that the chromatin acceptor sites may reside at marked distances from steroid regulated genes. Further research will hopefully identify the specific DNA sequences (i.e. acceptor site DNA sequences) that appear to be bound by these acceptor proteins (180) and determine the location of these sequences with respect to steroid-regulated genes.

It is important to note that many other laboratories have examined intact (whole) nuclei or chromatin for specific binding of a variety of steroid receptors. Examples of specific chromatin acceptor sites for PR are sheep hypothalamus (126), hamster uterus (35), and rat placenta (120). Chromatin acceptor sites that specifically bind estrogen receptors were found in the avian oviduct (45, 147), calf uterus (42, 140, 146), rat uterus (30), mouse uterus

(123), shark testes (144), human breast cancer cell lines (55, 159, 176), rodent malignant breast tissue (94, 158), and in mouse and sheep brain (105, 126). Further, specific chromatin acceptor sites for androgen receptors were reported for the rat prostate and Sertoli cells (96, 183a, 187), and for glucocorticoid receptors in rat liver, mouse mammary, and human leukemia cells (70, 145), and in human breast cancer cell lines (176). These chromatin acceptor sites also display a receptor-dependent, saturable, high-affinity binding using cell-free binding assays, as reported for the PR avian oviduct system. Where examined, all chromatin acceptor sites consisted of nonhistone proteins tightly bound to DNA and many of the acceptor sites were masked in the intact chromatin. More in-depth studies were carried out by Ruh and coworkers (140, 159, 160) utilizing the reconstituted acceptor sites whereby the dissociated acceptor proteins from calf uterine chromatin were reconstituted to pure DNA to generate specific acceptor sites for ER (140). Two classes (or species) of acceptor proteins were identified. More recent studies from this group reveal that antiestrogen receptor complexes bind to different acceptor sites (i.e. acceptor proteins) than do the estrogen receptor complexes (T. Ruh & M. Ruh, personal communication). This unique nuclear binding might explain some of the action of the antiestrogens.

More studies are under way to (a) further characterize the acceptor proteins, including this steroid receptor specificity, (b) characterize any associated specific DNA sequences, including the correlation between the acceptor site DNA sequences with those of the SREs described earlier, (c) determine the structure of the acceptor site DNA sequences when complexed with acceptor protein, (d) determine the evolutionary conservation of these sites, and (e) determine the location of these sites with respect to steroid-regulated genes. Answers to these questions should provide new insights into the mechanism of steroid regulation of gene expression.

The Nuclear Matrix as Acceptor Sites

A related class of nuclear acceptor sites has been identified as associated with the nuclear matrix. The nuclear matrix represents the residual structure after detergent treatment of nuclei, DNase I digestion, and high salt extraction. It reportedly consists of approximately 7% of the total nuclear protein and 2% of the total nuclear DNA and much of the heterogeneous nuclear RNA (10, 11, 13, 18). In these studies, nuclease- and salt-resistant localization of estrogen and androgen receptors has been identified in the nuclear matrices of avian liver and rat ventral prostate, respectively (9, 12). These sites display a high-affinity, saturable, tissue-specific, and steroid-specific binding. The majority of the receptors are associated with the internal ribonucleoprotein network (i.e. the internal nuclear matrix) of the total nuclear matrix structure (10–14). Similar nuclear localization of receptors has been identified for estradiol in the nuclear matrix of rat uterus, but not in rat lung or liver nuclear matrices (2, 13). Finally, using specific antireceptor antibodies in Western immunoblot analyses, Barrack and coworkers (3) have identified the presence of estrogen receptor molecules (67-kd species) in the nuclear matrix of female rat liver.

Barrack (9–11) and Colvard & Wilson (36) were also able to demonstrate the specific binding of isolated androgen receptor complexes to the isolated nuclear matrix of rat ventral prostate and rat Dunning prostate tumor respectively. The binding in both systems was saturable, high-affinity, tissue-specific (liver matrix showed little binding), and steroid and receptor dependent. These results suggest that the nuclear matrix of steroid target cells contains intact nuclear acceptor sites for steroid receptors and that these sites show binding properties similar to the chromatin acceptor sites and expected of true nuclear acceptor sites. The nuclear matrix appears to be associated with transcriptionally active genes, with rapidly synthesized RNA, with initiation sites for DNA replication, and with DNase I hypersensitive sites (10, 11, 13, 18, 32). Thus, this class of nuclear acceptor sites is associated with many of the biological functions that steroids regulate.

Spelsberg and coworkers (76) found that the chromatin acceptor sites for the avian oviduct PR (described above) are maintained not only after histones are removed by high salt solutions (190), but also after extensive nuclease (DNase I) digestion. The resulting protein DNA particles generated by the nuclease digestion of dehistonized avian oviduct chromatin resembled the nuclear matrix in composition of RNA and protein (representing about 5–10% of the nuclear protein) and 2–5% of the nuclear DNA. These sites displayed specific, saturable, and high-affinity binding ($K_d \sim 10^{-10}$M) of the PR (76). Therefore, since these chromatin acceptor site complexes have the same properties and were isolated with similar methods as the nuclear matrix, they are probably one and the same.

THE ROLE OF TRANSCRIPTION FACTORS IN EARLY AND LATE GENE RESPONSES

Early (Primary?) and Late (Secondary?) Gene Responses

Analysis of the molecular mechanisms by which activated steroid receptors interact with chromatin to regulate gene expression is complicated by the fact that different steroid responsive genes may be regulated at different periods and thus may be regulated by very different mechanisms. This is suggested by the wide variation in lag times that elapse between steroid administration and measurable changes in rate of transcription of different genes. Steroid hormones bind to their nuclear receptors and these steroid-receptor complexes are bound to their respective nuclear acceptor sites within five minutes after injection of the hormones into animals (109, 161). As shown in Figure 2, the

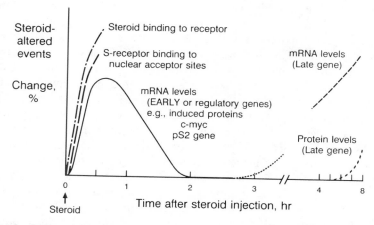

Figure 2 Outline of the chronology of events in the steroid regulation of gene expression in target tissues of an animal.

early or primary response genes show an immediate change in steady-state mRNA levels that can be measured within about 15 minutes after steroid administration. Examples of the rapid changes in mRNA levels are as follows: the early induced genes of rat uterus (44), the pS2 gene of MCF-7 human breast cancer cells (23), the *c*-myc gene in breast cancer cells (46), *n*-myc in rat uterus (116, 181), all showing induced transcription within about 15 minutes after estrogen administration, and finally, the *c*-myc proto-oncogene in the avian oviduct, which shows a decrease in mRNA levels within five minutes after progesterone administration (52).

In contrast, the bulk of the known structural genes studied for steroid regulation represent a second class of steroid responsive genes, called late genes, which may be secondary response genes. As shown in Figure 2, these late genes do not show a significant change in mRNA steady-state levels until one or more hours after steroid administration. An example of late steroid response is the estradiol induction of *Xenopus* liver vitellogenin mRNA, with the large increase in vitellogenin mRNA delayed until 90 minutes or more after estrogen administration (8a). Another example occurs in the avian oviduct, where there is a one- to three-hour lag period between the time progesterone or estrogen binds to nuclear acceptor sites and the increase in the mRNA levels of genes coding for the egg white proteins ovalbumin, ovomucoid, and lysozyme (72, 121, 152).

Role of Transcription Factors in Steroid Regulation of Gene Expression

Recently transcription factors were shown to bind at specific sites in or near several steroid-regulated genes. Two transcription factors (proteins) were shown to bind at specific sites in the glucocorticoid/progesterone sensitive promoter of the mouse mammary tumor virus long terminal repeat (MMTV-LTR) when transcription by this promoter is induced with glucocorticoid (40). These factors are present before hormone stimulation, but are prevented from or are incapable of binding to the MMTV-LTR DNA until the steroid is added. Another factor, active in estrogen-stimulated rooster liver but not in untreated liver, binds to a 14–base pair element in the third intron of the chicken vitellogenin gene and appears to stimulate transcription of the gene in vitro, even in the absence of estrogen receptor (86). Since cycloheximide does not block estrogen-induced transcription of liver vitellogenin genes, this intron-binding transcription factor is thought to be present in the unstimulated cells, and the addition of estrogen somehow activates the factor to bind to the DNA domain (86). Tissue-specific regulatory proteins also appear to mediate the steroid responsiveness of chicken lysozyme gene promoter, since transfection of a lysozyme/SV40 T-antigen fusion gene is induced by glucocorticoid in chicken oviduct cells, but not in chicken fibroblasts, even though both cell types have active glucocorticoid receptors (136).

In addition to the transcription factors described above, the RNA polymerase II requires three or more general protein transcription factors for the transcription of all structural genes (134, 135). Therefore, the steroid induction of transcription requires numerous protein factors in addition to the active receptor and RNA polymerase II. It should be mentioned that steroid induction of gene expression is also associated with changes in chromatin ultrastructure (19a, 57, 138), DNA methylation (17, 101, 148), and in the pattern of DNase I hypersensitive sites within chromatin (25, 90, 196). Some or all of these effects could well be mediated by regulatory proteins, which are rapidly regulated by steroids.

Role of the Early Genes as Regulatory Genes

Recognition of the distinct early and late transcriptional responses in midge salivary glands following administration of the steroid ecdysone led to the proposal that some of the early genes code for regulatory or transcription factors, which are required for transcription of the late genes (33, 34). This model has been applied to the steroid gene regulation systems by the authors (169, 172), and is described in the following section. The model is appealing because it can explain the variable lag times observed for steroid induction of transcription.

At the time of writing, there have been no reports describing the steroid-induced synthesis of transcription factors. However, there are reports of steroids regulating the activity of endogenous transcription factors (39, 40, 86). These factors could be activated by enzymatic modifications coded by the regulatory genes or their binding to chromatin might be facilitated by steroid-induced changes in chromatin. An example of a regulatory gene in steroid regulation of transcription factors comes from recent studies in this laboratory of progesterone action on c-myc proto-oncogene expression in the avian oviduct (52, 169), as well as of glucocorticoid action on c-myc in the avian oviduct (C. Rories et al, unpublished). Progesterone and/or glucocorticoids reduce the c-myc mRNA levels within five minutes in the avian oviduct, with a maximum of 70 to 90% within 20 minutes after injection of steroid. The c-myc gene codes for a nuclear protein that may positively regulate the genes involved in the initiation of DNA replication (63, 91, 174). Thus, a possible role of c-myc in the steroid regulation of cell proliferation exists. This system also could serve as an example of a steroid-regulated regulatory gene with the c-myc protein acting as a transcription factor, or possibly as an activator of transcription factors that regulate the expression of genes involved in control of cell division and growth. Support for this concept comes from other studies showing that c-myc is induced by estrogens (inducers of cell proliferation) in human breast cancer cells within 15 minutes after addition to the culture medium (46). Further, the mRNA of N-myc (another related proto-oncogene) was found to be induced by estrogens in the rat uterus within 15 minutes postinjection; however, changes in uterine c-myc mRNA were not observed until several hours later (116, 181). Similarly, glucocorticoids produce marked inhibition of the c-myc gene expression in a lymphosarcoma cell line, in which glucocorticoids repress cell proliferation (54).

MODELS OF STEROID ACTION

An Overall Model: Direct Action of Steroid Receptors on Regulatory Genes and the Functions of their Protein Products

With the information presently available, we have formulated a model for ovarian steroid action in Figure 3. The basic format for this model is similar to that described by Clever & Romball (33, 34) for the ecdysone-chromosome puff system. This model was developed to be in accord with the data presented in the preceding section and, is an extension of a similar model for steroid hormone action presented previously (169, 172). Beginning at the top left side of Figure 3 and following the arrows, steroid hormones enter target cells and bind to their receptors; the resulting complex then binds to the nuclear acceptor sites. These sites are located on a primary (1°) steroid regulatory element, possibly neighboring a regulatory gene (early gene) in the 5' flanking domain or even within the gene. This binding regulates the transcription of the regulatory gene within minutes after the steroid enters the target cell. In any given target cell, at any given time, there may be a few dozen of these regulatory genes responding to the steroid. Each of the regulatory genes codes for a regulatory protein, which could alter the expression of a multitude of genes via one of several possible pathways. In Pathway 1 some regulatory proteins could have important cytoplasmic/plasma membrane enzymatic activities (e.g. phosphorylation) that in turn cause changes in membrane transport, protein synthesis, protein processing, or protein secretion. Alternatively, in Pathway 2 the enzymatic regulatory proteins could modify nuclear factors that in turn could regulate chromatin structure, gene transcription as transcription factors, or possibly RNA processing. Lastly, in Pathway 3 the regulatory proteins could represent nuclear factors that directly regulate chromatin structure or gene transcription as transcription factors. In the latter two roles, the transcription factors would bind the secondary (2°) steroid regulatory elements residing either in the 5' flanking domains or within the steroid-regulated structural genes (late genes). Thus, the SREs residing near or within late genes would function as secondary SREs that bind transcription factors and not necessarily the steroid receptors. The regulation of structural (late gene) transcription would occur one to four hours after the steroid enters into the cell. Through these three pathways, each steroid-controlled regulatory gene could regulate the expression of a multitude of genes via transcription and/or posttranscriptional pathways. This simplified model explains some of the riddles related to steroid regulation of gene expression.

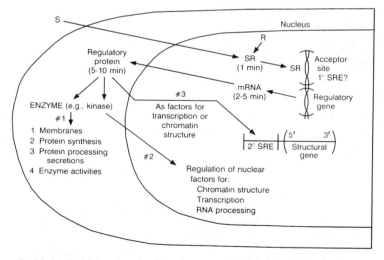

Figure 3   Model explaining the role of regulatory genes and their products (regulatory protein) in the action of steroids in target cells. The regulatory gene represents an early gene and the structural gene represents a late gene. The times represent estimated time of occurrence after the steroid enters the cell. The 1° SRE represents the primary steroid regulatory element; 2° SRE represents the secondary SRE.

Model for Direct Steroid Receptor Action on Early (Regulatory) Gene Transcription

Based on the above cited recent literature, we have designed a model to demonstrate how steroids might directly regulate the early regulatory gene transcription (Figure 4). This model does not address the possible early steroid regulation of mRNA processing, which might involve a direct steroid receptor interaction with nuclear RNAs (183b). The acceptor site may be located at a site distant to the SRE enhancer sequence, as shown in Figure 4, step 1, because (a) no nuclease footprints or zones of methylation protection have been observed on or adjacent to SRE, which would support the presence of tightly bound acceptor protein(s), and (b) there is evidence that reassociation of acceptor protein with DNA known to have an SRE fails to create a detectable acceptor site (T. C. Spelsberg, et al, unpublished data). In any event, the activated steroid receptor complex binds to the acceptor site with high affinity, and the receptor-acceptor complex then becomes associated with the nuclear matrix (Figure 4, step 2). Alternatively, the active receptor may bind an acceptor site containing an acceptor protein that is already

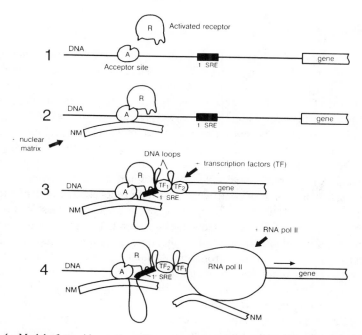

Figure 4 Model of steroid receptor action on gene transcription. R represents the receptor; A represents the acceptor protein; NM represents the nuclear matrix; TF_1/TF_2 represent transcription factors; $1°$ SRE represents the primary SRE; RNA pol II represents RNA polymerase II.

attached to the nuclear matrix (13). The DNA-binding domain of the matrix-bound receptor could then interact with the SRE, possibly displacing a negative regulatory factor (39), and facilitate the binding of transcription factors to specific sites in the promoter (Figure 4, step 3).

The binding of at least two transcription factors is shown to be steroid inducible (40). Some transcription factors may be tissue-specific and several may bind DNA in a cooperative fashion, possibly with DNA looping out between the protein-DNA complexes (106, 133, 150, 157) (see steps 3 and 4 of Figure 4). The protein-DNA complex formed at the promoter is then recognized by RNA polymerase II (Figure 4, step 4), and additional transcription factors bind to give rise to an active transcription complex with transcription of the gene ensuing (47). Nuclear matrix is shown in contact with RNA polymerase (Figure 4, step 4) to reflect the evidence that actively transcribed genes are associated with nuclear matrix (81, 197). The active receptor-acceptor complex is shown in continuous contact with the SRE (Figure 4, steps 3 and 4). However, the relatively weak in vivo footprint at the SREs (16, 40) suggests that the receptor-SRE interaction might actually be of a transient nature, with receptor dissociating from SRE after initiating the formation of the active transcription complex.

CONCLUSIONS

In the past six years, the area of steroid action on gene expression has been an exciting one owing to many rapid advances. The receptors have been purified, genomic clones of their genes have been isolated, and their primary structures determined. The molecular events involved in receptor activation and in the regulation of gene expression by the steroid receptor complexes are now being pursued. The role of the steroid regulatory elements (SRE) and transcription factors in the steroid regulation of gene expression is also under investigation and represents an area of potential breakthroughs. The chemical composition and locale of the nuclear acceptor sites (with respect to steroid regulated genes) has been an area of controversy and represents another area of exciting new information. Data in the literature indicate important roles for both the acceptor proteins and the DNA sequences they bind. The acceptor proteins are presented as proteins that help guide the steroid receptor complexes to the correct binding sites on the chromatin. A model is proposed whereby these acceptor proteins represent chromatin and/or nuclear matrix proteins that are bound to the genomic DNA at specific acceptor site DNA sequences neighboring regulatory genes (169, 172). These early regulatory genes in turn code for regulatory proteins, which have several possible functions described in the model. One of these functions is to regulate transcription factor binding to steroid regulatory elements resulting in the regulation of structural (late) gene expression (169, 172).

Literature Cited

1. Adler, S., Waterman, M. L., He, X., Rosenfeld, M. G. 1988. Steroid receptor-mediated inhibition of rat prolactin gene expression does not require the receptor DNA-binding domain. *Cell* 52: 685–95
2. Agutter, P. S., Birchall, K. 1979. Functional differences between mammalian nuclear protein matrices and pore-lamina complex laminae. *Exp. Cell Res.* 124: 453–60
3. Alexander, R. B., Greene, G. L., Barrack, E. R. 1987. Estrogen receptors in the nuclear matrix: direct demonstration using monoclonal antireceptor antibody. *Endocrinology* 120:1851–57
4. Anderson, J. N. 1984. The effect of steroid hormones on gene transcription. In *Biological Regulation and Development*, ed. R. F. Goldberger, K. R. Yamamoto, pp. 169–212. New York: Plenum
5. Anderson, J. N., Vanderbilt, J. N., Lawson, G. M., Tsai, M.-J., O'Malley, B. W. 1983. Chromatin structure of the ovalbumin gene family in the chicken oviduct. *Biochemistry* 22:21–30
6. Bailly, A., Atger, M., Atger, P., Cerbon, M. A., Alizon, M., et al. 1983. The rabbit uteroglobin gene. Structure and interaction with the progesterone receptor. *J. Biol. Chem.* 258:10384–89
7. Bailly, A., LePage, C., Rauch, M., Milgrom, E. 1986. Sequence specific DNA binding of the progesterone receptor to the uteroglobin gene: Effects of hormone, antihormone, and receptor phosphorylation. *EMBO J.* 5:3235–41
8a. Baker, H. J., Shapiro, D. J. 1978. Rapid accumulation of vitellogenin messenger RNA during secondary estrogen stimulation of *Xenopus laevis*. *J. Biol. Chem.* 253:4521–24
8b. Baker, M. E. 1986. Computer-based search for steroid and DNA binding sites of estrogen and glucocorticoid receptors. *Biochem. Biophys. Res. Commun.* 139: 281–86
8c. Baker, M. E. 1988. Similarity between the estrogen receptor and the DNA-binding domain of the tetracycline repressor. *Biochem. Biophys. Res. Commun.* 150:463–68
9. Barrack, E. R. 1983. The nuclear matrix of the prostate contains acceptor sites for androgen receptors. *Endocrinology* 113: 430–32
10. Barrack, E. R. 1987. Localization of steroid hormone receptors in the nuclear matrix. In *Steroid Hormone Receptors: Their Intracellular Localization*, ed. C. R. Clark, pp. 86–127. Chichester, England: Horwood
11. Barrack, E. R. 1987. Specific association of androgen receptors and estrogen receptors with the nuclear matrix: Summary and perspectives. In *Recent Advances in Steroid Hormone Action*, ed. V. K. Moudgil, pp. 85–107. New York: de Gruyter
12. Barrack, E. R., Coffey, D. S. 1980. The specific binding of estrogens and androgens to the nuclear matrix of sex hormone responsive tissues. *J. Biol. Chem.* 255:7265–75
13. Barrack, E. R., Coffey, D. S. 1982. Biological properties of the nuclear matrix: Steroid hormone binding. *Recent Prog. Horm. Res.* 38:133–95
14. Barrack, E. R., Coffey, D. S. 1983. The role of the nuclear matrix in steroid hormone action. *Biochem. Actions Horm.* 10:23–90
15. Beato, M., Arnemann, J., Chalepakis, G., Slater, E., Willmann, T. 1987. Gene regulation by steroid hormones. *J. Steroid Biochem.* 27:9–14
16. Becker, P. B., Gloss, B., Schmid, W., Strähle, U., Schütz, G. 1986. In vivo protein-DNA interactions in a glucocorticoid response element require the presence of the hormone. *Nature* 324:686–88
17. Becker, P. B., Ruppert, S., Schütz, G. 1987. Genomic footprinting reveals cell type-specific DNA binding of ubiquitous factors. *Cell* 51:435–43
18. Berezney, R. 1984. Organization and functions of the nuclear matrix in chromosomal nonhistone proteins. In *Chromosomal Nonhistone Proteins*, ed. L. S. Hnilica, 4:120–80. Boca Raton, Fla: CRC
19a. Bloom, K. S., Anderson, J. N. 1978. Fractionation of hen oviduct chromatin into transcriptionally active and inactive regions after selective micrococcal nuclease digestion. *Cell* 15:141–50
19b. Boyd, P. A., Spelsberg, T. C. 1979. Seasonal changes in the molecular species and nuclear binding of the chick oviduct progesterone receptor. *Biochemistry* 18:3685–90
20. Breathnach, R., Mandel, J. L., Chambon, P. 1977. Ovalbumin gene is split in chicken DNA. *Nature* 270:314–19
21. Brock, M., Shapiro, D. 1983. Estrogen regulates the absolute rate of transcription of the *Xenopus laevis* vitellogenin genes. *J. Biol. Chem.* 258:5449–55
22. Brock, M., Shapiro, D. 1983. Estrogen stabilizes vitellogenin mRNA against cytoplasmic degradation. *Cell* 34:207–14
23. Brown, A. M. C., Jeltsch, J.-M.,

Roberts, M., Chambon, P. 1984. Activation of pS2 gene transcription is a primary response to estrogen in the human breast cancer cell line MCF-7. *Proc. Natl. Acad. Sci. USA* 81:6344–48

24. Buetti, E., Kuhnel, B. 1986. Distinct sequence elements involved in the glucocorticoid regulation of the mouse mammary tumor virus promoter identified by linker scanning mutagenesis. *J. Mol. Biol.* 190:41–54

25. Burch, J. B. E., Evans, M. I. 1986. Chromatin structural transitions and the phenomenon of vitellogenin gene memory in chickens. *Mol. Cell. Biol.* 6:1886–93

26. Cato, A. C. B., Miksicek, R., Schütz, G., Arnemann, J., Beato, M. 1986. The hormone regulatory element of mouse mammary tumor virus mediates progesterone induction. *EMBO J.* 5:2237–40

27. Chandler, V. L., Maler, B. A., Yamamoto, K. R. 1983. DNA sequences bound specifically by glucocorticoid receptor in vitro render a heterologous promoter hormone responsive in vivo. *Cell* 33:489–99

28. Chen, C. L., Feigelson, P. 1979. Cycloheximide inhibition of hormonal induction of α_{2u}-globulin mRNA. *Proc. Natl. Acad. Sci. USA* 76:2669–73

29. Chuknyiska, R. S., Haji, M., Foote, R. H., Roth, G. S. 1984. Effects of in vivo estradiol administration of availability of rat uterine nuclear acceptor sites measured in vitro. *Endocrinology* 115:836–38

30. Chuknyiska, R. S., Haji, M., Foote, R. H., Roth, G. S. 1985. Age associated changes in nuclear binding of rat uterine estradiol receptor complexes. *Endocrinology* 116:547–51

31. Church, R. B., McCarthy, B. J. 1970. Unstable nuclear RNA synthesis following estrogen stimulation. *Biochem. Biophys. Acta* 199:103–14

32. Ciejek, E. M., Nordstrom, J. L., Tsai, M.-J., O'Malley, B. W. 1982. Ribonucleic acid precursors are associated with the chick oviduct nuclear matrix. *Biochemistry* 21:4945–53

33. Clever, U. 1964. Actinomycin and Puromycin: Effects on sequential gene activation by ecdysone. *Science* 146:794–95

34. Clever, U., Romball, C. G. 1966. RNA and protein synthesis in the cellular response to a hormone, ecdysone. *Proc. Natl. Acad. Sci. USA* 56:1470

35. Cobb, A. D., Leavitt, W. W. 1987. Characterization of nuclear acceptor sites for mammalian progesterone receptor: Comparison with the chick oviduct system. *Gen. Comp. Endocrinol.* 67:214–20

36. Colvard, D. S., Wilson, E. M. 1984. Androgen receptor binding to nuclear matrix in vitro and its inhibition by 8S androgen receptor promoting factor. *Biochemistry* 23:3479–86

37. Compton, J. G., Schrader, W. T., O'Malley, B. W. 1982. Selective binding of chicken progesterone receptor A subunit to a DNA fragment containing ovalbumin gene sequences. *Biochem. Biophys. Res. Commun.* 105:96–104

38. Conneely, O. M., Sullivan, W. P., Toft, D. O., Birnbaumer, M., Cook, R. 1986. Molecular cloning of the chicken progesterone receptor. *Science* 233:767–70

39. Cordingley, M. G., Richard-Foy, H., Lichter, A., Hager, G. L. 1987. The hormone response element of the MMTV LTR: A complex Regulatory Region. In *DNA: Protein Interactions and Gene Regulation*, ed. E. B. Thompson, J. Papaconstantinou, pp. 233–43. Austin: Univ. Texas Press

40. Cordingley, M. G., Riegel, A. T., Hager, G. L. 1987. Steroid-dependent interaction of transcription factors with the inducible promoter of mouse mammary tumor virus in vivo. *Cell* 48:261–70

41. Corthesy, B., Hipkind, R., Theulaz, I., Wahli, W. 1988. Estrogen-dependent in vitro transcription from the vitellogenin promoter in liver nuclear extracts. *Science* 239:1137–39

42. Cushing, C. L., Bambara, R. A., Helf, R. 1985. Interactions of estrogen-receptor and anti-estrogen-receptor complexes with nuclei in vitro. *Endocrinology* 116:2419–29

43. Dean, D. C., Knoll, B. J., Riser, M. E., O'Malley, B. W. 1983. A 5'-flanking sequence essential for progesterone regulation of an ovalbumin fusion gene. *Nature* 305:551–54

44. DeAngelo, A. B., Gorski, J. 1970. Role of RNA synthesis in the estrogen induction of a specific uterine protein. *Proc. Natl. Acad. Sci. USA* 66:693–700

45. DeBoer, W., Snippe, L., Ab, G., Gruber, M. 1984. Interaction of calf uterine estrogen receptors with chicken target cell nuclei. *J. Steroid Biochem.* 20:387–90

46. Dubik, D., Dembinski, T. C., Shiu, R. P. C. 1987. Stimulation of c-myc oncogene expression associated with estrogen-induced proliferation of human breast cancer cells. *Cancer Res.* 47:6517–21

47. Dynan, W. S., Tjian, R. 1985. Control of eukaryotic messenger RNA synthesis

by sequence-specific DNA-binding proteins. *Nature* 316:774–78

48. Edwards, D. P., Estes, P. A., Lawler-Heavner, J., Elashry-Stowers, D. 1988. Structural and functional properties of progesterone receptors. In *Steroid Receptors and Disease: Cancer, Autoimmune, Bone, and Circulatory Disorders*, ed. P. J. Sheridan, K. Blum, M. C. Trachtenberg, pp. 121–51. New York: Dekker

49. Emerson, B. M., Lewis, C., Felsenfeld, G. 1985. Interactions of specific nuclear factors with the nuclease-hypersensitive region of the chicken adult β-globulin gene: Nature of the binding domain. *Cell* 41:21–30

50. Evans, R. M., Hollenberg, S. M. 1988. Zinc fingers: Gilt by association. *Cell* 52:1–3

51. Feigelson, P., Kurtz, D. T. 1978. Hormonal modulation of α_{2u} globulin mRNA: Sequence measurements using a specific cDNA probe. *Cold Spring Harbor Symp. Quant. Biol.* 42:659–63

52. Fink, K. L., Wieben, E. D., Woloschak, G. E., Spelsberg, T. C. 1988. Rapid regulation of *c*-myc protooncogene expression by progesterone in the avian oviduct. *Proc. Natl. Acad. Sci. USA* 85:1796–1800

53. Folger-Bruce, K., Anderson, J. N., Hayward, M. A., Shapiro, D. J. 1983. Nuclease sensitivity and DNA methylation in estrogen regulation of *Xenopus laevis* vitellogenin gene expression. *J. Biol. Chem.* 258:8908–14

54. Forsthoefel, A., Thompson, E. A. 1988. Glucocorticoid regulation of transcription of the *c*-myc cellular protooncogene in P1798 cells. *Mol. Endocrinol.* In press

55. Frankel, F. R., Senior, M. B. 1986. The estrogen receptor complex is bound at unusual chromatin regions. *J. Steroid Biochem.* 24:983–88

56. Garcia, T., Buchou, T., Jung-Testas, I., Renoir, J.-M., Baulieu, E. E. 1987. Chick oviduct progesterone receptor phosphorylation: Characterization of a copurified kinase and phosphorylation in primary cultures. *J. Steroid Biochem.* 27:227–34

57. Garel, A., Axel, R. 1976. Selective digestion of transcriptionally active ovalbumin genes from oviduct nuclei. *Proc. Natl. Acad. Sci. USA* 73:3966–70

58. Giguere, V., Hollenberg, S. M., Rosenfeld, M. G., Evans, R. M. 1986. Functional domains of the human glucocorticoid receptor. *Cell* 46:645–52

59. Godowski, P. J., Rusconi, S., Miesfeld, R., Yamamoto, K. R. 1987. Glucocorticoid receptor mutants that are constitutive activators of transcriptional enhancement. *Nature* 325:365–68

60. Goldberger, A., Horton, M., Katzmann, J., Spelsberg, T. C. 1987. Characterization of the nuclear acceptor sites for the avian oviduct progesterone receptor using monoclonal antibodies. *Biochemistry* 26:5811–16

61. Goldberger, A., Littlefield, B. A., Katzmann, J., Spelsberg, T. C. 1986. Monoclonal antibodies to the nuclear binding sites of the avian oviduct progesterone receptor. *Endocrinology* 118:2235–41

62. Goldberg, A., Spelsberg, T. C. 1988. Partial purification and preparation of polyclonal antibodies against candidate chromatin acceptor proteins for the avian oviduct progesterone receptor. *Biochemistry* 27:2103–9

63. Gonda, T. J., Sheiness, D. K., Bishop, J. M. 1982. Transcripts from the cellular homologs of retroviral oncogenes: Distribution among chicken tissues. *Mol. Cell. Biol.* 2:617–24

64. Gorski, J., Gannon, F. 1976. Current models of steroid hormone action: a critique. *Annu. Rev. Biochem.* 28:425–50

65. Green, S., Chambon, P. 1987. Oestradiol induction of a glucocorticoid-responsive gene by a chimaeric receptor. *Nature* 325:75–78

66. Green, S., Kumar, V., Krust, A., Chambon, P. 1987. The oesterogen receptor: Structure and function. See Ref. 11, pp. 161–83

67. Greene, G. L., Gilna, P., Waterfield, M., Baker, A., Hort, Y., et al. 1986. Sequence and expression of human estrogen receptor complementary DNA. *Science* 231:1150–54

68. Gronemeyer, H., Turcotte, B., Quirin-Stricker, C., Bocquel, M. T., Meyer, M. E., et al. 1987. The chicken progesterone receptor: sequence, expression and functional analysis. *EMBO J.* 6:3985–94

69. Hager, L. J., McKnight, G. S., Palmiter, R. D. 1980. Glucocorticoid induction of egg white mRNAs in chick oviduct. *J. Biol. Chem.* 255:7796–7800

70. Hamana, K., Iwai, K. 1978. Glucocorticoid receptor complex binds to nonhistone protein and DNA in rat liver chromatin. *J. Biochem. (Tokyo)* 83:279–86

71. Harris, S. E., Means, A. R., Mitchell, W. M., O'Malley, B. W. 1973. Synthesis of ^{3}H DNA complementary to ovalbumin messenger RNA: Evidence for limited copies of the ovalbumin gene in chick oviduct. *Proc. Natl. Acad. Sci. USA* 70:3776–80

72. Harris, S. E., Rosen, J. M., Means, A. R., O'Malley, B. W. 1975. Use of a specific probe for ovalbumin messenger RNA to quantitate estrogen-induced gene transcripts. *Biochemistry* 14:2072–81

73. Higgins, S. J., Rousseau, G. G., Baxter, J. D., Tompkins, G. M. 1973. Nature of the nuclear acceptor sites for glucocorticoid and estrogen receptor complexes. *J. Biol. Chem.* 248:5873–79

74. Hollenberg, S. M., Giguere, V., Segui, P., Evans, R. M. 1987. Colocalization of DNA-binding and transcriptional activation functions in the human glucocorticoid receptor. *Cell* 49:39–46

75. Hora, J., Gosse, B., Rasmussen, K., Spelsberg, T. C. 1986. Estrogen regulation of the biological activity of the avian oviduct progesterone receptor and its ability to induce avidin. *Endocrinology* 119:1118–25

76. Hora, J., Horton, M., Toft, D., Spelsberg, T. C. 1986. Nuclease resistance and the enrichment of native nuclear acceptor sites for the avian oviduct progesterone receptor. *Proc. Natl. Acad. Sci. USA* 83:8839–43

77. Horwitz, K. B. 1987. The structure and function of progesterone receptors in breast cancer. *J. Steroid Biochem.* 27:447–57

78. Hynes, N. E., Groner, B., Sippel, A. E., Jeep, S., Wurtz, T., et al. 1979. Control of cellular content of chicken egg white protein specific RNA during estrogen administration and withdrawal. *Biochemistry* 18:616–24

79. Hynes, N., van Ooyen, A. J. J., Kennedy, N., Herrlich, P., Ponta, H., et al. 1983. Subfragments of the long terminal repeat cause of glucocorticoid responsive expression of mouse mammary tumor virus and an adjacent gene. *Proc. Natl. Acad. Sci. USA* 80:3637–41

80. Ivarie, R. D., O'Farrell, P. H. 1978. The glucocorticoid domain: Steroid-mediated changes in the rate of synthesis of rat hepatoma proteins. *Cell* 13:41–55

81. Jackson, D. A., Cook, P. R. 1985. Transcription occurs at a nucleoskeleton. *EMBO J.* 4:919–25

82. Jantzen, H.-M., Strähle, U., Gloss, B., Stewart, F., Schmid, W., et al. 1987. Cooperativity of glucocorticoid response elements located far upstream of the tyrosine aminotransferase gene. *Cell* 49:29–38

83. Jeltsch, J. M., Krozowski, Z., Quirin-Stricker, C., Gronemeyer, H., Simpson, R. J., et al. 1986. Cloning of chicken progesterone receptor. *Proc. Natl. Acad. Sci. USA* 83:5424–28

84. Jensen, E. V. 1987. Cytoplasmic versus nuclear localization of steroid hormone receptors: A historical perspective. See Ref. 10, pp. 13–25

85. Jost, J.-P., Moncharmont, B., Jiricny, J., Saluz, H., Hertner, T. 1986. In vitro secondary activation (memory effect) of avian vitellogenin II gene in isolated liver nuclei. *Proc. Natl. Acad. Sci. USA* 83:43–47

86. Jost, J.-P., Saluz, H., Jiricny, J., Moncharmont, B. 1987. Estradiol-dependent *trans*-acting factor binds preferentially to a dyad-symmetry structure within the third intron of the avian vitellogenin gene. *J. Cell. Biochem.* 35:69–82

87. Jost, J.-P., Seldram, M., Geiser, M. 1984. Preferential binding of estrogen-receptor complexes to a region containing the estrogen-dependent and hypomethylation site preceding the chicken vitellogenin II gene. *Proc. Natl. Acad. Sci. USA* 81:429–33

88. Katzenellenbogen, B. S. 1980. Dynamics of steroid hormone receptor action. *Annu. Rev. Physiol.* 42:17–25

89. Kaufmann, S. H., Okret, S., Wikstrom, A., Gustafsson, J., Shaper, J. J. 1986. Binding of the glucocorticoid receptor to the rat liver nuclear matrix. The role of disulfide bone formation. *J. Biol. Chem.* 261:11962–67

90. Kaye, J. S., Pratt-Kaye, S., Bellard, M., Dretzen, G., Bellard, F., et al. 1986. Steroid hormone dependence of four DNase I-hypersensitive regions located within the 7000-bp 5′ flanking segment of the ovalbumin gene. *EMBO J.* 5:277–85

91. Kelley, K., Siebenlist, U. 1986. The regulation and expression of *c*-myc in normal and malignant cells. *Annu. Rev. Immunol.* 4:317–38

92. Kirsch, T. M., Miller-Diener, A., Litwack, G. 1986. The nuclear matrix is the site of glucocorticoid receptor complex action in the nucleus. *Biochem. Biophys. Res. Commun.* 137:640–48

93. Klein-Hitpass, L., Schorpp, M., Wagner, U., Ryffel, G. U. 1986. An estrogen-responsive element derived from the 5′ flanking region of the *Xenopus* vitellogenin A2 gene functions in transfected human cells. *Cell* 46:1053–61

94. Klinge, C. M., Bambara, R. A., Zain, S., Helf, R. 1987. Estrogen receptor binding to nuclei from normal and neoplastic rat mammary tissues in vitro. *Cancer Res.* 47:2852–59

95. Klug, A., Rhodes, D. 1987. "Zinc fingers": a novel protein motif for nucleic

acid recognition. *Trends Biol. Sci.* 12: 464–69

96. Klyzsejko-Stefanowicz, L., Chui, J. F., Tsai, Y. H., Hnilica, L. S. 1976. Acceptor proteins in rat androgenic tissue chromatin. *Proc. Natl. Acad. Sci. USA* 73:1954–58

97. Knoll, B. J., Zarucki-Schulz, T., Dean, D. C., O'Malley, B. W. 1983. Definition of the ovalbumin gene promoter by transfer of an ovalglobin fusion gene into cultured cells. *Nucleic Acids Res.* 11:6733–54

98. Kon, O. L., Spelsberg, T. C. 1982. Nuclear binding of estrogen receptor complex: Receptor specific nuclear acceptor sites. *Endocrinology* 111:1925–35

99. Krust, A., Green, S., Argos, P., Kumar, V., Walter, P., et al. 1986. The chicken oestrogen receptor sequence: homology with v-erbA and the human oestrogen and glucocorticoid receptors. *EMBO J.* 5:891–97

100. Kumar, V., Green, S., Staub, A., Chambon, P. 1986. Localisation of the oestradiol-binding and putative DNA-binding domains of the human oestrogen receptor. *EMBO J.* 5:2231–36

101. Kuo, M. T., Mandel, J. L., Chambon, P. 1979. DNA methylation: correlation with DNase I sensitivity of chicken ovalbumin and conalbumin chromatin. *Nucleic Acids Res.* 7:2150–13

102. Lin, S., Riggs, A. D. 1975. The general affinity of lac repressor for E. coli DNA: Implications for the gene regulation in procaryotes and eucaryotes. *Cell* 4:107–11

103. Loosfelt, H., Atger, M., Misrahi, M., Guiochon-Mantel, A., Meriel, C., et al. 1986. *Proc. Natl. Acad. Sci. USA* 83:9045–49

104. Loosfelt, H., Fridlansky, F., Savouret, J.-F., Atger, M., Milgrom, E. 1981. Mechanism of action of progesterone in the rabbit endometrium. *J. Biol. Chem.* 256:3465–70

105. Lopez, A., Burgos, J., Ventanas, J. 1985. The binding of [³H]oestradiol receptor complex to hypothalamic chromatin of male and female mice. *Int. J. Biochem.* 17:1207–11

106. Maniatis, T., Goodbourn, S., Fischer, J. A. 1987. Regulation of inducible and tissue-specific gene expression. *Science* 236:1237–45

107. Martin-Dani, G., Spelsberg, T. C. 1985. Proteins which mask the nuclear binding sites of the avian oviduct progesterone receptor. *Biochemistry* 24:6988–97

108. Martinez, E., Givel, F., Wahli, W. 1987. The estrogen-responsive element as an inducible enhancer: DNA sequence requirements and conversion to a glucocorticoid-responsive element. *EMBO J.* 6:3719–27

109. McKnight, G. S., Palmiter, R. D. 1979. Transcriptional regulation of ovalbumin and conalbumin genes by steroid hormones in chick oviduct. *J. Biol. Chem.* 254:9050–58

110. Miesfeld, R., Godowski, P. J., Maler, B. A., Yamamoto, K. R. 1987. Glucocorticoid receptor mutants that define a small region sufficient for enhancer activation. *Science* 236:423–27

111. Miller, J., McLachlan, A. D., Klug, A. 1985. Repetitive zinc-binding domains in the protein transcription factor IIIA from *Xenopus* oocytes. *EMBO J.* 4: 1609–14

112. Miller, P. A., Ostrowski, M. C., Hager, G. L., Simons, S. S. Jr. 1984. Covalent and non-covalent receptor-glucocorticoid complexes preferentially bind to the same regions of the long terminal repeat of murine mammary tumor virus proviral DNA. *Biochemistry* 23:6883–89

113. Moen, R. C., Palmiter, R. D. 1980. Changes in hormone responsiveness of chick oviduct during primary stimulation with estrogen. *Dev. Biol.* 78:450–63

114. Moudgil, V. K., ed. 1987. *Recent Advances in Steroid Hormone Action.* New York: de Gruyter. 522 pp.

115. Mulvihill, E. R., LePennec, J. P., Chambon, P. 1982. Chicken oviduct progesterone receptor: Location of specific regions of high affinity binding in cloned DNA fragments of hormone-responsive genes. *Cell* 28:621–32

116. Murphy, L. J., Murphy, L. C., Friesen, H. G. 1987. Estrogen induction of N-myc and c-myc proto-oncogene expression in the rat uterus. *Endocrinology* 120:1882–88

117. O'Malley, B. W. 1984. Steroid hormone action in eukaryotic cells. *J. Clin. Invest.* 74:207–312

118a. O'Malley, B. W., Means, A. R. 1974. Female steroid hormones in target cell nuclei. *Science* 183:610–20

118b. O'Malley, B. W., McGuire, W. L., Kohler, P. O., Korenman, S. 1969. Studies on the mechanism of steroid hormone regulation of synthesis of specific proteins. *Recent Prog. Horm. Res.* 25:105–60

119. O'Malley, B. W., Roop, D. R., Lai, E. C., Nordstrom, J. L., Catterall, J. F., et al. 1979. The ovalbumin gene: Organization, structure, transcription, and regulation. *Recent Prog. Horm. Res.* 35:1–46

120. Ogle, T. F. 1987. Nuclear acceptor sites

for progesterone receptor complexes in rat placenta. *Endocrinology* 121:28–35

121. Palmiter, R. D., Moore, P. B., Mulvihill, E. R., Emtage, S. 1976. A significant lag in the induction of ovalbumin messenger RNA by steroid hormones: a receptor translocation hypothesis. *Cell* 8:557–72

122. Pastorcic, M., Wang, H., Elbrecht, A., Tsai, S. Y., Tsai, M.-J., et al. 1986. Control of transcription initiation in vitro requires binding of a transcription factor to the distal promoter of the ovalbumin gene. *Mol. Cell. Biol.* 6:2784–91

123. Pavlik, E. J., Van Nagell, J. R., Nelsen, K., Gallion, H., Donaldson, E. S., et al. 1986. Antagonism to estradiol in the mouse: Reduced entry of receptors complexed with 4-hydroxytamoxifen into Mg++ soluble chromatin fraction. *Endocrinology* 118:1924–34

124. Payvar, F., DeFranco, D., Firestone, G. L., Edgar, B., Wrange, O., et al. 1983. Sequences specific binding of glucocorticoid receptor to MTV DNA at sites within and upstream of the transcribed region. *Cell* 35:381–92

125. Payvar, F., Wrange, O., Carlstedt-Duke, J., Okret, S., Gustafsson, J. A., et al. 1981. Purified glucocorticoid receptors bind selectively in vitro to a cloned DNA fragment whose transcription is regulated by glucocorticoids in vivo. *Proc. Natl. Acad. Sci. USA* 78:6628–32

126. Perry, B. N., Lopez, A. 1978. The binding of [^{3}H]-labelled oestradiol- and progesterone-receptor complexes to hypothalmic chromatin of male and female sheep. *Biochem. J.* 176:873–83

127. Petkovich, M., Brand, N. J., Krust, A., Chambon, P. 1987. A human retinoic acid receptor which belongs to the family of nuclear receptors. *Nature* 330:444–50

128. Pfahl, M. 1983. Correlation of glucocorticoid receptor binding sites on MMTV proviral DNA with hormone inducible transcription. *Science* 222:1341–43

129. Picard, D., Yamamoto, K. R. 1987. Two signals mediate hormone-dependent nuclear localization of the glucocorticoid receptor. *EMBO J.* 6:3333–40

130. Pikler, G. M., Webster, R. A., Spelsberg, T. C. 1976. Nuclear binding of progesterone in hen oviduct: Binding to multiple sites in vitro. *Biochem. J.* 156:399–408

131. Ponta, H., Kennedy, N., Skroch, P., Hynes, N. E., Groner, B. 1985. Hormonal response region in the mouse mammary tumor virus long terminal repeat can be dissociated from the proviral promoter and has enhancer properties. *Proc. Natl. Acad. Sci. USA* 82:1020–24

132. Pratt, W. B. 1987. Transformation of glucocorticoid and progesterone receptors to the DNA-binding state. *J. Cell. Biochem.* 35:51–68

133. Ptashne, M. 1986. Gene regulation by proteins acting nearby and at a distance. *Nature* 322:697–701

134. Reinberg, D., Roeder, R. G. 1987. Factors involved in specific transcription by mammalian RNA polymerase II. Transcription factor IIS stimulates elongation of RNA chains. *J. Biol. Chem.* 262:3310–21

135. Reinberg, D., Roeder, R. G. 1987. Factors involved in specific transcription by mammalian RNA polymerase II. Purification and functional analysis of initiation factors IIB and IIE. *J. Biol. Chem.* 262:3331–37

136. Renkawitz, R., Beug, H., Graf, T., Matthias, P., Grez, M., et al. 1982. Expression of a chicken lysozyme recombinant gene is regulated by progesterone and dexamethasone after microinjection into oviduct cells. *Cell* 31:167–76

137. Renkawitz, R., Schütz, G., von der Ahe, D., Beato, M. 1984. Sequences in the promoter region of the chick lysozymes gene required for steroid regulation and receptor binding. *Cell* 37:503–10

138. Richard-Foy, H., Hager, G. L. 1987. Sequence-specific positioning of nucleosomes over the steroid-inducible MMTV promoter. *EMBO J.* 6:2321–28

139. Rosen, J. M., Matusik, R. J., Richards, D. A., Gupta, P., Rodgers, J. R. 1980. Multihormonal regulation of casein gene expression at the transcriptional and posttranscriptional levels in the mammary gland. *Recent Prog. Horm. Res.* 36:157–93

140. Ross, P., Ruh, T. S. 1984. Binding of the estradiol-receptor complex to reconstituted nucleoacidic protein from calf uterus. *Biochem. Biophys. Acta* 782:18–25

141. Roy, A. K., Clark, J. H. 1987. *Gene Regulation by Steroid Hormones III.* New York: Springer-Verlag. 302 pp.

142. Roy, A. K., Sarkar, F. H., Murtz, C. V. R., Majumdar, D., Demyan, W. F. 1986. Intra- and intracellular aspects of the hormonal regulation of α2u-globulin gene expression. See Ref. 141, pp. 234–46

143. Ruh, M. F., Singh, R. K., Bellone, C. J., Ruh, T. S. 1985. Binding of [^{3}H]triamcinolone acetonide-receptor complexes to chromatin from B-cell

leukemia line, BCL. *Biochim. Biophys. Acta* 844:24–33

144. Ruh, M. F., Singh, R. K., Mak, P., Callard, G. V. 1986. Tissue and species specificity of unmasked nuclear acceptor sites for the estrogen receptor of squalus testes. *Endocrinology* 118:811–17

145. Ruh, M. F., Singh, R. K., Ruh, T. S., Shyamala, G. 1987. Binding of glucocorticoid receptors to mammary chromatin acceptor sites. *J. Steroid Biochem.* 28:581–86

146. Ruh, T. S., Ross, P., Wood, D. M., Keene, J. L. 1981. The binding of [^{3}H]oestradiol receptor complexes to calf uterine chromatin. *Biochem. J.* 200:133–42

147. Ruh, T. S., Spelsberg, T. C. 1982. Acceptor sites for the estrogen receptor in hen oviduct chromatin. *Biochem. J.* 210:905–12

148. Saluz, H. P., Jiricny, J., Jost, J.-P. 1986. Genomic sequencing reveals a positive correlation between the kinetics of strand-specific DNA demethylation of the overlapping estradiol/glucocorticoid-receptor binding sites and the rate of avian vitellogenin mRNA synthesis. *Proc. Natl. Acad. Sci. USA* 83:7167–71

149. Scheidereit, C., Beato, M. 1984. Contacts between hormone receptor and DNA double helix within a glucocorticoid regulatory element of mouse mammary tumor virus. *Proc. Natl. Acad. Sci. USA* 81:3029–33

150. Schleif, R. 1987. Why should DNA loop? *Nature* 327:369–70

151. Schuh, S., Yonemoto, W., Brugge, J., Bauer, V. J., Riehl, R. M., et al. 1985. A 90,000-dalton binding protein common to both steroid receptors and Rous sarcoma virus transforming protein, pp60^{v-src}. *J. Biol. Chem.* 260:14292–96

152. Schütz, G., Nguyen-Huu, M. C., Giesecke, K., Hynes, N. E., Groner, B., et al. 1978. Hormonal control of egg white protein messenger RNA synthesis in the chicken oviduct. *Cold Spring Harbor Symp. Quant. Biol.* 42:617–24

153. Seiler-Tuyns, A., Walker, P., Martinez, E., Merillat, A.-M., Givel, F., et al. 1986. Identification of estrogen-responsive DNA sequences by transient expression experiments in a human breast cancer cell line. *Nucleic Acids Res.* 14:8755–70

154. Shapiro, D. J. 1982. Steroid hormone regulation of vitellogenin gene expression. *CRC Crit. Rev. Biochem.* 12:187–203

155. Shapiro, D. J., Nielsen, D. A., Blume, J. E., McKearin, D. 1987. Estrogen control of vitellogenin gene transcription

and mRNA stability. In *Steroid and Sterol Hormone Action*, ed. T. C. Spelsberg, R. Kumar, pp. 117–29. Boston: Nyhoff

156. Sheridan, P., Blum, K., Trachtenberg, M. C. 1988. *Steroid Receptors and Disease: Cancer, Autoimmune and Circulatory Disorders*, pp. 1–228. New York: Dekker

157. Short, N. J. 1987. Are some controlling factors more equal than others? *Nature* 326:740–41

158. Shyamala, G., Singh, R. K., Ruh, M. F., Ruh, T. S. 1986. Relationship between mammary ER and estrogenic sensitivity II: Binding of cytoplasmic receptor to chromatin. *Endocrinology* 119:819–26

159. Singh, R. K., Ruh, M. F., Butler, W. B., Ruh, T. S. 1986. Acceptor sites on chromatin for receptor bound by estrogen versus antiestrogens in antiestrogen-sensitive and resistant MCF-7 cells. *Endocrinology* 118:1087–95

160. Singh, R. K., Ruh, M. F., Ruh, T. S. 1984. Binding of [^{3}H]estradiol and [^{3}H]H1285 receptor complexes to rabbit uterine chromatin. *Biochem. Biophys. Acta* 800:33–40

161. Spelsberg, T. C. 1976. Nuclear binding of progesterone in chick oviduct: Multiple binding sites in vivo and transcriptional response. *Biochem. J.* 156:391–98

162. Spelsberg, T. C., Cox, R. F. 1976. Effects of estrogen and progesterone on transcription, chromatin and ovalbumin gene expression in the chick oviduct. *Biochim. Biophys. Acta* 435:376–90

163. Spelsberg, T. C., Goldberger, A., Hora, J., Horton, M., Littlefield, B. A. 1987. Characterization of the nuclear binding sites (acceptor sites) for a steroid receptor. See Ref. 141, pp. 111–36

164. Spelsberg, T. C., Goldberger, A., Horton, M., Hora, J. 1987. Nuclear acceptor sites for sex steroid hormone receptors in chromatin. *J. Steroid Biochem.* 27:133–47

165. Spelsberg, T. C., Gosse, B., Littlefield, A. B., Toyoda, H., Seelke, R. 1984. Reconstitution of native-like nuclear acceptor sites of the avian oviduct progesterone receptor: Evidence for involvement of specific chromatin proteins and specific DNA sequences. *Biochemistry* 23:5103–12

166. Spelsberg, T. C., Graham, M. L., Berg, N. J., Riehl, E., Coulam, C. B., et al. 1987. A nuclear binding assay to assess the biological activity of steroid receptors in isolated animal and human tissues. *Endocrinology* 121:631–44

167. Spelsberg, T. C., Halberg, F. 1980. Circannual rhythms in steroid receptor concentration and nuclear binding in chick oviduct. *Endocrinology* 107:1234–44

168. Spelsberg, T. C., Hora, J., Horton, M., Goldberger, A., Littlefield, B. A., et al. 1987. Specific DNA binding proteins and DNA sequences involved in steroid hormone regulation of gene expression. See Ref. 39, pp. 259–67

169. Spelsberg, T. C., Horton, M., Fink, K., Goldberger, A., Rories, C., et al. 1987. A new model for steroid regulation of gene transcription using chromatin acceptor sites and regulatory genes and their products. See Ref. 11, pp. 59–83

170. Spelsberg, T. C., Knowler, J., Boyd, P. A., Thrall, C. L., Martin-Dani, G. 1979. Support for chromatin acidic proteins as acceptors for progesterone in the chick oviduct. *J. Steroid Biochem.* 11:373–88

171. Spelsberg, T. C., Kumar, R. 1987. *Steroid and Sterol Hormone Action.* Boston: Nyhoff. 417 pp.

172. Spelsberg, T. C., Littlefield, B. A., Seelke, R., Martin-Dani, G., Toyoda, H., et al. 1983. Role of specific chromosomal proteins and DNA sequences in the nuclear binding sites for steroid receptors. *Recent Prog. Horm. Res.* 39:463–517

173. Strähle, U., Klock, G., Schütz, G. 1987. A DNA sequence of 15 base pairs is sufficient to mediate both glucocorticoid and progesterone induction of gene expression. *Proc. Natl. Acad. Sci. USA* 84:7871–75

174. Studzinski, G. P., Brelvi, Z. S., Feldman, S. C., Watt, R. A. 1986. Participation of c-myc protein in DNA synthesis of human cells. *Science* 234: 467–70

175. Sullivan, W. P., Smith, D. F., Beito, T. G., Krco, C. J., Toft, D. O. 1988. Hormone-dependent processing of the avian progesterone receptor. *J. Cell. Biol.* 36:103–19

176. Sun, L.-H. K., Pfendner, E. G., Senior, M. B., Frankel, F. R. 1983. Progesterone, glucocorticoid and estradiol receptors in MCF-7 cells bind to chromatin. *Mol. Cell. Endocrinol.* 30:267–78

177. Swaneck, G. E., Nordstrom, J. L., Kreuzaler, F., Tsai, M.-J., O'Malley, B. W. 1979. Effect of estrogen on gene expression in chicken oviduct: Evidence for transcriptional control of ovalbumin gene. *Proc. Natl. Acad. Sci. USA* 76: 1049–53

178. Tata, J. R., Ng, W. C., Perlman, A. J., Wolffe, A. P. 1986. Activation and regulation of vitellogenin gene family. See Ref. 141, pp. 205–33

179a. Thrall, C., Webster, R. A., Spelsberg, T. C. 1978. Steroid receptor interaction with chromatin. In *The Cell Nucleus*, ed. B. Harris, 6:461–526. New York: Academic

179b. Toft, D. O., Sullivan, W. P. 1988. Phosphorylation of the avian progesterone receptor. In *Receptor Phosphorylation*, ed. V. K. Moudgil, Boca Raton, Fla.: CRC Press. In press

180. Toyoda, T., Seelke, R., Littlefield, B. A., Spelsberg, T. C. 1985. Evidence for specific DNA sequences in the nuclear acceptor sites of the avian oviduct progesterone receptor. *Proc. Natl. Acad. Sci. USA* 82:4722–26

181. Travers, M. T., Knowler, J. T. 1987. Oestrogen-induced expression of oncogenes in the immature rat uterus. *FEBS Lett.* 211:27–30

182. Travers, A. 1983. Protein contacts for promoter location in eukaryotes. *Nature* 303:755

183a. Tsai, Y.-H., Sanborn, B. M., Steinberger, A., Steinberger, E. 1980. Sertoli cell chromatin acceptor sites for androgen receptor complexes. *J. Steroid Biochem.* 13:711–18

183b. Tymoczko, J. L., Lee, J. H. 1985. Chymotrypsin treatment of glucocorticoid receptor attenuates RNA-dependent inhibition of DNA binding. Evidence for a distinct RNA-binding site. *Biochim. Biophys. Acta* 846:193–99

184. von der Ahe, D., Janich, S., Scheidereit, C., Renkawitz, R., Schütz, G., et al. 1985. Glucocorticoid and progesterone receptors bind to the same sites in two hormonally regulated promoters. *Nature* 313:706–9

185. von der Ahe, D., Renoir, J.-M., Buchou, T., Baulieu, E. E., Beato, M. 1986. Receptors for glucocorticoids and progesterone recognize distinct features of a DNA regulatory element. *Proc. Natl. Acad. Sci. USA* 83:2817–21

186. Walker, P., Germond, J.-E., Brown-Luedi, M., Givel, F., Wahli, W. 1984. Sequence homologies in the region preceding the transcription initiation sites of the liver estrogen-responsive vitellogenin and apo-VLDLII genes. *Nucleic Acids Res.* 12:8611–26

187. Wang, T. Y. 1978. The role of nonhistone chromosomal proteins in the interaction of prostate chromatin with androgen receptor complex. *Biochem. Biophys. Acta* 518:81–88

188. Wasylyk, B., Kedinger, G., Corden, J., Brison, O., Chambon, P. 1980. Specific in vitro initiation of transcription on con-

albumin and ovalbumin genes and comparison with adenovirus-2 early and late genes. *Nature* 285:367–73

189. Waterman, M. L., Adler, S., Nelson, C., Greene, G. L., Evans, R. M., et al. 1988. A single domain of the estrogen receptor confers deoxyribonucleic acid binding and transcriptional activation of the rat prolactin gene. *Mol. Endocrinol.* 2:14–21

190. Webster, R. A., Pikler, G. M., Spelsberg, T. C. 1976. Nuclear binding of progesterone in hen oviduct: Role of acidic chromatin proteins in high-affinity binding. *Biochem. J.* 156:409–18

191. Weiler, I. J., Lew, D., Shapiro, D. J. 1987. The *Xenopus laevis* estrogen receptor: Sequence homology with human and avian receptors and identification of multiple estrogen receptor messenger ribonucleic acids. *Mol. Endocrinol.* 1:355–62

192. Weinberger, C., Thompson, C. C., Ong, E. S., Lebo, R., Gruol, D. J., et al. 1986. The c-erb-A gene encodes a thyroid hormone receptor. *Nature* 324:641–46

193. Welshons, W. V., Jordan, V. C. 1987. Heterogeneity of nuclear steroid hormone receptors with an emphasis on unfilled receptor sites. See Ref. 10, pp. 128–54

194a. White, R., Lees, J. A., Needham, M., Ham, J., Parker, M. 1987. Structural organization and expression of the mouse estrogen receptor. *Mol. Endocrinol.* 1:735–44

194b. Willmann, T., Beato, M. 1986. Steroid-free glucocorticoid receptor binds specifically to mouse mammary tumour virus DNA. *Nature* 324:688–91

195. Wiskocil, R., Bensky, P., Dower, W., Goldberger, R. F., Gordon, J. I., et al. 1980. Coordinate regulation of two estrogen-dependent genes in avian liver. *Proc. Natl. Acad. Sci. USA* 77:4474–78

196. Zaret, K. S., Yamamoto, K. R. 1984. Reversible and persistent changes in chromatin structure accompany activation of a glucocorticoid-dependent enhancer element. *Cell* 38:29–38

197. Zehnbauer, B. A., Vogelstein, B. 1985. Supercoiled loops and the organization of replication and transcription in eukaryotes. *BioEssays* 2:52–54

Annu. Rev. Physiol. 1989. 51:683–99

REGULATION OF GENE EXPRESSION BY GLUCOCORTICOIDS

Kerry L. Burnstein and John A. Cidlowski

Lineberger Cancer Research Center and Department of Physiology, University of North Carolina at Chapel Hill, Chapel Hill, North Carolina 27599

Introduction

Steroid hormones mediate profound physiological and developmental effects in higher eukaryotes. By interacting with their intracellular receptors in target cells, steroid hormones provide mechanisms for cellular communication and alterations in phenotypic response to environmental and internal stimuli. In response to hormone binding, steroid receptor proteins are thought to interact with specific target DNAs and, by an unknown mechanism, to modulate transcription of selected genes. As these molecules represent a family of ligand-dependent transcription factors, steroid receptors are being actively studied to understand their mode of action.

Of the hormone-receptor systems that have been examined, the glucocorticoid receptor is perhaps the most extensively characterized. Glucocorticoids are one class of steroid hormones first identified as mediating glycogen deposition in the liver. Subsequently, glucocorticoid activity was recognized in development, homeostasis, and the response to stress. This review focuses on transcriptional effects of glucocorticoids, including information pertaining to DNA sequences associated with target genes that are important for gene regulation by steroid. We discuss data made available by the recent cloning of the human (40), rat (53), and mouse (25) glucocorticoid receptors, as this cloning has profoundly affected studies involving steroid receptor structure and the role of these receptors in regulating gene expression. Finally, we point out stages of hormone action that might be subject to further regulation at the level of the receptor.

0066-4278/89/0315-0683$02.00

Mechanism of Glucocorticoid Action

Given that glucocorticoids are vital to many developmental and physiological processes, the presence of glucocorticoid receptors (GR) in almost all cell types is not surprising. GR from different tissues are thought to be identical, but the concentration of receptors depends on the cell type, the state of differentiation, the phase of the cell cycle, and the endocrine status of the cell. Cellular sensitivity to glucocorticoids is affected by receptor concentration but may also be altered by the presence of nonfunctional or modified receptor or by other cellular factors that modify receptor function (e.g. the receptor's ability to interact with or near target genes) (reviewed in 36, 56).

After diffusing into sensitive cells, glucocorticoids bind avidly but noncovalently to intracellular GR. This interaction between the receptor and its ligand results in activation or transformation of the hormone-receptor complex into a DNA-binding protein (56). Activated GR complexes reside in the nucleus as demonstrated by immunocytochemistry (reviewed in 87). By contrast, the location of the unliganded GR, cytoplasm or nucleus is unclear.

To understand the mechanism of receptor activation, researchers have examined and compared the structures of the unactivated and activated receptor complexes and have learned that activation is accompanied by alterations in the physicochemical properties of the receptor (reviewed in 6, 36). These alterations include decreased sedimentation rates, loss of non–steroid-binding components, and changes in chromatographic behavior on DEAE and DNA cellulose (38, 63, 83). Whether these changes in GR are a cause or a result of activation is unclear. Current models for activation favor the involvement of conformational changes in the oligomeric receptor structure that cause the dissociation of similar or dissimilar subunits (63, 84). This dissociation results in the unmasking of a DNA-binding region present in the receptor monomer (30). This model accounts for the observed structural and functional alterations. Consistent with this model is the finding that unactivated and activated receptors are similar in size (90–100 kD) as determined under denaturing electrophoresis conditions (19). Indirect evidence points to the presence of a 90-kD protein [called the 90-kD heat-shock protein for its immunological cross-reactivity to a chicken heat-shock protein associated with steroid-receptor complexes (13, 71)]. This protein is thought to dissociate from receptor after ligand binding and activation to yield the receptor monomer (44, 50, 71). Whether dissociation of the 90-kD protein occurs in vivo and is a consequence of activation is unknown.

After activation and receptor binding to chromatin, hormone-receptor complexes modulate the transcription of specific genes (reviewed in 66, 69, 91). The precise details of the molecular mechanism(s) that cause this effect have not been elucidated. Such information probably first requires development of adequate in vitro transcription systems that are capable of supporting GR-dependent gene expression. Such a system has recently been reported for an estrogen-inducible gene in nuclear liver extracts from *Xenopus laevis* (21); its development portends considerable progress in this area.

Activated GR preferentially binds to certain DNA sequences located upstream or occasionally downstream from the promoter of glucocorticoid-regulated genes; binding is required for transcriptional effects of the steroid-receptor complex. The target sequences for GR binding and regulation are referred to as GREs (glucocorticoid-responsive, or regulatory, elements), first identified in the long terminal repeat (LTR) of the mouse mammary tumor virus (MMTV) (58, 59, 60, 73). The MMTV-LTR has been linked to a variety of reporter genes that encode easily assayed proteins such as the Herpes virus thymidine kinase (HSV tk) or the bacterial enzyme chloramphenicol acetyltransferase (CAT); such reporter genes then become sensitive to glucocorticoid regulation (14, 34, 42). These plasmid constructs have been invaluable for testing transcriptional activation by mutant GR in transfected cells, as discussed below.

Domain Structure of Glucocorticoid Receptors

Sequence analysis of cloned steroid hormone receptor genes reveals a striking homology among these molecules and has led to the supposition that they are derived from a common ancestral gene (31, 49, 72, 88, 89). Certain regions of steroid receptors are more highly conserved than others, evidence that is consistent with earlier data that indicated steroid receptors are comprised of discrete functional domains. The domain structure of the GR was initially inferred from two sets of evidence: (*a*) the activity of receptor fragments produced by proteolytic digestion and (*b*) the examination of naturally occurring, truncated receptor mutants that lost or retained the capacity to bind ligand or DNA or to interact with antibodies directed against the primary immunogenic regions (36). The amino-terminal half of the receptor protein appears to be the most immunogenic and was also suspected of playing a modulatory role in transcription (28, 36). Ligand binding is localized to the carboxy-terminal portion of the receptor, while DNA binding is thought to be present at the approximate middle of the linear molecule. More precise mapping of these functional domains has progressed rapidly by mutational analysis of receptor cDNAs and is discussed below.

Recently, receptor mutants have been created by making insertions or deletions in the human GR (hGR) cDNA sequence; the mutants were then tested in vitro for their ability to bind DNA and hormone in coupled transcription/translation systems. Mutant receptors have also been examined in transfected cells, which lack endogenous functional GR, for the ability to transcriptionally activate glucocorticoid-responsive genes (24, 29, 30, 39, 52). The steroid receptor binding site for the synthetic glucocorticoid dexamethasone (dex) was mapped by deletion analysis to the carboxy-terminal 261 amino acids of the hGR (39), which confirmed results from the analysis of proteolytic receptor fragments (36). The steroid-binding domain could not be localized to a smaller receptor fragment, possibly because a minimum size is required to create a hydrophobic steroid-binding "pocket" (49). Surprisingly, deletion of the steroid-binding region (532–567 of hGR) resulted in a receptor that constitutively (i.e. independent of hormone) activated transcription in transfected cells (39). In contrast, the full-length GR cDNA stimulates transcription only after treatment with dex. This observation has also been made in similar experiments with both rat (30) and mouse (24) truncated GRs. Possibly the unliganded steroid-binding domain represses or somehow masks the DNA binding/transcriptional activation properties of the GR. Steroid binding to the receptor might cause the dissociation of the masking component from the DNA-binding region (30). It is unclear whether this repression is due to the direct interaction of the carboxy (steroid-binding) terminus of the receptor with the DNA-binding region or whether a non–steroid-binding component of the receptor complex [i.e. 90-kD heat-shock protein (61)] mediates repression by interacting with both the steroid-binding and DNA-binding domains.

The amino-terminal domain is the least conserved both in length and sequence among the steroid receptor family (31). GR from a mutant of the S49 mouse lymphoma cell line that lacks this domain are nonresponsive to hormone treatment. This evidence has prompted investigators to postulate a role for this region in transcription. These mutant receptors have an enhanced affinity for nonspecific DNA and display increased properties of nuclear transfer (nt[i]) probably because of their tight binding to DNA (reviewed in 28). Examination of the transcription-activating abilities of in vitro–derived mutants lacking hGR residues 77–262 of the amino-terminal domain reveals that this region is required for fully regulated transcriptional activity. Mutants lacking this segment display 10% of the activity of full-length GR (39). Deletions of comparable regions of rat (52) and mouse (24) GR have yielded similar findings. Danielsen et al (24) postulate that a cluster of acidic residues located in the mouse GR amino-terminal domain at amino acids 196–293 is responsible for the modulatory actions on transcription imposed by the amino-terminal domain. By neutralizing the charge of the basic DNA- and steroid-binding domains, the acidic residues may enable receptor to discriminate more effectively between specific and nonspecific DNAs. Interestingly, mutants lacking this acidic region (such as the nt[i] mutants) bind nonspecific DNA more avidly yet are not as effective at enhancing transcriptional activity (24, 25). Whether these mutants do in fact discriminate less efficiently between specific and nonspecific DNAs will be interesting to determine systematically.

The DNA-binding domain is the most highly conserved region among all steroid receptors examined thus far (3, 31). In addition, this region demonstrates a high degree of homology with the avian erythroblastosis viral oncogene product v-erb A and its cellular counterpart, the thyroid hormone receptor (49, 72, 88, 89). The DNA-binding domain is rich in cysteine, arginine, and lysine; nucleotide sequence data suggest that this domain has a structural motif similar to the *Xenopus laevis* 5S gene transcription factor TFIIIA (54) and to some other eukaryotic DNA-binding proteins (7). TFIIIA contains sequences that conform to a $Cys-X_{2-5}-Cys-X_{12}-His-X_{2-3}-His$ pattern [where X represents any amino acid (54)], which can adopt domains or "fingers" coordinated around a zinc atom. These "zinc fingers" are thought to bind DNA/RNA via hydrophilic amino acids (7). TFIIIA contains nine such fingers; GR could potentially form two (29). Whether or not the zinc finger–DNA-binding motif is relevant to DNA binding by GR is unknown; however, analysis of rat receptors with deletions of the region between 440 and 546, which encompasses the putative zinc fingers, indicates that this region is essential for DNA binding (70). Similarly, insertions that disrupt residues within the hypothetical hGR zinc fingers destroy DNA binding (29, 39). The DNA-binding domain of the protein appears to be quite resilient, as GR can be electrophoresed under denaturing conditions (which would presumably destroy zinc-coordinated domains) and subsequently renatured so that the domain regains the capacity to bind specific DNAs (75). Thus, this region is responsible for DNA binding, but whether or not selective binding by GR requires a zinc finger configuration is not understood.

Mutational analysis has delineated a core region of the receptor that contains information essential for both DNA binding and transcriptional activation (24, 39, 52). The core region of hGR corresponds to 88 amino acids from 404 to 491 and encompasses the Cys-rich region described above. Whether this 88–amino acid segment by itself can bind DNA and activate transcription has not been demonstrated, however. Furthermore, the data used to arrive at the designation of this core region are inconsistent. Human GR mutants that terminate at amino acid 491 or 488 bind DNA but cannot activate transcription, whereas a mutant lacking amino acids 491–515 is capable of binding DNA and enhancing transcription (39). This evidence suggests the importance of secondary structure required for a functional receptor. Nevertheless, Miesfeld et al (52) have found that a 150–amino acid rat GR peptide (407–556) binds DNA and retains the ability to activate transcription, albeit at a dramatically reduced level from full-length rat GR. These results suggest that the DNA-binding and transcriptional-activation functions are physically very close. The only separation of the two functions was seen in the hGR mutants discussed above, which had behavior inconsistent with that of other mutants from the same study (39).

Model of Transcriptional Activation by Glucocorticoids: Mouse Mammary Tumor Virus

Transcriptional activation of MMTV proviral DNA (the form integrated into host cell DNA) in response to glucocorticoids has become a paradigm for regulation of gene expression by steroid hormones. Because this model has been extensively reviewed (see 37, 65, 66), we mention only some salient features. The transcriptional induction of MMTV RNA by glucocorticoids is rapid, proceeds in the absence of protein synthesis, and is due to increased rates of transcription initiation (34, 66). Additionally, the response depends on the presence of the glucocorticoid receptor (67).

IDENTIFICATION OF GLUCOCORTICOID REGULATORY SEQUENCES   The proviral DNA itself, but not flanking cellular sequences, contains the regulatory sequences necessary for the observed transcription enhancement (10). Linkage of the long terminal repeat (LTR), which also contains the promoter region of the MMTV provirus, to a heterologous structural gene such as thymidine kinase (tk) (42) or dihydrofolate reductase (normally unresponsive to glucocorticoids) conferred hormonal inducibility upon the linked gene in transfection experiments (reviewed in 35, 66). Thus, sequences present on the 1.3-kb (kilobase) MMTV-LTR segment possess glucocorticoid regulatory properties. This type of gene transfer experiment has also been used to show that the glucocorticoid regulatory sequences in the LTR do not specifically require the MMTV promoter. Hormonal responsiveness can be conferred upon the heterologous tk promoter when the LTR minus its own promoter is placed upstream of the tk promoter (14). Additionally, Chandler et al (14) have shown that a 340-bp (base pair) MMTV-LTR restriction fragment, which contains sequences necessary for a glucocorticoid response, functions in both forward and reverse orientations and at variable distances relative to the heterologous tk promoter. Such properties are reminiscent of enhancer sequences, documented in certain viral genomes and in cellular DNA, and are responsible for increased transcriptional activity (reviewed in 8, 47).

Borders of the glucocorticoid regulatory sequences have been mapped more precisely by creating defined deletions within the MMTV-LTR and by linker scanning mutagenesis (11). These altered constructs were then tested for glucocorticoid-induced transcriptional activity in transfected cells. The glucocorticoid regulatory sites are located between -190 and -138 bp, with the transcription start site designated $+1$ (66). This region contains sequences that are capable of conferring glucocorticoid inducibility upon heterologous genes.

PHYSICAL MAPPING OF GLUCOCORTICOID RECEPTOR BINDING TO MMTV DNA   Gene regulatory proteins act by recognizing and preferentially binding to specific DNA sequences (62). In addition to the gene transfer studies mentioned earlier, analysis of the GR binding sites in MMTV have been conducted to determine if receptor binding sites coincide with the regulatory sites (59, 60). Receptor binding was demonstrated in the LTR and in the transcribed regions of the gene by protection of sequences from nuclease digestion (DNase I footprinting) (58). A family of octanucleotides related to the degenerate sequence 5' AGA(A/T)CAG(A/T) 3' are present at least once in each of nine nuclease footprints present in MMTV. In similar studies, Scheidereit et al (73) identified a hexanucleotide 5' TGTTCT 3' common to four GR binding sites present between −192 and −71 bp of the LTR. This hexamer is homologous to the complement of the octanucleotide described above. "Strong" footprints are found at sites between −189 and −135 (58) that correspond to the regulatory sequences identified by deletion analysis (discussed above).

The functional significance of GR binding sites that occur outside of the hormonal regulatory sequences is unclear. They may have some evolutionary significance as specific GR binding sites are found elsewhere, e.g. pBR322 (82). One caveat to all of these in vitro GR binding studies is that they are done under conditions of vast excess GR and are highly enriched in specific DNA sequences. Definitive data on the affinity of receptor for DNA are not available; thus, the question of whether specific DNA sequences are sufficient to direct the receptor to target genes is difficult to address.

Regulatory Regions Located on Other Glucocorticoid Responsive Genes

The identification in MMTV of glucocorticoid regulatory elements (GRE) that have enhancerlike properties and are bound by GR led to the search for similar regions associated with other glucocorticoid-regulated genes. These regulatory elements are bound by GR and have been identified at variable distances upstream from promoters (up to 2.5 kb from the transcription start site) and, in at least one case, have been found within the glucocorticoid-responsive gene itself. The genes for chicken lysozyme (64, 85, 86), human metallothionein IIA (46), rat tyrosine aminotransferase (4, 5, 43), tryptophan oxygenase (23), and human growth hormone (77) possess regions that confer glucocorticoid responsiveness upon heterologous reporter genes in transfected cells. The chicken lysozyme and human metallothionein genes contain GREs located only a few hundred base pairs from transcription initiation (−208 to −164, and −268 to −237, respectively) (46, 64). In contrast, a GRE is found in the first intron of the human growth hormone gene, at position +86 to +115 (77). These GREs bear homology with the consensus sequence also found in the MMTV-LTR: 5' (T/C)GGT-(A/T)CA(A/T)-TGT(T/C)CT 3' (46), which contains the hexanucleotide 5' TGTTCT 3' identified by

Scheidereit et al (73). This hexanucleotide may not be functionally complete, however, as evidenced by examples in which the presence of this sequence was not sufficient for transcriptional activation by GR (43, 46, 77).

MULTIPLE GREs ASSOCIATED WITH A SINGLE GENE   Hormone regulatory regions of the tyrosine aminotransferase (TAT) gene are located approximately 2.5 kb upstream from the transcription initiation site (5, 43). Two sequence elements were identified in this region that were homologous to the 16-bp GRE consensus sequence and were protected by GR from nuclease digestion. These two GREs appear to act cooperatively to induce transcription (43). The more proximal GRE does not induce transcription alone and is therefore not a true GRE; the more distal element is only 30% as active as the two elements combined. How transcription activation can be induced by sequences located so far from the promoter is not understood. These GREs are stronger inducers of transcription when placed more closely to the TAT promoter or the heterologous tk promoter; however, their requirement for cooperative interaction is unchanged. Why the more proximal TAT GRE cannot function alone is not understood, but Jantzen et al (43) suggest the reason may be related to the fact that the proximal GRE has less dyad symmetry than the distal GRE. (The possible role of symmetry in GRE function is discussed below.) The nature of the cooperative interaction between the two GREs of TAT is also a feature of this gene that necessitates further study, particularly once more highly purified preparations of receptor and other transcription factors become available that will allow receptor-dependent transcription in vitro.

Another hepatic gene, tryptophan oxygenase, also contains two GREs, located at −450 bp and −1.2 kb, that enhance transcription in an additive manner (23). Each GRE binds GR and induces transcription independently, but curiously, the proximal GRE requires additional sequences that are immediately upstream and are not footprinted by GR. Perhaps other GR binding sites thought to be nonfunctional also require additional sequences that were inappropriately deleted during construction of GRE-reporter plasmids. Such artifacts would complicate the gene-transfer studies used to identify GREs.

Plasmids have been constructed that contain multiple copies of the MMTV GRE, and these plasmids support higher levels of transcription in transfected cells than does the single-GRE–containing parent plasmid (81). Increased transcription occurs when the multiple GREs are separated such that one is present on either side of the *CAT* reporter gene or when the GREs are present in tandem either 5' to the promoter or 3' to the CAT gene. Thus, multiple GREs apparently are more effective at enhancing transcription than is a single GRE; in these experiments, the position of GREs in relation to one another was of little importance.

DIFFERENT STEROID RECEPTORS RECOGNIZE SIMILAR DNA REGULATORY ELEMENTS The chicken lysozyme gene can be regulated by several steroid hormones, including glucocorticoids and progestins. Results of nuclease protection studies show that the GR and progesterone receptor (PR) bind to overlapping regulatory sites located upstream of the lysozyme gene (85). Studies to determine the precise nucleotides that are in contact with receptor protein and therefore inaccessible to chemical methylation (methylation protection) revealed that the two receptors share only one nucleotide contact out of seven (86). In more recent studies (78), a 15-bp oligonucleotide was modeled after a GRE upstream of the TAT gene; this oligonucleotide contains partial dyad symmetry. When placed upstream of a fusion gene made up of the heterologous tk promoter and the CAT gene, this oligonucleotide was shown to mediate transcriptional activation in response to glucocorticoids and progestins in the breast cancer cell lines MCF7 and T-47D, respectively. When point mutations (single-base and double-base substitutions) were introduced at variable sites in this oligonucleotide, both progesterone and glucocorticoid inducibility were similarly decreased. These results suggest the importance of at least partial twofold symmetry for GR and PR recognition. They also indicate that GR and PR recognize the same 15-bp sequence and that mutations in this sequence similarly affect the ability of both receptors to induce transcription.

These data on PR and GR (78) seemingly contradict results from the methylation protection studies with the chicken lysozyme gene GRE (86). The reasons for discrepancies in the results of these two studies could originate at many levels because (a) nonidentical GRE sequences were examined and (b) one study examined DNA-protein contacts made in vitro using purified chick oviduct PR and rat liver GR, while the other study examined induction of transcription in transfected human cells. GR and PR appear to recognize very similar DNA sequences, however. This information implies that the differential hormonal control achieved by glucocorticoids and progestins on dually regulated genes is exerted through additional factors such as cell-specific transcription factors or through the actions of the other domains on the receptor molecule.

Results of similar studies using an oligonucleotide representing an estrogen regulatory element (ERE) have indicated that this element is not recognized by GR but can be converted to a GRE by 1–2 base substitutions provided symmetry is maintained (48). Thus, EREs and GREs are related but not identical.

The question of what dictates the unique response to a particular steroid has also been approached from a different perspective. Green & Chambon (32) created a hybrid receptor composed of the human GR DNA-binding domain and the human estrogen receptor (hER) steroid-binding and immunogenic domains. In transfection studies, this chimeric receptor activated, in an estradiol-dependent manner, the transcription of a cotransfected GRE-containing but not an ERE-containing plasmid. This experiment showed that, at least for the GR, the DNA-binding domain dictates what target genes are induced and elegantly proved that steroid receptors are comprised of functional domains. Analogous experiments using PR-GR chimeras may help resolve whether these two receptors actually recognize identical regulatory elements.

Negative Regulation of Gene Expression by Glucocorticoids

Research on the regulation of gene expression mediated by GR has focused mainly on transcriptional activation. Much less is known about how glucocorticoids inhibit transcription of certain genes, e.g. proopiomelanocortin (POMC) (15, 26) and prolactin (12), but this area is certain to be one of active research in the future. Since the regulation of POMC is reviewed elsewhere in this volume, we discuss only briefly the possible mechanisms of glucocorticoid-directed negative regulation. Possibly there exist DNA sequences analogous to GREs that serve instead to decrease transcription when bound by GR. Alternatively, the same GRE sequences associated with positively regulated genes may be present on negatively regulated genes but in different locations relative to the target gene. Since the location of GREs for "positive" genes is highly variable (anywhere from a few kilobases upstream from the promoter to within the gene), this option seems less likely unless subtle positional differences are important. Another possibility is that a different form of the GR interacts with "negative" genes and results in decreased transcription. Multiple GR forms from various tissues have been observed on two-dimensional gels (19) of GR labeled with the affinity ligand dexamethasone mesylate (76). Recent data suggest, however, that inhibition of transcription is not mediated by interaction of GR with DNA, since the DNA-binding domain of the receptor is not required (1). Interactions between GR and other proteins might therefore be important for transcriptional inhibition.

Glucocorticoid Receptor Regulation

Results of studies examining glucocorticoid sensitivity in normal, mutant, and transfected cells have reinforced the notion that a functional receptor is absolutely necessary although not sufficient to evoke a steroid response. The number of receptors generally correlates with the relative sensitivity of cells to steroids (9), although there are examples in which such correlation is not the case (27).

Glucocorticoids down-regulate levels of their own receptors by approximately 50–75% (16, 79). This down-regulation is reflected in (a) decreased levels of glucocorticoid binding (16, 79) and (b) decreased levels of GR mRNA (45, 57), which probably result from reduced receptor gene transcription (68). Because down-regulation occurs in the presence of cycloheximide and is specific for glucocorticoids at concentrations close to the steroid-binding affinity, GR probably mediates this phenomenon directly (16, 79). Autoregulation of GR represents a potentially powerful regulatory mechanism that has received considerably less attention than GR-mediated regulation of other genes.

Whether or not GR directly mediates reduced transcription of its own gene by interaction with GRE-like elements is not known. Results of in vitro footprinting experiments show that purified GR interacts with the 3' region of its gene, which is transcribed but not translated (57). Whether these binding sites play any role in GR regulation or if they even represent GR binding sites in vivo is not known. Down-regulation of hGR mRNA can be demonstrated in heterologous cells that have been transfected with an hGR cDNA (K. L. Burnstein & J. A. Cidlowski, submitted for publication). The cDNA used in these experiments lacks both the endogenous GR promoter and the 3' transcribed but untranslated region (containing the aforementioned GR binding sites). These results suggest that sequences within the hGR structural gene encode information necessary for down-regulation. Identification of these sequences is currently in progress.

Cellular GR concentrations also vary at different stages of the cell cycle (18). The finding that cellular responses to glucocorticoids essentially disappear during GII, M, and early GI phases has led investigators to examine the concentration and properties of receptors during the cell cycle (33, 80). The highest number of receptors, detected by binding to radiolabeled dex, were found during the S and GII phases in HeLa cells (18), and this increase was dependent on transcription and translation (17). Even during the nonresponsive stages of the cell cycle, cytoplasmic receptors were detected at levels sufficient to elicit a response to steroid (approximately 10,000 per cell); therefore, a strong correlation could not be made between hormonal responsiveness and cytoplasmic receptor number (17). Steroid binding to nuclear receptors was decreased, however, in GII, M, and early GI, which correspond to the hormone-insensitive stages. These stages are marked by the appearance of a more acidic GR form that may be related to the inability of cells to respond to steroid (22).

Potential Targets of Regulation in GR Action

We conclude this review with an overview of the points of possible regulation in the pathway of hormone receptor action. One of the early events in hormone receptor function is the binding of receptor to its cognate steroid molecule. Unliganded, heat-activated GR displays specificity in DNA binding in vitro (90); however, steroid hormone is required for this interaction to occur in vivo (4). GR forms that do not bind steroid have been reported recently in cells cultured under nonphysiological conditions (51, 74). Non–steroid-binding GR are generated when mouse thymoma cells are deprived of ATP for short time periods; this "null" receptor is located in the cell nucleus as detected by anti-GR antibody (51). Nuclear localization of this altered receptor contradicts conventional wisdom, which dictates that steroid binding is required for transformation and nuclear translocation. Perhaps steroid-binding capability is lost after nuclear translocation and this receptor form is trapped in the nucleus.

Non–steroid-binding GR have also been detected in HeLa cells following long-term treatment with high levels (10^{-6} M) of glucocorticoids (74). GR from these cells retain the capacity to bind specific DNAs at levels comparable to untreated cells (75). Whether non–steroid-binding receptors have a biological function is unclear; perhaps they become "regenerated" to wild-type receptors and vice versa. They may therefore represent a receptor form that is present in the normal pathway.

Transformation or activation to a DNA/chromatin-binding protein is a potential target for regulation. If activation is due to dissociation of a putative component of the GR complex such as the 90-kD heat-shock protein (50) or an RNA molecule (2), then perhaps control of activation can be exerted by modulation of intracellular levels of these components. Recent data suggest that the 90-kD protein is complexed to GR in intact cells. Results of these experiments also support the notion that the GR–90-kD protein complex is dissociated after glucocorticoid treatment (41).

After activation, GR-hormone complexes are thought to translocate to the nucleus, where they bind to specific DNA sequences in chromatin. As mentioned earlier, whether GREs alone are sufficient to target GR to specific genes remains unknown. Given that nonspecific DNA sequences are present in vastly higher concentrations than the specific GREs, envisioning a model in which GR binding is dictated solely by a short DNA sequence is difficult. That ancillary proteins (both chromatin associated and non–chromatin associated) are involved in specific GR-DNA recognition is therefore likely. In addition, GREs may reside in more accessible regions of the chromatin, which would aid in binding GR. Although altered sensitivity to nuclease has been observed in GRE-containing regions of chromatin (5, 92), whether this hormone-induced DNase sensitivity is a consequence or cause of receptor binding is not known.

Another "black box" in the regulation of receptor action is the fate of the steroid hormone–receptor complex after DNA binding. Is there cycling between the DNA-bound and DNA-free states and, if so, what are the kinetics of these events? Does the presence of receptor on DNA "recruit" other transcription factors (20)? One aspect of receptor action that has not been extensively addressed is the removal of the receptor from the nucleus after transcriptional networks have been activated. Is the receptor targeted to lysosomes for degradation or is it reused? Cyclic models examining receptor kinetics have been described that feature GR recycling (55), but factors involved in the regulation of these events have not been elucidated.

Clearly, many aspects of steroid hormone receptor function are still not understood. Fortunately, though, technical and intellectual resources for addressing these problems continue to expand and progress can be expected in understanding the regulation of gene expression by glucocorticoid receptors and the regulation of these steroid-dependent transcription factors themselves.

ACKNOWLEDGMENTS

We thank Debbie Bellingham, Dave Dyer, Victoria Allgood, and Marcia Gaido for editorial comments on this review and Wayne Balkan for assistance in preparing the manuscript. Our research is supported by National Institutes of Health grants AM32460, AM32459, and AM32078. K. L. B. is a postdoctoral fellow of the Lineberger Cancer Research Center and is supported by National Institutes of Health training grant 5T32CA09156 and by a National Institutes of Health NRSA fellowship F32GM12686.

Literature Cited

1. Adler, S., Waterman, M. L., He, X., Rosenfeld, M. G. 1988. Steroid receptor-mediated inhibition of rat prolactin gene expression does not require the receptor DNA-binding domain. *Cell* 52:685–95

2. Ali, M., Vedeckis, W. V. 1987. Interaction of RNA with transformed glucocorticoid receptor. *J. Biol. Chem.* 262:6778–84

3. Arriza, J. L., Weinberger, C., Cerelli, G., Glaser, T. M., Handelin, B. L., et al. 1987. Cloning of the human mineralocorticoid receptor complementary DNA: structural and functional kinship with the glucocorticoid receptor. *Science* 237:268–75

4. Becker, P. B., Gloss, B., Schmid, W., Strähle, U., Schütz, G. 1986. In vivo protein-DNA interactions in a glucocorticoid response element require the presence of the hormone. *Nature* 324:686–88

5. Becker, P. B., Renkawitz, R., Schütz, G. 1984. Tissue-specific DNase I hypersensitive sites in the 5'-flanking sequences of the tryptophan oxygenase and the tyrosine aminotransferase genes. *EMBO J.* 3:2015–20

6. Bellingham, D. B., Cidlowski, J. A. 1988. The glucocorticoid receptor: functional implications of protein and gene structure. In *Steroid Receptors and Disease,* ed. P. J. Sheridan, K. Blum, M. C. Tractenberg, pp. 97–119. New York: Dekker

7. Berg, J. M. 1986. Potential metal binding domains in nucleic acid binding proteins. *Science* 232:485–87

8. Boss, M. A. 1983. Enhancer elements in immunoglobulin genes. *Nature* 303:281–82

9. Bourgeois, S., Newby, R. F. 1979. Correlation between glucocorticoid receptor and cytolytic response of murine lymphoid cell lines. *Cancer Res.* 39:4749–51

10. Buetti, E., Diggelmann, H. 1983. Glucocorticoid regulation of mouse mammary tumor virus: identification of a short essential DNA region. *EMBO J.* 2:1423–29

11. Buetti, E., Kühnel, B. 1986. Distinct sequence elements involved in the glucocorticoid regulation of the mouse mammary tumor virus promoter identified by linker scanning mutagenesis. *J. Mol. Biol.* 190:379–89

12. Camper, S. A., Yao, Y. A. S., Rottman, F. M. 1985. Hormonal regulation

of the bovine prolactin promoter in rat pituitary tumor cells. *J. Biol. Chem.* 260:12246–51

13. Catelli, M. G., Binart, N., Jung-Testas, I., Renoir, J. M., Baulieu, E.-E., et al. 1985. The common 90-kd protein component of non-transformed '8S' steroid receptors is a heat shock protein. *EMBO J.* 4:3131–35

14. Chandler, V. L., Maler, B. A., Yamamoto, K. R. 1983. DNA sequences bound specifically by glucocorticoid receptor in vitro render a heterologous promoter responsive in vivo. *Cell* 33:489–99

15. Charron, J., Drouin, J. 1986. Glucocorticoid inhibition of transcription from episomal proopiomelanocortin gene promoter. *Proc. Natl. Acad. Sci. USA* 83:8903–7

16. Cidlowski, J. A., Cidlowski, N. B. 1981. Regulation of glucocorticoid receptors by glucocorticoids in cultured HeLa cells. *Endocrinology* 109:1975–82

17. Cidlowski, J. A., Cidlowski, N. B. 1982. Glucocorticoid receptors and the cell cycle: evidence that the accumulation of glucocorticoid receptors during the S phase of the cell cycle is dependent on ribonucleic acid and protein synthesis. *Endocrinology* 110:1653–62

18. Cidlowski, J. A., Michaels, G. A. 1977. Alteration in glucocorticoid binding site number during the cell cycle in HeLa cells. *Nature* 266:643–45

19. Cidlowski, J. A., Richon, V. 1984. Evidence for microheterogeneity in the structure of human glucocorticoid receptors. *Endocrinology* 115:1588–97

20. Cordingley, M. G., Riegel, A. T., Hager, G. L. 1987. Steroid-dependent interaction of transcription factors with the inducible promoter of mouse mammary tumor virus in vivo. *Cell* 48:261–70

21. Corthésy, B., Hipskind, R., Theulaz, I., Wahli, W. 1988. Estrogen-dependent in vitro transcription from the vitellogenin promoter in liver nuclear extracts. *Science* 239:1137–39

22. Currie, R. A., Cidlowski, J. A. 1982. Identification of modified forms of human glucocorticoid receptors during the cell cycle. *Endocrinology* 110:2192–94

23. Danesch, U., Gloss, B., Schmid, W., Schütz, G., Schule, R., Renkawitz, R. 1987. Glucocorticoid induction of the rat tryptophan oxygenase gene is mediated by two widely separated glucocorticoid responsive elements. *EMBO J.* 6:625–30

24. Danielsen, M., Northrop, J. P., Jonklaas, J., Ringold, G. M. 1987. Domains of the glucocorticoid receptor involved in specific and nonspecific deoxyribonucleic acid binding, hormone activation, and transcriptional enhancement. *Mol. Endocrinol.* 1:816–22

25. Danielsen, M., Northrop, J. P., Ringold, G. M. 1986. The mouse glucocorticoid receptor: mapping of functional domains by cloning, sequencing, and expression of wild-type and mutant receptor proteins. *EMBO J.* 5:2513–22

26. Eberwine, J. H., Roberts, J. L. 1984. Glucocorticoid regulation of proopiomelanocortin gene transcription in the rat pituitary. *J. Biol. Chem.* 259:2166–70

27. Fanger, B. O., Currie, R. A., Cidlowski, J. A. 1986. Regulation of epidermal growth factor receptors by glucocorticoids during the cell cycle in HeLa S$_3$ cells. *Arch. Biochem. Biophys.* 249:116–25

28. Gehring, U. 1987. Steroid hormone receptors: biochemistry, genetics, and molecular biology. *Trends Biochem. Sci.* 12:399–402

29. Giguère, V., Hollenberg, S. M., Rosenfeld, M. G., Evans, R. M. 1986. Functional domains of the human glucocorticoid receptor. *Cell* 46:645–52

30. Godowski, P. J., Rusconi, S., Miesfeld, R., Yamamoto, K. R. 1987. Glucocorticoid receptor mutants that are constitutive activators of transcriptional enhancement. *Nature* 325:365–68

31. Green, S., Chambon, P. 1986. A superfamily of potentially oncogenic hormone receptors. *Nature* 324:615–17

32. Green, S., Chambon, P. 1987. Oestradiol induction of a glucocorticoid-responsive gene by a chimaeric receptor. *Nature* 325:75–78

33. Griffen, M. J., Ber, R. 1969. Cell cycle events in the hydrocortisone regulation of alkaline phosphatase in HeLa S$_3$ cells. *J. Cell Biol.* 40:297–304

34. Groner, B., Hynes, N. E., Rahmsdorf, U., Ponta, H. 1983. Transcription initiation of transfected mouse mammary tumor virus LTR DNA is regulated by glucocorticoid hormones. *Nucleic Acids Res.* 11:4713–24

35. Groner, B., Kennedy, N., Skroch, P., Hynes, N. E., Ponta, H. 1984. DNA sequences involved in the regulation of gene expression by glucocorticoid hormones. *Biochem. Biophys. Acta* 781:1–6

36. Gustafsson, J.-Å., Carlstedt-Duke, J., Poellinger, L., Okret, S., Wikström, A.-C., et al. 1987. Biochemistry, molecular biology, and physiology of the glucocorticoid receptor. *Endocrine Rev.* 8:185–234

37. Hager, G., Richard-Foy, H., Kessel, M., Wheeler, D., Lichtler, A. C., Ostrowski, M. 1984. The mouse mammary tumor virus model in studies of glucocorticoid regulation. *Rec. Prog. Horm. Res.* 40:121–42

38. Holbrook, N. J., Bodwell, J. E., Jeffries, M., Munck, A. 1983. Characterization of nonactivated and activated glucocorticoid receptor complexes from intact rat thymus cells. *J. Biol. Chem.* 258:6477–85

39. Hollenberg, S. M., Giguère, V., Segui, P., Evans, R. M. 1987. Colocalization of DNA-binding and transcriptional activation functions in the human glucocorticoid receptor. *Cell* 49:39–46

40. Hollenberg, S. M., Weinberger, C., Ong, E. S., Cerelli, G., Oro, A., et al. 1985. Primary structure and expression of a functional human glucocorticoid receptor cDNA. *Nature* 318:635–41

41. Howard, K. J., Distelhorst, C. W. 1988. Evidence for intracellular association of the glucocorticoid receptor with the 90-kDa heat shock protein. *J. Biol. Chem.* 263:3474–81

42. Hynes, N., van Ooyen, A. J. J., Kennedy, N., Herrlich, P., Ponta, H., Groner, B. 1983. Subfragments of the large terminal repeat cause glucocorticoid-responsive expression of mouse mammary tumor virus and of an adjacent gene. *Proc. Natl. Acad. Sci. USA* 80:3637–41

43. Jantzen, H.-M., Strähle, U., Gloss, B., Stewart, F., Schmid, W., et al. 1987. Cooperativity of glucocorticoid response elements located far upstream of the tyrosine aminotransferase gene. *Cell* 49:29–38

44. Joab, I., Radanyi, C., Renoir, M., Buchou, T., Catelli, M.-G., et al. 1984. Common non-hormone binding component in non-transformed chick oviduct receptors of four steroid hormones. *Nature* 308:850–53

45. Kalinyak, J. E., Dorin, R. I., Hoffman, A. R., Perlman, A. 1987. Tissue-specific regulation of glucocorticoid receptor mRNA by dexamethasone. *J. Biol. Chem.* 262:10441–44

46. Karin, M., Haslinger, A., Holtgreve, H., Richards, R. I., Krauter, P., et. al. 1984. Characterization of DNA sequences through which cadmium and glucocorticoid hormones induce human metallothionein-IIA gene. *Nature* 308:513–19

47. Khoury, G., Gruss, P. 1983. Enhancer elements. *Cell* 33:313–14

48. Klock, G., Strähle, U., Schütz, G. 1987. Oestrogen and glucocorticoid responsive elements are closely related but distinct. *Nature* 329:734–36

49. Krust, A., Green, S., Argos, P., Kumar, V., Walter, P., et al. 1986. The chicken oestrogen receptor sequence: homology with v-erbA and the human oestrogen and glucocorticoid receptors. *EMBO J.* 5:891–97

50. Mendel, D. B., Bodwell, J. E., Gametchu, B., Harrison, R. W., Munck, A. 1986. Molybdate-stabilized nonactivated glucocorticoid-receptor complexes contain a 90-kDa non-steroid binding phosphoprotein that is lost on activation. *J. Biol. Chem.* 264:3758–63

51. Mendel, D. B., Bodwell, J. E., Munck, A. 1986. Glucocorticoid receptors lacking hormone-binding activity are bound in nuclei of ATP-depleted cells. *Nature* 324:478–80

52. Miesfeld, R., Godowski, P. J., Maler, B. A., Yamamoto, K. R. 1987. Glucocorticoid receptor mutants that define a small region sufficient for enhancer activation. *Science* 236:423–27

53. Miesfeld, R., Rusconi, S., Godowski, P. J., Maler, B. A., Okret, S., et al. 1986. Genetic complementation of a glucocorticoid receptor deficiency by expression of cloned receptor cDNA. *Cell* 46:389–99

54. Miller, J., McLachlan, A. D., Klug, A. 1985. Repetitive zinc-binding domains in the protein transcription factor IIIA from *Xenopus* oocytes. *EMBO J.* 4:1609–14

55. Munck, A., Holbrook, N. J. 1984. Glucocorticoid receptor complexes in rat thymus cells. *J. Biol. Chem.* 259:820–31

56. Munck, A., Leung, K. 1977. Glucocorticoid receptors and mechanism of action. In *Receptors and Mechanism of Action of Steroid Hormones*, ed. J. R. Pasqualini, 2:311–97. New York: Dekker

57. Okret, S., Poellinger, L., Dong, Y., Gustafsson, J.-Å. 1986. Down-regulation of glucocorticoid receptor mRNA by glucocorticoid hormones and recognition by the receptor of a specific binding sequence within a receptor cDNA clone. *Proc. Natl. Acad. Sci. USA* 83:5899–5903

58. Payvar, F., DeFranco, D., Firestone, G. L., Edgar, B., Wrange, Ö., et al. 1983. Sequence-specific binding of glucocorticoid receptor to MTV DNA at sites within and upstream of the transcribed region. *Cell* 35:381–92

59. Payvar, F., Wrange, Ö., Carlstedt-Duke, J., Okret, S., Gustafsson, J.-Å., Yamamoto, K. R. 1981. Purified gluco-

corticoid receptors bind selectively in vitro to a cloned DNA fragment whose transcription is regulated by glucocorticoids in vivo. *Proc. Natl. Acad. Sci. USA* 78:6628–32

60. Pfahl, M. 1982. Specific binding of the glucocorticoid-receptor complex to the mouse mammary tumor virus proviral promoter region. *Cell* 31:475–82

61. Pratt, W. B., Jolly, D. J., Pratt, D. V., Hollenberg, S. M., Giguère, V., et al. 1988. A region in the steroid binding domain determines formation of the non-DNA binding 9S glucocorticoid receptor complex. *J. Biol. Chem.* 263:267–73

62. Ptashne, M., 1986. Gene regulation by proteins acting nearby and at a distance. *Nature* 322:697–701

63. Raaka, B. M., Samuels, H. H., 1983. The glucocorticoid receptor in GH_1 cells. *J. Biol. Chem.* 258:417–25

64. Renkawitz, R., Schütz, G., von der Ahe, D., Beato, M. 1984. Sequences in the promoter region of the chicken lysozyme gene required for steroid regulation and receptor binding. *Cell* 37:503–10

65. Ringold, G. M. 1983. Regulation of mouse mammary tumor virus gene expression by glucocorticoid hormones. *Curr. Top. Microbiol. Immunol.* 106:79–103

66. Ringold, G. M. 1985. Steroid hormone regulation of gene expression. *Annu. Rev. Pharmacol. Toxicol.* 25:529–66

67. Ringold, G. M., Yamamoto, K. R., Tomkins, G. M., Bishop, J. M., Varmus, H. E. 1975. Dexamethasone induction of mouse mammary tumor virus RNA: A system for studying glucocorticoid action. *Cell* 6:299–305

68. Rosewicz, S., McDonald, A. R., Maddux, B. A., Goldfine, I. D., Miesfeld, R. L., Logsdon, C. D. 1988. Mechanism of glucocorticoid receptor downregulation by glucocorticoids. *J. Biol. Chem.* 263:2581–84

69. Rousseau, G. G. 1984. Control of gene expression by glucocorticoid hormones. *Biochem. J.* 224:1–12

70. Rusconi, S., Yamamoto, K. R. 1987. Functional dissection of the hormone and DNA binding activities of the glucocorticoid receptor. *EMBO J.* 6:1309–15

71. Sanchez, E. R., Toft, D. O., Schlesinger, M. J., Pratt, W. B. 1985. Evidence that the 90k-Da phosphoprotein associated with the untransformed L-cell glucocorticoid receptor is a murine heat shock protein. *J. Biol. Chem.* 260: 12398–401

72. Sap, J., Muñoz, A., Damm, K., Goldberg, Y., Ghysdael, J., et al. 1986. The c-*erb*-A protein is a high-affinity receptor for thyroid hormone. *Nature* 324: 635–40

73. Scheidereit, C., Geisse, S., Westphal, H. M., Beato, M. 1983. The glucocorticoid receptor binds to defined nucleotide sequences near the promoter of mouse mammary tumor virus. *Nature* 304:749–52

74. Silva, C. M., Jewell, C. M., Cidlowski, J. A. 1987. Non-steroid binding forms of glucocorticoid receptor in dexamethasone treated HeLa S3 cells. *J. Cell. Biochem. Suppl.* 11A:124

75. Silva, C. M., Tully, D. B., Petch, L. A., Jewell, C. M., Cidlowski, J. A. 1987. Application of a protein blotting procedure to the study of human glucocorticoid receptor interactions with DNA. *Proc. Natl. Acad. Sci. USA* 84: 1744–48

76. Simons, S. S. Jr., Thompson, E. B. 1981. Dexamethasone 21-mesylate: an affinity label of glucocorticoid receptors from rat hepatoma tissue culture cells. *Proc. Natl. Acad. Sci. USA* 78:3541–45

77. Slater, E. P., Rabenau, O., Karin, M., Baxter, J. D., Beato, M. 1985. Glucocorticoid receptor binding and activation of a heterologous promoter by dexamethasone by the first intron of the human growth hormone gene. *Mol. Cell. Biol.* 5:2984–92

78. Strähle, U., Klock, G., Schütz, G. 1987. A DNA sequence of 15 base pairs is sufficient to mediate both glucocorticoid and progesterone induction of gene expression. *Proc. Natl. Acad. Sci. USA* 84:7871–75

79. Svec, F., Rudis, M. 1981. Glucocorticoids regulate the glucocorticoid receptor in the AtT-20 cell. *J. Biol. Chem.* 256:5984–87

80. Tomkins, G. M., Gelehrtr, T. D., Granner, D., Martin, D., Samuels, H. H., Thompson, E. B. 1969. Control of specific gene expression in higher organisms. *Science* 166:1474–80

81. Toohey, M. G., Morley, K. L., Peterson, D. O. 1986. Multiple hormone-inducible enhancers as mediators of differential transcription. *Mol. Cell. Biol.* 6:4526–38

82. Tully, D. B., Cidlowski, J. A. 1987. pBR322 contains glucocorticoid regulatory element DNA consensus sequences. *Biochem. Biophys. Res. Commun.* 144: 1–10

83. Vedeckis, W. V. 1981. Activation and chromatographic properties of the AtT-20 mouse pituitary tumor cell line glucocorticoid receptor. *Biochemistry* 20: 7237–45

84. Vedeckis, W. V. 1983. Subunit dissociation as a possible mechanism of glucocorticoid receptor activation. *Biochemistry* 22:1983–89

85. von der Ahe, D., Janich, S., Scheidereit, C., Renkawitz, R., Schütz, G., Beato, M. 1985. Glucocorticoid and progesterone receptors bind to the same sites in two hormonally regulated promoters. *Nature* 313:706–9

86. von der Ahe, D., Renoir, J.-M., Buchou, T., Baulieu, E.-E., Beato, M. 1986. Receptors for glucocorticosteroid and progesterone recognize distinct features of a DNA regulatory element. *Proc. Natl. Acad. Sci. USA* 83:2817–21

87. Walters, M. 1985. Steroid hormone receptors and the nucleus. *Endocr. Rev.* 6:512–43

88. Weinberger, C., Hollenberg, S. M., Rosenfeld, M. G., Evans, R. M. 1985. Domain structure of human glucocorticoid receptor and its relationship to the v-*erb*-A oncogene product. *Nature* 318:670–72

89. Weinberger, C., Thompson, C. C., Ong, O. S., Lebo, R., Gruol, D. J., Evans, R. M. 1986. The c-*erb*-A gene encodes a thyroid hormone receptor. *Nature* 324:641–46

90. Willmann, T., Beato, M. 1986. Steroid-free glucocorticoid receptor binds specifically to mouse mammary tumour virus DNA. *Nature* 324:688–91

91. Yamamoto, K. R. 1985. Steroid receptor regulated transcription of specific genes and gene networks. *Annu. Rev. Genet.* 19:209–52

92. Zaret, K. S., Yamamoto, K. R. 1984. Reversible and persistent changes in chromatin structure accompany activation of a glucocorticoid-dependent enhancer element. *Cell* 38:29–38

Annu. Rev. Physiol. 1989. 51:701–14

EFFECTS OF INSULIN ON GENE TRANSCRIPTION

Miriam H. Meisler and Georgette Howard

Department of Human Genetics, University of Michigan Medical School, Ann Arbor, Michigan 48109–0618

INTRODUCTION

The peptide hormone insulin acts through a variety of mechanisms to regulate the direction and rate of carbohydrate metabolism. Protein kinase, cAMP, and phosphoinositides have been studied as potential mediators of the cytoplasmic effects of insulin (2, 6, 10). The isolation of many insulin-regulated genes by molecular cloning during the past five years has stimulated interest in the role of transcriptional regulation in insulin action. In the first phase of this molecular era, the concentrations of mRNAs for insulin-regulated proteins have been quantitated. Significant changes in steady-state concentrations of several mRNAs in response to insulin have been demonstrated. These studies have been summarized in recent reviews (13, 15, 18).

Currently attention is focused on the molecular mechanisms responsible for these changes in mRNA concentration. The steady-state concentration of a messenger RNA is determined by a sequence of events that includes initiation of transcription by RNA polymerase II, elongation of the transcript, termination of transcription, mRNA capping, polyadenylation, splicing, transport to the cytoplasm, and eventual degradation. Recent progress in the study of eukaryotic gene expression demonstrates that the first step in this process, initiation of transcription, can be regulated by the binding of nuclear proteins to *cis*-acting DNA sequences (26). For example, DNA-binding proteins are known to mediate transcriptional effects of steroid hormones, cAMP, and various low-molecular-weight effectors. This is not a well established mechanism of action for peptide hormones. Whether the effects of insulin on enzyme concentration result from this type of transcriptional regulation is the subject of this review.

701

0066–4278/89/0315–0701$02.00

Two experimental methods have been used to address this question: (*a*) biochemical measurement of the rate of gene transcription, by incorporation of radiolabelled precursors into messenger RNA, and (*b*) gene transfer and expression of cloned DNA containing regulatory sequences. We briefly discuss the interpretation of data obtained by these methods, and review their recent application to insulin-regulated genes.

EXPERIMENTAL CONSIDERATIONS

Demonstration of Transcriptional Regulation

NUCLEAR ELONGATION ASSAY   Cloned cDNA or exonic sequences from genomic clones are required for this assay. To measure the incorporation of precursors into mRNA, isolated nuclei are incubated in the presence of [^{32}P]UTP for a period of two to thirty minutes. RNA is extracted and the radioactivity incorporated into a specific messenger RNA is isolated by hybridization with the corresponding unlabeled DNA, which can be immobilized on nitrocellulose filters for convenience. Radioactivity bound to the filters is quantitated in a liquid scintillation counter or by densitometry of x-ray film. Reinitiation of transcription during this assay is very inefficient, especially in the presence of the detergent sarcosyl (17). The radioactivity incorporated into a specific mRNA during the assay therefore is proportional to the number of partial transcripts present in the nuclei. This radioactivity is taken as a measure of the "transcription rate" of the gene at the time of isolation of the nuclei (7).

One problem in the application of nuclear elongation to insulin-regulated genes is the limited sensitivity of the assay. Many insulin-regulated genes are expressed at low levels, accounting for much less than 1% of the messenger RNA in the cell, and the effects of insulin on these mRNA concentrations are often only two- to three-fold in magnitude. Consider a typical assay, in which one million cpm are incorporated into total RNA. The majority of this newly synthesized RNA will be ribosomal RNA. Depending upon the cell type, messenger RNA will account for roughly 3% of the total, or 30,000 cpm. An mRNA that comprises 1% of the total mRNA will then contain only 300 cpm. The "transcription rate" of this messenger RNA can be expressed in ppm: 300 cpm of specific hybridization divided by one million cpm incorporated into total RNA gives a transcription rate of 300 ppm. For a less abundant mRNA, the signal would be correspondingly smaller.

Measurements of such small signals in the presence of a large excess of nonspecific radioactivity result in considerable variation between replicate assays. In order to increase the radioactivity incorporated into low abundance mRNAs, the assay time has sometimes been extended up to one hour, without confirmation that incorporation remains linear during this period. Long incubations also introduce the possibility that regulation of processing steps subsequent to transcription could influence the final level of incorporated radioactivity. Finally, there is some question as to whether the results of assays with isolated nuclei provide an accurate reflection of the in vivo rates of transcription. Direct measurement of transcription rates in vivo would be of great value for confirmation of nuclear elongation assays; one method for such measurement has recently been described (40).

GENE TRANSFER   Genomic clones that include upstream promoter and regulatory sequences are required for these studies. The effect of insulin on cloned genes has been studied after gene transfer to cultured cells and to transgenic mice. When an insulin-responsive cultured cell line of the appropriate cell type is available, gene expression can be studied either by stable chromosomal integration of the cloned gene, or by transient assay of a population of transfected cells (28). Analysis of transgenic mice provides the advantage of expression in normal cells under physiological conditions (32).

It is frequently assumed that hormone responses during transient assay are the result of transcriptional regulation. Since transient assays are carried out for 24 to 48 hours, hormonal effects on mRNA processing and stability could also contribute to the final concentration of mRNA. If the results are based on determination of protein concentration or enzyme activity, effects of insulin on translation may also contribute to differences between treated and untreated cultures.

Demonstration that a transferred gene is regulated by insulin establishes that cis-acting sequences within the transferred DNA are responsible for the regulation. However, it is not possible to distinguish between transcriptional and posttranscriptional regulatory mechanisms if the transferred gene includes untranslated leader sequences, coding sequences, or introns. Transcriptional regulation can be unambiguously demonstrated with hybrid genes containing only nontranscribed sequences from the insulin-responsive gene fused to a nonregulated reporter gene. In this case, if expression of the fusion gene is insulin-responsive, then regulation of transcription initiation would be strongly indicated as the mechanism of insulin action.

A practical complication in the construction of hybrid genes is the lack of convenient restriction sites separating 5' flanking sequences from transcribed sequences. Ideally, they would be separated by enzymatic cleavage between nucleotides -1 and $+1$ of the regulated gene. In practice, the location of convenient restriction sites requires the inclusion of short stretches of transcribed sequences from the insulin-regulated gene, raising the possibility that posttranscriptional effects of these sequences on processing or on mRNA stability may influence the expression of the reporter gene.

Direct versus Indirect Effects of Insulin

Many effects of insulin were discovered as differences between diabetic and normal animals. Some of these may actually be caused by the other hormones, growth factors, and metabolites that are altered in diabetic animals. To be considered a direct effect of insulin, the response to insulin should be reproducible in cultured cells, and should be mediated by binding to the insulin receptor. However, even transcriptional effects of insulin that meet these criteria probably do not require direct molecular interaction of insulin with the transcriptional apparatus. Some of the second messenger molecules that mediate the cytoplasmic effects of insulin could mediate transcriptional effects as well. We are not aware of any evidence of sequence-specific binding to DNA by insulin or the insulin receptor. Transcriptional effects of insulin that are direct effects in the physiological sense are thus likely to be mediated at the molecular level by other nuclear proteins.

POSITIVE EFFECTS OF INSULIN

Demonstration of the effects of insulin on gene expression requires prior depletion of endogenous insulin from the experimental system. This can be accomplished in whole animal studies by administration of streptozotocin, a β cell-specific toxin. Streptozotocin treatment produces an irreversible diabetic state in which responses to injected insulin can be demonstrated. When an insulin-responsive cell line is studied, insulin depletion is obtained by growth in the absence of serum for several days prior to treatment with insulin. Proteins that are positively regulated by insulin include the hepatic enzymes glucokinase, pyruvate kinase, and glyceraldehyde-3-phosphate dehydrogenase (GAPDH), the pancreatic enzyme amylase, and the proto-oncogene c-fos.

Glucokinase

Liver-specific glucokinase (EC2.7.1.1) catalyzes the phosphorylation of glucose to glucose-6-phosphate, the first step in hepatic glucose metabolism. Glucokinase mRNA cannot be detected in liver of streptozotocin diabetic animals, but it reappears within one hour of insulin treatment (21). Kinetic analysis of the reappearance of glucokinase mRNA and protein was used to derive an estimated half-life of two to three hours for the mRNA and >30 hours for the protein. Nuclear elongation experiments were carried out using liver nuclei isolated at various times after administration of insulin to diabetic animals. A 20-fold increase in transcription rate was observed 45 minutes after administration of insulin. This rapid increase in mRNA synthesis suggests that insulin influences either transcription initiation or processing of the glucokinase mRNA. The effect of insulin on transcription of glucokinase is mimicked by treatment of diabetic rats with vanadate (12).

Pyruvate Kinase

L-type pyruvate kinase (EC 2.7.1.40) catalyzes the final step in glycolysis, conversion of phosphoenolpyruvate plus ADP to pyruvate plus ATP. In diabetic animals, the abundance of this mRNA is greatly reduced. Transcription rates were measured in a nuclear elongation assay using liver nuclei from diabetic animals. Insulin therapy produced a seven-fold increase in transcription rate, from 123 ± 81 to 762 ± 456 ppm (30). The maximal response was observed within 16 hours of insulin treatment. Similar rapid effects on transcription of pyruvate kinase were observed after refeeding of starved animals (29, 42). These studies indicate that the physiologic effect of insulin in vivo is to increase synthesis of pyruvate kinase mRNA.

Amylase

Alpha-amylase (EC 3.2.1.1) is the digestive enzyme that initiates the conversion of dietary starch to glucose. The amylase mRNA is abundant in the acinar cells of the pancreas, where it comprises more than 20% of the mRNA. Certain pancreatic amylase genes, including rat *Amy-2* and mouse *Amy-2.2*, appear to depend upon insulin for expression. In streptozotocin-diabetic animals these amylase mRNAs are reduced to undetectable levels, and treatment of the diabetic animals with insulin restores high levels of mRNA (8, 23, 31). Transfer of the intact *Amy-2.2* gene to transgenic animals demonstrated that *cis*-acting sequences close to the structural gene are responsible for the effects of insulin (31). An amylase/CAT hybrid gene containing the *Amy-2.2* sequence -208 to $+19$ has also been transferred to the germ line of transgenic mice (31a). The hybrid gene was expressed specifically in pancreas of the transgenic animals. Treatment of the transgenic animals with streptozotocin reduced CAT activity and mRNA to undetectable levels, and normal levels of CAT activity were restored after administration of insulin to the diabetic mice. These studies have localized the insulin-responsive sequences of this gene to a 227-bp DNA fragment and indicate that transcription of amylase is repressed in diabetic mice.

Glyceraldehyde-3-Phosphate Dehydrogenase (GAPDH)

The glycolytic enzyme GAPDH (EC 1.2.1.12) is regulated by insulin in liver cells and in adipocytes. The human gene has recently been cloned and studied by gene transfer methods (1). The intact GAPDH gene and a GAPDH/CAT hybrid gene were transfected into adipocyte and hepatoma cell lines. Stable transformants were isolated by selection for expression of the co-transfected *neo* gene. To evaluate response to insulin, the stably transformed cells were serum-starved for one to three days and then treated with insulin for 16 hours. The concentration of the GAPDH mRNA was increased three-fold in the hepatoma cells and ten-fold in the adipocytes. A five-fold increase in CAT activity of insulin-treated cells was demonstrated in stable transformants containing the hybrid gene.

Transient expression of the GAPDH/CAT hybrid gene was also measured in the hepatoma cell line. An increase of three- to four-fold in CAT activity was observed in the cells cultured in the presence of insulin. These studies demonstrate that the inductive effect of insulin on human GAPDH expression is mediated through *cis*-acting sequences located between −487 and +20 of the human GAPDH gene.

c-fos

The proto-oncogene *c*-fos is expressed in many tissues. In cultured adipocytes, the abundance of the *c*-fos mRNA is increased within ten minutes of exposure of the cells to insulin (38). Transient expression of a hybrid construct containing sequences −356 to +109 of *c*-fos fused to the CAT structural gene has been studied in transfected cells (39). Two lines of Chinese hamster ovary cell lines were used in these studies, one producing high levels of a normal insulin receptor protein, and the other producing a truncated insulin receptor protein that binds insulin but lacks tyrosine kinase activity (9). In the cells containing the normal insulin receptor, there was a three-fold increase in the abundance of the *c*-fos/CAT transcript (measured by a ribonuclease protection assay) during a 45-minute insulin treatment. There was no corresponding increase in the cell line producing the truncated receptor. This result demonstrates that regulation of *c*-fos by insulin is mediated by the insulin receptor, and suggests that the kinase activity of the receptor is essential for this regulation.

A mutant *c*-fos derivative containing four base substitutions within the 20-bp serum response element (−320 to −299) did not respond to insulin (39). This DNA element is also required for induction of *c*-fos by phorbol 12-myristate 13-acetate, which suggests that both inducers act through the same transcription factor. While these sequences are evidently required for regulation by insulin, it has not been demonstrated that they are sufficient for this effect. Transfer of the serum response element to a non-insulin-regulated promoter will be required to demonstrate that this element can be considered an insulin-responsive enhancer.

The *c*-fos protein is associated with a complex that activates transcription of genes containing AP1 binding sites (33). The rapid induction of *c*-fos protein could result in increased transcription of other insulin-responsive genes, as in Figure 1C (page 710).

NEGATIVE EFFECTS OF INSULIN

Insulin exerts opposing effects on hepatic glycolysis and gluconeogenesis. The rate of glycolysis is increased by positive regulation of pyruvate kinase and GAPDH, while the rate of gluconeogenesis is reduced by negative regulation of phosphoenolpyruvate carboxykinase (PEPCK). A negative effect of insulin on growth hormone expression has also been reported.

PEPCK

Two isozymes of PEPCK (PEPCK, EC 4.1.1.32) are expressed in mammalian liver and kidney. Mitochondrial PEPCK appears not to be regulated by insulin. Cytosolic PEPCK is a key enzyme in gluconeogenesis and is regulated by several hormones. The negative effect of insulin on cytoplasmic PEPCK has been extensively studied (16, 18, 19).

PEPCK transcription was studied by nuclear elongation assay using nuclei from the insulin-responsive hepatoma H4IIE (14, 16, 35). In the presence of cAMP, insulin reduces the transcription rate from ~ 1500 to ~ 150 ppm. In unstimulated cells, the constitutive transcription rate of ~ 180 ppm is further reduced to less than 50 ppm by addition of insulin to the culture medium.

The expression of three different fusion genes containing rat PEPCK gene promoter was studied by gene transfer. A construct containing PEPCK sequences −450 to +73 fused to the first exon of human growth hormone gene was transferred to the germ line of transgenic mice (27). The effects of diet on expression of the construct in liver was consistent with a response mediated by insulin. However, since the growth hormone gene may itself be regulated by insulin, it is necessary to examine additional constructs to determine whether the dietary effects are mediated by sequences derived from PEPCK or from growth hormone.

A PEPCK/CAT fusion gene containing rat PEPCK sequences between −600 and +69 is also responsive to insulin (25). The fusion gene was transfected into H4IIE hepatoma cells, and the effect of hormones on CAT activity was ascertained after 18 hours of expression. The presence of insulin (10 nM) was sufficient to prevent the two- to three- fold stimulation of CAT activity produced by incubation with dexamethasone alone or cAMP alone. Insulin also prevented the five-fold stimulation produced by dexamethasone and cAMP together.

A different result was observed in a stably transformed rat hepatoma cell line (41). In this work, a hybrid gene containing PEPCK sequences −548 to +73 was fused to the thymidine kinase structural gene. The PEPCK/tk construct was regulated by cAMP and glucocorticoids with no negative effect in the presence of insulin.

The latter two studies are consistent with the possibility that the PEPCK sequences between −548 and −600, which were present in the CAT fusion gene but not in the tk construct, could be required for negative regulation of the PEPCK/CAT construct by insulin.

Other differences between the two studies include the expression assays used: stable transformants in the first study and transient assays in the second. These and other interpretations are discussed in reference (25).

Growth Hormone

Nuclear elongation experiments were carried out in primary cultures of pituitary cells (43). In the presence of 7 nM insulin, transcription of the growth hormone gene was reduced from ~ 40 ppm to 15 ppm. This effect was blocked by anti-insulin receptor serum. Subsequently, the regulation of a 2.6-kb fragment containing the intact growth hormone gene was studied in the choriocarcinoma cell line JEG3. In transient expression experiments, a high concentration of insulin (200 nM) was required to observe an effect on growth hormone production (44). The authors suggest that regulation of growth hormone may be mediated through the insulin-like growth factor I receptor rather than the insulin receptor.

OTHER GENES

Thyroglobulin

Thyroglobulin, the precursor of active thyroid hormone, is the major protein synthesized in the thyroid gland. There is some evidence of thyroid deficiency in diabetic rodents and humans (reviewed in 34). Nuclear elongation assays on cultured thyroid cells demonstrated a two-fold increase in the presence of insulin, from ~ 800 to ~ 1700 ppm (34). However, similar effects were observed with IGF-1 and the effects of insulin and IGF-1 were not additive. Therefore it remains uncertain whether insulin functions physiologically as a regulator of thyroglobulin expression.

Glutamine Synthetase

Glutamine synthetase is expressed in many cell types and functions in amino acid metabolism. Both positive and negative effects of insulin on glutamine synthetase have been reported. In the cultured adipocyte line 3T3-L1, the transcription rate, measured by nuclear elongation, is increased from ~ 100 to 250 ppm by dexamethasone (3). This induction is prevented by insulin (3). The same authors have measured transcription of the amplified glutamine synthetase gene in a CHO cell line. In these cells, insulin alone produced a two-fold increase in transcription, from ~ 200 to 400 ppm (4). The reason for the opposite results in the two cell lines remains to be established.

Albumin

There are conflicting reports regarding the effects of insulin on transcription of albumin. As measured by the nuclear elongation assay on isolated liver nuclei, the rate of transcription of albumin was 700 ppm in untreated rats and only 350 ppm in diabetic rats (24). When nuclei were isolated from primary cultures of rat hepatocytes, a six-hour exposure to 100-nM insulin increased albumin transcription from ~ 70 to 115 ppm (24). However, in the hepatoma cell line H4IIE, 2-pM insulin produced a roughly 4–fold reduction in albumin transcription (37). The conflict between these data could be related to the transformed state of the hepatoma cells.

SUMMARY OF DIRECT EFFECTS OF INSULIN

The currently available evidence for effects of insulin on mRNA synthesis is summarized in Table 1. Many of these effects are small in magnitude and difficult to measure with the available methods. Additional studies are required to confirm these observations.

Three general mechanisms by which insulin may regulate transcription are represented in Figure 1. All three propose an insulin-responsive protein (IRP) whose conformation is altered by the action of insulin. This protein could bind to specific DNA sequences and influence transcription directly (Figure 1A). Successful transfer of insulin-responsive sequences to heterologous promoters would establish the validity of this model.

Other mechanisms of transcriptional activation and inactivation in response to insulin cannot be excluded by the available data. The IRP might catalyze a covalent modification of a transcriptional regulator protein resulting in altered activity, perhaps by phosphorylation or dephosphorylation (Figure 1B), or the IRP could produce a stable complex with a transcriptional regulator, thereby modifying its activity (Figure 1C). The effects of several hormones on the same gene could then be integrated through their independent effects on a common DNA binding protein. When mechanisms B and C are involved, it

Table 1   Quantitative effects of insulin on mRNA concentration and transcription

Gene	Effect on mRNA concentration (insulin/control)	Effect on transcription (insulin/control)	Reference
Amylase*	>100[a]	Not done	23, 31
Casein	>100[+c]	>1000-fold	5
GAPDH*	10[c]	3- to 10-fold	1
Glucokinase	>10[a]	20-fold	21
Growth hormone	0.5[c]	15 ppm/40 ppm	43
PEPCK*	0.5[c]	50 ppm/177 ppm	14
Pyruvate kinase	>10[a]	800 ppm/100 ppm	30

[+]Requires the presence of other hormones in addition to insulin.
*Gene transfer data summarized in Table 3.
[a]Measured in whole animal experiments.
[c]Measured in cultured cells.

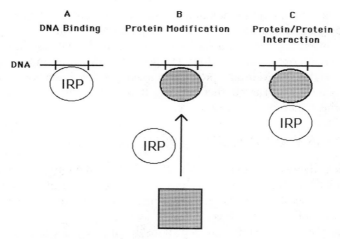

Figure 1 Molecular mechanisms for transcriptional effects of insulin. The IRP represents an insulin-responsive protein whose conformation is altered in response to insulin. Three mechanisms by which an IRP could influence transcription are indicated. (*A*) IRP binds to a specific, *cis*-acting enhancer and alters transcription of the adjacent gene; (*B*) IRP catalyzes the covalent modification of a transcription factor, changing its effect on transcription; (*C*) Stable, noncovalent binding of IRP to a transcription factor changes its effect on transcription.

will not be possible to separate a *cis*-acting insulin responsive DNA element from sequences mediating the effects of other hormones. See note added in proof, page 714.

INTERACTION WITH OTHER HORMONES

Many of the enzymes regulated by insulin are also regulated by glucocorticoids and cAMP (Table 2). The effect of cAMP on these genes is opposite in direction to the insulin effect. Under normal physiological conditions, these regulators coexist and interact to influence transcription. Additive effects are expected if the hormones act independently through different *cis*-acting sequences (Figure 1*A*). The conditions of independence and additivity have been demonstrated for regulation of PEPCK by glucocorticoids and by cAMP (35), but this has not yet been demonstrated for insulin.

In some cases, insulin alone does not induce gene expression, but its presence is required in combination with other inducers. Casein transcription has been measured by the nuclear elongation assay using nuclei from mammary gland explants maintained in short-term culture (5). In the presence of serum, cortisol, prolactin, and insulin, the original level of transcription (6400 ppm) was maintained during the culture period. However, if insulin was omitted from the culture medium, transcription of casein was not detected. Insulin alone in the medium did not maintain casein transcription. A

Table 2 Multifactorial regulation of insulin-responsive genes

Gene	Tissue	Insulin	Glucocorticoids	cAMP	Thyroid
Amylase	Pancreas	Pos	Pos		
Growth hormone	Pituitary	Neg	Pos	Pos	Pos
Casein	Mammary	Pos	Pos		
c-fos	Many	Pos			
GAPDH	Many	Pos			
Glucokinase	Liver	Pos	Pos	Neg	Pos
PEPCK	Liver, kidney	Neg	Pos	Pos	Pos
Pyruvate kinase	Liver	Pos		Neg	

similar situation has been observed for *Xenopus* ovalbumin gene (11). Induction of ovalbumin transcription by estrogen requires the presence of insulin in the culture medium. The permissive effect of insulin on this induction can be replaced by elevated cAMP levels, which suggests that the effects may involve protein phosphorylation (11). Models *B* and *C* in Figure 1 may be involved in cases in which insulin is necessary but not sufficient for the action of other hormones.

CONCLUSIONS AND FUTURE DIRECTIONS

A major goal will be the precise identification of *cis*-acting DNA sequences responsive to insulin. The recent isolation of insulin-responsive promoter/enhancer regions from four insulin-regulated genes (Table 3) indicates that this will be feasible. It will be necessary, however, to determine whether the insulin-response of these genes can be separated from other regulatory sequences and transferred to heterologous promoters. Comparison of the available sequences did not reveal obvious consensus elements common to these promoters. Since insulin is known to change the concentrations of a variety of

Table 3 Localization of insulin-responsive sequences by gene transfer[a]

Gene	Effect of insulin on expression of construct	Gene sequences in construct	Assay system	Reference
Amylase	>100 fold	−208 to +19	Transgenic mice	31a
c-fos	2–3-fold	−356 to +109	Transient	39
GAPDH	3–4-fold	−487 to +20	Stable+transient	1
PEPCK	2–3-fold	−600 to +69	Transient	25

[a]Hybrid constructs containing the indicated sequences from the regulated genes were fused to the bacterial chloramphenicol acetyltransferase gene. Regulation of the hybrid construct by insulin was assayed either in transgenic mice or by transfection of DNA into cultured cells, as described in the text.

intracellular signals, more than one of these regulators may interact with sequences in different genes.

A second important line of research is the isolation of insulin-responsive proteins directly involved in transcriptional effects, the IRP of Figure 1. For proteins that bind specifically to DNA two promising methods are available: biochemical isolation of nuclear proteins based on their high affinity for specific DNA sequences (22), and screening of expression libraries using oligonucleotide probes containing the binding sequences (36). Isolation of regulatory factors, which influence transcription through protein/protein interaction (Figure 1*B* and *C*), will require new methods. Mutant cell lines deficient in specific regulatory proteins could be used to isolate the defective gene. A general strategy for selection of this type of mutant cell line was recently described (20). If insertional mutagenesis were used in the production of such mutant lines, the mutagenized genes could be recovered by molecular cloning, using the inserted DNA as hybridization probe. Correction of the mutant cell lines by transfection with expression libraries could also be used to isolate the defective genes.

At present, the question as to whether insulin influences gene transcription appears to have been answered in the affirmative. The next few years should see confirmation of the preliminary studies currently available, as well as elucidation of the molecular details of these transcriptional effects.

ACKNOWLEDGMENT

Preparation of this chapter, and our studies of the effects of insulin on the amylase gene, have been supported by USPHS grants GM 24872 and DK 36089, the Michigan Diabetes Research and Training Center P60 DK 20572, and the Gastrointestinal Hormone Research Core Center P30 DK 34933. G.H. is recipient of National Research Service award F32 DK 08137. We are grateful to Lisa Campeau for superb assistance with the manuscript.

Literature Cited

1. Alexander, M. C., Lomanto, M., Nasrin, N., Ramaika, C. 1988. Insulin regulates glyceraldehyde-3-phosphate dehydrogenase (GAPDH) gene expression through *cis*-acting DNA sequences. *Proc. Natl. Acad. Sci. USA* 85:5092–96
2. Belfrage, P., Donner, J., Stralfors, P., eds. 1986. *Mechanisms of Insulin Action.* Amsterdam: Elsevier. 409 pp.
3. Bhandari, B., Miller, R. E. 1987. Glutamine synthetase gene transcription in cultured 3T3-L1 adipocytes: Regulation by dexamethasone, insulin, and dibutyryl cyclic AMP. *Mol. Cell. Endocrinol.* 51:7–11
4. Bhandari, B., Wilson, R. H., Miller, R. E. 1987. Insulin and dexamethasone stimulate transcription of an amplified glutamine synthetase gene in Chinese hamster ovary cells. *Mol. Endocrinol.* 1:403–7
5. Chomczynski, P., Qasba, P., Topper, Y. J. 1984. Essential role of insulin in transcription of the rat 25,000 molecular weight casein gene. *Science* 226:1326–28
6. Czech, M. P., ed. 1985. *Molecular Basis of Insulin Action.* New York: Plenum. 473 pp.
7. Derman, E., Krauter, K., Walling, L.,

Weinberger, C., Ray, M., et al. 1981. Transcriptional control in the production of liver-specific mRNAs. *Cell* 23:731–39

8. Dranginis, A., Morley, M., Nesbitt, M., Rosenblum, B. B., Meisler, M. H. 1984. Independent regulation of nonallelic pancreatic amylase genes in diabetic mice. *J. Biol. Chem.* 259:12216–19

9. Ellis, L., Clauser, E., Morgan, D. O., Edery, M., Roth, R. A., et al. 1986. Replacement of insulin receptor tyrosine residues 1162 and 1163 compromises insulin-stimulated kinase activity and uptake of 2-deoxyglucose. *Cell* 45:721–32

10. Espinal, J. 1987. Mechanism of insulin action. *Nature* 328:574–75

11. Evans, M. I., McKnight, G. S. 1984. Regulation of the ovalbumin gene: effects of insulin, adenosine 3', 5'-monophosphate, and estrogen. *Endocrinology* 115:368–77

12. Gil, J., Miralpeix, M., Carreras, J., Bartrons, R. 1988. Insulin-like effects of vanadate on glucokinase activity and fructose 2,6-biphosphate levels in the liver of diabetic rats. *J. Biol. Chem.* 263:1868–71

13. Goodrich, A. G., Hanson, R. W., eds. 1986. *Metabolic Regulation: Applications of Recombinant DNA Techniques.* *Ann. NY Acad. Sci.,* Vol. 478

14. Granner, D. K., Andreone, T., Sasaki, K., Beale, E. 1983. Inhibition of transcription of the phosphoenolpyruvate carboxykinase gene by insulin. *Nature* 305:549–51

15. Granner, D. K., Sasaki, K., Andreone, T., Beale, E. 1986. Insulin regulates expression of the phosphoenolpyruvate carboxykinase gene. *Recent Prog. Horm. Res.* 42:111–41

16. Granner, D. K., Sasaki, K., Chu, D. 1986. Multihormonal regulation of phosphoenolpyruvate carboxykinase gene transcription: The dominant role of insulin. *Ann. NY Acad. Sci.* 478:175–90

17. Groudine, M., Peretz, M., Weintraub, H. 1981. Transcriptional regulation of hemoglobin switching in chicken embryos. *Mol. Cell. Biol.* 1:281–88

18. Hanson, R. W., Hatzoglou, M., McGrane, M. M., Rottman, F. M., Wagner, T. 1988. Molecular biology and nutrition research. *Natl. Res. Counc. Symp. Frontiers Nutr. Sci.* In press

19. Hod, Y., Cook, J. S., Weldon, S. L., Short, J. M., Wynshaw-Boris, A., et al. 1986. Differential expression of the genes for the mitochondrial and cytosolic forms of phosphoenolpyruvate carboxykinase. *Ann. NY Acad. Sci.* 478:31–45

20. Hofstetter, P., Kikinis, Z., Altus, M. S., Pearson, D., Nagamine, Y. 1987. A new genetic approach for studying hormonal regulation of urokinase-type plasminogen activator gene expression in LLC-PK$_1$ cells. *Mol. Cell. Biol.* 7:4535–41

21. Iynedjian, P. B., Gjinovci, A., Renold, A. E. 1988. Stimulation by insulin of glucokinase gene transcription in liver of diabetic rats. *J. Biol. Chem.* 263:740–44

22. Kadonaga, J. T., Tjian, R. 1986. Affinity purification of sequence-specific DNA binding proteins. *Proc. Natl. Acad. Sci. USA* 83:5889–93

23. Korc, M., Owerbach, D., Quinto, C., Rutter, W. J. 1981. Pancreatic islet-acinar cell interaction: Amylase messenger RNA levels are determined by insulin. *Science* 213:351–53

24. Lloyd, C. E., Kalinyak, J. E., Hutson, S. M., Jefferson, L. S. 1987. Stimulation of albumin gene transcription by insulin in primary cultures of rat hepatocytes. *Am. J. Physiol.* 252:C205–14

25. Magnuson, M. A., Quinn, P. G., Granner, D. K. 1987. Multihormonal regulation of phosphenolpyruvate carboxykinase-chloramphenicol acetyltransferase fusion genes: Insulin's effects oppose those of cAMP and dexamethasone. *J. Biol. Chem.* 262:14917–20

26. Maniatis, T., Goodbourn, S., Fischer, J. A. 1987. Regulation of inducible and tissue-specific gene expression. *Science* 236:1237–45

27. McGrane, M. M., deVente, J., Yun, J., Bloom, J., Parks, E., et al. 1988. Tissue specific expression and dietary regulation of a chimeric phosphoenolpyruvate carboxykinase/bovine growth hormone gene in transgenic mice. *J. Biol. Chem.* 263:11443–51

28. Miller, J. H., Calos, M. P., eds. 1987. *Current Communications in Molecular Biology: Gene Transfer Vectors for Mammalian Cells.* New York: Cold Spring Harbor Lab. 169 pp.

29. Munnich, A., Lyonnet, S., Chauvet, D., Van Schaftingen, E., Kahn, A. 1987. Differential effects of glucose and fructose on liver L-type pyruvate kinase gene expression in vivo. *J. Biol. Chem.* 262:17065–71

30. Noguchi, T., Inoue, H., Tanaka, T. 1985. Transcriptional and post-transcriptional regulation of L-type pyruvate kinase in diabetic rat liver by insulin and dietary fructose. *J. Biol. Chem.* 260:14393–97

31. Osborn, L. O., Rosenberg, M. P., Kel-

ler, S. A., Meisler, M. 1987. Tissue-specific and insulin-dependent expression of a pancreatic amylase gene in transgenic mice. *Mol. Cell. Biol.* 7:326–34

31a. Osborn, L. O., Rosenberg, M. P., Keller, S. A., Ting, C.-N., Meisler, M. 1988. Insulin response of a hybrid amylase/CAT gene in transgenic mice. *J. Biol. Chem.* 263:16519–22

32. Palmiter, R. D., Brinster, R. L. 1986. Germline transformation of mice. *Annu. Rev. Genet.* 20:465–99

33. Rauscher, F. J. III, Sambucette, L. C., Curran, T., Distel, R. J., Spiegelman, B. M. 1988. Common DNA binding site for fos protein complexes and transcription factor AP-1. *Cell* 52:471–80

34. Santisteban, P., Kohn, L. D., Di Lauro, R. 1987. Thyroglobulin gene expression is regulated by insulin and insulin-like growth factor 1, as well as thyrotropin, in FRTL-5 thyroid cells. *J. Biol. Chem.* 262:4048–52

35. Sasaki, K., Cripe, T. P., Koch, S. R., Andreone, T. L., Petersen, D. D., et al. 1984. Multihormonal regulation of phosphoenolpyruvate carboxykinase gene transcription: The dominant role of insulin. *J. Biol. Chem.* 259:15242–51

36. Singh, H., LeBowitz, J. H., Baldwin, A. S., Sharp, P. A. 1988. Molecular cloning of an enhancer binding protein: isolation by screening of an expression library with a recognition site DNA. *Cell* 52:415–23

37. Straus, D. S., Takemoto, C. D. 1987. Insulin negatively regulates albumin mRNA at the transcriptional and post-transcriptional level in rat hepatoma cells. *J. Biol. Chem.* 262:1955–60

38. Stumpo, D. J., Blackshear, P. J. 1986. Insulin and growth factor effects on *c*-fos expression in normal and protein

kinase C-deficient 3T3-L1 fibroblasts and adipocytes. *Proc. Natl. Acad. Sci. USA* 83:9453–57

39. Stumpo, D. J., Stewart, T. N., Gilman, M. Z., Blackshear, P. J. 1988. Identification of *c*-fos sequences involved in induction by insulin and phorbol esters. *J. Biol. Chem.* 263:1611–14

40. Watson, G., Paigen, K. 1988. mRNA synthesis rates in vivo for androgen inducible sequences in mouse kidney. *Mol. Cell. Biol.* 8:2117–24

41. Wynshaw-Boris, A., Short, J. M., Loose, D. S., Hanson, R. W. 1986. Characterization of the phosphoenolpyruvate carboxykinase (GTP) promoter-regulatory region. 1. Multiple hormone regulatory elements and the effects of enhancers. *J. Biol. Chem.* 261:9714–20

42. Vaulont, S., Munnich, A., Decaux, J.-F., Kahn, A. 1986. Transcriptional and post-transcriptional regulation of L-type pyruvate kinase gene expression in rat liver. *J. Biol. Chem.* 261:7621–25

43. Yamashita, S., Melmed, S. 1986. Insulin regulation of rat growth hormone gene transcription. *J. Clin. Invest.* 78:1008–14

44. Yamashita, S., Ong, J., Melmed, S. 1987. Regulation of human growth hormone gene expression by insulin-like growth factor 1 in transfected cells. *J. Biol. Chem.* 262:13254–57

45. Chu, D. T. W., et al. 1988. *J. Biol. Chem.* 263:13007–11

46. Stanley, F. 1988. *J. Biol. Chem.* 263:13444–48

47. Lee, K., et al. 1985. *J. Biol. Chem.* 260:16433–38

48. Sasaki, K., Granner, D. K. 1988. *Proc. Natl. Acad. Sci. USA* 85:2954–58

49. Curran, T., Franza, B. R. 1988. *Cell* 55:395–97

NOTE ADDED IN PROOF

Recent reports describe the effect of insulin on transcription of gene 33 hepatoma cells (45) and transcription of prolactin in a pituitary-derived cell line (46). A positive effect of insulin on transcription of gene 33 in liver was previously observed in vivo (47). Insulin appears to exert its primary effect on the initiation of transcription PEPCK, with secondary effect on the rate of elongation (48). New information on the role of *c*-fos in transcriptional activation (49) is consistent with its function as an intermediate in the transcriptional effects of insulin by the mechanism proposed in Figure 1C.

Annu. Rev. Physiol. 1989. 51:715-26

HORMONAL REGULATION OF POMC GENE EXPRESSION

Dominic J. Autelitano, James R. Lundblad, Mariann Blum, and James L. Roberts

Fishberg Research Center of Neurobiology, Mt. Sinai School of Medicine, New York, New York 10029

INTRODUCTION

Proopiomelanocortin (POMC) is perhaps the best studied of the three opioid peptide precursor genes. As well as coding for the opioid peptide β-endorphin, the POMC gene also gives rise to several important biologically active peptides, including ACTH and α-melanocyte stimulating hormone (for reviews see 27, 73). The major site of expression of the POMC gene is the pituitary gland. In addition, the POMC gene is expressed in several brain regions and in a multitude of extracranial tissues. The fact that the POMC gene is expressed in such a variety of cell types, and is under such complex differential regulation, makes it an important model system for understanding how different regulatory factors and intracellular mechanisms interact to establish the required level of gene expression.

The presence of only one functional POMC gene has been reported for several mammalian species, although the mouse has been shown to contain an additional POMC pseudogene that does not produce a functional mRNA (54). The structure of the POMC gene is similar among all mammalian species, and contains 3 exons, separated by 2 relatively large introns.

POMC-like mRNA has been demonstrated in a variety of extrapituitary tissues including brain regions such as the hypothalamus, amygdala and cerebral cortex (21), ovary and testis (16, 18, 19, 35, 36, 41, 44, 55, 63), adrenal medulla (42), spleen macrophages (53), duodenum, and stomach (23). The size of the mature POMC mRNA transcript appears to be similar in pituitary and spleen macrophages (~1100 bases) (53), while in hypothalamus, POMC mRNA transcripts seem to be identical to pituitary except for a

715

0066-4278/89/0315-0715$02.00

longer poly(A) tail (40). Recent studies show that in peripheral tissues such as testes, POMC transcripts that are 200–400 bases shorter have been detected that contain no exon 1 or exon 2 sequences, and are derived via heterogeneous transcription initiation sites near the 5' end of exon 3 (40, 45). Alternate forms of POMC mRNA also exist in rat pituitary tissue as a result of differential splicing between exon 1 and exon 2, which leads to the inclusion of an additional 30 nucleotides within the 5' untranslated portion of the mRNA (60). Although the functional significance of these altered POMC mRNA transcripts is not yet clear, they do appear to vary in a tissue-specific manner. Similarly, regulation of these tissue-specific POMC mRNA transcripts by a multitude of hormonal, neurohormonal, and neurotransmitter factors occurs differentially and is discussed below.

PITUITARY

CRF/AVP

The effects of CRF on POMC gene expression in pituitary anterior lobe (AL) and neurointermediate lobe (NIL) have been examined both in vitro and in vivo. Rapid stimulation of POMC gene transcription was observed in primary cultures of AL cells following treatment with CRF (25, 30, 31). In short-term cultures of rat NIL cells, Eberwine and colleagues (25) demonstrated that CRF could rapidly increase POMC gene transcription, but at 10-fold higher doses than needed for AL cultures. Gagner & Drouin (31) failed to show any effect of CRF on POMC gene transcription in NIL cultures. Recent studies further demonstrated that injection of exogenous CRF into rats results in rapid (<30 min) increases in POMC gene transcription in both AL and NIL, although the magnitude and duration of the response differs between the two pituitary lobes (8). The rise measured in POMC gene transcription following CRF administration suggests that there may be associated rapid increases in the level of nuclear mRNA precursor. Northern blots of nuclear RNA isolated from CRF-treated AtT20 cells (mouse corticotroph tumor cell line) show the presence of a large-molecular-weight POMC RNA species that is presumably the POMC primary transcript (2). In addition, Autelitano et al (8) have shown that following injection of exogenous CRF into rats, changes in the levels of pituitary POMC primary transcript accurately reflect alterations in gene transcription.

The stimulation of POMC gene transcription by CRF leads to increased amounts of nuclear primary transcript, which if efficiently spliced may lead to increased levels of mature POMC mRNA. In all in vivo studies reported, administration of exogenous CRF by a variety of routes for at least 3 days results in a 50–400% increase in the level of POMC mRNA in AL (8, 14, 37, 54). In contrast, long-term administration of CRF to rats was shown to decrease NIL levels of POMC mRNA in several studies (8, 37, 54), while having no effect in another study (14). The differential effects of CRF on AL and NIL POMC gene expression in vivo may be partly due to differences in transcriptional responsiveness of corticotrophs and melanotrophs to exogenous CRF (8, 25). The increase in POMC mRNA levels in primary cultures of rat AL cells and in AtT20 cells following exposure to CRF suggests that this factor acts directly on these cells to increase POMC mRNA (2, 48, 50). Unlike its long-term effect in vivo, CRF administration causes an increase in POMC mRNA levels in cultured NIL cells (48, 50). The reason for the differential effect of CRF on NIL POMC gene expression in vivo versus in vitro is not clear but might suggest that CRF has both direct and indirect actions on NIL POMC.

Although the effect of AVP (both alone and in combination with CRF) on ACTH release is well documented (see 6 for review), its effects on POMC gene expression in pituitary have not yet been fully characterized. Recently in a preliminary report, it was shown that AVP had no effect on either basal or on CRF-stimulated levels of POMC mRNA in rat AL cultures (56).

Glucocorticoids

It is well established that the secretion and synthesis of ACTH and other AL POMC-derived peptides are under the negative feedback influence of adrenal corticosteroids (43). Nakanishi et al (59) initially demonstrated an increase in POMC mRNA activity in extracts of whole pituitary from adrenalectomized (ADX) rats, which was prevented by simultaneous administration of glucocorticoids. Later studies using hybridization methods (12, 69), and in situ hybridization histochemistry (28, 33) indicated that the main effect of adrenalectomy was on AL POMC mRNA levels (>10-fold increases); NIL POMC mRNA levels were affected only slightly (a small decrease). Within 1 hour of ADX, POMC gene transcription in AL is elevated (12) and remains elevated even at 14 days post-surgery (26). Injection of dexamethasone (DEX) to ADX rats results in > 10-fold decrease in this elevated transcription rate within 30 minutes (30), and a reversal in the elevated POMC mRNA levels after several days (12). As shown by in situ hybridization with a probe specific for the first intron (or intervening sequence) of the POMC gene, adrenalectomy increased the autoradiographic signal over each positive cell but also increased the total number of positive cells in the AL (28). Thus, the large increases in AL POMC gene expression after adrenalectomy may be due to both an increase in transcription rate per individual cell and in the number of cells transcribing the POMC gene.

Adrenalectomy, however, removes a feedback signal for both the corticotroph itself and the hypothalamus. It increases the content and biosynthesis of the hypothalamic releasing factors AVP and CRF (6). Thus, the large increases in POMC mRNA levels following adrenalectomy are due to removal of a direct inhibitory influence on the corticotroph and to an increase in "hypothalamic drive" on the corticotroph. Dallman et al (22) show that ADX rats with anterolateral hypothalamic disconnection, relative to sham-ADX lesioned rats, do not have higher levels of anterior pituitary POMC mRNA despite removal of the feedback influence of corticosteroids.

Direct effects of glucocorticoids on corticotroph POMC gene expression have been demonstrated in both primary cultures of anterior pituitaries and in the AtT20 cell line (25, 30, 31, 58, 66). The transcription rate of the POMC gene is maximally inhibited within 20 minutes of addition of glucocorticoids and detectably reduced from control at 10 minutes. The inhibition of transcription rate by dexamethasone in culture occurs in the presence of the protein synthesis inhibitor cycloheximide (31) and thus may be a direct effect of GR-glucocorticoid complex itself and not due to the induction of a repressorlike molecule.

Gene transfer studies indicate DNA sequences responsible for direct negative regulation of transcription of the rat POMC gene lie within 706 nucleotides of the transcription start site (15). The mechanism apparently does not require tissue-specific factors since POMC fusion genes introduced into murine mammary epithelial cells (15) or murine fibroblasts (39) are negatively regulated by dexamethasone to roughly the same extent as the endogenous POMC gene in AtT20 corticotrophic tumor cells. The role of the glucocorticoid receptor as a positive *trans*-acting factor has been extensively described (84); however, the mechanisms involved in negative regulation of transcription by the glucocorticoid receptor are not known.

While both glucocorticoids and CRF have been shown to have a direct effect on POMC gene transcription, the corticotroph is never exposed to only one of these hormones in the absence of the other but is under the influence of a combination of both in the intact animal. POMC gene transcription rate in AL cultures simultaneously exposed to CRF and dexamethasone were found to be intermediate between control levels and those of CRF alone (30, 31). In addition to the effects of glucocorticoids on CRF-stimulated secretion (1, 80), short-term glucocorticoid pretreatment of AL cultures inhibits CRF-stimulated transcription of the POMC gene (25). The inhibitory effects of DEX pretreatment on CRF-stimulated transcription occur before inhibition of CRF-stimulated secretion in the same cultures. When CRF was given first to the cultures, subsequent glucocorticoid addition had no effect at a time period (60 minutes) when CRF maximally stimulated POMC gene transcription. However, glucocorticoids were fully inhibitory when added after only 10 minutes of CRF stimulation. The molecular and cellular mechanisms involved in these interactions are not currently understood. CRF-stimulated processes may regulate glucocorticoid receptor function in the corticotroph, glucocorticoids could interfere with CRF-stimulated signal transduction (for example, cAMP formation; see 11, 34), or alternatively the interaction could be at the genomic level between the glucocorticoid receptor and a *trans*-acting factor mediating the stimulatory effects of CRF on POMC gene transcription.

Regulation of POMC gene expression by glucocorticoids in the intermediate lobe (IL) of the pituitary is more complex. Under normal circumstances the IL melanotroph does not express detectable levels of glucocorticoid receptor (GR) (3, 65, 79), but GR may be induced (or 'depressed') in vivo through isolation of the IL from neural influences (5, 71), or after in vitro culture (4, 5). The in vitro appearance of GR may be prevented by dopamine or dopamine agonists, which suggests that the tonic influence of hypothalamic dopamine on the IL suppresses expression of the GR gene (4). Eberwine et al (25) demonstrated an inhibitory effect of glucocorticoids on basal POMC gene transcription as well as the inhibition of subsequent CRF-stimulated POMC gene expression in IL cells after 3 to 4 days in culture. Gagner & Drouin (31), however, failed to show an effect of dexamethasone on POMC gene transcription under similar circumstances, perhaps because of differences in culture conditions. If the effect of glucocorticoids observed in vitro is due to the appearance of GR in the melanotroph, then expression of GR may be sufficient to mediate the inhibitory transcriptional response and corticotroph-specific factors may not be required for inhibition of POMC gene expression. This conclusion is supported by gene transfer studies described above. Two recent in vivo studies, however, demonstrate stimulation of IL POMC mRNA levels by glucocorticoids in rats chronically treated with the dopamine antagonist haloperidol (7), or in rats with medial basal hypothalamic lesions that remove neural input to the IL (71). Thus while glucocorticoids can modulate POMC gene expression in the IL, the physiological mechanisms involved appear to be quite different from those involved in suppression of POMC gene expression in the AL.

Dopamine/GABA

Unlike the AL, the POMC-producing melanotrophs of the IL are poorly vascularized (83) but receive a rich innervation of neurotransmitter substances such as dopamine (13), GABA (61, 76), and serotonin (29, 46). The best studied of these neurotransmitters in relation to POMC gene expression in pituitary is dopamine. In the IL of the pituitary, POMC-derived peptide secretion is under inhibitory dopaminergic control (62, 74) and is mediated via D2 receptors that are negatively coupled to adenylate cyclase (57). Hollt and colleagues (38) were the first to demonstrate that chronic blockade of IL dopamine receptors by haloperidol led to a time-dependent increase in POMC mRNA levels in NIL that was reversible after discontinuation of the drug. Chen et al (17) and Pritchett & Roberts (64) further demonstrated that injection of the dopamine receptor agonist, bromocryptine, substantially decreased POMC mRNA in rat NIL but like haloperidol had no effect on AL POMC mRNA. The specificity of the dopamine effects on pituitary POMC mRNA is further reinforced by in vitro studies using short-term cultures of rat pituitary AL and NIL cells (48). In these studies, dopamine or bromocriptine-induced inhibition of NIL POMC mRNA was antagonized by haloperidol, while none of these dopaminergic agents had any effect on AL POMC mRNA. The alterations in POMC mRNA in NIL in response to dopaminergic manipulation are at least partly due to effects on gene transcription, since the dopamine receptor antagonist haloperidol has been reported to increase POMC transcription 3–4-fold in rat NIL for up to 16 hours after a single injection (64).

GABA appears to be colocalized with dopamine in the group of tubero-hypophyseal neurons that project to the IL (77), and like dopamine, it exerts an inhibitory influence on secretion of POMC peptides from the IL (75). The role of GABA in the regulation of pituitary POMC mRNA was investigated by inhibiting in vivo the GABA catabolic enzyme GABA-transaminase, thereby increasing the levels of GABA in hypothalamus and pituitary (49). Loeffler and colleagues (49) showed that this treatment caused a time-dependent 40–60% decrease in NIL POMC mRNA levels, while having no effect on AL. In vitro studies further showed that the effect was a direct action of GABA on melanotroph cells (49).

BRAIN

Pulse-labeling studies by Liotta et al (47) first demonstrated that the hypothalamus was a site of POMC biosynthesis. Northern blot and solution hybridization analysis further demonstrated the presence of POMC mRNA in hypothalamus, amygdala, and cerebral cortex and indicated that this transcript was expressed in brain at 1–2 orders of magnitude less than in AL (21). The use of in situ hybridization studies elegantly confirmed the presence of POMC mRNA in a disperse group of neurons located in the periarcuate region of the hypothalamus (32), and in combination with retrograde dye tracing techniques, it was shown that these POMC containing neurons had projections to diverse areas of the brain (82).

Some or all of these hypothalamic POMC-producing neurons have been implicated in maintenance of reproductive function, since the levels of POMC-derived peptides vary in response to the estrous cycle (9) and gonadal steroid levels (78). The use of a quantitative RNA dot-blot technique reveals that in ovariectomized rats, estrogen treatment decreases by 40% the hypothalamic levels of POMC mRNA (81), while in situ hybridization studies suggest that this decrease is due to a reduction in the level of POMC mRNA expression per cell (70). In addition, Roberts and colleagues (68) demonstrated that estrogen treatment led to rapid and sustained inhibition of POMC gene transcription in the hypothalamus, which presumably is at least partly responsible for the estrogen-induced decrease in POMC mRNA.

Since POMC gene expression in AL and NIL appears to be distinctly different in its sensitivity to glucocorticoid hormones, it is of interest to determine if POMC gene expression in brain is glucocorticoid responsive. Using sensitive solution hybridization techniques, Birnberg et al (12) demonstrated that 14 days following adrenalectomy the level of POMC mRNA expression in hypothalamus was unchanged. In contrast, Beaulieu and colleagues (10) showed that 7 days after adrenalectomy increases in POMC mRNA in hypothalamus occured and that this response was reversed by treatment with either dexamethasone or corticosterone.

GONADS

POMC mRNA was first described in rat testis by Pintar and colleagues (63) in 1984. In these studies, Northern blot analysis of adult rat testicular extracts revealed the presence of a POMC mRNA transcript that was at least 200 nucleotides shorter than the pituitary transcript and also demonstrated that this POMC-like mRNA was localized in the majority of Leydig cells. The existence of a shortened POMC-like mRNA in testis was confirmed by Chen et al (19) in several species, as well as in mouse Leydig cell lines. The immunocytochemical localization of N-acetylated, and C-terminally shortened endorphinlike molecules within the seminiferous tubules, suggested that testicular germ cells might also synthesize POMC (20). The use of in situ hybridization studies showed that POMC mRNA was not localized to all Leydig cells and that the highest density of labeling was associated with Leydig cells in close approximation to seminiferous tubules in certain stages of the cycle (35). Furthermore, POMC mRNA was shown to be present in spermatagonia and spermatocytes in tubules that were closely associated with POMC-expressing Leydig cells (35). Northern blot analysis of enriched preparations of testicular germ cells indicated that the POMC mRNA transcript expressed within the testicular tubules was also several hundred nucleotides shorter than in pituitary (36, 44). Northern blot analysis of ovarian RNA extracts revealed the presence of a POMC mRNA transcript that is similar in size to that expressed in testis (16). Although the presence of POMC-derived peptides has been localized predominantly to the luteal cells of the ovary (51, 52, 72), the precise localization of ovarian POMC mRNA has not been reported.

Several studies addressed the role of gonadotropins and gonadal steroids on the levels of POMC mRNA in ovary and testis. Pregnant mare serum gonadotropin (PMSG) priming of immature rats was shown to increase dramatically the ovarian levels of POMC mRNA (16, 55). Using PMSG-primed granulosa cells as a model, Melner and colleagues (55) demonstrated the potent stimulatory effects of luteinizing hormone and androgen on ovarian POMC mRNA and further showed that these effects could be obtained in vivo. Since the levels of ovarian POMC mRNA are under the influence of gonadotropins and gonadal steroids, changes in the reproductive status of the animal might be expected to lead to alterations in ovarian POMC gene expression. The level of ovarian POMC mRNA in pregnant rats is 2–4-fold higher than in cycling rats (16, 41) but remains fairly constant throughout the estrous cycle (41). Similarly, in testis, human chorionic gonadotropin stimulated the expression of POMC mRNA, while adrenalectomy had no effect (18).

As discussed above, the short POMC mRNA transcripts found in gonads contain no exon 1 or exon 2 sequences but rather initiate transcription at heterogeneous sites near the 5' end of exon 3. A major question raised is whether or not these transcripts can be efficiently translated, since no signal peptide would be present and none of the short transcripts could code for a complete POMC molecule (40, 45). The presence of low levels of pituitary-sized POMC mRNA has also been detected in gonads (45) and it has been suggested that this transcript is responsible for the translation of POMC-derived peptides. Since most regulatory studies to date used Northern blots, the current body of data suggests that the more prevalent shorter POMC transcripts are regulated in gonadal tissue, although changes in the normal length transcript may have gone undetected in these studies because of the latter's extremely low abundance. If, indeed, these hormonally regulated short transcripts are translated, it will be of interest to determine the exact nature of the translation products, since their sequences predict abnormal peptide sequence and the lack of a valid signal peptide raises questions about proper processing of the prohormone.

CONCLUSIONS

The current body of literature on the hormonal regulation of the POMC gene suggests that this gene is responsive to extremely complex, tissue-specific modes of regulation. The wide spectrum of potential biological activities of the peptides encoded for by the POMC gene reflect the diverse range of cell types that express POMC. In turn, these different cell types with unique tissue environments and receptor complements regulate expression of the POMC gene in a differential manner. The differential effects of dopamine, GABA, CRF, and glucocorticoids on AL versus NIL POMC gene expression further exemplify the tissue-or cell-specific control of this gene. Several laboratories are currently attempting to identify promoter sequences and transcription factors that are involved in mediating the effects of these hormonal agents on POMC gene expression (24, 54, 67). Precise characterization of the genomic sequences and transcription factors responsible for transcriptional regulation of the POMC gene in response to these various regulatory agents will provide further answers regarding the complex differential control of this gene in various tissues.

ACKNOWLEDGMENTS

This work was supported by National Institutes of Health grant DK27484 (JLR). D. J. A. was supported in part by a Fulbright post-doctoral fellowship.

Literature Cited

1. Abou-Samra, A.-B., Catt, K. J., Aguilera, G. 1986. Biphasic inhibition of adrenocorticotropin release by corticosterone in cultured anterior pituitary cells. *Endocrinology* 119:972–77
2. Affolter, H.-U., Reisine, T. 1985. Corticotropin releasing factor increases proopiomelanocortin messenger RNA in mouse anterior pituitary tumor cells. *J. Biol. Chem.* 260:15477–81
3. Antakly, T., Eisen, H. J. 1984. Immunocytochemical localization of glucocorticoid receptor in target cells. *Endocrinology* 115:1984–89
4. Antakly, T., Mercille, S., Cote, J. P. 1987. Tissue-specific dopaminergic regulation of the glucocorticoid receptor in the rat pituitary. *Endocrinology* 120:1558–62
5. Antakly, T., Sasaki, A., Liotta, A. S., Palkovits, M., Krieger, D. T. 1985. Induced expression of the glucocorticoid receptor in the rat intermediate pituitary lobe. *Science* 229:277–79
6. Antoni, F. A. 1986. Hypothalamic control of adrenocorticotropin secretion: advances since the discovery of 41-residue corticotropin-releasing factor. *Endocrine Rev.* 7:351–78
7. Autelitano, D. J., Clements, J. A., Nikolaidis, I., Canny, B. J., Funder, J. W. 1987. Concomitant dopaminergic and glucocorticoid control of pituitary proopiomelanocortin messenger ribonucleic acid and β-endorphin levels. *Endocrinology* 121:1689–96
8. Autelitano, D. J., Blum, M., Lopingco, M., Allen, R. G., Roberts, J. L. 1988. Differential regulation of anterior and intermediate pituitary lobe proopiomelanocortin gene expression by CRF occurs both at the transcriptional and posttranscriptional levels. Submitted to *Neuroendocrinology*
9. Barden, N., Merand, Y., Rouleau, D., Garon, M., Dupont, A. 1981. Changes in the beta endorphin content of discrete hypothalamic nuclei during the estrous cycle of the rat. *Brain Res.* 204:441–45
10. Beaulieu, S., Gagne, B., Barden, N. 1988. Glucocorticoid regulation of proopiomelanocortin messenger ribonucleic acid content of rat hypothalamus. *Mol. Endocrinol.* 2:727–31
11. Bilezikjian, L. M., Vale, W. 1983. Glucocorticoids inhibit CRF induced production of cAMP in cultured anterior pituitary cells. *Endocrinology* 113:657–62
12. Birnberg, N. C., Lissitzky, J.-C., Hinman, M., Herbert, E. 1983. Glucocorticoids regulate proopiomelanocortin gene expression in vivo at the levels of transcription and secretion. *Proc. Natl. Acad. Sci. USA* 80:6982–86
13. Bjorklund, A., Moore, R. Y., Nobin, A., Stenevi, U. 1973. The organization of tubero-hypophyseal and reticulo-infundibular catecholamine neuron systems in the rat brain. *Brain Res.* 51:171–91
14. Bruhn, T. O., Sutton, R. E., Rivier, C. L., Vale, W. W. 1984. Corticotropin-releasing factor regulates proopiomelanocortin ribonucleic acid levels in vivo. *Neuroendocrinology* 39:170–75
15. Charron, J., Drouin, J. 1986. Glucocorticoid inhibition of transcription from episomal proopiomelanocortin gene promoter. *Proc. Nat. Acad. Sci. USA* 83:8903–07
16. Chen, C.-L., Chang, C.-C., Krieger, D. T., Bardin, C. W. 1986. Expression and regulation of proopiomelanocortin-like gene in the ovary and placenta: comparison with the testis. *Endocrinology* 118:2382–89
17. Chen, C.-L., Dionne, F. T., Roberts, J. L. 1983. Regulation of the proopiomelanocortin mRNA levels in rat pituitary by dopaminergic compounds. *Proc. Natl. Acad. Sci. USA* 80:2211–2215
18. Chen, C.-L., Madigan, M. B. 1987. Regulation of testicular proopiomelanocortin gene expression. *Endocrinology* 121:590–596
19. Chen, C.-L., Mather, J. P., Morris, P. L., Bardin, C. W. 1984. Expression of proopiomelanocortin-like gene in the

testis and epididymis. *Proc. Natl. Acad. Sci. USA* 81:5672–75

20. Cheng, M. C., Clements, J. A., Smith, A. I., Lolait, S. J., Funder, J. W. 1985. N-acetyl endorphin in rat spermatagonia and primary spermatocytes. *J. Clin. Invest.* 75:832–35

21. Civelli, O., Birnberg, N., Herbert, E. 1982. Detection and quantitation of pro-opiomelanocortin mRNA in pituitary and brain tissues from different species. *J. Biol. Chem.* 257:6783–87

22. Dallman, M. F., Makara, G. B., Roberts, J. L., Levin, N., Blum, M. 1985. Corticotrope response to removal of releasing factors and corticosteroids in vivo. *Endocrinology* 117:2190–97

23. DeBold, C. R., Nicholson, W. E., Orth, D. N. 1988. Immunoreactive pro-opiomelanocortin (POMC) peptides and POMC-like messenger ribonucleic acid are present in many rat nonpituitary tissues. *Endocrinology* 66:2648–57

24. Drouin, J., Charron, J., Gagner, J.-P., Jeannotte, L., Nemer, M., et al. 1987. Pro-opiomelanocortin gene: a model for negative regulation of transcription by glucocorticoids. *J. Cell. Biochem.* 35: 293–304

25. Eberwine, J. H., Jonassen, J. A., Evinger, M. J. Q., Roberts, J. L. 1987. Complex transcriptional regulation by glucocorticoids and corticotropin-releasing hormone of proopiomelanocortin gene expression in rat pituitary cultures. *DNA* 6:483–92

26. Eberwine, J. H., Roberts, J. L. 1984. Glucocorticoid regulation of pro-opiomelanocortin gene transcription in the rat pituitary. *J. Biol. Chem.* 259: 2166–70

27. Eipper, B. A., Mains, R. E. 1980. Structure and biosynthesis of pro-adrenocorticotropin/endorphin and related peptides. *Endocrine Rev.* 1:1–27

28. Fremeau, R. T. Jr., Lundblad, J. R., Pritchett, D. B., Wilcox, J. N., Roberts, J. L. 1986. Regulation of pro-opiomelanocortin gene transcription in individual cell nuclei. *Science* 234:1265–69

29. Friedman, E., Krieger, D. T., Mezey, E., Leranth, C. S., Brownstein, M. J., et al. 1983. Serotonergic innervation of the rat pituitary intermediate lobe: decrease after stalk section. *Endocrinology* 112:1943–47

30. Gagner, J.-P., Drouin, J. 1985. Opposite regulation of pro-opiomelanocortin gene transcription by glucocorticoids and CRH. *Mol. Cell. Endocrinol.* 40:25–32

31. Gagner, J.-P., Drouin, J. 1987. Tissue-specific regulation of pituitary pro-opiomelanocortin gene transcription by corticotropin-releasing hormone, 3',5'-cyclic adenosine monophosphate, and glucocorticoids. *Mol. Enocrinology* 10: 677–82

32. Gee, C. E., Chen, C.-L., Roberts, J. L., Thompson, R., Watson, S. J. 1983. Identification of proopiomelanocortin neurons in rat hypothalamus by in situ cDNA-mRNA hybridization. *Nature* 306:374–76

33. Gee, C. E., Roberts, J. L. 1983. In situ hybridization histochemistry: a technique for study of gene expression in single cells. *DNA* 2:157–63

34. Giguere, V., Labrie, F., Cote, J., Coy, D. H., Sueiras-Diaz, J. et al. 1982. Stimulation of cyclic AMP accumulation and corticotropin release by synthetic ovine corticotropin-releasing factor in rat anterior pituitary cells; Site of glucocorticoid action. *Proc. Natl. Acad. Sci. USA.* 79:3466–69

35. Gizang-Ginsberg, E., Wolgemuth, D. J. 1985. Localization of mRNAs in mouse testes by in situ hybridization distribution of α-tubulin and developmental stage specificity of proopiomelanocortin transcripts. *Dev. Biol.* 111:293–305

36. Gizang-Ginsberg, E., Wolgemuth, D. J. 1987. Expression of the pro-opiomelanocortin gene is developmentally regulated and affected by germ cells in the male mouse reproductive system. *Proc. Natl. Acad Sci. USA* 84:1600–04

37. Hollt, V., Haarmann, I. 1984. Corticotropin-releasing factor differentially regulates proopiomelanocortin messenger ribonucleic acid levels in anterior as compared to intermediate pituitary lobes of rats. *Biochem. Biophys. Res. Commun.* 124:407–15

38. Hollt, V., Haarmann, I., Seizinger, B. R., Herz, A. 1982. Chronic haloperidol treatment increases the level of in vitro translatable messenger ribonucleic acid coding for the β-endorphin/adrenocorticotropin precursor proopiomelanocortin in the pars intermedia of the rat pituitary. *Endocrinology* 110:1885–91

39. Israel, A., Cohen, S. N. 1985. Hormonally mediated negative regulation of human proopiomelanocortin gene expression after transfection into mouse L cells. *Mol. Cell. Biol.* 5:2443–53

40. Jeannotte, L., Burbach, J. P. H., Drouin, J. 1987. Unusual proopiomelanocortin ribonucleic acids in extrapituitary tissues: intronless transcripts in testes and long poly (A) tails in hypothalamus. *Mol. Endocrinol.* 1:749–57

41. Jin, D. F., Muffly, K. E., Okulicz, W. C., Kilpatrick, D. L. 1988. Estrous cycle- and pregnancy-related differences in expression of the proenkephalin and proopiomelanocortin genes in the ovary and uterus. *Endocrinology* 122:1466–71

42. Jingami, H., Nakanishi, S., Imura, H., Numa, S. 1984. Tissue distribution of messenger RNAs coding for opioid peptide precursors and related RNA. *Eur. J. Biochem.* 142:441–47

43. Keller-Wood, M. E., Dallman, M. F. 1984. Corticosteroid inhibition of ACTH secretion. *Endocrine Rev.* 5:1–24

44. Kilpatrick, D. L., Borland, K., Jin, D. F. 1987. Differential expression of opioid peptide genes by testicular germ cells and somatic cells. *Proc. Natl. Acad. Sci. USA* 84:5695–99

45. Lacaze-Masmonteil, T., De Keyzer, Y., Luton, J.-P., Kahn, A., Bertagna, X. 1987. Characterization of proopiomelanocortin transcripts in human nonpituitary tissues. *Proc. Natl. Acad. Sci. USA* 84:7261–65

46. Leranth, C. S., Palkovits, M., Krieger, D. T. 1983. Serotonin immunoreactive nerve fibres and terminals in the rat pituitary gland: light- and electron-microscopic studies. *Neuroscience* 9:289–96

47. Liotta, A. S., Gildersleeve, D., Brownstein, M. J., Krieger, D. T. 1979. Biosynthesis in vitro of immunoreactive 31,000 dalton corticotropin/β-endorphin-like material by bovine hypothalamus. *Proc. Natl. Acad. Sci. USA* 76:1448–51

48. Loeffler, J.-P., Demeneix, B. A., Kley, N. A., Hollt, V. 1988. Dopamine inhibition of proopiomelanocortin gene expression in the intermediate lobe of the pituitary. *Neuroendocrinology* 47:95–101

49. Loeffler, J.-P., Demeneix, B. A., Pittius, C. W., Kley, N., Haegele, K. D. et al. 1986. GABA differentially regulates the gene expression of proopiomelanocortin in rat intermediate and anterior pituitary. *Peptides* 7:253–58

50. Loeffler, J.-P., Kley, N., Pittius, C. W., Hollt, V. 1985. Corticotropin-releasing factor and forskolin increase proopiomelanocortin messenger RNA levels in rat anterior and intermediate cells in vitro. *Neurosci. Lett.* 62:383–87

51. Lolait, S. J., Autelitano, D. J., Lim, A. T. W., Smith, A. I., Toh, B. H. et al. 1985. Ovarian immunoreactive β-endorphin and estrous cycle in the rat. *Endocrinology* 117:161–68

52. Lolait, S. J., Autelitano, D. J., Markwick, A. J., Toh, B. H., Funder, J. W. 1986. Co-expression of vasopressin with β-endorphin and dynorphin in individual cells from the ovaries of Brattleboro and Long-Evans rats: immunocytochemical studies. *Peptides* 7:267–76

53. Lolait, S. J., Clements, J. A., Markwick, A. J., Cheng, C., McNally, M. et al. 1986. Pro-opiomelanocortin messenger ribonucleic acid and posttranslational processing of beta endorphin in spleen macrophages. *J. Clin. Invest.* 77:1776–79

54. Lundblad, J. R., Roberts, J. L. 1988. Regulation of proopiomelanocortin gene expression in pituitary. *Endocrine Rev.* 9:135–58

55. Melner, M. H., Young, S. L., Czerwiec, F. S., Lyn, D., Puett, D. et al. 1986. The regulation of granulosa cell proopiomelanocortin messenger ribonucleic acid by androgens and gonadotropins. *Endocrinology* 119:2082–88

56. Menefee, J. K., DeBold, C. R. 1988. Phorbol ester stimulates ACTH release but does not increase POMC mRNA levels in rat anterior pituitary cells. *Proc. Ann. Meet. Endocrine Soc. 70th, New Orleans* (Abstr. No. 806)

57. Munemura, M., Cote, T. E. Tsuruta, K., Eskay, R. L., Kebabian, J. W. et al. 1980. The dopamine receptor in the intermediate lobe of the rat pituitary gland: pharmacologial characterization. *Endocrinology* 107:1676–83

58. Nakamura, N, Nakanishi, S., Sueoka, S., Imura, H., Numa, S. 1978. Effects of steroid hormones on the level of corticotropin messenger RNA activity in cultured mouse-pituitary-tumor cells. *Eur. J. Biochem.* 86:61–66

59. Nakanishi, S., Kita, T., Taii, S., Imura, H., Numa, S. 1977. Glucocorticoid effect on the level of corticotropin messenger RNA activity in rat pituitary. *Proc. Natl. Acad. Sci. USA* 74:3283–86

60. Oates, E., Herbert, E. 1984. 5' sequence of porcine and rat pro-opiomelanocortin mRNA. *J. Biol. Chem.* 259:7421–25

61. Oertel, W. H., Mugnaini, E., Tappaz, M. L., Weise, V. K., Dahl, A.-L. et al. 1982. Central GABAergic innervation of neurointermediate pituitary lobe: biochemical and immunocytochemical study in the rat. *Proc. Natl. Acad. Sci. USA* 79:675–79

62. Penny, R. J., Thody, A. J. 1978. An improved radioimmunoassay for α-melanocyte-stimulating hormone (α-MSH) in the rat: serum and pituitary α-MSH levels after drugs which modify catecholaminergic neurotransmission. *Neuroendocrinology* 25:193–203

63. Pintar, J. E., Schacter, B. S., Herman, A. B., Durgerian, S., Krieger, D. T. 1984. Characterization and localization of proopiomelanocortin messenger RNA in adult rat testis. *Science* 225:632–34

64. Pritchett, D. B., Roberts, J. L. 1987. Dopamine regulates expression of the glandular-type kallikrein gene at the transcriptional level in the pituitary. *Proc. Natl. Acad. Sci. USA* 84:5545–49

65. Rees, H., Stumpf, W., Sar, M., Petrusz, P. 1977. Autoradiographic studies of ³H-dexamethasone uptake by immunocytochemically characterized cells of the rat pituitary. *Cell Tissue Res.* 182:347–56

66. Roberts, J. L., Budarf, M. J., Baxter, J. D., Herbert, E. 1979. Selective reduction of proadrenocorticotropin/endorphin protein and messenger ribonucleic acid activity in mouse pituitary tumor cells by glucocorticoids. *Biochemistry* 18:4907–15

67. Roberts, J. L., Lundblad, J. R., Eberwine, J. H., Fremeau, R. T., Salton, S. R. J. 1987. Hormonal regulation of POMC gene expression in pituitary. *Ann. NY Acad. Sci.* 512:275–85

68. Roberts, J. L., Wilcox, J. N., Blum, M. 1985. The regulation of proopiomelanocortin gene expression by estrogen in the rat hypothalamus. In *Role of DNA Activity in the Brain*, ed. A. Giuditta, pp. 112–122. New York: Raven

69. Schachter, B. S., Johnson, L. K., Baxter, J. D., Roberts, J. L. 1982. Differential regulation by glucocorticoids of proopiomelanocortin mRNA levels in the anterior and intermediate lobes of the rat pituitary. *Endocrinology* 110:1442–44

70. Schachter, B. S., Pfaff, D. W., Shivers, B. D. 1986. Quantitative in situ hybridization for studying estrogen's effect on hypothalamic endorphin gene expression. *Proc. Ann. Meet. Soc. for Neurosci. 16th. Washington, D.C.* (Abstr. No. 4.4.)

71. Seger, M. A., van Eekelen, J. A. M., Kiss, J. Z., Burbach, J. P. H., de Kloet, E. R. 1988. Stimulation of proopiomelanocortin gene expression by glucocorticoids in the denervated rat intermediate pituitary gland. *Neuroendocrinology* 47:350–57

72. Shaha, C., Margioris, A., Liotta, A. S., Krieger, D. T., Bardin, C. W. 1984. Demonstration of immunoreactive β-endorphin- and α3-melanocyte-stimulating hormone-related peptides in the ovaries of neonatal, cyclic, and pregnant mice. *Endocrinology* 115:378–84

73. Smith, A. I., Funder, J. W. 1988. Proopiomelanocortin processing in the pituitary, central nervous system, and peripheral tissues. *Endocrine Rev.* 9:159–79

74. Tilders, F. J. H., Mulder, A. H. 1975. In vitro demonstration of melanocyte-stimulating hormone release inhibiting action of dopaminergic nerve fibres. *J. Endocrinol.* 64:63P–64P

75. Tomiko, S. A., Taraskevich, P. S., Douglas, W. W. 1983. GABA acts directly on cells of pituitary pars intermedia to alter hormone output. *Nature* 301:706–07

76. Vincent, S. R., Hokfelt, T., Wu, J.-Y. 1982. GABA neuron systems in hypothalamus and the pituitary gland: immunocytochemical demonstration using antibodies against glutamate decarboxylase. *Neuroendocrinology* 34:117–25

77. Vuillez, P., Perez, S. C., Stoeckel, M. E. 1987. Colocalization of GABA and tyrosine hydroxylase immunoreactivities in the axons innervating the neurointermediate lobe of the rat pituitary: an ultrastructural immunogold study. *Neurosci. Lett.* 79:53–58

78. Wardlaw, S. L., Thoron, L., Frantz, A. G. 1982. Effects of sex steroids on brain beta endorphin. *Brain Res.* 245:327–31

79. Warembourg, M. 1975. Radioautographic study of the rat brain and pituitary after injection of ³H dexamethasone. *Cell Tissue Res.* 161:183–91

80. Widmaier, E. P., Dallman, M. F. 1984. The effects of corticotropin-releasing factor on adrenocorticotropin secretion from perfused pituitaries in vitro: rapid inhibition by glucocorticoids. *Endocrinology* 115:2368–74

81. Wilcox, J. N., Roberts, L. R. 1985. Estrogen decreases rat hypothalamic proopiomelanocortin messenger ribonucleic acid levels. *Endocrinology* 117:2392–96

82. Wilcox, J. N., Roberts, J. L., Chronwall, B. M., Bishop, J. F., O'Donohue, T. O. 1986. Localization of proopiomelanocortin mRNA in functional subsets of neurons defined by their axonal projections. *J. Neurosci. Res.* 16:89–96

83. Wingstrand, K. G. 1966. Microscopic anatomy, nerve supply and blood supply of the pars intermedia. In *The Pituitary Gland*, ed. G. W. Harris, B. T. Donovan, 3:1–27. Berkeley/Los Angeles: Univ. Calif. Press

84. Yamamoto, K. R. 1985. Steroid receptor regulated transcription of specific genes and gene networks. *Annu. Rev. Genet.* 19:209–52

SPECIAL TOPIC: POLARITY OF EPITHELIAL CELLS: INTRACELLULAR SORTING AND INSERTION

Introduction, Douglas C. Eaton, *Section Editor*

Department of Physiology, Emory University Medical School, Atlanta, Georgia 30322

The development of plasma membranes may have marked one of the most significant events in the evolutionary development of life as we know it on earth. Associated with this compartmentalization of the cell was a specific new problem; the cell was now required to distinguish between those cellular components that were necessary to form the plasma membrane and those that were required to remain in the cytoplasm. In this context, sorting methods for both proteins and lipids evolved to target cellular components to the plasma membrane (and to various other cellular organelles).

Later, in an evolutionary sense, this problem of sorting organellar components became more complicated with the advent of polarized tissues. The traditional example of a polarized tissue is the various classes of epithelial tissues which line the body cavities of higher organisms, but other cell types often display significant polarization as well: neurons are polarized in a dendritic vs axonal fashion, while endothelial cells are polarized in a manner reminiscent of epithelial cells. Despite the general nature of the sorting problem typified by these other examples, the polarization of epithelial cells is so striking that a large fraction of the work that has examined polarity-determining signals has been directed towards understanding the sorting processes in various types of epithelial tissues. The polarity of epithelial tissues is remarkable since the membranes of cells facing the lumen of the body compartment defined by the tissue may differ from the opposite or basal membrane in structure, protein content and even lipid content. This special topic section reflects the interest in the development of polarity in epithelial tissues and the sorting mechanisms that lead to the polarization.

To begin the section, Dr. Joseph Handler provides an overview of the sorting process and presents a unique perspective on mechanisms for polarization with particular respect given to the polarization of membrane lipids. In his overview he also points out one of the features of epithelial tissues that make such tissues interesting subjects for studies of polarization. That is, many viruses are released from epithelial cells in a polarized fashion. This observation implies that, associated with the viral coat protein, there is a signal that directs the viral particle to a specific target membrane of the epithelial cell. While this is no different than the cell's endogenous proteins, the ability to easily identify viral proteins and to genetically manipulate the proteins' primary structure has lead to viral proteins being used as generalized models for the sorting of membrane proteins. In this section, both Drs. Enrique Rodriguez-Boulan and Pedro Salas and, in a separate chapter, Dr. Michael Roth describe such approaches in an attempt to identify the sorting signals for viral proteins.

Of course, while the viral coat proteins are probably sorted in a manner similar to cellular proteins, they are, nonetheless, foreign. Therefore, the issue of whether endogenous proteins are sorted in a manner similar to viral proteins is addressed in a chapter by Drs. Hubbard, Stieger, and Bartles.

I view the chapters described above to be an examination of the sorting process at a molecular level. Clearly, sorting at a molecular level is finally reflected in the macroscopic organization of the cell. To deal with polarization at a cellular level, Dr. Dennis Brown describes the polarized targeting and recycling of membrane vesicles in renal cells. Such vesicle insertion represents a primary mechanism for inserting or removing large numbers of protein molecules from specific cellular membranes. Finally, Drs. Cereijido, Contreras, and Gonzales-Mariscal describe the sequence of events that lead to the repolarization of cultured epithelial cells after the complete loss of polarity associated with re-plating the cells. A similar sequence of events must take place during normal embryonic development as epithelial cells polarize to perform their normal function of separating two body compartments.

Therefore, this section represents a broad spectrum of approaches to the problem of epithelial polarity and cellular sorting ranging from the molecular biology of model systems to the cellular physiology of the development of polarization.

Annu. Rev. Physiol. 1989. 51:729–40

OVERVIEW OF EPITHELIAL POLARITY

Joseph S. Handler[1]

Laboratory of Kidney and Electrolyte Metabolism, National Heart, Lung, and Blood Institute, National Institutes of Health, Bethesda, Maryland 20892

INTRODUCTION

Polarity is the structural and functional hallmark of epithelia. The apical plasma membrane, facing the organism's exterior (the lumen of the gut, renal tubule, glandular duct, or bile canaliculus) differs in many important respects from the basolateral plasma membrane that is apposed to adjacent epithelial cells (lateral plasma membrane), and to the basement membrane (basal plasma membrane) and interior of the organism. Vectorial transport, a principal function of epithelia, depends on the polar distribution of plasma membrane constituents. To the extent that the same transporter is present in the apical and basolateral plasma membrane of an epithelial cell, substrate would be pumped into or out of the cell, rather than vectorially, across the epithelium. Figure 1 is an often reproduced schematic that depicts the complex structure of intestinal epithelium. The apical plasma membrane, depicted with many microvilli, is the special organelle that gives the epithelium its specific functional characteristics. The basolateral plasma membrane, on the other hand, shares many characteristics with the plasma membranes of nonpolar cells. It is usually the location of the (Na + K)-ATPase, receptors for hormones and growth factors, transporters for ions and nutrients, and is the site of attachment to the basement membrane or other supporting material. Its special characteristics complement the special characteristics of the apical plasma membrane. For example, in epithelia that transport glucose from apical to basal surface, the apical membrane contains a sodium-coupled glucose transporter that moves glucose into the cell based on the driving force

---

[1]Current address: Division of Nephrology, Johns Hopkins University School of Medicine, Baltimore, Maryland 21205

0066-4278/89/0315-0729$02.00

for sodium entry, and the basolateral membrane contains a different transporter that facilitates glucose exit down its own concentration gradient. Tight junctions, another special organelle of epithelia, form a continuous belt between cells at the apical pole of epithelia, and act as barriers to leakage through the space between cells, thereby maintaining the efficiency of vectorial transport. An excellent review on epithelial surface polarity was published earlier in this series (42). In this overview, I discuss issues that are not the subject of other articles in this series on polarity of epithelia, as well as some issues that have not received much attention.

Much of our current understanding of epithelial polarity has come from studies of epithelia in culture. Madin-Darby canine kidney (MDCK) cells have been used for most studies, in part for historical reasons. They are a good choice for they are easy to grow, are well polarized, have tight junctions whose function is readily assayed, transport electrolytes vectorially, and respond to polypeptide hormones. Other kidney-derived epithelial cell lines [A6 (5, 44, 48), LLC-PK$_1$ (30, 31)], and primary cultures of thyroid (18, 19,

Figure 1 Schematic of an epithelium. The apical plasma membrane is rich in microvilli and faces the lumen. It is separated from the basolateral plasma membrane by the tight junction. The basolateral plasma membrane contains gap junctions, desmosomes, and hemidesmosomes. Microfilaments in the core of microvilli are connected to apical zone filaments. Tonofilaments (intermediate filaments), attached to desmosomes and hemidesmosomes form a structural framework. Reproduced from Reference 14 with permission.

28, 54) and mammary (41) cells behave similarly. Epithelial cell culture literally becomes tissue culture. Although seeded sparsely as single cells that may not be polarized, the culture is an organized epithelial tissue when grown to confluence. As in naturally occurring epithelia, cultured epithelial cells grow with their basal plasma membranes against the supporting surface, attached by many if not all of the attachment factors employed by naturally occurring epithelia. The apical surface faces the culture medium. To the extent that the tight junctions at the apical pole of the cell are effective seals, they limit access of medium to the basolateral surface, which in situ faces the nutrient extracellular fluid but in culture faces the petri dish. The demonstration that epithelial cells can be cultured on a porous support (4, 20, 21) that allows medium access to both surfaces of the epithelium was important. When epithelial cells are cultured on a porous surface, a culture technique that recognizes the functional consequences of epithelial polarity, they differentiate more than cells cultured on the customary solid plastic tissue culture dish (12, 41, 50). Although epithelia in situ are more difficult to study, effective methods have been developed and considerable information gathered about their polarity. One article in this series focuses on studies of liver cells in situ (A. Hubbard, this volume).

Epithelial polarity is usually considered in terms of the apical versus basolateral plasma membrane. It is important to recognize that the entire cell is polarized. The polarity of internal organelles contributes to epithelial function. For example, special vesicles that shuttle transporters into and out of the apical or basolateral plasma membrane are located adjacent to that plasma membrane (these vesicles are discussed extensively in D. Brown's article in this volume). Mitochondria are typically located toward the basal pole of the cell near ATP-consuming (Na + K)-ATPase. Cytoskeletal elements are polarized as well. At the basal surface of the cell, ankyrin and fodrin, cytoskeletal binding proteins, colocalize with (Na + K)-ATPase (27), and actin filaments co-localize with attachment sites (32). At the apical surface of the cell (Figure 1), the core of microvilli is composed of bundles of actin filaments that are linked within the apical cytoplasm to actin filaments that form the terminal web. Intermediate filaments form a framework that runs from the nuclear matrix to hemidesmosomes in the basal plasma membrane and to desmosomes in the lateral plasma membrane, structurally connecting adjacent epithelial cells (7) (Figure 1). Eventually we will have to understand the genesis and turnover of all organelles in the cell in order to understand epithelial polarity.

DEVELOPMENT OF POLARITY

Most epithelial cells in situ and in culture become polarized as they form during cell division. Cell division has a special polarization in epithelia. It has been studied most thoroughly in thyroid follicular epithelia in situ (54). The cleavage furrow forms perpendicular to the apical membrane, so that each daughter cell receives apical and basolateral plasma membrane, as well as all other organelles from the parent cell. As the cleavage furrow contracts, the shrinking intercellular bridge between daughter cells migrates toward the apical surface and a new tight junction forms just basal to the cleavage furrow. The new tight junction is continuous with tight junctions between daughter cells and neighboring cells. Those tight junctions are apparently not disturbed. As cell division is completed, the intercellular bridge is sloughed into the apical environment, which leaves the new tight junction in place. Thus, for most epithelial cells, in situ and in culture, the template for polarity has been present throughout their lifetime, an inheritance from epithelial ancestors.

Not all epithelial cells form from other epithelial cells. During embryogenesis, epithelial cells form from nonepithelial cells, and some epithelial cells divide with the cleavage furrow parallel to the apical surface to form an epithelial cell and a nonpolarized cell. Regulation of these processes is not understood (45).

Epithelial cells are programmed to become polarized, even when the maternal template is not available. This is evident in cultured epithelial cells. They are routinely subcultured by exposure to trypsin and a calcium chelator. After several minutes, the cells separate from each other and their attachment surface to form a suspension of single cells. If the cells are kept in suspension, apical and basolateral membrane markers migrate in a global fashion and polarity is lost. A similar loss of polarity takes place when naturally occurring epithelia are dissociated into single cells (8, 29, 55). When the single cells settle on the surface of a culture vessel, the plasma membrane in contact with the attachment surface appears to become the basal plasma membrane (34). The genesis of polarity in single cells is of particular interest for single cells do not have complete tight junctions. Tight junctions play an important role in epithelial polarity. Aspects of that role and the genesis of polarity are discussed later in this overview and more thoroughly in other articles in this series (Cereijido, Rodriguez-Boulan, this volume) and elsewhere (3, 10).

MAINTENANCE OF POLARITY

Maintenance of plasma membrane polarity can be considered in terms of several functions. Replacement of degraded membrane proteins and the reinsertion of endocytosed components are discussed in other articles in this volume (Hubbard, Rodriguez-Boulan, Brown, Rose). Less information is available about the prevention of movement of plasma membrane components to the opposite plasma membrane by diffusion.

Plasma membrane lipids as well as some membrane proteins diffuse freely in the plane of the membrane. A structure at the juncture of the apical and basolateral plasma membrane, probably the tight junction, serves as a barrier to diffusion. Although considerable evidence supports that role for the tight junction, it is not established, in part because the molecular structure of the tight junction is not known. It is appropriate to evaluate some of the arguments that point to the barrier role of the tight junction, for some of the arguments are imperfect. (*a*) Disruption of tight junctions, typically accomplished by chelation of calcium, results in loss of polarity of plasma membrane constituents (8, 29, 55). This may reflect the barrier role played by tight junctions. Alternatively, it may reflect an effect of chelation of calcium on the function of unidentified structures that maintain the polar distribution of membrane components as well as the integrity of the tight junction. (*b*) When calcium is restored to the culture, there is a temporal correlation between the reformation of tight junctions and repolarization of membrane proteins (1, 13, 37). Resorting of dispersed membrane proteins requires more than the imputed barrier function of the tight junction; it requires a sorting function (3). (*c*) There is a correlation between transepithelial electrical resistance, an estimate of tight junction function, and the degree of polarity of membrane proteins (13). The correlation could well be a manifestation of the coordinated differentiation of many cell functions as a cultured epithelium matures. Such a correlation has been found, for example, between transepithelial electrical resistance, the morphology of an epithelium, and the function of membrane proteins (15). (*d*) Finally, not all membrane proteins are free to diffuse in the membrane. Some proteins are linked to cytoskeletal elements, which are also polarized (6, 26). The role of the tight junction in maintaining the polarity of lipid distribution is discussed below.

Polarity in the distribution of plasma membrane proteins is apparently complete. Although transporters such as the $Na+/H+$ exchanger or the Cl^-/HCO_3^- exchanger are located in the apical plasma membrane of some epithelia and in the basolateral membrane of others, these are not necessarily the same proteins at both surfaces. No protein has been shown to reside in both the apical and basolateral plasma membrane of the same epithelial cell. The observation that enveloped viruses bud from infected epithelial cells in a polarized manner provided a powerful model for studying the sorting of apical versus basolateral membrane proteins (35). The polarity of virus budding depends on polarized distribution of the glycoproteins of the virus envelope (33). Since highly specific antibodies are available, and many of these glycoproteins have been cloned and sequenced, their behavior can be studied by gene transfection, which eliminates the side effects of virus infection. It also allows the application of in vitro mutagenesis to delineate the structural characteristics necessary for polar sorting (see articles in this volume by Rodriguez-Boulan and by Rose).

Epithelial polarity is also manifest in the lipid composition of apical and basolateral plasma membranes. The difference in the lipid composition of the two membranes varied among the epithelia examined, but this is difficult to evaluate since it depends on the degree of purification of the membrane fractions (2, 22). Since viruses obtain their envelopes as they bud through the plasma membrane of their host cell, the lipid composition of the envelope reflects the lipid composition of that plasma membrane. Analysis of the lipids of viruses that have budded from the apical or basolateral plasma membrane yielded clear information about the polar distribution of plasma membrane lipids (50). Viruses budding from the apical plasma membrane were enriched in phosphatidylethanolamine and phosphatidylserine; viruses emerging from the basolateral surface were enriched in phosphatidylcholine, sphingomyelin, and phosphatidylinositol. The differences were not virus specific, for when the epithelial cells were kept in suspension so that they did not polarize, the envelopes of both viruses had the same lipid composition.

How are lipids inserted in the plasma membrane of epithelial cells in a polar fashion? Lipids are synthesized in the endoplasmic reticulum. Their sorting to cell organelles has been examined by adding lipids with fluorescent markers to cultured cells and following their fate (17). Adapting the fluorescent lipid technique to epithelia grown on a porous support became possible with the development of confocal fluorescence microscopy (52). NBD-ceramide taken up by MDCK cells accumulated in the region of the Golgi complex at low temperatures, where it was converted to more complex lipids. When the temperature was raised to 37°C, fluorescence shifted from the Golgi region to the apical and basal plasma membranes where fluorescent lipids accumulated in the external leaflet of the membrane bilayer. The two major fluorescent lipids, C_6-NBD-glucosylceramide and C_6-NBD-sphingomyelin, were both more concentrated in the apical plasma membrane than in the basolateral plasma membrane, but not to the same degree, an indication of specificity in their sorting. The characteristics or signals that result in sorting of lipids and how sorting is accomplished remain unknown.

Fluorescence microscopy was also used to explore the mechanism by which the polar distribution of freely diffusing membrane lipids is maintained (5, 51, 52). Apparently, lipids in the inner leaflet of the plasma membrane diffuse freely past the region of the tight junction within the membrane. Lipids in the outer leaflet do not diffuse past the region of the tight junction. Glycolipids (44), the C_6-NBD-glucosylceramide and C_6-NBD-sphingomyelin studied by confocal fluorescence microscopy (52), and a variety of other fluorescent lipids, which characteristically are found in the outer leaflet of the membrane bilayer, all remain in the apical or basolateral plasma membrane in which they are initially incorporated (5, 51). Lipids in the inner leaflet, including those that flip-flop between the leaflets of the bilayer and thus gain access to the inner leaflet, distribute to both apical and basolateral plasma membranes (5, 51). The evidence indicates that there is a barrier to diffusion of lipids in the outer leaflet of the bilayer, whereas lipids in the inner leaflet diffuse freely. The barrier is in the region of the tight junction, and is perhaps part of the tight junction. Its structure is unknown.

EPITHELIAL PLASTICITY

Environment determines the polarity of epithelia. The importance of contact in determining the location of the basal surface of the epithelium is illustrated by the effect of an overlay of collagen on a cultured epithelium. Before the overlay, the basal surface is in contact with the culture surface, e.g. the culture dish, and the apical surface faces up toward the medium. Contact of collagen with the apical plasma membrane results in remodeling of the epithelium so that epithelial cysts form within the collagen. The basal surface of the cyst is in contact with the collagen, the apical surface faces the lumen. Remodeling results from cell migration and cell division (11).

The plasticity of epithelial structure is dramatically illustrated by the response of primary cultures of thyroid epithelial cells to changes in the composition of the culture medium. When cultured in a vessel treated to prevent cell attachment, they grow in suspension and form hollow spheres. In the usual culture medium with 5 or 10% serum, thyroid epithelia orient with their apical surface out, toward the culture medium (this is the orientation most epithelial cell lines adopt under these conditions). When seeded in medium containing thyrotropin or other agents that raise cell cAMP levels (19), or in medium with a low concentration (0.5%) of serum, epithelia form with their in situ orientation, apical surface in toward the follicle lumen. Raising the concentration of serum to 5% after normal polarity is established in medium with 0.5% serum results in complete reversal of polarity over a few days (28). Both morphological and functional markers undergo the reversal. Originally toward the lumen, the apical membrane with characteristic microvilli and tight junctions between adjacent cells, as well as the Golgi apparatus between the nucleus and the apical membrane, finally orient toward the surface facing the outside of the follicle. The smooth basolateral plasma membrane, originally toward the outside, finally forms the lumenal surface. During this remarkable transition cells pass through a stage in which microvilli and tight junctions are at both the lumenal and external surface of the same cell. Reversal of the polarity of the plasma membrane precedes reversal of the polarity of intracellular organelles.

Equally striking is the report of reversal of polarity of the early chick embryo epiblast epithelium in response to reversal of transepithelial electric potential (46). Normally, the transepithelial potential difference is 15–20 mV, basal surface positive, and apical to basal transport of tracer Na^+ is ten times tracer Na^+ flux from basal to apical surface. As in other epithelia, tight junctions are located at the apical surface, and the $(Na + K)$-ATPase, assayed by the polarity of $[^3H]$ouabain binding, is located at the basal surface. Reversal of polarity occurs in response to an imposed transepithelial electric potential equal to but opposite in direction to the potential the epithelium normally generates. After three hours of imposed reverse electric potential, tight junctions appear at what was originally the basal surface of the epithelium, and $[^3H]$ouabain binding to the original apical surface exceeds binding to the basal surface. Basal to apical tracer sodium flux exceeds apical to basal flux. Flux in both directions is inhibited by strophanthidin. Transepithelial resistance falls markedly in the period of imposed reversed potential difference, so the transition may occur in the absence of effective tight junctions. I am unaware of similar experiments in other epithelia.

The experimental reversal of polarity is noteworthy for there is evidence that intercalated cells in mammalian kidney undergo partial reversal of polarity under physiological conditions. Intercalated cells comprise about 25% of the cells in the cortical collecting duct of the rabbit. They belong to the general category of mitochondria-rich cells, an epithelial cell type that transports H^+ vectorially. They are rich in mitochondria and in carbonic anhydrase activity, and have characteristic rod-shaped particles in freeze-fracture electron micrographs of the plasma membrane that extrudes H^+. The rod-shaped particles are thought to represent an ATP-consuming H^+ pump. The H^+ pumps reside in the plasma membrane and in vesicles that lie under the plasma membrane. The vesicles serve as a reservoir of H^+ pumps that are inserted in the plasma membrane in response to stimuli that evoke increased H^+ pumping. There are two types of intercalated cells in the cortical collecting duct. One type, with rod-shaped particles in the apical plasma membrane, secretes H^+ into the lumen of the tubule. The other type, with rod-shaped particles in the basolateral plasma membrane, secretes HCO_3^- (or absorbs H^+ from lumen to blood). The HCO_3^--secreting cell in the rabbit binds peanut lectin at its lumenal surface (16, 39). The evidence for reversal consists of the finding that more than 90% of intercalated cells are of the HCO_3^--secreting type in rabbits on their usual alkaline diet. When rabbits are placed on an acid diet, which stimulates H^+ secretion into the urine, the number of H^+-secreting cells increases and the number of HCO_3^--secreting cells decreases so that there are equal numbers of the two cell types. There is no change in the total number of intercalated cells (40). Cell division is extremely rare and insufficient to explain the change, so the change is attributed to reversal of polarity of the H^+ pump. Preliminary findings (38; G. J. Schwartz, personal communication) indicate that a similar change occurs in response to in vitro acidosis. The findings and interpretation are provocative, albeit somewhat indirect. It should be noted that this reversal of polarity is selective for elements involved in H^+ and HCO_3^- movement. Tight junctions and the Na^+,K^+-ATPase remain in place. The turtle urinary bladder also contains both types of mitochondria-rich cell and secretes H^+ or HCO_3^-, depending on metabolic conditions (47). Since turtle bladders survive in vitro for over 24 hours, it may be easier to examine reversal in this organ. Histochemical or immunochemical evidence of cells in intermediate stages of reversal of polarity, similar to the documentation presented for thyroid cells (28), would be compelling.

In some epithelia, membrane proteins shuttle from one surface to the other, conveying bound ligands across the cell. This vesicle-mediated process, termed transcytosis, may convey very small amounts of fluid as well (9, 53). Secretions such as bile, saliva, and milk contain high levels of immunoglobulin IgA that have been transcytosed. In the intestine of suckling rats, IgG is transcytosed from lumen to blood. Secretory and absorptive transcytosis are mediated by different binding proteins. In both processes, the immunoglobulin binding protein is initially inserted into the membrane where it first binds the immunoglobulin (basolateral for IgA, apical for IgG) and then moves to the opposite membrane where the immunoglobulin is released, because of proteolytic cleavage of a segment of the binding protein (secretion of IgA), or because of reduced affinity secondary to a change in pH (absorption of IgG). The immunoglobulin binding proteins are endocytosed in vesicles that contain other membrane components that are separated during transcytosis (24). The signals involved in sorting the binding proteins during transcytosis are unknown. In vitro mutagenesis and transfection of the gene for the IgA receptor into MDCK cells have begun to clarify this issue (23).

CONCLUDING REMARKS

Many cell types are polarized. Endothelial cells are polarized like epithelial cells, have tight junctions, and attachment determines their basal surface (25). Neurons, myocytes, and even fertilized ova exhibit their own type of polarity that is essential for their function. In a trivial sense, all attached cells in culture are polarized in that they have basal attachment sites and related intracellular stress fibers. Epithelial polarity is the result of genetically programmed organelle formation and distribution that is finally shaped by the cell's environment. New techniques such as those that allow access to the interior of the cell for study of vesicular transport and organelle movement (36, 43) should sustain the rapid advance of knowledge in this field.

Literature Cited

1. Balcarova-Stander, J., Pfeiffer, S. E., Fuller, S. D., Simons, K. 1984. Development of cell surface polarity in the epithelial Madin-Darby canine kidney (MDCK) cell line. *EMBO J.* 3:2687–94
2. Brasitus, T. A., Schachter, D. 1980. Lipid dynamics and lipid protein interactions in rat enterocyte basolateral and microvillus membranes. *Biochemistry* 19:2763–69
3. Cereijido, M., Gonzalez-Mariscal, L., Avila, G., Contreras, R. G. 1988. Tight Junctions. *CRC Crit. Rev. Anat. Sci.* 1:171–92
4. Cereijido, M., Robbins, E. S., Donlan, W. J., Rotunno, C. A., Sabatini, D. D. 1978. Polarized monolayers formed by epithelial cells on a permeable and translucent support. *J. Cell Biol.* 77:853–80
5. Dragsten, P. R., Blumenthal, R., Handler, J. S. 1981. Membrane asymmetry in epithelia: is the tight junction a barrier to diffusion in the plasma membrane? *Nature* 294:718–22
6. Drenckhahn, D., Franz, H. 1986. Identification of actin-, alpha-actinin-, and vinculin-containing plaques at the lateral membrane of epithelial cells. *J. Cell Biol.* 102:1843–52
7. Fey, E. G., Wan, K. M., Penman, S. 1984. Epithelial cytoskeletal framework and nuclear matrix-intermediate filament scaffold: three-dimensional organization and protein composition. *J. Cell Biol.* 98:1973–84
8. Fujimoto, T., Ogawa, K. 1982. Energy-dependent transformation of mouse gall bladder epithelial cells in a Ca^{2+}-depleted medium. *J. Ultrastruct. Res.* 79:327–40
9. Goligorsky, M. S., Hruska, K. A. 1986. Transcytosis in cultured proximal tubular cells. *J. Membr. Biol.* 93:237–47
10. Gumbiner, B. 1987. Structure, biochemistry, and assembly of epithelial tight junctions. *Am. J. Physiol.* 253 *(Cell Physiol. 22):* C749–C758
11. Hall, H. G., Farson, D. A., Bissell, M. J. 1982. Lumen formation by epithelial cell lines in response to collagen overlay: A morphogenetic model in culture. *Proc. Natl. Acad. Sci. USA* 79:4672–76
12. Handler, J. S., Preston, A. S., Steele, R. E. 1984. Factors affecting the differentiation of epithelial transport and responsiveness to hormones. *Fed. Proc.* 43:2221–24
13. Herzlinger, D. A., Ojakian, G. K. 1984. Studies on the development and maintenance of epithelial cell surface polarity with monoclonal antibodies. *J. Cell Biol.* 98:1777–87
14. Hull, B. E., Staehelin, L. A. 1979. The terminal web. *J. Cell Biol.* 81:67–82
15. Lang, M. A., Muller, J., Preston, A. S., Handler, J. S. 1986. Complete response to vasopressin requires epithelial organization in A6 cells in culture. *Am. J. Physiol. 250 (Cell Physiol.):* C138–C145
16. LeHir, M., Kaissling, B., Koeppen, B. M., Wade, J. B. 1982. Binding of peanut lectin to specific epithelial cell types in kidney. *Am. J. Physiol.* 242:C117–C120
17. Lipsky, N. G., Pagano, R. E. 1983. Sphingolipid metabolism in cultured fibroblasts: microscopic and biochemical studies employing a fluorescent ceramide analogue. *Proc. Natl. Acad. Sci. USA* 80:2608–12
18. Mauchamp, J., Chambard, M., Gabrion, J., Verrier, B. 1983. Polarized multicellular structures designed for the "in vitro" study of thyroid cell function and polarization. *Methods Enzymol.* 98:477–86
19. Mauchamp, J., Verrier, B., Chambard, M., Charrier, B., Remy, L., Michel-Bechet, M. 1979. Polarity of three-dimensional structures derived from isolated long thyroid cells in primary culture. *Cell Tissue Res.* 204:417–30
20. Michalopoulos, G., Pitot, H. C. 1976. Primary culture of parenchymal liver cells on collagen membranes. *Exp. Cell Res.* 94:70–78
21. Misfeldt, D. S., Hamamoto, S. T., Pitelka, D. 1976. Transepithelial transport in culture. *Proc. Natl. Acad. Sci. USA* 73:1212–16
22. Molitoris, B. A., Simon, F. R. 1985. Renal cortical brush-border and basolateral membranes: cholesterol and phospholipid composition and relative turnover. *J. Membr. Biol.* 83:207–15
23. Mostov, K. E., Breitfeld, P., Harris, J. M. 1987. An anchor-minus form of the polymeric immunoglobulin receptor is secreted predominantly apically in Madin-Darby canine kidney cells. *J. Cell Biol.* 105:2031–36
24. Mostov, K. E., Simister, N. E. 1985. Transcytosis. *Cell* 43:389–90
25. Muller, W. A., Gimbrone, M. A. Jr. 1986. Plasmalemmal proteins of cultured vascular endothelial cells exhibit apical-basal polarity: analysis by surface-selective iodination. *J. Cell Biol.* 103:2389–2402

26. Nelson, W. J., Veshnock, P. J. 1987. Ankyrin binding to $(Na^+ + K^+)$ATPase and implications for the organization of membrane domains in polarized cells. *Nature* 328:533–36

27. Nelson, W. J., Veshnock, P. J. 1987. Modulation of fodrin (membrane skeleton) stability by cell-cell contact in Madin-Darby canine kidney epithelial cells. *J. Cell Biol.* 104:1527–37

28. Nitsch, L., Wollman, S. H. 1980. Ultrastructure of intermediate stages in polarity reversal of thyroid epithelium in follicles in suspension culture. *J. Cell Biol.* 86:875–80

29. Pisam, M., Ripoche, P. 1976. Redistribution of surface macromolecules in dissociated epithelial cells. *J. Cell Biol.* 71:907–20

30. Rabito, C. A., Karish, M. V. 1982. Polarized amino acid transport by an epithelial cell line of renal origin (LLC-PK1). The basolateral systems. *J. Biol. Chem.* 257:6802–8

31. Rabito, C. A., Karish, M. V. 1983. Polarized amino acid transport by an epithelial cell line of renal origin (LLC-PK1). The apical systems. *J. Biol. Chem.* 258:2543–47

32. Rapraeger, A., Jalkanen, M., Bernfield, M. 1986. Cell surface proteoglycan associates with the cytoskeleton at the basolateral cell surface of mouse mammary epithelial cells. *J. Cell Biol.* 103:2683–96

33. Rodriguez-Boulan, E. 1983. Membrane biogenesis, enveloped RNA viruses, and epithelial polarity. *Mod. Cell Biol.* 1:119–70

34. Rodriguez-Boulan, E., Paskiet, K. T., Sabatini, D. D. 1983. Assembly of enveloped viruses in MDCK cells: polarized budding from single attached cells and from clusters of cells in suspension. *J. Cell Biol.* 96:866–74

35. Rodriguez-Boulan, E., Sabatini, D. D. 1978. Asymmetric budding of viruses in epithelial monolayers: A model system for study of epithelial polarity. *Proc. Natl. Acad. Sci. USA* 75:5071–75

36. Sambuy, Y., Rodriguez-Boulan, E. 1988. Isolation and characterization of the apical surface of polarized Madin-Darby canine kidney epithelial cells. *Proc. Natl. Acad. Sci. USA* 85:1529–33

37. Sang, U. H., Saier, M. H. Jr., Ellisman, M. H. 1979. Tight junction formation is closely linked to the polar redistribution of intramembranous particles in aggregating MDCK epithelia. *Exp. Cell. Res.* 12:384–91

38. Satlin, L. M., Schwartz, G. J. 1988. In vitro metabolic acidosis (MA) stimulates

endocytic activity of cortical collecting duct (CCD) intercalated cells (IC). *Kidney Int.* 33:406 (Abstr.)

39. Schuster, V. L., Bonsib, S. M., Jennings, M. L. 1986. Two types of collecting duct mitochondria-rich (intercalated) cells: lectin and band 3 cytochemistry. *Am J. Physiol.* 251:C347–C355

40. Schwartz, G. J., Barasch, J., Al-Awqati, Q. 1985. Plasticity of functional epithelial polarity. *Nature* 318:368–71

41. Shannon, J. M., Pitelka, D. R. 1981. The influence of cell shape on the induction of functional differentiation in mouse mammary cells in vitro. *In Vitro* 17:1016–28

42. Simons, K., Fuller, S. D. 1985. Cell surface polarity in epithelia. *Annu. Rev. Cell Biol.* 1:243–88

43. Simons, K., Virta, H. 1987. Perforated MDCK cells support intracellular transport. *EMBO J.* 6:2241–47

44. Spiegel, S., Blumenthal, R., Fishman, P. H., Handler, J. S. 1985. Gangliosides do not move from apical to basolateral plasma membrane in cultured epithelial cells. *Biochim. Biophys. Acta* 821:310–18

45. Stern, C. D. 1984. A simple model for early morphogenesis. *J. Theor. Biol.* 107:229–42

46. Stern, C. D., MacKenzie, D. O. 1983. Sodium transport and the control of epiblast polarity in the early chick embryo. *J. Embryol. Exp. Morphol.* 77:73–98

47. Stetson, D. L., Steinmetz, P. R. 1985. Alpha and beta types of carbonic anhydrase-rich cells in turtle bladder. *Am J. Physiol. 249 (Renal Fluid Electrolyte Physiol. 18):* F553–F565

48. Turner, R. J., Thompson, J., Sariban-Sohraby, S., Handler, J. S. 1985. Monoclonal antibodies as probes of epithelial membrane polarization. *J. Cell Biol.* 101:2173–80

49. Valentich, J. D. 1982. Basal lamina assembly by the dog kidney epithelial cell line MDCK. *9th Cold Spring Harbor Conf. Cell Proliferation* pp. 567–79

50. van Meer, G., Simons, K. 1982. Viruses budding from either the apical or the basolateral membrane domain of MDCK cells have unique phospholipid compositions. *EMBO J.* 1:847–52

51. van Meer, G., Simons, K. 1986. The function of tight junctions in maintaining differences in lipid composition between the apical and the basolateral cell surface domains of MDCK cells. *EMBO J.* 5:1455–64

52. van Meer, G., Stelzer, E. J. K., Wijnaendts-van-Resandt, R. W., Simons,

K. 1987. Sorting of sphingolipids in epithelial (Madin-Darby canine kidney) cells. *J. Cell Biol.* 105:1623–35

53. von Bonsdorff, C. H., Fuller, S. D., Simons, K. 1985. Apical and basolateral endocytosis in Madin-Darby canine kidney (MDCK) cells grown on nitrocellulose filters. *EMBO J.* 4:2781–92

54. Zeligs, J. D., Wollman, S. H. 1979. Mitosis in thyroid follicular epithelial cells in vivo. *J. Ultrastruct. Res.* 66:288–303

55. Ziomek, C. A., Schulman, S., Edidin, M. 1980. Redistribution of membrane proteins in isolated mouse intestinal epithelial cells. *J. Cell Biol.* 86:849–57

Annu. Rev. Physiol. 1989. 51:741–54

EXTERNAL AND INTERNAL SIGNALS FOR EPITHELIAL CELL SURFACE POLARIZATION

Enrique Rodriguez-Boulan and Pedro J. I. Salas[1]

Department of Cell Biology and Anatomy, Cornell University Medical School, 1300 York Ave, New York, NY 10021

CELL POLARITY

Although every eukaryotic cell has some degree of polarity, in transporting epithelia, polarity is a property of the tissue as a whole. Each cell is kept in register with neighboring cells via three specific junctions; from apical to basal poles, they are the tight junction (zonula occludens), the belt desmosome (zonula adherens), and the desmosome (macula adherens) (67, 85). Tight junctions are characteristic of epithelial cells. They constitute a "gate" (that controls the paracellular permeability to ions and macromolecules) and a "fence" (that segregates apical and basolateral proteins and lipids) [(24), see Cereijido et al, in this volume].

How Polarized are Epithelial Cells?

Studies with a variety of apical-specific and basolateral-specific markers indicate that, with few exceptions (54, 76), proteins (enzymes, transporters, hormone receptors) are quite polarized, usually 10–100 times (67, 85). Little information is available, however, on the differences in total protein compositions of both domains in different epithelial cells. Using cell fractionation, Fujita et al (16) found large differences between the plasma membrane protein composition of apical and basolateral membranes of mouse intestinal cells. Labelling procedures are presently more useful than cell fractionation in defining the composition of the apical and the basolateral surface of cultured cells. Lactoperoxidase iodination (62), galactosylation of a ricin-resistant

[1]Current address: Instituto de Investigaciones Bioquimicas, Fundacion Campomar, CONICET, Av Patricias Argentinas 435, 1405 Buenos Aires, Argentina

741

Madin-Darby Canine Kidney (MDCK) mutant line (4), and a biotin labelling procedure (82) reveal dramatic differences between the integral and peripheral protein composition of apical and basolateral surfaces of confluent MDCK cells grown on filters.

Lipid compositions also appear different in the two membranes. Hansson et al (26) analyzed the lipid content of two viruses, influenza and vesicular stomatitis virus (VSV), that bud from the apical and the basolateral membrane domains, respectively. Because the lipid compositions of the viruses reflect the compositions of the original membranes, their results demonstrate increased amounts of phosphatidylcholine and decreased levels of phosphatidylethanolamine in the basolateral surface. Clearly, the most interesting observation is the concentration of glycolipids in the apical surface, particularly glucosylceramide and galactosylceramide; the former is more abundant in strain I and the latter in strain II MDCK cells (26). These authors estimated that, if all surface glycolipids are present in the exoplasmic leaflet of the cell membrane, these glycolipids must occupy most of this leaflet in the apical plasma membrane. Recent evidence indicates that the polarized glycolipid distribution results from both vectorial delivery to the apical surface (90) and the tight junctional fence, which blocks diffusion of lipids in the external but not internal leaflet of the plasmalemma (13, 89).

Another striking difference between apical and basolateral membranes appears to be the localization of glycoproteins linked to the plasma membrane via a phosphatidylinositol glycosan (GPI) moiety. This novel class of glycoproteins [see Low & Saltiel (34) for review] includes several well-established apical proteins, such as trehalase, alkaline phosphatase, and 5' nucleotidase. In MDCK cells, five major proteins of this class are all apical (33). This result suggests the exciting possibility that a covalently linked glycolipid may play the role of an apical sorting signal in epithelial cells.

MAINTENANCE OF EPITHELIAL POLARITY AT STEADY STATE

The large differences in composition between epithelial surface domains are maintained by a combination of intracellular sorting, anchoring to a domain-specific submembrane cytoskeleton, and recycling of surface components. Much of our present knowledge of the mechanisms that sort apical and basolateral plasma membrane proteins along their intracellular pathway comes from data obtained in MDCK cells infected with enveloped RNA viruses (67, 71). The membrane proteins of these viruses, which are model plasma membrane proteins, are polarized in epithelial cells. Influenza hemagglutinin (HA) is targeted to the apical surface of MDCK cells, while VSV G glycoprotein is expressed on the basolateral surface [(70), for review see Rodriguez-Boulan (67)].

Intracellular Sorting of Viral Envelope Glycoproteins: How General is this Mechanism?

Apically targeted HA and basolaterally targeted G protein are both synthesized in the rough endoplasmic reticulum and share a common intracellular pathway until the transmost cisterna of the Golgi apparatus (17, 63, 79, 80), from where they are transported to the surface in small (~200 nm), smooth vesicles (64, 69). Transport from the Golgi apparatus to the respective surface appears to be vectorial for both HA and G, as shown by experiments in which anti-HA, anti-G antibodies or proteases were added to the opposite surface and failed to affect transport (40, 44, 57), by immunofluorescence (80), and by immunoelectron microscopy (64, 69). When the cells are incubated at 20°C, the transport of both HA and G is blocked at the level of a distal compartment of the Golgi apparatus (39, 57), the trans Golgi network (TGN), kinetically located only 5 min away from the cell surface. The TGN is considered the sorting site (23).

Using a photocrosslinkable form of ouabain as a probe, Caplan et al (7) recently showed that $Na^+K^+ATPase$, a typical basolateral glycoprotein, is delivered vectorially to the basolateral membrane of MDCK cells. Conversely, a pulse-chase, cell-fractionation approach provided evidence that sucrase isomaltase and other apical proteins of intestinal epithelium, as well as hepatocyte apical markers, may reach the apical surface via the basolateral membrane [(2, 27, 36); see Hubbard et al, this volume]. Whether these divergent results stem from the different experimental approaches or represent actual differences in the sorting pathways of intestinal, liver, and kidney cells is unknown. Studies in which the same methodology is used for the same markers in different epithelial cells are necessary to elucidate this crucial point.

Recycling

The magnitude of the contribution of recycling of surface components to epithelial surface polarity is not yet clear. Research shows that VSV G protein incorporated into the apical membrane of MDCK cells via virus fusion is partially transcytosed to the basal membrane (38, 56). Conversely, no transport of $Na^+K^+ATPase$ from the apical to the basal membrane was detected under conditions that caused large amounts of $Na^+K^+ATPase$ to be trapped in the apical surface (11). The apical pumps were removed with a half-time of 80 min and were presumably degraded in the lysosomes, since they never reappeared in the cell surface. ATPase inserted in the basolateral surface originated in intracellular pools.

Default Secretory and Membrane Transport Pathways in Epithelial Cells

Recent work highlights the important role played by oligomerization in the intracellular migration of plasma membrane proteins. VSV G protein and HA become trimers soon after synthesis in the endoplasmic reticulum (ER), and this oligomerization is apparently essential for their transport (12, 18, 32). Conversely, some proteins destined to remain in the ER lumen share a tetrapeptide, Lys-Asp-Glu-Leu; when this tetrapeptide is removed, they are secreted (48). Similarly, removal of cytoplasmic or hydrophobic sequences from rotaviral, adenoviral, or coronaviral glycoproteins, which are normal residents of the ER or Golgi apparatus, results in their progression to the plasma membrane or in their secretion (35, 55, 59). Thus, the hypothesis is that transport to the plasma membrane is a default pathway followed by proteins that have no sorting or retention signals for other compartments [see Pfeffer & Rothman (58) for review].

The problem of the default pathway in epithelial cells has been reviewed recently by Matlin (37). For secretory proteins, the concept is quite clear: the default pathway is the pathway followed by the bulk fluid volume. In MDCK cells, this default pathway is approximately equal for exocytosis toward the apical and the basal surface (45). Many endogenous and transfected secretory proteins are secreted in equal amounts toward the apical and basal medium in MDCK cells. The exceptions are an apical 80-kD marker, a basolaterally targeted laminin, and proteoglycans (8, 21, 88). For these exceptions, an intracellular receptor, presumably in the Golgi apparatus, probably recognizes specific sorting features of these proteins that mediate their incorporation into apically or basolaterally targeted vesicles.

For epithelial membranes, the default pathway is the path followed by the bulk of the membrane lipid flow during transport to the cell surface. There is no accurate estimate of this parameter. If, as in secretion, the default membrane pathway distributes proteins equally toward both membranes, sorting signals must be present in both apical and basolateral proteins. The striking differences between apical and basolateral integral membrane protein compositions (discussed above) indicate the existence of stringent sorting mechanisms. Because practically no protein is found at similar levels in both surface domains (82), the default pathway is unlikely to distribute proteins equally to both surfaces. In fact, current evidence indicates that the bulk lipid flow to apical and basal membranes is qualitatively different, i.e. glycolipids are transported preferentially to the apical surface (90). Thus, sorting of apical and basal proteins might be based on their differential affinities for the apically and basolaterally targeted bulk lipid flows.

Sorting Signals for Apical and Basolateral Targeting

Removal of N-linked carbohydrates by treatment of infected cells with tunicamycin (22) or their modification by lectin-resistance mutations (43) does not impair the correct sorting of influenza HA and VSV G proteins. Thus, the sorting information must be contained in the protein part of the molecule. To explore the nature of the sorting information, chimeras and truncated forms of apical and basolateral viral glycoproteins were expressed via appropriate expression vectors in MDCK cells and in a polarized monkey kidney cell line. In spite of some contradictory results, most of the data currently support the idea that sufficient sorting information lies in the ectoplasmic (intraluminal) domain of the viral glycoproteins. Deletion of the cytoplasmic domain of Semliki forest virus E2 glycoprotein does not prevent its basolateral localization (73). Likewise, deletion of the cytoplasmic domain of neuraminidase does not prevent its apical localization (31). Deletion of transmembrane and cytoplasmic domains resulted in polarized apical secretion of HA in one study (75) and in nonpolarized secretion of truncated viral glycoproteins in two other studies (19, 86). Chimeric proteins consisting of the ectoplasmic domain of influenza HA and the transmembrane and cytoplasmic domains of VSV G protein (HAG) are targeted to the apical membrane (41, 75). Similarly, a chimeric protein containing the ectoplasmic domain of VSV G and cytoplasmic and transmembrane domains of influenza HA (GHA) is transported to the basal surface (42). A different result was reported for a similar type of chimera (except that only the cytoplasmic segment was replaced) by Puddington et al (60); in this case, the GHA protein lost its polarized expression.

Recently, the poly-Ig receptor has been cloned, sequenced, and expressed via a retroviral vector in MDCK cells, where it is targeted to the basolateral surface and transcytosed to the apical membrane as in other epithelial cells (46). Removal of the cytoplasmic domain of the protein resulted in its direct targeting to the apical surface (47). When both the transmembrane and cytoplasmic domains were deleted, the resultant secretory protein was secreted toward the apical medium (45). These results suggest that the cytoplasmic domain of the poly-Ig receptor contains the basolateral sorting information, while the apical sorting information is contained in the ectoplasmic domain.

Although the fact that some proteins may contain more than one sorting domain cannot be ignored, some of the contradictory results from different investigators are likely due to different degrees of alteration of the tertiary and quaternary structures in the chimeric or truncated proteins. More experiments are needed using proteins with easily assayable functions (e.g. enzymes or receptors) to examine the possible alterations of the tertiary or quaternary structure caused by the mutations introduced.

An alternative approach to the use of chimeric or mutant proteins is to study proteins that naturally lack cytoplasmic domains. As mentioned above, results of experiments in which GPI-anchored plasma membrane proteins were localized in MDCK cells suggest an apical sorting role for the GPI moiety (33). We are now testing this possibility using a stringent molecular biology approach. If addition of the GPI moiety to proteins that are normally secreted without polarity (or to the basolateral surface) turns them into apical-surface proteins, the sorting role of the GPI anchor will be confirmed.

Finally, a third approach is the study of "natural polarity mutants." Na^+K^+ ATPase, normally a basolateral marker, has an apical localization in choroid plexus and retinal pigmentary epithelium. H^+-ATPase has opposite localizations in different cells of the kidney collecting tubule (6, 83). Study of these interesting cases may yield useful information on the nature of the apical and basolateral sorting signals and on the mechanisms that control the establishment and maintenance of surface polarity in epithelia.

Role of the Cytoskeleton

The role of the cytoskeleton in the vectorial delivery of plasma membrane proteins in epithelial cells is controversial. While two groups reported that cytoskeletal-disrupting drugs did not affect the basolateral targeting of VSV G protein (65, 77), opposite results were reported for influenza HA. Salas et al (77) found no effect, whereas Rindler et al (65) reported increased missorting of HA to the basolateral surface. The different results may be related to the difficulty in depolymerizing the entire microtubular network, to secondary effects of the drugs that take longer to get established, and/or to problems in the quantitation of HA polarity. The polarity ratio for HA is considerably lower than for budding virions (1 : 10, as opposed to 1 : 500 for the virus). The most clear result by Rindler et al, observed after considerably longer colchicine incubation times than needed to depolymerize the microtubular network, was the decreased polarity of influenza virus budding; the ratio was reduced to ~1 : 10, which is close to the polarity ratio of HA (P. J. I. Salas, unpublished results). The polarity of HA was reduced only by 10–20% under the same conditions (77). Thus, the polarity of influenza virus budding may depend on additional factors besides the asymmetric surface distribution of HA, such as perhaps the vectorial delivery of nucleocapsids or M protein, which might involve the microtubular network. The possibility should be considered that microtubules contribute to the stringency of apical sorting by keeping the Golgi apparatus in its central apical position in the cell (72). In the presence of microtubule inhibitors, the Golgi apparatus becomes peripheral, which may explain an increase in the rate of missorting of apical proteins, normally quite high (10–15%) for influenza HA. The definitive solution of this problem requires alternative approaches to microtubule inhibitors, such as video-enhanced microscopy and in vitro reconstitution of vesicular transport to the apical surface.

Restrictions to Lateral Mobility by the Submembrane Cytoskeleton

Once a plasma membrane protein reaches its target surface domain, what keeps it there? There are three possible (nonexcluding) factors: (a) the tight junctional fence, (b) the lack of signals for clustering into coated pits and endocytosis, and (c) a retention signal, e.g. for interaction with the submembrane cytoskeleton or with another protein linked to the cytoskeleton.

As mentioned, tight junctions constitute a fence for integral membrane proteins and for lipids in the exoplasmic leaflet of the membrane bilayer. Certain proteins, e.g. influenza HA (74), are not endocytosed or recycled. Replacement of G cytoplasmic sequences for corresponding HA sequences promotes recycling of HA, which suggests but does not prove that the information for recycling is in the cytoplasmic portion of G (74). The most clear evidence for restriction of membrane protein diffusion by interaction with the submembrane cytoskeleton has been obtained in the erythrocyte for the complex formed by band 3, ankyrin, and spectrin (5, 52, 84, 87). Interestingly, all of these molecules were recently reported in association with the basolateral membrane of kidney cells (14). Nelson and Veshnock (49–51) reported the formation of an insoluble basolateral fodrin (nonerythroid form of spectrin) network in MDCK cells and its association with Na^+K^+ ATPase. Salas et al (79) showed that, under conditions in which the cortical cytoskeleton of MDCK cells is well preserved, incompletely polarized apical markers are preferentially extracted by Triton X-100 from the basolateral surface and vice versa for basolateral markers. Furthermore, under conditions in which the basolateral fodrin cytoskeleton is not assembled (e.g. lack of cell-cell contacts), basolateral proteins are completely extracted by Triton X-100. These results suggest that retention signals in plasma membrane proteins, like the ones described above for ER proteins, play an important role in the maintenance of epithelial surface polarity.

ESTABLISHMENT OF SURFACE POLARITY BY EPITHELIAL CELLS

Although the polarization of epithelial cells is guided by their own genetic program, the expression of this polarization program clearly depends on the presence of specific external clues. This dependence is best seen in epithelial cells in culture that, when dissociated from the monolayer by protease digestion and chelating agents, become rounded and largely randomize their surface components (68). After plating on an adequate substrate, the cells spread, make contact with other cells, and with time, reestablish a confluent monolayer. This process of acquisition of polarity depends largely on specific cell-cell and cell-substrate interactions that define the lateral and the basal epithelial surfaces, respectively. The apical surface is defined by default as the surface that interacts neither with cells or substrate.

Cell-Substrate Interactions

To study the role of the substrate, independently of cell-cell contacts, in the development of polarity, dissociated cells can be replated either very sparsely or in the presence of micromolar levels of calcium, which blocks the development of cell-cell contacts but does not detach the cells from the substrate (20, 91). Sparse MDCK cells or monolayers kept in micromolar calcium exhibit incomplete polarity. The budding of enveloped viruses is still considerably polarized (68). An apical marker (184 kD) is excluded from the attached surface, but several basolateral antigens, including $Na^+K^+ATPase$, are not polarized (1, 11, 28, 91). Polarization of the basolateral markers fully depends on the establishment of cell-cell contacts. These results suggest that cell-substrate interactions are sufficient to induce apical but not basolateral polarization. The inductive role of the extracellular matrix (ECM) in epithelial polarity has also been highlighted by the dramatic polarity reversal of cells from isolated thyroid follicles upon exposure of their apical surfaces to collagen (9, 10, 53).

The ECM receptors involved in induction of epithelial polarity are still unknown. Salas et al (81) recently reported that the initial attachment of MDCK cells to the substrate occurs via a relatively small population of type I collagen receptors. Attachment to collagen triggers the secretion of laminin; therefore, whether collagen or laminin receptors are critical for the development of polarity in this system is unclear. In a related observation, Ingber et al (30) showed that pancreatic tumor epithelial cells unable to synthesize their own basement membrane components polarize their cytoplasmic organelles upon plating only on laminin but not on several other ECM components. Perhaps basal recruitment of ECM receptors during cell attachment triggers epithelial cell polarization via organization of a basal membrane cytoskeleton that excludes the apical surface proteins.

Role of Cell-Cell Contacts

Epithelial and neural cells feature strong intercellular adhesion mechanisms mediated by specific cell adhesion molecules (CAMs) and intercellular junctions. CAMs appear to play critical roles during embryogenesis by regulating tissue organization and cell migration [for review see Edelman (15)]. Epithelial CAMs are L-CAM and the related molecule uvomorulin; other CAMs will probably be identified in the future. Cloning and sequencing of CAM cDNAs have shown that most are transmembrane glycoproteins (15, 66). Interestingly, L-CAM and uvomorulin have extensive sequence homology and display putative calcium-binding domains in each of three internally repeated ectoplasmic regions (66).

The role of CAMs in the establishment of epithelial polarity is suggested by several lines of evidence. In kidney epithelium, uvomorulin becomes detectable 12 h after completion of induction in the tubules but is absent from the glomerular epithelium, which implies the existence of additional, unidentified CAMs that play roles in early epithelial organization (94). Polyclonal and monoclonal antibodies against uvomorulin dissociate early confluent or sub-confluent MDCK monolayers; they also block the recovery of electrical resistance upon calcium addition to monolayers developed in micromolar calcium (3, 25, 29). Vega-Salas et al (91) recently showed that cell-cell interactions are required for polarization of a basolateral 63-kD MDCK marker but not for polarization of an apical 184-kD protein. Distribution of the 184-kD protein between intracellular and surface pools, however, was controlled by cell-cell contacts. In subconfluent cells and in monolayers prevented from forming contacts by incubation in micromolar calcium levels, more than 60% of the 184-kD protein was stored in large microvilli-rich intracellular vacuoles (vacuolar apical compartment, or VAC) (92). VACs were exocytosed toward regions of cell-cell contact upon addition of Ca^{2+} (93). Interestingly, VACs express other apical markers, such as influenza HA in infected cells, but exclude basolateral markers. Similar structures have been morphologically described in tumors of epithelial lineage (61); they may play an important role in the development of the apical surface during epithelial differentiation.

Recent work by Nelson & Veshnock (49–51) provides a possible explanation for the role of cell-cell interactions on the polarization of basolateral proteins. Establishment of cell-cell contacts results in the development of an insoluble fodrin/ankyrin network under the basolateral surface. ATPase formed a very high molecular weight complex with this network (51). Presumably, uvomorulin is an important stabilizer of this complex, since conditions that result in its removal from the cell surface (such as proteolysis or calcium chelation) also cause disruption of the complex (50).

CONCLUSIONS

The introduction of well-characterized epithelial cell lines and the use of exogenous polarized epithelial markers (viral glycoproteins, transfected receptors) have considerably increased our understanding of the mechanisms that control epithelial cell polarization. Current views indicate that this control results from the expression of a particular epithelial differentiation program in response to external signals from ECM components and other cells. Important elements in this program are cellular receptors for ECM molecules and cell adhesion molecules. These signals induce the cellular asymmetry via the assembly of domain-specific submembrane cytoskeletons and specific intercellular junctions. Once the monolayer is formed and the plasma membrane domains are segregated, the degree of polarization of surface components is increased and regulated by vectorial exocytosis of newly synthesized proteins and lipids, removal and degradation of incorrectly localized proteins, and perhaps, transcytosis of some surface components. The relative contribution of each of these mechanisms will be understood only after extensive experimentation. Domain-specific linkage to the cytoskeleton and the tight junctional fence provide mechanisms to restrict plasma membrane proteins to the correct surface domain. The molecular biological approach to understanding the nature of the sorting signals responsible for apical and basolateral targeting has not provided clearcut answers yet. It is not yet known whether a modification in the surface localization of a protein is a direct consequence of the removal of targeting information or an indirect effect of the mutation on the tertiary or quaternary structure of the protein that results in the destruction of the signal. Within these limitations, several lines of evidence indicate that the sorting information is localized in the ectoplasmic domain of the proteins. No explanation currently describes how such information would be read and used by the cell to target apical or basolateral molecules to their correct surface domain. A useful model on apical/basolateral targeting in epithelial cells would allow for a unified explanation of both protein and lipid sorting. Exciting developments should come soon regarding the nature of the basic mechanisms of epithelial cell polarization and the role of epithelial polarity in cell and developmental biology.

Acknowledgments

This work was supported by grants from the National Institutes of Health and the American Heart Association, New York branch. E. R.-B. is a recipient of an Established Investigator Award from the American Heart Association.

Literature Cited

1. Balcarova-Stander, J., Pfeiffer, S. E., Fuller, S. D., Simons, K. 1984. Development of cell surface polarity in the epithelial Madin Darby canine kidney (MDCK) cell line. EMBO J. 3:2687–94
2. Bartles, J. R., Feracci, H. M., Stieger, B., Hubbard, A. L. 1987. Biogenesis of the rat hepatocyte plasma membrane in vivo: comparison of the pathways taken by apical and basolateral proteins using subcellular fractionation. J. Cell Biol. 105:1241–52
3. Behrens, J., Birchmeier, W., Goodman, S. L., Imhof, B. A. 1985. Dissociation of MDCK epithelial cells by the monoclonal antibody anti-Arc-1: mechanistic aspects and identification of the antigen as a component related to uvomorulin. J. Cell Biol. 101:1307–15
4. Brandli, A. W., Hansson, G. C., Rodriguez-Boulan, E., Simons, K. 1988. A polarized epithelial cell mutant deficient in translocation of UDP-galactose into the Golgi complex. J. Biol. Chem. In press

5. Branton, D., Cohen, C., Tyler, J. 1981. Interaction of cytoskeletal proteins on the human erythrocyte membrane. Cell 24:24–32
6. Brown, D., Hirsch, S., Gluck, S. 1988. An H^+-ATPase in opposite plasma membrane domains in kidney epithelial cell subpopulations. Nature 331:622–24
7. Caplan, M. J., Anderson, H. C., Palade, G. E., Jamieson, J. D. 1986. Intracellular sorting and polarized cell surface delivery of (Na^+, K^+) ATPase, an endogenous component of MDCK cell basolateral plasma membranes Cell 46:623–31
8. Caplan, M. J., Stow, J. L., Newman, A. P., Madri, J., Anderson, H. C., et al. 1987. Dependence on pH of polarized sorting of secreted proteins. Nature 329:632–35
9. Chambard, M. J., Gabrion, J., Mauchamp, J. 1981. Influence of collagen gel on the orientation of epithelial cell polarity: follicle formation from iso-

lated thyroid cells and from preformed monolayers. *J. Cell. Biol.* 91:157–67

10. Chambard, M., Verrier, B., Gabrion, J., Mauchamp, J., 1984. Polarity reversal of inside-out thyroid follicles cultured within collagen gel: reexpression of specific functions. *Biol. Cell.* 51: 315–25

11. Contreras, R. G., Avila, G., Gutierrez, C., Bolivar, J. J., Gonzalez-Mariscal, L., Rodriguez-Boulan, E., Cereijido, M. 1989. Repolarization of Na^+K^+ ATPase during reformation of Madin Darby Canine Kidney (MDCK) monolayers. *Am. J. Physiol.*

12. Copeland, C. S., Doms, R. W., Bolzau, E. M., Webster, R. G., Helenius, A. 1986. Assembly of influenza hemagglutinin trimers and its role in intracellular transport. *J. Cell Biol.* 103:1179–81

13. Dragsten, P. R., Handler, J. S., Blumenthal, R. 1982. Fluorescent membrane probes and the mechanism of maintenance of cellular asymmetry in epithelia. *Fed. Proc.* 41:48–53

14. Drenckhahn, D., Schluter, K., Allen, D. P., Bennett, V. 1985. Colocalization of band 3 with ankyrin and spectrin at the basal membrane of intercalated cells in the rat kidney. *Science* 230:1287–89

15. Edelman, G. M. 1986. Cell adhesion molecules in the regulation of animal form and tissue pattern. *Annu. Rev. Cell Biol.* 2:81–116

16. Fujita, M., Kawai, K., Asano, S., Nakao, N. 1973. Protein components of two different regions of an intestinal plasma epithelial cell membrane. *Biochim. Biophys. Acta* 307:141–51

17. Fuller, S. D., Bravo, R., Simons, K. 1985. An enzymatic assay reveals that proteins destined for the apical and basolateral domains of an epithelial cell line share the same late Golgi compartment. *EMBO J.* 4:297–307

18. Gething, M. J., McCammon, K., Sambrook, J. 1986. Expression of wild type and mutant forms of influenza hemagglutinin: the role of folding in intracellular transport. *Cell.* 46:939–50

19. Gonzalez, A., Rizzolo, L., Rindler, M., Adesnik, M., Sabatini, D. D., Gottlieb, T. 1987. Nonpolarized secretion of truncated forms of the influenza hemagglutinin and the vesicular stomatitis virus G protein from MDCK cells. *Proc. Natl. Acad. Sci. USA* 84:3738–42

20. Gonzalez-Mariscal, L., Chavez de Ramirez, B., Cereijido, M. 1985. Tight-junction formation in cultured epithelial cells (MDCK). *J. Membr. Biol.* 86:113–25

21. Gottlieb, T. A., Beaudry, G., Rizzolo, L., Colman, A., Rindler, M., Adesnik, M., Sabatini, D. 1985. *Proc. Natl. Acad. Sci. USA* 83:2100–4

22. Green, R., Meiss, H. K., Rodriguez-Boulan, E. 1981. Glycosylation does not determine the segregation of viral envelope proteins in the plasma membrane of epithelial cells. *J. Cell Biol.* 89:230–39

23. Griffiths, G., Simons, K. 1986. The trans Golgi network: Sorting at the exit site of the Golgi complex. *Science* 234:438–43

24. Gumbiner, B. 1987. Structure, biochemistry and assembly of epithelial tight junctions. *Am. J. Physiol.* 253: C749–C758

25. Gumbiner, B., Simons, K. 1986. A functional assay for proteins involved in establishing an epithelial occluding barrier: identification of a uvomorulin-like polypeptide. *J. Cell Biol.* 102:457–68

26. Hansson, G. C., Simons, K., van Meer, G. 1986. Two strains of the Madin-Darby canine kidney (MDCK) cell line have distinct glycolipids compositions. *EMBO J.* 5:483–89

27. Hauri, H. P., Quaroni, A., Isselbacher, K. J. 1979. Biogenesis of intestinal plasma membrane: Posttranslational route and cleavage of sucrase-isomaltase. *Proc. Natl. Acad. Sci. USA* 76:5183–86

28. Herzlinger, D. A., Ojakian, G. K. 1984. Studies on the development and maintenance of epithelial cell surface polarity with monoclonal antibodies. *J. Cell. Biol.* 98:1777–87

29. Imhoff, B. A., Vollmers, H. P., Goodman, S. L., Birchmeier, W. 1983. Cell-cell interaction and polarity of epithelial cells: specific perturbation using a monoclonal antibody. *Cell* 35:667–75

30. Ingber, D. E., Madri, J. A., Jamieson, J. D. 1986. Basement membrane as a spatial organizer of polarized epithelia. *Am. J. Pathol.* 122:129–39

31. Jones, L. V., Compans, R. W., Davis, A. R., Bos, T. J., Nayak, D. P. 1985. Surface expression of influenza virus neuraminidase, an aminoterminal anchored viral membrane glycoprotein in polarized epithelial cells. *Mol. Cell. Biol.* 5:2181–89

32. Kreis, T. E., Lodish, H. F. 1986. Oligomerization is essential for transport of vesicular stomatis virus glycoprotein to the cell surface. *Cell* 46:929–37

33. Lisanti, M., Sargiacomo, M., Graeve, L., Saltiel, A., Rodriguez-Boulan, E., 1988. Polarized distribution of glycosyl-phosphatidylinositol anchored proteins

in a renal epithelial cell line. *Proc. Natl. Acad. Sci. USA* In press

34. Low, M., Saltiel, A. 1988. Structural and functional roles of glycosyl-phosphatidylinositol in membranes. *Science* 239:268–74

35. Machamer, C. E., Rose, J. K. 1987. A specific transmembrane domain of a coronavirus E1 glycoprotein is required for its retention in the Golgi region. *J. Cell Biol.* 105:1205–14

36. Massey, D., Feracci, H., Gorvel, J.-P., Rigal, A., Soulie, J. M., Maroux, S. 1987. Evidence for the transit of aminopeptidase N through the basolateral membrane before it reaches the brush border of enterocytes. *J. Membr. Biol.* 96:19–25

37. Matlin, K. S. 1986. The sorting of proteins to the plasma membrane in epithelial cells. *J. Cell Biol.* 103:2565–68

38. Matlin, K. S., Bainton, D., Pesonen, M., Genty, N., Louvard, D., Simons, K., 1983. Transfer of a viral envelope glycoprotein from the apical to the basolateral plasma membrane of MDCK cells. I. Morphological evidence. *J. Cell Biol.* 97:627–37

39. Matlin, K. S., Simons, K. 1983. Reduced temperature prevents transfer of a membrane glycoprotein to the cell surface but does not prevent termina glycosylation. *Cell* 34:233–43

40. Matlin, K. S., Simons, K. 1984. Sorting of an apical plasma membrane glycoprotein occurs before it reaches the surface in cultured epithelial cells. *J. Cell Biol.* 99:2131–39

41. McQueen, N., Nayak, D. P., Stephens, E. B., Compans, R. W. 1986. Polarized expression of a chimeric protein in which the transmembrane and cytoplasmic domains of the influenza virus hemagglutinin have been replaced by those of the vesicular stomatitis virus G protein. *Proc. Natl. Acad. Sci. USA* 83:9318–22

42. McQueen, N., Nayak, D. P., Stephens, E. B., Compans, R. W. 1987. Basolateral expression of a chimeric protein in which the transmembrane and cytoplasmic domains of vesicular stomatitis virus G protein have been replaced by those of influenza virus hemagglutinin. *J. Biol. Chem.* 262:16233–40

43. Meiss, H. K., Green, R. F., Rodriguez-Boulan, E. 1982. Lectin resistant mutants of polarized epithelial cells. *Mol. Cell. Biol.* 2:1287–94

44. Misek, D. E., Bard, E., Rodriguez-Boulan, E. 1984. Biogenesis of epithelial cell polarity: intracellular sorting and

vectorial exocytosis of an apical plasma membrane glycoprotein. *Cell* 39:537–46

45. Mostov, K. E., Breitfeld, P., Harris, J. 1987. An anchor-minus form of the polymeric immunoglobulin receptor is secreted predominantly apically in Madin-Darby canine kidney cell. *J. Cell Biol.* 105:2031–36

46. Mostov, K. E., Deitcher, D. L. 1986. Polymeric immunoglobulin receptor expressed in MDCK transcytose IgA. *Cell* 46:613–21

47. Mostov, K. E., de Bruyn Kops, A., Deitcher, D. L. 1986. Deletion of the cytoplasmic domain of the polymeric immunoglobulin receptor prevents basolateral localization and endocytosis. *Cell* 47;359–64

48. Munro, S., Pelham, H. R. B. 1987. A C-terminal signal prevents secretion of luminal ER proteins. *Cell* 48:899–907

49. Nelson, W. J., Veshnock, P. J. 1986. Dynamics of membrane-skeleton (fodrin) organization during development of polarity in Madin-Darby canine kidney cells. *J. Cell Biol.* 103:1751–66

50. Nelson, W. J., Veshnock, P. J. 1987. Modulation of fodrin (membrane skeleton) stability by cell-cell contact in Madin-Darby canine kidney epithelial cell. *J. Cell Biol.* 104:1527–37

51. Nelson, W. J., Veshnock, P. J. 1987. Ankyrin binding to (Na^+-K^+) ATPase and implications for the organization of membrane domains in polarized cells. *Nature* 328:533–36

52. Niggli, V., Burger, M. M. 1987. Interaction of the cytoskeleton with the plasma membrane. *J. Membr. Biol.* 100:97–121

53. Nitsch, L., Wollman, S. H. 1980. Ultrastructure of intermediate stages in polarity reversal of thyroid epithelium in follicles in suspension culture. *J. Cell Biol.* 86:875–80

54. Ojakian, G. K., Romain, R. E., Herz, R. E. 1987. A distal nephron glycoprotein that has different cell surface distributions in MDCK cell sublines. *Am. J. Physiol.* 253:C433–43

55. Paabo, S., Bhat, B. M., Wold, W. S. M., Peterson, P. A. 1987. A short sequence in the COOH-terminus makes an adenovirus membrane glycoprotein a resident of the endoplasmic reticulum. *Cell* 50:311–17

56. Pesonen, M., Simons, K. 1983. Transepithelial transport of a viral membrane glycoprotein implanted into the apical plasma membrane of Madin-Darby canine kidney cells. II. Immunological quantitation. *J. Cell Biol.* 97:638–43

57. Pfeiffer, S., Fuller, S. D., Simons, K. 1985. Intracellular sorting and basolateral appearance of the G protein of vesicular stomatitis virus in MDCK cells. *J. Cell Biol.* 101:470–76

58. Pfeffer, S. R., Rothman, J. E. 1987. Biosynthetic protein transport and sorting by the endoplasmic reticulum and Golgi. *Annu. Rev. Biochem.* 56:829–52

59. Poruchynsky, M. S., Tyndall, C., Both, G. W., Sato, F., Bellamy, A. R., Atkinson, P. H. 1985. Deletions into a NH$_2$-terminal hydrophobic domain result in secretion of Rotavirus VP7, a resident endoplasmic reticulum membrane glycoprotein. *J. Cell Biol.* 101:2199–2209

60. Puddington, L., Woodgett, C., Rose, J. K. 1987. Replacement of the cytoplasmic domain alters sorting of a viral glycoprotein in polarized cells. *Proc. Natl. Acad. Sci. USA* 84:2756–60

61. Remy, L. 1986. The intracellular lumen: origin, role and implications of a cytoplasmic neostructure. *Biol. Cell.* 56:97–106

62. Richardson, J. C. W., Simmons, N. L. 1979. Demonstration of protein asymmetries in the plasma membrane of cultured renal (MDCK) epithelial cells by lactoperoxidase-mediated iodination. *FEBS Lett.* 105:201–4

63. Rindler, M. J., Ivanov, I. E., Plesken, H., Rodriguez-Boulan, E., Sabatini, D. D. 1984. Viral glycoproteins destined for apical or basolateral plasma membrane domains traverse the same Golgi apparatus during their intracellular transport in doubly infected Madin Darby Canine Kidney cells. *J. Cell Biol.* 98:1304–19

64. Rindler, M. J., Ivanov, I. E., Plesken, H., Sabatini, D. D. 1985. Polarized delivery of viral glycoproteins to the apical and basolateral plasma membranes of Madin-Darby canine kidney cells infected with temperature sensitive viruses. *J. Cell Biol.,* 100:136–51

65. Rindler, M. J., Ivanov, I. E., Sabatini, D. D. 1987. Microtubule-acting drugs lead to the nonpolarized delivery of the influenza hemagglutinin to the cell surface of polarized Madin-Darby canine kidney cells. *J. Cell Biol.* 104:231–52

66. Ringwald, M., Schuh, R., Vestweber, D., Eistetter, H., Lottspeich, F., et al. 1987. The structure of cell adhesion molecule uvomorulin. Insights into the molecular mechanism of Ca^{2+} dependent cell adhesion. *EMBO J.* 6:3467–53

67. Rodriguez-Boulan, E. 1983. Membrane biogenesis, enveloped RNA viruses and epithelial polarity. In *Modern Cell Biology,* ed. B. Satir, 1:119–70. New York: Liss

68. Rodriguez-Boulan, E., Paskiet, K. T., Sabatini, D. D. 1983. Assembly of enveloped viruses in MDCK cells: Polarized budding from single attached cells and from clusters of cells in suspension. *J. Cell Biol.* 96:866–74

69. Rodriguez-Boulan, E., Paskiet, K., Salas, P. J. I., Bard, E. 1984. Intracellular transport of influenza virus hemagglutinin to the apical surface of Madin-Darby canine kidney cells. *J. Cell Biol.* 98:308–19

70. Rodriguez-Boulan, E., Pendergast, M. 1980. Polarized distribution of viral envelope proteins in the plasma membrane of infected epithelial cells. *Cell* 20:45–54

71. Rodriguez-Boulan, E., Sabatini, D. D. 1978. Asymmetric budding of viruses in epithelial monolayers: a model system for study of epithelial polarity. *Proc. Natl. Acad. Sci. USA* 75:5071–75

72. Rogalski, A. A., Singer, S. J. 1984. Associations of elements of the Golgi apparatus with microtubules. *J. Cell Biol.* 99:1092–1100

73. Roman, L. M., Garoff, H. 1986. Alteration of the cytoplasmic domain of the membrane-spanning glycoprotein p62 of Semliki Forest virus does not affect its polar distribution in established lines of Madin Darby canine kidney cells. *J. Cell Biol.* 103:2607–18

74. Roth, M. G., Doyle, C., Sambrook, J., Gething, M. J. 1986. Heterologous transmembrane and cytoplasmic domains direct functional chimeric influenza virus into the endocytic pathway. *J. Cell Biol.* 102:1271–83

75. Roth, M. G., Gundersen, D., Patil, N., Rodriguez-Boulan, E. 1987. The large external domain is sufficient for the correct sorting of secreted or chimeric influenza virus hemagglutinins in polarized monkey kidney cells. *J. Cell Biol.* 104:769–82

76. Sabanero, M., Gonzalez-Robles, A., Meza, I. 1985. Characterization of a 36,000-dalton protein from the surface of Madin-Darby canine kidney cells involved in cell attachment and spreading. *J. Cell Biol.* 100:2001–7

77. Salas, P. J. I., Misek, D. E., Vega-Salas, D. E., Gundersen, D., Cereijido, M., Rodriguez-Boulan, E. 1986. Microtubules and actin filaments are not critically involved in the biogenesis of epithelial cell surface polarity. *J. Cell Biol.* 102:1853–67

78. Salas, P. J. I., Vega-Salas, D. E., Hochman, J., Rodriguez-Boulan, E., Edidin, M. 1988. Domain specific attachment to the submembrane cytoskeleton: a mechanism involved in the maintenance of epithelial surface polarity. *J. Cell Biol.* In press

79. Salas, P. J. I., Vega-Salas, D. E., Misek, D. E., Bard, E., Rodriguez-Boulan, E. 1984. Intracellular sorting of plasma membrane glycoproteins in epithelial cells. *Ann. NY Acad. Sci.* 435:337–40

80. Salas, P. J. I., Vega-Salas, D. E., Misek, D., Rodriguez-Boulan, E. 1985. Intracellular routes of apical and basolateral plasma membrane proteins to the surface of epithelial cells. *Pflügers Arch.* 405:s152–57

81. Salas, P. J. I., Vega-Salas, D. E., Rodriguez-Boulan, E. 1987. Collagen receptors mediate early events in the attachment of epithelial (MDCK) cells. *J. Membr. Biol.* 98:223–36

82. Sargiacomo, M., Lisanti, M., Graeve, L., LeBivic, A., Rodriguez-Boulan, E. 1989. Integral and peripheral protein composition of the apical and basolateral membrane domains in MDCK cells. *J. Membr. Biol.* In press

83. Schwartz, G. J., Barasch, J., Al-Awqati, Q. 1985. Plasticity of functional epithelial polarity. *Nature* 318:368–71

84. Sheetz, M. P., Schindler, M., Koppel, D. E. 1980. Lateral mobility of integral membrane proteins is increased in spherocytic erythrocytes. *Nature* 285:510–11

85. Simons, K., Fuller, S. D. 1985. Cell surface polarity in epithelia. *Annu. Rev. Cell Biol.* 1:243–88

86. Stephens, E. B., Compans, R. W. 1986. Nonpolarized expression of a secreted murine leukemia virus glycoprotein in polarized epithelial cells. *Cell* 47:1053–59

87. Tsuji, A., Ohnishi, S. 1986. Restriction of the lateral motion of band 3 in the erythrocyte membrane by the cytoskeletal network: dependence on spectrin association state. *Biochemistry* 25:6133–39

88. Urban, J., Parczyk, K., Leutz, A., Kayne, M., Kondor-Koch, C. 1987. Constitutive apical secretion of an 80-kD sulfated glycoprotein complex in the polarized epithelial Madin-Darby canine kidney cell line. *J. Cell Biol.* 105:2735–43

89. van Meer, G., Simons, K. 1986. The function of tight junctions in maintaining differences in lipid composition between the apical and the basolateral cell surface domains of MDCK cells. *EMBO J.* 5:1455–64

90. van Meer, G., Stelzer, E. H. K., Wijnaendts-van-Resandt, R. W., Simons, K. 1987. Sorting of sphingolipids in epithelial (Madin-Darby canine kidney) cells. *J. Cell Biol.* 105:1623–35

91. Vega-Salas, D. E., Salas, P. J. I., Rodriguez-Boulan, E. 1987. Formation of the apical pole of epithelial (Madin-Darby canine kidney) cell: polarity of an apical protein is independent of tight junctions while segregation of a basolateral marker requires cell-cell interactions. *J. Cell Biol.* 104:905–16

92. Vega-Salas, D. E., Salas, P. J. I., Rodriguez-Boulan, E. 1987. Modulation of the expression of an apical plasma membrane protein of Madin-Darby canine kidney epithelial cells: cell-cell interactions control the appearance of a novel intracellular storage compartment. *J. Cell Biol.* 104:1249–59

93. Vega-Salas, D. E., Salas, P. J. I., Rodriguez-Boulan, E. 1988. Exocytosis of vacuolar apical compartment (VAC): a cell-cell contact controlled mechanism for the establishment of the apical plasma membrane domain in epithelial cells. *J. Cell Biol.* 107:1717–28

94. Vestweber, D., Kemler, R., Ekblom, P. 1985. Cell-adhesion molecule uvomorulin during kidney development. *Dev. Biol.* 112:213–21

Annu. Rev. Physiol. 1989. 51:755–70

BIOGENESIS OF ENDOGENOUS PLASMA MEMBRANE PROTEINS IN EPITHELIAL CELLS

A. L. Hubbard and B. Stieger

Department of Cell Biology and Anatomy, Johns Hopkins University School of Medicine, Baltimore, Maryland 21205

J. R. Bartles

Department of Cell Biology and Anatomy, Northwestern University Medical School, Chicago, Illinois 60611

INTRODUCTION

The plasma membrane (PM) is a complex and dynamic macromolecular assembly. Its complexity is particularly evident in polarized epithelial cells, where specialized domains exist to carry out diverse functions within one continuous and fluid lipid bilayer (57). The basolateral domain of epithelial cells faces the internal milieu and is functionally analogous to the PM of nonepithelial cells. It is also specialized for adhesion to the basal lamina and to other cells. The apical domain of epithelial cells faces the external medium and is considered the differentiated surface, since it displays the specialized structures and carries out the specialized functions that largely define each epithelium.

Integral glycoproteins constitute a particularly interesting class of membrane molecules in epithelial cells. They mediate a number of dynamic processes occurring at the PM and have been detected in both surface domains of epithelial cells (e.g. 36, 57). Most are transmembrane (e.g. 36), which means that unique sequences are available at both the external and cytoplasmic faces of the bilayer for interaction with each environment. Furthermore, the presence of N-linked oligosaccharides on the external segments of these proteins places constraints on the intracellular pathways that they must

755

0066-4278/89/0315-0755$02.00

traverse in their biogenesis. It is clear that membrane glycoproteins are synthesized, modified, and transported through much of the same pathway as are lysosomal and secretory proteins [i.e. the endoplasmic reticulum → Golgi complex (ER→GC) biogenetic pathway] (34). Furthermore, many recent studies have focused on the signals, sites, and mechanisms of sorting that must occur within this pathway.

An emerging view of sorting is that two classes of signals may (or may not) be present on molecules in the ER → GC biogenetic pathway. One class consists of retention signals that, given the appropriate receptor and environment, will retain a molecule in a particular compartment. The only example so far identified is the C-terminal tetrapeptide sequence on several soluble ER proteins (44). The other class consists of positive signals that are recognized by specific receptors, which segregate a molecule from the general population and transport it to a specific location. There are two examples in this category: mannose-6-phosphate on the N-linked oligosaccharides in lysosomal enzymes (35), and as-yet-unidentified sequences/conformations on regulated secretory proteins (10, 45). On the basis of recent morphological studies, the *trans*-most cisterna of the Golgi complex (45), or a corresponding tubulovesicular array the *trans*-Golgi network (26, 45), has been implicated as the site where positive sorting signals operate in the biogenetic pathway. Molecules lacking either type of signal are thought to be constitutively secreted or, for PM proteins, expressed at the cell surface. In epithelial cells, yet a third class of signals must exist that segregates proteins destined for the apical and basolateral membrane domains. The presence of analogous molecules in the PM of nonpolarized cells and the basolateral membrane in polarized cells suggests that these membrane proteins may have no positive sorting signals and that their route to the cell surface represents a default pathway. Therefore, the domain-specific signal would be on the apical proteins.

The questions of where and how domain-specific sorting occurs in polarized epithelial cells have been addressed using both in vitro and in vivo systems. The MDCK (Madin-Darby canine kidney) cell line has been the predominant in vitro model for two reasons. First, it forms a polarized monolayer in culture, and second, enveloped viruses have been shown to infect these monolayers and mature in a polarized fashion, thus providing investigators with well-characterized membrane glycoproteins whose biogenesis can be studied with little interference by endogenous proteins (56). Much has been learned with this model, which is reviewed elsewhere in this volume. However, the MDCK cell is an in vitro system that must be validated and extended by the study of endogenous membrane proteins, both in cultured epithelial cell systems and in systems where the normal tissue architecture is maintained. Therefore, in this review we focus on what is known about the sorting of endogenous PM glycoproteins in epithelial cells. We also discuss the endogenous secretory proteins of epithelial cells, because our recent results have led us to hypothesize that these two classes of constitutively expressed molecules share a common pathway to the PM.

BIOSYNTHETIC ROUTES OF ENDOGENOUS PLASMA MEMBRANE PROTEINS

After synthesis, transport, and glycosylation together within the ER and GC, newly synthesized domain-specific PM glycoproteins have three possible routes to their sites of function. (*a*) They can be segregated within the cell in a late/post-Golgi location with each type inserted directly into the correct domain. (*b*) They can be transported to all domains, inserted randomly, and then subsequently retrieved and delivered to the correct domain. (*c*) They all can be transported to one domain and those destined for the other domain subsequently segregated and delivered there.

Studies on the sorting of exogenous viral envelope glycoproteins in MDCK cells have convincingly established that influenza HA (a model apical plasma membrane protein) and VSV G protein (a model basolateral PM protein) reach the *trans*-portion of the Golgi together, are sorted intracellularly, and are each shipped directly to the correct PM domain (route *a*, above). The evidence is discussed elsewhere in this volume and has also been reviewed by others (39, 56, 57).

Table 1 presents a summary of studies on the biosynthetic routes taken by endogenous PM proteins in hepatocytes, enterocytes, and MDCK cells. Liver and intestine have been the organs of choice for all of the in vivo biosynthetic studies to date. These epithelia are more homogeneous than those in other major organs (e.g. the kidney) and are amenable to subcellular fractionation methods yielding preparations that are relatively enriched in apical and basolateral membranes (4, 41). However, subcellular fractionation never yields a pure preparation of any organelle, thus it is important to consider likely contaminants that could influence the results. Furthermore, yields of a particular organelle in the fractions that are finally analyzed are always less than 100% and often less than 10% and make extrapolations to the intact cell problematic.

Basolateral Proteins

Relatively few studies have focused on the biosynthetic route taken by endogenous basolateral proteins to the PM (Table 1). In the intestine such proteins would be present on nonepithelial cells as well as enterocytes. This is not a problem in liver, where hepatocytes comprise 70% of the cell population (8) and hepatocyte-specific basolateral proteins have been identified and

Table 1 Studies of biosynthetic routes taken by endogenous plasma membrane proteins[a]

Tissue	Protein(s)	Species	Approach	Route to plasma membrane Direct	Route to plasma membrane Via other domain	Evidence	Reference
Basolateral							
	(Na^+-K^+)–ATPase	MDCK (dog kidney)	^{35}S-methionine ippt[b] SDS gels and ARG	Yes	No	Antibody against covalently linked ouabain	12
	Polymeric IgA-receptor	MDCK, transfected	^{35}S-methionine ippt SDS gels and ARG	Yes	No	Antibody against secretory component	43
Liver	CE 9 AGSP-receptor	Rat in vivo	^{35}S-methionine ippt SDS gels and ARG	Yes	No	Kinetics	5
Apical Liver	Membrane glycoproteins	Rat in vivo	^3H-fucose fluorography of SDS gels and specific radioactivity in fractions	No	Yes	Kinetics	18

	Aminopeptidase N Dipeptidylpeptidase IV HA 4	Rat in vivo	^{35}S-methionine ippt SDS gels and ARG	No	Yes	Kinetics	5
Small Intestine	Membrane glycoproteins	Rat in vivo	^{3}H-fucose fluorography of SDS gels and specific radioactivity in fractions	Yes	Yes	Kinetics	50
	Sucrase-isomaltase	Rat in vivo	^{3}H-fucose ippt with determination of radioactivity	No	Yes	Kinetics	28
	Aminopeptidase N	Rat in vivo	^{3}H-leucine ippt with determination of radioactivity	Yes	No	Kinetics	1
	Aminopeptidase N	Pig organ culture	^{35}S-methionine ippt SDS gels and ARG	Yes	No	Accessibility to proteases	15
	Aminopeptidase N	Rabbit in vivo	^{35}S-methionine ippt SDS gels and ARG	No	Yes	Kinetics	37

[a] All studies used an approach based on subcellular fractionation. In all the studies the radiolabeled proteins were found maximally in the Golgi fraction after 15 to 30 minutes and were present in significant amounts in the plasma membrane fractions after 45 minutes.
[b] ippt: isolation of proteins by immunoprecipitation.
[c] SDS gels: separation of proteins by sodium dodecyl sulfate polyacrylamide gel electrophoresis. ARG: autoradiography.

studied (31). In these and MDCK cells, when endogenous, newly synthesized basolateral proteins were followed to the PM, they were found only in the basolateral domain, whether probed directly (in intact MDCK cell monolayers) or through membrane domain fractionation (in liver). Thus neither apical nor random insertion followed by retrieval appear to be the sorting options used for basolateral proteins by these cells.

Apical Proteins in Liver

Evans et al (18) were perhaps the first to suggest that newly synthesized glycoproteins were transferred via a membrane-mediated path from the basolateral to the apical PM of rat hepatocytes in vivo. However, their sinusoidal subfraction showed extensive contamination by GC and mature forms of specific integral hepatocyte PM proteins were not considered.

Our recent experiments examining the sorting of endogenous rat hepatocyte PM proteins included three apical proteins, aminopeptidase N, dipeptidylpeptidase IV, and a ~105-kd protein called HA 4 (Table 1). We measured the rates of appearance of the newly synthesized apical and basolateral proteins in a highly purified preparation of intact hepatocyte PM and in apical and basolateral PM vesicle fractions. The newly synthesized, mature (terminally glycosylated), apical and basolateral PM proteins were found to reach the hepatocyte PM at approximately the same route, with maximal specific radioactivity reached after 45 minutes of chase. In light of the results in virally infected MDCK cells, we were surprised to find that all of the newly synthesized proteins—apical and basolateral—were present at 45 minutes of chase in vesicles that appeared to be bona fide basolateral PMs by several independent criteria. (a) They fractionated as basolateral PM in sucrose density gradients and in free-flow electrophoresis. (b) They could be separated from the bulk of the likely organellar contaminants, including vesicles derived from the trans-Golgi cisternae and endosomes. (c) They contained proven basolateral constituents as judged from vesicle immunoadsorption experiments. (d) Finally, they were oriented in an ectoplasmic-side-out fashion, as expected for vesicles derived from the PM but not for those derived from intracellular organelles. At chase times greater than 45 minutes, the newly synthesized apical proteins began to appear in the apical plasma membrane vesicles, but they did so at different rates. Thus, in hepatocytes, sorting occurs at or after the basolateral surface (route c above) rather than at an intracellular location as in MDCK cells.

Apical Proteins in Intestine

The lumenal surface of the small intestine is lined by an epithelium that is a mixture of mucin-secreting cells (the goblet cells) and columnar absorptive cells (enterocytes). Enterocytes originate in the crypts, differentiate their apical membrane (the brush border) during migration up the villus, and are sloughed into the gut lumen after about 2–3 days (29). This rapid cellular turnover means that there is substantial biosynthesis of apical membrane proteins, which has facilitated studies on the sorting routes taken by two brush border enzymes, sucrase-isomaltase and aminopeptidase N (Table 1). Unfortunately, the results are contradictory and allow no conclusions to be drawn at present. Two common features might have contributed to the controversy. (*a*) A single (different) fractionation technique was used in each study, making the influence of contaminations difficult to assess. (*b*) A single apical protein was chosen for study. There is, therefore, clearly a need for thorough reexamination of the sorting pathways in intestine in which several proteins from each of the two domains are followed and multiple fractionation techniques are applied. The discovery of permanent, differentiated enterocytelike epithelial cell lines (48, 49, 54) might provide a useful alternative to some of these problems.

BIOSYNTHETIC ROUTES OF SECRETORY PROTEINS

Most eukaryotic cells secrete proteins into their environment. These molecules are either: (*a*) packaged without significant concentration into vesicles and continuously discharged by exocytosis (the constitutive pathway), or (*b*) concentrated at the level of the *trans*-Golgi and stored in secretory granules until exocytosis is initiated by some external stimulus (the regulated pathway) (10, 19).

Regulated Secretory Pathways

Much is known about the regulated secretory pathways operating within polarized epithelial cells such as the exocrine pancreas or parotid (3, 46). However, the biogenetic pathways for apical and basolateral PM proteins are as yet unexplored in these cells. Since the secretory granule membrane has a protein composition that is simpler and largely distinct from that of the apical domain (11), with which the former fuses upon stimulation, it is presumed that newly synthesized apical proteins are delivered via a pathway that is different from the one taken by regulated secretory proteins. Furthermore, the constitutive nature of PM protein expression points to constitutive secretory pathways in polarized epithelial cells as the more likely of the routes for delivery of domain-specific PM proteins.

Constitutive Secretory Pathways

There have been few studies of constitutive secretion in polarized epithelial cells other than hepatocytes. Table 2 presents a list of the endogenous proteins that are known to be continuously secreted by two cell lines in vitro and by

Table 2 Secretion of endogenous proteins

Cell	Protein	Secretion		Perturbation	Reference
		Apical	Basolateral		
Hepatocytes (rat perfused liver)	albumin major plasma proteins	No	Yes		40
MDCK (canine kidney)	81 kd glycoprotein	Yes	No	Chloroquine leads to intracellular accumulation and reduced secretion	24
MDCK	80 kd glycoprotein complex (30–40 kd)	Yes	No	No effect of chloroquine Tunicamycin leads to nonpolarized secretion	33, 60
MDCK	laminin heparan sulfate proteoglycan cathepsin D	No No No	Yes Yes No	NH$_4$Cl leads to nonpolarized secretion	13
Caco-2 (human large intestine)	lipoproteins	No	Yes	—	59

hepatocytes in vivo. It is clear that MDCK cells constitutively secrete distinct sets of endogenous proteins from both their apical and basolateral surfaces. In addition, a variety of exogenous secretory proteins introduced into MDCK cells by transfection appear to be secreted constitutively from both apical and basolateral surfaces, as though they were not recognized by the MDCK cells' sorting machinery (24, 33).

In contrast to MDCK cells, hepatocytes have only a basolaterally directed secretory pathway (14, 32, 40). This is the pathway along which the hepatocyte constitutively secretes the major plasma proteins. The proteins present in intrahepatic bile are not secreted directly into bile, but are derived from the plasma either by paracellular leakage through the intercellular space and the hepatocytes' tight junctions or by fluid-phase or receptor-mediated transcytosis (14, 32). That the hepatocyte does not have an apically directed secretory pathway may be related to its apparent use of a basolateral-to-apical transcytotic pathway for the delivery of apical PM proteins.

Use of the human intestinal cell line, Caco-2, for biogenetic studies is just beginning, and thus far only a basolateral secretory route has been identified in these cells (59).

A UNIFYING HYPOTHESIS

There appears to be an interesting correlation between the sorting pathways for PM proteins and constitutive secretory proteins within different polarized epithelial cell types (6). The MDCK cell, which can constitutively secrete in either the apical or basolateral direction, ships its apical PM proteins directly from the Golgi complex to the apical PM. In contrast, the hepatocyte, which has no apically directed pathway for constitutive secretion, employs a basolateral-to-apical transcytotic route for the delivery of its apical PM proteins. At present, there are insufficient data to allow us to determine whether this correlation will extend to epithelial cells other than the hepatocyte and MDCK.

Theoretically, the relationship between constitutive secretion and domain-specific PM expression could be expressed at any of a number of levels. At one extreme, both classes of proteins, PM and constitutive secretory, may be sorted by the same mechanism and delivered in the same post-Golgi transport vesicles (27). This possibility seems unlikely, at least for the MDCK cell, in which ammonium chloride treatment alters the polarity of constitutive laminin and heparan sulfate proteoglycan secretion, without affecting the sorting of an exogenous PM protein (influenza HA) (13, 38) or an endogenous basolateral plasma membrane protein (the Na^+,K^+-ATPase) (12). Even though constitutive secretory proteins (albumin and transferrin) and an exogenous PM protein (VSV G protein) have been colocalized in putative secretory vesicles in the Hep G2 human hepatoma cell line (58), more recent morphological evidence suggests that albumin may be sorted from an endogenous PM protein (the asialoglycoprotein receptor) in the *trans*-portion of the Golgi in rat hepatocytes in vivo (21). The problem with both of these morphological studies is that they fail to distinguish newly synthesized secretory and membrane proteins from the preexisting ones. This distinction is crucial because there is a large intracellular pool of asialoglycoprotein receptors (62) whose localization might obscure those of the newly synthesized molecules. Alternatively, this apparent relationship between the pathways of constitutive exocytic vesicular traffic operating within a single epithelial cell type could be more indirect. There could be separate sorting mechanisms and transport vesicles for PM and constitutive secretory proteins in polarized epithelial cells, but both pathways might be subject to certain generalized directional constraints, such as those that could result from restricting the spatial distributions of microtubules or perhaps other cytoskeletal elements. Microtubules have been postulated to serve as tracks that guide vesicular traffic within cells (10, 61). It is interesting to note that microtubule-disrupting drugs, such as colchicine, appear to impair sorting of apical PM proteins in MDCK cells (53, but see 55), rat hepatocytes (16; B. Stieger & A. L. Hubbard, unpublished), and rat small intestine (17, 47, 51).

REMAINING QUESTIONS

We are still far from a complete molecular understanding of PM protein sorting in epithelial cells. In fact, no firm generalizations can yet be made because the biogenesis of only a limited number of endogenous (or exogenous) proteins has been definitively established in only two epithelial cell types. Consequently, numerous questions remain, of which only a few are mentioned here.

Is There Cell-Type-Specific PM Protein Sorting?

Clearly there is a need to expand the study of endogenous PM protein biogenesis both to additional apical proteins, since they are the molecules that are sorted differently in MDCK cells and hepatocytes, and to additional types of polarized epithelial cells. As mentioned, the intestine and at least one regulated secretory epithelium deserve careful attention. Identification of the constitutive secretory pathways that exist in these cells is also an important issue in order to test the hypothesis we have advanced above. Perhaps hepatocytes are unique among epithelial cells in the route and manner they use to sort apical proteins. If so, detailed structural comparisons of several liver apical proteins become important, with particular attention to amino acid sequence differences or to any co- or posttranslational modifications that might serve as cell-type-specific sorting signals. Introduction of several apical proteins of the hepatocyte (and perhaps constitutive secretory proteins as well) into heterologous epithelial cells (e.g. MDCK and Caco-2 cells) by transfection followed by detailed examination of the sorting pathways taken by these molecules could also be quite valuable.

Where are the Sorting Sites?

Since the routes taken by apical proteins in the rat hepatocyte in vivo and MDCK cells in vitro are different, the sorting sites must also be different. Where are they? In MDCK cells, morphological colocalization of the model PM glycoproteins, VSV G and influenza HA, throughout the Golgi (52) and their biochemical co-accumulation in the *trans*-portion of the organelle by incubation at 20°C (20) have focused attention on this subcompartment as the site where segregation of apical from basolateral PM proteins most likely occurs. However, no morphological separation has yet been observed, nor has the acidic nature of this portion of the Golgi (2) been established in MDCK cells (see below).

Our results indicate that the hepatocyte sorts its apical and basolateral PM proteins after their initial insertion into the basolateral domain of the plasma membrane (5). Therefore, we predict that one type of vesicular carrier would first deliver all PM molecules to the basolateral membrane. Then, either (*a*) the apical proteins could be selectively incorporated into endocytic vesicles formed at the basolateral surface and transported to the apical surface; or (*b*) both basolateral and apical glycoproteins could be internalized and sorted intracellularly, with the basolateral proteins being recycled back to the basolateral surface and the apical proteins being delivered to the apical surface. In the first case, the sorting would occur at the PM. In the second case, the sorting would presumably occur in an endocytic compartment, not unlike the one that has been postulated to function in the sorting of recycling basolateral receptors (e.g. the asialoglycoprotein receptor) and transcytotic receptors (e.g. the polymeric IgA receptor) following endocytosis in rat hepatocytes in vivo (23). This compartment is acidic (63).

Which Vesicles Transport PM Proteins?

Very little is known about the vesicles involved in the transport of constitutively expressed PM proteins from the Golgi complex to the surface of either polarized or nonpolarized cells. These vesicles would appear to be very short-lived, since VSV G protein trapped in the *trans*-Golgi network by incubation at 20°C begins to appear at the PM within just a few minutes following warming to 32°C (25). Those vesicles delivering exogenous PM proteins, such as VSV G protein in Hep G2 cells (58) or in CHO cells, (7) or influenza HA in AtT-20 cells or in pancreatic B cells (45), are relatively small electronlucent structures with diameters in the range of 100–300 nm, which are presumably derived by budding off of the *trans*-Golgi cisterna (25, 45). In the case of the hepatocyte, it would appear that the most likely vesicles to carry the newly synthesized apical and basolateral PM proteins from the *trans*-Golgi to the basolateral PM are engaged in transport of the hepatocyte's constitutive secretory proteins, such as albumin and transferrin, to its basolateral surface. These vesicles also typically fall within the range of 100–300 nm in diameter and display an electronlucent core, which often contains what appear to be very low density lipoprotein particles (21, 64). Likewise, the most likely candidates for mediating the transcytotic movement of the apical proteins would be the 110–160 nm diameter endosomal vesicles that have been implicated in the transcytosis of the polymeric IgA and its receptor in hepatocytes in vivo (23, 30).

The difficulties associated with isolating the carriers involved in PM protein delivery are numerous. Not only are these vesicles short-lived, but they have no currently known organellar marker activities and may have only a small fraction of the domain-specific molecules, owing to the continuous nature of the delivery. These features make immunoadsorption of such vesicles with antibodies to the cytoplasmic portions of PM proteins impractical. However, careful kinetic experiments, together with reversible perturbation of the transport pathways by low temperature or drug treatment, may eventually allow identification, isolation, and biochemical characterization of the relevant carriers of PM proteins.

What are the Sorting Mechanisms?

As discussed earlier, domain-specific signals must exist on at least one set of epithelial cell PM proteins that serve to segregate them from those destined for the other domain. Although we presume that the apical proteins contain the structural information, there is no direct evidence for this at present. It is possible that basolateral proteins contain a retention signal. Despite prodigious efforts, the definitive identification of a sorting signal on any PM protein has proven to be difficult (see Roth, this volume). Perhaps this is due not only to signals that are conformational rather than linear, but also to the existence of a hierarchy of signals (or receptors) that operates differently in different cellular compartments. That is, one signal (or recognition molecule) may be dominant in a particular site (owing to environmental conditions) but another signal becomes dominant in a second site. In this regard, the recent work of Mostov and colleagues (42, 43) on the sorting of the liver pIgA receptor in MDCK cells deserves comment.

This PM protein in hepatocytes is normally delivered to the basolateral domain and then later shuttled to the apical domain as the result of some sorting event that occurs in an endosomal compartment (23). In MDCK cells, it must be initially sorted from apical proteins in the *trans*-Golgi network, which means that this liver molecule has a signal that can be read by the MDCK sorting machinery there. That the truncated (cytoplasmic tail-minus and the cytoplasmic and membrane-spanning segment-minus) derivations in MDCK are sorted directly to the apical domain suggests (*a*) that the cytoplasmic tail's basolateral sorting signal is dominant when it comes to sorting signal recognition in the *trans*-Golgi network, (*b*) that the truncated protein is sorted by a similar mechanism whether membrane-attached or soluble, and (*c*) that perhaps there is some similarity between the apical sorting machinery (signals, receptors, environment?) present in the *trans*-Golgi network and the endocytic sorting compartment. A detailed examination of these sorting pathways and the effects of various drugs on sorting of the intact and truncated pIgA receptor in both MDCK and polarized hepatocytes seems warranted.

The fact that the two possible sites of PM protein sorting in both MDCK cells (the *trans*-Golgi network) and hepatocytes (endosomes) are acidic suggests that pH may play a role in reversible signal recognition and the segregation of apical from basolateral PM proteins. Trafficking of the cation-independent, mannose-6-phosphate receptor and its ligand (a lysosomal enzyme) between these two compartments provides a useful paradigm (9, 19, 22, 35). However, pH sensitivity appears not to be a mechanism for signal recognition in MDCK cell PM sorting, since weak bases have no effect on the sorting of influenza HA to the apical or Na^+,K^+-ATPase to the basolateral membrane. The effect of weak bases on hepatocyte apical protein sorting has not yet been examined. Nonetheless, other possibilities need to be explored, for example, membrane potential and/or other ionic conditions. Both in vitro reconstitution of sorting as well as isolation and biochemical characterization of the *trans*-Golgi and endosomes will be necessary to resolve this issue.

ACKNOWLEDGMENTS

We thank Arlene Daniel for help in preparing this manuscript. A.L.H. is supported by the National Institutes of Health (GM29185), B.S. by the Swiss National Science Foundation (83.396.0.86), and J.R.B. by National Institutes of Health (DK34138).

Literature Cited

1. Ahnen, D. J., Santiago, N. A., Cezard, J.-P., Gray, G. M. 1982. Intestinal aminooligopeptidase. In vivo synthesis on intracellular membranes of rat jejunum. *J. Biol. Chem.* 257:12129–35
2. Anderson, R. G. W., Pathak, R. K. 1985. Vesicles and cisternae in the trans Golgi apparatus of human fibroblasts are acidic compartments. *Cell* 40:635–43
3. Arvan, P., Castle, J. D. 1987. Phasic release of newly synthesized secretory

proteins in the unstimulated rat exocrine pancreas. *J. Cell Biol.* 104:243–52
4. Bartles, J. R., Braiterman, L. T., Hubbard, A. L. 1985. Endogenous and exogenous domain markers of the rat hepatocyte plasma membrane. *J. Cell Biol.* 100:1126–38
5. Bartles, J. R., Feracci, H. M., Stieger, B., Hubbard, A. L. 1987. Biogenesis of the rat hepatocyte plasma membrane in vivo: comparison of the pathways taken

by apical and basolateral proteins using subcellular fractionation. *J. Cell Biol.* 105:1241–51

6. Bartles, J. R., Hubbard, A. L. 1988. Plasma membrane protein sorting in epithelial cells: Do secretory pathways hold the key? *Trends Biochem. Sci.* 13:181–84

7. Bergmann, J. E., Singer, S. J. 1983. Immunoelectron microscopic studies of the intracellular transport of the membrane glycoprotein (G) of vesicular stomatitis virus in infected Chinese Hamster ovary cells. *J. Cell Biol.* 97:1777–87

8. Blouin, A., Bolender, R. P., Weibel, E. R. 1977. Distribution of organelles and membranes between hepatocytes and nonhepatocytes in the rat liver parenchyma. A stereological study. *J. Cell Biol.* 72:441–55

9. Brown, W. J., Goodhouse, J., Farquhar, M. G. 1986. Mannose-6-phosphate receptors for lysosomal enzymes cycle between the Golgi complex and endosomes. *J. Cell Biol.* 103:1235–47

10. Burgess, T. L., Kelly, R. B. 1987. Constitutive and regulated secretion of proteins. *Annu. Rev. Cell Biol.* 3:243–93

11. Cameron, R. S., Castle, J. D. 1984. Isolation and compositional analysis of secretion granules and their membrane subfraction from the rat parotid gland. *J. Membr. Biol.* 79:127–44

12. Caplan, M. J., Anderson, H. C., Palade, G. E., Jamieson, J. D. 1986. Intracellular sorting and polarized cell surface delivery of $(Na^+,K^+)ATPase$, an endogenous component of MDCK cell basolateral plasma membranes. *Cell* 46:623–31

13. Caplan, M. J., Stow, J. L., Newman, A. P., Madri, J., Anderson, H. C., et al. 1987. Dependence on pH of polarized sorting of secreted proteins. *Nature* 329:632–35

14. Coleman, R. 1987. Biochemistry of bile secretion. *Biochem. J.* 244:249–61

15. Danielsen, E. M., Cowell, G. M. 1985. Biosynthesis of intestinal microvillar proteins. Evidence for an intracellular sorting taking place in, or shortly after, from the Golgi complex. *Eur. J. Biochem.* 152:493–99

16. Durand-Schneider, A.-M., Maurice, M., Dumont, M., Feldmann, G. 1987. Effect of colchicine and phalloidin on the distribution of three plasma membrane antigens in rat hepatocytes: comparison with bile duct ligation. *Hepatology* 7:1239–48

17. Ellinger, A., Pavelka, M., Gangl, A. 1983. Effect of colchicine on rat small

intestinal absorptive cells. II. Distribution of label after incorporation of [³H]fucose into plasma membrane glycoproteins. *J. Ultrastruct. Res.* 85:260–71

18. Evans, W. H., Flint, N. A., Vischer, P. 1980. Biogenesis of hepatocyte plasma-membrane domains. Incorporation of [³H]fucose into plasma-membrane and Golgi-apparatus glycoproteins. *Biochem. J.* 192:903–10

19. Farquhar, M. G. 1985. Progress in unraveling pathways of Golgi traffic. *Annu. Rev. Cell Biol.* 1:447–88

20. Fuller, S. D., Bravo, R., Simons, K. 1985. An enzymatic assay reveals that proteins destined for the apical or basolateral domains of an epithelial cell line share the same late Golgi compartments. *EMBO J.* 4:297–307

21. Geuze, H. J., Slot, J. W., Schwartz, A. L. 1987. Membranes of sorting organelles display lateral heterogeneity in receptor distribution. *J. Cell Biol.* 104:1715–23

22. Geuze, H. J., Slot, J. W., Strous, G. J. A. M., Hasilik, A., Von Figura, K. 1985. Possible pathways for lysosomal enzyme delivery. *J. Cell Biol.* 101:2253–62

23. Geuze, H. J., Slot, J. W., Strous, G. J. A. M., Peppard, J., Von Figura, K., et al. 1984. Intracellular receptor sorting during endocytosis: comparative immunoelectron microscopy of multiple receptors in rat liver. *Cell* 37:195–204

24. Gottlieb, T. A., Beaudry, G., Rizzolo, L., Colman, A., Rindler, M., et al. 1986. Secretion of endogenous and exogenous proteins from polarized MDCK cell monolayers. *Proc. Natl. Acad. Sci. USA* 83:2100

25. Griffiths, G., Pfeiffer, S., Simons, K., Matlin, K. 1985. Exit of newly synthesized membrane proteins from the trans cisterna of the Golgi complex to the plasma membrane. *J. Cell Biol.* 101:949–64

26. Griffiths, G., Simons, K. 1986. The trans Golgi network: sorting at the exit site of the Golgi complex. *Science* 234:438–43

27. Gumbiner, B., Kelly, R. B. 1982. Two distinct intracellular pathways transport secretory and membrane glycoproteins to the surface of pituitary tumor cells. *Cell* 28:51–59

28. Hauri, H.-P., Quaroni, A., Isselbacher, K. J. 1979. Biogenesis of intestinal plasma membrane: posttranslational route and cleavage of sucrase-isomaltase. *Proc. Natl. Acad. Sci. USA* 76:5183–86

29. Henning, S. J. 1985. Ontogeny of enzymes in the small intestine. *Annu. Rev. Physiol.* 47:231–45

30. Hoppe, C. A., Connolly, T. P., Hubbard, A. L. 1985. Transcellular transport of polymeric IgA in the rat hepatocyte: biochemical and morphological characterization of the transport pathway. *J. Cell Biol.* 101:2113–23

31. Hubbard, A. L., Bartles, J. R., Braiterman, L. T. 1985. Identification of rat hepatocyte plasma membrane proteins using monoclonal antibodies. *J. Cell Biol.* 100:1115–25

32. Kloppel, T. M., Brown, W. R., Reichen, J. 1986. Mechanisms of secretion of proteins into bile: studies in the perfused rat liver. *Hepatology* 6:587–94

33. Kondor-Koch, C., Bravo, R., Fuller, S. D., Cutler, D., Garoff, H. 1985. Exocytotic pathways exist to both the apical and the basolateral cell surface of the polarized epithelial cell MDCK. *Cell* 43:297–306

34. Kornfeld, R., Kornfeld, S. 1985. Assembly of asparagine-linked oligosaccharides. *Annu. Rev. Biochem.* 54:631–64

35. Kornfeld, S. 1987. Trafficking of lysosomal enzymes. *FASEB J.* 1:462–68

36. Lodish, H. F., Braell, W. A., Schwartz, A. L., Strous, G. J. A. M., Zilberstein, A. 1981. Synthesis and assembly of membrane and organelle proteins. *Int. Rev. Cytol. Suppl.* 12:247–307

37. Massey, D., Feracci, H., Gorvel, J.-P., Rigal, A., Soulie, J. M., et al. 1987. Evidence for the transit of aminopeptidase N through the basolateral membrane before it reaches the brush border of enterocytes. *J. Membr. Biol.* 96:19–25

38. Matlin, K. S. 1986. Ammonium chloride slows transport of the influenza virus hemagglutinin but does not cause mis-sorting in a polarized epithelial cell line. *J. Biol. Chem.* 261:15172–78

39. Matlin, K. S. 1986. The sorting of proteins to the plasma membrane in epithelial cells. *J. Cell Biol.* 103:2565–68

40. Miller, L. L., Bly, C. G., Watson, M. L., Bale, W. F. 1951. The dominant role of the liver in plasma protein synthesis. A direct study of the isolated perfused rat liver with the aid of lysine-ϵ-C^{14}. *J. Exp. Med.* 94:431–53

41. Moktari, S., Feracci, H., Gorvel, J.-P., Mishal, Z., Rigal, A., et al. 1986. Subcellular fractionation and subcellular localization of aminopeptidase N in the rabbit enterocytes. *J. Membr. Biol.* 89:53–63

42. Mostov, K. E., Breitfeld, P., Harris, J.

M. 1987. An anchor-minus form of the polymeric immunoglobin receptor is secreted predominantly apically in Madin-Darby Canine Kidney cells. *J. Cell Biol.* 105:2031–36

43. Mostov, K. E., de Bruyn Kops, A., Deitcher, D. L. 1986. Deletion of the cytoplasmic domain of the polymeric immunoglobulin receptor prevents basolateral localization and endocytosis. *Cell* 47:359–64

44. Munro, S., Pelham, H. R. B. 1987. A C-terminal signal prevents secretion of luminal ER proteins. *Cell* 48:899–907

45. Orci, L., Ravazzola, M., Amherdt, M., Perrelet, A., Powell, S. K., et al. 1987. The *trans*-most cisternae of the Golgi complex: a compartment for sorting of secretory and plasma membrane proteins. *Cell* 51:1039–51

46. Palade, G. 1975. Intracellular aspects of the process of protein synthesis. *Science* 189:347–58

47. Pavelka, M., Ellinger, A., Gangl, A. 1983. Effect of colchicine on rat small intestinal absorptive cells. I. Formation of basolateral microvillus borders. *J. Ultrastruct. Res.* 85:249–59

48. Pinto, M., Appay, M.-D., Simon-Assmann, P., Chevalier, G., Dracopoli, N., et al. 1982. Enterocytic differentiation of cultured human colon cancer cells by replacement of glucose by galactose in the medium. *Biol. Cell* 44:193–96

49. Pinto, M., Robine-Leon, S., Appay, M.-D., Kedinger, M., Triadou, N., et al. 1983. Enterocyte-like differentiation and polarization of the human colon carcinoma cell line Caco-2 in culture. *Biol. Cell* 47:323–30

50. Quaroni, A., Kirsch, K., Weiser, M. M. 1979. Synthesis of membrane glycoproteins in rat small-intestinal villus cells. Redistribution of L-[1,5,6-^{3}H]fucose-labelled membrane glycoproteins among Golgi, lateral basal and microvillus membranes in vivo. *Biochem. J.* 182:203–12

51. Quaroni, A., Kirsch, K., Weiser, M. M. 1979. Synthesis of membrane glycoproteins in rat small-intestinal villus cells. Effect of colchicine on the redistribution of L-[1,5,6-^{3}H]fucose-labelled membrane glycoproteins among Golgi, lateral basal and microvillus membranes. *Biochem. J.* 182:213–21

52. Rindler, M. J., Ivanov, I. E., Plesken, H., Rodriguez-Boulan, E., Sabatini, D. D. 1984. Viral glycoproteins destined for apical or basolateral plasma membrane domains traverse the same Golgi apparatus during their intracellular trans-

port in doubly infected Madin-Darby Canine Kidney cells. *J. Cell Biol.* 98:1304–19

53. Rindler, M. J., Ivanov, I. E., Sabatini, D. D. 1987. Microtubule-acting drugs lead to the nonpolarized delivery of the influenza hemagglutinin to the cell surface of polarized Madin-Darby Canine Kidney cells. *J. Cell Biol.* 104:231–41

54. Rousset, M. 1986. The human colon carcinoma cell lines HT-29 and Caco-2: two in vitro models for the study of intestinal differentiation. *Biochimie* 68: 1035–40

55. Salas, P. J. I., Misek, D. E., Vega-Salas, D. E., Gundersen, D., Cereijido, M., et al. 1986. Microtubules and actin filaments are not critically involved in the biogenesis of epithelial cell surface polarity. *J. Cell Biol.* 102:1853–67

56. Salas, P. J. I., Vega-Salas, D., Misek, D., Rodriguez-Boulan, E. 1985. Intracellular routes of apical and basolateral plasma membrane proteins to the surface of epithelial cells. *Pflügers Arch.* 405:S152–S157

57. Simons, K., Fuller, S. D. 1985. Cell surface polarity in epithelia. *Annu. Rev. Cell Biol.* 1:243–288

58. Strous, G. J. A. M., Willemsen, R., van Kerkhof, P., Slot, J. W., Geuze, H. J., et al. 1983. Vesicular stomatitis virus glycoprotein, albumin, and transferrin are transported to the cell surface via the same Golgi vesicles. *J. Cell Biol.* 97:1815–22

59. Traber, M. G., Kayden, H. J., Rindler, M. J. 1987. Polarized secretion of newly synthesized lipoproteins by the Caco-2 human intestinal cell line. *J. Lipid Res.* 28:1350–63

60. Urban, J., Parczyk, K., Leutz, A., Kayne, M., Kondor-Koch, C. 1987. Constitutive apical secretion of an 80-kD sulfated glycoprotein complex in the polarized epithelial Madin-Darby Canine Kidney cell line. *J. Cell Biol.* 105:2735–43

61. Vale, R. D. 1987. Intracellular transport using microtubule-based motors. *Annu. Rev. Cell Biol.* 3:347–78

62. Wall, D. A., Hubbard, A. L. 1985. Receptor-mediated endocytosis of asialoglycoproteins by rat liver hepatocytes: biochemical characterization of the endosomal compartments. *J. Cell Biol.* 101:2104–12

63. Yamashiro, D. J., Maxfield, F. R. 1984. Acidification of endocytic compartments and the intracellular pathways of ligands and receptors. *J. Cell. Biochem.* 26:231–46

64. Yokota, S., Fahimi, H. D. 1981. Immunocytochemical localization of albumin in the secretory apparatus of rat liver parenchymal cells. *Proc. Natl. Acad. Sci. USA* 78:4970–74

Annu. Rev. Physiol. 1989. 51:771–84

VESICLE RECYCLING AND CELL-SPECIFIC FUNCTION IN KIDNEY EPITHELIAL CELLS

Dennis Brown

Renal Unit, Massachusetts General Hospital and Department of Pathology, Harvard Medical School, Boston, Massachusetts 02114

INTRODUCTION

The recycling of plasma membrane components by exocytosis and endocytosis is a general phenomenon that allows cells to regulate the variety and/or the number of membrane proteins that are required for specific cellular functions. While recycling events have been studied extensively for many receptors and their associated ligands, other membrane proteins including specific transporters, channels, and enzymes also appear to be regulated by similar mechanisms. This establishment, maintenance, and modulation of plasma membrane domains is of critical importance to the function of polarized epithelial cells, which are responsible for the vectorial transport of many ions and molecules between distinct extracellular compartments (9, 26, 29). Epithelial cells lining the urinary tubule show many remarkable examples of plasma membrane polarity, and much of our current knowledge concerning the generation of epithelial cell polarity has come from studies using kidney epithelial cells in culture (29).

In vivo the kidney must respond quickly to alterations in the extracellular environment in order to maintain body fluid and electrolyte homeostasis. Thus the reabsorptive and secretory capacity of the epithelial cells lining the urinary tubule is constantly changing; in some cases, this change occurs by shuttling specific plasma membrane components to and from the cell surface by means of specialized transport vesicles. This phenomenon is particularly well developed in the kidney collecting duct, which contains two distinct types of epithelial cells, principal cells and intercalated cells. Both of these

771

0066-4278/89/0315-0771$02.00

cell types modulate the function of their plasma membranes by the insertion and removal of specific components that are packaged into exo- and endocytotic vesicles. In the intercalated cell a proton-pumping ATPase is recycled between a characteristic set of vesicles and the plasma membrane (13, 28); in the principal cell, a "water channel" is moved to and from the apical membrane following vasopressin stimulation of these cells (18, 23, 36). In both cell types vesicles with a distinct cytoplasmic coat are involved in the shuttling process, but our work reveals that the coating material is different in the two systems. In principal cells, clathrin-coated vesicles participate in the endocytotic phase of water channel recycling (3, 6); in intercalated cells, recycled vesicles are coated with the cytoplasmic domains of proton pumps, a major molecule transported by these vesicles (1).

WATER CHANNEL RECYCLING IN PRINCIPAL CELLS

Principal cells of the kidney collecting duct respond to the antidiuretic hormone, vasopressin, by increasing the water permeability of the apical plasma membrane from a virtually water-impermeable state to a normal level of permeability that is generally associated with most biological membranes. This alteration of membrane permeability allows osmotic equilibration to occur between the urine in the tubule lumen and the hypertonic interstitium of the kidney medulla; it is of critical importance to the maintenance of body fluid homeostasis. On the basis of many morpho-functional studies, carried out mainly on the toad urinary bladder (a vasopressin-sensitive model of the collecting duct), it is believed that proteinaceous water channels located within the membranes of some cytoplasmic vesicles are delivered by exocytosis to the apical plasma membrane following vasopressin stimulation (18, 23, 36). These water-permeable patches of membrane are incorporated into the previously impermeable membrane and result in the observed increase in membrane permeability.

These specialized membrane patches can be visualized using the freeze-fracture technique, where they appear as discrete aggregates or clusters of intramembranous particles (IMPs) within the lipid bilayer (7, 15, 18, 19). These IMP clusters are closely related to vasopressin-induced transepithelial water flow in all vasopressin-sensitive epithelia so far examined, i.e. amphibian urinary bladder, amphibian epidermis, and collecting duct principal cells. Most importantly, IMP clusters appear on the apical plasma membrane of principal cells in parallel with the increase in urinary concentration in vasopressin-treated Brattleboro rats that lack endogenous vasopressin (15). By a combination of thin section and freeze-fracture electron microscopy, Brown & Orci showed (3) that these vasopressin-induced clusters are located in clathrin-coated pits on the apical plasma membrane of principal cells

(Figure 1). This was achieved by exposing the cells to the polyene antibiotic, filipin, which leaves clathrin-coated domains intact, but perturbs the structure of the rest of the plasma membrane (Figure 1A and B). The protein A-gold technique confirms that the coated domains associated with apical plasma membranes of principal cells contain clathrin (Figure 1C). The specific anticlathrin antibody used was kindly provided by Dr. Daniel Louvard, Pasteur Institute, Paris. Using horseradish peroxidase as a marker, Brown et al subsequently showed that vasopressin induces clathrin-mediated endocytosis in principal cells (6). Endocytosis occurs even in the continued presence of the hormone, an indication that apical membrane segments, presumably containing the IMP clusters, are continuously recycled during hormone action. However, upon removal of the hormonal stimulus, an even greater endocytotic uptake of tracer occurs and IMP clusters disappear from the plasma membrane (17, 36). This indicates that during vasopressin withdrawal water-permeable patches are removed from the apical membrane, but exocytosis no longer occurs, or is markedly reduced. The membrane, therefore, returns to its previous water-impermeable state. Clathrin-mediated endocytosis has been extensively investigated in other cell types, particularly in relation to the internalization of cell surface receptors (14). Its role in the principal cell apical membrane appears to reflect an adaptation of a similar mechanism for the internalization of specific segments of plasma membrane, but it is important to realize that in this case the internalized molecules are mediators of the final biological effect of the hormone and are not hormone receptors, which are located on the basolateral plasma membrane. However, the precise mechanism of water channel uptake may be somewhat different in the toad bladder, where an involvement of clathrin-coated pits has not yet been demonstrated.

This description of the cell biology of vasopressin action predicts that endocytotic vesicles whose recycling is induced by the hormone should carry water channels on their limiting membranes and should, therefore, be highly permeable to water. By allowing these vesicles to endocytose 6-carboxyfluorescein or FITC-dextran introduced into the tubule lumen, we measured their water permeability directly using the technique of fluorescence quenching. The rate of shrinkage of isolated vesicles upon exposure to a hypertonic solution, coupled to the activation energy of this process, reveals the presence of a water channel in membranes. Data show that endosomes that are internalized in the presence, but not in the absence, of vasopressin do indeed have permeability properties consistent with the presence of a water channel (34).

There are still many unresolved questions concerning the mechanism of vasopressin action on membrane permeability. While current evidence strongly suggests that recycling of a water channel is responsible for the biological action of the hormone, we still have little notion of the nature of this channel.

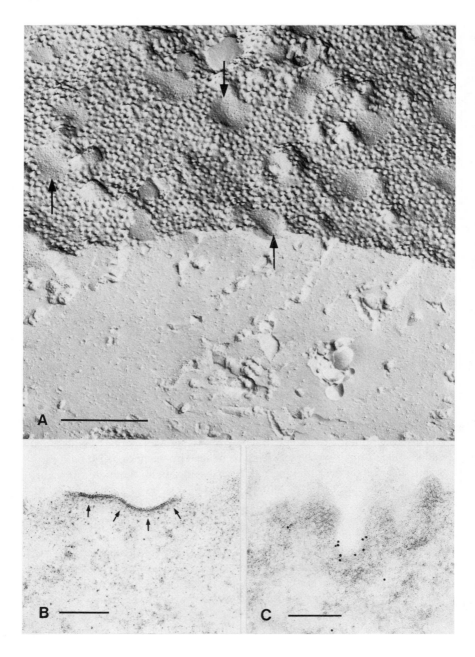

Is it a single transmembrane protein, or does the appearance of IMP clusters on the apical membrane alter the local protein-lipid environment so that water can now move rapidly between the proteins, rather than through an aqueous pore? In addition, it is possible that the permeability of the water channel may be modulated after it is in place in the apical membrane (8), which would provide another level at which membrane water permeability may be controlled.

In the collecting duct, the mode of formation of the IMP clusters on the apical membrane is unknown. Although events in the toad bladder indicate that exocytosis of preformed IMP clusters occurs (23, 36), this has not yet been shown in the kidney. This is because the IMP clusters in the principal cell have a looser morphology than in the bladder, and they cannot be readily identified on intracellular vesicles that have a high degree of membrane curvature. In the toad bladder the IMP clusters form tightly packed arrays on membranes and they can easily be followed by freeze-fracture as they recycle. Because IMP clusters in the kidney are associated with clathrin-coated pits, it is possible that the morphologically detectable clusters reflect only part of the cycle, i. e. the endocytotic phase. If water channel clusters are inserted intact into the apical membranes of principal cells by exocytosis, then they must rapidly associate with a clathrin coat following insertion. An alternative explanation is that water channels are not initially clustered, but only assume this form upon becoming concentrated into coated pits prior to internalization. Answers to these questions will require further purification of the recycled

←———

Figure 1 (A) Freeze-fracture replica of apical region of a principal cell from a homozygous Brattleboro rat treated with exogenous vasopressin. After fixation the tissue was exposed to filipin, which disrupts most of the apical membrane, but leaves vasopressin-induced IMP clusters intact *(arrows)*. These clusters are believed to be specific water-permeable patches in the membrane in which water channels are concentrated. As shown in Figures 1*B* and 1*C*, they correspond to clathrin-coated pits on the apical plasma membrane. Bar = 0.5 μm.

(B) Thin section of part of the apical region of a principal cell from a Brattleboro rat, treated with vasopressin. Following exposure to filipin, as in Figure 1*A*, most of the apical plasma membrane loses its trilaminar structure. However, selected regions are not perturbed by filipin and these regions have an underlying clathrin coat on the cytoplasmic side of the membrane *(arrows)*. Since these areas are unique in their resistance to filipin deformation, they must correspond to the membrane domains that contain the IMP aggregates shown in Figure 1*A*. Bar = 0.2μm.

(C) Apical region of a principal cell from kidney collecting duct, embedded at low temperature in Lowicryl K4M and incubated to reveal clathrin antigenic sites using the protein A-gold technique. The anti-clathrin antibody was provided by Dr. Daniel Louvard, Pasteur Institute, Paris. This procedure was used to show that the vasopressin-induced coated pits on the apical membrane of principal cells were clathrin-coated pits. In some cases, these coated invaginations took the form of omega figures, as shown here, whereas other coated membrane regions were only slightly indented, or flat, as shown in Figure 1*B*. Bar = 0.2 μm vesicles, and identification of specific proteins as candidate water channels; initial steps in this direction have been reported recently for the toad urinary bladder (16).

PROTON PUMP RECYCLING IN INTERCALATED CELLS

By reabsorbing filtered bicarbonate and regenerating bicarbonate consumed by metabolic processes, the kidney plays a key role in acid-base homeostasis. This is accomplished by net acid secretion and is performed mainly by the proximal tubule and the collecting duct (10). Proton secretion in the collecting duct is carried out primarily by a highly specialized subpopulation of cells known as intercalated cells and is mediated by an ATP-dependent proton pump (11, 12, 33). Intercalated cells are members of a family of cells known collectively as "mitochondria-rich" cells, which are found in a variety of transporting epithelia. They are all rich in carbonic anhydrase, they all have characteristic rod-shaped IMPs when examined by freeze-fracture, and as their name suggests, they contain large numbers of mitochondria compared to the adjacent cells in the same epithelia (25). Much of our current understanding of the role of mitochondria-rich cells in transepithelial proton transport has come from work on the turtle urinary bladder epithelium (30), which contains large numbers of these cells. Several morpho-functional studies reveal alterations in the appearance of these cells under different conditions that modify epithelial proton secretion (20, 21). These modifications are especially evident at the level of the apical plasma membrane, where the number and size of apical microvilli and microplicae can vary enormously. The number of specialized rod-shaped IMPs in the apical plasma membrane of these cells is also highly variable.

It is now clear that when proton secretion is stimulated by systemic acidosis or by increasing the pCO_2 of the serosal bathing solution in vitro, specialized vesicles that are located in the cytoplasm of intercalated cells move to and fuse with the plasma membrane, thus inserting proton pumps into the membrane (13, 21, 28, 31). The characteristic features of these transporting vesicles are illustrated in Figure 2. The endocytotic nature of these vesicles was subsequently shown using horseradish peroxidase as a tracer (5). The vesicles are, therefore, involved in the shuttling of proton pumps both to and from the plasma membrane (Figure 2A). Initially the presence of proton pumps on the limiting membrane of the vesicles was demonstrated using fluorescent pH markers to determine the pH of the vesicle interior (13, 28). Our recent work focuses on the use of specific antibodies to localize H^+ATPase molecules in intercalated cells and on the use of the rapid-freeze, deep-etch procedure to examine the cytoplasmic domain of membrane-associated proton pumps (1, 2).

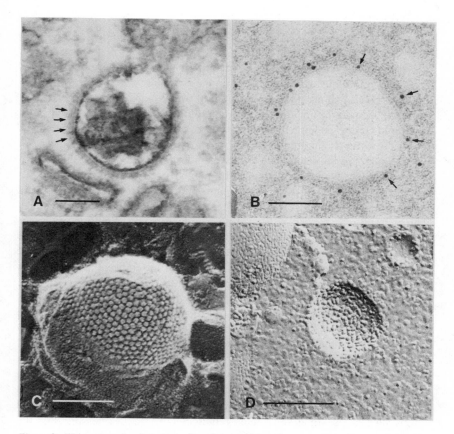

Figure 2 This composite plate shows four characteristics of the specialized proton-transporting vesicles that are found in the cytoplasm of intercalated cells.

(A) Vesicle from an intercalated cell that has internalized horseradish peroxidase from the collecting duct lumen. The HRP is mainly localized in the stud-coated vesicles *(arrows)*, which demonstrates their role in endocytosis. Bar = 0.2 μm.

(B) Vesicle that has been labeled using the protein A-gold technique to localize proton pumps. The section was incubated first with an affinity-purified antibody against the 70-kd subunit of the bovine medullary proton pump, followed by 8-nm protein A-gold complexes. The gold particles are located over the cytoplasmic coat of this vesicle *(arrows)*; hence the 70-kd subunit forms part of the cytoplasmic domain of the proton pump. Bar = 0.1 μm.

(C) Cytoplasmic surface of a vesicle from a toad bladder mitochondria-rich cell that was rapidly frozen, deep-etched, and rotary-shadowed with platinum and carbon. The cytoplasmic studs, seen in the previous figures are about 10 nm in diameter and form tightly packed hexagonal arrays on the vesicle. These studs represent the cytoplasmic domain of proton pumps. Bar = 0.1 μm (Reproduced from 1.)

(D) Cytoplasmic vesicle from an intercalated cell, seen by conventional freeze-fracture. Many rod-shaped IMPs are present on the P-face of these vesicles *(center)*, whereas complementary elongated depressions are visible on the E-face *(top left)*. These IMPs probably represent a specialized integral membrane protein that is associated with intercalated cell membranes, and may either be part of the transmembrane domain of the proton pump itself, or a membrane component that is targeted to the same membrane domains as the proton pump. Bar = 0.2 μm.

Rapid-Freezing and Freeze-Fracture

The specialized vesicles that transport proton pumps in these cells are, as described in the Introduction, coated on their cytoplasmic surface with stud-like projections that are unrelated to clathrin (4). We now know that the studs represent the cytoplasmic domains of the proton pumps carried by the vesicles (1). Rapid-freeze, deep-etch views of the studs reveal paracrystalline arrays of 10-nm projections that are hexagonally packed on the cytoplasmic surface of parts of the plasma membrane, and on vesicle membranes (Figure 2C). Identical images were obtained when immunoaffinity-purified bovine medullary proton pumps were incorporated into pure phospholipid liposomes and examined by the same procedure (1). Using conventional freeze-fracture, characteristic rod-shaped IMPs are found on membranes (both plasma membranes and intracellular vesicle membranes) from intercalated cells (Figure 2D) and all other members of the mitochondria-rich cell family thus far examined (25). These IMPs, which are presumed to represent a special class of integral membrane protein, may be part of the proton pump, perhaps the transmembrane domain (30). This idea is supported by the work of Stetson & Steinmetz (32), who describe two types of mitochondria-rich cells in the turtle bladder, one having rod-shaped IMPs and studs on the apical plasma membrane, and the other having basolateral studs and basolateral rod-shaped IMPs. These are believed to be proton-secreting and bicarbonate-secreting cells, respectively (see below). However, rod-shaped IMPs were not a feature of liposomes into which purified proton pumps had been incorporated, and they are not found in all cells that have immunocytochemically detectable pumps such as proximal convoluted tubule cells (25). It is possible that the rod-shaped IMP represents a particular form of the pump that is different in some cells, or it may be a distinct protein that is targeted to the same domains as the pump in some, but not all cells. Finally, the rod-shaped IMP could be a protein-lipid complex whose formation depends on the lipid composition of the membrane.

Immunocytochemical Localization of Proton Pumps

To provide further evidence that the stud-coated membrane domains contain subunits of the proton pump, polyclonal, affinity-purified antibodies against the 31-, 56-, and 70-kd subunits of the bovine proton pump were used to immunolabel intercalated cells using the protein A-gold technique on thin sections of kidney embedded in Lowicryl K4M (1, 2, 27). Gold particle label was found associated with the stud-coated regions of the plasma membrane, as well as with the specialized vesicles that are involved in the transport of proton pumps in these cells (Figures 2B and 3A). In the medulla all intercalated cells (with the exception of some cells in the initial portion of outer stripe collecting ducts) had a heavy apical labeling with the antibodies, consistent with data showing that medullary collecting ducts have a high rate of hydrogen ion secretion (10). In contrast, intercalated cells in the cortical collecting duct had three patterns of labeling (Figure 3B). Some had apical pumps, some had basolateral pumps, and some had a nonpolar, diffuse localization that, at the electron microscopic level, was accounted for mainly by the labeling of numerous cytoplasmic vesicles, although labeling of free cytoplasmic subunits could not be ruled out. This is consistent with physiological evidence that the cortical collecting duct can secrete either net acid or net bicarbonate under different physiological conditions (22). It was previously proposed that cells with apical and basolateral proton pumps could coexist in the cortical collecting duct (28). Moreover, Schwartz et al (28) provided evidence suggesting that at least some intercalated cells could reverse their functional polarity by transferring proton pumps from their apical plasma membrane to their basolateral membrane and vice versa. This would occur as the acid-base status of the animal changed. Our data show an inverse relationship between the number of cortical intercalated cells with basolateral and diffuse staining within individual animals, which suggests that at least these classes of cells may be interconvertible (2). The percentage of apically stained cells varies less among different animals, but, nevertheless, the variation is sufficient (between 30 and 50%) to suggest that these cells, too, may not be a completely static population. Clearly, intercalated cells from animals that have been rendered acidotic or alkalotic must be examined and quantified to determine the distribution of cells in the three staining categories with respect to the total population of intercalated cells. A recent thin section study examining intercalated cells in different acid-base conditions concluded that not all cortical cells modulate their morphological appearance under different conditions, which may mean that some cells have a fixed phenotype (35).

These observations pose fundamental questions concerning the mode of targeting the proton pump in intercalated cells. It is generally believed that information that determines whether a given protein will be inserted into the apical or the basolateral plasma membrane of epithelial cells is contained within the protein molecule itself (9). We must now determine whether the proton pump is targeted in a different way, or whether the subunit composition of this multisubunit enzyme is different in the two membrane domains; it is possible, for example, that the targeting information will be contained in a pump subunit against which antibodies are not yet available. At present, our antibodies against four of the major subunits that comprise about 80% of the mass of the pump all co-localize in the same membrane regions.

Another intriguing question that remains concerns the assembly of the pump in the transporting vesicles. Based on extraction of pump subunits from kidney vesicles at pH 11.5, it appears that the 31-, 56-, and 70-kd subunits

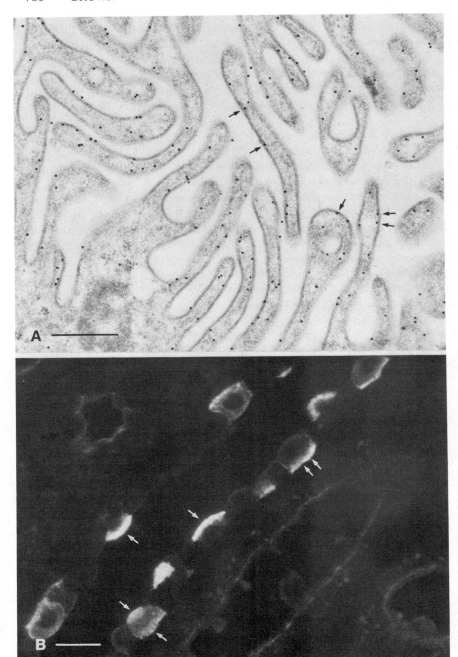

are, as expected from the rapid-freeze and immunocytochemical studies, peripheral membrane proteins (2). A 25-kd subunit, on the other hand, is not removed from membranes at high pH, which suggests that it may be an integral membrane protein. Since it is probable that this subunit is produced in the rough endoplasmic reticulum, whereas the three others are made on free ribosomes, where does assembly of the complete pump occur and what factors regulate assembly of the pump? These questions may eventually be answered by immunocytochemical approaches combined with analysis of isolated cell vesicle fractions.

Finally, the bovine medullary proton pump is an enzyme composed of many subunits, in common with some other proton pumps isolated from different sources (33). The subunit structure of the pump is similar when it is isolated using two completely independent procedures, which indicates that all subunits are part of, or closely associated with, the enzyme (11, 12). However, the roles of the individual subunits are at present unknown, and it will be important to determine which of the isolated subunits are critical for proton pumping activity, and which may have other functions, such as targeting the pump to specific membrane domains. This type of analysis has already been performed for some proton pumps and candidate subunits for the transmembrane proton channel and the catalytic site have been identified (33).

SUMMARY

Epithelial cell function depends on the precise delivery of newly synthesized and recycled membrane components to specific plasma membrane domains. The establishment and maintenance of apical and basolateral plasma membrane domains of quite distinct composition enable epithelia to undertake the vectorial transport of fluid, ions, and a variety of other molecules from one compartment to another. In many epithelia this capacity for transepithelial transport can be rapidly and reversibly modulated by prevailing physiological

←——

Figure 3 *(A)* Section through the apical microvilli and microplicae of an intercalated cell following embedding in Lowicryl K4M. The section was incubated with specific antibody against the 70-kd subunit of the proton pump, and antigenic sites were revealed using 15-nm protein A-gold complexes. In sections perpendicular to the plasma membrane, the cytoplasmic coat (see also Figure 2) can be seen, and the majority of the gold particles are located directly over or close to this coating material *(arrows)*. Bar = 0.2 μm.

(B) Semithin (1 μm) section of Epon-embedded rat kidney cortex incubated by indirect immunofluorescence to reveal the 31-kd subunit of proton pumps. Whereas all intercalated cells in the inner stripe (and most of the outer stripe) of the outer medulla have only apical proton pumps, three distinct patterns of labeling are found in cortical collecting ducts. Some cells have uniquely apical labeling *(single arrow)*, others have basolateral labeling *(double arrows)*, and a third population of cells has a more diffuse pattern of labeling that is not restricted to one pole of the cell *(arrows)*. Bar = 20 μm. (Reproduced from 2.)

conditions. For example, in the collecting duct of the kidney the two epithelial cell types have both evolved efficient systems that enable such alterations in cell-specific function to occur in response to different stimuli. In both vasopressin-sensitive principal cells and the acid-secreting intercalated cells, specialized membrane patches containing water channels and proton pumps, respectively, are inserted into and removed from plasma membranes on demand and thus dramatically alter the properties of plasma membranes in these cells. Although the basic mechanism in both cells is the recycling of vesicles containing the membrane components of interest, the specific details of the process appear different in the two cell types. In the principal cell vesicle recycling is induced by a specific hormone, vasopressin, and involves clathrin-coated vesicles in the endocytotic step of the cycle. The vesicles that deliver water channels to the cell surface have not yet been identified. In the intercalated cell the transporting vesicles are highly specialized and are coated with the cytoplasmic domains of proton pumps. These vesicles do not have a clathrin coat and therefore represent a distinct class of coated vesicle. As more becomes known about transporting vesicles that are involved in different functions within the cell, it is becoming increasingly clear that it is no longer valid to separate vesicles simply into coated, i.e. clathrin-coated, and smooth vesicles. Three types of coating material have already been described on so-called coated vesicles (1, 14, 24), and it is likely that as our ability to detect the cytoplasmic domains of more proteins involved in intracellular transport increases, we will find that all vesicles are coated, but some are more coated than others. These coating molecules will include the cytoplasmic domains of proteins that are being delivered by the vesicles, as well as specific proteins that are involved in vesicle targeting, vesicle movement, and vesicle fusion or fission.

ACKNOWLEDGMENTS

I am indebted to many colleagues who have made major contributions over the last several years to the work described in this review. This work has received continuous support from the Swiss National Science Foundation and from the National Institutes of Health. D. B. is an Established Investigator of the American Heart Association.

Literature Cited

1. Brown, D., Gluck, S., Hartwig, J. 1987. Structure of the novel membrane-coating material in proton-secreting epithelial cells and identification as an H^+ATPase. *J. Cell. Biol.* 105:1637–48
2. Brown, D., Hirsch, S., Gluck, S. 1988. An H^+ATPase in opposite plasma membrane domains in kidney epithelial cell subpopulations. *Nature* 331:622–24
3. Brown, D., Orci, L. 1983. Vasopressin stimulates formation of coated pits in rat kidney collecting ducts. *Nature* 302: 253–55
4. Brown, D., Orci, L. 1986. The "coat" of kidney intercalated cell tubulovesicles does not contain clathrin. *Am. J. Physiol.* 250:C605–C608
5. Brown, D., Weyer, P., Orci, L. 1987. Non-clathrin coated vesicles are involved in endocytosis in kidney collect-

ing duct intercalated cells. *Anat. Rec.* 218:237–42

6. Brown, D., Weyer, P., Orci, L. 1988. Vasopressin stimulates endocytosis in kidney collecting duct principal cells. *Eur. J. Cell Biol.* 46:336–41

7. Chevalier, J., Bourguet, J., Hugon, J. S. 1974. Membrane associated particles: distribution in frog urinary bladder epithelium at rest and after oxytocin treatment. *Cell Tissue Res.* 152:129–40

8. Chevalier, J., Parisi, M., Bourguet, J. 1983. The rate limiting step in hydrosmotic response of frog urinary bladder. A freeze-fracture study of different temperatures and medium pH. *Cell Tissue Res.* 228:345–55

9. Garoff, H. 1985. Using recombinant DNA techniques to study protein targeting in the eukaryotic cell. *Annu. Rev. Cell Biol.* 1:403–45

10. Giebisch, G. 1986. Mechanisms of renal tubule acidification. *Klin. Wochenschr.* 64:853–61

11. Gluck, S., Caldwell, J. 1987. Immunoaffinity purification and characterization of H^+ATPase from bovine kidney. *J. Biol. Chem.* 262:15780–89

12. Gluck, S., Caldwell, J. 1988. Proton-translocating ATPase from bovine kidney medulla: partial purification and reconstitution. *Am. J. Physiol.* 254:F71–F79

13. Gluck, S., Cannon, C., Al-Awqati, Q. 1982. Exocytosis regulates urinary acidification in turtle bladder by rapid insertion of H^+ATPase into the luminal membrane. *Proc. Natl. Acad. Sci. USA* 79:4327–31

14. Goldstein, J. L., Anderson, R. G. W., Brown, M. S. 1979. Coated pits, coated vesicles and receptor-mediated endocytosis. *Nature* 279:679–85

15. Harmanci, M. C., Stern, P., Kachadorian, W. A., Valtin, H., DiScala, V. A. 1980. Vasopressin and collecting duct intramembranous particle clusters: a dose-response relationship. *Am. J. Physiol.* 239:F560–F564

16. Harris, H. W., Murphy, H. E., Willingham, M. C., Handler, J. S. 1987. Isolation and characterization of specialized regions of toad urinary bladder apical plasma membrane involved in the water permeability response to antidiuretic hormone. *J. Membr. Biol.* 96:175–86

17. Harris, H. W., Wade, J. B., Handler, J. S. 1986. Transepithelial water flow regulates apical membrane retrieval in antidiuretic-hormone-stimulated toad urinary bladder. *J. Clin. Invest.* 78:703–12

18. Hays., R. M. 1983. Alteration of lumi-

nal membrane structure by antidiuretic hormone. *Am. J. Physiol.* 245:C289–C296

19. Kachadorian, W. A., Levine, S. D., Wade, J. B., DiScala, V. A., Hays, R. M. 1977. Relationship of aggregated intramembranous particles to water permeability in vasopressin-treated toad urinary bladder. *J. Clin. Invest.* 59:576–81

20. Kaissling, B. 1982. Structural aspects of adaptive changes in renal electrolyte secretion. *Am. J. Physiol.* 243:F211–F226

21. Madsen, K. M., Tisher, C. C. 1986. Structural-functional relationships along the distal nephron. *Am. J. Physiol.* 250:F1–F15

22. McKinney, T. D., Burg, M. B. 1977. Bicarbonate transport by rabbit cortical collecting tubules. *J. Clin. Invest.* 60:766–68

23. Muller, J., Kachadorian, W. A., DiScala, V. A. 1980. Evidence that ADH-stimulated intramembrane particle aggregates are transferred from cytoplasmic to luminal membranes in toad bladder epithelial cells. *J. Cell Biol.* 85:83–95

24. Orci, L., Glick, B. S., Rothman, J. E. 1986. A new type of coated vesicular carrier that appears not to contain clathrin: its possible role in protein transport within the Golgi stack. *Cell* 46:171–84

25. Orci, L., Humbert, F., Brown, D., Perrelet, A. 1981. Membrane ultrastructure in urinary tubules. *Int. Rev. Cytol.* 73:183–242

26. Rindler, M. J., Ivanov, I. E., Rodriguez-Boulan, E., Sabatini, D. D. 1982. Biogenesis of epithelial cell plasma membranes. In *Membrane Recycling. Ciba Found. Symp.*, 92:184. London: Pitman

27. Roth, J., Bendayan, M., Orci, L. 1978. Ultrastructural localization of intracellular antigens by the use of protein A-gold complex. *J. Histochem. Cytochem.* 26:1074–81

28. Schwartz, G. L., Barasch, J., Al-Awqati, Q. 1985. Plasticity of functional epithelial cell polarity. *Nature* 318:368–71

29. Simons, K. 1987. Membrane traffic in an epithelial cell line derived from the dog kidney. *Kidney Int.* 32(Suppl. 23):S201–S207

30. Steinmetz, P. R. 1986. Cellular organization of urinary acidification. *Am. J. Physiol.* 251:F173–F187

31. Stetson, D. L., Steinmetz, P. R. 1983. Role of membrane fusion in CO_2 stimulation of proton secretion by turtle

bladder. *Am. J. Physiol.* 245:C113–C120

32. Stetson, D. L., Steinmetz, P. R. 1985. α and β types of carbonic anhydrase-rich cells in turtle bladder. *Am. J. Physiol.* 249:F553–F565

33. Stone, D. 1988. Proton translocating ATPases: issues in structure and function. *Kidney Int.* 33:767–74

34. Verkman, A. S., Lencer, W., Brown, D., Ausiello, D. A. 1988. Endosomes from kidney collecting tubule cells contain the vasopressin-sensitive water channel. *Nature.* 333:268–69

35. Verlander, J. W., Madsen, K. M., Tisher, C. C. 1988. Effect of acute respiratory acidosis on two populations of intercalated cells in rat cortical collecting duct. *Am. J. Physiol.* 253:F1142–F1156

36. Wade, J. B., Stetson, D. L., Lewis, S. A. 1981. ADH action: evidence for a membrane shuttle mechanism. *Ann. NY Acad. Sci.* 372:106–17

Annu. Rev. Physiol. 1989. 51:785–95

DEVELOPMENT AND ALTERATION OF POLARITY

Marcelino Cereijido, Rubén G. Contreras, and Lorenza Gonzalez-Mariscal

Department of Physiology and Biophysics. Center of Research and Advanced Studies, México

INTRODUCTION

At the beginning of this century, Galeotti (28, 29) explained the electrical potential across the frog skin by assuming that its epithelium is more permeable to Na^+ in the direction of pond-side to blood side than in the reverse direction; his proposal was scorned because it was considered in violation of the laws of Thermodynamics. We now know that Galeotti's assumption was correct: Epithelial cells exhibit vectorial transport due to an asymmetric distribution of pumps, channels, and carriers in their apical or basolateral poles. However, we do not yet know how this polarization is achieved and maintained.

Although the fence like properties of the tight junction cannot sort membrane components per se: the tight junction (TJ) has been regarded as the cause of this polarity on the basis that: (a) Proteins were considered to diffuse freely in the plane of the membrane and required a fence to retain them in a given domain. (b) A TJ would afford such a fence because it forms a continuous seal that circles the cell at the limit between the apical and the basolateral regions. (c) Opening of the TJ by removal of Ca^{2+} and addition of chelating agents results in a loss of polarization (for a review see 13). These observations have since been reinterpreted, and experimental conditions have been introduced (a) to follow polarization and junction formation in model systems (14–16, 74, 77, 79), (b) to delay polarization and TJ formation (30), (c) to open and reseal already established TJs (43), (d) to promote TJ formation in cells that lack this structure (3, 20, 25, 26, 55, 61, 67, 68, 84, 88), and (e) to perturb a previously established polarity (7, 17–19, 52). These

785

0066-4278/89/0315-0785$02.00

approaches have yielded information on the development of polarity and TJs, as well as on the complex interrelationship between the two phenomena.

POLARITY OF NONEPITHELIAL CELLS

Polarity is a steady state situation resulting from molecular sorting of the traffic between the cell surface and internal organelles (see Rodriguez-Boulan & Salas, Hubbard et al, Brown, and Roth, this volume), which may even be observed in cells that lack TJs. Thus, microorganisms such as *Caulobacter crescentus* exhibit an asymmetric distribution of membrane features (65, 82); skeletal muscle fibers present acetylcholine receptors in restricted domains of their membrane (52); osteoclasts confine proton-ATPase to their ruffled border (5); and viruses are known to bud selectively only from specific areas on the surface of presumptive myocytes (62).

DEVELOPMENT OF POLARITY

When cells from lines that retain a considerable degree of polarization are harvested with trypsin-EDTA (ethylene diamine tetracetic acid), they lose this asymmetry, but regain it upon plating. Since the degree of development and sealing of TJs in these preparations can be easily assessed from the magnitude of transepithelial electrical resistance (TER) (Figure 1, curve 1), the study of polarization and, in particular, its relationship to TJs has been greatly stimulated. (15, 16). The asymmetric distribution of several glycoproteins on the surface of Madin-Darby canine kidney (MDCK) cells, both at subconfluent and confluent densities, shows a strong correlation with the development of TJs (33). Furthermore, some membrane antigens are incorporated in a polarized fashion into either apical or basolateral membranes only in cells with high, but not with low TER (59). In these cells there is a higher density of intramembranous particles (IMP) in the basolateral than in the apical region (12); the number of IMPs decreases during harvesting, but increases simultaneously with the development of TJs (35, 36). An analogous phenomenon was observed with the distribution of Na,K-ATPase, an enzyme normally confined to the basolateral side of MDCK cells (12, 34, 39).

However, the time course of polarization is not always parallel to that of TJ formation. Thus, polarization of alkaline phosphatase and γ-glutamyl transpeptidase in LLC-PK$_1$ cells is delayed with respect to the development of the TJs (68). Similarly, apical localization of alkaline phosphatase and basolateral localization of Na,K-ATPase are first observed after the formation of TJ in fetal rat colon (21). Therefore, whenever processes occur according to their spontaneous time courses, TJ development occurs simultaneously or precedes polarization, as if the latter has to wait until a fence is established. Conversely, Caldwell & McLaughin (10) observed that in distrophic rats, Na,K-ATPase loses its polarization in the apical pole of the retinal pigment cells and redistributes over the whole surface, coinciding with a breakdown of the TJ. However, these observations do not necessarily demonstrate that polarization depends on a fence provided by the TJ. The possibility exists that polarity and TJs result from simultaneous but independent mechanisms.

DEVELOPMENT OF POLARITY INDEPENDENT OF THE TJ

Epithelial cells cultured in suspension for 12–15 h display high affinity binding sites for soluble collagen, and their occupancy by collagen triggers the exocytosis of a second population of low-affinity binding sites. When

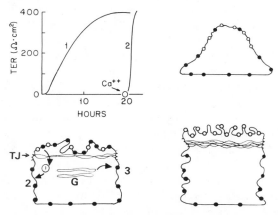

Figure 1   Relationship between polarity and tight junctions (TJ). *(upper left)* MDCK cells plated at confluence on a permeable support form TJs and develop a transepithelial electrical resistance (TER) that reaches a maximun in 10–15 h (curve 1) (15, 16). However, if 1 h after plating, monolayers are switched to Ca-free medium, they do not form TJs nor develop TER (circle) (31, 32). *(upper right)* These cells' basolateral markers (e.g. Na,K-ATPase: full circles) are distributed at random, but some of their apical markers may be (open circles) asymmetricly distributed in spite of the absence of TJs (92). If Ca^{2+} is added 20 hours after plating, TJs are quickly assembled and TER develops with much faster kinetics *(upper left,* curve 2) (31, 32). *(bottom left)* The quick formation of TJs traps some basolateral components on the apical (wrong) side. However, these TJs are gradually removed (step 1) until the cell achieves its correct polarization *(bottom right).* When G protein from the envelope of vesicular stomatitis viruses [a molecule normally addressed to the basolateral membrane (77)] is artificially inserted in the apical membrane, it is removed and readdressed to the basolateral domain (65) (step 1 *bottom left*). Na,K-ATPase is also removed from the apical domain but is not reinserted into the basolateral membrane. In this case the cell inserts a newly synthesized enzyme in the basolateral domain (R. G. Contreras et al, unpublished results). These processes demonstrate that the asymmetric distribution of membrane proteins may occur in the absence, or even in spite of the presence of TJs.

collagen is presented in the form of a solid support, these receptors are recruited to the membrane facing the adherent surface (81). This attachment permits a certain degree of polarization even in the absence of TJs (4, 5, 37, 44, 72, 75). Rapraeger et al (69) proposed that cell surface proteoglycan acts as a matrix receptor that binds epithelial cells to the underlying basement membrane, that this structure permits anchoring and spatial orientation of the cytoskeleton, and that this organelle provides in turn a framework for regional distribution of membrane components. Development of polarization sometimes requires contact with neighboring cells to trigger or orient the apical-basolateral axis (see 49). Absence of neighbors prompts cells to divide and enter a stage in which polarity is not yet expressed. Therefore, it is conceivable that the requirement of surrounding and contacting cells may not necessarily stem from the need for specific signals.

Although most epithelial cell lines polarize when attached to bare substrates, such as naked glass or plastic, the degree of polarization achieved is much higher when cells are grown on a collagen gel matrix or on a nitrocellulose filter (3, 24, 32, 71, 83, 86). Sometimes cells condition their own support. Thus, MDCK cells asymmetrically secrete the laminin and heparan sulphate proteoglycans that constitute their basement membrane (11). But in other cases, differentiation and polarity are not due to attachment to specific components, but to the fact that these substrates permit the access of nutrients from the basolateral side as in natural epithelia. Thus, cultures of mammary epithelium on collagen gels start secretion of milk proteins only when gels are released from the culture dish and allowed to contract and form a floating pad (24, 57), or when they are cultured on a Millipore filter (62); A6 cells only respond to antidiuretic hormones when grown in a chamber on permeable support (85). Likewise, endothelial cells only form TJs when cultured on a substrate coated with extracellular matrix (83).

The degree of polarization, as well as the specific proteins polarized at a given moment, varies during the cell cycle (1) and may require different triggers. MDCK cells plated at confluence and switched to Ca-free media show a negligible value of TER due to the absence of TJs (Figure 1). In these cells microvilli occupy only the free (luminal) border, but IMPs (31) and Na,K-ATPase (R. G. Contreras et al, unpublished results) are not polarized. Antigens on the other hand offer a somewhat complex picture. Antigens that occupy the apical domain in monolayers with TJs show a considerably degree of polarity even in the absence of TJs, but basolateral antigens exhibit a random distribution (91). Cells from the embryonic rat pancreas show clear polarization at stages in which TJs are not yet observed (41). Taken together, these studies indicate: (*a*) Polarization as well as synthesis, assembling, and sealing of TJs are greatly influenced by cell contacts, either with neighboring cells or with the substrate. (*b*) The same cell may express asymmetric distribution of certain membrane protein species, while the distribution of other proteins is random. (c) At least in some cases, polarization does not require TJs.

DEVELOPMENT OF POLARIZATION IN SPITE OF TJs

Polarization of certain membrane components not only may take place in the absence of the fence constituted by the TJs, but it may also proceed in spite of this structure. Thus, thyroid epithelial cells isolated from porcine or rat glands and cultured in suspension in the absence of thyroid stimulating hormone (TSH) form inside-out follicles, structures in which the cell polarity is inverted with respect to the initial orientation in the gland so that the apical surface, characterized by microvilli and limited by TJs, faces the culture medium (27, 47, 48). When the apical surface of these inside-out vesicles is coated with a hydrated collagen matrix, a lumen is formed in the center of the group of cells and polarity reverses so that now microvilli face the inner side, and TJs migrate in the plane of the membrane towards the basal pole, giving rise to a typical polarized follicle (6, 7, 17). A similar reversing phenomenon was observed in suspended aggregates of LLC-PK$_1$ cells (55, 92). A reversal of polarity was also observed in ectoderm cells extirpated from early gastrula and replaced in an inverted position (93). However, this phenomenon does not seem to depend exclusively on collagen, as reversal of polarity in thyroid epithelial cells may also be provoked by increasing the concentration of serum in the bathing medium (58).

Epithelial cells can transcytose, in a polarized fashion, a variety of molecules such as immunoglobulins, hormones, growth factors, and viral proteins from one pole to the other (42, 53). Some membrane components are first inserted in the basolateral region and transported in a later step to a permanent apical position (8, 45). During normal biogenesis in MDCK cells, vesicular stomatitis G protein is targeted to the basolateral side (77) as are native membrane proteins (2). However, when this protein is incorporated into the apical surface via virus fusion, it is quickly endocytosed and partially redistributed to the basolateral surface as if it were a newly synthesized basolateral protein (46, 64). Gonzalez-Mariscal et al observed that when Ca^{2+} is added to cells that have been incubated in Ca-free media for 20 h, TJs form with fast kinetics (30, 31), thus trapping roughly one third of the Na,K-ATPase on the apical (wrong) domain (Figure 1, curve z). This enzyme is nevertheless removed from this position with a half time of about 80 min. However, Na,K-ATPase is not relocated on the basolateral (correct) side, as in the case of viral protein G (R. G. Contreras et al, unpublished observations).

ROLE OF THE CYTOSKELETON

The interaction between membrane proteins and cytoplasmic structural proteins is thought to play an important role in the maintenance of polarity of the plasma membrane, as well as in the assembly and sealing of TJs (9, 40, 50, 51, 70). When cells are treated with drugs like cytochalasin B, TJs open and cells lose their polarity. However, it is not possible to determine if loss of polarity is causally related to loss of TJs. When polarized membrane proteins of MDCK cells are extracted with Triton X100 in a buffer that preserves the cytoskeleton, they are preferentially extracted from the incorrect domain. These results indicate that cytoskeletal anchoring is most effective for proteins that are anchored in the correct domain (80). Na,K-ATPase is almost completely confined to the basolateral side (12), but only 50% of it is immobilized (38). Ankyrin binds to the cytoskeleton and to Na,K-ATPAase, which has a basolateral distribution (56). This anchoring could actively prevent mixing of membrane proteins through the formation of topographically fixed structures on the membrane. When an anti-fodrin antibody or its Fab fragment are applied to permeabilized chromaffin cells, they specifically inhibit Ca^{2+}-induced catecholamine release by exocytosis, which suggests that fodrin and the cytoskeleton participate in the asymmetric secretion of proteins (63). However, association with the cytoskeleton does not seem to be a universal requirement. Thus, in MDCK cells in which the development of TJs was blocked by the use of drugs that interfere with the cytoskeleton, viruses bud only from their correct target membrane (79).

POLARIZATION OF MEMBRANE LIPIDS

Membrane lipids have a comparatively small degree of polarization. Some lipidic species are inserted asymetrically (91), but due to their ability to diffuse freely in the plane of the plasma membrane (74, 88), their restriction to a given pole of the cell requires a fence like the TJ. However, the efficiency of this restriction seems to be limited to lipids confined to the outer leaflet of the plasma membrane. Thus, Dragsten and coworkers (22, 23) marked the apical pole with two different types of lipid probes that were shown to diffuse freely in the plane of this membrane; the first type, with a negligible flip-flopping rate, could not pass beyond the TJ to gain access to the basolateral region. The second type, which had a measurable flip-flop rate, appeared on the basolateral side. They concluded that although none of the lipid probes can traverse the TJ, molecules of the second type were able to flip-flop from the outer to the inner leaflet of the apical membrane, diffuse on this leaflet until they reached the basolateral domain, and then jump back to the outer leaflet, and thus appear in the basolateral region. This interpretation, which implies that the TJ is only an extracellular fence (84), was confirmed by van Meer and coworkers (89) by fusing liposomes containing fluorescent lipids to the apical membrane of MDCK cells. When these liposomes were incorporated asymmetrically only in the outer leaflet, no transference of fluorescence to the basolateral region was observed. However when fused liposomes contained fluorescent probes in both leaflets, probes rapidly diffused to the basolateral domain after fusion. This indicates that apical-basolateral asymmetries in the distribution of lipids are due to the composition of the outer leaflet.

SUMMARY

Overall polarization of the plasma membrane of epithelial cells is the sum of the individual polarizations of its components. These individual polarizations in turn, may vary independently in degree (apical/basolateral ratio) and may be expressed at different stages of the cell cycle. They occur in response to cell contacts, nature of the support, and presence of triggering hormones; once established, polarizations may be subject to disruption and resorting. Epithelial cells transcytose receptors, insert membrane mechanisms during a particular period of the cell cycle, remove and relocate misplaced membrane components, and even completely reverse their polarity in the presence of well established TJs. TJs are not responsible for polarization but, ironically, they should be regarded as a result of the polarization process itself (31). The polarization of single cells, such as neurons and muscle cells mentioned at the beginning of this article, may represent extreme cases of cells that polarize but do not produce TJs. However, if an asymmetrically inserted protein is subsequently released from underlying anchoring structures (e.g. the cytoskeleton) to become free (e.g. 50% of Na,K-ATPase in MDCK cells), then the TJ may play a role in confining the free fraction to the apical or to the basolateral region. But even if TJs fail to completely segregate membrane components, mechanisms can restore polarization as in the case of the Na,K-ATPase trapped on the apical side. Lipid polarization seems to depend on the existence of the fence like character of the TJs and to the best of our knowledge lipid polarization is only found in epithelial cells with well established TJs.

ACKNOWLEDGMENT

We acknowledge the generous economic support of CONACYT, COSNET, and COSBEL, SA de CV of México, as well as the NIH (research grant AM26481).

Literature Cited

1. Agabian, N., Evinger, M., Parker, E. 1979. Generation of asymmetry during development. Segregation of type specific proteins in Caulobacter. J. Cell Biol. 81:123–36
2. Amerongen, H. M., Mack. J. A., Wilson, J. M., Bilbo, P. R., Neutra, M. R. 1987. A lateral membrane protein in intestinal epithelial cells. J. Cell Biol. 105:146a
3. Arthur, F. E., Shivers, R., Bowman, P. D. 1987. Astrocite mediated induction of tight junctions in brain capillary endothelium: an efficient in vitro model. Dev. Brain Res. 36:155–59
4. Balcarova-Stander, J., Pfeiffer, S. E., Fuller, S. D., Simons, K. 1984. Development of cell surface polarity in the epithelial Madin-Darby canine kidney (MDCK) cell line. EMBO J. 3:2687–94
5. Baron, R., Neff, L., Louvard, D., Courtoy, P. J. 1985. Cell-mediated extracellular acidification and bone resorption: evidence for a low pH in resorbing lacunae and localization of a 100-kD lysosomal membrane protein at the osteoclast ruffled border. J. Cell Biol. 101:2210–22
6. Barriere, H., Chambard, M., Mauchamp, J., Gabrion, J. 1986. Polarity reversal of inside-out follicles cultured within collagen gel: a structural study. Biol. Cell 57:39–52
7. Barriere, H., Chambard, M., Selzner, J., Mauchamp, J., Gabrion, J. 1988. Polarity reversal of inside-out thyroid follicles cultured with collagen gel: structure of the junctions assessed by freeze-fracture and lanthanum permeability. Biol. Cell. 62:133–44
8. Bartles, J. R., Feracci, H. M., Stieger, B., Hubbard, A. L. 1987. Biogenesis of the rat hepatocyte plasma membrane in vivo: comparison of the pathways taken by apical and basolateral proteins using subcellular fractionation. J. Cell Biol. 105:1241–51
9. Bentzel, C. J., Hainau, B., Ho, S., Huis, W., Edelman, A., et al. 1980. Cytoplasmic regulation of tight-junctions permeability: effect of plant cytokinins. Am. J. Physiol. 239:C75–89
10. Caldwell, R. B., McLaughin, B. J. 1984. Redistribution of Na-K-ATPase in the dystrophic rat retinal pigment epithelium. J. Neurocytol. 13:895–910
11. Caplan, J. M., Stow, J. L., Newman, A. P., Madri, J., Anderson, H. G., et al. 1987. Dependence on pH of polarized sorting of secreted proteins. Nature 329:632–35
12. Cereijido, M., Ehrenfeld, J., Meza, I., Martinez-Palomo, A. 1980. Structural and functional membrane polarity in cultured monolayers of MDCK cells. J. Membr. Biol. 52:147–59
13. Cereijido, M., Gonzalez-Mariscal, L., Avila, G., Contreras, R. G. 1988. Tight junctions. CRC Crit. Rev. Anat. Sci. 1: 171–91
14. Cereijido, M., Meza, I., Martinez-Palomo, A. 1981. Occluding junctions in cultured epithelial monolayers. Am. J. Physiol. 240:C96–102
15. Cereijido, M., Robbins, E. S., Dolan, W. J., Rotunno, C. A., Sabatini, D. D. 1978. Polarized monolayers formed by epithelial cells on a permeable and translucent support. J. Cell Biol. 77:853–80
16. Cereijido, M., Rotunno, C. A., Robbins, E. S., Sabatini, D. D. 1978. Polarized epithelial membranes produced in vitro. In Membrane Transport Processes, ed. J. F. Hoffman, pp. 443–61. New York: Raven
17. Chambard, M., Gabrion, J., Mauchamp, J. 1981. Influence of collagen gel on the orientation of epithelial cell polarity: follicle formation from isolated thyroid cells and from preformed monolayers. J. Cell Biol. 91:157–66
18. Chambard, M., Verrier, B., Gabrion, J., Mauchamp, J. 1984. Polarity reversal on inside-out thyroid follicle cultured with collagen gel: reexpression of specific functions. Biol. Cell 51:315–26
19. Chevalier, J., Pinto da Silva, P. 1987. Osmotic reversal induces assembly of tight junction strands at the basal pole of toad bladder epithelial cells but does not reverse cell polarity. J. Membr. Biol. 95:199–208
20. Cohen, E., Talmon, A., Faff, O., Bacher, A., Ben-Shaul, Y. 1985. Formation of tight junctions in epithelial cells. Exp. Cell Res. 156:103–16
21. Colony, P. C., Neutra, M. R. 1983. Epithelial differentiation in the fetal rat colon: plasma membrane phosphatase activities. Dev. Biol. 97:349–63
22. Dragsten, P. R., Blumenthal, R., Handler, J. S. 1981. Membrane asymmetry in epithelia: is the tight junction a barrier to diffusion in plasma membrane. Nature 294:718–22
23. Dragsten, P. R., Handler, J. S., Blumenthal, R. 1982. Fluorescent membrane probes and the mechanism of maintenance of cellular asymmetry in epithelia. Fed. Proc. 41:48–53
24. Emerman, J. T., Pitelka, D. 1977. Maintenance and induction of morpho-

logical differentiation in dissociated mammary epithelium. *In Vitro* 13:316–78

25. Faff, O., Cohen, E., Bacher, A., Ben-Shaul, Y. 1988. Protease-induced formation of focal tight junctions in HT-29 adenocarcinoma cells does not require extracellular calcium. *Biochim. Biophys. Acta* 905:48–56

26. Faff, O., Mitreiter, R., Muckter, H., Ben-Shaul, Y., Bacher, A. 1988. Rapid formation of tight junctions in HT-29 human adenocarcinoma cells by hypertonic salt solutions. *Exp. Cell Res.* 177:60–72

27. Fayet, G., Pacheco, H., Tixier, R. 1970. Sur la reassociation in vitro des cellules isolees de thyroide de porc et la biosynthese de la thyroglobuline. I. Conditions pour l'induction des reassociations cellulaires par la thyreostimuline. *Bull. Soc. Chim. Biol.* 52:299–306

28. Galeotti, G. 1904. Concerning the EMF which is generated at the surface of animal membranes on contact with different electrolytes. *Z. Phys. Chem.* 49:542–53

29. Galeotti, G. 1907. Ricerche di elettrofisiologia secondo i criteri dell'elettrochimica. *Z. Allg. Physiol.* 6:99–108

30. Gonzalez-Mariscal, L., Borboa, L., Lopez-Vancell, R., Beaty, G., Cereijido, M. 1985. Electrical properties of MDCK cells. In *Tissue Culture of Epithelial Cells,* ed. M. Taub, pp. 25–36. London: Plenum

31. Gonzalez-Mariscal, L., Chavez de Ramirez, B., Cereijido, M. 1985. Tight junction formation in cultured epithelial cells (MDCK). *J. Membr. Biol.* 86:113–25

32. Grover, A., Andrews, G., Adamson, E. D. 1983. Role of laminin in epithelium formation by F9 aggregates *J. Cell Biol.* 97:137–44

33. Herzlinger, D. A., Ojakian, G. K. 1984. Studies on the development and maintenance of epithelial cell surface polarity with monoclonal antibodies. *J. Cell Biol.* 98:1777–87

34. Hoi Sang, U., Evans-Layng, M. 1982. Polar redistribution of Na-K-ATPase in aggregating MDCK cells. *Exp. Cell Res.* 146:192–98

35. Hoi Sang, U., Saier, M. H., Ellisman, M. H. 1979. Tight junction formation is closely linked to the polar redistribution of intramembranous particles in aggregating MDCK epithelia. *Exp. Cell Res.* 122:384–92

36. Hoi Sang, U., Saier, M. H., Ellisman, M. H. 1980. Tight junction formation in the establishment of intramembranous

particle polarity in aggregating MDCK cells. *Exp. Cell Res.* 128:223–35

37. Ingber, D. E., Madri, J. A., Jamieson, J. D. 1986. Basement membrane as a spatial organizer of polarized epithelia. *Am. J. Pathol.* 122:129–39

38. Jesaitis, A. J., Yguerabide, J. 1986. The lateral mobility of the (Na, K+)-dependent ATPase in Madin-Darby canine kidney cells. *J. Cell Biol.* 102:1256–63

39. Louvard, D. 1980. Apical membrane aminopeptidase appears at sites of cell-cell contact in cultured epithelial cells. *Proc. Natl. Acad. Sci. USA* 77:4132–36

40. Madara, J. M., Berenberg, D., Carlson, S. 1986. Effects of cytochalasin D on occluding junctions of intestinal absorptive cells: further evidence that the cytoskeleton may influence paracellular permeability and junctional charge selectivity. *J. Cell Biol.* 102:2125–36

41. Madden, M. E., Sarras, M. P. 1985. Development of an apical plasma membrane domain and tight junctions during histogenesis of the mammalian pancreas. *Dev. Biol.* 112:427–42

42. Maratos-Flier, E., Kao, C. Y., Verdin, E. M., King, G. L. 1987. Receptor-mediated vectorial transcytosis of epidermal growth factor by Madin-Darby canine kidney cells. *J. Cell Biol.* 105:1595–1601

43. Martinez-Palomo, A., Meza, I., Beaty, G., Cereijido, M. 1980. Experimental modulation of occluding junctions in a cultured transporting epithelium. *J. Cell Biol.* 87:736–45

44. Mason, P. W., Lu, M. L., Jacobson, B. S. 1987. Cell substrate adhesion-induced redistribution of proteins among the apical, basal, and internal domains of the plasma membrane of HeLa cells spreading on gelatin. *J. Biol. Chem.* 262:3746–53

45. Massey, D., Feracci, H., Gorvel, J P., Rigal, A., Maroux, S. 1987. Evidence for the transit of aminopeptidase N through the basolateral membrane before it reaches the brush border of enterocytes. *J. Membr. Biol.* 96:19–26

46. Matlin, K. S., Bainton, D., Pesonen, M., Genty, N., Louvard, D., Simons, K. 1983. Transfer of a viral envelope glycoprotein from the apical to the basolateral plasma membrane of MDCK cells. I. Morphological evidence. *J. Cell Biol.* 97:627–37

47. Mauchamp, J., Chambard, M., Bernard, P. 1979. Morphological and electrical polarity of the thyroid epithelium reconstructed in culture. In *Hormonal Control of Epithelium Transport,* ed. J.

Bourget, J. Chevalier, M. Parisi, P. Ripoche, pp. 43–52. Paris: Institut National de la Sante et de la Recherche Medicale

48. Mauchamp, J., Margotat, A., Chambard, M., Charrier, B., Remy, L., Michel-Bechet, M. 1979. Polarity of three-dimensional structures derived from isolated pig thyroid cells in primary culture. *Cell Tissue Res.* 204:417–30

49. Mesnil, M., Fraslin, J., Piccoli, C., Yamasaki, H., Guguen-Guillouzo, C. 1987. Cell contact but no junctional communication (dye coupling) with biliary epithelial cells is required for hepatocytes to maintain differentiated properties. *Exp. Cell Res.* 173:524–33

50. Meza, I., Ibarra, G., Sabanero, M., Martinez-Palomo, A., Cereijido, M. 1980. Occluding junctions and cytoskeletal components in a cultured transporting epithelium. *J. Cell Biol.* 87:746–54

51. Meza, I., Sabanero, M., Stefani, E., Cereijido, M. 1982. Occluding junctions in MDCK cells modulation of transepithelial permeability by the cytoskeleton. *J. Cell. Biochem.* 18:407–21

52. Miledi, R. 1960. The acetylcholine sensitivity of frog muscle fibres after complete or partial denervation. *J. Physiol.* 151:1–23

53. Mostov, K. E., Simister, N. E. 1985. Transcytosis. *Cell* 43:389–90

54. Muckter, H., Ben-Shaul, Y., Bacher, A. 1988. ATP requirement for induced tight junction formation in HT-29 adenocarcinoma cells. *Eur. J. Cell Biol.* In press

55. Mullin, J. M., O'Brien, P. G. 1987. Spontaneous reversal of polarity of the voltage across LLC-PK1 renal epithelial cell sheets. *J. Cell. Physiol.* 133:515–22

56. Nelson, W. J., Veshnock, P. 1987. Ankyrin binding to (Na+K) ATPase and implications for the organization of membrane domains in polarized cells. *Nature* 328:533–35

57. Neville, C. 1987. Mammary cultures on floating gels: a model system for mammary function. *News Physiol. Sci.* 2:107–11

58. Nitsch, L., Wollman, S. H. 1987. Cell polarity and water transport in thyroid epithelial cells in separated follicles in suspension culture. *Scanning Electron Microsc.* 1:1279–86

59. Ojakian, G. K., Romain, R. E., Herz, R. 1987. A distal nephron glycoprotein has a different cell surface distributions on MDCK cell sublines. *Am. J. Physiol.* 253:C433–43

60. Ophir, I., Cohen, E., Bacher, A., Ben-Shaul, Y. 1988. Studies on the role of protein synthesis in the induced formation of tight junctions in HT-29 adenocarcinoma cells. Submitted for publication

61. Parry, G., Cullen, B., Kaetzel, C., Kramer, R., Moss, L. 1987. Regulation of differentiation and polarized secretion in mammary epithelial cells maintained in culture: extracellular matrix and membrane polarity influences. *J. Cell Biol.* 105:2043–51

62. Peng, I., Dennis, J. E., Rodriguez-Boulan, E., Fischman, D. A. 1987. Epithelial polarity in presumptive myocardial cells. *J. Cell Biol.* 105:145a

63. Perrin, D., Langley, K., Aunis, D. 1987. Anti-fodrin secretion from permeabilized chromaffin cells. *Nature* 326:498–501

64. Pesonen, M., Simons, K. 1983. Transepithelial transport of a viral membrane glycoprotein implanted into the apical plasma membrane of Madin-Darby canine kidney cells. II. Immunological quantitation. *J. Cell Biol.* 97:638–43

65. Poindexter, J. S. 1964. Biological properties and classification of the Caulobacter group. *Bacteriol. Rev.* 28:231–95

66. Polak-Charcon, S., Ben-Shaul, Y. 1978. Tight junction assembly in human adenocarcinoma cell line: relations to cytoskeletal elements. *9th Int. Congr. Electron Microscopy, Toronto,* 2:334–35

67. Polak-Charcon, S., Shoham, J. J., Ben-Sahul, Y. 1978. Junction formation in tripsinized cells of human adenocarcenoma cell line. *Exp. Cell Res.* 116:1–13

68. Rabito, C. A., Kreisberg, J. L., Wight, D. 1984. Alkaline phosphatase and γ-glutamyltransepeptidase as polarization markers during the organization of LLC-PK1 cells into an epithelial membrane. *J. Biol. Chem.* 259:574–82

69. Rapraeger, A., Jalkanen, M., Bernfield, M. 1986. Cell surface proteoglycan associates with the cytoskeleton at the basolateral cell surface of mouse mammary epithelial cells. *J. Cell Biol.* 103:2683–96

70. Rassat, J., Robenek, H., Themann, H. 1982. Cytochalasin B effects of the gap and tight junctions of mouse hepatocytes in vivo. *J. Submicrosc. Cytol.* 14:427–39

71. Ritzki, T. M., Ritzki, R. M. 1983. Basement membrane polarizes lectin binding sites of Drosophila larval fat body cells. *Nature* 303:340–42

72. Rodman, J. S., Kerjaschki, D., Merisko, E., Farquhar, M. G. 1984. Presence

of an extensive clathrin coat on the apical plasmalemma of the rat kidney proximal tubule cell. *J. Cell Biol.* 98:1630–36

73. Rodriguez-Boulan, E. 1983. Membrane biogenesis, enveloped RNA viruses, and epithelial polarity. *Mod. Cell Biol.* 1: 119–70

74. Rodriguez-Boulan, E., Misek, D., Vega-Salas, D., Salas, P. J., Bard, E. 1985. Protein sorting in the secretory pathway. *Curr. Top. Membr. Transp.* 24:251–94

75. Rodriguez-Boulan, E., Paskiet, K. T., Sabatini, D. D. 1983. Assembly of enveloped viruses in Madin-Darby canine kidney cells: polarized budding from single attached cells and from clusters of cells in suspension. *J. Cell Biol.* 96: 886–74

76. Rodriguez-Boulan, E., Paskiet, K. T., Salas, P. J. I., Bard, E. 1984. Intracellular transport of influenza virus hemagglutinin to the apical surface of Madin-Darby canine kidney cells. *J. Cell Biol.* 98:308–19

77. Rodriguez-Boulan, E. J., Pendergast, M. 1980. Polarized distribution of viral envelope glycoprotein in the plasma membrane of infected epithelial cells. *Cell* 20:45–54

78. Rodriguez-Boulan, E. J., Sabatini, D. D. 1978. Asymmetric budding of viruses in epithelial monolayers: a model system for the study of epithelial cell polarity. *Proc. Natl. Acad. Sci. USA* 75:5071–75

79. Salas, P., Misek, I., Vega-Salas, D. E., Gundersen, D., Cereijido, M., Rodriguez-Boulan, E. 1986. Microtubules and actin filaments are not critically involved in the biogenesis of epithelial cell surface polarity. *J. Cell Biol.* 102:1853–67

80. Salas, P., Vega-Salas, D. E., Hochman, J., Rodriguez-Boulan, E., Edidin, M. 1988. Selective anchoring in the specific plasma membrane domain: a role in the biogenesis of epithelial cell polarity. *J. Cell Biol.* Submitted for publication

81. Salas, P., Vega-Salas, D. E., Rodriguez-Boulan, E. 1987. Collagen receptors mediate early events in the attachment of epithelial (MDCK) cells. *J. Membr. Biol.* 98:223–36

82. Shapiro, L. 1985. Generation of polarity during Caulobacter cell differentiation. *Annu. Rev. Cell Biol.* 1:173–207

83. Shivers, R., Arthur, F. E., Bowman, P. D. 1988. Induction of gap junction and brain endothelium-like tight junctions in cultured bovine endothelial cells: local control of cell specialization. *J. Submicrosc. Cytol. Pathol.* 20: 1–14

84. Spiegel, S., Blumenthal, R., Fishman, P. H., Handler, J. S. 1985. Gangliosides do not move from apical to basolateral plasma membrane in cultured epithelial cells. *Biochim. Biophys. Acta* 821:310–18

85. Steele, R. E., Preston, A. S., Johnson, J. P., Handler, J. S. 1986. Porousbottom dishes for culture of polarized cells. *Am. J. Physiol.* 20:C136–39

86. Sugrue, S., Hay, E. D. 1981. Response of basal epithelial cell surface and cytoskeleton to solubilized extracellular matrix molecules. *J. Cell Biol.* 91:45–54

87. Talmon, A., Cohen, E., Bacher, A., Ben-Shaul, Y. 1984. Separation of induction and expression of tight junction formation mediated by proteinases. *Biochim. Biophys. Acta* 769:505–7

88. Turner, R. J., Thompson, J., Sariban-Sohraby, S., Handler, J. S. 1985. Monoclonal Antibodies as probes of epithelial membrane polarization. *J. Cell Biol.* 101:2173–80

89. van Meer, G., Gumbiner, B., Simons, K. 1986. The tight junction does not allow lipid molecules to diffuse from one epithelial cell to the next. *Nature* 322:639–41

90. van Meer, G., Stelzer, E. H. K., Wijnaendts-van Resandt, R., Simons, K. 1987. Sorting of sphingolipids in epithelial (Madin-Darby canine kidney) cells. *J. Cell Biol.* 105:1623–35

91. Vega-Salas, D. E., Salas, P., Gundersen, D., Rodriguez-Boulan, E. 1987. Formation of the apical pole of epithelial Madin-Darby canine kidney cells: polarity of an apical protein is independent of tight junctions while segregation of a basolateral marker requires cell-cell interactions. *J. Cell Biol.* 104:905–16

92. Wohlwend, A., Montesano, R., Vassalli, J. D., Orci, L. 1985. LLC-PK1 cysts: a model for the study of epithelial polarity. *J. Cell Physiol.* 125:533–39

93. Zeng, M., Zhou, M. 1987. Experimental reversion of the polarity of gastrula ectoderm cell. *Acta Biol. Exp. Sinica* 20: In press

Annu. Rev. Physiol. 1989. 51:797–810

MOLECULAR BIOLOGICAL APPROACHES TO PROTEIN SORTING

Michael G. Roth

Department of Biochemistry, University of Texas Southwestern Medical Center, Dallas, Texas 75235-9038

INTRODUCTION

Epithelial cells in culture provide an excellent experimental system for investigation of one of the fundamental questions of cellular organization, the problem of how a cell recognizes, packages, and targets membrane proteins to specific destinations and how segregation of these proteins is maintained once they are put in place. To achieve a detailed understanding of the chemical processes controlling this intracellular traffic, one must be able to perturb sorting mechanisms in ways that make clear the causal relations of events in the transport pathway. Genetic manipulations have traditionally provided powerful tools for achieving just the kind of specific and limited changes in complex systems that allow their analyses. Molecular biology now provides opportunities to employ genetic approaches to problems, such as the sorting of membrane proteins in epithelial cells in culture, where biochemical, physiological, and cytological techniques have been well developed but genetics has been difficult to apply.

The discussion that follows will review the contributions that molecular biological approaches have made to our understanding of three aspects of the sorting problem: the location of glycoprotein features that are recognized during sorting; whether there is an unsorted exocytic pathway in epithelial cells; and the location of features important for the endocytosis and transcytosis of glycoproteins in epithelial cells. Other chapters in this volume discuss possible mechanisms for sorting epithelial cell surface proteins; thus, the emphasis of this chapter is on the technical and conceptual problems inherent in the use of expression vectors in differentiated cells.

797

0066-4278/89/0315-0797$02.00

PRACTICAL ASPECTS OF THE USE OF EXPRESSION VECTORS IN EPITHELIAL CELLS

The use of expression vectors is often called reverse genetics since one starts with a gene, either mutated or not, and introduces it into cells with the intention of creating a certain cellular phenotype. Just as traditional genetic approaches can be used to select cells containing mutations that are either induced transiently through environmental manipulations (conditional mutants) or are constitutive (unconditional), vectors can be chosen to give either transient or permanent gene expression. Ideally, one would like to have a vector that could be used for both transient and permanent expression. Such an ideal vector does not yet exist for use in epithelial or other types of differentiated cells and choosing among existing vectors inevitably involves certain compromises. For example, the only vectors that can deliver genes into confluent epithelial cells at high efficiency are those that can be packaged into virus particles and the recombinant viruses grown up as stocks with infectious titers greater than 10^7 infectious units per milliliter. Such virus vectors can attain levels of gene expression that are more than sufficient for biochemical or immunocytochemical analysis, but they are lytic and cause epithelial cells to lose surface polarity at some period after infection. This complicates the analysis of sorting phenomena when the interval during which polarity is maintained is brief and the synchrony of the infection is low. In contrast, vectors that are not toxic to the cell have, with few exceptions, given low levels of gene expression and have been delivered into cells at low frequency. This has the practical result of limiting the use of these vectors either to nonquantitative transient expression experiments or to experiments employing lines of permanently transfected cells selected for levels of expression that are much greater than average. A list of vectors that have been used in epithelial cells is provided in Table 1.

Certain vectors and transcriptional promotors require a specific cellular environment to be maximally active, thus at the beginning of an experiment a decision must be made as to whether a choice of a certain vector will determine the selection of a cell type or vice versa. In some of the experiments described in this review the choice has been made to find a polarized cell that supports the replication of an efficient expression vector. In other experiments, the primary choice was to select a well-characterized epithelial cell line and attempt to adapt previously existing expression vectors for use in those cells. In every case the choice of the vector and cell type had important effects on the experimental protocols and to some degree influenced the experimental outcome.

A final point important for choosing an expression vector is the level of gene expression required for the use of an experimental technique that may be

Table 1 Expression vectors used in epithelial cells

Vector	Promoter	Gene expressed[a]	Reference
SV40 (virus)	SV40 late	HA HAG HA[sec]	38
		H1GA HA	25
		NA SN10	17
Vaccinia	Vaccina p7.5	G MuLV–gp70/p15E	43
		HA F-MCFV–gp70/p15E	42
Retrovirus	MuLV LTR	Polyimmunoglobulin receptor	26
	MuLV LTR	v-src c-src	45
pSV2 plasmid	SV40 early	Lysozyme neo[r]	18
		G; HA	14
		Growth hormone lysozyme $\alpha_{2\mu}$-globulin S L κ chain	13
		TG, THA	12
		G; GHA; neo[r]	31
Plasmid	SV40 early	SFV p62 mutants neo[r]	35
	Human MT IIa	p62-d4	35
Plasmid	HSV TK	Bovine prochymosin	13
Plasmid	HSV TK	Neo[r]	12
Bovine papilloma virus-derived plasmid	Mouse MT I	HA	[b]
Plasmid	MSV LTR	Rat nerve growth factor	[c]

[a]Abbreviations: neo[r], TN5 phosphotransferase. SFV, Semliki Forest virus. HSV TK, Herpes Simplex virus I thymidine kinase. MT, metallothioneine. TG, truncated G protein. THA, truncated HA. HA[sec], secreted HA. HAG, HA-G chimera. H1GA, HA-G chimera. NA, influenza virus neuraminidase. SN10, neuraminidase with altered cytoplasmid domain. MuLV, murine leukemia virus. F-MCFV, Friend mink cell focus inducing virus. MSV, Moloney murine sarcoma virus. LTR, long terminal repeat.
[b]M. G. Roth, unpublished.
[c]E. Rodriguez-Boulan, unpublished.

crucial for the success of an experiment. In the past, difficulties in achieving adequate levels of protein production have resulted in experiments that used techniques lacking the sensitivity necessary to accomplish the stated goals of the research. Some of the recent contradictory reports describing the transport and ultimate location of glycoproteins expressed from recombinant genes introduced into epithelial cells are probably due to this problem.

SITE-DIRECTED MUTAGENESIS AS AN APPROACH TO IDENTIFYING FEATURES RECOGNIZED DURING SORTING IN EPITHELIAL CELLS

Viral glycoproteins were the obvious choices for the first experiments employing recombinant DNA techniques to investigate sorting of cell-surface proteins. In epithelial cells, viral glycoproteins are sorted to either the apical or basolateral surfaces (34). With the exception of the immunoglobulins and histocompatibility antigens, more is known about the relationship of biosynthesis, structure, and function of the glycoproteins of several simple enveloped viruses than about any others. These data are of critical importance for interpreting the results of experiments that employ mutagenesis in an attempt to locate recognition signals important for sorting. In addition, the genes for glycoproteins of enveloped viruses that bud from either the apical or basolateral surface domains of epithelial cells were expressed from recombinant vectors much earlier than were those of cellular glycoproteins known to be distributed in a polarized manner.

The first question to be addressed using recombinant vectors was that of whether viral proteins other than the glycoproteins are involved in sorting. This problem was solved by finding polarized cells that would support the replication of recombinant SV40 expression vectors that had previously been shown to produce large amounts of protein in nonpolarized cells (5, 7, 9–11, 37, 47). Primary cultures of African Green monkey kidney cells were infected with recombinant SV40 viruses in which the late SV40 genes had been replaced with a gene encoding hemagglutinin (HA) of influenza virus, and during early periods of HA synthesis the protein was observed to be sorted to the apical surface of a majority of the cells in the culture (36). Similar results using different vectors and cells were subsequently reported for another apical glycoprotein, the influenza virus neuraminidase (NA) (17), and for several basal glycoproteins of viral (43) and cellular origin (1, 28).

The viral glycoproteins used for early sorting experiments all are oriented in the membrane with a large external domain, a single transmembrane domain, and a quite small cytoplasmic domain. In principle, the recognition event required for sorting viral glycoproteins could involve any of these three topologically distinct domains, and the location of features important for this recognition would have quite different implications for the nature of the cellular sorting mechanism. For example, recognition of the external domain would imply that sorting involved important events in the lumen of organelles of the transport pathway and would be consistent with sorting both secretory and membrane-bound proteins by a single mechanism. If receptors were involved in this event, either they must be sorted intracellularly themselves, or they must appear at least transiently at the plasma membrane. Recognition of the cytoplasmic domains of transmembrane proteins would be compatible with a cytoplasmic sorting agent that might both recruit proteins into transport vesicles and mediate a recognition event between the vesicles and destination membranes. Direct involvement of transmembrane domains in sorting would be most easily understood as part of a process that relies upon aggregation of classes of proteins. An obvious way to distinguish between these possibilities would be to specifically mutate, delete, or exchange one of these domains using recombinant DNA techniques.

Of course, implicit in this approach is the requirement that changes in one domain be largely independent of the others. At the time that the first mutagenesis experiments began to investigate sorting properties, the relationship between folding and oligomerization of viral glycoproteins and their transport had not been established. However, two lines of evidence suggested that, at least for HA and NA, it would be possible to introduce changes into the cytoplasmic domain without changing the structure of the external domain. First, the three-dimensional structure of the external domain had been solved by X-ray diffraction of crystals of HA that had been proteolytically cleaved at a site 10 amino acids from the predicted start of the transmembrane region (48). The truncated proteins in these crystals were found to be stable HA trimers that retained hemagglutinating activity. Similarly, NA tetramers proteolytically cleaved from the virus retained neuraminidase activity. The three-dimensional structure determined by X-ray diffraction of crystals of soluble NA suggested that, as was the case for HA, the transmembrane and cytoplasmic domains played minor roles, if any, in determining the shape of the protein (44). Secondly, it had been shown that a genetically truncated HA gene lacking its transmembrane and cytoplasmic domains could be secreted from the cell (11, 23). Based on this evidence, several laboratories set out to make mutant and chimeric glycoproteins as a means of determining whether recognition of glycoproteins during sorting occurs in the cytoplasm or in the lumen of the transport pathway. However, it was subsequently determined that the structure of the external domain of HA is definitely influenced by the nature of the transmembrane domain and perhaps by the cytoplasmic domain (9, 37). Thus the original premise of independent domains is not strictly correct for HA (and probably many other glycoproteins). This means that observations of the loss of sorting properties in a mutant protein cannot be interpreted without information about the degree of structural change to the protein. Unfortunately, there have been few studies in which both the sorting properties and structure of mutant proteins have been investigated in any detail. Nevertheless, in some experiments, chimeric or mutated glycoproteins retained their original sorting properties, and these results provide strong evidence that the recognition of apical proteins is a luminal event.

Transient Expression Experiments

Two different recombinant virus vectors have proven useful for transient expression of mutant and chimeric glycoprotein genes in polarized cells, SV40-late replacement vectors (10, 38) and recombinant vaccinia viruses (3, 43). In addition, experiments employing transient expression of proteins in MDCK cells transfected with plasmid vectors have been reported (14, 33);

however, the levels of expression using those systems were too low to allow quantitative measurements and that approach is not currently in use.

In the SV40–late replacement vectors, the genes encoding the viral capsid proteins have been deleted from the late transcriptional unit and replaced with a gene for a glycoprotein. The viral capsid genes are then supplied by a coinfecting helper virus with a defective early gene that makes it dependent upon the presence of the expression vector for replication. High-titer stocks of recombinant SV40 viruses are prepared by transfecting both vector and helper DNA into permissive monkey cells, followed by serial passage of the resulting virus to prepare virus stocks capable of infecting 100% of the cells in a culture. Recombinant SV40 viruses replicate to several thousand copies per cell, which results in the production of large amounts of protein. Thus experiments requiring brief intervals of incorporation of radioactive amino acids into nascent polypeptides, or experiments employing immunocytochemistry and electron microscopy, are easily performed using these vectors. SV40-late replacement viruses have been widely used for studies of glycoprotein biosynthesis in both polarized and nonpolarized monkey cells (5, 7, 9–11, 15, 23, 25, 36, 39, 46, 47) and the results of these studies demonstrate quite conclusively that the virus has little effect on the constitutive secretory pathway until quite late during infection. However, because of packaging constraints imposed by the SV40 capsid, the size of the gene that can be inserted into the late region is limited to approximately 2200 base pairs. In addition, SV40 replicates only in cells of African Green or Rhesus monkey origin and this precludes the use of other well-characterized polarized epithelial cells lines. However, a continuous Rhesus monkey kidney cell line, MA104, contains polarized cells. A subline derived from these cells, MA104.11 (38), resembles the MDCK strain II (32) cell line morphologically and electrically, and has proven useful as a host for SV40-virus vectors.

Two sets of experiments have been performed employing MA104.11 cells infected with recombinant SV40 vectors that expressed either wild-type or mutant forms of the influenza virus HA (38) or NA (17) proteins. In the first, the techniques of immunocytochemistry and electron microscopy were used to compare the localization of wild-type NA and a mutant NA in which the 10 amino acids of the amino-terminal cytoplasmic domain had been changed to a random 9 amino acids (17). Greater than 90% of either the wild-type or the mutant NA was detected at the apical surface of polarized MA104.11 cells and it was concluded that NA does not require its native cytoplasmic domain for sorting in epithelial cells.

Similarly, Roth and colleagues constructed a chimeric HAG gene encoding a protein in which the external domain of HA was joined to the transmembrane and cytoplasmic domains of the vesicular stomatitis virus (VSV) G protein, a glycoprotein that is normally sorted to the basolateral plasma membrane in epithelial cells (38). MA104.11 cells, grown on filters in mini-Marbrook chambers, were infected with recombinant SV40 vectors expressing either HAG, wild-type HA, or HA^{sec}, a truncated form of HA containing the entire external domain but lacking the transmembrane and cytoplasmic domains. MA104.11 cells were shown to retain polarized characteristics for the first 28 to 32 hours after infection with recombinant SV40 vectors, after which the infected cell culture increasingly contained cells with nonpolarized HA. During the early period when HA expression was polarized, HA^{sec} that had been metabolically labeled with ^{35}S methione was secreted almost exclusively into the medium above the apical cell surface and HAG, like HA, was observed to be present at 9 times greater concentration at the apical surface than at the basolateral. These experiments indicated that the external domain of HA is sufficient for sorting the protein in MA104.11 cells, thus any recognition of HA must occur in the lumen of the transport pathway. It is more difficult to draw conclusions about the role of the G protein cytoplasmic domain in the chimeric protein. If the G cytoplasmic domain retained its normal shape in HAG, then the sorting signal in the HA external domain is dominant and the G sequences may, or may not, contain sorting information. Although HAG was recognized by an antibody specific for the G cytoplasmic domain, it is not certain that the G sequences retained their entire native conformation in HAG.

Very similar experiments were reported by McQueen et al (25), using a recombinant vaccinia vector to express wild-type or a mutant HA-G protein in MDCK cells. In the vaccinia vector system, a gene of interest is placed under the control of a vaccinia promoter in an insertion plasmid that contains vaccinia DNA flanking the subcloning site. Cells are infected with vaccinia and then transfected with the insertion plasmid two hours later. At low frequency, infecting vaccinia virus DNA recombines with the insertion plasmid, and recombinant viruses are subsequently identified by filter hybridization or by selection for some activity encoded by the insertion plasmid (3, 20). These recombinant viruses are then plaque purified and high-titer stocks are prepared. Vaccinia has a wide host range and can incorporate at least 25,000 bases of foreign DNA (41). However, vaccinia viruses are quite lytic and their use requires care so that the cellular functions under study are not destroyed before they can be measured. Under the proper conditions, MDCK cells infected with recombinant vaccinia viruses have been shown to sort correctly several different viral glycoproteins (43). Using this system, McQueen and colleagues infected MDCK cells with a recombinant virus encoding a protein, H1GA, in which the external domain of the HA was joined to the transmembrane and cytoplasmic domains of the G protein (25). By radioimmuno assay, immunocytochemistry, and electron microscopy, this protein was observed to be sorted correctly to the apical surface of MDCK cells 4 hours after infection.

Stephens & Compans (42) infected MDCK cells with vaccinia virus vectors that carried either the wild-type or a truncated gene encoding the gp70/p15E envelope protein of Friend mink cell focus inducing virus. For comparison they used a vaccinia vector to express the wild-type HA in MDCK cells. In these experiments, 100% of the HA was detected at the apical cell surface and 100% of the gp70/p15E at the basolateral domain. The truncated protein was detected in equal amounts in the medium from each side of MDCK cell monolayers grown on filters. Since the effects of the truncation on the structure of the secreted glycoprotein were not investigated, the cause for the change in sorting properties of that protein is currently unknown.

Continuous Cell Lines Expressing Exogenous Glycoproteins

The sorting of chimeric or mutant glycoproteins has been studied by several groups through the creation of permanent lines of epithelial cells expressing genes carried by plasmid vectors. Roman & Garoff investigated the sorting of the Semliki Forest virus (SFV) p62 envelope protein precursors in MDCK cells that had been cotransfected with a plasmid expression vector and neomycin resistance marker and selected with the neomycin analogue G418 (35). As is typical of transfected MDCK cells, in these experiments colonies expressing the SFV proteins were isolated at a frequency approximately 100 times lower than is commonly attained with fibroblasts such as NIH 3T3 cells. In addition, the level of SFV proteins synthesized was low, requiring the use of blotting techniques for their detection. Nevertheless, by three separate assays, wild-type p62 and mutants lacking cytoplasmic p62 sequences were demonstrated to be correctly sorted to the basal domain of MDCK cells. Thus, for at least one of the basal class of glycoproteins, recognition required for sorting occurs either in the lumen of the transport pathway or within the lipid bilayer.

Using a quite similar approach, Puddington et al (31) constructed chimeric genes encoding proteins in which the external and transmembrane domains of the VSV G protein were joined to the cytoplasmic domain of either HA or IgM and transfected them into MDCK cells. Isolation of cells expressing these genes proved to be quite difficult and expression of the proteins required treatment of the cells with sodium butyrate for extended periods. Under these conditions, the G-μ protein was detected only at internal membranes and the G-HA protein was observed by immunofluorescence to be present at both basolateral and apical MDCK surfaces. The conformational state of the mutant G-HA protein was not reported and the implications of these findings in regard to the location of sorting information are not yet clear.

Using a similar pSV2-derived vector, Gonzalez et al established MDCK cell lines that expressed truncated forms of either HA or G (12). Detection of the proteins in these cells required pretreatment with butyrate for 24 to 48 hours prior to prolonged labeling with radioactive methionine; under these conditions both the truncated G and HA were secreted from cells in monolayers in a nonpolarized fashion and the cells were reported to maintain electrical resistance. The conformational state of the mutant proteins was unknown and the authors of this study concluded that although the sequences missing from HA or G were important for sorting, it was possible that they contributed to the overall structure of the protein rather than serving as a feature recognized during sorting.

Although MDCK cells are by far the best-characterized continuous epithelial cell line and are the cells of choice for investigations of glycoprotein sorting, they are difficult to transfect with exogenous DNA. Clones of MDCK cells surviving selection for a marker transfected into them usually express a cotransfected gene of interest at low levels. In contrast, a continuous line of epithelial cells derived from pig kidney, LLC-PK1, can be transfected by standard calcium phosphate protocols at an efficiency nearly as high as achieved with NIH 3T3 cells (M. G. Roth, unpublished results). From a population of these cells that had survived selection with G418 after cotransfection with a neomycin resistance marker and a bovine papilloma virus-derived vector expressing HA (40), high expression cell lines were selected by fluorescence-activated flow cytometry. These cells have remained polarized and have stably expressed HA at a level of approximately 3×10^6 molecules per cell for over two years and contain 40 to 80 copies of the papilloma virus vector as an episome (M. G. Roth, manuscript in preparation). Thus LLC-PK1 cells are a promising cell line for use as a polarized cell host for recombinant expression vectors, particularly those derived from papilloma virus.

INTRODUCTION OF SIGNAL-LESS PROTEINS INTO EPITHELIAL CELLS

The sorting of glycoproteins to the surface domains in epithelial cells could occur through mechanisms that actively recognize and sequester proteins into transport vesicles destined for each arm of the pathway; alternatively, there could be a mechanism that selects proteins for transport to one of the surface domains and excludes others. Proteins not selected for the sorted pathway would then reach the surface by the unsorted or default pathway. Several groups have attempted to distinguish between these possibilities by introducing into MDCK cells genes that encode proteins normally absent from that cell type under the assumption that such proteins would lack features important for sorting. The results of these experiments have largely confirmed this assumption and indicate that, for MDCK cells at least, sorting is likely to be required for polarized transport of secreted proteins to either membrane domain.

MDCK cells transfected with a plasmid vector carrying a gene encoding chicken lysozyme have been isolated after selection with G418 (18). The rate of lysozyme synthesis in one of these cell lines, Lys-16, was sufficient for pulse chase protocols without the need for treatment with butyrate to enhance transcription. Since lysozyme was secreted by all of the cells in Lys-16 cultures, it was possible to demonstrate that polarized Lys-16 cells in electrically tight monolayers secreted lysozyme in equivalent amounts from both the apical and basal surfaces. The simplest interpretation of these results is that sorting in these cells involves active recognition of proteins, and in the absence of recognition, proteins can reach either surface. Similar results have been obtained by other workers using transient expression systems, however, in these experiments it was difficult to establish that the transfected cells, which were a minority of the population, were in fact polarized (13).

TRANSCYTOSIS AND ENDOCYTOSIS OF MUTANT OR CHIMERIC GLYCOPROTEINS IN EPITHELIAL CELLS

The complexity of protein sorting that occurs in the exocytic pathway in epithelial cells is matched by sorting of proteins during endocytosis. Certain proteins, such as HA, are excluded from the endocytic pathway and remain at the surface domain into which they are originally inserted (19, 37). Other proteins, such as the transferrin receptor, are continually internalized and returned to the proper surface domain with extremely high fidelity (8, 22). Another protein, the polyimmunoglobulin receptor, is endocytosed from the same basolateral surface as the transferrin receptor, but is then rapidly transcyotsed to the apical surface (28).

The sorting of the polyimmunoglobulin receptor in epithelial cells has been investigated through expression of specifically altered cDNAs from a recombinant retrovirus vector (27). In this system, the cDNA of interest is placed under the control of a retrovirus LTR in a vector that also carries a selectable marker gene that is usually controlled by its own promoter (2). The vector lacks retrovirus genes but contains sequences needed for packaging viral RNA. After transfection into an appropriate helper cell line, the vector cDNA is transcribed and packaged into virions (4, 21). These virus particles are then used to deliver the vector into cells where a reverse-transcribed DNA copy is intergrated into the host DNA as a provirus. The production of viruses by the packaging cell lines is inefficient and results in virus stocks of relatively low infectious titer, thus, after infection of target cells with the packaged vector, the uninfected cells must be removed from the culture by selection for the marker gene carried by the vector. Most cells carrying the vector provirus will contain only one, so extensive screening is often necessary to identify cells with levels of protein expression sufficient for certain techniques such as immunocytochemistry.

Using a retrovirus vector, Mostov and colleagues established MDCK cell lines expressing either the wild-type polyimmunoglobulin receptor, a receptor lacking its cytoplasmic domain, or a receptor lacking both the transmembrane and cytoplasmic domains (26, 27). In MDCK cells, the wild-type receptor appears to follow the normal transport pathway, traveling first to the basal surface where it is rapidly internalized (a process that is independent of ligand binding) and is then transported to the apical plasma membrane. At some point during this process (probably at the apical surface) the external domain of the receptor is proteolytically cleaved and released into the apical medium. In contrast, the receptor lacking its cytoplasmic domain was shown to be defective for endocytosis and appeared predominantly at the apical surface in MDCK cells (27). Similarly, the more extensively truncated receptor was secreted into the medium above the apical surface of MDCK cells in confluent monolayers (26). These findings are consistent with other recent reports indicating that the cytoplasmic domains of cell-surface receptors contain features required for entry into coated pits (6, 16, 19, 30, 39). Furthermore, since proteins such as lysozyme and growth hormone are secreted from both surface domains in MDCK cells (13, 18), polarized secretion of the truncated polyimmunoglobulin receptor indicates that the external domain of the receptor is likely to carry information required for apical sorting in its external domain. If the external domains of the mutant polyimmunoglobulin receptors are not altered by the changes in the cytoplasmic or transmembrane domains, these results suggest that the cytoplasmic domain contains a dominant signal necessary for sorting the protein to the basolateral surface. However, the degree to which the protein structure of the mutant proteins has been altered has not been investigated, thus the possibilities remain that structural rearrangements in the external domains of the mutants either cause them to lose a dominant basolateral signal or to be excluded from the pathway to the basolateral surface, effectively sorting them to the apical domain.

Like the polyimmunoglobulin receptor, the VSV G protein is transported first to the basolateral surface and has the capacity to enter the endocytic pathway (14, 24, 29, 37). G protein has also been shown to be capable of transcytosis in MDCK cells (24). Although the endocytosis of G protein in polarized cells has not been studied extensively, it has been observed that the surface distribution of G protein expressed from a cDNA is less polarized than is G protein observed at early periods of infection of epithelial cells with VSV. It is quite likely that in virus-infected cells, G protein is incorporated into virions at the basal surface and kept from entering the endocytic pathway. However, in the absence of other VSV proteins, G might be internalized and either recycled to the basolateral domain or transcytosed to the apical surface. Thus the steady state distribution of G protein will depend upon sorting occurring during both exocytosis and endocytosis.

SUMMARY

The use of recombinant DNA technology to introduce specifically altered genes into epithelial cells has passed through its introductory phase. Enough data have accumulated to indicate the major problems and opportunities for this approach. The greatest opportunity is for locating the features of glycoproteins that are recognized during sorting through the expression of specifically altered proteins in epithelial cells. The results of experiments of this kind briefly summarized here emphasize the need for detailed analyses of the effects of specific mutations on the structure of the mutant proteins. In addition, progress will require quantitative results that have been difficult to obtain to date. To accomplish this, the level of expression of mutant proteins in polarized cells must be higher than previously has been the case. This in turn requires that an effort be made to identify vectors specifically adapted for use in epithelial cells.

ACKNOWLEDGMENTS

M.G.R. is supported by grants CD-299 from the American Cancer Society, GM37547 from the National Institute of General Medical Sciences, and 86G-091 from the American Heart Association Texas Affiliate.

Literature Cited

1. Caplan, M. J., Anderson, H. C., Palade, G. E., Jamieson, J. D. 1986. Intracellular sorting and polarized cell surface delivery of (Na$^+$, K$^+$)ATPase, an endogenous component of MDCK cell basolateral plasma membranes. *Cell* 46:623–31
2. Cepko, C. L., Roberts, B. E., Mulligan, R. C. 1984. Construction and applications of a highly transmissible murine retrovirus shuttle vector. *Cell* 37:1053–62
3. Chakrabarti, S., Brechling, K., Moss, B. 1985. Vaccinia virus expression vector: coexpression of β-galactosidase provides visual screening of recombinant virus plaques. *Mol. Cell. Biol.* 5:3403–9
4. Cone, R. D., Mulligan, R. C. 1984. High-efficiency gene transfer into mammalian cells: generation of helper-free recombinant retrovirus with broad mammalian host range. *Proc. Natl. Acad. Sci. USA* 81:6349–53
5. Davis, A. R., Bos, T. J., Nayak, D. P. 1983. Active influenza virus neuraminidase is expressed in monkey cells from cDNA cloned in simian virus 40 vectors. *Proc. Natl. Acad. Sci. USA* 80:3976–80
6. Davis, C. G., van Driel, I. R., Russell, D. W., Brown, M. S., Goldstein, J. L. 1987. The low density lipoprotein receptor: identification of amino acids in the cytoplasmic domain required for rapid endocytosis. *J. Biol. Chem.* 262:4075–82
7. Doyle, C., Roth, M. G., Sambrook, J., Gething, M.-J. 1985. Mutations in the cytoplasmic domain of the influenza virus heagglutinin affect different stages of intracellular transport. *J. Cell Biol.* 100:704–14
8. Fuller, S. D., Simons, K. 1986. Transferrin receptor polarity and recycling accuracy in "tight" and "leaky" strains of Madin-Darby canine kidney cells. *J. Cell Biol.* 103:1767–79
9. Gething, M.-J., McCammon, K., Sambrook, J. 1986. Expression of wild-type and mutant forms of influenza hemagglutinin: the role of folding in intracellular transport. *Cell* 46:939–50
10. Gething, M.-J., Sambrook, J. 1981. Cell-surface expression of influenza haemagglutinin from a cloned DNA copy of the RNA gene. *Nature* 293:620–25
11. Gething, M.-J., Sambrook, J. 1982. Construction of influenza haemaggluti-

nin genes that code for intracellular and secreted forms of the protein. *Nature* 300:598–603

12. Gonzalez, A., Rizzolo, L., Rindler, M. J., Adesnik, M., Sabatini, D. D., Gottlieb, T. A. 1987. Nonpolarized secretion of truncated forms of the influenza hemagglutinin and the vesicular stomatitus virus G protein from MDCK cells. *Proc. Natl. Acad. Sci. USA* 84:3738–42

13. Gottlieb, T. A., Beaudry, G., Rizzolo, L., Colman, A., Rindler, M., et al. 1986. Secretion of endogenous and exogenous proteins from polarized MDCK cell monolayers. *Proc. Natl. Acad. Sci. USA* 83:2100–4

14. Gottlieb, T. A., Gonzalez, A., Rizzolo, L., Rindler, M. J., Adesnik, M., Sabatini, D. D. 1986. Sorting and endocytosis of viral glycoproteins in transfected polarized epithelial cells. *J. Cell Biol.* 102:1242–55

15. Hiebert, S. W., Paterson, R. G., Lamb, R. A. 1985. Hemagglutinin-neuraminidase protein of the paramyxovirus simian virus 5: nucleotide sequence of the mRNA predicts an N-terminal membrane anchor. *J. Virol.* 54:1–6

16. Honegger, A. M., Dull, T. J., Felder, S., Van Obberghen, E., Bellot, F., et al. 1987. Point mutation at the ATP binding site of EGF receptor abolishes protein-tyrosine kinase activity and alters cellular routing. *Cell* 51:199–209

17. Jones, L. V., Compans, R. W., Davis, A. R., Bos, T. J., Nayak, D. P. 1985. Surface expression of influenza virus neuraminidase, an amino-terminally anchored viral membrane glycoprotein, in polarized epithelial cells. *Mol. Cell. Biol.* 5:2181–89

18. Kondor-Koch, C., Bravo, R., Fuller, S. D., Cutler, D., Garoff, H. 1985. Exocytic pathways exist to both the apical and the basolateral surface of the polarized epithelial cell MDCK. *Cell* 43:297–306

19. Lazarovits, J., Roth, M. G. 1988. A single amino acid change in the cytoplasmic domain allows the influenza virus hemagglutinin to be endocytosed through coated pits. *Cell* 53:743–52

20. Mackett, M., Smith, G. L., Moss, B. 1984. General method for production and selection of infectious vaccinia virus recombinants expressing foreign genes. *J. Virol.* 49:857–64

21. Mann, R., Mulligan, R. C., Baltimore, D. 1983. Construction of a retrovirus packaging mutant and its use to produce helper-free defective retrovirus. *Cell* 33:153–59

22. Maratos-Flier, E., Kao, C.-Y. Y., Ver-

din, E. M., King, G. L. 1987. Receptor-mediated vectorial exocytosis of epidermal growth factor by Madin-Darby canine kidney cells. *J. Cell Biol.* 105:1595–1602

23. Markoff, L., Lin, B.-C., Sveda, M. M., Lai, C.-J. 1983. Glycosylation and surface expression of the influenza virus neuraminidase requires the N-terminal hydrophobic region. *Mol. Cell Biol.* 4:8–16

24. Matlin, K., Bainton, D. F., Pesonen, M., Louvard, D., Genty, N., Simons, K. 1983. Transepithelial transport of a viral membrane glycoprotein implanted into the apical plasma membrane of Madin-Darby canine kidney cells. *J. Cell Biol.* 97:627–37

25. McQueen, N., Nayak, D. P., Stephens, E. B., Compans, R. W. 1986. Polarized expression of a chimeric protein in which the transmembrane and cytoplasmic domains of the influenza virus hemagglutinin have been replaced by those of the vesicular stomatitis virus G protein. *Proc. Natl. Acad. Sci. USA* 83:9318–22

26. Mostov, K. E., Breitfeld, P., Harris, J. M. 1987. An anchor-minus form of the polymeric immunoglobulin receptor is secreted predominantly apically in Madin-Darby canine kidney cells. *J. Cell. Biol.* 105:2031–36

27. Mostov, K. E., de Bruyn Kops, A., Deitcher, D. L. 1986. Deletion of the cytoplasmic domain of the polymeric immunoglobulin receptor prevents basolateral localization and endocytosis. *Cell* 47:359–64

28. Mostov, K. E., Deitcher, D. L. 1986. Polymeric immunoglobulin receptor expressed in MDCK cells transcytoses IgA. *Cell* 46:613–21

29. Personen, M., Simons, K. 1984. Transcytosis of the G protein of vesicular stomatitis virus after implantation into the apical membrane of Madin-Darby canine kidney cells. I. Involvement of endosomes and lysosomes. *J. Cell Biol.* 99:796–802

30. Prywes, R., Livneh, E., Ullrich, A., Schlessinger, J. 1986. Mutations in the cytoplasmic domain of EGF receptor affect EGF binding and receptor internalization. *EMBO J.* 9:2179–90

31. Puddington, L., Woodgett, C., Rose, J. K. 1987. Replacement of the cytoplasmic domain alters sorting of a viral glycoprotein in polarized cells. *Proc. Natl. Acad. Sci. USA* 84:2756–60

32. Richardson, J. C. W., Scalera, V., Simmons, N. L. 1981. Identification of two strains of MDCK cells which resemble

separate nephron tubule segments. *Biochim. Biophys. Acta* 673:26–36

33. Rizzolo, L. J., Finidori, J., Gonzalez, A., Arpin, M., Ivanov, I. E., et al. 1985. Biosynthesis and intracellular sorting of growth hormone-viral envelope glycoprotein hybrids. *J. Cell Biol.* 101:1351–62

34. Rodriguez-Boulan, E., Pendergast, M. 1980. Polarized distribution of viral envelope proteins in the plasma membrane of infected epithelial cells. *Cell* 20:45–54

35. Roman, L. M., Garoff, H. 1986. Alteration of the cytoplasmic domain of the membrane-spanning glycoprotein p62 of Semliki Forest virus does not affect its polar distribution in established line of Madin-Darby canine kidney cells. *J. Cell Biol.* 103:2607–18

36. Roth, M. G., Compans, R. W., Giusti, L., Davis, A., Nayak, D., et al. 1983. Influenza virus hemagglutinin expression is polarized in cells infected with recombinant SV40 viruses carrying cloned hemagglutinin DNA. *Cell* 33:435–43

37. Roth, M. G., Doyle, C., Sambrook, J., Gething, M.-J. 1986. Heterologous transmembrane and cytoplasmic domains direct functional chimeric influenza virus hemagglutinins into the endocytic pathway. *J. Cell Biol.* 102:1271–83

38. Roth, M. G., Gundersen, D., Patil, N., Rodriguez-Boulan, E. 1987. The large external domain is sufficient for the correct sorting of secreted or chimeric influenza virus hemagglutinins in polarized monkey kidney cells. *J. Cell Biol.* 104:769–82

39. Rothenberger, S., Iacopetta, B. J., Kühn, L. C. 1987. Endocytosis of the transferrin receptor requires the cytoplasmic domain but not its phosphorylation site. *Cell* 49:423–31

40. Sambrook, J., Rodgers, L., White, J., Gething, M.-J. 1985. Lines of BPV-transformed murine cells that constitutively express influenza virus hemagglutinin. *EMBO J.* 4:91–103

41. Smith, G. L., Moss, B. 1983. Infectious poxvirus vectors have capacity for at least 25,000 base pairs of foreign DNA. *Gene* 25:21–28

42. Stephens, E. B., Compans, R. W. 1986. Nonpolarized expression of a secreted murine leukemia virus glycoprotein in polarized epithelial cells. *Cell* 47:1053–59

43. Stephens, E. B., Compans, R. W. Earl, P., Moss, B. 1986. Surface expression of viral glycoproteins is polarized in epithelial cells infected with recombinant vaccinia viral vectors. *EMBO J.* 5:237–45

44. Varghese, J. N., Laver, W. G., Colman, P. M. 1983. Structure of the influenza virus glycoprotein antigen neuraminidase a 2.9 Å resolution. *Nature* 303:35–40

45. Warren, S. L., Andel, L. M., Nelson, W. J. 1988. Elevated expression of pp60$^{c\text{-}src}$ alters a selective morphogenetic property of epithelial cells in vitro without a mitogenic effect. *Mol. Cell Biol.* 8:632–46

46. White, J. M., Helenius, A. A., Gething, M.-J. 1982. The haemagglutinin of influenza virus expressed from a cloned gene promotes membrane fusion. *Nature* 300:658–59

47. Wills, J. W., Srinivas, R. V., Hunter, E. 1984. Mutations of the Rous sarcoma virus env gene that affect the transport and subcellular location of the glycoprotein products. *J. Cell Biol.* 99:3011–23

48. Wilson, I. A., Skehel, J. J., Wiley, D. C. 1981. The haemagglutinin membrane glycoprotein of influenza virus: structure at 3 Å resolution. *Nature* 289:366–73

RESPIRATORY PHYSIOLOGY

Introduction, Robert E. Forster, *Section Editor*

It has been known for over a century that several organs can respond to a decrease in arterial P_{O_2} and actuate homeostatic responses. However there is still no agreement as to the precise cellular or molecular mechanism by which P_{O_2} is sensed.

The fundamental process is presumably a chemical reaction and the obvious candidate is the reduction of molecular oxygen by cytochrome aa₃ in the mitochondrion. In this model a lower arterial P_{O_2} could decrease oxidative phosphorylation, thus reducing available ATP, which could trigger a cascade of responses. However according to reported measurements in mitochondrial suspensions, the P_{O_2} in the neighborhood of a mitochondrion has to fall to about 1 mm Hg before the reduction of cytochrome aa_3 will lower oxidative phosphorylation significantly.

Thus the question follows as to whether the P_{O_2} decrease from the arterial blood, at 100 mm Hg, to the mitochondrion is normally this great, and transforms the inquiry to an investigation of tissue P_{O_2}. This is another major unanswered physiological question of sufficient importance to stimulate semi-annual international meetings (ISOTT or the International Society for Oxygen Transport in Tissues). Of course there may be, and undoubtedly are, other fundamantal mechanisms of oxygen sensing.

Tamura, Hazeki, Nioka, and Chance review the present state of our knowledge of control of mitochondrial respiration, particularly the recent results of nuclear magnetic resonance as well as optical spectroscopic methods applied in vivo.

The best known oxygen sensor is the peripheral chemoreceptor near the

811

carotid sinus, the carotid body, and Acker discusses the state of our views of its function today and proposes mechanisms.

Another well known homeostatic response to lowered arterial P_{O_2} is increased hematopoiesis, which results from stimulation of the erythropoietin-producing cells of the kidney. Bauer and Kurtz review the status of this field, the recognition of the erythropoietin-producing cells and the heterogeniety of renal tissue P_{O_2}.

Muscle makes up a majority of body tissue and provides the best known model for the delivery of O_2 from the capillaries to the mitochondria, and for calculation of tissue P_{O_2} from the capillaries to the mitochondria, and for calculation of tissue P_{O_2} gradients. Wittenberg and Wittenberg review oxygen transport in muscle, with particular attention paid to the importance of myoglobin in facilitating this flux.

Annu. Rev. Physiol. 1989. 51:813–34

IN VIVO STUDY OF TISSUE OXYGEN METABOLISM USING OPTICAL AND NUCLEAR MAGNETIC RESONANCE SPECTROSCOPIES

Mamoru Tamura and Osamu Hazeki

Biophysics Division, Research Institute of Applied Electricity, Hokkaido University, Sapporo, Japan

Shoko Nioka and Britton Chance

Department of Biochemistry and Biophysics, School of Medicine, University of Pennsylvania, Philadelphia, Pennsylvania 19104 USA

INTRODUCTION

This review summarizes several optical approaches for monitoring the tissue oxygenation state. These are correlated with magnetic resonance spectroscopy (MRS) studies of tissue energy metabolism. We focus here mainly on cardiac and brain tissues because of their high oxygen sensitivity.

RESPIRATORY CHARACTERISTICS OF MITOCHONDRIA

Respiration rate is governed by adenosine diphosphate (ADP), inorganic phosphate (P_i), in particular oxygen as emphasized here, and by various other factors. These factors, in turn, govern the redox states of cytochrome a_3 and pyridine nucleotide. Near equilibrium among phosphate potentials, pyridine nucleotide and cytochrome a_3 was proposed for cell suspensions (118, 160) and has been tested analytically in isolated mitochondria, cell suspensions,

813

0066-4278/89/0315-0813$02.00

and perfused organs at low [O_2] values (49, 168). However, the near equilibrium approach is now found to be inconsistent with MRS of in vivo and in vitro studies of the myocardium (101), and the kinetic control described below is preferred (see Equation 3).

When the oxygen was limited and cytochrome largely reduced, respiration rate of mitochondria (130), shown in Equation 1, was tested over wide ranges of oxygen concentrations (10^{-7}–10^{-10}M) (33, 130) by using bacterial luminescence as a "gold standard" of oxygen indication (116). For an irreversible reaction of reduced cytochrome oxidase (a^{2+}_3) with oxygen O_2 the rate is simply expressed:

$$\frac{dO_2}{dt} = k_1 \, [a^{2+}_3][O_2] \tag{1}$$

where k_1 is the second order rate constant for the reaction of cytochrome oxidase and oxygen.

The apparent K_m value for oxygen is calculated from the quotient of the pseudo first order reaction velocity constant for the removal of the second electron from molecular oxygen, k_3 over k_1 ($K_m = K_3/K_1$). The oxygen dependence of respiration rate and cytochrome a^{2+}_3, shown in Equation 3, gives values of P50$_{a3}$ in active respiration with sufficient Pi and ADP (state 3) and resting respiration with sufficient Pi, but no ADP (state 4) (40).

The redox state of the mitochondrial respiratory components has been well established under hypoxic conditions. The half maximal reduction of pyridine nucleotide, $P_{50_{PN}}$, occurs at [O_2] of 0.08 μM in state 3 in vitro (140). Similarly, P_{50} of cytochrome $a+a_3$ occurs at 0.15 μM [O_2] in state 3 and at less than 0.04 μM [O_2] in state 4, which demonstrates the energy dependence of oxygen affinity. P_{50} of cytochrome c depends on the respiration rate ranging from 0.27 to 0.03 μM [O_2] in state 3 and state 4 respectively (117). There is a linear increase of the P_{50} for cytochrome c with increasing respiratory rate (130, 140). Critical [O_2] was found to be 0.09 μM for mitochondrial state 3 respiration (112, 116). Below this [O_2], insufficient ATP is generated and endogenous Ca^{2+} is released from the mitochondria. Incomplete reduction of cytochromes is observed in anoxic cells and isolated mitochondria when ATP is produced by glycolysis or is supplemented (energized state) (117).

Reduction of cytochrome $a+a_3$ does not occur in parallel with the reduction of cytochrome c since their relation depends on the energy state and respiration rate. Similar nonlinear relationships are also observed between the pyridine nucleotide and cytochrome $a+a_3$. Two and possibly three copper atoms (59, 166) are present in cytochrome oxidase with different redox and optical properties which behave differently from the heme $a+a_3$ (11, 19, 111).

The half-maximal reduction of optically detectable copper (Cu_a) in isolated mitochondria occurs at [O_2] of 0.08 μM in both state 4 and state 3 (72). The simultaneous redox plots indicate energy state and tissue oxygen concentration (64, 147, 149, 157).

Optical absorption can determine [cytochrome a^{2+}_3] and permit a calculation of oxygen consumption at high respiration rates as in Equation 1 or can measure the oxygenation of myoglobin (see Gradient Coherence section below).

Multiple Controls of Mitochondrial Respiration

The possibility of substrate and oxygen controls of oxidative metabolism is implicit in the experimental results obtained from the mature myocardium. For the first time, greater precision of the MRS data, obtained from the dog heart in vivo, permitted the conclusion that not only is ATP constant as work increases, but so are phosphocreatine (PCr), and to the extent that it can be determined, P_i. Recent MRS studies (29, 43) show that the perfused heart does not display the same metabolic characteristics when glucose is a substrate as when palmitate is the substrate; in the latter case ADP control ($K_m \sim$ 20 μM) can be determined in the skeletal tissue (101). Thus, in in vivo studies, metabolic control cannot be assigned exclusively to ADP + P_i, but may include other constitutents of the general equation for oxidative metabolism:

$$3ADP + 3P_i + NADH + 4H^+ + \tfrac{1}{2} O_2 = 3ATP + NAD^+ + 4H_2O. \tag{2}$$

NADH and oxygen may exert more control of myocardial metabolism as the work increases; ADP and P_i may be constant while NADH and oxygen vary. First, Hansord (60) and Denton (46) proposed that cytosolic calcium activates mitochondrial pyruvate dehydrogenase and that the higher calcium levels found with greater work increase activity of the dehydrogenase, and hence raise [NADH]. Second, it is possible that local oxygen delivery is regulated in accordance with work to supplement mitochondrial function as the work increases (28, 29).

The data on heart are inconsistent with the near-equilibrium proposal (159, 160); in fact, kinetic control (Equation 3; 28) is more appropriate than might be expected of the metabolically active myocardium (101). An appropriate framework for kinetic control is the modified Michaelis-Menten formulation (29), which in its simplest and approximate form is

$$\frac{V}{V_{max}} = \frac{1}{1 + \dfrac{K_1}{ADP} + \dfrac{K_2}{P_i} + \dfrac{K_3}{NADH} + \dfrac{K_4}{O_2}} ; \tag{3}$$

where K_1 to K_4 are the K_ms of substrates in the oxidative phosphorylation enzyme system (Equation 2).

This is an elaboration of the Michaelis-Menten equation for enzyme activity that is (a) a steady state formulation of kinetic control, and (b) one in which the enzyme itself is the system of oxidative metabolism. In order that any substrate be regulatory, it must be at a concentration approximating that of its affinity constant; if it is large compared to its affinity constant, it will not be regulatory for those particular conditions. In the myocardium where there is a potential for multiple controls, all four constituents may be of the same order as their respective K_ms designated K_1–K_4 and hence regulatory. In skeletal muscle, NADH, oxygen, and probably P_1 are large compared to their K_ms and ADP is regulatory, a situation that may also exist in the brain (31, 154). Equation 3 unifies the ideas of metabolic control in these different tissues. One complication is that the K_ms are interdependent, and as one takes control, it modulates the effective value of the others. Nevertheless, the expression accounts for the existing data and is unique and useful in directing experimental studies.

APPROACHES TO RESPIRATION AND OXYGEN IN TISSUE

Introduction

Unlike the oxygen microelectrode, which at best samples the superficial tissue layer, techniques using electromagnetic radiation (light and radio waves) have various advantages for monitoring the oxygen and metabolite concentration deep within the living tissue. The methods have a short response time, are nondestructive, and permit continuous monitoring of the oxygen state as well as the energy state. The applicable frequency range extends from ultra-violet (UV) to radio-frequency (rf). The basic principle of optical monitoring for tissue oxygen has been well established by the use of optically responsive indicators such as mitochondrial cytochromes, oxygen carrying hemoproteins, and several oxygen-related heme-enzymes (17).

Figure 1 shows the scheme of the calibration curve of optically active intrinsic oxygen sensors as studied in vitro, except PCr/P_i, which was measured in cat brain and $[O_2]$ was taken from venous outflow. The degrees of oxygenation-deoxygenation of hemoglobin and myoglobin indicate the oxygen concentrations in the circulatory system and cytosolic space of tissue, respectively. The oxidation-reduction of cytochrome $a+a_3$ indicates mainly $[O_2]$ in the mitochondrial space. The redox change of pyridine nucleotide (PN) also gives us mitochondrial $[O_2]$ (140). The ratio PCr/P_i, which has a linear relation to phosphorlation potential as determined by phosphorus MRS, indicates oxygen levels as well as energy state and follows a profile similar to mitochondrial cytochrome (28, 29) and pyridine nucleotide (108).

Examples of sensitive intracellular oxygen indicators are yeast hemoglobin (115), leg hemoglobin (1), and ascaris hemoglobin (116). Figure 2 shows an example of determination of intracellular PO_2 by yeast hemoglobin (115), which can be increased by genetic methods in *S. cerevisiae* (36). The yeast hemoglobin is a convenient intracellular indicator for the quantitative measurement of oxygen concentrations up to $10^{-9}M$, at its K_m, and verifies the high O_2 affinity of cytochrome oxidase in cells. (See page 834 for Fig. 1 and 2).

Many extrinsic oxygen probes are available, such as pyrene butyric acid in liver (97) and brain (103), as it will pass through the blood brain barrier under mannitol stress. Lifetime measurements of oxygen quenching fluorescence (99), and most recently, phosphorescence, can be used to measure very low oxygen concentrations down to $10^{-9}M$ (151). Extrinsic probes may be linear with respect to oxygen concentration according to the Stern-Volmer relationship (99).

Fluorinated carbon emulsion was used to measure oxygen concentration (150), since oxygen changes relaxation times in fluorine MRS. This technique can be applied to whole body imaging to localize the hypoxia (85), but the O_2 sensitivity is low. However, rapidly respiring groups or clumps of cells in tissues cause O_2 gradients that require validation with intracellular probes such as intracellular hemoglobin, or extrinsic probes trapped inside cells such as pH and Ca indicators.

Ultraviolet to Visible Spectroscopy

The redox changes of respiratory components can be measured in the range of 300–650 nm. Pyridine nucleotide can be measured by fluorescence at 366 nm with excitation at 450 nm with a mercury lamp (35, 105). Fluorescence of mitochondria originates mainly from NADH in the matrix space (22). Artifacts arose with the use of lasers, such as the frequency-doubled nitrogen laser, the helium-cadmium laser, and the 334 nm line of the mercury arc (123), and consisted of (*a*) greatly increased tissue damage, (*b*) excitation of pigments whose responses are not correlated with that of NADH and (*c*) inadequate hemoglobin compensation. Since tissue damage by ultraviolet light decreases at wavelengths above 360 nm, and since a variety of compensatory procedures are available at 366 nm (108), the 366 nm mercury arc line is recommended.

Microfluorometry of the brain surface showed responses to hypoxia that were unaffected by hemoglobin interference because it focused on regions sparse in blood vessels (38). Large fiber-optic systems covering 10 mm² of the brain surface, including major blood vessels, require compensation for changes in hemoglobin absorption with deoxygenation. Kobayashi (98) used a compensating wavelength of hemoglobin in the red region (77, 98). Extrinsic dyes such as rhodamine (106) have been used for compensation (48).

Satisfactory compensation for hemoglobin absorption changes can be tested by the arterial injection of bolus of saline. In a dog brain at 366 nm, the reflectance signal contained nearly the same contribution from hemoglobin as the fluorescence signal, as judged by comparison with the microscopic technique.

In in vivo conditions, hemoglobin masks almost all the cytochromes. Attempts have been made to measure the fluorescence of heart NADH but interference from blood hemoglobin as well as from myoglobin absorption was not completely eliminated (93). Similarly, myoglobin and hemoglobin absorption cannot be separated in vivo in heart and skeletal tissue. The overlap of the spectra of myoglobin and cytochrome was analyzed quantitatively by the Kubelka-Munk theory of photon-diffusion (163). Conventional dual-wavelength spectrophotometry and multicomponent analysis give almost the same results (53, 70). Such observations, undertaken in white muscle and hemoglobin/myoglobin free cell suspensions, were less difficult to pursue than in red muscles, i.e. either skeletal or cardiac muscles where the myoglobin absorption changes may interfere with the absorption measurements of cytochromes, so that special corrections are needed for cytochrome analysis.

Redox changes of cytochrome $a + a_3$ in the heart can be measured at 605–620 nm where the molar ratio of myoglobin to cytochrome $a + a_3$ in the myocardium is $8 : 1$ (147). In the rapidly respiring Langendorf-perfused heart, the parallel between the absorption changes of myoglobin and b cytochrome in a graded hypoxia (gradient coherence) was at first believed to be an optical artifact due to inadequate separation of the cytochrome and myoglobin signals. However, the use of ethyl hydrogen peroxide to convert myoglobin to the ferryl form, which is unresponsive to O_2, indicated that the interferences were of small consequence in this parallelism (148). Optical studies of suspensions of slowly respiring myocytes and mixtures of mitochondria with myoglobin clearly showed the optical technique can separate cytochrome and myoglobin signals at the concentrations of 1 to 10 respectively for physiological cardiac tissue, but in these models no coherence was observable (81, 82, 162). Perfused rat thigh muscle, where myoglobin: cytochrome $a + a_3$ is $4 : 1$, shows coherence in graded hypoxia (146). In contrast, no reduction of cytochrome could be detected during hypoxia of the intact dog muscle, although myoglobin deoxygenation was observed by microspectrophotometry (66, 67). Periodic redox changes of cytochrome $a + a_3$ were reported during the cardiac cycle (48, 104).

Two-Dimensional Displays of Flavoprotein (Fp), Pyridine Nucleotide Redox State

A number of attempts have been made to provide a 2-D display of the redox state in animals and humans. The first method employed a high resolution (50 μ) micro-fluorometer (139) which scanned the brain surface in a rectangular array over 6 × 3.5 mm and produced a difference map in minutes. While the hypoxic stress over long intervals may have caused additional changes, the experimental results in normoxic and hypoxic rat brain indicated that hypoxia was distributed unevenly over the surface.

Freeze trapping affords an opportunity to observe heterogeneity in three dimensions by fluorophotography (107); hypoxia/ischemia induces a macroscopic heterogeneity shown as "black holes" where the infarct ablates the fluorescence signal itself (155). Large scale heterogeneity was also observed unexpectedly for reduced NADH in the caudus putamen and thalamus in normoxia (73) because the pentobarbital anesthesia used affects mitochondria uniformly (25). Two dimensional scanning of serial sections gives three dimensional images of metabolic heterogeneity in the brain (37) with a resolution of about 50 μ in each section, and <10 μ in the third dimension due to scattering in ice crystals. This system has been used to scan freeze-trapped gerbil brains under conditions of spreading depression, both in space and time (62, 63). The NADH and flavoprotein fluorescence were enhanced about ten-fold due to the reduction in non-radiative transitions at low temperatures and the enhanced tissue scattering. Furthermore, since the flavoprotein (Fp) signal increases with oxidation and the NADH (PN) signal decreases, the ratio Fp/PN was found to normalize the effects of different distributions of mitochondria in different parts of the brain tissue. Reflectance spectrophotometry for cytochromes can also be employed for redox mapping in the brain.

In order to obtain real-time two-dimensional scans of the brain, a flying spot scanner employing NADH or flavoprotein fluorescence (39) was developed for recording changes of the redox state of the brain following the surgical supplementation of the blood supply by an external to internal carotid artery anastomosis in which some 30 patients were examined (6). Here, the object was to present to the surgeon rapid two-dimensional scans, or histogram displays, of fluorescence intensity. Such histograms proved invaluable in identifying whether small portions of the tissue under observation had received more oxygen following the anastomosis (6).

Red Light to Infrared Spectroscopy

The absorption coefficient of hemoglobin in the near-red region (630–830 nm) is relatively small, light penetrates deep in tissues, and the light scattering according to Kubelka-Munck is somewhat less. Millikan may have used these wavelengths because of fortuitous leaks of the green and red filters (110). Butler & Norris (15) demonstrated transmission in this region through opaque materials and Jobsis applied this technique to cat and neonate heads (74).

Dual wavelength spectrophotometry of hemoglobin developed by Millikan (110) can use any appropriate wavelength pair, for example, 910 nm and 760 nm which are absorption maxima for oxyhemoglobin and deoxyhemoglobin respectively. The apparatus becomes more complex when the ∼10% contribution to absorption of the copper component of cytochrome a+a₃ in the oxidized state at 830 nm is to be included. In this case, four wavelengths are used and various algorithms based upon animal models, the transilluminated head of cat (74) and rat (58, 66, 74), used for studies in neonates (44, 74, 78, 167). An additional peak at 870 nm, which was not observed in vitro, was identified (C. A. Piantadosi, personal communication).

In animal models, hemoglobin oxygenation, blood volume, and the redox state of cytochrome copper have been measured in the head under various conditions such as carotid occlusion (75) and change of intracranial pressure (16). Simultaneous changes in the near-red absorbance were also reported in the human palm (144), rat skeletal muscle (131), and dog heart (74). In the rat, with fluorocarbon substituted for blood, the absorption change of copper cytochrome a+a₃ was analyzed in more detail (52, 69, 74, 87–90, 164); Kariman showed that the redox change is energy dependent (87). Hazeki (66, 67) demonstrated a linear relationship between absorbance and hematocrit, but found that the absorption coefficients of hemoglobin in oxy and deoxy forms in situ differed from those of purified hemoglobin. Light scattering of cells in tissues has been studied by others (80, 122, 137, 138, 158).

Time Resolved Spectroscopy (TRS)

Since tissues scatter incident light significantly, the Beer-Lambert law is not directly applicable for quantitative analysis of tissue pigments. Delpy et al (45, 153, 165), Blumberg (13), Wilson & Adam (158), and Barbour (7, 21) have calculated the distribution of the light intensity in a scattering material containing an absorber and have laid the theoretical framework for photon migration in tissues. Most recently, Patterson (21), Wilson & Adam (158) and Shinnar (21) have superimposed theoretical and experimental data on photon migration using Monte Carlo or random walk theories. TRS measures time of light transit in a sample, and thus the optical path length in tissue, and can avoid the problem produced by scattering on the continuous wave spectroscopy (CWS) (30). The propagation of light or photon migration in brain tissue is highly efficient (20% loss cm⁻¹) and relatively independent of wavelength (<10% change 630–800 nm). Decreased propagation of light in brain tissue is largely due to incremental absorption by hemoglobin or cytochromes (32).

Two approaches are being used to time resolve the first arrival photons that have followed a straight line on a minimal optical path with negligible lateral migration. Whilst nearly all incident photons change their direction in living tissue after having traveled an absorption length (13), a few straight line emergent photons may be detected with high power laser input and highly time-resolved detection. The complementary scheme is to measure the population of "late emergent" photons from the brain, i.e. those having travelled everywhere within the brain. The number of emergent photons in brain containing hemoglobin decreases exponentially with time or distance travelled, the slope $\mu = \frac{1}{L} (\ln I)$ increases as the absorption by hemoglobin increases. Typical values for the brain containing oxyhemoglobin are 0.05 cm^{-1}, and at 760 and 630 nm this value increases as the hemoglobin is deoxygenated. In animal models, quantitative correlations between tissue analysis of brain and this slope change have been achieved (30, 32). While imaging with continuous light has been proposed by some, it has very limited possibilities for reconstruction since the optical pathlength is not known (113, 156, 167). TRS is potentially better for imaging since the presence of absorbing objects attenuates the migrating photons, and algorithms similar to those of computer tomography (CT) technology seem applicable.

Quantitative correlations between the deoxygenation of known amounts of hemoglobin and the TRS measured slope change have been achieved (30, 32). Moreover, the quantitation of hemoglobin changes by TRS in a particular location, observed also by continuous wave spectroscopy (CSW), affords a measure of the pathlength for the latter (32).

Magnetic Resonance Spectroscopy (MRS)

Magnetic Resonance Spectroscopy affords noninvasive biochemical evaluation by phosphorus MRS (^{31}P MRS) (54, 121) of energy related metabolites, ADP, PCr, P_i, and lipid related components, such as phosphoethanolamine and phosphoglycerol choline. Proton MRS (^{1}H) has the capability of measuring lactate, aspartate, Cr + PCr, (5, 10, 169) and many of the carbon compounds, particularly glycogen, which can be studied by ^{31}C MRS (44). Among the unique features of MRS biochemistry in vivo is that physiological conditions can both be observed and maintained, and thus many approaches that involve the establishment of steady states of metabolites are now available for study; whereas previously homeostatic controls could only be evaluated indirectly. Repeated observations on the same animal obviate the necessity for matched controls in many studies. Longitudinal observations over long periods are particularly feasible with human subjects because of the noninvasive nature of MRS. Most important for the biochemical/ physiological study is the fact that the free thermodynamically active forms of substrates are quantified permitting the first insight on the free phosphate in the cell by direct measurements, since Seraydarian et al (132) observed in 1961 that the analytical determinations of P_i were time dependent. Thus, some limitations of biochemical tissue assays are avoided, namely alteration of labile tissue chemicals during sampling and assay and inability to obtain multiple assays in the same sample or to identify free forms of substrates.

Although MRS is advantageous in many respects, it has significant weaknesses that are often overlooked by enthusiastic investigators. First of all, it is essentially a "blunt" tool. Concentrations less than 0.3 mM are difficult to determine; for example, determination of 2.3 mM ATP with ± 10% accuracy in the brain require averaging over 15 minutes. Secondly, absolute concentrations require detailed calibrations that are often beyond the skills or facilities available to most investigators. Thus, analytical values for the most stable metabolite are often taken as a calibration for the MRS study. Ratios of concentrations can be determined by MRS, providing there is an adequately long interval between radio-frequency interrogations and adequate resolution of peaks to ensure against undesirable overlap of components. Line broadening may be due to heterogeneity of the sample and to the presence of adventitious paramagnets or cations that may bind the phosphorus compounds, for example magnesium and calcium binding of ATP.

Free adenosine diphosphate (ADP) is important in many metabolic control transitions since it was shown in 1955 to govern the rate of mitochondrial electron transport (40) (see Equation 3). In organs that do not contain creatine kinase, ADP is hard to determine by MRS unless assumptions are made about the chemical mechanisms. However, when a number of kinases dealing with ADP and AMP are near equilibrium (154), then the adenine nucleotides can be computed from the equilibrium constants. Under certain simplified conditions, Pi/PCr is proportional to ADP with a proportional constant of 1 to 33 at pH 7.1. However, the assumption of near equilibrium of creatine kinase in the cell must be verified by experimentation, often by the MRS technique of saturation transfer (12, 133). When these requirements are satisfied, MRS becomes a most useful tool for exploring the kinetics and thermodynamics of energy metabolism in the cytosolic space. Reasonable assumptions permit calculation of the phosphate potential ATP/ADP $\times$ P_i, directly from PCr and P_i as PCr $(/P_i)^2$ at a constant pH, with assumptions about the size of the free creatine pool.

STUDIES OF TISSUE ENERGY METABOLISM

Oxygen Gradient-Gradient Coherence and Oxygen

The critical $[O_2]$ in an outflow from an organ and in the cytosol has been reported to be much higher in tissue than in isolated mitochondria (49, 160) see also Jobsis (76, 126). The differences depend on the nature of oxygen concentration gradients in rapidly respiring tissue and are discussed in this section.

In rapidly respiring tissue, a microscopic heterogeneity arises in the pericapillary tissue: the portion at the arterial end of the capillary will have a different P_{O_2} from the distal portion in addition to the radial differences (37). This type of heterogeneity has been examined by measuring the absorbance change of two oxygen indicators (Figure 1). A typical example is the perfused rat heart (3), where the myoglogin deoxygenation in progressive hypoxia (and recovery) is proportional to the cytochrome $a+a_3$ reduction at high metabolic rates (147). Under these conditions, myoglobin can be substituted for cytochrome in Equation 1, enabling a determination of O_2 (27, 41). This plot of myoglobin deoxygenation versus cytochrome reduction is termed a correlation or coherence diagram and the proportional phenomenon is called a "gradient coherence" (29, 40). Under these conditions, a 5-torr oxygen gradient exists, presumably between cytosolic and mitochondrial spaces.

Computer simulations verify the coherence diagram. The calculated gradients are small at lower oxygen consumption rates but at high rates, the gradient coherence is readily demonstrated and gradients can reach over 10 torr per micron in a model simulating typical cytosolic/mitochondrial dimensions of the myocyte (41). Figure 3 graphically illustrates the effect of respiration rate upon the responses of myoglobin and cytochrome to low, medium, and high metabolic flux. At low respiration rates the myoglobin becomes deoxygenated prior to the cytochrome reduction. At medium respiration rates the myoglobin deoxygenation overlaps cytochrome reduction and at the highest rates the two are indistinguishable. (See page 834, Fig. 3).

The dependence of coherence upon respiration rate has been overlooked by many investigators. Honig et al (42, 55–57, 71) proposed uniform distribution of oxygen in the cell interior, reporting the uniform distribution of myoglobin oxygenation of a single muscle cell in the previously exercised dog skeletal muscle based on the oxygen diffusion theory. Lubbers & Starlingers (135) found gradient coherence but proposed macroscopic heterogeneity (nonuniform) distribution of hypoxic cells in the perfused heart (W. D. Lubbers, personal communication), which we termed geometric coherence (27). Isolated cardiac myocytes fail to respire rapidly enough to show gradient coherence; measurement of respiration rate, myoglobin oxygenation, and redox state of cytochrome $a+a_3$ (159) showed no detectable gradient existed between cytosol and mitochondria. On the other hand, Jones (83, 84) reported that gradient coherence existed in the cell interior. The much lower oxygen consumption of the cell preparations compared to intact tissues may account for the observed differences. Gradient coherence diminished when oxygen consumption was lowered by cooling the perfused heart (W. D. Lubbers, personal communication). Coherence was also obtained in perfused liver for cytochrome-c and urate oxidase while the more slowly respiring glycolate did not show coherence (114). In brain, there exists a large oxygen gradient between blood and mitochondria, and a PaO_2 of 20 mm Hg is critical for the production of lactate and reduction of cytochrome $a+a_3$ (142). However, unlike cardiac and skeletal tissues, myoglobin is lacking and therefore the experimental evidence of a cytosolic oxygen gradient has not been obtained.

Cardiac and Skeletal Muscle

Measurement of the NADH of skeletal muscle during stimulation was first employed to bridge the gap between isolated mitochondria and cell suspensions and tissues (18, 26, 32, 92). The level of NAD reduction was found to be high in the resting state, consistent with observations of a "resting" mitochondrial suspension (state 4) while stimulation caused rapid step-wise oxidations of NADH at various twitch rates until a plateau was reached, [the state 4 to state 3 transition observed in mitochondria (40)]. With slight increases of stimulation, an abrupt transition from normoxic to hypoxic conditions occurred suggesting that the inward diffusion of oxygen became rate limiting (18, 32) indicating the anaerobic threshold of the perfused, stimulated muscle. A calculation of the expected breakdown of ATP and the increase of ADP thereby suggested that only small amounts of ADP were necessary to activate mitochondrial function in vivo, consistent with ADP control of mitochondrial respiration in muscle (32).

The complexities of the NADH response may also involve substrate control of oxidative phosphorylation as described above. With sufficient $[O_2]$, NADH indicates the substrate level, while when $[O_2]$ is limited, NADH responds to the oxygen tension (29). Thus, NADH can be an indicator for both substrate and oxygen levels (see Equation 3).

The estimation of intracellular $[O_2]$ in the cardiac and skeletal tissues have been quantitated by myoglobin absorption change (2, 37, 57, 86, 104, 147, 149, 157). Pyridine nucleotide begins to be reduced at a cytosolic $[O_2]$ lower than 6 μM (107, 147). Lactate release starts to increase at $[O_2]$ of 10 μM at which level oxygen consumption also begins to fall, but is constant above this. Thus, critical $[O_2]$ in vasculature for the heart was concluded to be <10 μM, almost tenfold higher than that in isolated mitochondria (76, 89). The same investigators (82, 83) reported similar results with isolated myocytes although others disagree (91, 100, 124, 127, 162). Constancy of respiration rate as $[O_2]$ fell to 10 μM can be explained partly by concomitant increases of ADP, cytochrome a^{2+}_3, and NADH (49, 161) (see Equation 3).

The critical $[O_2]$ determines the direction of redox shift of pyridine nucleotide in metabolic activation as in muscle contraction or electrical activity (102). In the isolated perfused rat heart, oxidation of pyridine nucleotide and reduction of cytochrome $a+a_3$ paralleled the increase of oxygen consumption with work (117) and at the same time, lactate release increased slightly (128). An increased oxygen consumption by the heart required increased ADP and caused a change of pyridine nucleotide of 18% of the full-scale change that was obtained by complete aerobic anoxic transition. At $[O_2]$ lower than 10 μM, increased NADH was associated with decreasing oxygen consumption, concomitant with the deoxygenation of myoglobin (2) as was observed in frog sartorius muscle (26, 32). Perfused rat thigh muscle, where myoglobin and cytochrome $a+a_3$ is $4:1$, also show coherence in graded hypoxia (149). In contrast, no reduction of cytochrome could be detected in hypoxia of the intact dog muscle, although myoglobin deoxygenation was observed (66). The perfused heart gave a nonparallel relationship between NADH and cytochrome $a+a_3$ reduction. The same was observed with mitochondrial suspensions in state 3 respiration (Figure 1), which suggests that the mitochondria of the normal beating perfused heart are idling in state 3 (PCr/P_i = 5 to 10). In contrast, Kanaide et al (86) showed a nearly linear relationship between these two components that suggests that the heart was near state 3 (157). However, heart oxygenation and substrate delivery must be monitored in such cases.

Metabolic Fluctuations in Cardiac Tissue

Fabel and Lübbers (50) monitored oxymyoglobin in the mammalian heart as an indication of $[O_2]$ and concluded that no fluctuations occurred during the cardiac cycle. Tamura et al (145, 147, 150), meanwhile, showed that myoglobin was more oxygenated during systolic than diastolic periods in the crystalloid perfused heart. However, they noted diminished fluctuations as small amounts of hemoglobin were added to the perfusate and concluded that minimization of fluctuations of tissue PO_2 was the proper physiologic function of Hb and Mb. Makino et al (104) obtained similar results, even in hypoxia (50, 64, 104) indicating that homeostatsis of O_2 delivery is maintained at the high PaO_2 values that they used.

Heterogeneity

Flash photographic techniques (23, 136) have been used for these fluorescence studies and more recently a reticon detector (129). The photographs clearly demonstrated the nonuniform distribution of hypoxic or anoxic areas in the cardiac tissue, in low flow ischemic/anoxia more than in anoxic/anoxia. Although the nonlinear aspect of the photographic recordings of NADH fluorescence could cause overestimation of the gradients, steep gradients have been found by optical and metabolite analysis of freeze-clamped tissue (62, 63). On the basis of NADH fluorescent patches, myoglobin should also show patchiness but changes observed by spectrophotometry in the degree of deoxygenation of myoglobin do not have the resolution of the fluorescence photography and may be interpreted as an average of normoxic areas and anoxic areas.

Brain Studies

The redox state of the brain mitochondrial respiratory chain is altered by moderate electrical stimulation or seizure. An initial oxidation of PN followed by reduction (77, 106, 124) is associated, with maximal and prolonged electrical activation of the brain, respectively (47, 48). The extent of oxidation of pyridine nucleotide and duration of stimulation are parallel in normoxia (48, 125). Oxidation of cytochrome $a+a_3$ during electrical stimulation in normoxia (124) was first measured at 605–590 nm wavelengths and considered free of hemoglobin interference (94–96). In graded hypoxia, there is a transition in the effect of electrical stimulation from oxidation in normoxia to no response, and then to a reduction in severe hypoxia. This transition is considered to be diagnostic of the critical oxygenation state of the tissue.

The initial studies of the redox changes in the hypoxic brain were made with a fluorescence microscope that was employed either in a stationary mode at a single point where small blood vessels were observed (38), or in a scanning mode in two dimensions (139). When a normoxic rat was made to breathe nitrogen (no oxygen), after a 30 second lag period, the redox state of the brain with dura intact changed from normoxic to hypoxic reduced state over less than 30 seconds (24). These initial results were unaffected by a change in hemoglobin absorption because the fluorescence measurement was restricted to a small aperture, 10–20 u, and focused on an area with few blood vessels and with penetration depths of about 0.5 mm (18, 38). A simple time sharing of signals permitted simultaneous measurements of NADH and hemoglobin (38, 61). NAD reduction in hypoxia did not occur until 80% deoxygenation of hemoglobin occurred.

Cytochrome Oxygen Affinity in Brain Tissue

Highly reduced cytochrome $a+a_3$ was found to be present in the blood perfused brain inspiring at 20 to 100% oxygen (68, 142). More recently, Sylvia and Piantadosi (141) found cytochrome oxidase, cytochrome c, and cytochrome b to be reduced at very nearly the same P_{O_2}, and PCr was constant until reduction of these cytochromes had occurred (see also 119). Similar observations were reported using near-red wavelengths (65). Thus cytochromes b and c of brain mitochondria behave as isolated mitochondria in the absence of hemoglobin. Rosenthal and his colleagues (109) using anesthetized rat brain found that K^+ depolarization did not occur until cytochrome a reduction occurred. The early reduction of cytochromes observed both by Rosenthal (126) and Wilson (158, 159) is not observed in suspensions of baker's yeast containing copious reserves of ATP and polyphosphates (20). It is noteworthy that these yeast cells neither clump nor contain hemoglobin and thus the results are consistent with the above studies of fluorocarbon-perfused brains. These results confirm the earlier studies of Bashford et al (8, 9) who rapidly freeze-trapped and redox-scanned the surface and sections of the gerbil brain at ~100°K as in normoxia and hypoxia. Hemoglobin was deoxygenated prior to cytochrome $a+a_3$ reduction which occurred only at very low P_{O_2}s.

Clinical Applications

The changes of blood volume and redox state of cytochrome copper of the brain using near-red spectroscopy were demonstrated with human volunteers under conditions of hyperventilation (75) and hypercapnia (75, 165). Clinically, upon compression of the carotid artery (51), different behaviors of regional cerebral blood volume, hemoglobin oxygen saturation, and cytochrome redox levels were demonstrated between normal volunteers and patients. In these human studies, data from fluorocarbon-substituted cat brains was assumed transferable to humans for the calibration algorithm (120, 123, 143, 168). However, it was recently found that photons migrate over much longer pathlengths in the larger human brain and now the transferability of measurement on the small animal head is open to question (30).

Phosphorus nuclear magnetic resonance is in no detectable way affected by the presence or absence of hemoglobin and gives titrations of energy dependence that show changes when optical studies indicate hemoglobin to be nearly completely deoxygenated. This method has proven itself to be very useful in a wide variety of clinical applications (54).

The bedside monitoring of cerebral oxygenation for the newborn baby affords a useful trend indicator (4, 14, 129, 165). The possibility that the TRS technology can be used to calibrate the mean optical path of these trend indicators and allow quantitation of the hemoglobin changes would greatly enhance their clinical utility (30).

Literature Cited

1. Appleby, C. A. 1962. The oxygen equilibrium of leg hemoglobin. *Biochem. Biophys. Acta* 60:226–35
2. Araki, R., Tamura, M., Yamazaki, I. 1983. The effect of intracellular oxygen concentration of lactate release, pyridine nucleotide reduction and respiration rate in the rat cardiac tissue. *Circ. Res.* 53:448–55
3. Araki, R., Tamura, M., Yamazaki, I. 1986. A role of prostaglandin I_2 in hypoxia-induced increase in coronary flow in the perfused rat heart. *Adv. Exp. Med. Biol.* 200:323–31
4. Arridge, S. R., Cope, M., van der Zee, P., Milson, P. J., Delpy, D. T. 1986. Visualization of the oxygenation state of the brain and muscle in newborn infants by near-infrared transillumination. In *Information Processing in Medical Imaging*, ed. S. L. Bacharach, pp. 155–76. New York: Nijhoff
5. Arus, C., Barany, M., Westler, W. M., Markley, J. L. 1984. ^{1}H NMR of intact muscle at 11 T. *FEBS Lett.* 165:231–37
6. Austin, G., Jutzy, R., Chance, B., Barlow, C. 1978. Noninvasive monitoring of human brain oxidative metabolism. In *Frontiers of Biological Energetics*, ed. D. L. Dutton, J. S., Leigh, A. Scapa, pp. 1445–55. New York: Academic
7. Barbour, R. L., Sotak, C. H., Levy, G. C., Chan, S H. 1984. Use of gated perfusion to study early effects of anoxia on cardiac energy metabolism: a new ^{31}P NMR method. *Biochemistry* 23:6053–6062
8. Bashford, C. L., Barlow, C. H., Chance, B., Haselgrove, J. 1980. The oxidation-reduction state of cytochrome oxidase in freeze trapped gerbil brains. *FEBS Lett.* 113:78–80
9. Bashford, C. L., Barlow, C. H., Chance, B., Haselgrove, J., Sorge, J. 1982. Optical measurements of oxygen delivery and consumption in gerbil cerebral-cortex. *Am. J. Physiol.* 242:C265–C71
10. Behar, K. L., Rothyman, D. L., Schulman, R. G., Petroff, O. A. C., Prichard, J. W. 1984. Detection of cerebral lactate in vivo during hypoxemia by ^{1}H NMR at

relatively low field strengths (1.9 T). *Proc. Natl. Acad. Sci. USA* 81:2517–19

11. Beinert, H., Shaw, R. W., Hansen, R. E., Hartzell, C. R. 1980. Studies on the origin of the near-infrared (800–900 nm) absorption of cytochrome-c oxidase. *Biochem. Biophys. Acta* 591:458–70

12. Bittl, J. A., Balschi, J. A., Ingwall, J. S. 1987. The effects of norepinephrine infusion on myocardial high energy phosphate content and turnover in the living rat. *J. Clin. Invest.* 79:1852–59

13. Blumberg, B. 1987. Light propagation in human tissues: The physical origin of the inhomogeneous scattering mechanisms. *Biophys. J.* 51:288a

14. Brazy, J. E., Darrell, V. L., Mitnick, M. H., Jobsis, F. F. 1985. Non-invasive observations. *Pediatrics* 75:217–25

15. Butler, W. L., Norris, K. H. 1962. The spectrophotometry of dense light scattering material. *Arch. Biochem. Biophys.* 87:31–40

16. Cairns, C. B., Fillipo, D., Proctor, H. J. 1985. A non-invasive method for monitoring the effects of increased intracranial pressure with near-infrared spectrophotometry. *Surg. Gynecol. Obstet.* 161:145–48

17. Chance, B. 1954. Spectrophotometry of intracellular respiratory pigments. *Science* 120:767–75

18. Chance, B. 1965. Reaction of oxygen with the respiratory chain in cells and tissues. *J. Gen. Physiol.* 49:163–88

19. Chance, B. 1966. Spectrophotometric observations of absorbance changes in the infrared region in suspension of mitochondrial and in submitochondrial particles. *Biochemistry of Copper*, ed. J. Peisach, P. Aisen, W. E. Blumberg, pp. 283–303. New York: Academic

20. Chance, B. 1988. Early reduction of cytochrome c in hypoxia. *FEBS Lett.* 226:343–46

21. Chance, B. 1988. *Photon Migration in Tissues*. New York: Plenum. In press

22. Chance, B., Baltscheffsky, H. 1958. Respiratory enzymes in oxidative phosphorylation. VII. Binding of intramitochondrial reduced pyridine nucleotide. *J. Biol. Chem* 233:736–39

23. Chance, B., Barlow, C. 1976. Ischemic areas in perfused rat hearts: measurement by NADH fluorescence photography. *Science* 193:909–10

24. Chance, B., Cohen, P., Jobsis, F., Schoener, B. 1962. Intracellular oxidation-reduction states in vivo. *Science* 137:499–508

25. Chance, B., Hollunger, G. 1963. Inhibition of electron and energy transfer in mitochondria. I. Effects of amytal, thiopental, rotenone, progesterone, and methylene glycol. *J. Biol. Chem.* 238:418–31

26. Chance, B., Jobsis, F. F. 1959. Changes in fluoresence in a frog Sartorius muscle following a twitch. *Nature* 184:195–96

27. Chance, B., Kobayashi, K., Nakazawa, H. 1988. Metabolic heterogeneity in rapidly metabolizing tissues. *J. Appl. Cardiol.* Submitted

28. Chance, B., Leigh, J. S. Jr., Clark, B. J., Maris, J., Kent, J. et al. 1985. Control of oxidative metabolism and oxygen delivery in human skeletal muscle: a steady-state analysis of the work/energy cost transfer function. *Proc. Natl. Acad. Sci. USA* 82:8384–88

29. Chance, B., Leigh, J. S. Jr., Kent, J., McCully, K., Nioka, S., et al. 1986. Multiple controls of oxidative metabolism in living tissues as studied by phosphorous magnetic resonance. *Proc. Natl. Acad. Sci. USA* 83:9458–62

30. Chance, B., Leigh, J. S., Miyake, H., Smith, D. S., Nioka, S., et al. 1988. Comparison of time resolved and unresolved measurements of deoxygenation in brain. *Proc. Natl. Acad. Sci. USA* 85:4971–75

31. Chance, B., Leigh, J. S. Jr., Nioka, S., Sinwell, T., Younkin, D., Smith, D. S. 1987. An approach to the problem of metabolic heterogeneity in brain: ischemia and reflow after ischemia. *Ann. NY Acad. Sci.* 508:309–20

32. Chance, B., Mauriello, G., Aubert, X. M. 1962. ADP arrival at muscle mitochondria following a twitch. In *Muscle as a Tissue*, ed. K. Rodahl, S. M. Horvath, pp. 128–45. New York: McGraw-Hill

33. Chance, B., Nioka, S., Kent, J., McCully, K., Fountain, M., et al. 1988. Time resolved spectroscopy of hemoglobin and myoglobin in resting and ischemic muscle. *Anal. Biochem.* 174:698–707

34. Chance, B., Oshino, N. 1978. Luminous bacteria as an oxygen indicator. *Methods Enzymol.* 57:223–26

35. Chance, B., Oshino, N., Sugano, T., Mayevsky, A. 1973. Basic principles of tissue oxygen determination from mitochondrial signals. In *Oxygen Transport to Tissue*, ed. H. Bicher, D. F. Bruley, pp. 277–92. New York: Plenum

36. Chance, B., Powers, L., Poyton, R. O., Waterland, R. 1988. Subunit control of cytochrome oxidase. *Biophys. J.* 53:373a

37. Chance, B., Quistorff, B. 1978. Studies of tissue oxygen gradients by single and

multiple indicators. *Adv. Exp. Med. Biol.* 94:331–38

38. Chance, B., Schoener, B., Schindler, F. 1964. The intracellular oxidation-reduction state. In *Oxygen in the Animal Organism*, ed. F. Dickens, E. Neil, pp. 367–88. London: Pergamon

39. Chance, B., Silverstein, B., Mayevsky, A. 1980. Heterogenity of metabolic states of cerebral cortex in vivo. In *Cerebral Metabolism and Neural Functions*, ed. J. V. Passoneau, R. A. Hawkins, W. D. Lust, pp. 77–84. Baltimore: Williams & Wilkens

40. Chance, B., Williams, G. 1955. Respiratory enzymes in oxidative phosphorylation: I. Kinetics of oxygen utilization. *J. Biol. Chem.* 217:383–93

41. Chance, E. M., Chance, B. 1987. Oxygen delivery to tissue: calculation of oxygen gradients in the cardiac cell. *Adv. Exp. Med. Biol.* 222:69–75

42. Clark, A., Clark, P. A. A., Connett, R. J., Gayeski, T. E. J., Honig, C. R. 1987. How large is the drop in PO_2 between cytosol and mitochondria? *Am. J. Physiol.* 252:C583–87

43. Clark, B. J., Smith, D., Chance, B. 1987. Metabolic consequences of oxygen transport studied with phosphorus nuclear magnetic resonance spectroscopy. In *Oxygen Transport and Utilization*, ed. C. W. Bryan-Brown, S. M. Ayres, Ch. 7, pp. 144–70. Fullerton, CA: Soc. Crit. Care Med.

44. Cohen, S. M. 1983. Simultaneous ^{13}C and ^{31}P NMR studies of perfused rat liver. *J. Biol. Chem.* 258:14294–14308

45. Cope, M., Delpy, D. T., Reynolds, E. O. R., Wray, S., Wyatt, J., van der Zee, P. 1987. Methods of quantitating cerebral near-infrared spectroscopy data. *Adv. Exp. Med. Biol.* 222:183–89

46. Denton, R. M., McCormack, J. G. 1985. Ca^{+2} transport by mammalian mitochondria and its role in hormone action. *Am. J. Physiol.* 249:E543–54

47. Dora, E. 1984. A simple cranial window technique for optical monitoring of cerebrocortical microcirculation and NAD/NADH redox state. Effect of mitochondrial electron transport inhibitors and anoxic anoxia. *J. Neurochem.* 42:101–8

48. Dora, E., Gyulai, L., Kovack, A. G. B. 1983. Determinants of brain activation-induced cortical NAD/NADH response in vivo. *Brain Res.* 229:61–72

49. Erecinska, M., Wilson, D. F., Nishiki, K. 1978. Homeostatic regulation of cellular energy metabolism; experimental characterization in vivo and fit to a model. *Am. J. Physiol.* 234:C82–C89

50. Fabel, H., Lubbers, D. W. 1965. Measurements of reflection spectra of the beating rabbit heart in situ. *Biochem. Z.* 341:351–56

51. Ferrari, M., Azmette, E., Giannini, I., Sideri, G., Fieschi, C., Carpi, A. 1986. Effects of carotid artery compression test on regional cerebral blood volume, hemoglobin oxygen saturation and cytochrome c oxidase level in cerebrovascular patients. *Adv. Exp. Med. Biol.* 200:213–21

52. Ferrari, M., Giannini, I., Capri, A., Fasella, P. 1983. Non-invasive near-infrared spectroscopy of brain in fluorocarbon exchanged rats. *Physiol. Chem. Phys. Med. NMR* 15:107–13

53. Figulla, H. R., Hoffman, J., Lubbers, D. W. 1984. Evaluation of reflection spectra of the isolated heart by multicomponent spectral analysis in comparison to other evaluation methods. *Adv. Exp. Med. Biol.* 169:821–30

54. Gadian, D. G. 1982. *Nuclear Magnetic Resonance and its Applications to Living Systems.* Oxford: Clarendon

55. Gayeski, T. E. J., Honig, C. R. 1986. Oxygen gradients from sarcolemma to cell interior in red muscle at maximal VO_2. *Am. J. Physiol.* 251:H789–99

56. Gayeski, T. E. J., Honig, C. R. 1986. Oxygen transport in rest-work transition illustrates new functions for myoglobin. *Am. J. Physiol.* 248:H914–21

57. Gayeski, T. E. J., Honig, C. R. 1986. Shallow intracellular O_2 gradient and absence of perimitochondrial O_2 "wells" in heavily working red muscle. *Adv. Exp. Med. Biol.* 200:487–94

58. Giannini, I., Ferrari, M., Carpi, A., Fasella, P. 1982. Rat-brain monitoring by near-infrared spectroscopy: an assessment of possible clinical significance. *Physiol. Chem. Phys.* 14:295–305

59. Griffith, D. E., Wharton, D. C. 1961. Studies on the electron transport system. Purification and properties of cytochrome oxidase. *J. Biol. Chem.* 236:1850–56

60. Hansford, R. G. 1985. Relation between mitochondrial calcium transport and control of energy metabolism. *Rev. Physiol. Biochem. Pharmacol.* 102:2–72

61. Harrison, M., Sick, T. J., Rosenthal, M. 1985. Mitochondrial redox responses to cerebral ischemia produced by fourvessel occlusion in the rat. *Neurol. Res.* 7:142–47

62. Haselgrove, J. C., Barlow, C. H., Chance, B. 1980. The third distribution of metabolic states in gerbil brain during the course of spreading depression. See Ref. 39, pp. 72–76

63. Haselgrove, J. C., Barlow, C. H., Eleff, E., Chance, B., Lebordias, S. 1981. Correlation of electrical signals and mitochondrial redox state during spreading depression. In *Oxygen Transport to Tissue. Adv. Physiol. Sci.*, ed. A. G. B. Kovach, E. Dora, M. Kessler, I. A. Silver, 25:25–26. Budapest: Pergamammon

64. Hassinen, I. E., Hiltunen, J. K., Takala, T. E. S. 1981. Reflectance spectrophotometric monitoring of the isolated perfused rat heart as a method of measuring the oxidation-reduction state. *Cardiovas. Res.* 15:86–91

65. Hazeki, O., Seiyama, A., Tamura, M. 1987. Near-infrared spectrophotometric monitoring of hemoglobin and cytochrome aa₃ in situ. *Adv. Exp. Med. Biol.* 215:283–89

66. Hazeki, O., Tamura, M. 1988. Quantitative analysis of hemoglobin oxygenation state of rate brain in situ by near-infrared spectrophotometry. *J. Appl. Physiol.* 64:796–802

67. Hazeki, O., Tamura, M. 1988. Near-infrared quadruple wavelength spectrophotometry of rat head. *Adv. Exp. Med. Biol.* 222: In press

68. Hempel, F. G., Jobsis, F. F., LaManna, J. C., Rosenthal, M., Saltzman, H. A. 1977. Oxidation of cerebral cytochrome aa₃ by oxygen plus carbon dioxide at hyperboric pressures. *J. Appl. Physiol.* 43:873–79

69. Hempel, F. G., Kariman, K., Saltzman, H. A. 1980. Redox transitions in mitochondria of cat cerebral-cortex with seizures and hemorrhagic hypotension. *Am. J. Physiol.* 238:H249–56

70. Hoffmann, J., Lubbers, D. W. 1986. *Adv. Exp. Med. Biol.* 200:125–30

71. Honig, C. R., Gayeski, T. E. J., Federspiel, W., Clark, A., Clark, P. 1984. Muscle O₂ gradients from hemoglobin to cytochrome: new concepts, new complexities. *Adv. Exp. Med. Biol.* 169:23–28

72. Hoshi, S., Hazeki, O., Tamura, M. 1988. Redox behaviour of visible copper in mitochondria at low PO₂. *Adv. Exp. Med. Biol.* 222: In press

73. Ishikawa, T., Tamura, M., Nakamura, S., Ikeda, M., Nagai, K. 1984. Topographic analysis of the redox state of rat brain by NADH fluorescence photography of cross section. *J. Biochem.* 95:213–21

74. Jobsis, F. F. 1977. Non-invasive, infrared monitoring of cerebral and myocardial oxygen sufficiency and circulatory parameters. *Science* 198:1264–67

75. Jobsis, F. F. 1979. Oxidative metabolic effects of cerebral hypoxia. *Adv. Neurology* 26:299–318

76. Jobsis, F. F. 1972. Oxidative metabolism at low PO₂. *Fed. Proc.* 31:1404–13

77. Jobsis, F. F. 1985. NIROS-copy: noninvasive near infrared monitoring of cellular oxygen sufficiency. *Adv. Exp. Med. Biol.* 191:833–41

78. Jobsis, F. F., Keizer, J. H., LaMann, J. C., Rosenthal, M. 1977. Reflectance spectrophotometry of cytochrome aa₃ in vivo. *J. Appl. Physiol.* 43:858–72

79. Jobsis, F. F., O'Connor, M., Vitale, A., Vreman, H. 1971. Intracellular redox changes in functioning cerebral cortex. Metabolic effects of epileptiform activity. *J. Neurophysiol.* 34:735–49

80. Johnson, C. C. 1970. Optical diffusion in blood. *IEEE Trans. Biomed. Eng.* BME-17:129–33

81. Jones, D. P. 1986. Intracellular diffusion gradient of O₂ and ATP. *Am. J. Physiol.* 250:C663–75

82. Jones, D. P., Kennedy, F. G. 1982. Intracellular O₂ gradients in cardian myocytes. Lack of a role for myoglobin in facilitation of intracellular diffusion. *Biochem. Biophys. Res. Commun.* 105:419–24

83. Jones, D. P., Kennedy, F. G. 1986. Analysis of intracellular oxygenation of isolated adult cardiac myocytes. *Am. J. Physiol.* 250:C384–90

84. Jones, D. P., Mason, H. S. 1978. Gradients of O₂ concentration in hepatocytes. *J. Biol. Chem.* 253:4874–80

85. Joseph, P. M., Fishman, J. E., Mukherji, B., Sloviter, H. 1985. In vivo ¹⁹F NMR imaging of the cardiovascular system. *J. Comput. Assist. Tomography* 9:1012–1019

86. Kanaide, H., Yoshimura, R., Makino, N., Nakamura, M. 1982. Regional myocardial function and metabolism during acute coronary occlusion. *Am. J. Physiol.* 242:H980–89

87. Kariman, K., Burkhart, D. S. 1985. Heme-copper relationship of cytochrome oxidase in rat brain in situ. *Biochem. Biophys. Res. Commun.* 126:1022–28

88. Kariman, K., Burkhart, D. S. 1985. Non-invasive in vivo spectrophotometric monitoring of brain cytochrome aa₃ revisited. *Brain Res.* 360:203–13

89. Kariman, K., Hempel, F. G., Jobsis, F. F. 1983. In vivo comparison of cytochrome aa₃ redox state and tissue PO₂ in transient anoxia. *J. Appl. Physiol.* 55:1057–1063

90. Kariman, K., Jobsis, F. F., Saltzman, H. A. 1983. Cytochrome aa₃ reoxida-

tion. Early indicators of metabolic recovery from hemorrhagic shock in rats. *J. Clin. Invest.* 72:180–91

91. Katz, I. R., Wittenberg, J. B., Wittenberg, B. A. 1984. Monoaminic oxidase, an intracellular probe of oxygen pressure in isolated cardiac myocytes. *J. Biol. Chem.* 259:7504–9

92. Katz, L. A., Koretsky, A. P., Balaban, R. S. 1987. Respiratory control in the glucose perfused heart: a ^{31}P NMR and NADH fluorescence study. *FEBS Lett.* 221:270–76

93. Kedem, J., Mayevsky, A., Sonn, J., Acad, B. A. 1981. An experimental approach for evaluation of the O_2 balance in local myocardial regions in vivo. *Q. J. Exp. Physiol.* 66:501–14

94. Kreisman, N. R., Hodin, R. A., Brizzee, B. L., Rosenthal, M., Sick, T. J., Busto, R., Ginsberg, M. D. 1987. Seizure-associated pulmonary edema and cerebral oxygenation in the rat. *J. Appl. Physiol.* 62:658–67

95. Kreisman, N. R., LaManna, J. C., Rosenthal, M., Sick, T. J. 1981. Oxidative metabolic responses with recurrent seizures in rat cerebral cortex: Role of systemic factors. *Brain Res.* 218:175–88

96. Kreisman, N. R., Sick, T. J., LaManna, J. C., Rosenthal, M. 1981. Local tissue oxygenation-cytochrome aa_3 redox relationship. *Brain Res.* 218:161–74

97. Knopp, I. A., Longmuir, I. S. 1972. Intracellular measurement of oxygen by quenching of fluorescence of pyrenebutyric acid. *Biochem. Biophys. Acta* 279:393–97

98. Kobayashi, S., Nishiki, K., Kaede, K., Ogata, E. 1971. Optical consequences of blood substitution on tissue oxidation-reduction state microfluorometry. *J. Appl. Physiol.* 31:93–96

99. Lakowicz, J. R. 1984. *Principles of Fluorescence Spectroscopy*, pp. 238–76. New York: Plenum

100. LaManna, J. C., Light, A. I., Peretsman, S. J., Rosenthal, M. 1983. Oxygen insufficiency during hypoxic hypoxia in rat-brain cortex. *Brain Res.* 293:313–18

101. Lew, B. T., Mohanakrishnan, P., Ugurbil, K., From, A. H. L. 1988. Regulation of rat heart respiration by Ca^{+2} activation of intramitochondrial dehydrogenases: studies with ruthenium red. *Soc. Magnetic Resonances Med., 7th Ann. Meet., San Francisco,* Aug. 20–26, Vol. 1, p. 290

102. Lipton, P. 1973. Effects of membrane depolarization on nicotinamide nucleotide fluorescence in brain slices. *Biochem. J.* 136:999–1009

103. Longmuir, I. S., Knopp, J. A. 1976. Measurement of tissue oxygen with a fluorescent probe. *J. Appl. Physiol.* 41:598–602

104. Makino, N., Kanaide, H., Yoshimura, R., Nakamura, M. 1983. Myoglobin oxygenation remains constant during the cardiac cycle. *Am. J. Physiol.* 245:H237–43

105. Mayevsky, A. 1984. Brain NADH redox state monitored in vivo by fiber optic surface fluorometry. *Brain Res. Rev.* 7:49–68

106. Mayevsky, A., Chance, B. 1975. Metabolic responses of the awake cerebral cortex to anoxia hypoxia spreading depression and epileptiform activity. *Brain Res.* 98:149–65

107. Mayevsky, A., Kaplan, H., Haveri, J., Haselgrove, J., Chance, B. 1986. Three-dimensional metabolic mapping of the freeze-trapped brain: effects of ischemia in the mongolian gerbil. *Brain Res.* 367:63–72

108. Mayevsky, A., Nioka, S., Subramanian, V. H., Chance, B. 1988. Brain oxidative metabolism of the newborn dog: correlation between ^{31}P NMR spectroscopy and pyridine nucleotide redox state. *J. Cereb. Blood Flow Metab.* 8:201–7

109. Milito, S. J., Raffin, C. N., Rosenthal, M., Sick, T. J. 1988. Potassium ion hemostasis and mitochondrial redox activity in brain: relative changes as indicators of hypoxia. *J. Cereb. Blood Flow Metab.* 8:155–62

110. Millikan, G. A. 1942. The oximeter, and instrument for measuring continuously the oxygen saturation of arterial blood in man. *Rev. Sci. Instrum.* 13:434–44

111. Nicholls, P., Chanady, G. A. 1982. Titration and steady state behaviour of 830 nm chromophore in cytochrome-c oxidase. *Biochem. J.* 203:541–49

112. Nishiki, K., Erecinska, M., Wilson, D. F. 1979. Effect of amytal on metabolism of perfused rat-heart: Relationship between glycolysis and oxidative-phosphorylation. *Am. J. Physiol.* 237:221–30

113. Ohlsson, P., Grunderson, J., Nilson, D. M. 1980. Diaphanography: A method for evaluation of the female breast. *World J. Surg.* 4:701–7

114. Oshino, N., Jamieson, D., Chance, B. 1975. The properties of hydrogen peroxide production under hyperoxic and hypoxic conditions of perfused rat liver. *Biochem. J.* 146:53–65

115. Oshino, R., Oshino, N., Chance, B., Hagihara, B. 1973. Studies on yeast

hemoglobin. The properties of yeast hemoglobin and its physiological function in the cell. *Eur. J. Biochem.* 35:23–33

116. Oshino, R., Oshino, N., Tamura, M., Kobilinski, L., Chance, B. 1972. A sensitive bacterial luminescence probe for O_2 in biochemical systems. *Biochem. Biophys. Acta* 273:5–7

117. Oshino, N., Sugano, T., Oshino, R., Chance, B. 1974. Mitochondrial function under hypoxic conditions. The steady states of cytochrome $a+a_3$ and their relation to mitochondrial energy states. *Biochem. Biophys. Acta* 368:298–310

118. Owen, C. S., Wilson, D. F. 1974. Control of respiration by the mitochondrial phosphorylation state. *Arch. Biochem. Biophys.* 161:581–91

119. Piantadosi, C. A., Jobsis, F. F. 1984. Spectrophotometry of cerebral cytochrome aa_3 in bloodless rats. *Brain Res.* 305:89–94

120. Piantadosi, C. A., Sylvia, A. L., Jobsis, F. F. 1987. Differences in brain cytochrome responses to carbon monoxide and cyanide in vivo. *J. Appl. Physiol.* 62:1277–84

121. Radda, G. K. 1986. The use of NMR spectroscopy for the understanding of disease. *Science* 233:640–45

122. Rea, P. A., Crowe, J., Wickramasinghe, Y., Rolfe, P. 1985. Non-invasive optical methods for the study of cerebral metabolism in the human newborn; a technique for the future? *J. Med. Eng. Tech.* 9:160–66

123. Renault, G., Sinet, M., Muffat-Joly, M., Cornillault, J., Pocidalo, J. J. 1985. In situ monitoring of myocardial metabolism by laser fluorimetry: Relevance of a test of local ischemia. *Lasers Surg. Med.* 5:111–22

124. Rosenthal, M., Jobsis, F. F. 1971. Intracellular redox changes in functioning cerebral cortex II. Effect of direct cortical stimulation. *J. Neurophysiol.* 34:750–62

125. Rosenthal, M., LaManna, J. C. 1975. Effect of ouabain and phenobarbital on the kinetics of cortical metabolism transients associated with evoked potentials. *J. Neurochem.* 24:111–16

126. Rosenthal, M., LaManna, J. C., Jobsis, F. F., Levasseur, J. E., Kontos, H. A., Patterson, J. L. 1976. Effects of respiratory gases on cytochrome-A in intact cerebral-cortex: Is there a critical PO_2? *Brain Res.* 108:143–54

127. Rosenthal, M., Martel, D., LaManna, J. C., Jobsis, F. F. 1976. In situ studies of oxidative energy metabolism during transient cortical ischemia in cats. *Exp. Neurol.* 50:477–97

128. Sagisaki, K., Tamura, M., Yamazaki, I. 1984. The effect of K^+ concentration on the energy metabolism in perfused rat heart. *J. Biochem.* 95:1091–1103

129. Salama, G., Lombardi, R., Elson, J. 1987. Maps of optical action potentials and NADH fluoresence in intact work hearts. *Am. J. Physiol.* 252:H381–94

130. Schlinder, F. 1965. PhD thesis. Univ. Penna.

131. Seiyama, A., Hazeki, O., Tamura, M. 1988. Non-invasive quantitative analysis of blood oxygenation in rat skeletal muscle. *J. Biochem.* 103:419–24

132. Seraydarian, K., Mommaerts, W. F. H. M., Wallner, A., Guillory, R. J. 1961. An estimation of the true inorganic phosphate content of frog sartorius muscle. *J. Biol. Chem.* 236:2071–2075

133. Shoubridge, E. A., Briggs, R. W., Radda, G. K. 1982. ^{31}P NMR saturation transfer measurements of the steady state rates of creatine kinase and ATP synthetase in rat brain. *FEBS Lett.* 104:288–92

134. Deleted in proof

135. Starlinger, H., Lubbers, D. W. 1973. Ploarographic measurement of the oxygen pressure performed simultaneously with optical measurements of the redox state of the respiratory chain in suspensions of mitochondrial under steady state conditions at low oxygen tensions. *Pfleugers Arch.* 341:15–22

136. Steenbergen, C., Deleeuw, G., Barlow, C., Chance, B., Williamson, J. R. 1977. Heterogeneity of the hypoxic state in perfused rat heart. *Circ. Res.* 41:606–15

137. Steinke, J. M., Shepherd, A. P. 1986. Role of light scattering in whole blood oxymetry. *IEEE Trans. Biomed. Eng.* BME-33:294–301

138. Steinke, J. M., Shepherd, A. P. 1987. Reflectance measurement of hematocrit and oxyhemoglobin saturation. *Am. J. Physiol.* 253:H147–53

139. Stuart, B. H., Chance, B. 1974. NADH brain surface scanning and 3-D computer display. *Brain Res.* 76:473–79

140. Sugano, T., Oshino, N., Chance, B. 1974. Mitochondrial functions under hypoxic conditions. The steady states of cytochrome-c reduction and of energy metabolism. *Biochem. Biophys. Acta* 347:340–58

141. Sylvia, A. L., Piantadosi, C. A. 1988. O_2 dependence of in vivo brain cyto-

chrome redox responses and energy-metabolism in bloodless rats. *J. Cereb. Blood Flow Metab.* 8:163–72

142. Sylvia, A. L., Piantadosi, C. A., Jobsis, F. F. 1985. Energy metabolism and in vivo cytochrome-c oxidase redox relationships in hypoxic rat brain. *Neurol. Res.* 7:81–88

143. Sylvia, A. L., Proctor, H. J., Goldsmith, M. M., Jobsis, F. F. 1982. Exchange transfusion with fluosol-43: In vivo assessment of cerebral cytochrome-c oxidase redox state. *J. Trauma* 22:815–19

144. Takada, M., Tamura, T., Tamura, M. 1987. Non-invasive near-infrared measurements of human arm tissues in vivo. *Adv. Exp. Med. Biol.* 215:301–4

145. Tamura, M., Araki, R., Harada, K., Yamazaki, I. 1986. Myoglobin-probed optical studies on cardiac oxygen fluctuations in hemoglobin-free isolated perfused rat heart. In *New Approach in Cardiac Mechanics and its Control* ed. Kitamura, Abe, Segawa, pp. 89–97. New York/London/Paris/Tokyo: Gordon & Breach Sci.

146. Tamura, M., Nomura, Y., Hazeki, O. 1988. Near-infrared oxygen monitoring. Fundamentals and feasibility for imaging. In *"Photon-migration in the Tissue"*, ed. B. Chance. New York: Plenum.

147. Tamura, M., Oshino, N., Chance, B., Silver, I. 1978. Optical measurements of intracellular oxygen concentration of rat heart in vitro. *Arch. Biochem. Biophys.* 191:8–22

148. Tamura, M., Oshino, N., Chance, B. 1982. Some characteristics of hydrogen and alkylhydroperoxides metabolizing systems in cardiac tissue. *J. Biochem.* 92:1019–1031

149. Tamura, M., Seiyama, A., Hazeki, O. 1987. Spectroscopic characteristics of rat skeletal and cardian tissues in the visible and near-infrared region. *Adv. Exp. Med. Biol.* 215:297–300

150. Taylor, J., Deutsch, C. 1988. ^{19}F Nuclear magnetic resonance: Measurements of $[O_2]$ and pH in biological systems. *Biophys. J.* 43:227–33

151. Vanderkooi, J. M., Maniara, G., Green, T. J., Wilson, D. F. 1987. An optical method for measurement of dioxygen concentration based upon quenching of phosphorescence. *J. Biol. Chem.* 262:5476–82

152. Deleted in proof

153. van der Zee, P., Delpy, D. T. 1987. Simulation of the point spread function for light in tissue by a monte carlo method. *Adv. Exp. Med. Biol.* 215:179–91

154. Veech, R. L., Lawson, J. W. R., Cornell, N. W., Krebs, H. A. 1979. Cytosolic phosphorylation potential. *J. Biol. Chem.* 254:6538–47

155. Welsh, F. A., Rieder, W. 1978. Evaluation of in situ freezing of cat brain by NADH fluorescence. *J. Neurochem.* 37:199–309

156. Wiernsperger, N., Sylvia, A. L., Jobsis, F. F. 1981. Incomplete transient ischemia: A non-destructive evaluation of in vivo cerebral metabolism and hemodynamics in rat brain. *Stroke* 12:864–68

157. Williamson, J. R., Rich, T. L. 1983. Mitochondrial function in normal and hypoxic states of myocardium. In *Advance in Myocardiology*, ed. Chazov, Sacks, Rona, pp. 271–85. New York: Plenum

158. Wilson, B. C., Adam, C. T. 1983. A monte carlo model for the dependence of cellular energy metabolism. *Arch. Biochem. Biophys.* 195:485–93

159. Wilson, D. F., Erecinska, M., Drown, C., Silver, I. A. 1979. The oxygen dependence of cellular energy metabolism. *Arch. Biochem. Biophys.* 195:485–93

160. Wilson, D. F., Owen, C. S., Mela, L., Weiner, L. 1973. Control of mitochondrial respiration by the phosphate potential. *Biochem. Biophys. Res. Commun.* 53:326–33

161. Wilson, D. F., Stubbs, M., Oshino, M., Erecinska, M. 1974. Thermodynamic relationship between the mitochondrial oxidation-reduction reactions and cellular ATP levels in asirtes tumor cells and perfused rat liver. *Biochemistry* 13:5303–11

162. Wittenberg, B. A., Wittenberg, J. B. 1985. Oxygen pressure gradients in isolated cardiac myocytes. *J. Biol. Chem.* 260:6548–54

163. Wodnick, R., Lubbers, D. W. 1974. Quantitative evaluation of reflection spectra of living tissue. *Hoppe-Seyler's Z. Physiol. Chem.* 355:583–94

164. Wyatt, J. S., Cope, M., Delpy, D. T., Wray, S., Reynolds, E. O. R. 1988. Characterization of near-infrared absorption spectra of cytochrome aa_3 and hemoglobin for the non-invasive monitoring of cerebral oxygenation. *Biochem. Biophys. Acta.* 933:184–92

165. Wyatt, J. S., Cope, M., Delpy, D. T., Wray, S., Reynolds, E. O. R. 1986. Quantification of cerebral oxygenation and hemodynamics in sick newborn infants by near-infrared spectrophotometry. *Lancet* 2 (8515):1063–1066

166. Yewey, G. L., Caughey, W. S. 1987. Metals and activity of bovine heart cytochrome-c oxidase are independent of polypeptide subunit-III, subunit-VIII, subunit-A, and subunit-B: *Biochem. Biophys. Res. Commun.* 148:1520–26
167. Yamashita, Y., Suzuki, S., Miyaki, S., Hayakawa,, T. 1988. The neonate brain (NIR) and breast imaging using transillumination. See Ref. 146

168. Yoshiya, I., Shimada, Y., Tanaka, K. 1980. Spectrophotometric monitoring of arterial oxygen saturation in the finger tip. *Med. Biol. Eng. Comput.* 18:27–32
169. Yoshizaki, K., Radda, G. K., Inubushi, T., Chance, B. 1987. ¹H- and ³¹P-NMR studies on smooth-muscle of bullfrog stomach. *Biochim. Biophys. Acta* 928: 36–44

NOTE ADDED IN PROOF.

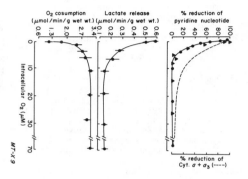

Figure 1   See page 816 for reference.

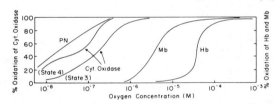

Figure 2   See page 817 for reference.

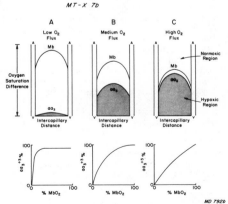

Figure 3   See page 823 for reference.

Annu. Rev. Physiol. 1989. 51:835–44

P_{O_2} CHEMORECEPTION IN ARTERIAL CHEMORECEPTORS

H. Acker

Max-Planck-Institut fuer Systemphysiologie, Rheinlanddamm 201, 4600 Dortmund 1, West Germany

INTRODUCTION

Arterial chemoreceptors are not restricted to the carotid bodies, which are located dorsal to the common carotid artery bifurcation, but are also present in the aortic arch region, where several groups of such cells are referred to as aortic bodies. The chemosensory function of aortic bodies is well known (6), and their ultrastructure is identical to that of the carotid body.

Moreover, small chemoreceptor units have been found in the carotid bifurcation region at some distance from the carotid body itself and even around the common carotid artery of the cat. Ultrastructural features of small chemoreceptor units are identical to those of the carotid body. Consequently, it seems justified to extrapolate the data on the carotid body to the whole arterial chemoreceptor system (48).

The carotid body detects changes in the chemical composition, tonicity, and temperature of its environment either in vivo or in a saline-superfused in vitro preparation (22). Sensory discharges of the sinus nerve increase in frequency when environmental O_2 tension (P_{O_2}) or pH falls, when CO_2 tensions (P_{CO_2}) increases, or when temperature or tonicity increase. Conversely, the discharge frequency decreases with increasing P_{O_2}, low P_{CO_2}, alkalinity, a fall in environmental temperature, or when the medium is made hyposmotic. In addition, chemical substances such as NaCN, hormones, and K^+ ions also stimulate these receptors (22). The aim of this article is to develop some ideas about the chemoreceptor mechanism in the carotid body, especially with regard to P_{O_2} chemoreception. The author would like to stimulate the discussion about chemoreceptor mechanisms and is aware that his ideas are open for criticism due to their necessary subjective origin.

835

0066-4278/89/0315-0835$02.00

P_{O_2} chemoreception is a process where oxygen serves not only as an electron acceptor in the respiratory chain for energy production, but also interacts with other cellular components to produce a signal that tells specialized cells to switch on auxiliary mechanisms to lessen hypoxic cell damages.

Clarifying this process may have an impact on understanding other cellular processes in organs that display P_{O_2} chemosensitive reactions (2). Three major P_{O_2} chemosensitive reactions are known to occur in the carotid body and must be related to intracellular events: transmitter release, flow changes, and nerve ending excitation. This article can only attempt to explain chemoreception at present because definitive experimental evidence on the molecular level is lacking.

THE P_{O_2} FIELD IN THE CAROTID BODY IN VIVO AND IN VITRO

Tissue oxygen tension in the carotid body in vivo has been measured with microelectrodes. The tissue P_{O_2} measured by Acker et al (4) for the cat carotid body and Weigelt et al (46) for the rabbit carotid body was in the range of 0–100 torr and with the frequency histogram left shifted with a mean value of about 20 torr, whereas Whalen et al (47) found mean P_{O_2} values of 40–50 torr and top values up to 100 torr. These low P_{O2} findings were unexpected since the carotid body possesses a high total flow and a small arterio-venous oxygen concentration difference (23, 42). Degner & Acker (17) recalculated the left-shifted P_{O_2} histogram of the carotid body on the basis of a microscopical serial reconstruction, published physiological data, and a mathematical model. Differences in the capillary length seemed to be the main reason for different P_{O_2} histograms. A reduction of 40% in the capillary length shifted the mean value of the P_{O_2} histogram from 20 torr to 50 torr. Furthermore, the authors (17) could calculate carotid body local flow velocities in the range of local flow velocities in other organs. Hydrogen clearances could directly measure these values in the carotid body (0.01–0.10) cm/s with a mean value of 0.02 cm/s) (27). A total flow of the carotid body of about 2000 rn/100 g/min signifies local flow values of less than 10% of the total flow, which is in agreement with estimates of local flow by Acker & O'Regan (5). The carotid body vascular structure with arterio-venous anastomoses or short arterio-venous interconnections is the morphological basis for this large heterogeneity between local and total flow (31).

The P_{O_2} gradient in superfused carotid body in vitro (18) flattens towards the center, with steep gradients at high P_{O_2} levels in the superfusion medium and shallow P_{O_2} gradients at low P_{O_2} levels. These changes in the P_{O_2} gradients supply sufficient oxygen to the carotid body tissue by diffusion, even under low P_{O_2} values (30 torr) in the superfusion medium (18).

THE POSSIBLE MECHANISMS OF P$_{O_2}$ CHEMORECEPTION

The respiratory chain of the carotid body mitochondria has often been proposed as the most probable candidate for a P$_{O_2}$ sensor. Anichkow & Belinki (10) as well as Joels & Neil (28) assumed that chemosensory excitation, especially under hypoxia, is caused by a decrease in ATP levels in the carotid body tissue. Obeso et al (37) measured a decrease in ATP of about 30%, changing the oxygenation from 100% O$_2$ to 20% O$_2$ in the superfusion medium of the carotid body in vitro, which probably supports the ATP hypothesis. Biscoe (13) proposed that energy depletion under hypoxia triggers the nervous discharge by producing membrane instability in the sensory nerve endings. Using several inhibitors and uncouplers of the respiratory chain, Mulligan et al (35) clearly showed that P$_{O_2}$ chemoreception in the carotid body is not possible without a functioning respiratory chain. However, the need for energy during chemoreception seems to be low since two hours of glucose-free superfusion are needed to abolish the hypoxia-induced increase in nervous discharge (19). Thus, it was of interest to investigate the respiratory chain of the carotid body directly. The absolute level of the oxygen consumption under control conditions depends on the type of oxygen supply (see Table 1). The blood-perfused carotid body reveals oxygen consumption values of about 0.12 μl O$_2$ min^{-1} (38, 42), whereas the long-time saline-perfused carotid body (38) or the nonperfused carotid body in vivo and in vitro, with an oxygen supply from the outside (3, 18, 29, 47), show oxygen consumption values of about 0.021 μl O$_2$ min^{-1} (for review see 23). Since the oxygen supply in both cases was measured to be sufficient (4, 18, 46, 47), the question must be raised whether perfusing the carotid body with blood has an uncoupling effect on the mitochondria, which results in increased oxygen consumption and decreased ATP production. The difference in oxygen consumption in addition to the difference of the ATP content support this suggestion (Table 1). Obeso et al (37) found an ATP content of the superfused carotid body in vitro of about 0.4 nmol/ carotid body (cb) whereas Acker & Starlinger (9) published a value of 0.087 nmol/cb for the blood-perfused organ in vivo. A factor five can be calculated for the difference in oxygen consumption as well as for the difference in ATP content (see Table 1). The respiratory chain seems to be further specialized in that there is a P$_{O_2}$-dependent oxygen consumption (3, 29, 42, 47). The P$_{O_2}$-dependent oxygen consumption was accompanied by a change in tissue pH (19) during variations in the oxygen pressure. Even moderate hypoxia decreased the oxygen consumption and acidified the carotid body tissue. This phenomenon can be interpreted as participation of aerobic glycolysis with chemoreception. The importance of glycolysis was also demonstrated by ultrastructural studies of intramitochondrial junctions (49) visible predominantly in type-I glomus cells. The number of intramitochondrial junctions increased during hypoxia. This increase can be avoided by inhibiting glycolysis. Aerobic glycolysis causes a compensatory increase in ATP production in the glycolytic pathway; the net production of H^+ ions by ATP hydrolysis, however, cannot be further regulated by the impaired respiratory chain under hypoxia (14). An unchanged ATP level in the hypoxic carotid body in vivo was observed by Acker & Starlinger (9). The P_{O_2}-dependent oxygen consumption could be caused by two mechanisms even though the normal mitochondria have a P_{O_2}-independent oxygen consumption down to a P_{O_2} of 0.1 torr (16). The first mechanism is a competition between glycolytic ATP production and mitochondrial ATP production for ADP, and the second, a competition for NADH, H^+ between the lactate dehydrogenase (LDH) and the respiratory chain. The participation of LDH is in agreement with findings of Petrova (40), which showed that 20 min of hypoxia induced a distinct increase of LDH isoenzymes, mostly composed of M subunits, in the rat carotid body.

A further characterization of the respiratory chain in the carotid body was done by photometry. By using a dual-wavelength photometer Mills & Jöbsis (32) measured a low and high affinity of cytochrome aa_3 for P_{O_2}. This unusual behavior was interpreted as a P_{O_2} sensing process; Nair et al (36) developed a model of P_{O_2} chemoreception on the basis of this finding, combining metabolism and chemoreceptor activity. However, Acker & Eyzaguirre (2a) demonstrated that the dual wavelength method is invalid in the superfused mouse carotid body due to uncontrolled behavior of the isosbestic points. They proceeded with a whole spectrum analysis, covering the wavelength range between 500 nm and 620 nm. Figure 1 shows a hypoxic- and cyanide-difference spectrum of the superfused rat carotid body; clearly, the spectra differ markedly. The cyanide spectrum shows a distinct trough at 550 nm, which can be related to reduced cytochrome c (16). Acker & Eyzaguirre (2a) used the cyanide spectra to calculate the cytochrome content of the carotid body with the values listed in Table 1. The ratio of cytochrome c content to

Table 1 Activity characteristics of the carotid body respiratory chain

Carotid body	Oxygen consumption μl O_2/min/cb[a]	ATP nmol/cb	Cytochrome c 10^{-3} μg/g	Cytochrome aa_3 fr.w.[b]
Blood perfusion	0.12 (38, 42)	0.087 (9)	—	—
Saline perfusion superfusion	0.021 (3, 18, 29, 38, 47)	0.4 (37)	1.89 (2a)	0.97 (2a)

[a] cb=carotid body.
[b] g fr. w.=gram fresh weight.

cytochrome *aa₃* content is 1.9, which is close to the values reported for the kidney (43) and suggests a normal proportion of both cytochromes in the carotid body. The hypoxic-difference spectrum shows two distinct peaks at 530 nm and 560 nm. Contamination of hemoglobin was excluded (2a) since hypoxia and cyanide application resulted in a similar spectral characteristic of hemoglobin (24). It was, therefore, hypothesized that an unknown pigment is responsible for the hypoxic-difference spectrum in the carotid body.

A second P_{O_2} chemosensor process was discussed with respect to endothelial cells (7). It was demonstrated that hypoxia, cyanide, and dithioerythrite (a thiol group donor) could activate a calcium ATPase in these cells (7). Since in red cells calcium ATPase could be activated as a thiol-rich protein (26) by reducing agents that split disulfide bonds, the involvement of glutathione peroxidase as a P_{O_2} sensor in carotid body endothelial cells was suggested (7).

THE EFFECTORS OF P_{O_2} CHEMORECEPTION

P_{O_2} chemoreception is generally defined as a P_{O_2}-dependent transmitter release from type I cells that generates action potentials in the postsynaptic

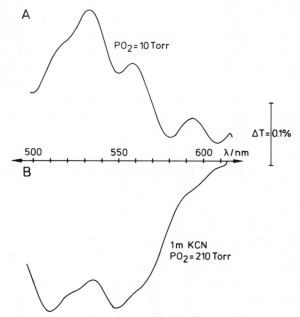

Figure 1 (A) Hypoxic and (B) cyanide absorption-difference spectra of the rat carotid body in vitro. ΔT = light transmission change. δ = light wavelength, P_{O_2} = oxygen pressure in the superfusion medium.

afferent nerve endings. The involvement of calcium as an effector in this process was shown by an increased exocytosis of transmitter-containing vesicles of type-I cells after external application of the calcium ionophore A 23187 (25). Bernon et al (11) increased chemoreceptive discharge by calcium-containing liposomes, which are able to penetrate cell membranes and to load the cytosol of type-I cells with calcium. The decrease in oxygen consumption and the increase in the carotid body tissue pH by lowering the P_{O_2} may be an ideal mechanism to interconnect oxygen pressure variations and chemoreceptor nervous activity; this mechanism could utilize changes in intracellular calcium activity to control transmitter release since mitochondria and cytosolic pH are involved in the regulation of the cytosolic calcium level (15). This assumption is supported by findings of Acker (1) and Delpiano & Acker (21a), which showed that the extracellular calcium activity decreased under hypoxia with a concomitant increase in the extracellular potassium activity. Pietruschka's (41) measurement of hypoxia-induced calcium influx into cultured type-I cells confirmed that the calcium influx into carotid body cells is enhanced under hypoxia. However, recent patch clamp studies on type I cells in tissue culture could not find a hypoxia-induced increase of calcium inward currents; whereas the potassium outward current was impaired under these conditions (21, 30a).

Endothelial cells isolated from microvessels react to hypoxia with a decrease in the intracellular calcium level (7); this result may explain the very sensitive P_{O_2} vasodilatation of the carotid body microvessels (44).

cAMP is another possible effector that is found in the carotid body tissue (33) and increases under hypoxia (20), which might stimulate enzyme induction as in the case of tyrosin hydroxylase (22). This mechanism could be of importance to understand the increase of catecholamine content in the carotid body under long-term hypoxia (22).

THE EFFECTS OF P_{O_2} CHEMORECEPTION

Figure 2 gives an overview of the major cell elements in the carotid body and their involvement in the three P_{O_2} chemosensitive reactions: transmitter release, flow changes, and nerve ending excitation. One has to differentiate between the stimulus of hypoxia and anoxia since chemoreceptor nervous activity declines in anoxia or at very low P_{O_2} values (34). It seems that the carotid body has lost its capability to respond to very low oxygen levels after birth, since the fetal carotid body is able to establish a normal response curve with very low P_{O_2} values. This response curve is reset during the first week of life to higher P_{O_2} values (13a). The whole vascular system of the adult carotid body, including arterioles, capillaries, and venules, vasodilates as P$_{O_2}$ goes from hyperoxic to anoxic values (44), which is accompanied by a decreased local flow velocity (27). At the molecular level, calcium ATPase may be activated by thiol groups, which decreases the level of intracellular calcium (7) and relaxes contractile elements, as has been described for endothelial cells (45). The energy requirement during transmitter release and nerve ending excitation under hypoxia seems to be low, as discussed above. Although the mechanism of transmitter release and nervous excitation is not known, this process seems to be switched on under hypoxia without reduction of the respiratory chain. Therefore, it was hypothesized that a pigment is involved, as already suggested by other authors (30), perhaps regulating the activity of the respiratory chain by controlling the electron flux and thus influencing the intracellular calcium content to facilitate transmitter release. The transmitters themselves may generate action potentials (22) or increase the calcium influx into type-I cells for further transmitter release (39, 41), either by depolarization or hyperpolarization (8, 21b, 22), with compensatory ionic changes, perhaps in case of potassium regulated by glial cell-like type-II cells (21b). During anoxia, the reduction of the respiratory chain is obvious and concomitantly, the action potential rate declines, which indicates the lack of energy, the lack of a transmitter, or the inability of nerve endings to generate impulses on their own at a sufficient high impulse rate, as suggested by experiments on sinus nerve regeneration (12).

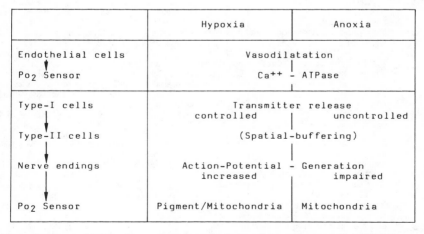

Figure 2 Presumable P$_{O_2}$ chemoreception mechanisms and the subsequent effects in different carotid body cell elements under hypoxia and anoxia.

Literature Cited

1. Acker, H. 1980. The meaning of tissue P_{O_2} and local blood flow for the chemoreceptive process of the carotid body. *Fed. Proc.* 39:2641–47
2. Acker, H., ed. 1988. *Oxygen Sensing in Tissues.* Berlin: Springer-Verlag. 212 pp.
2a. Acker, H., Eyzaguirre, C. 1987. Light absorbance changes in the mouse carotid body during hypoxia and cyanide poisoning. *Brain Res.* 409:380–85
3. Acker, H., Lübbers, D. W. 1977. The kinetic of local tissue P_{O_2} decrease after perfusion stop within the carotid body of the cat in vivo and in vitro. *Pflügers Arch.* 369:135–40
4. Acker, H., Lübbers, D. W., Purves, M. J. 1971. Local oxygen tension field in the glomus caroticum of the cat and its change at changing arterial P_{O_2}. *Pflügers Arch.* 329:136–55
5. Acker, H., O'Regan, R. G. 1981. The effects of stimulation of autonomic nerves on carotid body blood flow in the cat. *J. Physiol.* 315:99–110
6. Acker, H., O'Regan, R. G., eds. 1983. *Physiology of the Peripheral Arterial Chemoreceptors.* Amsterdam: Elsevier. 477 pp.
7. Acker, H., Pietruschka, F., Dufau, E. 1987. The effect of hypoxia and cyanide on intracellular calcium in cloned endothelial cells of brain microvessels. *Pflügers Arch.* 408:R72
8. Acker, H., Pietruschka, F. 1984. Membrane potential of cultured carotid body glomus cells under normoxia and hypoxia. *Brain Res.* 3M:148–51
9. Acker, H., Starlinger, H. 1984. Adenosine triphosphate content in the cat carotid body under different arterial O_2 and CO_2 conditions. *Neurosci. Lett.* 50:175–79
10. Anichkow, S. W., Belinki, M. R., eds. 1963. *Pharmacology of the Carotid Body Chemoreceptors.* Oxford: Pergamon. 225 pp.
11. Bernon, R., Leitner, L. M., Roumy, M., Verna, A. 1983. Effects of ion-containing liposomes upon the chemoafferent activity of the rabbit carotid body superfused in vitro. *Neurosci. Lett.* 35:289–95
12. Bingmann, D., Caspers, H., Kienecker, E. W., Knoche, H. 1978. Chemoreceptive properties of the carotid sinus nerve after its implantation into the external carotid artery. *J. Physiol.* 284:163P–164P
13. Biscoe, T. 1971. Carotid body: structure and function. *Physiol. Rev.* 51:437–95
13a. Blanco, C. E., Davies, G. S., Hamon, M. A., McCooke, H. B. 1984. The response to hypoxia of arterial chemoreceptors in fetal sheep and newborn lambs. *J. Physiol.* 351:25–37
14. Busa, W. B., Nuccitelli, R. 1984. Metabolic regulation via intracellular pH. *Am. J. Physiol.* 246:R409–R438
15. Carafoli, E., Crompton, M. 1978. The regulation of intracellular calcium. *Curr. Top. Membr. Trans.* 10:151–216
16. Chance, B., Legallais, V., Sorge, J., Graham, N. 1975. A versatile time-sharing multichannel spectrophotometer, reflectometer and fluorometer. *Anal. Chem.* 66:498–514.
17. Degner, F., Acker, H. 1986. Mathematical analysis of tissue P_{O_2} distribution in the cat carotid body. *Pflügers Arch.* 407:305–11
18. Delpiano, M., Acker, H. 1980. Relationship between tissue P_{O_2} and chemoreceptor activity of the carotid body in vitro. *Brain Res.* 195:85–93
19. Delpiano, M., Acker, H. 1985. Extracellular pH changes in the superfused cat carotid body during hypoxia and hypercapnia. *Brain Res.* 342:273–80
20. Delpiano, M., Starlinger, H., Acker, H. 1985. Changes in the cAMP content of the superfused cat carotid produced by initial P_{O_2} decrease in the medium. *Pflügers Arch.* 405:R37
21. Delpiano, M., Flesheler, J., Acker, H., Pietruschka, F. 1988. Ionic channels in rabbit carotid body type I-cells. *Pflügers Arch.* 411:R73
21a. Delpiano, M., Acker, H. 1989. Hypoxic and hypercyanic responses of $[Ca^{++}]_o$ and $[k^+]_o$ in the cat carotid body in vitro. *Brain Res.* In press
21b. Duchen, M. R., Caddy, K. W. T., Kirby, G. C., Patterson, D. L., Ponte, J., Biscoe, T. J. 1988. Biophysical studies of the cellular elements of the rabbit carotid body. *Neurosci.* 26(1):291–311
22. Eyzaguirre, C., Fidone, J. 1980. Transduction mechanisms in carotid body: glomus cells, putative neurotransmitters and nerve endings. *Am. J. Physiol.* 239 (*Cell Physiol.* 8):C135–C152
23. Eyzaguirre, C., Fitzgerald, R. S., Lahiri, S., Zapata, P. 1983. Arterial Chemoreceptors. In *Handbook of Physiology—The Cardiovascular System,*

ed. J. T. Shepherd, F. M. Abboud, pp. 557–621. Bethesda, Md.: Am. Physiol. Soc.

24. Fasman, G. D. 1976. *Handbook of Biochemistry and Molecular Biology,* 3:176–81. Cleveland: CRC

25. Grönblad, M., Akerman, K. E., Eränko, O. 1979. Induction of exocytosis from glomus cells by incubation of the carotid body of the rat with calcium and ionophore A23187. *Anat. Rec.* 195:387–95

26. Hebbel, R. P., Shalev, O., Foker, W., Rank, B. H. 1986. Inhibition of erythrocyte Ca^{2+} ATPase by activated oxygen through thiol- and lipid-dependent mechanisms. *Biochim. Biophys. Acta* 862:8–16

27. Hilsmann, J., Degner, F., Acker, H. 1987. Local flow velocities in the cat carotid body. *Pflügers Arch.* 410:204–11

28. Joels, N., Neil, E. 1963. The excitation mechanism of the carotid body. *Br. Med. Bull.* 19:21–4

29. Leitner, L. M., Liaubet, M. J. 1971. Carotid body oxygen consumption of the cat in vitro. *Pflügers Arch.* 323:315–22

30. Lloyd, B. B., Cunningham, D. J. C., Goode, R. 1968. Depression of hypoxic hyperventilation in man by sudden inspiration of carbon monoxide. In *Arterial Chemoreceptors,* ed. R. W. Torrance, pp. 145–48. Oxford: Blackwell

30a. Lópes-Barneo, J., Lópes-Lópes, J. R., Ureña, J., Gonsáles, C. 1988 Chemostransduction in the carotid body: K$^+$ current modulated by P$_{O_2}$ in type I chemoreceptor cells. *Science* 241:580–82

31. McDonald, D. M., Larue, D. T. 1983. The ultrastructure and connections of blood vessels supplying the rat carotid body and carotis sinus. *J. Neurocytol.* 12:117–53

32. Mills, E., Jöbsis, F. F. 1972. Mitochondrial respiratory chain of carotid body and chemoreceptor response to changes in oxygen tension. *J. Neurophysiol.* 35:405–28

33. Mir, A. K., Pallot, D. J., Nahorski, S. R. 1983. Biogenic amine-stimulated cyclic adenosine-3',5'-monophosphate formation in the rat carotid body. *J. Neurochem.* 41:663–69

34. Müller, U., Prühs, D., Oehlke-Unterholzner, C., Wiemer, W. 1984. Comparison of carotid chemoreceptors and baroreceptors reactions to anoxia and ischemia. In *The Peripheral Arterial*

Chemoreceptors, ed. D. J. Pallot, pp. 9–16. Croom Helm, England: Oxford Univ. Press

35. Mulligan, E., Lahiri, S., Storey, B. T. 1981. Carotid body O$_2$ chemoreception and mitochondrial oxidative phosphorylation. *J. Appl. Physiol.* 51:438–46

36. Nair, P. K., Buerk, D. G., Whalen, W. J. 1986. Cat carotid oxygen metabolism and chemoreception described by a two-cytochrome model. *Am. J. Physiol.* 250:H202–H207

37. Obeso, A., Almaraz, L., Gonzales, C. 1985. Correlation between adenosine triphosphate levels, dopamine release and electrical activity in the carotid body: support for the metabolic hypothesis of chemoreception. *Brain Res.* 348:64–68

38. O'Regan, R. G. 1979. Responses of the chemoreceptors of the cat carotid body perfused with cell-free solutions. *Ir. J. Med. Sci.* 148:78–85

39. O'Regan, R. G., Acker, H. 1988. Effects of changes in chemoreceptor activity on extracellular K$^+$ and Ca^{2+} activities in the cat carotid body. *Brain Res.* 445:268–79

40. Petrova, N. V. 1974. Effect of hypoxia on the lactate dehydrogenase isoenzyme composition in the rat carotid body. *Bull. Exp. Biol. Med.* 78:1005–6

41. Pietruschka, F. 1985. Calcium influx in cultured carotid body cells is stimulated by acetylcholine and hypoxia. *Brain Res.* 347:140–43

42. Purves, M. J. 1970. The effect of hypoxia, hypercapnia and hypertension upon carotid body blood flow and oxygen consumption in the cat. *J. Physiol.* 209:395–416

43. Schollmeyer, P., Klingenberg, M. 1962. Über den Cytochromgehalt tierischer Gewebe. *Biochem. Z.* 335:426–39

44. Seidl, E., Acker, H., Teckhaus, L. 1979. Quantitative Erfassung des Gefässvolumens des Glomus caroticum der Katze unter den Bedingungen der Normoxie, Hypoxie und Hypercapnie. *Microsc. Acta* 3:185–89

45. Weigelt, H., Fujii, F., Lübbers, D. W., Hauck, G. 1981. Specialized endothelial cell in frog mesentery. Attempt of an electrophysiological characterization. *Bibl. Anat.* 20:89–93

46. Weigelt, H., Seidl, E., Acker, H., Lübbers, D. W. 1980. Distribution of oxygen partial pressure in the carotid body region and in the carotid body (rabbit). *Pflügers Arch.* 388:137–42

47. Whalen, W. J., Nair, P., Sidebotham, T., Spanda, J., Lacerna, M. 1981. Cat carotid body. Oxygen consumption and other parameter. *J. Appl. Physiol.* 50:129–33

48. Verna, A. 1979. Ultrastructure of the carotid body in the mammals. *Int. Rev. Cytol.* 60:271–330

49. Verna, A., Talib, N., Barets, A. 1987. Hypoxia induced intermitochondrial junctions in the rabbit carotid body: an ultrastructural and experimental study. In *Chemoreceptors in Respiratory Control,* ed. J. A. Ribeiro, D. J. Pallot, pp. 1–10. Croom Helm, England: Oxford Univ. Press

Annu. Rev. Physiol. 1989. 51:845–56

OXYGEN SENSING IN THE KIDNEY AND ITS RELATION TO ERYTHROPOIETIN PRODUCTION

C. Bauer and A. Kurtz

Physiologisches Institut der Universität Zürich, Winterthurerstrasse 190, 8057 Zürich, Switzerland

INTRODUCTION

More than 30 years ago the kidney in adult mammals was found to be an essential component of a regulatory feedback loop that controls the number of red blood cells and thereby the oxygen capacity of the blood. The kidney releases a hormone, erythropoietin, that stimulates erythrocyte formation in the bone marrow (26). The rate of release of erythropoietin from the kidney is greatly enhanced by various forms of hypoxia, such as hypoxic hypoxia, anemia, and carbon monoxide poisoning (27). The question that arises, therefore, is whether the oxygen sensor that controls the production of erythropoietin resides outside or inside the kidney. Results of experiments obtained on animals without functioning arterial chemoreceptors as well as with artificially perfused kidneys or renal hypoperfusion point toward an intrarenal localization of the oxygen sensor (9, 27, 50). In this context, the renal oxygen sensor is operationally defined as a receptor mechanism that controls the production of erythropoietin.

This overview aims to conceptualize present knowledge on the physiological parameters relevant for the transduction mechanism in the kidney through which the synthesis of erythropoietin might be stimulated. More specifically we discuss (a) the type of oxygen signal that regulates erythropoietin production, (b) the location of the oxygen sensor within the kidney, and (c) the transduction mechanism that generates effector molecules that might stimulate the synthesis of erythropoietin.

845

WHAT KIND OF OXYGEN SIGNAL IS PERCEIVED BY THE RENAL OXYGEN SENSOR?

Oxygen Supply to the Normoxic Kidney

THE DISTRIBUTION OF OXYGEN IN THE NORMAL KIDNEY IS NOT HOMOGENEOUS Normally the kidney receives a relatively large share of the cardiac output (about 20–25%), which is necessary for filtration and excretion of waste products. Consequently, the volume of oxygen transported to the kidney is large compared with the overall oxygen consumption; only 8–10% of the oxygen delivered to the kidney is actually used. Nonetheless, the kidney is remarkably susceptible to hypoperfusion; acute renal failure is a frequent complication of hypotension caused by hypovolemia or shock and significantly outnumbers the incidence of brain, liver, or heart failure in the same clinical condition (11, 54).

Such a disproportion between oxygen delivery and susceptibility toward hypoperfusion can be reconciled by gradients of oxygen availability within the renal parenchyma. In 1960 Aukland & Krog (2) demonstrated in exposed kidneys of anesthetized dogs that the renal cortex pO_2 and the urine pO_2 are much lower than the venous blood pO_2. Furthermore, clamping of the renal artery or induction of anemia lowered pO_2 in the cortex and outer medulla but not the inner medulla (1, 2). These results are in keeping with the demonstration of Baumgärtl and co-workers that large variations in respired oxygen concentration mostly affect cortical pO_2 (6). These authors also found that 85% of the pO_2 frequency distribution in the dog renal cortex is below the pO_2 in the renal vein. The critical pO_2, i.e. the pO_2 below which oxygen consumption falls, is also quite high: 35 torr in the venous effluent of the isolated perfused kidney (17), as compared with the critical pO_2 in renal cortical tissue of approximately 10 torr (40). These results are best explained by oxygen shunting that drains oxygen from the arterial to the venous segment of the capillaries, not only in the medulla but also in the renal cortex (6, 11, 40, 41, 53). Note that the peritubular capillary plexus in the renal cortex possesses a hairpinlike configuration. Thus, the glomerular capillaries, efferent arterioles, and their initial peritubular capillary subdivisions pass through, and are intimately surrounded by, capillaries with a lower pO_2 (32, 57). This anatomical arrangement allows for diffusion of oxygen from arterial to venous blood and is equivalent to postglomerular shunting. In addition, significant preglomerular shunting apparently exists from the intralobular artery to the intralobular vein. This type of oxygen shunt lowers the pO_2 in the superficial glomeruli of the Munich Wistar rat to pO_2 values between 40 and 50 torr (53). In summary, the evidence suggests there are considerable inhomogeneities of oxygen supply within the kidney cortex, despite the fact that the kidney is supplied with large amounts of oxygen.

Renal Function During Hypoxia

THE OXYGEN CONSUMPTION OF THE KIDNEY IS NOT GREATLY ALTERED UNDER HYPOXIC CONDITIONS   From the large body of data on the reactions of body fluid volumes and renal function in high-altitude hypoxia or anemia, the following picture emerges: Under conditions of moderate hypoxia (arterial $pO_2 > 35$ torr in hypoxic hypoxia; hematocrit approximately 20% in anemic hypoxia), renal blood flow and glomerular filtration rate do not change significantly [reviewed in (23)]. This evidence can be explained partly by the observation that the renal blood flow does not increase in proportion to the rise in cardiac output that occurs in hypoxia (22). Only in conditions of severe hypoxia have some investigators observed a relative decrease in the glomerular filtration rate in comparison with renal blood flow, which leads to a decrease in filtration fraction (1, 56, 63). Furthermore, the initial hemoconcentration observed under conditions of acute arterial hypoxia is apparently caused by an increase of renal sodium and water excretion. This hypoxia-induced natriuresis is, however, most likely controlled by extrarenal factors (7, 23, 24, 39) and cannot be explained by a direct inhibition of tubular reabsorptive function caused by a shortage of oxygen. The fact that at moderate degrees of hypoxia the filtration fraction remains more or less constant is important, because it indicates that the workload of the kidney stays constant. The workload of the kidney is determined by the amount of sodium that must be reabsorbed per unit time. Because the sodium reabsorption largely governs the oxygen consumption of the kidney (16, 30, 38, 60), the global oxygen consumption of the kidney would not be expected to change significantly under hypoxic conditions, and this result is observed experimentally (60). Even under conditions in which the filtration fraction is decreased, the oxygen consumption of the kidney remains unaltered; this phenomenon appears to be related to more efficient oxygen extraction from the blood by an increase in the pO_2 gradients between the peritubular capillaries and the oxygen-consuming cells (1).

The Information Coding of the Renal Oxygen Sensor

THE RENAL OXYGEN SENSOR DETECTS CHANGES IN VENOUS PO_2 An exponential relationship between the plasma levels of erythropoietin and the degree of hypoxia has been well established (19). Before considering the oxygen signal that controls erythropoietin formation, we offer a brief background on erythropoietin, highlighting the newest developments in this field. In 1977 Miyake, Kung, & Goldwasser (46) described the purification of the hormone from the urine of anemic patients. Since then, the gene coding for human erythropoietin has been cloned and the amino acid deduced from the gene structure (45). Erythropoietin is a glycoprotein with a mass of approximately 34,000 daltons, of which some 40% is represented by the carbo-

848   BAUER & KURTZ

hydrate part. The protein part consists of 166 amino acids with both O-linked and *N*-linked saccharides, which are the anchor for the complex carbohydrate structure (52). cDNA clones for human erythropoietin have been isolated, and the expression of erythropoietin cDNA clones has been achieved (25, 42, 51). Furthermore, the advent of molecular probes has yielded evidence that hypoxia leads to an accumulation of erythropoietin mRNA in the kidney, which regulates erythropoietin production (8, 10, 55).

We define the sensitivity of the oxygen renal sensor that controls erythropoietin production by the amount of hormone produced at a given degree of hypoxia. Under steady state conditions, the serum level of erythropoietin is proportional to the production rate because there is no indication of direct, oxygen-dependent regulation of erythropoietin degradation. Furthermore, the sensitivity of the oxygen sensor presumably depends upon the ratio of oxygen supply to the kidney and oxygen consumption of the kidney. An increase in the oxygen transport capacity should therefore lead to a decrease in the stimulus to the oxygen sensor and thereby to a reduced erythropoietin response. We have tested this hypothesis by exposing mice with different hematocrit values to an atmosphere containing either 8% O_2 or 0.1% CO in air. Figure 1 shows that there is an inverse relationship between erythropoietin response and oxygen transport capacity of the blood. These results indicate that (*a*) the renal oxygen sensor records changes in the ratio of oxygen supply to oxygen demand and (*b*) it is sensitive to the venous pO_2 because this variable changes when the oxygen transport capacity of the blood increases or decreases.

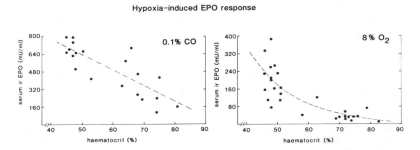

Figure 1 The relationship between hematocrit and hypoxia-induced erythropoietin (EPO) response. Mice were rendered polycythemic during a 15-day period of intermittent (20–22 h/day) normobaric hypoxic hypoxia (7–8% O_2). Four and 12 days later, polycythemic animals together with normocythemic controls were exposed to either hypoxic hypoxia (8% O_2) (*right*) or carbon monoxide (0.1% CO) (*left*) for 3 hs. The EPO-response induced by this hypoxic stress is plotted against the hematocrit values of the animals [taken from Ref. 32a with the permission of Karger (Basel)].

THE LOCATION OF THE RENAL OXYGEN SENSOR

Erythropoietin Production and the Oxygen Sensor Are Located in the Renal Cortex

The next question regards the location of the renal oxygen sensor that is involved in the elaboration of erythropoietin. Assuming the sensor is sensitive to oxygen supply and tubular oxygen consumption, one expects a decrease in the sensitivity of the oxygen sensor when tubular oxygen consumption is reduced by interference of transport rates. By using site-specific transport inhibitors, researchers should be able to localize those tubular structures that are associated with the hypoxia-dependent erythropoietin formation. We have used acetazolamide (proximal tubule), furosemide (loop of Henle), hydrochlorothiazide (early distal tubule), and acetazolamide (late distal tubule) in mice and produced in every case a highly significant natriuresis, which is indicative of a reduced tubular sodium reabsorption. Only when the proximal tubular sodium reabsorption was inhibited by approximately 30%, however, was the hypoxia-induced erythropoietin response elicited by 8% O_2 or 0.1% carbon monoxide significantly reduced (K.-U. Eckardt, A. Kurtz, C. Bauer, unpublished results). From the data shown in Figure 1 and the results obtained with the site-specific transport inhibitors, we conclude that the pO_2 in the peritubular capillaries of the convoluted and straight proximal tubule is the essential variable involved in the regulation of erythropietin production. This idea agrees with two recent reports in which cells containing erythropoietin mRNA were localized in the kidney cortex by using in situ hybridization (31, 37). The mRNA encoding the erythropoietin was detected mainly in the kidney cortex in the peritubular interstitium in close proximity to the basolateral membrane of the cortical tubules. The two groups of authors suggest that the endothelial cells of the peritubular capillaries are the ones that produce erythropoietin.

From a physiological point of view, this location is sensible because the cells are physically positioned to measure the ratio of oxygen supply (from the capillary lumen) to oxygen consumption (from the basolateral membrane of the tubuli). Further experiments are necessary, however, to prove that the cells that produce erythropoietin are of endothelial origin. Remember that endothelial cells also release prostacyclin under hypoxic conditions (12). This derivative of arachidonic acid metabolism stimulates erythropoietin production in cultures of renal cells (33). Therefore, locally produced prostacyclin could, in an autocrine fashion, stimulate erythropoietin formation in the erythropoietin-producing cells.

THE TRANSDUCTION MECHANISM OF THE RENAL OXYGEN SENSOR

The Biochemistry of Oxygen Sensing

ATP COULD BE AN EFFECTOR MOLECULE IN OXYGEN-DEPENDENT BIOLOG-
ICAL REACTIONS   The fact that the oxygen dependence of mitochondrial
oxidative phosphorylation extends well into the physiological range, i.e. up to
pO_2 values of 60 torr (18, 29), is critical to the understanding of oxygen-
dependent physiological reactions. It allows mitochondria to function as
tissue oxygen sensors by converting information on intracellular pO_2 values
into a metabolic signal, which is represented by $[ATP]/[ADP][P_i](64, 65)$.
Therefore, in terms of receptor physiology, the mitochondria themselves
would act as oxygen sensors by converting the signal "hypoxia" into a change
of cytosolic $[ATP]/[ADP][P_i]$, which can be regarded as effector molecules in
this transduction mechanism.

Recall that $[ATP]/[ADP][P_i]$ not only governs electron flow and oxidative
phosphorylation in the mitochondria but that individual components of this
three-membered family are important links among the activities of glycolysis,
the citric acid cycle, and oxidative phosphorylation Apart from these more
general interactions, ATP at physiological concentrations can control a number of cellular variables such as a voltage-independent K^+ conductivity in
cardiac muscle (48) and pancreatic B cells (15). Furthermore, a reduced
availability of ATP to the enzyme phosphatidylinositol-4-phosphate kinase
(43) appears to lead to a decrease in the contractility of smooth muscle under
hypoxic conditions (14).

In the kidney, a tight coupling is observed between oxidative metabolism
and the Na,K-ATPase activity, which thereby accounts for the tight coupling
between Na^+ transport and oxidative metabolism (44, 58). Results from
several experiments have led to the hypothesis that there are
microheterogeneities within cells with regard to the delivery of ATP from
mitochondrial oxidative phosphorylation to the Na,K-ATPase (3, 59) located
at the basolateral side of kidney epithelial cells in association with the
cytoskeletal protein ankyrin (47). Furthermore, that the proximal tubule has
quite a low capacity to maintain [ATP] via glycolytic sources is interesting
(4). A decrease in oxygen supply to the proximal tubules with a subsequent
fall of $[ATP]/[ADP][P_i]$ is therefore a more direct indicator of a hypoxic
condition in the proximal tubules compared with the more distal parts of the
nephron, which have a much higher glycolytic reserve (4, 13). In addition, a
hierarchy exists in the maintenance of energy-dependent processes in the
proximal tubule such that ATP used for transport can be "borrowed" from
other ATP-dependent processes in conditions of reduced oxidative
phosphorylation (59). Such a preferential delivery of ATP to the Na,K-

ATPase under conditions of reduced ATP availability would lead to local imbalances of the ATP distribution at the cytosolic side of the plasma membrane and ATP-dependent regulatory mechanisms could be set in motion.

The ATP Dependency of Prostaglandin Formation

PROSTAGLANDINS SEEM TO BE INVOLVED IN THE ELABORATION OF ERYTHROPOIETIN   How can the results described above be translated into an oxygen sensor that governs erythropoietin production? We can provide only a conceptual framework, which arises from the following observations: (a) A functioning prostaglandin system is necessary for the elaboration of hypoxia-induced erythropoietin production [reviewed in (20, 27)]. (b) Under hypoxic conditions, the renal excretion of prostaglandins increases (61). (c) Addition of arachidonic acid and prostaglandins of the E type to the perfusion fluid increases the release of erythropoietin in artificially perfused kidneys [reviewed in 20, 27)]. (d) Stimulation of NaCl transport in layers of a high-resistance renal epithelial cell line led to a stimulation of oxygen consumption and release of prostaglandin E$_2$ from the basolateral side of the cells (34, 35). (e) The same increase in prostaglandin E$_2$ release can be achived by treating these cells with the uncouplers of oxidative phosphorylation, amobarbital and rotenone (35). The entirety of these results led to the proposal that the hypoxia-induced release of prostaglandin E$_2$ is due to a local fall of ATP at the basolateral side of the membrane of these cells. The enzyme that would be inhibited by a shift of ATP to the Na,K-ATPase is acyl-Co-A-synthetase, which has a high Km for ATP of approximately 4.5 mM. Inhibition of this enzyme results in the inhibition of reesterification of arachidonic acid, the rate-limiting substrate for prostaglandin synthesis (5, 35, 62).

Whilst such a scheme, in which hypoxia leads to production of prostaglandin E$_2$ by a local decrease in ATP, can explain some aspects of the hypoxia-induced and prostaglandin-mediated elaboration of erythropoietin, problems remain as to the nature of the oxygen-sensing mechanism. The first is the way by which prostaglandins enhance the transcription rate of the gene coding for erythropoietin under conditions of hypoxia. Some investigators suggest that prostaglandin E$_2$ stimulates adenylate cyclase and that the erythropoietin gene would therefore belong to those genes whose promoter is regulated by cAMP-dependent protein kinases [reviewed in (20, 27)]. The evidence on which this hypothesis rests is circumstantial, however, and more direct experiments need to be done before the cAMP-dependency of the erythropoietin gene can be accepted.

Second, as Jones (28) has indicated, many oxygen-dependent biochemical reactions are found in the kidney. All of these oxygen-dependent reactions would not easily explain the fact that erythropoietin is continuously produced by normoxic kidneys. Perhaps the low but constant production of prostaglandins in the normal kidney (62) is sufficient to maintain normal day-to-day erythropoietin production. The mere fact, however, that normal erythropoietin production is so delicately regulated renders unlikely the possibility that the normal production rate depends on a single effector system such as the prostaglandins.

Another metabolic indicator of renal hypoxia or renal metabolic rate is adenosine [reviewed in (49)]. The enzyme that dephosphorylates AMP to adenosine, ecto-5'-nucleotidase, is found in distinct regions of the kidney cortex. Enzyme activity is present in the brush border of the proximal tubule, highest in the P_1 segments with decreasing intensity in the P_2 and P_3 segments and also in the peritubular and perivascular fibroblasts of the cortical labyrinth (B. Kaissling, personal communication). In two recent reports it was shown that administration of adenosine leads to an increase of erythropoietin formation in mice (60a) and in insolated perfused kidneys (49a), possibly by binding to a cell surface receptor of the A_2-subclass. Adenosine is known, however, to cause a transient fall in renal blood flow (49) and a persistent reduction in glomerular filtration rate (22a). It is not clear, therefore, if adenosine enhances erythropoietin formation by an intrarenal decrease in blood flow or by a direct effect on the hormone-producing cells.

SUMMARY AND PERSPECTIVES

Under normal circumstances there is a constant relationship between global renal blood flow and global renal oxygen consumption that is reflected by the linear dependency of oxygen consumption upon sodium reabsorption (16, 30, 38, 60). Due to the marked heterogeneity of tissue pO_2 within the kidney, however, a reduction of oxygen delivery to the kidney leads to even more pronounced changes of local tissue pO_2, almost exclusively in the kidney cortex and the outer region of the medulla (11, 53, 54). We summarize the possible function of the renal oxygen sensor that controls erythropoietin formation with the aid of Figure 2.

Two possibilities are considered: First, the oxygen sensor is localized within the erythropoietin (EPO)-producing cell, perhaps specialized endothelial cells (31, 37) in the peritubular capillaries of the proximal tubule. One of the biochemical messengers in such a case could be prostacyclin, which is released from endothelial cells under certain conditions of hypoxia (12) and stimulates erythropoietin formation in cultures of renal cells (33). In this scheme, the role of the tubular cell would be that of an oxygen sink that merely soaks away oxygen and thereby records changes in oxygen supply. The second possibility is that the proximal tubule generates a biochemical signal that acts on the erythropoietin-producing cell. Such a signal could be

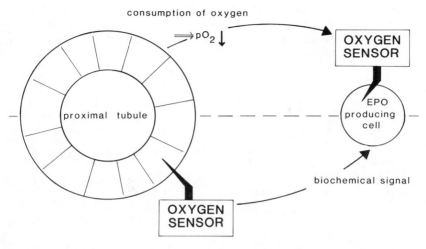

Figure 2   Schema for two possible mechanisms of the renal oxygen sensor. *Right:* The oxygen sensor is located in the erythropoietin (EPO) producing cell and responds to oxygen taken away from the proximal tubule. *Left:* The sensor is located in the tubular wall and conveys information to the EPO producing cell by chemical messengers.

prostaglandin E$_2$, which is released from the basolateral side of renal epithelial cells when there is a mismatch between oxygen supply and oxygen consumption (35). Other biochemical signals such as ATP or adenosine (21, 49) can also be considered candidates in this transduction mechanism. Nucleotides such as ATP or ADP stimulate prostacyclin release from endothelial cells (21). The hierarchy of ATP-consuming reactions in the proximal tubule, with Na,K–ATPase apparently at the top, is important to consider (58, 59). Therefore, under hypoxic conditions, metabolic indicators could be generated without compromising tubular reabsorptive function.

What about the "gain" that amplifies the hypoxic signal? In the case of erythropoietin production, the gain could be represented by an increase in the number of hormone-producing cells as the severity of hypoxia increases. Determining the specific relationships between the degree of hypoxia, the level of erythropoietin mRNA in a given cell, and the number of hormone-producing cells provides a thrilling task for future research, not only with specific regard to the regulation of hypoxia-induced erythropoietin production, but also for questions related to the general laws of signal recognition and signal processing.

ACKNOWLEDGMENTS

We are grateful to Kai-Uwe Eckardt, Hartmut Osswald, Ulrich Pohl, and Hans-Joachim Schurek for many helpful discussions. We also express our thanks to Olga Stoupa for her most diligent secretarial help. The authors' research was partly supported by the Swiss National Science Foundation, the Roche Research Foundation, and the Hartmann Müller Stiftung für medizinische Forschung.

Literature Cited

1. Aperia, A. C., Liebow, A. A., Roberts, L. E. 1968. Renal Adaptation to Anemia. *Circ. Res.* 22:489–500
2. Aukland, K., Krog, J. 1960. Renal oxygen tension. *Nature* 188:671
3. Aw, T. Y., Jones, D. P. 1985. ATP concentration gradients in cytosol of liver cells during hypoxia. *Am. J. Physiol.* 249:C385–92
4. Bagnasco, S., Good, D., Balaban, R., Burg, M. 1985. Lactate production in isolated segments of the rat nephron. *Am. J. Physiol.* 248:F522–26
5. Bauer, C. 1988. Metabolic events that may activate erythropoietin production in the hypoxic kidney. In *Oxygen Sensing in Tissues*, ed. H. Acker, pp. 93–101. Berlin: Springer-Verlag
6. Baumgärtl, H., Leichtweiss, H. P., Lübbers, D. W., Weiss, C., Huland, H. 1972. The oxygen supply of the dog kidney: measurements of intrarenal pO$_2$. *Microvasc. Res.* 4:247–57
7. Behm, R., Gerber, B., Griffel, D., Spee, B., Zingler, C. 1987. Comparison of the response of renal sodium excretion to almitrine and hypoxia in conscious normotensive and spontaneously hypertensive rats. *Biomed. Biochim. Acta* 46:999–1004
8. Beru, N., McDonald, J., Lacombe, C., Goldwasser, E. 1986. Expression of the erythropoietin gene. *Mol. Cell. Biol.* 6:2571–75
9. Beynon, G. W., Balfour, W. E. 1973. The carotid body and erythropoiesis in the rat. *Nature (New Biol.)* 243:61–62
10. Bondurant, M. C., Koury, M. J. 1986. Anemia induces accumulation of erythropoietin mRNA in the kidney and liver. *Mol. Cell. Biol.* 6:2731–33
11. Brezis, M., Rosen, S., Silvo, P., Epstein, F. H. 1984. Selective vulnerability of the medullary thick ascending limb to anoxia in the the isolated perfused rat kidney. *J. Clin. Invest.* 73:182–90
12. Busse, R., Förstermann, U., Matsuda, H., Pohl, U. 1984. The role of prostaglandins in the endothelium-mediated vasodilatory response to hypoxia. *Pflügers Arch.* 401:77–83
13. Chamberlain, M. E., Mandel, L. J. 1987. Na$^+$-K$^+$-ATPase activity in

medullary thick ascending limb during short-term anoxia. *Am. J. Physiol.* 252:F838–43
14. Coburn, R. F., 1988. ATP-sensing reactions and oxygen chemoreception. In *Receptors and Reflexes During Breathing*, ed. S. Lahiri, New York: Oxford Univ. Press
15. Cook, D. L., Hales, N. 1984. Intracellular ATP directly blocks K$^+$ channels in pancreatic B-cells. *Nature* 311:271–73
16. Deetjen, P., Kramer, K. 1961. Die Abhängigkeit des O$_2$-Verbrauchs der Niere von der Na-Rückresorption. *Pflügers Arch.* 273:636–50
17. Dume, T., Koch, K. M., Karuse, H. H., Ochwadt, B. 1966. Kritischer venöser Sauerstoffdruck an der erythrocytenfrei perfundierten isolierten Rattenniere. *Pflügers Arch.* 290:89–100
18. Erecinska, M., Wilson, D. F. 1982. Regulation of cellular energy metabolism. *J. Membr. Biol.* 70:1–14
19. Erslev, A. J., Caro, J., Miller, O., Silver, R. 1980. Plasma erythropoietin in health and disease. *Ann. Clin. Lab. Sci.* 10:250–57
20. Fisher, J. W., McGonigle, R., Beckman, B. 1986. Control mechanisms in kidney erythropoietin production. In *Kidney Hormones*, ed. J. W. Fisher, 3:463–74. London: Academic
21. Gordon, J. L. 1986. Extracellular ATP: effects, sources and fate. *Biochem. J.* 233:309–19
22. Grupp, I., Grupp, G., Holmes, J. C., Fowler, N. O. 1972. Regional blood flow in anemia. *J. Appl. Physiol.* 33:456–61
22a. Hall, J. E., Granger, J. P. 1986. Renal hemodynamics and arterial pressure during chronic intrarenal adenosine infusion in conscious dogs. *Am. J. Physiol.* 250:F32–F39
23. Honig, A. 1983. Role of the arterial chemoreceptors in the reflex control of renal function and body fluid volumes in acute arterial hypoxia. In *Physiology of the Peripheral Arterial Chemoreceptors*, ed. H. Acker, R. G. O'Regan, pp. 395–429, Amsterdam: Elsevier
24. Honig, A., Wedler, B., Zingler, C., Ledderhos, C., Schmidt, M. 1985. Kid-

ney function during arterial chemoreceptor stimulation. III. Long-lasting inhibition of renal tubular sodium reabsorption due to pharmacological stimulation of the peripheral arterial chemoreceptors with almitrine bismesylate. *Biomed. Biochim. Acta* 44:1659–72

25. Jacobs, K., Shoemaker, C., Rudersdorf, R., Neill, S., Kaufmann, J., et al. 1985. Isolation and characterization of genomic and cDNA clones of human erythropoietin. *Nature* 313:806–10

26. Jacobson, L. O., Goldwasser, E., Fried, W., Plzak, L. 1957. Role of the kidney in erythropoiesis. *Nature* 179:633–34

27. Jelkmann, W. 1986. Renal erythropoietin: properties and production. *Rev. Physiol. Biochem. Pharmacol.* 104: 140–215

28. Jones, D. P. 1986. Renal metabolism during normoxia, hypoxia and ischemic injury. *Annu. Rev. Physiol.* 43:33–50

29. Kashiwagura, T., Wilson, D. F., Erecinska, M. 1984. Oxygen dependence of cellular metabolism: the effect of O₂ tension on gluconeogenesis and urea synthesis in isolated rat hepatocytes. *J. Cell. Physiol.* 120:13–18

30. Kiil, F., Aukland, K., Refsum, H. E. 1961. Renal sodium transport and oxygen consumption. *Am. J. Physiol.* 201:511–16

31. Koury, S. T., Bondurant, M. C., Koury, M. J. 1988. Localization of erythropoietin synthesizing cells in murine kidney by in situ hybridization. *Blood* 71:524–27

32. Kriz, W., Kaissling, B. 1985. Structural organisation of the mammalian kidney. In *The Kidney: Physiology and Pathophysiology,* ed. D. W. Seldin, G. Giebisch, 1:265–306. New York: Raven

32a. Kurtz, A., Eckardt, K.-U., Tannahill, L., Bauer, C. 1988. Regulation of erythropoietin production. *Contrib. Nephrol.* 66:1–16

33. Kurtz, A., Jelkmann, W., Pfeilschifter, J., Bauer, C. 1985. Role of prostaglandins in hypoxia-stimulated erythropoietin production. *Am. J. Physiol.* 249:C3–8

34. Kurtz, A., Pfeilschifter, J., Brown, C. D. A., Bauer, C. 1986. NaCl transport stimulates prostaglandin release in cultured renal epithelial (MDCK) cells. *Am. J. Physiol.* 250:C676–81

35. Kurtz, A., Pfeilschifter, J., Malmström, K., Woodson, R. D., Bauer, C. 1987. Mechanism of NaCl transport-stimulated prostaglandin formation in MDCK cells. *Am. J. Physiol.* 252:C307–14

36. Deleted in press

37. Lacombe, C., Da Silva, J. L., Bruneval,

P., Fournier, J. G., Wendling, F., et al. 1988. Peritubular cells are the site of erythropoietin synthesis in the murine hypoxic kidney. *J. Clin. Invest.* 81:620–23

38. Lassen, N. A., Munck, O., Thaysen, J. H. 1961. Oxygen consumption and sodium reabsorption in the kidney. *Acta Physiol. Scand.* 51:371–84

39. Ledderhos, C., Quies, W., Schuster, R., Peters, R. 1987. Renal hemodynamics and excretory function of healthy young men during stimulation of their peripheral arterial chemoreceptors by almitrine bismesylate. *Biomed. Biochim. Acta* 12:1035–42

40. Leichtweiss, H. P., Lübbers, D. W., Weiss, C., Baumgärtl, H., Reschke, W. 1969. The oxygen supply of the rat kidney. Measurements of intrarenal pO₂. *Pflügers Arch.* 309:328–49

41. Levy, M. N., Imperial, E. S. 1961. Oxygen shunting in renal cortical and medullary capillaries. *Am. J. Physiol.* 200:159–62

42. Lin, F. K., Suggs, S., Lin, C. H., Browne, J., Smalling, R., et al. 1985. Cloning and expression of the human erythropoietin gene. *Proc. Natl. Acad. Sci. USA* 82:7580–84

43. Lundberg, G. A., Jergil, B., Sunder, R. 1985. Subcellular localization and enzymatic properties of rat liver phosphatidylinositol-4-phosphate kinase. *Biochim. Biophys. Acta* 846:379–87

44. Mandel, L. J., Balaban, R. S. 1981. Stoichiometry and coupling of active transport to oxidative metabolism in epithelial tissues. *Am. J. Physiol.* 240: F357–71

45. McDonald, J. D., Lin, F.-K., Goldwasser E. 1986. Cloning, sequencing, and evolutionary analysis of the mouse erythropoietin gene. *Mol. Cell. Biol.* 6:842–48

46. Miyake, T., Kung, C. H. K., Goldwasser, E. 1977. Purification of human erythropoietin. *J. Biol. Chem.* 252: 5558–64

47. Nelson, W. J., Veshnak, P. J. 1987. Ankyrin binding to (Na⁺-K⁺) ATPase and implications for the organisation of membrane domains in polarized cells. *Nature* 328:533–36

48. Noma, A. 1985. ATP-regulated single K channels in cardiac muscle. *Nature* 305:147–48

49. Osswald, H. 1983. Adenosine and renal function. In *Regulatory Function of Adenosine,* ed. R. M. Berne, T. W. Roll, R. Rubio, pp. 399–415. London: Nijhof

49a. Paul, P., Rothmann, S. A., Meagher,

R. C. 1988. Modulation of erythropoietin production by adenosine. *J. Lab. Clin. Med.* 112:168–73

50. Paulo, L. G., Fink, G. D., Roh, B. L., Fisher, J. W. 1973. Influence of carotid body ablation on erythropoietin production in rabbits. *Am. J. Physiol.* 224:442–44

51. Powell, J. S., Berkner, K. L., Lebo, R. V., Adamson, J. W. 1986. Human erythropoietin gene: High level expression in stably transfected mammalian cells and chromosome localization. *Proc. Natl. Acad. Sci. USA* 83:6465–69

52. Sasaki, H., Bothner, B., Dell, A., Fukuda, M. 1987. Carbohydrate structure of erythropoietin expressed in Chinese hamster ovary cells by a human erythropoietin cDNA. *J. Biol. Chem.* 262:12059–76

53. Schurek, H. J. 1988. Die Nierenmarkhypoxie: Ein Schlüssel zum Verständnis des akuten Nierenversagens? *Klin. Wochenschr.* 66:828–35

54. Schurek, H. J., Kriz, W. 1985. Morphological and functional evidence for oxygen deficiency in the isolated perfused rat kidney. *Lab. Invest.* 53:145–55

55. Schuster, S. J., Wilson, J. H., Erslev, A. J., Caro, J. 1987. Physiologic regulation and tissue localization of renal erythropoietin messenger RNA. *Blood* 70:316–18

56. Selkurt, E. E. 1953. Influence of hypoxia on renal circulation and on excretion of electrolytes and water. *Am. J. Physiol.* 172:700–8

57. Smith, H. 1951. *The Kidney. Structure and Function in Health and Disease*, pp.

10–14. New York: Oxford Univ. Press

58. Soltoff, S. P. 1986. ATP and the regulation of renal cell function. *Annu. Rev. Physiol.* 48:9–31

59. Soltoff, S. P., Mandel, L. J. 1984. Active ion transport in the renal proximal tubule. III. The ATP dependence of the Na-Pump. *J. Gen. Physiol.* 84:643–62

60. Thurau, K. 1961. Renal Na reabsorption and O_2 uptake in dogs during hypoxia and hydrochlorothiazide infusion. *Proc. Soc. Exp. Biol. Med.* 106:714–17

60a. Ueno, M., Brookins, J., Beckman, B., Fisher, J. W. 1988. A_1 and A_2 adenosine receptor regulation of erythropoietin production. *Life Sci.* 43:229–37

61. Walker, B. R. 1982. Diuretic response to acute hypoxia in the conscious dog. *Amer. J. Physiol.* 243:F440–46

62. Walker, L. A., Frölich, J. C. 1987. Renal prostaglandins and leukotrienes. *Rev. Physiol. Biochem. Pharmacol.* 107:2–72

63. Weismann, D. N. 1981. Altered renal hemodynamic and urinary prostaglandin response to acute hypoxemia after inhibition of prostaglandin synthesis in the anesthetized dog. *Circ. Res.* 48:632–40

64. Wilson, D. F., Erecinska, M. 1985. Effect of oxygen concentration on cellular metabolism. *Chest* 885:2295–2325

65. Wilson, D. F., Owen, C. S., Erecinska, M. 1979. Quantitative dependence of mitochondrial oxidative phosphorylation on oxygen concentration: A mathematical model. *Arch. Biochem. Biophys.* 195:494–504

Annu. Rev. Physiol. 1989. 51:857–78
Copyright © 1989 by Annual Reviews Inc. All rights reserved

TRANSPORT OF OXYGEN IN MUSCLE

Beatrice A. Wittenberg and Jonathan B. Wittenberg

Department of Physiology & Biophysics, Albert Einstein College of Medicine, Bronx, New York 10461

INTRODUCTION

Red muscles, despite access to an infinite reservoir of air and drawing their oxygen supply from alveolar air of $P_{O_2} \simeq 100$ torr, actually operate in sustained steady states of volume-average sarcoplasmic oxygen pressure near 3 torr. At these oxygen pressures, sarcoplasmic myoglobin is partially saturated with oxygen; intracellular myoglobin offers an endogenous probe of sarcoplasmic oxygen pressure. The heart and red skeletal muscles can vary their rate of work and their rate of steady state oxygen utilization 20-fold in response to sustained demand. Most (at least 85%) of the oxygen consumed by muscle is used for mitochondrial oxidative phosphorylation (89). That the rate of mitochondrial ATP genesis can also vary 20-fold follows logically. Here we ask how the massive and variable flow of oxygen to muscle mitochondria is achieved at near-constant low sarcoplasmic oxygen pressure.

We address intracellular events within the myocyte with particular attention to the role of myoglobin. We report the facts and let them speak and draw inferences as closely as possible to the experimental findings. In passing, we allude to some mathematical or numerical treatments of oxygen transport and diffusion but do not attempt a critical review or analysis. The role of myoglobin in oxygen supply to muscle, pioneered by Millikan (86), is reviewed elsewhere (73, 125, 133, 134). Also, the molecular mechanism of intracellular myoglobin function is discussed in greater detail in an upcoming review (J. B. Wittenberg, B. A. Wittenberg, in preparation).

MYOGLOBIN

Myoglobin, which is present in most vertebrate hearts and in many vertebrate striated and smooth muscles, is also widely if erratically expressed throughout

857

the animal, plant, and bacterial kingdoms. It is a relatively small protein, monomeric in all vertebrate systems, and contains 153 amino acid residues in a compactly folded polypeptide chain with a molecular weight of approximately 17,000. There is one heme per molecule, and one diatomic oxygen molecule is bound reversibly. The outside of the molecule is composed mainly of hydrophilic residues (96), and possibly as a consequence, myoglobin molecules in concentrated solution slide past each other with minimal frictional interaction (98, 112), a property favoring myoglobin-facilitated oxygen diffusion within the sarcoplasm. The structure of the gene is known in mice, men, and seals (8, 9, 115). The amino acid sequence and the three-dimensional structure of the molecule are remarkably constant, although there is sufficient diversity to permit construction of a vertebrate family tree (100).

Myoglobin occurs at significant concentrations in the hearts of all large vertebrates. The concentration in skeletal muscle fibers is linked closely to the requirement for sustained work (86). Bird gizzard offers a unique case of a smooth muscle doing sustained hard work; the myoglobin concentration is high. The myoglobin content of muscles increases dramatically with exercise (86, 95, 133) and even increases in a predominantly white muscle cross-innervated with the nerve from a red muscle (84). There is, to date, no correlated study of morphometric change and myoglobin content in response to exercise training. Myoglobin content of muscles is proportional to the cytochrome oxidase content (76, 133). The concentration of myoglobin in the hearts of most species falls near 200 μmol/kg wet weight (101). The concentration in skeletal muscle can be higher (101, 133) and is perhaps correlated with the larger cell size and more widely spaced capillaries (e.g. 26).

The concentration of myoglobin-bound oxygen in the sarcoplasm of the heart or skeletal muscle performing sustained work in a steady state exceeds the concentration of dissolved oxygen. Consider, by example, a cardiac myocyte that contains 200 μM myoglobin half saturated with oxygen; the myoglobin-bound oxygen concentration is 100 μM. Taking P_{50} (equilibrium oxygen pressure at half saturation) = 2.3 torr, the sarcoplasmic free-oxygen concentration will approximate 3.2 μM at 37°C, and the ratio of myoglobin-bound oxygen to free oxygen will approximate 30:1.

Myoglobin in situ enjoys relatively unhindered rotational diffusion (77). The rate of translational diffusion, albeit unknown, is presumably no more than 10-fold less than that in dilute solution (98, 133). The diffusion coefficient of free, dissolved oxygen in muscle is approximately 0.8 times that in dilute solution (79).

Myoglobin in vertebrate tissue binds oxygen reversibly. Ferric myoglobin is held to an undetectable concentration by action of the enzyme system metmyoglobin reductase (61, 104, 108, 131). Oxygenation of isolated myoglobin is independent of pH and is not modulated by other effectors (1).

Oxygen affinity (105, 129) as well as the partition between oxygen and carbon monoxide (130) are nearly the same in the heart cell as in purified myoglobin.

MYOGLOBIN–REPORTED SARCOPLASMIC OXYGEN PRESSURE

Millikan (85) first used the spectroscopically reported fractional oxygenation of myoglobin 50 years ago to measure "muscle metabolism" in situ in a blood-perfused working muscle. He found myoglobin to function in states of partial oxygenation. This finding has been abundantly confirmed in working heart (32, 43) and skeletal muscle (38, 40, 42, 86).

Sarcoplasmic oxygen pressure can be calculated from the spectroscopically observed fractional saturation of myoglobin and the value of P_{50}. The assumption of near equilibrium for respiring myocytes has been validated (87, 136). Gayeski & Honig use the value $P_{50} = 5.3$ torr, determined for isolated dog myoglobin at 37°C (e.g. 43), in their calculations. Tamura et al (105) report $P_{50} = 2.4$ torr for myoglobin in situ in the saline-perfused rat heart at 25°C. We find $P_{50} = 1.3$ torr (129) and 2.3 torr (unpublished results) for myoglobin in situ in isolated rat cardiac myocytes at 30°C and 37°C, respectively, and we use these values in our calculations. Volume-average sarcoplasmic oxygen pressure, reported by the fractional oxygenation of myoglobin in situ, has been studied in blood-perfused skeletal muscle, in the blood-perfused heart in situ, and in saline-perfused heart. The last has been used mainly to evaluate changes during the cardiac cycle, since the oxygen supply is compromised in the absence of erythrocytes.

Heart

A direct measure of fractional saturation of myoglobin within myocytes of the blood-perfused heart beating in situ has been achieved by Gayeski & Honig (43). The exposed surface of the dog ventricle was frozen rapidly by contact with a massive heat sink precooled in liquid nitrogen. Saturation of myoglobin with oxygen was measured by reflectance microspectrophotometry within individual cells chosen near the frozen surface. The validity of the measurement depends critically on the extent to which the speed of freezing outraces change from the in vivo state. The authors present credible evidence that the freezing rate is adequate to preserve the volume-average myoglobin saturation as it was in the living state (39, 43). Myoglobin saturation was never less than 30–35%. The striking result is that myoglobin saturation is narrowly distributed near half saturation in all of the population of cells examined. The results were independent of heart rate, cardiac output, arterial oxygen pressure, and moderate changes in work load and were the same in the several mammalian species examined. An implication is that oxygen pressure within the cardiac myocyte is closely controlled.

These findings agree with those of Coburn et al, who measured ^{14}CO binding to myoglobin and deduced that myoglobin is partially deoxygenated in the heart (20) and skeletal muscle (18, 19).

There is disagreement about possible fluctuation of myoglobin oxygenation during the heart beat [reviewed in (52)]. No measurements have been reported for blood-perfused hearts. Some transmittance or reflectance spectroscopic observations of the saline-perfused heart (103, 105) suggest fluctuations with phases that depend on the conditions of the experiments. Others report no change or a small decrease during systole (32, 54, 80). Blood oxygen stores would be expected to damp this already small change.

Skeletal Muscle

Skeletal muscles, by the nature of the work they do, are inhomogeneous and are made of many fiber types and diverse motor units. The experimental situation chosen by Gayeski & Honig (40, 42) to impose some homogeneity on the in situ, blood-perfused dog gracilis muscle was a series of maximal twitch contractions at relatively low frequency, 2, 4, and 6 Hz, with near-maximal oxygen uptake at 6 Hz. Myoglobin saturation, as before, was determined by reflectance spectrophotometry of the quick-frozen muscle. Myoglobin oxygenation, measured in large populations of cells, always exceeded 25% (38, 39).

During normal muscle contraction, those motor units active at any one time would receive stimuli at 10–30 Hz, thereby achieving a local steady state characterized by end-capillary oxygen pressure in the associated capillaries near the lower inflection of the erythrocyte oxygen equilibrium curve, e.g. $P_{O_2} = 20$ torr (133). Gayeski & Honig (42) reported that one muscle, driven at 4 Hz, approximates this steady state, with an end-capillary P_{O_2} for the whole muscle near 22 torr. Myoglobin in cells sampled from this muscle was about half saturated with oxygen (mean 57%, range 45–67%).

INTRACELLULAR GRADIENTS OF OXYGEN PRESSURE

Intact Heart

Gayeski & Honig (43) reported that myoglobin saturation of 32% within an illustrative, individual myocyte of the beating, blood-perfused heart was homogeneous throughout the sarcoplasm, even though an arteriole and three capillaries abutted this particular cell.

Skeletal Muscle

Myoglobin saturation in cross sections of gracilis muscle was relatively homogeneous within the confines of a single cell (40). The largest variations observed in a typical cell were approximately 20%. Variations observed were not correlated with proximity of capillaries or distance from the center. Myoglobin saturation in adjacent cells, often similar, sometimes differed markedly (40, 58). Myoglobin saturation followed for distances of 800 μm along individual fibers of the muscle stimulated at 6Hz fluctuated randomly. Gayeski & Honig concluded that there is no suggestion of intracellular radial gradients of myoglobin saturation, no suggestion of gradients radiating from capillaries, and no evidence for a decrement of tissue oxygenation along the length of a capillary.

Isolated Cardiac Myocytes

Suspensions of cardiac myocytes freshly isolated from hearts of adult rats (126–128) have been used to establish the magnitude of gradients of oxygen pressure within the respiring myocyte (64, 129). We emphasize that these are adult cells that retain the properties they enjoyed in the heart; they are not cultured cells. Suspensions of cells offer the advantages of homogeneity and accurate control of extracellular oxygen pressure. The diffusion path for oxygen is defined precisely. Cellular architecture is preserved, but tissue architecture has been lost. In particular, oxygen from the extracellular medium has access to the entire surface of the isolated myocyte, whereas capillaries in the intact heart are in contact with perhaps only a fifth of the cell surface. The isolated myocytes are not working against an external load, and their oxygen uptake closely reflects that of the heart at rest. Mitochondrial oxidative phosphorylation in the isolated cardiac myocyte is tightly coupled, as shown by a 20-fold increase in oxygen uptake in response to treatment with uncouplers of oxidative phosphorylation (129). Wittenberg & Wittenberg (129, 130) and Katz et al (64) used a moderate concentration of the uncoupler of mitochondrial oxidative phosphorylation, CCCP, to increase the oxygen uptake of cardiac myocytes reversibly to a rate near that of the beating rat heart performing work under moderate load. They used a steady state system in which oxygen consumed by the myocyte is replenished from a gas phase. The experiment is open to the criticism (124) that oxygen entering the solution from the gas phase will be more concentrated near the interface. For this reason, and to bring unstirred layers surrounding each cell to constant and minimum thickness, stirring in these experiments were made as vigorous as possible without damaging the suspended myocytes.

Katz et al (64) used the activity of monoamine oxidase, a flavoenzyme located at the outer mitochondrial membrane, to report the chemical activity of dissolved oxygen at this locus. Working near the optimal sensitivity of the assay, approximately 7 torr extracellular P_{O_2}, they found that the difference in oxygen pressure from the extracellular environment to the outer mitochondrial membrane, even in rapidly respiring cardiac myocytes, is at most 2 torr. Wittenberg & Wittenberg (129) used the fractional oxygen saturation of intracellular myoglobin to report volume-average sarcoplasmic oxygen pressure. This also is an equilibrium measure of local chemical activity of oxygen. Optimal sensitivity is near 1.3 torr. Sarcoplasmic oxygen pressure was found to be nearly the same as extracellular oxygen pressure in resting cells and only about 2 torr less in rapidly respiring myocytes. Part of this latter difference may be ascribed to the oxygen pressure drop across the unstirred layer that must surround each cell. Four probes reflect the availability of oxygen reacting with mitochondrial cytochrome oxidase with optimal sensitivity near 0.1–0.2 torr: the fractional oxidation of cytochrome oxidase, the fractional oxidation of cytochrome c, respiratory oxygen uptake, and lactate accumulation. These probes showed no large change until sarcoplasmic myoglobin was more than half deoxygenated. The pressure drop from sarcoplasmic to mitochondrial compartments was calculated assuming that the apparent P_{50} of oxygen dependence was the same in situ as it was in isolated muscle mitochondria studied under similar conditions. This pressure drop is 0.2 torr or less. These experiments prove that oxygen pressure gradients within the respiring myocyte are small indeed and that this is true at ambient and cytoplasmic P_{O_2} near 0.1, 1.3, and 7 torr.

Perimitochondrial Gradients

Kennedy & Jones (69) claim very steep oxygen pressure gradients in cardiac myocytes. Their results may in part reflect insufficient stirring in the apparatus used (123, 129). Recalculation of their data (15, 16), taking appropriate values for oxygen diffusivity and mitochondrial oxygen affinity, suggests that their findings are consistent with a very small pressure drop across the sarcoplasm. Very steep local oxygen pressure gradients, as much as several torr, immediately adjacent to intracellular mitochondria of myocytes have been suggested (69, 105, 118). Gayeski & Honig (41) did not observe such gradients in tissue, and Cole et al (24) found no such gradients surrounding isolated mitochondria. Wilson & Rumsey (123), Clark et al (15, 16), and Wittenberg & Wittenberg (129) discount the idea of steep perimitochondrial gradients.

OXYGEN SUPPLY TO INTRACELLULAR MITOCHONDRIA

In this section, we inquire whether mitochondria of cardiac or red skeletal muscle are oxygen-limited in steady states of normal muscle function. We do not address hypoxic or ischemic states.

   Oxygen uptake and fractional oxidation of cytochrome oxidase of resting isolated cardiac myocytes at 30°C begin to decline sharply with decreasing extracellular P_{O_2} ("critical P_{O_2}") as the fractional saturation of sarcoplasmic myoglobin reaches 30% (recalculated from 129). Respiration, cytochrome oxidase reduction, and cytochrome c reduction are half maximal only when myoglobin becomes largely deoxygenated ($<$ 15%, recalculated from 129). Notably, the minimum myoglobin oxygenation encountered in cells of the working heart or skeletal muscle, 25–30% (38–40, 43), is never less than the myoglobin saturation at the critical oxygen pressure of isolated myocytes.

The oxygen pressure required by isolated mitochondria may be compared with oxygen pressure available in the myoctye. Wilson et al (124) reviewed the oxygen dependence of isolated mitochondria. The oxygen concentration for half-maximal respiratory rate depends strongly on the metabolic status of the mitochondria. Respiration of well-coupled heart (94) or skeletal muscle (24) mitochondria, studied in slowly changing or steady states, was half maximal near 0.02–0.2 torr. These values are commensurate with the sarcoplasmic oxygen pressure at which respiration of isolated cardiac myocytes is half maximal, 0.1 or 0.25 torr in resting or rapidly respiring myocytes, respectively (recalculated from 129). They are less than sarcoplasmic oxygen pressure, roughly 1.3 torr at 30°C and 2.3 torr at 37°C, of myocytes operating in steady states of half saturation of myoglobin with oxygen.

We conclude that mitochondria in the cardiac myocyte first become oxygen limited when sarcoplasmic myoglobin is less than 30% saturated with oxygen and do not lack strongly for oxygen until sarcoplasmic myoglobin is largely desaturated. Mitochondria in the working heart, where sarcoplasmic myoglobin oxygenation is closely controlled near 50% (43), are not oxygen limited.

TISSUE GRADIENTS OF OXYGEN PRESSURE

Oxygen Pressure Difference: Capillary to Sarcoplasm

Wittenberg & Wittenberg (129) and Katz et al (64) found gradients of oxygen pressure within the sarcoplasm to be small and concluded that the largest part of the oxygen pressure difference from the capillary lumen to mitochondria of the working heart must be extracellular. The mean oxygen pressure drop is the difference between mean capillary oxygen pressure, which is conserved near 20–25 torr in cardiac and red skeletal muscle capillaries (e.g. 107, 133), and volume-average sarcoplasmic oxygen pressure, which is centered near 2 torr in the working state. The directly measured oxygen pressure difference is very large. Gayeski & Honig (43) found sarcoplasmic myoglobin 32% saturated (P_{O_2} = 1.1 torr) at a point in a cardiac myocyte only 2 μm removed from an arteriole that had interior oxygen pressure of 63 torr. They report numerous measurements in working gracilis muscle of myoglobin-sensed oxygen pressure of 0.6–1.8 torr at points only 5 μm removed from blood-filled capillaries with internal P_{O_2} of 20–30 torr (40, 58). Since capillary oxygen supply is matched closely to mitochondrial oxygen demand (113), we may regard the steep pressure drop across the capillary wall as an integral aspect of tissue oxygen supply and inquire how it is achieved and controlled.

CALCULATED OXYGEN PRESSURE DIFFERENCE ACROSS THE CAPILLARY WALL   The capillary wall offers by far the smallest area in the cellular diffusion path from capillary to mitochondrion; the oxygen flux per unit area must be highest at this point (134). A unit area of capillary lumenal surface supplies five units of sarcolemmal area, 50–200 units of mitochondrial surface, and up to 600 units of the much-folded mitochondrial inner membrane, where cytochrome oxidase consumes oxygen (2, 26, 60, 97). The oxygen pressure gradient across the capillary wall may be estimated from measured parameters. We consider first morphometric data and the rate of muscle oxygen consumption alone. We take the general case of the heart or red skeletal muscle consuming oxygen at a maximal sustainable steady rate (106, 107, 114, 133). The oxygen uptake per unit volume of mitochondria in such muscles may be taken as nearly constant and is close to 5 ml oxygen cm^{-3} min^{-1} (59, 60). Furthermore, a unit volume of mitochondria, in heart and diverse muscles of several animals, is supplied by a constant length of capillary, 14 km capillary length cm^{-3} mitochondria (26). Combining these numbers and taking the inner capillary diameter as 4.6 μm (26, 116), we obtain the oxygen flux across the capillary wall: 2.5×10^{-3} ml O_2 cm^{-2} min^{-1}. The Krogh diffusion coefficient for oxygen in muscle at 37°C is known accurately: 2.9×10^{-8} ml O_2 cm^{-1} min^{-1} $torr^{-1}$ (68, 79). The effect of cell membranes in the diffusion path may be neglected. These membranes are very thin; the diffusion coefficient of oxygen in membranes exceeds that for water (36), and cell membranes offer no barrier to oxygen flow (21). The remaining parameter, the diffusion path length from erythrocyte to sarcoplasm, is not known with any precision. As a minimum we take the observed mean thickness of the capillary wall, 0.2 μm (26, 116), and calculate the oxygen pressure difference across the wall as 2–4 torr. A more realistic estimate of the erythrocyte-sarcolemma distance might be 0.5 μm (3), in which case the pressure drop across the capillary wall required to meet metabolic demand would be 5–10 torr.

Landis & Pappenheimer (75), considering different parameters: morphometric data, and the measured permeability of the pulmonary capillary, estimate the pressure drop across the muscle capillary wall to be 3–8 torr.

ROLE OF THE ERYTHROCYTE   The foregoing calculation tacitly assumes that the entire endothelial lining of the capillary is exposed to a homogeneous oxygen pressure and that the outflowing oxygen is replenished in instantaneous equilibrium with hemoglobin-bound oxygen in the erythrocyte. In reality the observed oxygen outflux from the capillary is the time average of discontinuous delivery as individual red cells, which are separated by columns of plasma, make their way single file through the capillary (33, 55, 57). Additionally, the rate of oxygen egress from red blood cells is twofold to threefold less than the rate of oxygen dissociation from oxyhemoglobin (17, 21, 51, 93). The effect of these kinetic phenomena is to increase the equilibrium pressure head required to drive oxygen into the tissue from 5–10 torr to 10–20 torr (33, 55).

ROLE OF FACILITATED DIFFUSION   Myoglobin-facilitated oxygen diffusion in a working myocyte brings the very low sarcoplasmic oxygen pressure to within a molecular diameter of the sarcolemmal boundary. Results of experiments by Cole et al (24) show how this effect comes about. Myoglobin, added to a suspension of respiring mitochondria, accelerates the entry of oxygen from a gas phase and increases steady state solution P_{O_2}. The explanation is that deoxymyoglobin captures oxygen immediately as it crosses the interface; the newly formed oxymyoglobin diffuses away to discharge its oxygen as it comes into near equilibrium with the bulk solution. The effect is to make the oxygen pressure gradient from capillary lumen to the sarcoplasm more steep, thereby enhancing the oxygen flux.

Oxygen Pressure Gradient: Erythrocyte to Mitochondrion

Krogh in 1919 enunciated the now-classic view of oxygen pressure gradients in tissue [(74) see (133) for a review of later extensions of Krogh's theory]. He considered that each capillary supplied a cylinder of tissue surrounding it and posited a monotonic fall in oxygen pressure from erythrocyte to the cylinder periphery. Implicit in this treatment is the assumption that the effective diffusion coefficient for oxygen is the same everywhere in the tissue volume. We now recognize that this assumption does not hold for cardiac or red skeletal muscle, in which myoglobin-facilitated diffusion greatly accelerates oxygen movement within the sarcoplasm. Katz et al (64), Wittenberg & Wittenberg (129), and, independently, Honig and colleagues (58) prefer to consider that the gradient of oxygen pressure from erythrocyte to mitochondrion in these tissues is discontinuous; it is very steep across the capillary wall and almost flat within the sarcoplasm. The largest part of the oxygen pressure difference, 20 torr, from the capillary lumen to mitochondria of the working heart or skeletal muscle must be extracellular.

REQUIREMENT FOR MYOGLOBIN IN MUSCLE

A number of reagents, hydroxylamine (131), substituted hydrazines or nitrite (131), and hydroperoxides (105), have been used to convert intracellular myoglobin to higher oxidation states that do not bind oxygen. These reagents are without apparent effect on isolated mitochondria (24, 131), nor do they interfere with neuromuscular transmission, excitation-contraction coupling, autoregulation of blood flow, or mitochondrial oxidative phosphorylation in intact skeletal muscle (23) and muscle fibers (131). Nitrite does not affect heart rate, left ventricular pressure development, oxygen consumption, or ATP and phosphocreatine concentration in the fully aerobic, saline-perfused heart (109).

Myoglobin-Supported Contractile Function

The first attempt to establish a functional deficit when myoglobin was selectively inactivated (25) used the fluorocarbon-perfused dog heart and was defeated by formation of pericapillary edema. Blockade of myoglobin function in the saline-perfused fish heart causes work output to decline at low but not high oxygen pressure (4, 13). Blockade of myoglobin function in the saline-perfused rat heart, observed continuously by ^{31}P nuclear magnetic resonance depletes ATP and phosphocreatine rapidly in hypoxic hearts but not at all in hearts perfused near 1 atmosphere P_{O_2} (109). Myoglobin blockade in isolated kitten heart papillary muscles at low P_{O_2} (12) produced a new steady state characterized by significantly reduced maximal rate of relaxation of the muscle, a sensitive measure of the availability of ATP. Extremes of low oxygen pressure in the perfusate or bathing medium were required to demonstrate myoglobin-dependent ATP generation in each of these experiments. These results provide evidence that work output at low oxygen pressure is dependent on functional myoglobin.

Cole (22, 23) studied prolonged steady states of sustained isometric contraction of the blood-perfused gastrocnemius-plantaris muscle of the dog, in situ with the nerve supply intact. Both isometric twitch tension and oxygen uptake were reduced significantly after blockade of myoglobin function. Interestingly, muscle blood flow remained unchanged, and oxygen extraction decreased, which suggests that functional myoglobin transports oxygen to mitochondria. Cole's results establish unequivocally that myoglobin supports oxygen availability at the mitochondria of muscles operating in physiologically normal states.

Myoglobin-Mediated Vectorial Transport of Oxygen

We turn to the question of myoglobin-mediated vectorial transport of oxygen through red muscle. De Koning et al (27) studied steady state oxygen transfer across thin layers, 400–800 μm, of respiring chicken gizzard (a myoglobin-containing smooth muscle) in the presence and absence of carbon monoxide to block myoglobin oxygenation. They concluded from a mathematical treatment of simultaneous oxygen diffusion and consumption that their data demonstrate myoglobin-facilitated oxygen transport within the muscle. The above-mentioned experiments by Braunlin et al (12) showed myoglobin-dependent function in kitten papillary muscles that are about 500 μm thick; inhibition of function was reversed by increased oxygen pressure, which implied vectorial oxygen transport. Wittenberg et al (131) showed that functional myoglobin enhances steady state oxygen consumption by bundles, 300–900 μm thick, of fibers teased from pigeon breast muscle. The effect of nitrite blockade of myoglobin function was greatest near 50 torr ambient P_{O_2} and was reversed at higher oxygen pressure, which implies diffusion-limited oxygen movement. Respiration returned to normal when the action of intracellular enzymes restored sarcoplasmic myoglobin to the oxygenated state. We conclude that myoglobin mediates vectorial oxygen transport in muscle cells.

MYOGLOBIN-FACILITATED OXYGEN DIFFUSION

Translational diffusion of oxymyoglobin molecules, each carrying pick-a-back a diatomic oxygen molecule, results in diffusion of bound oxygen molecules through the sarcoplasm. This phenomenon is called myoglobin-facilitated oxygen diffusion (87, 88, 132, 133, 136). In the presence of gradients of oxygen pressure and myoglobin oxygen saturation, facilitated diffusion generates a flux of bound oxygen. Although myoglobin diffuses at one twentieth the rate of free-oxygen diffusion, myoglobin concentration, as noted, exceeds free-oxygen concentration in working muscles approximately thirtyfold, and the fluxes of free and myoglobin-bound oxygen in sarcoplasm are expected to be of the same order. Facilitated diffusion by enhancing the flux of oxygen through the sarcoplasm maintains constant, ample free-oxygen and myoglobin-bound oxygen concentrations at the mitochondrion.

Three conditions must be met for facilitated diffusion to contribute an oxygen flux over and above the flux of free dissolved oxygen: *(a)* myoglobin must be present at significant concentration, *(b)* myoglobin must be partially desaturated with oxygen somewhere in the system, and *(c)* myoglobin must be free to undergo translational diffusion within the sarcoplasm. The first two conditions are clearly satisfied within cardiac and red skeletal myocytes. The third has resisted experimental study, although rotational diffusion has been demonstrated (77). One idea that is reasonable to consider is that vectorial transport of oxygen in sarcoplasm is achieved by myoglobin-facilitated oxygen diffusion.

MYOGLOBIN-MEDIATED OXYGEN DELIVERY TO MITOCHONDRIA

In the preceding sections, we demonstrated that myoglobin, by facilitating oxygen diffusion, maintains an ample free-oxygen concentration at the muscle mitochondrion. We now describe experiments in which isolated cardiac myocytes are flooded with superabundant oxygen (130). Sarcoplasmic myoglobin is essentially fully oxygenated, and facilitated diffusion contributes no additional oxygen flux. The oxygen requirements of isolated cardiac myocytes are fully met at less than 1 torr (129). The oxygen pressures used in these experiments exceed 20- to 200-fold that needed to saturate the simple diffusive flow of oxygen to cytochrome oxidase. In this circumstance, low levels of carbon monoxide selectively block myoglobin function without perturbing cytochrome oxidase and abolish approximately one third of the steady state oxygen uptake. The extent of this inhibition of respiration is directly proportional to the fraction of total myoglobin in the carbon monoxide form. Accordingly the myoglobin-dependent component of the oxygen uptake is proportional to the fraction of sarcoplasmic myoglobin combined with oxygen. The myoglobin-mediated oxygen flow is dependent on electron flux through the mitochondrial respiratory chain and supports ATP generation. We conclude that cardiac mitochondria accept two additive simultaneous flows of oxygen: a flow of dissolved oxygen to cytochrome oxidase and a flow of myoglobin-bound oxygen to a mitochondrial terminus. The latter is called myoglobin-mediated oxygen delivery to mitochondria.

RESPIRATORY CONTROL

Mitochondrial ATP genesis must stay in step with sarcoplasmic ATP consumption, with the rate of myoglobin-mediated oxygen supply, and with the rate at which oxygen enters the myocyte from the capillary. Relevant aspects of control of respiration have been reviewed recently in isolated mitochondria (11, 123), in cells other than muscle (31, 120, 121), and in heart (45, 52, 89, 117, 118). Brand & Murphy (11) inquire profoundly into the points of contact between the mitochondrion and its surrounding cytoplasm at which control may be exerted. At each control point, the thermodynamic parameters, e.g. oxidation/reduction potential, phosphate potential, and proton motive force, must be distinguished from the kinetic parameters, e.g. electron flow, oxygen uptake, and rate of ATP genesis. Those components of the electron transport chain that have been probed in isolated cardiac myocytes, NAD(P)H/NAD(P) (30), cytochrome b of ubiquinone/cytochrome c oxidoreductase (130), and cytochrome c (129), are each partially reduced at physiological oxygen pressure, which permits modulation of electron flow in response to changing ATP demand. Operation of several potential control points has been investigated in cardiac muscle. In the saline-perfused heart, different steps in oxidative phosphorylation may be made rate limiting (6, 110). With glucose as the sole exogenous substrate, control is apparent at the level of NADH generation. In the presence of exogenous pyruvate, or when

NADH supply is otherwise made nonlimiting, control is apparent at the level of ADP and P_i. We begin our description with electron input into the mitochondrial NADH/NAD pool and end with oxygen delivery from myoglobin.

Calcium-Sensitive Dehydrogenases and the Supply of NADH

Cytosolic calcium ion concentration, itself a rigidly controlled parameter in working muscle, regulates the activity of pyruvate dehydrogenase and other calcium-sensitive dehydrogenases in the cardiac myocyte (28, 29, 49, 72, see also 34, 48, 50, 83), which in turn regulate the rate of generation of mitochondrial NADH and the potential flow of electrons to the electron transport chain. Under conditions in which ADP and P_i are abundantly available, NADH and/or the rate of NADH generation limits the rate of oxidative phosphorylation in the saline-perfused heart (6, 65, 110). Conversely under conditions of fixed NADH supply, [ADP] and [P_i] increase in response to increasing work load (66). A nuclear magnetic resonance study (56) demonstrated calcium-modulated oxygen consumption and energy balance in the saline-perfused heart.

Adenine Nucleotide Phosphorylation Status

In the steady state, ATP, which is cleaved to ADP and P_i during muscle work, must be regenerated at the same rate it is consumed. The important control of mitochondrial electron flow and oxygen consumption by the rate at which ADP is returned to the mitochondria and/or by extramitochondrial adenine nucleotide phosphorylation status has been reviewed recently (e.g. 11, 44, 52). Concomitant change in phosphorylation potential, the ratio [ATP]/[ADP][P_i], and oxygen uptake have been demonstrated in the saline-perfused heart (46, 53, 90, 92, 102, 123) under appropriate conditions of exogenous substrate availability (37, 82, 102). Erecinska & Wilson (31) and Wilson & Rumsey (123), from studies of isolated mitochondria and diverse nonmuscle cells, perceived the following general interactive relations. "At constant [NADH]/[NAD] the respiratory rate is strongly dependent on [ATP]/[ADP][P_i]," and "At constant [ATP]/[ADP] [P_i] the respiratory rate is strongly dependent on [NADH]/[NAD]."

When mitochondrial NADH is abundant and nonlimiting, the rate of oxidative phosphorylation in the saline-perfused heart (67, 110) or isolated mitochondria (14, 62) is directly proportional to [ADP] and/or [P_i]. Under this condition mechanical activity of cardiac muscle can control respiration directly.

Coronary blood flow in the saline-perfused heart supplied with appropriate substrate increases linearly with decreasing values of the ratio

[ATP]/[ADP][P$_i$] (91, 92, 102). Whether there is a causal relation between these phenomena, and how information transfer is achieved are open questions.

The noninvasive probe ^{31}P nuclear magnetic resonance has been used to monitor pH, [ATP], [phosphocreatine], and [P$_i$] in the beating, blood-perfused rat, dog, and human hearts (7, 10, 47, 66). Balaban et al (5) and Kantor et al (63) showed that the relative concentrations of ATP and phosphocreatine remained unchanged throughout the cardiac cycle and were not changed by a fivefold increase in work output (5, 63).

Oxygen

Respiration of cardiac myocytes (129) and of diverse cells without myoglobin (31, 78, 99, 119–122) is independent of oxygen pressure to less than 1 torr. Erecinska & Wilson (31), and Wilson & coworkers (122, 123) advanced the thesis that cells compensate for decreased oxygen availability by increasing the fractional reduction of cytochrome c, which favors electron flow through cytochrome oxidase and preserves the rate of respiratory oxygen uptake. They report that in non-myoglobin-containing cells, cytochrome c becomes reduced as a continuous function of oxygen pressure below 100 torr, with reduction becoming more marked below 30 torr (120–124). In contrast, in the cardiac myocyte, myoglobin oxygenation decreases gradually along the hyperbolic oxygen equilibrium curve from nearly 100% at 60 torr to 50% at 1.3 torr, with no detectable change in cytochrome c reduction (129). In the cardiac myocyte, myoglobin may maintain oxygen delivery to cytochrome oxidase to less than 1 torr extracellular oxygen pressure.

Oxymyoglobin

Myoglobin-mediated oxygen delivery enhances oxidative phosphorylation in the cardiac myocyte (130). Conversely, we may consider electron flow and myoglobin-mediated oxygen delivery as linked functions: oxymyoglobin concentration may regulate electron flow through the respiratory chain. Although we can measure neither oxymyoglobin nor free-oxygen concentration at the interface of sarcoplasm and mitochondrion, the known shallow intracellular gradients of sarcoplasmic myoglobin oxygenation imply that concentrations of both are relatively large. An interesting consequence of myoglobin-facilitated oxygen diffusion is that the ratio of myoglobin-bound to free oxygen at the mitochondrial surface must exceed the volume-average ratio, which is 30:1 (87, 133). These circumstances favor control of mitochondrial electron flow by sarcoplasmic oxymyoglobin concentration.

An expected change in capillary blood flow was not found in skeletal muscle after blockade of myoglobin oxygenation (23). This result raises the possibility of a role of functional myoglobin in the sequence of events that results in the opening or closing of muscle capillaries.

RATES OF OXYGEN UTILIZATION AND ATP GENERATION

Only four unidirectional rates are accessible to measurement in the isolated cardiac myocyte or perfused heart: *(a)* oxygen uptake, which is related to the net rate of ATP formation; *(b)* the unidirectional rate of ATP synthesis from ADP and P_i, which is catalyzed by mitochondrial inner membrane proton-ATPase (70, 71, 110); (This is the key enzyme of mitochondrial oxidative phosphorylation, which regenerates ATP consumed in the cell); *(c)* the rate of creatine kinase–catalyzed formation of ATP from phosphocreatine and ADP (81, 110, 111); and *(d)* the net rate of ATP hydrolysis that results from muscle contraction and ion transport (110). Those rates involving ATP, ADP, P_i, and phosphocreatine are measured by nuclear magnetic resonance magnetization transfer techniques.

Mitochondrial oxygen uptake is irreversible. Since there is no reverse reaction, the measured rate is equal to the unidirectional rate. Mitochondrial oxygen uptake is related to net mitochondrial oxidative phosphorylation by the P:O ratio. In the intact myocardium, under conditions in which aerobic glycolysis makes no contribution to ATP generation, nuclear magnetic resonance measurements of unidirectional rates give the best available estimate of this ratio. The estimate is P:O = 2.34 (110).

The mitochondrial proton-ATPase, particularly at high workloads in the heart, operates unidirectionally in the direction of ATP synthesis (110), and the unidirectional rate is nearly equal to the net rate of ATP synthesis.

Ugurbil and colleagues (110), from nuclear magnetic resonance studies, reach the conclusion that "regulation of oxidative phosphorylation in the myocardium is based on kinetic rather than thermodynamic mechanisms. The rate of oxidative phosphorylation appears to be determined by the availability of its various substrates, and one of the key enzymes involved in this process, the mitochondrial proton-ATPase, is working unidirectionally." The rate of the reaction catalyzed by the proton-ATPase is controlled in part by the concentration of ADP (6, 14, 62) and P_i (67) available to the inner mitochondrial membrane.

CONCLUSIONS

Cardiac and red skeletal muscle myocytes sustain a massive and variable flow of oxygen to the mitochondrion at near-constant low sarcoplasmic oxygen pressure. Blockade of myoglobin oxygenation reduces oxygen consumption and work output of heart and muscle. Myoglobin-facilitated oxygen diffusion mediates a large part of the total oxygen flux through the sarcoplasm, and most of the oxygen consumed arrives at the mitochondrion pick-a-back aboard myoglobin molecules.

Cardiac mitochondria accept two additive simultaneous flows of oxygen: the well-known flow of dissolved oxygen to cytochrome oxidase and a flow of myoglobin-bound oxygen (called myoglobin-mediated oxygen delivery) to a mitochondrial terminus. The oxymyoglobin-mediated oxygen flow is dependent on electron flow through the mitochondrial electron transport chain and supports ATP generation. Sarcoplasmic oxymyoglobin concentration may modulate electron flow in the mitochondrial electron transport chain.

Gradients of myoglobin saturation and oxygen pressure within the myocytes are shallow and do not exceed 2–3 torr. The oxygen pressure difference from the capillary lumen to the sarcoplasm is large, 15–20 torr, and the gradient of oxygen pressure across the capillary wall is steep.

Mitochondria in the normal working heart do not lack for oxygen. Sarcoplasmic myoglobin oxygenation is held near half saturation, at which point change in oxygen pressure is maximally buffered by equilibrium with myoglobin. Oxygen limitation of respiratory oxygen consumption is observed only below 30% saturation of sarcoplasmic myoglobin with oxygen. Notably myoglobin saturation in individual myocytes of normal working heart and muscle does not fall below this level.

The working myocyte in blood-perfused heart or skeletal muscle operates in steady states in which myoglobin oxygenation is closely controlled near half saturation; ATP, ADP, P_i, and phosphocreatine concentrations are unchanging; and end-capillary oxygen pressure is always the same (near the lower inflection of the erythrocyte oxygen equilibrium curve). Oxygen flow to the mitochondrion, electron throughput in the mitochondrial respiratory chain, and the rate of ATP genesis may vary twentyfold in response to changing work load. Calcium-mediated modulation of enzyme activities at the substrate level may increase the rate at which NADH is made available to the mitochondrial respiratory chain. The rate of oxidative phosphorylation depends also on the rate at which ADP and P_i are returned to the mitochondrion. The increased demand for oxygen in response to increased workload is met by opening more capillaries with a concomitant increase in blood flow.

There need be no unique rate-limiting step in normal working muscle. Oxygen delivery is not rate limiting. The flows of oxygen, ATP, ADP, P_i, and substrate-donated electrons through working muscle may better be regarded as a family of steady states, which when perturbed, will always return to their starting point by some kind of relaxation process, however complex (35).

Literature Cited

1. Antonini, E., Brunori, M. 1971. Hemoglobin and myoglobin in their reactions with ligands. Amsterdam: North-Holland

2. Anversa, P., Loud, A. V., Giacomelli, F., Weiner, J. 1978. Absolute morphometric study of myocardial hypertrophy in experimental hypertension II. Ultrastructure of myocytes and interstitium. *Lab. Invest.* 38:597–609

3. Anversa, P., Olivetti, G., Melissari, M., Loud, A. V. 1980. Stereological measurement of cellular and subcellular hypertrophy and hyperplasia in papillary muscle of the adult rat. *J. Mol. Cell. Cardiol.* 12:781–95

4. Bailey, J. R., Driedzic, W. R. 1986. Function of myoglobin in oxygen consumption by isolated perfused fish hearts. *Am. J. Physiol.* 251:R1144–R1150

5. Balaban, R. S., Kantor, H. L., Katz, L. A., Briggs, R. W. 1986. Relation between work and phosphate metabolite in the in vivo paced mammalian heart. *Science* 232:1121–23

6. Balaban, R. S., Koretsky, A., Katz, L. 1987. NMR investigations of cellular energy metabolism. *Ann. NY Acad. Sci.* 508:48–52

7. Blackledge, M. J., Rajagopalan, B., Oberhaensli, R. D., Bolas, N. M., Styles, P., Radda, G. K. 1987. Quantitative studies of human cardiac metabolism by ^{31}P rotating frame NMR. *Proc. Natl. Acad. Sci. USA* 84:4283–87

8. Blanchetot, A., Price, M., Jeffreys, A. J. 1986. The mouse myoglobin gene. Characterization and sequence comparison with other mammalian myoglobin genes. *Eur. J. Biochem.* 159:469–74

9. Blanchetot, A., Wilson, V., Wood, D., Jeffreys, A. J. 1983. The seal myoglobin gene: An unusually long globin gene. *Nature* 301:732–34

10. Bottomley, P. A. 1985. Noninvasive study of high-energy phosphate metabolism in human heart by depth resolved ^{31}P NMR spectroscopy. *Science* 229:769–72

11. Brand, M. D., Murphy, M. P. 1987. Control of electron flux through the respiratory chain in mitochondria and cells. *Biol. Rev.* 62:141–93

12. Braunlin, E. A., Wahler, G. M., Swayze, C. R., Lucas, R. V., Fox, I. J. 1986. Myoglobin facilitated oxygen diffusion maintains mechanical function of mammalian cardiac muscle. *Cardiovasc. Res.* 20:627–36

13. Canty, A. A., Driedzic, W. R. 1987. Evidence that myoglobin does not support heart performance at maximal levels of oxygen demand. *J. Exp. Biol.* 128:469–73

14. Chance, B., Williams, G. R. 1956. The respiratory chain and oxidative phosphorylation. *Adv. Enzymol.* 17:65–134

15. Clark, A. Jr., Clark, P. A. A. 1985. Local oxygen gradients near isolated mitochondria. *Biophys. J.* 48:931–38

16. Clark, A. Jr., Clark, P. A. A., Connett, R. J., Gayeski, T. E. J., Honig, C. R. 1987. How large is the drop in oxygen pressure between cytosol and mitochondrion? *Am. J. Physiol.* 252:C583–C587

17. Clark, A. Jr., Federspiel, W. J., Clark, P. A. A., Cokelet, G. R. 1985. Oxygen delivery from red cells. *Biophys. J.* 47:171–81

18. Clark, B. J., Coburn, R. F. 1975. Mean myoglobin oxygen tension during exercise at maximal oxygen uptake. *J. Appl. Physiol.* 39:135–44

19. Coburn, R. F., Mayers, L. B. 1971. Myoglobin oxygen tension determined from measurements of carboxymyoglobin in skeletal muscle. *Am. J. Physiol.* 220:66–74

20. Coburn, R. F., Ploegmakers, F., Gondrie, P., Abboud, R. 1973. Myocardial myoglobin oxygen tension. *Am. J. Physiol.* 224:870–76

21. Coin, D. T., Olson, J. S. 1979. The rate of oxygen uptake by human red blood cells. *J. Biol. Chem.* 254:1178–90

22. Cole, R. P. 1982. Myoglobin function in exercising skeletal muscle, *Science* 216:523–25

23. Cole, R. P. 1983. Skeletal muscle function in hypoxia: effect of alteration of intracellular myoglobin. *Resp. Physiol.* 53:1–14

24. Cole, R. P., Sukanek, P. C., Wittenberg, J. B., Wittenberg, B. A. 1982. Mitochondrial function in the presence of myoglobin. *J. App. Physiol.* 53:1116–24

25. Cole, R. P., Wittenberg, B. A., Caldwell, P. R. B. 1978. Myoglobin function in the isolated fluorocarbon perfused dog heart. *Am. J. Physiol.* 234:H567–H572

26. Conley, K. E., Kayar, S. R., Rosler, K., Hoppeler, H., Weibel, E. R., Taylor, C. R. 1987. Adaptive variation in the mammalian respiratory system in relation to energetic demand: IV. Capillaries and their relationship to oxidative capacity. *Resp. Physiol.* 69:47–64

27. de Koning, L., Hoofd, J. C., Kreuzer, F. 1981. Oxygen transport and the function of myoglobin. Theoretical model and experiments in chicken gizzard smooth muscle. *Pflügers Arch.* 389: 211–17

28. Denton, R. M., McCormack, J. G. 1980. On the role of the calcium transport cycle in heart and other mammalian mitochondria. *FEBS Lett.* 119:1–8

29. Denton, R. M., McCormack, J. G. 1983. Mechanism of pyruvate dehydrogenase activation by increased cardiac work. *J. Mol. Cell. Cardiol.* 15:369–82

30. Eng, J., Lynch, R. M., Balaban, R. S. 1988. NADH fluorescence spectroscopy and imaging of single cardiac myocytes. *Biophys. J.* 53:197a

31. Erecinska, M., Wilson, D. F. 1982. Regulation of cellular energy metabolism. *J. Membr. Biol.* 70:1–14

32. Fabel, H., Lubbers, D. W. 1965. Measurements of reflection spectra of the beating rabbit heart in situ. *Biochem. Z.* 341:351–56

33. Federspiel, W. J., Popel, A. S. 1986. A theoretical analysis of the effect of the particulate nature of blood on oxygen release in capillaries. *Microvasc. Res.* 32:164–89

34. Fein, A., Tsacopoulos, M. 1988. Activation of mitochondrial oxidative metabolism by calcium ions in *Limulus* ventral photoreceptor. *Nature* 331:437–40

35. Fichera, G., Sneider, M. A., Wyman, J. 1977. On the existence of a steady state in a biological system. *Proc. Natl. Acad. Sci. USA* 74:4182–84

36. Fischkoff, S., Vanderkooi, J. M. 1975. Oxygen diffusion in biological and artificial membranes determined by the fluorochrome pyrene. *J. Gen. Physiol.* 65:663–76

37. From, A. H. L., Petein, M. A., Michurski, S. P., Zimmer, S. D., Ugurbil, K. 1986. ^{31}P NMR studies of respiratory regulation in the intact myocardium. *FEBS Lett.* 206:257–61

38. Gayeski, T. E. J., Connett, R. J., Honig, C. R. 1985. Oxygen transport in rest-work transition illustrates new functions for myoglobin. *Am. J. Physiol.* 248: H914–H921

39. Gayeski, T. E. J., Connett, R. J., Honig, C. R. 1987. The minimum intracellular oxygen pressure for maximum cytochrome turnover in red muscle in situ. *Am. J. Physiol.* 252: H906–H915

40. Gayeski, T. E. J., Honig, C. R. 1986. Oxygen gradients from sarcolemma to cell interior in a red muscle at maximal oxygen consumption. *Am. J. Physiol.* 251:789–99

41. Gayeski, T. E. J., Honig, C. R. 1986. Shallow intracellular oxygen gradients and absence of perimitochondrial oxygen wells in heavily working red muscle. *Adv. Exp. Med. Biol.* 200:495–514

42. Gayeski, T. E. J., Honig, C. R. 1988. Intracellular oxygen pressure in the long axis of individual fibers in working gracilis muscle. *Am. J. Physiol.* 254:H1179–86

43. Gayeski, T. E. J., Honig, C. R. 1989. Intracellular oxygen pressure in individual cardiac myocytes in dog, cat, rabbit, ferret, and rat. *Am. J. Physiol.* In press

44. Gibbs, C. 1985. The cytoplasmic phosphorylation potential. Its possible role in the control of myocardial respiration and cardiac contractility. *J. Mol. Cell. Cardiol.* 17:727–31

45. Gibbs, C. L., Chapman, J. B. 1979. Cardiac energetics. In *Handbook of Physiology*, ed. R. M. Berne. 1:775–804. Bethesda, MD: Am. Physiol. Soc.

46. Giesen, J., Kammermeier, H. 1980. Relationship of phosphorylation potential and oxygen consumption in isolated perfused rat hearts. *J. Mol. Cell. Cardiol.* 12:891–907

47. Grove, T. H., Ackerman, J. J. H., Radda, G. K., Bore, P. J. 1980. Analysis of rat heart in vivo by phosphorus nuclear magnetic resonance. *Proc. Natl. Acad. Sci. USA* 77:299–302

48. Hansford, R. G. 1985. Relation between mitochondrial calcium transport and control of energy metabolism. *Rev. Physiol Biochem. Pharmacol.* 102:1–72

49. Hansford, R. G. 1987. Relation between cytosolic free calcium ion concentration and the control of pyruvate dehydrogenase in isolated cardiac myocytes. *Biochem. J.* 241:145–51

50. Hansford, R. G., Staddon, J. M. 1987. The relationship between the cytosolic free calcium ion concentration and the control of pyruvate dehydrogenase. In *Cell Calcium and Control of Membrane Transport*, ed. L. J. Mandel, D. C. Eaton, 42:242–57. New York: Rockefeller Univ. Press

51. Harrington, J. P., Elbaum, D., Bookchin, R. M., Wittenberg, J. B., Nagel, R. L. 1977. Ligand kinetics of hemoglobin S containing erythrocytes. *Proc. Natl. Acad. Sci. USA* 74:203–6

52. Hassinen, I. E. 1986. Mitochondrial respiratory control in the myocardium. *Biochim. Biophys. Acta* 853:135–51

53. Hassinen, I. E., Hiltunen, J. K. 1975.

Respiratory control in isolated perfused rat heart. Role of the equilibrium relations between the mitochondrial electron carriers and the adenylate system. *Biochim. Biophys. Acta* 408:319–30

54. Hassinen, I. E., Hiltunen, J. K., Takala, T.E.S. 1981. Reflectance spectrophotometric monitoring of the isolated perfused heart as a method of measuring the oxidation-reduction state of cytochromes and oxygenation of myoglobin. *Cardiovasc. Res.* 15:86–91

55. Hellums, J. D. 1977. The resistance of oxygen transport in the capillaries relative to that in the surrounding tissue. *Microvasc. Res.* 13:131–36

56. Hoerter, J. A., Miceli, M. V., Renlund, D. J., Jacobus, W. E., Gerstenblith, G., Lakatta, E. G. 1986. A phosphorus-31 nuclear magnetic resonance study of the metabolic, contractile, and ionic consequences of induced calcium alterations in the isovolumic rat heart. *Circ. Res.* 58:539–51

57. Honig, C. R., Frierson, J. L., Gayeski, T. E. J. 1989. Anatomical determinants of oxygen flux density at coronary capillaries. *Am. J. Physiol.* In press

58. Honig, C. R., Gayeski, T. E. J., Federspiel, W., Clark, A., Clark, P. 1984. Muscle oxygen gradients from hemoglobin to cytochrome: new concepts, new complexities. *Adv. Exp. Med. Biol.* 169:23–38

59. Hoppeler, H., Kayar, S. R., Claassen, H., Uhlmann, E., Karas, R. H. 1987. Adaptive variation in the mammalian respiratory system in relation to energetic demand: III. Skeletal muscles: setting the demand for oxygen. *Resp. Physiol.* 69:27–46

60. Hoppeler, H., Lindstedt, S. L. 1985. Malleability of skeletal muscle in overcoming limitations: Structural elements. *J. Exp. Biol.* 115:355–64

61. Hultquist, D. E., Sannes, L. J., Juckett, D. A. 1984. Catalysis of methemoglobin reduction. *Curr. Topics Cell. Regul.* 24:287–300

62. Jacobus, W. E., Moreadith, R. W., Vandegaer, K. M. 1982. Mitochondrial respiratory control. Evidence against the regulation of respiration by extramitochondrial phosphorylation potentials or by [ATP]/[ADP] ratios. *J. Biol. Chem.* 257:2397–2402

63. Kantor, H. L., Briggs, R. W., Metz, K. R., Balaban, R. S. 1986. Gated in vivo examination of cardiac metabolites with ^{31}P nuclear magnetic resonance. *Am. J. Physiol.* 251:H171–175

64. Katz, I. R., Wittenberg, J. B., Wittenberg, B. A. 1984. Monoamine oxidase an intracellular probe of oxygen pressure in isolated cardiac myocytes. *J. Biol. Chem.* 259:7504–9

65. Katz, L. A., Koretsky, A. P., Balaban, R. S. 1987. Respiratory control in the glucose-perfused heart. A ^{31}P NMR and NADH fluorescence study. *FEBS Lett.* 221:270–76

66. Katz, L. A., Koretsky, A. P., Balaban, R. S. 1988. The activation of dehydrogenase activity and cardiac respiration. A ^{31}P NMR study. *Am. J. Physiol.* 255:H185–88

67. Katz, L. A., Swain, J. A., Portman, M. A., Balaban, R. S. 1988. Intracellular pH and inorganic phosphate content of the heart in vivo: A ^{31}P NMR study. *Am. J. Physiol.* 255:H189–96

68. Kawashiro, T., Nusse, W., Scheid, P. 1975. Determination of diffusivity of oxygen and carbon dioxide in respiring tissue. Results in rat skeletal muscle. *Pflügers Arch.* 359:231–51

69. Kennedy, F. G., Jones, D. P. 1986. Oxygen dependence of mitochondrial function in isolated rat cardiac myocytes. *Am. J. Physiol.* 250:C374–C383

70. Kingsley-Hickman, P., Sako, E. Y., Andreone, P A., St. Cyr, J. A., Michurski, S., et al. 1986. ^{31}P NMR measurement of ATP synthesis rate in perfused intact rat hearts. *FEBS Lett.* 198:159–63

71. Kingsley-Hickman, P. B., Sako, E. Y., Mohanakrishnan, P., Robitaille, P. M., From, A. H. L., Foker, J. E., Ugurbil, K. 1987. ^{31}P NMR studies of ATP synthesis and hydrolysis kinetics in the intact myocardium. *Biochemistry* 26: 7501–10

72. Kobayashi, K., Neely, J. R. 1983. Mechanism of pyruvate dehydrogenase activation by increased cardiac work. *Mol. Cell. Cardiol.* 15:369–82

73. Kreuzer, F., Hoofd, L. 1987. Facilitated diffusion of oxygen and carbon dioxide. In *Handbook of Physiology*, ed. L. E. Farhi, S. M. Tenney, 4:89–111. Bethesda, Md.: Am. Physiol. Soc.

74. Krogh, A. 1919. The number and distribution of capillaries in muscle with calculations of the oxygen pressure head necessary for supplying the tissue. *J. Physiol.* 52:409–15

75. Landis, E. M., Pappenheimer, J. R. 1963. Exchange of substances through the capillary walls. In *Handbook of Physiology*, ed. W. F. Hamilton, P. Dow., 2:961–1034. Bethesda, MD.: Amer. Physiol. Soc.

76. Lawrie, R. A. 1953. The activity of the cytochrome system in muscle and its relation to myoglobin. *Biochem. J.* 55:298–305

77. Livingston, D. J., La Mar, G. N., Brown, W. D. 1983. Myoglobin diffusion in bovine heart muscle. *Science* 220:71–73

78. Lloyd, D., Mellor, H., Williams, J. L. 1983. Oxygen affinity of the respiratory chain of *Acanthamoeba castellanii*. *Biochem. J.* 214:47–51

79. Mahler, M., Louy, C., Homsher, E., Peskoff, A. 1985. Reappraisal of diffusion, solubility and consumption of oxygen in frog skeletal muscle, with applications to muscle energy balance. *J. Gen. Physiol.* 86:105–34

80. Makino, N., Kanaide, H., Yoshimura, R., Nakamura, M. 1983. Myoglobin oxygenation remains constant during the cardiac cycle. *Am. J. Physiol.* 245: H237–H243

81. Matthews, P. M., Bland, J. L., Gadian, D. G., Radda, G. K. 1982. A ^{31}P NMR saturation transfer study of the regulation of creatine kinase in the rat heart. *Biochim. Biophys. Acta* 721:312–320

82. Matthews, P. M., Williams, S. R., Seymour, A. M., Schwartz, A., Dube, G., et al. 1982. A ^{31}P NMR study of some metabolic and functional effects of the inotropic agents epinephrine and ouabain, and the ionophore RO2–2985 (X537A) in the isolated, perfused rat heart. *Biochim. Biophys. Acta* 720:163–71

83. McCormack, J. G., Denton, R. M. 1986. Calcium ion as a second messenger within mitochondria. *Trends Biochem. Sci.* 11:258–62

84. McPherson, A., Tokunaga, J. 1967. The effects of cross-innervation on the myoglobin concentration of tonic and phasic muscles. *J. Physiol.* 188:121–29

85. Millikan, G. A. 1937. Experiments on muscle hemoglobin in vivo; the instantaneous measurement of muscle metabolism. *Proc. R. Soc. London Ser. B* 123:218–41

86. Millikan, G. A. 1939. Muscle hemoglobin. *Physiol. Rev.* 19:503–23

87. Murray, J. D. 1971. On the molecular mechanism of facilitated oxygen diffusion by haemoglobin and myoglobin. *Proc. R. Soc. London Ser. B* 178:95–110

88. Murray, J. D. 1977. *Lectures On Nonlinear-Differential-Equation Models in Biology.* pp. 42–82. Oxford: Clarendon

89. Neely, J. R., Morgan, H. E. 1974. Substrate and energy metabolism of the heart. *Annu. Rev. Physiol.* 36:413–59

90. Nishiki, K., Erecinska, M., Wilson, D. F. 1978. Energy relationships between cytosolic metabolism and mitochondrial respiration in rat heart. *Am. J. Physiol.* 234:C73–C81

91. Nuutinen, E. M., Nelson, D., Wilson, D. F., Erecinska, M. 1983. Regulation of coronary blood flow: effects of 2,4-dinitrophenol and theophylline. *Am. J. Physiol.* 244:H396–H405

92. Nuutinen, E. M., Nishiki, K., Erecinska, M., Wilson, D. F. 1982. Role of mitochondrial oxidative phosphorylation in regulation of coronary flow. *Am. J. Physiol.* 243:H159–H169

93. Olson, J. S. 1981. Stopped-flow, rapid mixing measurements of ligand binding to hemoglobin and red cells. *Methods Enz.* 76:631–51

94. Oshino, N., Sugano, T., Oshino, R., Chance, B. 1974. Mitochondrial function under hypoxic conditions: The steady states of cytochrome a, a_3 and their relation to mitochondrial energy states. *Biochim. Biophys. Acta* 368:298–310

95. Pattengale, K., Holloszy, J. O. 1967. Augmentation of skeletal muscle myoglobin by a program of treadmill running. *Am. J. Physiol.* 213:783–85

96. Perutz, M. F., Kendrew, J. C., Watson, H. C. 1965. Structure and function of hemoglobin. II. Some relations between polypeptide chain configuration and amino acid sequence. *J. Mol. Biol.* 13:669–78

97. Reichmann, H., Hoppeler, H., Mathieu-Costello, O., von Bergen, F., Pette, D. 1985. Biochemical and ultrastructural changes of skeletal muscle mitochondria after chronic electrical stimulation in rabbits. *Pflügers Arch.* 404:1–9

98. Riveros-Moreno, V., Wittenberg, J. B. 1972. The self-diffusion coefficients of myoglobin and hemoglobin in concentrated solutions. *J. Biol. Chem.* 247:895–901

99. Robiolio, M., Rumsey, W. L., Wilson, D. F. 1989. Oxygen diffusion and mitochondrial respiration in neuroblastoma cells. *Am. J. Physiol.* Submitted for publication

100. Romero-Herrera, A. E., Lehmann, H., Joysey, K. A., Friday, A. E. 1978. On the evolution of myoglobin. *Philos. Trans. R. Soc. London Ser. B* 283:61–163

101. Schuder, S., Wittenberg, J. B., Haseltine, B., Wittenberg, B. A. 1979. Spectrophotometric determination of

myoglobin in cardiac and skeletal muscle; Separation from hemoglobin by subunit exchange chromatography. *Anal. Biochem.* 92:473–81

102. Starnes, J. W., Wilson, D. F., Erecinska, M. 1985. Substrate dependence of metabolic state and coronary flow in perfused rat heart. *Am. J. Physiol.* 249:H799–H806

103. Tamura, M., Araki, R., Harada, K., Yamazaki, I. 1986. Myoglobin-proved optical studies on cardiac oxygen fluctuations in the hemoglobin-free isolated perfused rat heart. In *New Approaches in Cardiac Mechanics,* ed. K. Kitamura, H. Abe, K. Sagawa, pp. 87–89. New York: Gordon and Breach

104. Tamura, M., Araki, R., Ishikawa, T., Sagisaka, K., Yamazaki, I. 1980. Direct observation of reduction of met- and ferrylmyoglobins in the hemoglobin-free perfused rat heart. *J. Biochem. Tokyo* 88:1211–13

105. Tamura, M., Oshino, N., Chance, B., Silver, I. A. 1978. Optical measurements of intracellular oxygen concentration of rat heart in vitro. *Arch. Biochem. Biophys.* 191:8–22

106. Taylor, C. R. 1987. Structural and functional limits to oxidative metabolism: Insights from scaling. *Annu. Rev. Physiol.* 49:135–46

107. Taylor, C. R., Karas, R. H., Weibel, E. R., Hoppeler, H. 1987. Adaptive variation in the mammalian respiratory system in relation to energetic demand: II. Reaching the limits to oxygen flow. *Resp. Physiol.* 69:7–26

108. Taylor, D. J., Hochstein, P. 1982. Reduction of metmyoglobin in myocytes. *J. Cell. Mol. Cardiol.* 14: 133–40

109. Taylor, D. J., Matthews, P. M., Radda, G. K. 1986. Myoglobin-dependent oxidative metabolism in the hypoxic rat heart. *Resp. Physiol.* 63:275–83

110. Ugurbil, K., Kingsley-Hickman, P. B., Sako, E. Y., Zimmer, S., Mohanakrishnan, P., et al. 1987. ^{31}P NMR studies of the kinetics and regulation of oxidative phosphorylation in the intact myocardium. *Ann. NY Acad. Sci.* 508:265–86

111. Ugurbil, K., Petein, M., Maiden, R., Michurski, S., From, A. H. 1986. Measurement of an individual rate constant in the presence of multiple exchanges: Application to myocardial creatine kinase reaction. *Biochemistry* 25:100–7

112. Veldkamp, W. B., Votano, J. R. 1976. Effects of intermolecular interaction on

protein diffusion solution. *J. Phys. Chem.* 80:2794–2801

113. Weibel, E. R. 1987. Scaling of structural and functional variables in the respiratory system. *Annu. Rev. Physiol.* 49:147–59

114. Weibel, E. R., Taylor, C. R., Hoppeler, H., Karas, R. H. 1987. Adaptive variation in the mammalian respiratory system in relation to energetic demand: I. Introduction to problem and strategy. *Resp. Physiol.* 69:1–6

115. Weller, P., Jeffreys, A. J., Wilson, V., Blanchetot, A. 1984. Organization of the human myoglobin gene. *EMBO J.* 3:439–46

116. Wiedeman, M. P. 1984. Architecture. In *Handbook of Physiology,* ed. E. M. Renkin, C. C. Michel, 4:11–40. Bethesda, Md.: Am. Physiol. Soc.

117. Williamson, J. R. 1979. Mitochondrial function in the heart. *Annu. Rev. Physiol.* 41:485–506

118. Williamson, J. R., Rich, T. L. 1983. Mitochondrial function in normal and hypoxic states of the myocardium. *Adv. Myocardiol.* pp. 271–85

119. Wilson, D. F. 1982. Regulation of in vivo mitochondrial oxidative phosphorylation. In *Membranes and Transport,* ed. A. N. Martonosi, 1:349–55. New York: Plenum

120. Wilson, D. F., Erecinska, M. 1985. Effect of oxygen on cellular metabolism. *Chest* 885:229S–232S

121. Wilson, D. F., Erecinska, M., Drown, D., Silver, I. A. 1979. The oxygen dependency of cellular energy metabolism. *Arch. Biochem. Biophys.* 195:485–93

122. Wilson, D. F., Owens, C. S., Holian, A. 1977. Control of mitochondrial respiration: A quantitative evaluation of the roles of cytochrome c and oxygen. *Arch. Biochem. Biophys.* 182:749–62

123. Wilson, D. F., Rumsey, W. L. 1988. Factors modulating the oxygen dependence of mitochondrial oxidative phosphorylation. *Adv. Exp. Med. Biol.* 222:121–31

124. Wilson, D. F., Rumsey, W. L., Green, T. J., Vanderkooi, J. M. 1988. The oxygen dependence of mitochondrial oxidative phosphorylation measured by a new optical method for measuring oxygen concentration. *J. Biol. Chem.* 263:2712–18

125. Wittenberg, B. A. 1988. Oxygen delivery and oxidative phosphorylation in isolated ventricular myocytes. In CRC Handbook "Isolated Adult Cardiomyocytes", Baton Rouge: CRC

126. Wittenberg, B. A., Doeller, J. E., Gupta, R. K., White, R. L. 1988. Measurement of sarcolemmal permeability and intracellular pH, free magnesium, and high energy phosphates of isolated heart cells. In *Biology of Isolated Adult Cardiac Myocytes*, ed. W. A. Clark, R. S. Decker, T. K. Borg, pp. 118–29. Amsterdam: Elsevier

127. Wittenberg, B. A., Robinson, T. F. 1981. Oxygen requirements, morphology, cell coat and membrane permeability of calcium tolerant myocytes from hearts of adult rats. *Cell Tissue Res.* 216:231–51

128. Wittenberg, B. A., White, R. L., Ginzberg, R. D., Spray, D. C. 1986. Effect of calcium on the dissociaton of the mature rat heart into individual and paired myocytes: Electrical properties of cell pairs. *Circ. Res.* 59:143–50

129. Wittenberg, B. A., Wittenberg, J. B. 1985. Oxygen pressure gradients in isolated cardiac myocytes. *J. Biol. Chem.* 260:6548–54

130. Wittenberg, B. A., Wittenberg, J. B. 1987. Myoglobin-mediated oxygen delivery to mitochondria of isolated cardiac myocytes. *Proc. Natl. Acad. Sci. USA* 84:7503–7

131. Wittenberg, B. A., Wittenberg, J. B., Caldwell, P.R.B. 1975. Role of myoglobin in the oxygen supply to red skeletal muscle. *J. Biol. Chem.* 250:9038–43

132. Wittenberg, J. B. 1966. The molecular mechanism of hemoglobin-facilitated oxygen diffusion. *J. Biol. Chem.* 241:104–14

133. Wittenberg, J. B. 1970. Myoglobin facilitated oxygen diffusion and the role of myoglobin in oxygen entry into muscle. *Physiol. Rev.* 50:559–636.

134. Wittenberg, J. B., Wittenberg, B. A. 1981. Facilitated oxygen diffusion by oxygen carriers. In *Oxygen and Living Process,* ed. D. L. Gilbert, pp. 177–99. New York: Springer-Verlag

135. Deleted in proof

136. Wyman, J., 1966. Facilitated diffusion and the possible role of myoglobin as a transport mechanism. *J. Biol. Chem.* 241:115–21

SUBJECT INDEX

879

tissue plasminogen activator
synthesis and, 247-48,
249
Gonads
proopiomelanocortin and,
721-22
G proteins, 229-41
adenylyl cyclase inhibition
and, 217-18
cardiovascular system regulation and, 233-40
muscarinic receptor reconstitution and, 222
phospholipase activation and,
108-9
receptor-operated calcium-ion
channels and, 116
structure of, 230-33
Growth factors
peptide, 192-93
renal epithelial cell proliferation and, 33-48
tissue plasminogen activator
synthesis and, 247
See also specific type
Growth hormone
insulin and, 708
insulin-like growth factor-1
and, 43
urine epidermal growth factor
and, 68-69

H

Heart
α-adrenergic effects in, 239-
40
β-adrenergic receptor-
mediated effects in, 234-
36
glycolysis and membrane
function in, 343
muscarinic receptor-mediated
effects in, 236-39
myocytes of
fractional saturation of,
859-60
myoglobin saturation in, 860
Heparin
fibroblast growth factors binding to, 46
Hepatocytes
bile acid retention in, 162-63
epidermal growth factor responses in
pertussis toxin sensitive,
108
Heterokaryons
muscle gene expression in,
181
Hippocampal cells
T current in, 377

Hippocampus
neuronal processes in, 517-19
Histamine
cytosolic free calcium ion
and, 118
intracellular calcium-ion release and, 319
prostacyclin synthesis and,
249
tissue plasminogen activator
synthesis and, 248
Histidine
uptake of
regulation of, 134
Hormone response element, 52-
53
Hormones
cellular calcium-ion fluxes
and, 107-19
endoplasmic reticulum
calcium-ion pump and,
93
Hydrazines
intracellular myoglobin and,
865-66
Hydroperoxides
intracellular myoglobin and,
865-66
β-Hydroxybutyrate
anion transport and, 420
Hydroxylamine
intracellular myoglobin and,
865-66
3α-Hydroxysteroid de-
hydrogenases
bile acid transport and, 168-
72
Y' bile acid binders and,
167-68
Hyperglycemia
aldohexose transport and, 130
Hypertension
endogenous digoxin and, 7
Hyperthyroidism
glomerular filtration rate and,
21
Hypokalemia
renal hypertrophy and, 41
Hypothalamus
proopiomelanocortin synthesis
in, 720-21
Hypothyroidism
glomerular filtration rate and,
21
Hypoxia
renal function during, 847

I

Indomethacin
bile acid transport and, 169-
71

epidermal growth factor and,
75-76
Inositol lipid metabolism
muscarinic stimulation of, 218
Inositol lipid turnover
phospholipase C and, 218
Inositol 1,3,4,5-
tetrakisphosphate
fertilization membrane formation and, 88
pancreatic acinar cells and,
152
Inositol 1,4,5-trisphosphate
calcium release and, 84, 96
endoplasmic reticulum,
218, 321-22
intracellular, 112-14
potassium-ion channels and,
395
production and metabolism of
regulation of, 109-11
In situ hybridization
muscarinic receptors and, 221
Insulin
effects of
direct vs. indirect, 704
negative, 706-8
positive, 704-6
epidermal growth factor and,
74
gene transcription and, 701-12
glucose carrier regulation and,
3-4
glucose transport and, 460
interactions with other hormones, 710-11
proximal tubular hypertrophy
and, 26
receptor for
tyrosine kinase activity in,
39
tyrosine kinase activity of,
193
Insulin-like growth factor-1
receptor for
tyrosine kinase activity in,
39, 193
Insulin-like growth factors
renal epithelial cell proliferation and, 34, 42-44
Integumental nutrient transport,
585-97
features of, 585-86
mechanism of, 586-93
role of, 593-96
Interferon
cultured myocytes and, 195
Interleukin-1
PAI-1 secretion and, 252-53
prostacyclin synthesis and,
249
tissue plasminogen activator
mRNA levels and, 249

CUMULATIVE INDEXES

CONTRIBUTING AUTHORS, VOLUMES 47–51

CHAPTER TITLES, VOLUMES 47–51

Annual Reviews Inc.

A NONPROFIT SCIENTIFIC PUBLISHER

4139 El Camino Way
P.O. Box 10139
Palo Alto, CA 94303-0897 • USA

Annual Reviews Inc. publications may be ordered directly from our office by mail, Telex, or use our Toll Free Telephone line (for orders paid by credit card or purchase order*, and customer service calls only); through booksellers and subscription agents, worldwide; and through participating professional societies. Prices subject to change without notice. ARI Federal I.D. #94-1156476

- **Individuals:** Prepayment required on new accounts by check or money order (in U.S. dollars, check drawn on U.S. bank) or charge to credit card—American Express, VISA, MasterCard.
- **Institutional buyers:** Please include purchase order number.
- **Students:** $10.00 discount from retail price, per volume. Proof of student status must be provided (photocopy of student I.D. or signature of department secretary is acceptable). Students must send orders direct to Annual Reviews. Orders received through bookstores and institutions requesting student rates will be returned. You may order at the Student Rate for a maximum of 3 years.
- **Professional Society Members:** Members of professional societies that have a contractual arrangement with Annual Reviews may order books through their society at a reduced rate. Check with your society for information.
- **Toll Free Telephone orders:** Call 1-800-523-8635 (except from California) for orders paid by credit card or purchase order and customer service calls only. California customers and all other business calls use 415-493-4400 (not toll free). Hours: 8:00 AM to 4:00 PM, Monday-Friday, Pacific Time. *Written confirmation is required on purchase orders from universities before shipment.
- **Telex: 910-290-0275**

Regular orders: Please list the volumes you wish to order by volume number.
Standing orders: New volume in the series will be sent to you automatically each year upon publication. Cancellation may be made at any time. Please indicate volume number to begin standing order.
Prepublication orders: Volumes not yet published will be shipped in month and year indicated.
California orders: Add applicable sales tax.
Postage paid (4th class bookrate/surface mail) **by Annual Reviews Inc.** Airmail postage or UPS, extra.

ANNUAL REVIEWS SERIES		Prices Postpaid per volume USA & Canada/elsewhere	Regular Order Please send:	Standing Order Begin with:
			Vol. number	Vol. number
Annual Review of ANTHROPOLOGY				
Vols. 1-14	(1972-1985)	$27.00/$30.00		
Vols. 15-16	(1986-1987)	$31.00/$34.00		
Vol. 17	(1988)	$35.00/$39.00		
Vol. 18	(avail. Oct. 1989)	$35.00/$39.00	Vol(s). _____	Vol. _____
Annual Review of ASTRONOMY AND ASTROPHYSICS				
Vols. 1, 4-14, 16-20	(1963, 1966-1976, 1978-1982)	$27.00/$30.00		
Vols. 21-25	(1983-1987)	$44.00/$47.00		
Vol. 26	(1988)	$47.00/$51.00		
Vol. 27	(avail. Sept. 1989)	$47.00/$51.00	Vol(s). _____	Vol. _____
Annual Review of BIOCHEMISTRY				
Vols. 30-34, 36-54	(1961-1965, 1967-1985)	$29.00/$32.00		
Vols. 55-56	(1986-1987)	$33.00/$36.00		
Vol. 57	(1988)	$35.00/$39.00		
Vol. 58	(avail. July 1989)	$35.00/$39.00	Vol(s). _____	Vol. _____
Annual Review of BIOPHYSICS AND BIOPHYSICAL CHEMISTRY				
Vols. 1-11	(1972-1982)	$27.00/$30.00		
Vols. 12-16	(1983-1987)	$47.00/$50.00		
Vol. 17	(1988)	$49.00/$53.00		
Vol. 18	(avail. June 1989)	$49.00/$53.00	Vol(s). _____	Vol. _____
Annual Review of CELL BIOLOGY				
Vol. 1	(1985)	$27.00/$30.00		
Vols. 2-3	(1986-1987)	$31.00/$34.00		
Vol. 4	(1988)	$35.00/$39.00		
Vol. 5	(avail. Nov. 1989)	$35.00/$39.00	Vol(s). _____	Vol. _____

ANNUAL REVIEWS SERIES		Prices Postpaid per volume USA & Canada/elsewhere	Regular Order Please send:	Standing Order Begin with:
			Vol. number	Vol. number

Annual Review of COMPUTER SCIENCE

Vols. 1-2	(1986-1987)................	$39.00/$42.00		
Vol. 3	(1988)	$45.00/$49.00		
Vol. 4	(avail. Nov. 1989)...........	$45.00/$49.00	Vol(s). _____	Vol. _____

Annual Review of EARTH AND PLANETARY SCIENCES

Vols. 1-10	(1973-1982)................	$27.00/$30.00		
Vols. 11-15	(1983-1987)................	$44.00/$47.00		
Vol. 16	(1988)	$49.00/$53.00		
Vol. 17	(avail. May 1989)...........	$49.00/$53.00	Vol(s). _____	Vol. _____

Annual Review of ECOLOGY AND SYSTEMATICS

Vols. 2-16	(1971-1985)................	$27.00/$30.00		
Vols. 17-18	(1986-1987)................	$31.00/$34.00		
Vol. 19	(1988)	$34.00/$38.00		
Vol. 20	(avail. Nov. 1989)...........	$34.00/$38.00	Vol(s). _____	Vol. _____

Annual Review of ENERGY

Vols. 1-7	(1976-1982)................	$27.00/$30.00		
Vols. 8-12	(1983-1987)................	$56.00/$59.00		
Vol. 13	(1988)	$58.00/$62.00		
Vol. 14	(avail. Oct. 1989)	$58.00/$62.00	Vol(s). _____	Vol. _____

Annual Review of ENTOMOLOGY

Vols. 10-16, 18	(1965-1971, 1973)			
20-30	(1975-1985)................	$27.00/$30.00		
Vols. 31-32	(1986-1987)................	$31.00/$34.00		
Vol. 33	(1988)	$34.00/$38.00		
Vol. 34	(avail. Jan. 1989)...........	$34.00/$38.00	Vol(s). _____	Vol. _____

Annual Review of FLUID MECHANICS

Vols. 1-4, 7-17	(1969-1972, 1975-1985).......	$28.00/$31.00		
Vols. 18-19	(1986-1987)................	$32.00/$35.00		
Vol. 20	(1988)	$34.00/$38.00		
Vol. 21	(avail. Jan. 1989)...........	$34.00/$38.00	Vol(s). _____	Vol. _____

Annual Review of GENETICS

Vols. 1-19	(1967-1985)................	$27.00/$30.00		
Vols. 20-21	(1986-1987)................	$31.00/$34.00		
Vol. 22	(1988)	$34.00/$38.00		
Vol. 23	(avail. Dec. 1989)...........	$34.00/$38.00	Vol(s). _____	Vol. _____

Annual Review of IMMUNOLOGY

Vols. 1-3	(1983-1985)................	$27.00/$30.00		
Vols. 4-5	(1986-1987)................	$31.00/$34.00		
Vol. 6	(1988)	$34.00/$38.00		
Vol. 7	(avail. April 1989)	$34.00/$38.00	Vol(s). _____	Vol. _____

Annual Review of MATERIALS SCIENCE

Vols. 1, 3-12	(1971, 1973-1982)...........	$27.00/$30.00		
Vols. 13-17	(1983-1987)................	$64.00/$67.00		
Vol. 18	(1988)	$66.00/$70.00		
Vol. 19	(avail. Aug. 1989)...........	$66.00/$70.00	Vol(s). _____	Vol. _____

Annual Review of MEDICINE

Vols. 9, 11-15	(1958, 1960-1964)			
17-36	(1966-1985)................	$27.00/$30.00		
Vols. 37-38	(1986-1987)................	$31.00/$34.00		
Vol. 39	(1988)	$34.00/$38.00		
Vol. 40	(avail. April 1989)	$34.00/$38.00	Vol(s). _____	Vol. _____